CE 75/
5

P 283 284

7 problems

LP 51.
    Highway relocation

May 6   7:15

· Polaris

Compute Magnetic

Bearing Declination

Scale Lat + Long from map

Final

June 5

1:30   4:30

ROUTE SURVEYING

by

CARL F. MEYER

Professor of Civil Engineering
Worcester Polytechnic Institute

SECOND EDITION

Published by

INTERNATIONAL TEXTBOOK COMPANY
SCRANTON, PENNSYLVANIA

THE HADDON CRAFTSMEN, INC.
SCRANTON, PENNSYLVANIA

8035

PREFACE TO THE SECOND EDITION

The wide acceptance of the first edition of this book has not only been gratifying, but is proof that engineering teachers were ready to accept some important departures from the traditional handbook type of text on this subject. Although this new edition maintains the same basic approach, many important additions and changes have been made, the most significant being:

(1) A new chapter on "Aerial Photography in Route Surveying," which does not duplicate the technical principles found in textbooks on photogrammetry but instead lays emphasis on the special applications of this new science to route-location. Advantages, limitations, costs, and modern examples are treated in a condensed, though practical, manner.

(2) A complete revision of the chapter on "Curve Problems in Highway Design." This was made necessary by the publication in 1954 of a new *Policy on Geometric Design of Rural Highways* by the American Association of State Highway Officials. The new policy contains extensive changes that make many of the earlier recommendations obsolete. It is a monumental work that is bound to exert a strong influence on the geometric aspects of modern highway design for many years.

(3) Revision of the chapter on Vertical Curves ("Parabolic Curves"), principally to change the notation so as to agree with that in the *AASHO Policy*, but also to include some new material, such as the practical problem of passing a vertical curve through a fixed point.

(4) In the chapter on "Earthwork," some further clarification and expansion of the mass diagram and its practical applications.

(5) Several improvements in the chapter on "Spirals," including (apparently for the first time in any textbook on route surveying) a simple traverse solution for that troublesome problem—the completely-spiraled compound curve.

(6) Further expansion of the traverse method of solving compound curve problems.

(7) New Tables XVII-A and XVII-B, which provide an original and rapid method of correcting level-section earthwork quantities for the effect of transverse ground slope.

(8) A table of functions of numbers (Table XXVII), conveniently located at the end of the book.

(9) Numerous minor changes in practically every chapter, all made with the object of improving the clarity of the presentation.

Table XXVII is reprinted from *Railroad Curves and Earthwork*, 7th ed., by C. Frank Allen, by permission of Professor Allen's estate and of his publisher, the McGraw-Hill Book Company, Inc.

C.F.M.

Worcester, Massachusetts
January 1956

CONTENTS

Part I: Basic Principles

1. Route Location 1
2. Simple Curves 12
3. Compound and Reverse Curves 39
4. Parabolic Curves 53
5. Spirals 68
6. Earthwork 96

Part II: Practical Applications

7. Special Curve Problems 137
8. Curve Problems in Highway Design 159
9. Railroad Surveys 231
10. Highway Surveys 266
11. Surveys for Other Routes 282
12. Aerial Photography in Route Surveying 290

Appendix: Partial Theory of the Spiral 311

Part III. Tables 1
Index 313

PART I
BASIC PRINCIPLES

CHAPTER 1

ROUTE LOCATION

1–1. Introduction.—This chapter comprises an outline of the basic considerations affecting the general problem of route location. The material is non-mathematical, but it is necessary for a clear understanding of the purposes served by the technical matters in the remaining chapters of Part I. Specific practical applications of these basic considerations to the location of highways, railroads, and other routes of transportation and communication are given in Part II.

1–2. Definition of Route Surveying.—Route surveying includes all field work and requisite calculations (together with maps, profiles, and other drawings) involved in the planning and construction of any route of transportation. If the word *transportation* be taken to refer not only to the transportation of persons but also to the movement of liquids and gases and to the transmission of power and messages, then route surveying is a very broad subject. Among the important engineering structures thus included are: highways and railroads; aqueducts, canals, and flumes; pipe lines for water, sewage, oil, and gas; cableways and belt conveyors; and power, telephone, and telegraph transmission lines.

Though this definition of route surveying serves to distinguish the subject from other branches of surveying, it is customary to assume that projects designated as route surveys have considerable magnitude. The setting of a few telephone poles along a highway or the staking out of several blocks of city street scarcely fits the definition. There must be definite termini a considerable distance apart. In such a situation, route surveys are for two purposes: (1) determining the best *general route* between the termini; (2) fixing the alignment, grades, and other details of the *selected route*. Sound engineering principles require that the route be chosen in such a way that the project may be constructed and operated with the greatest economy and utility.

1–3. Relation of Project to Economics.—Every route-surveying project involves economic problems both large and small. *By far the most important question is whether or not to construct the project.* Essentially, this decision is based on a comparison of the cost of the enterprise with the probable financial returns or social advantages to be expected. In some cases the question can be answered after a careful preliminary study without field work; in others, extensive surveys and cost estimates must first be made.

However simple or complex the project may be, it is rarely possible for the engineer alone to answer this basic economic question. To his studies must be added those of the persons responsible for the financial and managerial policies of the organization. In the case of a public project the broad social and political objectives also carry weight.

The engineer responsible for conducting route surveys is not solely a technician. In addition to his indispensable aid in solving the larger economic problems, he is continually confronted with smaller ones in the field and office. For example, the relatively simple matter of deciding which of several methods is to be used in developing a topographic map of a strip of territory is, basically, an economic problem that involves the purpose of the survey, the terrain, and the equipment and personnel available.

1–4. Relation of Project to Design.—Design problems in route location are closely related to route surveying. Some matters of design must precede the field work; others are dependent on it. For example, in order that the field work for a proposed new highway may be done efficiently, the designers must have chosen—at least tentatively—not only the termini and possible intermediate connections but also such design details as the number of traffic lanes, width of right-of-way, maximum grade, minimum radius of curve, and minimum sight distance. On the other hand, considerable field work must be done before the designers can fix the exact alignment, grade elevations, shoulder widths, and culvert locations to fit the selected standards safely and with the greatest over-all economy. The interrelationship between modern highway surveying and design is outlined in Art. 10-2.

1–5. Basic Factors of Alignment and Grades.—In route location it is usually found that the termini and possible intermediate controlling points are at different elevations. Moreover, the topography and existing physical features rarely permit a straight location between the points. These circumstances invariably require the introduction of vertical and horizontal changes in direction; therefore, grades, vertical curves, and horizontal curves are important features of route surveying and design.

Curvature is not inherently objectionable. Though a straight line is the shortest distance between two points, it is also the most monotonous—a consideration of some aesthetic importance in the location of scenic highways. The device of curvature gives the designer limitless opportunities to fit a location to the natural swing of the topography in such a way as to be both pleasing and economical. Excessive or poorly designed curvature, however, may introduce serious operating hazards, or may add greatly to the costs of constructing, maintaining, or operating over the route.

Steep grades are likely to have the same effects on safety and costs as excessive curvature. It should be emphasized, nevertheless, that problems of curves and grades are ordinarily interrelated. Thus, on highway and railroad location it is often the practice to increase the distance between two fixed points in order to reduce the grade. This process, known as "development," necessarily adds to the total curvature. It is not always a feasible solution, for the added curvature may be more objectionable than the original steep grade.

The aim of good location should be the attainment of consistent conditions with a proper balance between curvature and grade. This is especially true in highway location, owing to the fact that each vehicle is individually operated and the driver often is unfamiliar with the particular highway. Many highway accidents occur at a point where there is a sudden and misleading variation from the condition of curvature, grade, or sight distance found on an adjacent section of the same highway. To produce a harmonious balance between curvature and grade, and to do it economically, requires that the engineer possess broad experience, mature judgment, and a thorough knowledge of the objectives of the project.

1-6. Influence of Type of Project.—The type of route to be built between given termini has a decided influence on its location. As an example, the best location for a railroad would not necessarily be the most suitable one for a power-transmission line. A railroad requires a location having fairly flat grades and curves. Moreover, there are usually intermediate controlling points such as major stream and highway crossings, mountain passes, and revenue-producing markets. In contrast, power is transmitted as readily up a vertical cable as along a horizontal one. Grades, therefore, have no significance, and river and highway crossings present no unusual problems. Where changes in direction are needed, they are made at angle towers. Consequently, the alignment is as straight as possible from generating station to sub-station.

1-7. Influence of Terrain.—The character of the terrain between termini or major controlling points is apt to impress a characteristic pattern upon a route location, particularly in the case of a highway or a railroad. Terrain may be generally classified as *level*, *rolling*, or *mountainous*.

In comparatively level regions the line may be straight for long distances, minor deviations being introduced merely to skirt watercourses, to avoid poor foundations, or possibly to reduce land damages. On an important project, however, the artificial control imposed by following section lines or other political subdivisions should not be permitted to govern.

In rolling country the location pattern depends on the orientation of the ridges and valleys with respect to the general direction of the route. Parallel orientation may result in a *valley line* having flat grades, much curvature, frequent culverts and bridges, and fill in excess of cut; or it may permit a *ridge line* (from which the word *highway* originated) on which the alignment and drainage problems are simpler. To connect two such situations, and also in case the ridges are oblique to the general direction of the route, there may be a *side-hill line*. This has the characteristics of uniformly rising grades, curvature fitted to the hillsides, and relatively light, balanced grading.

Where the ridges and valleys are approximately at right angles to the general direction of the route, the typical pattern which results may be called a *cross-drainage line*. Here the location of passes through the ridges and the location of crossings over the major streams constitute important controlling points between which the line may be of the side-hill type. Generally, a cross-drainage line involves steep grades, heavy grading with alternate cuts and fills, expensive bridges, and curvature considerably less than that on a valley line.

Mountainous terrain imposes the severest burden upon the ingenuity of the locating engineer. No simple pattern or set of rules fits all situations. Short sections of each of the types of lines previously described must be inserted as conditions require. "Development," even to the extent of switchbacks and loops, may be the only alternative to expensive tunnel construction.

1–8. Sequence of Field and Office Work.—The definition of route surveying stated in Art. 1–2 referred to field work and calculations concerning both planning and construction. Though these operations vary with different organizations, and particularly with the nature and scope of the project, the following is a typical outline of the sequence of field and office work:

For Planning

(a) The conception of the project, and preliminary office studies regarding its desirability and feasibility.

(b) Field *reconnaissance* of the terrain between the termini, followed by further office studies and recommendation report.

(c) *Preliminary surveys* over one or more locations along the general route recommended in the reconnaissance report.

(d) *Office studies* consisting of preparation of a map from preliminary survey data; projection of a tentative alignment and profile; and preliminary estimate of quantities and cost.

(e) *Location survey* involving staking of projected location, complete with curves; minor adjustment of alignment and grades; cross-sectioning for more accurate earthwork estimate; ties to property lines and existing im-

provements; and field measurements for design of miscellaneous structures.

For Construction

(*f*) *Office work* including preparation of specifications and
drawings covering all details of the project; negotiations
for acquiring right-of-way or easement; and advertising
for bids.

(*g*) *Construction surveys* including reestablishment of final
location; setting reference stakes, grade stakes, and
slope stakes for controlling the construction; making
periodic measurements and estimates of work done, to
serve as a basis for partial payments to the contractor;
taking final cross-sections and other measurements of
the completed project, to serve as a basis both for final
payment and for preparation of "record" plans; and
setting right-of-way monuments in accordance with prepared legal descriptions.

1–9. Importance of the Reconnaissance.—Second in importance to the primary question—whether or not to build
the project—is the selection of the *general route* between the
termini.   This is usually determined by the *reconnaissance*.

The statement by Wellington,* "*The reconnaissance must
not be of a line, but of an area,*" is a most apt one.   The extent
of the area depends, of course, on the type of project and the
nature of the terrain, but the area must be broad enough to
cover all practicable routes joining the termini.   Of particular
importance is the need for guarding against the natural
tendency to favor an obviously feasible location.   It is
possible that country which is covered with tangled under-
growth, or is otherwise rough for foot travel on reconnaissance,
may hide a much better location than is available in more
settled or open territory.

With regard to the importance of the "art of reconnaissance"
and the attitude of the engineer toward it, nowhere will more
effective comments be found than in Wellington's classic
treatise.*   Though written by that author in 1887 for the

---

*Reprinted by permission from *Economic Theory of the Location of Rail-
ways* by A. M. Wellington, published by John Wiley & Sons, Inc., 1915.

instruction of engineers on railroad location, the following statements are timeless in their application to all types of route location:

"... there is nothing against which a locating engineer will find it necessary to be more constantly on his guard than the drawing of hasty and unfounded conclusions, especially of an unfavorable character, from apparent evidence wrongly interpreted. If his conclusions on reconnaissance are unduly favorable, there is no great harm done— nothing more at the worst will ensue than an unnecessary amount of surveying; but a hasty conclusion that some line is not feasible, or that further improvements in it cannot be made, or even sometimes—often very absurdly—that no other line of any kind exists than the one which has chanced to be discovered—these are errors which may have disastrous consequences.

"On this account, if for no other, the locating engineer should cultivate ... what may be called an optimistic habit of mind. He should not allow himself to enter upon his work with the feeling that any country is seriously difficult, but rather that the problem before him is simply to find the line, which undoubtedly exists, and that he can only fail to do so from some blindness or oversight of his own, which it will be his business to guard against.

"For the reason that there is so much danger of radical error *in the selection of the lines to be surveyed* (or, rather, of the lines not to be examined), it results that THE WORST ERRORS OF LOCATION GENERALLY ORIGINATE IN THE RECONNAISSANCE. This truth once grasped, the greatest of all dangers, over-confidence in one's own infallibility, is removed."

If, as often happens, the reconnaissance is entrusted to one engineer, he should have mature experience in the promotional, financial, and engineering aspects of similar projects. It is not enough that he be an experienced locating engineer, for such a man is likely to concentrate upon the purely physical possibilities of a route and to overlook the related commercial or social values. Furthermore, he should be able to sense the significance of present trends and their probable effect upon the future utility of the project, or to realize when to seek a specialist's advice in such matters.

1–10. Purposes of Preliminary Surveys.—A preliminary survey follows the general route recommended in the reconnaissance report. The most important purpose of such a survey is to obtain the data for plotting an accurate map of a strip of territory along one or more promising routes. This map serves as the basis for projecting the final alignment and profile, at least tentatively. Enough data are also obtained from which to make an estimate of earthwork quantities, of the sizes of drainage structures, and needed right-of-way. Taken together, these data permit the compilation of a fairly close cost estimate.

Preliminary surveys differ greatly in method and precision. Invariably, however, there is at least one traverse (compass, stadia, or transit-and-tape) which serves as a framework for the topographical details. Elevations along the traverse line and tie measurements to existing physical features are essential. Accurate contours may or may not be needed, the requirement depending on the type of the project.

Detailed methods of running preliminary surveys adapted to particular types of routes will be found in Chapters 9, 10, and 11.

1–11. Proper Use of Topography.—On new locations of routes over which grades are particularly important, an accurate contour map is indispensable. A relocation of an existing route, such as a highway, may sometimes be made by revising the preliminary survey directly on the ground. This method, termed "field location" or "direct location," is not recommended for a new line. It is true that some engineers seem to have uncanny ability for locating a satisfactory line—though not necessarily the best one—by direct field methods. This natural gift is not to be belittled, but it should be subordinated in difficult terrain to careful office studies aided by a contour map.

The primary purpose of the contour map is to serve as a basis for making a "paper location" of the final center line. On such a map the locating engineer is able to scan a large area at once. By graphical methods he can study various locations in a small fraction of the time required for a field party to survey the lines on the ground. Furthermore, he is not subject to the natural optical illusions which often mislead even the most experienced engineer in the field. An added advantage of the contour map, provided it is extensive enough, is to supply visible evidence that no better line has been overlooked.

It is possible, however, to put too much reliance upon map topography. Particularly to be avoided is the temptation to control the work from the office by making such a meticulous paper location, even to the extent of complete notes for staking all curves, that the field work of final location becomes a mere routine of carrying out "instructions from headquarters." No contour map, no matter how accurate it may be, can impress upon the mind more forcibly than field examination such details as the true significance of length and depth of cuts and fills; the nature of the materials and foundations; susceptibility to slides, snow drifting, and other maintenance difficulties; or the aesthetic values of the projected location. At best, the map facilitates making what might be termed a "semi-final location," which is to be further revised in minor details during the location survey.

1–12. Function of Location Survey.—The purpose of the location survey is to transfer the paper location, complete with curves, to the ground. It is too much to expect that this line on the ground will conform to the paper location in every detail. It is almost certain that there will be minor deviations, resulting usually from errors in the preliminary traverse or in the taking or plotting of the topography. An exact agreement does not assure the excellence of the location; it merely proves the geometric accuracy of the field and office work. Consequently, regardless of the "fit" with the paper location, the engineer should be constantly on watch for opportunities to make those minor adjustments in alignment or grades which only close observation of the field conditions will reveal.

When staked, the final location is usually cross-sectioned for closer determination of earthwork quantities. In addition, tie measurements to property lines are made to serve for preparing right-of-way descriptions, and all necessary field data are obtained to permit the detailed design of miscellaneous structures.

1–13. Relation of Surveying to Engineering.—Before we leave these basic considerations to study the technical aspects of route surveying, it should be pointed out that surveying and mapping, as ordinarily practiced, are not engineering; they are merely methods of obtaining and portraying data needed as a prelude to the design and construction of engineering works.

During the study of the chapters which follow, it will be natural for the student to concentrate on the geometrical and instrumental techniques. However, the course in Route Surveying will not reach its potential value unless it is more than drill in field and office practice. The student, stimulated by the instructor's examples and illustrations, should attempt to look beyond the technical details and gain some insight into the factors which lead to the conception of a particular project. Knowledge of those factors will give him a better appreciation of the engineering surveys—their planning, the controlling specifications, and the usefulness of the data to the designers.

To be of the greatest usefulness, without being unduly costly, the surveys, maps, and computations should be only as complete and accurate as needed for the ultimate purpose. For some purposes the utmost in accuracy is required. For others, extreme niceties are too costly and time-consuming; they may be replaced by approximate methods and short cuts. As an example, much time is often wasted in "exact" calculation of yardage estimates prior to construction, only to find that shrinkage, compaction, overbreak, or stripping allowances change the estimated values by large amounts. This is not to imply that grading calculations may always be done by approximate methods. Accuracy is always required, for example, in determination of yardage for payment to contractors. One trait of a good engineer is his judgment of the degree of precision required in obtaining data and computing values for use.

Surveying and mapping are essential prerequisites to engineering design for mass transportation. Despite the growing file of good maps, the rapid modernization of our transportation systems is creating expanding demands for surveying and mapping services. In the field of highway engineering alone, the total distance covered by surveys and resurveys for a recent year was estimated to reach 26,000 miles. In designing a large transportation project, extensive surveying operations are involved in the early reconnaissance, in the detailed preliminary and location surveys, and in all the work leading to the preparation of topographic maps, profiles, cross sections, and other working drawings. If to these there are added the construction layout and "as-built" record surveys, it is apparent that a large portion of the total engineering costs is absorbed by surveying and mapping.

In contrast to the leisurely pace of highway construction in the early part of this century, wherein the ordinary piece-meal survey served the purpose, we now have vast and costly projects. The magnitude and complexity of the 427-mile New York State Thruway and the heavily traveled turnpikes of Pennsylvania, New Jersey, Ohio, and Massachusetts are current examples. Even these may be dwarfed by larger projects already conceived, such as the Mississippi River Parkway, for which map reconnaissance of 50,000 square miles has yielded over 8,000 miles of alternate routes.[19] Survey and mapping methods must be designed to keep pace with the advanced design and construction techniques used on such vast projects.

The use of photogrammetric methods (described in Chapter 12) represents the most important advance in surveying and mapping for modern mass transportation. In addition to reducing mapping costs, photogrammetry can save time, which may be translated into a substantial reduction in interest charges during construction.

In fitting surveying and mapping into the plans for a transportation project, saving in time by use of short-cut methods should not be achieved at the expense of reduction in the ultimate required accuracy. Time saved by short cuts in control surveys, for example, may be lost many times over in transferring the paper location to the ground or in monumenting the right of way. During construction, one field change caused by poor original surveys may delay the work longer than the time saved earlier by the short-cut survey methods.

By keeping in mind the ultimate accuracies required for the various phases of a project and adopting well-planned, skillfully executed methods of surveying and mapping, even at the expense of some extra time, the whole project will have a firmer base around which the design and construction operations can be planned. This kind of surveying and mapping is true engineering.

---

[19]See bibliography at the end of Chapter 12.

CHAPTER 2

SIMPLE CURVES

2-1. Foreword.—Every route has a calculable geometric alignment. The form may be a simple series of straight lines and angles, as in the case of a power transmission line, or it may be an intricate combination of straight lines and curves.

The primary purpose of any curve is to provide the required change in direction in the form best suited to the operating characteristics. Secondary considerations are reasonable economy in construction cost and ease of staking the curve in the field.

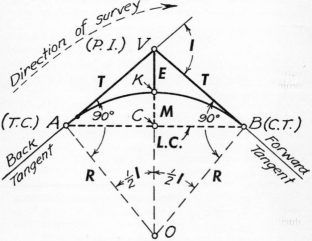

Fig. 2-1. Simple-curve layout

Horizontal curves are usually arcs of circles or of spirals. Generally, the circular arc makes up the greater portion of a curve. The arcs of varying radii, or spirals, provide a gradual transition between the circular arc and the tangents.

Vertical curves joining straight sections of grade line are invariably parabolic arcs. When vertical and horizontal curves overlap, their study is simplified by considering them separately.

2-2. Definitions and Notation.—A *simple curve* consists of a circular arc tangent to two straight sections of a route. Though spiral transitions are commonly used at the ends of circular arcs on modern highways and railroads, a thorough knowledge of the simple curve—its basic geometry, calculation, and method of staking—is necessary for an understanding of more complex curve problems.

There is no universally accepted notation. That shown in Fig. 2-1, however, is commonly used in recent practice. (In this diagram, parts of the curve layout frequently surveyed in the field are drawn as solid lines, whereas geometric construction lines and curve parts infrequently surveyed are shown dotted.) The intersection of the tangents at V is called the *vertex*, or *point of intersection*, abbreviated P.I. The deflection angle between the tangents is denoted by I; it is equal to the *central angle* of the curve. For a survey progressing in the direction indicated, the tangent up to the P.I. is called the *initial tangent*, or *back tangent*; that beyond the P.I. is the *forward tangent*. The beginning of the circular arc at A is known as the T.C. (tangent to curve); the end at B, as the C.T. (curve to tangent). In a simple curve the T.C. and the C.T. are equidistant from the P.I. The T.C. is sometimes designated as the P.C. (point of curve) or B.C. (beginning of curve). Corresponding terms for the C.T. are P.T. (point of tangent) and E.C. (end of curve).

Certain lines on the curve layout are very useful in calculations or for field work. Those shown in Fig. 2-1 are: the distance from the P.I. to the T.C. (or C.T.), known as the *tangent distance*, T; the distance from the P.I. to the mid-point K of the *curve*, called the *external distance*, E; and the *radius* of the circular arc, designated by R. Also shown, though of lesser importance, are the *long chord*, L.C., which is the distance between the T.C. and the C.T.; and the *middle ordinate*, M, or the distance from the mid-point C of the long chord to the mid-point K of the curve.

2-3. General Formulas.—From Fig. 2-1 the following important relations may be written practically by inspection:

$$T = R \tan \tfrac{1}{2}I \qquad\qquad (2\text{-}1)$$

$$E = R \sec \tfrac{1}{2}I - R = R \operatorname{exsec} \tfrac{1}{2}I \qquad (2\text{-}2)$$

$$\text{L.C.} = 2\,R \sin \tfrac{1}{2}I \qquad\qquad (2\text{-}3)$$

$$M = R - R \cos \tfrac{1}{2}I = R \operatorname{vers} \tfrac{1}{2}I \qquad (2\text{-}4)$$

If tables of exsecants and versed sines are not available, the most convenient formula for calculation by logarithmic or natural functions may be chosen from among the following relations:

$$E = T \tan \tfrac{1}{4}I \qquad\qquad (2\text{-}5)$$

$$E = R \tan \tfrac{1}{2}I \tan \tfrac{1}{4}I \qquad\qquad (2\text{-}6)$$

$$M = R \sin \tfrac{1}{2}I \tan \tfrac{1}{4}I \qquad\qquad (2\text{-}7)$$

$$M = R(1 - \cos \tfrac{1}{2}I) \qquad\qquad (2\text{-}8)$$

The remaining formulas needed for computing and staking a simple-curve layout are developed in the articles which follow.

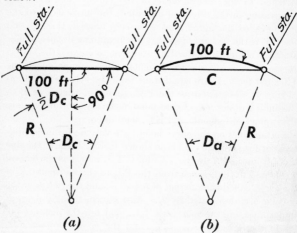

Fig. 2-2. Definitions of degree of curve

2-4. Degree of Curve.—The curvature of a circular arc is perfectly defined by its radius. However, where the radius is long, as on modern highway and railroad alignment, the center of the curve is inaccessible or remote. In this case the radius is valueless for surveying operations, though still needed in certain computations; it must be replaced by a different characteristic of the curve, which is more directly useful in the field. The characteristic commonly used is known as the *degree of curve*, D. Though several definitions of degree of curve may be found, all are based upon the fact that a circle is a curve having a constant angular change in direction per unit of distance. The two most widely used are the chord definition and the arc definition of D.

According to the *chord definition* the degree of curve is the central angle subtended by a 100-foot chord. It is denoted by D_c, as indicated in Fig. 2–2(a).

According to the *arc definition* the degree of curve is the central angle subtended by a 100-foot arc. It is denoted by D_a, as indicated in Fig. 2–2(b).

By inspection of Fig. 2–2(a), it is seen that

$$\sin \tfrac{1}{2}D_c = \frac{50}{R} \qquad (2\text{–}9)$$

In Fig. 2–2(b),

$$D_a : 100 = 360° : 2\pi R$$

from which

$$D_a = \frac{5,729.58}{R} \qquad (2\text{–}10)$$

It is rarely necessary to use equation 2–9 or equation 2–10. When D is given, the value of R or log R should be taken from Table I. For approximate calculations using either definition of D,

$$D = \frac{5,730}{R} \qquad (2\text{–}11) \textbf{ Approx.}$$

Neither definition of D is perfectly adapted to all phases of calculation and field work. Both involve certain approximations in field work, done the most convenient way, and certain small corrections where a high degree of precision is required. The chord definition has been used almost invariably by the railroads. It is sometimes called the "railroad definition" of D. On the other hand, highway practice has tended toward greater use of the arc definition. However, modern standards of alignment for high-speed operation over both railroads and highways have practically reduced to an academic matter all controversy over the merits of a particular definition.

A 2° curve computed and staked according to either definition is substantially the same curve on the ground. Nevertheless, it will usually be necessary for the engineer to conform to the definition of D used by the organization with which he is associated. Moreover, he may frequently be required to use the other definition of D, as in performing calculations for fitting a relocation to existing alignment. For these reasons the theoretical treatment in this book covers both definitions. The tables in Part III are exceptionally complete, as they are designed to simplify curve calculations based upon either definition of D.

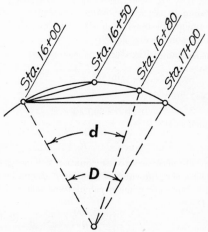

Fig. 2-3. Subchords

2-5. Measurements on Curves.—Regardless of whether the chord definition or the arc definition of D is used, measurements along a curve must be made by taping a series of chords. An isolated curve may be staked conveniently by dividing the central angle into an equal number of parts. The resulting chords with their directions determined by any appropriate method then form an inscribed polygon of equal sides. However, on most route surveys the curves are parts of the continuous alignment over which it is convenient to carry the regular survey stationing without a break. In consequence, a curve rarely begins or ends at a whole station; accordingly, chords less than 100 feet long, called *subchords*, will adjoin the T.C. and the C.T. The methods of treating these subchords are responsible for the slight approximations or corrections mentioned in Art. 2–4.

Fig. 2–3 represents a portion of a circular arc having certain stakes located thereon. For the chord definition of D, stations 16 and 17 will be exactly 100 feet apart as measured along the chord joining those stations. For the arc definition, however, the stations will be slightly closer together since, by definition, they are separated by exactly 100 feet as measured around the arc.

It is frequently necessary to set stakes on a curve at closer intervals than at whole stations, as at sta. 16+50, for example. The only logical position for this stake is exactly midway between stations 16 and 17, regardless of the definition of D. Thus, sta. 16+50 would be separated from the adjacent whole stations by chords which are of equal length but are *not 50 feet long*. They would be slightly greater or slightly less than 50 feet, the actual length depending on the definition of D. Such chords are loosely referred to as "50-foot subchords."

On precise work, however, it is advisable to use a more definite terminology. All uncertainty is eliminated by calling the actual length of a chord its *true length*, and designating as the *nominal length* the value found by taking the difference between the stationing at the ends of the chord. The nominal length may be further illustrated by imagining the arc in Fig. 2–3 between stations 16 and 17 to be divided into exactly 100 equal parts. Theoretically, sta. 16+80 is at the 80th division, and it is joined to sta. 16 by an 80-foot *nominal subchord*; but it is located in the field by taping a *true subchord* of 80 ± feet from sta. 16.

A summary on lengths of subchords follows:

> **For chord definition of D**—*True subchords are* **longer** *than nominal subchords.*
>
> **For arc definition of D**—*True subchords are* **shorter** *than nominal subchords; nominal subchords are equal to true lengths of arc.*

If d, Fig. 2–3, is the central angle subtended by any nominal subchord c_n, then $d : D = c_n : 100$, or

$$d = \frac{c_n D}{100} \qquad (2\text{–}12)$$

The true subchord is

$$c_t = 2\,R\,\sin\tfrac{1}{2}d \qquad (2\text{–}13)$$

Note the analogy of formula 2–13 to formula 2–3. True subchords are given in Table II.

2–6. Length of Curve.—The *length of curve, L,* is the nominal distance around the curve. It equals the difference between the stationing of the C.T. and the T.C.

For either definition of D,

$$L : 100 = I : D$$

or

$$L = \frac{100 I}{D} \qquad (2\text{–}14)$$

For the arc definition of D, formula 2–14 obviously gives the true length of the total circular arc; whereas, for the chord definition, it gives the total length of the 100-foot chords and nominal subchords between the T.C. and C.T. In the latter case the true length of arc is slightly greater than L. If needed, it may be obtained theoretically from the relation $L = \dfrac{IR}{57.2958}$; but a more practical method is to use Table II or Table VI.

Example.—*Given:* $I = 34°14'$; $D_c = 9°$; $R = 637.275$ (Table I).

$34° = 0.593412$ rad. (Table VI)	True length of arc
$14' = 0.004072$ rad. (Table VI)	$= 0.597484 \times 637.275$
Sum $= 0.597484$ rad. (Table VI)	$= 380.76$

For check of above by Table II see example on page 19.

2–7. Use of Tables.—The formulas developed thus far may be solved with the aid of tables of logarithmic or natural trigonometric functions. However, certain calculations are expedited, or even eliminated, by using special curve tables. The example on page 19, given in outline form, illustrates the use of some of the tables given in Part III.

Example.—*Given:* $I = 34°14'$; $D = 9°$.

For chord definition of D	For arc definition of D

For chord definition of *D*

$T = 1764.5 \div 9$ (Table VIII)
$= 196.06$
$+\quad 0.19$ (Table IX)
$T = \overline{196.25}$

$E = 265.5 \div 9$ (Table VIII)
$= 29.50$
$+\quad 0.03$ (Table X)
$E = \overline{29.53}$

$\text{L.C.} = 2R \sin \tfrac{1}{2}I$
Result, using Tables I and
XX (or XXII): L.C. $= 375.12$

$M = R \text{ vers } \tfrac{1}{2}I$
Result, using Tables I and
XX (or XXIII): $M = 28.23$

$$L = \frac{100I}{D} = \frac{100 \times 34.2333}{9}$$

or, to avoid decimals of degrees, convert I and D to minutes, giving

$$L = \frac{205,400}{540} = 380.37$$

For true length of arc (if needed) use arc for 1 sta. $= 100.103$ (Table II). Then, excess arc in L stations $= 0.103 \times 3.80 = 0.39$.
Therefore, true arc length $= 380.37 + 0.39 = 380.76$

Examples of true subchords

Nominal	True	
100	100	
50	50.04	(Table II)
82.48	82.51	(Table III)

For arc definition of *D*

$T = 1764.5 \div 9$ (Table VIII)
$= 196.06$

$E = 265.5 \div 9$ (Table VIII)
$= 29.50$

$\text{L.C.} = 2R \sin \tfrac{1}{2}I$
Result, using Tables I and
XX (or XXII): L.C. $= 374.74$

$M = R \text{ vers } \tfrac{1}{2}I$
Result, using Tables I and
XX (or XXIII): $M = 28.20$

$$L = \frac{100I}{D}$$

Compute L as shown in adjacent column, giving
$$L = 380.37$$

From definition of D_a, the true length of arc equals L as computed above.

Examples of true subchords

Nominal	True	
100	99.90	(Table II)
50	49.99	(Table II)
82.48	82.42	(Table IV)

The example on page 19 not only shows the utility of certain tables but also gives an idea of the effect of using different definitions of D. Whether the differences between the computed values of corresponding parts of the curve are insignificant or important depends on the circumstances. If the curve is one staked on semi-final location prior to grading, they are probably unimportant; if the curve is staked on final location, for setting track centers or forms for concrete paving, the differences are large enough to warrant close adherence to a particular definition of D in all calculations. On modern high-speed alignment where D is 3° or less, the two definitions of D give practically the same results.

2–8. Locating the T.C. and C.T.—In locating a curve on a projected alignment, the tangents are run to an intersection at the P.I., the angle I is measured, and the stationing is carried forward along the back tangent as far as the P.I. (see Art. 7–3 for a description of the process when the P.I. is inaccessible). The degree of curve will usually have been selected from the paper-location study. If it has not been, a suitable value may be determined by measuring the approximate E (or T) needed to give a good fit with the topography. The tabulated E (or T) for a 1° curve (Table VIII) divided by the approximate E (or T) gives a value of D which will fit the field conditions. Usually this D is rounded off to a figure convenient for calculation, and of course it must be within the limiting specifications for the project.

The values of T and L are next computed, and from them the stationing of the T.C. and C.T. are determined as follows:

$$\text{Sta. T.C.} = \text{Sta. P.I.} - T$$

$$\text{Sta. C.T.} = \text{Sta. T.C.} + L \text{ (nominal)}$$

For staking and checking the curve it is necessary to set hubs at the T.C. and the C.T. This is done by taping the calculated T backward and forward from the P.I. Sometimes it is more convenient to set the T.C. by taping from a nearer hub (P.O.T.) on the back tangent. In case the curve is long or the terrain is difficult for taping, it is also advisable to set a check hub at the mid-point of the curve by taping the *exact value* of E from the P.I. along the bisector of the angle.

2–9. Deflection-Angle Method.—The convenient deflection-angle method of locating points on a simple curve is based on a proposition in geometry: *an angle formed by a tangent and a chord is measured by one-half the intercepted arc.*

In Fig. 2–4, a, b, and c represent 100-ft stations on a portion of a simple curve, a being less than one station beyond the T.C. By definition, as indicated in Figs. 2–2(a) and 2–2(b), each central angle between full stations is equal to D; the angle subtended by the first subchord is d_1, Fig. 2–3. The angles VAa, VAb, and VAc in Fig. 2–4 are known as the *deflection angles*, or *total deflections*, to the stations on the curve. From the foregoing proposition they are equal to one-half the corresponding central angles. Thus, the deflection angle to locate c from a set-up at the T.C. is $\frac{1}{2}(d_1+2D)$.

The *subdeflection* for the fractional station to a is $\frac{1}{2}d_1$; it is equal to $\frac{c_1D}{200}$, c_1 being the nominal subchord length (see formula 2–12). It is apparent that, once the first subdeflection has been calculated, the total deflections to the remaining full stations are readily found by adding successive increments of $\frac{1}{2}D$. Between the last full station on the curve and the C.T., there will be a second subchord, c_2. Its subdeflection $\frac{1}{2}d_2$ should be calculated and added to the total deflection up to the last full station. If the sum equals $\frac{1}{2}I$, the arithmetic is checked.

In practice, subdeflections are usually small and are best computed in minutes from either of the following formulas:

$$\tfrac{1}{2}d \text{ (in minutes)} = 0.3 \ c_n \ D° \qquad (2\text{–}15)$$

$$\tfrac{1}{2}d \text{ (in minutes)} = c_n \times \text{defl. per ft*} \qquad (2\text{–}16)$$

The distances taped in connection with the deflection angles *are not* the rays from the T.C. to the various points on the curve. Theoretically they are the successive true chords from point to point, starting at the T.C. Therefore, once the deflection angles have been figured, there is practically no added computation. However, the non-coincidence of tape and line of sight may be slightly confusing in the field work.

---

*In formula 2–16, *defl. per ft* means "deflection in minutes per foot of nominal chord" (or per foot of station). Thus, if $D=9°=540'$, $\frac{1}{2}D=270'$ and defl. per ft$=2.7'$. Values of defl. per ft are listed in Table I.

Example.—*Given:* Sta. P.I. $= 24+63.8$; $I = 34°14'$. Stakes
to be set for semi-final highway location; curve to pass approximately 30 ft inside vertex; stakes needed at full stations and
half-stations; distances to tenths and deflections to nearest
minute adequate. Use arc definition of D.

Approx. $D_a = \dfrac{265.5}{30} = 8.85°$ (Table VIII). Round off to 9°
curve with defl. per ft $= 2.7'$. The problem now becomes that
in Art. 2–7, from which $T = 196.1$, $L = 380.4$, and $E = 29.5$.

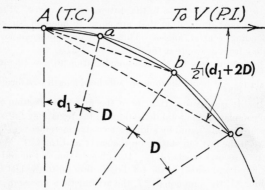

Fig. 2–4. Deflection-angle method

Sta. P.I. $= 24+63.8$
$-T = 1+96.1$

Sta. T.C. $= 22+67.7$ $c_1 = 32.3$ $\frac{1}{2}d_1 = 2.7 \times 32.3 = 1°27'$
$+L = 3+80.4$ 23 to 26 $= 300.0$ $\frac{1}{2}D \times 3 = 13°30'$

Sta. C.T. $= 26+48.1$ $c_2 = 48.1$ $\frac{1}{2}d_2 = 2.7 \times 48.1 = 2°10'$

                               Sum $= 380.4$ Sum $= 17°07'$
                                      $= L$ $= \frac{1}{2}I$
                               (check)   (check)

There follows a typical form for setting up the notes on the
left-hand page of the field book. Notes run upward in order
to simplify orienting sketches on the right-hand page, where
the center line is used to represent the survey line.

Form of notes for simple curve

Sta.	Point	Total Defl.	Calc. Bearing	Mag. Bearing	Curve Data
27					$I = 34°14'$
+50					$D_a = 9°$ rt.
+48.1	⊙C.T.	17°07′	N50°41′E	N50½°E	P.I. $= 24+63.8$
26		14°57′			$T = 196.1$
+50		12°42′			$L = 380.4$
25	⊙	10°27′			$E = 29.5$
+50		8°12′			Defl. per ft
24		5°57′			$= 2.7'$
+50	⊙	3°42′			
23		1°27′			
+67.7	⊙T.C.	0°00′	N16°27′E	N16½°E	
+50					
22					

2–10. Transit Set-ups on Curve.—In the preceding description the implication is that the entire curve is staked from a set-up at the T.C. This is often true. However, there are

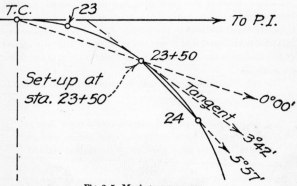

Fig. 2–5. Moving up on curve

circumstances (see Art. 2–11) which make this procedure impracticable or even impossible. Should such be the case, *deflections are computed as though for a set-up at the T.C.* By proper manipulation of the transit it can be set up at any staked point on the curve, and the staking can then continue from that set-up without altering the previously computed deflections.

Fig. 2–5 shows the first portion of the curve calculated in Art. 2–9. It is assumed that the curve has been staked as far as sta. 23+50 from a set-up at the T.C., and that conditions make it difficult to sight beyond from that set-up. If, with the transit moved to sta. 23+50, the vernier is set to 0° and the telescope is inverted and then backsighted to the T.C. and plunged, the condition will be as represented by the dotted line from the T.C. through sta. 23+50. If now the upper motion is loosened and the telescope is turned clockwise, the line of sight will be on the local tangent when the vernier reads 3°42' and will be in the correct direction for locating sta. 24 when the vernier reads 5°57'. These facts follow directly from the geometric principle noted at the beginning of Art. 2–9.

An extension of Fig. 2–5 would show that, for a set-up at sta. 25 with the transit to be oriented by a backsight to the previous set-up at sta. 23+50, the vernier should first be set at 3°42' *on the correct side of 0°*. Backsighting with the telescope reversed and then plunging would permit sighting the remaining points on the curve by using the total deflections opposite those stations in the transit notes. No added calculations are required if this method is followed; the only record of the set-ups is the symbol ⊙ in the *Point* column of the notes on page 23.

The preceding description may be summarized in a rule-of-thumb:

> *To move up on curve and retain original notes, occupy any station and backsight to any other station with the* **vernier** *set to the total deflection of the* **station sighted.**

Occasionally it may be desired to have the vernier read 0° when the line of sight is on the *local tangent* to the curve at a new set-up, as at the C.C. of a compound curve (see Art. 3–12). To do this the vernier must be set at the *difference between the tabulated deflections for station sighted and station* *occupied.** As in applying the rule-of-thumb, the surveyor must be careful to set the *vernier reading* for the backsight *on the correct side of 0°.*

2–11. Comments on Field Work.—*Transit set-ups* for staking the curve must be started at the T.C. or C.T. For short curves which are entirely visible from one set-up, it is preferable to occupy the C.T. and to tape the chords toward it from the T.C. By so doing, the longer sights are taken before possible settlement of the transit occurs. Moreover, one set-up is eliminated, for the transit is then in position for lining in the stakes along the forward tangent. For a set-up at the C.T., the transit is oriented by backsighting to the T.C. with the vernier reading 0° or to the P.I. with the vernier set at $\frac{1}{2}I$. In either case it is wise to check the angle to the other point, in order to verify the equality of the tangent distances.

In case the field conditions require one or more set-ups on the curve, it is good practice to occupy the T.C. first and to tape in a forward direction, moving up the transit according to the rule-of-thumb stated in Art. 2–10. The final portion of the curve is best located by setting up at the C.T. and taping *backward* to the previous set-up. This practice insures good tangencies at the T.C. and C.T., and throws any slight error into the curve where it is more easily adjusted.

A long curve, or one having a large central angle, may justify intermediate set-ups even though the entire curve is visible from either end. The consideration here is the required degree of accuracy in setting the points on the curve. When the tape and the line of sight intersect at a large angle, it is possible for the chainman to swing one end of the tape through a certain distance without detection by the transitman, thus throwing off the position of the point and introducing an accumulative taping error. The amount of this swing—and its relative importance on the particular work—is best deter-

---

*When this book is used as a textbook for a course in Route Surveying, it is recommended that students be given the opportunity to compute and stake at least one simple curve at this point in their study. Doing so will help to fix the principles more firmly in mind and contribute toward a better appreciation of the practical suggestions which follow.

mined by trial in the field.   As a general guide, the deflection angle from the transit to the taping point should be kept under 25° or 30°.

Field checks should be made at every convenient opportunity.   In locating the T.C. and the C.T., it is good insurance to double-chain the tangent distances, at least until the chainmen have demonstrated the reliability of their first measurements.   Less time will be lost if the check chaining is done while curve deflections are being computed.   Setting a check point at the middle of the curve may also be advisable (see Art. 2–8).

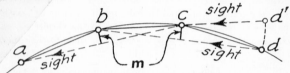

Fig. 2–6. Check of stake positions

Before definitely setting each stake on the curve, the head chainman should sight to the second stake back and verify the middle ordinate *m* to the intervening stake.   (See Fig. 2–6.) A sudden change in middle ordinate (for equidistant points on the curve) will reveal a mistake in setting off the deflection angle.   Otherwise, such an error might go undetected at the time or even fail to show up in the final closing check if the curve is flat.

The final check occurs at the extremity of the last chord taped.   This may be at the T.C., at the C.T., or at any intermediate stake previously set.   The best method is to mark an independent point by measuring the required distance and deflection from the final set-up.   The distance between this point and its theoretical equivalent at the stake previously set is a direct measure of the error of closure in the traverse around the tangent distances and curve chords.   This error should be consistent with the survey methods, the difficulty of the terrain, and the requirements of the project.

Chord lengths used in running curves depend principally on the degree of curve and on the purpose of the survey.   On *flat curves* in easy terrain, full stations suffice for the field work and for most construction purposes. Thus, for D_c true chords between full stations are exactly 100 feet long, and the end subchords may be considered equal to their nominal lengths (see Tables II and III). For D_a the end subchords may also be taken equal to their nominal (arc) lengths, but the chord for each of a long series of full stations may require a slight correction in order to reduce the systematic error in taping (see Tables II and IV).

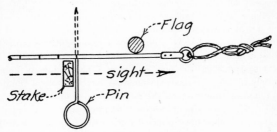

Fig. 2–7. Setting station stakes

On *sharp curves*, or in difficult terrain requiring frequent cross-sections, additional points between full stations are needed. Whether it is necessary to use true subchords instead of nominal subchords depends on the accuracy required. Table II shows at a glance the effect of the sharpness of the curve on the true lengths of nominal full chords and subchords. When Table II is used in conjunction with Tables III and IV, any degree of accuracy is readily obtainable. Study of Table II shows in general that chord corrections are unnecessary on curves flatter than about 5°. On sharper *chord-definition curves*, corrections may be eliminated by using 100-ft chords; whereas, on sharper *arc-definition curves*, shorter nominal subchords serve the same purpose.

Stakes are set on curves where needed for subsequent field work or for controlling construction. A tacked *hub*, with a *guard stake* designating the point and stationing, is set at each transit station. Important points, such as the P.I., T.C., and C.T., are carefully referenced. Points not occupied by the transit are identified by *station stakes*, which are driven and marked as in profile leveling.

Station stakes used for cross-sectioning prior to construction need not be individually centered by the transit. Doing this is of no practical value, and it wastes time if the stakes are hidden by grass or brush. A rapid method is shown in Fig. 2–7. The head chainman first obtains line from the transitman and then sets a range pole (flag) off line about the width of a stake and a few tenths of a foot beyond the station. He next verifies the middle ordinate (see Fig. 2–6). Then he stretches the tape tangent to the range pole and sets a chaining pin at the exact distance. Finally, he uses the point of the range pole to make a hole beside and slightly behind the point where the pin enters the ground, and proceeds to the next station with the pole and tape. The stakeman immediately drives a marked station stake into the hole at the pin, at the same time keeping the moving tape to one side with his foot. The pin should not be disturbed in the process; it remains in place until pulled by the rear chainman after the next forward pin is set.

By following the foregoing method on tangents and flat curves, station stakes will always be close enough in both line and distance. On sharp curves where the angle between tape and line of sight is large, it may be slightly better to set the range pole practically on the line of sight.

In setting points on curves the head chainman can expedite the work by placing himself quickly on line at the point to be set. One method of doing this, especially suited to open country, is for the head chainman to range forward the proper chord distance along a line through the last two stakes, placing himself in position as at d' in Fig. 2–6. By then pacing inward the known chord-offset distance (Art. 2–14), he will be in approximately the correct position for setting the required point at d. With experience the head chainman will invariably be in the field of view by the time the transitman sets off the deflection angle and sights.

Many variations are possible in the technique described. The range pole may be dispensed with for short sights in open country. Another device used where frequent *plus points* are required is to set those station stakes directly at the proper division on the tape and to move the tape forward at each full station. The important factors to consider are speed, accuracy consistent with the needs, and avoidance of taping errors. In all cases, carrying the taping forward by *chaining from pin to pin* is advisable.

After grading, all points on curves which are set to control construction details must be more carefully centered than in the methods just described.

On pavements or in other locations where stakes cannot be driven, the points are chiseled or marked with keel, or a nail may be driven flush through a small square of red cloth. Guard stakes marked with the stationing are set at a convenient offset distance to one side.

Minor obstacles to setting calculated points on curves are often met in running location prior to clearing or grading. These should not be permitted to delay the field work.

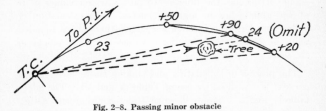

Fig. 2–8. Passing minor obstacle

Fig. 2–8 shows another sketch of the first portion of the curve calculated in Art. 2–9. If the line of sight to sta. 24 were to hit a large tree, for example, it could be backed off to the left of the tree for setting a stake at any convenient plus point. Thus, if sta. 23+90 were in the clear, its deflection would be $40 \times 2.7'$ greater than that just used to set sta. 23+50. The calculations—$40 \times 2.7' = 108' = 1°48'$ and $3°42' + 1°48' = 5°30'$—may be made mentally in a few seconds. After the station stake at 23+90 is set, another new plus point to the right of the tree (such as 24+20) could be staked by following a similar process; or else the taping could proceed from sta. 23+90 directly to the next calculated point at sta. 24+50.

A minor obstacle on the curve itself (such as a large boulder at sta. 24) could be by-passed by the same method.

Major obstacles are treated in Chapter 7.

2-12. Even-Radius Curves.—Some organizations, including a few highway departments, do not use the degree of curve designation either in calculations or in field work. Instead, a curve is chosen on the basis of its radius, which usually is a round number. Deflections are calculated theoretically from the following proportion:

$$\text{deflection}:\tfrac{1}{2}\text{ arc length} = 360°:2\,\pi\,R$$

This reduces to

$$\text{defl. (in minutes)} = \frac{1,718.873}{R} \times \text{arc length} \qquad (2\text{--}17)$$

This method has the advantage that radii may be selected which are convenient for calculating curve parts. The *radius* would also mean more to the average person than the *degree*, should it become the practice to post warning values of R at the approaches to highway curves. The calculation of deflections, however, is much less simple than with a rounded value of D, and their fractional values are inconvenient in the field.

The process of calculating and staking these "even-radius curves" is expedited by use of Tables V and VI. The latter table is used to compute L when I and R are given. Other curve parts are found from the usual formulas (see Art. 2–3). Table V gives directly most of the data concerning deflections and chord lengths needed in the field. Subchord deflections are readily computed from the tabulated deflections per foot.

2-13. Metric Curves.—In countries having the metric system, distances are usually measured with a 20-meter tape, and a "station" is nominally a distance of 10 meters. On route surveys either the radius in meters or the degree of curve may be used in selecting and staking curves. However, the customary metric "degree of curve" D_m differs from those already defined not only in unit of measurement but in angle and length of chord (or arc) as well. Specifically, D_m is the *deflection angle* for a chord (or arc) of *20 meters*. Thus, by analogy from equations 2–9 and 2–10,

$$\sin D_m \text{ (chord def.)} = \frac{10}{R_m} \qquad (2\text{--}18)$$

and

$$D_m \text{ (arc def.)} = \frac{572.958}{R_m} \qquad (2\text{--}19)$$

Also, by analogy from equation 2–14,

$$L_m = \frac{10\,I}{D_m} \qquad (2\text{--}20)$$

It is not necessary to use special metric-system tables to compute and stake metric curves. The foregoing simple relations used in connection with the tables in Part III of this book will enable an engineer to handle any metric-curve problem. If Table VIII is used, for example, the tangents and externals for a 1° metric curve are *one-tenth* the tabulated values (for the same central angle). This fact follows from equations 2–10 and 2–19.

For a quick comparison between *metric* and *foot* curves, it is well to remember that for curves of the same radius the ratio between D and D_m is about 3 to 1 (actually 3.048 to 1). In other words, a curve of given D_m is about 3 times as sharp as one having the same numerical value of D.

2–14. Staking by Offsets.—There is no good substitute for the deflection-angle method when points must be set quickly and accurately on long-radius curves. It is mathematically possible, however, to devise several other methods based either upon *angles from the P.I.* or upon *offsets*. The former basis is rarely practicable, but there are occasions where an offset method is very useful.

The offset methods* are known as:

(*a*) Chord offsets

(*b*) Middle ordinates

(*c*) Tangent offsets

(*d*) Ordinates from a long chord

---

*Following the derivation of some needed mathematical relations, only the chord-offset method is described in detail. Abbreviated descriptions of the remaining methods are enough to serve as a basis for applying them.

The *chord offset, tangent offset,* and *middle ordinate* for a *full station* are designated by C.O., T.O., and M.O.; corresponding terms for any other distance are c.o., t, and m. The *true chord* for a *full station* is *100 feet* or *C*, the length depending on the definition of *D*.

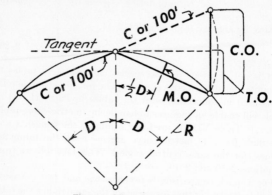

Fig. 2–9. Offsets for full station

From Fig. 2–9 the following *exact* relations may be written practically by inspection:

$$C = 2 R \sin \tfrac{1}{2} D_a \qquad (2\text{–}21)$$

$$\text{C.O. (chord def.)} = 200 \sin \tfrac{1}{2} D_c \qquad (2\text{–}22)$$

$$\text{C.O. (arc def.)} = 2 C \sin \tfrac{1}{2} D_a \qquad (2\text{–}23)$$

$$\text{T.O.} = \tfrac{1}{2} \text{ C.O.} \qquad (2\text{–}24)$$

$$\text{M.O.} = R \text{ vers } \tfrac{1}{2} D \qquad (2\text{–}25)$$

Also, by similar triangles,

$$\text{C.O.}:100 \text{ (or } C) = 100 \text{ (or } C):R$$

Hence,

$$\text{C.O. (chord def.)} = \frac{100^2}{R} \qquad (2\text{–}26)$$

and

$$\text{C.O. (arc def.)} = \frac{C^2}{R} \qquad (2\text{–}27)$$

Four useful *approximate* relations are:

$$\text{M.O.} = \tfrac{1}{3} \text{ C.O.} \qquad (2\text{–}28) \text{ Approx.}$$

$$\text{C.O.} = 1\tfrac{3}{4} D \qquad (2\text{–}29) \text{ Approx.}$$

$$t = \tfrac{7}{8} s^2 D \text{ } (s \text{ is chord in } stations) \qquad \text{(2–30) Approx.}$$

$$m \text{ (in inches for a 62-ft chord)} = D \qquad \text{(2–31) Approx.}$$

The approximate 8:4:1 ratio of the chord offset, tangent offset, and middle ordinate is worth memorizing (mnemonic: "eight for one").

Offsets for any subchord (or subarc) may be found by first determining the values for a full station and then applying the principle that c.o., t, and m are proportional to the *squares* of the subchords (or subarcs).

Table I contains values of certain of the full-station offsets. The explanatory notes preceding that table show its usefulness in obtaining any offsets accurately.

Chord offsets, sometimes called "deflection distances," provide a means of setting station stakes rapidly when a transit is not available. If the tapeman sights past his plumb-bob cord, surprising accuracy is possible. It is invariably adequate for surveys made prior to clearing and grading.

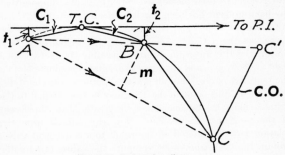

Fig. 2–10. Staking by offsets

In Fig. 2–10 (curvature greatly exaggerated) the P.I. and the tangent points are assumed to have been set by the usual methods. If the transitman and some of the field party now proceed along the forward tangent for purposes of setting stakes or measuring the angle I for the next curve, three men (or even two) can set the station stakes on the curve left behind.

The procedure follows: Knowing the stationing of the T.C., calculate the subchords c_1 and c_2 to the adjacent full stations at A and B (sta. A is on the curve produced backward). Then calculate t_1 and t_2, which are the tangent offsets for the subchords. The field work may now be started after range poles have been set at convenient points on the tangent. Establish a temporary point at A by the "swing offset" method. Locate the station stake at B similarly. Range the line AB ahead a full-station chord to C', and locate the next station stake at C by the C.O. Continue around the curve by full-chord offsets (obviously, half-stations or quarter-stations could be used instead) until the full station preceding the C.T. has been set. Make the final check by measuring the last subchord and the swing offset to the forward tangent; check them against their theoretical values.

In an exceptional situation, a curve may be selected to fit the topography and may be completely staked without use of the transit or tables of any kind; it is assumed that the principles are understood and that the approximate relations 2–29 and 2–30 have been memorized. For example, suppose that the back tangent has been partially cleared, but the P.I. has not been established and D has not been chosen. To run the curve, set the T.C. at a point fitting the topography, tape toward the P.I. a certain distance (possibly 200 feet), take a right angle by eye, and measure t to a suitable random point on the tentative curve. For all practical purposes the chord distance c from this point to the T.C. may be taken equal to the distance along the tangent unless t is greater than 20 per cent of the tangent measurement. Now compute D from the relation 2–30, and round off the result to a convenient value. Obtain the C.O. from 2–29, compute the values of t for the subchords at the T.C. by means of the square relation, and stake the complete curve by chord offsets as previously described. No check can be made at the C.T. unless I (and consequently L and the stationing of the C.T.) can be determined by some means.

Middle ordinates are also useful in staking a curve by tape alone. Their most valuable use, however, is in checking and realigning existing curves on railroads. (See Art. 9–17.)

In staking problems, first locate full stations either side of the T.C. by swing tangent offsets, as in the chord-offset method just described. Then set the next full station by sighting from the rear station along a line m feet inside the forward station, and measure the full chord distance from the forward station (see Fig. 2–10). Continue this process to the stake before the C.T., and make the final check as in the chord-offset method. (Fractional stations could be used instead of full stations.)

It should be noted that, when stakes are set at full stations, the distance m is the middle ordinate for two stations; consequently, $m = \text{T.O.} = \frac{1}{2}$ C.O.

Topographical conditions sometimes make this method preferable to chord offsets. It is probably better on sharp curves, regardless of topography, because the offsets are only half as long.

Tangent offsets provide a handy means of setting station stakes by tape alone. The method is essentially one of rectangular coordinates, the T.C. being used as the origin and the tangent being used as an axis.

The deflection $\frac{1}{2}d$ to the first regular station is first computed. The tangent distance to this station is $c \cos \frac{1}{2}d$, and its offset is $c \sin \frac{1}{2}d$. Coordinates of remaining full stations are obtained by adding increments of $C \cos (d + \frac{1}{2}D)$ and $C \sin (d + \frac{1}{2}D)$, $C \cos (d + \frac{3}{2}D)$ and $C \sin (d + \frac{3}{2}D)$, etc., where C is the chord for a full station. Since in most cases $C = 100$ feet, the computation is very simply performed by using natural sines and cosines. As a check on the computations, the coordinates of the C.T. should equal $R \sin I$ and $R \operatorname{vers} I$. If tangent distances fall beyond the P.I., it is probably better to calculate the second half of the curve with reference to the C.T. and the forward tangent.

In the field, set temporary stakes at the calculated tangent distances. Then locate the station stakes at the intersections of the tangent offsets and the chords from the preceding stations.

Ordinates from a long chord are also based upon rectangular coordinates. As in the tangent-offset method, the origin is at the T.C., but the axis is along a convenient long chord. If the chord is the L.C. of the curve, simple relations for the

coordinates of the station stakes may be expressed (these will
not be derived). However, it is difficult to imagine many
practical situations in which one of the foregoing methods
would not be better than this.

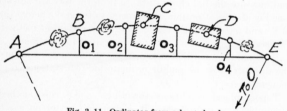

Fig. 2–11. Ordinates from a long chord

Perhaps the most useful application of this method is in
setting stakes at odd plus points between a series of minor
obstacles on a curve. Fig. 2–11 illustrates such a situation.
Station E is set by turning a deflection angle with the transit
at A and taping the chord AE, which is $2\,R \sin \frac{1}{2}AOE$.
Stakes set sufficiently close for cross-sectioning are then located
by taping the offsets $o_1, o_2, \ldots$ at convenient points along AE.
If the segments of AE at any ordinate are designated by s_1
and s_2 (units are stations), then the length of the ordinate in
feet is found from the relation

$$o = \tfrac{7}{8}\, s_1\, s_2\, D \qquad\qquad \textbf{(2–32) Approx.}$$

Note the resemblance between formulas 2–32 and 2–30.

2–15. Problems

NOTE.—Answers are given only for odd-numbered problems. Unless
otherwise stated, linear measurements in data and answers are expressed to
hundredths; values may be rounded off to tenths if desired by the instructor.
Certain of the practical problems in Art. 7–19 may also be assigned, particularly numbers 1, 2, and 4.

1. *Given:* $I = 37°51'$; $D_c = 6°20'$. *Find:* T, E, L.C., M, L,
and true length of arc. Compute by formulas, and check by
tables. *Answers:* $T = 310.34$; $E = 51.72$; L.C. $= 587.12$; $M =$
48.93; $L = 597.63$; true length $= 597.94$.

2. *Given:* $I = 87°17'$; $D_c = 15°$. *Find:* T, E, L.C., M, L, and
true length of arc. Compute by formulas, and check by
tables.

3. *Given:* Same data as Problem 1, but use D_a. *Find: T, E,* L.C., *M*, and *L*. Compute by formulas, and check by tables. *Answers: T* = 310.18; *E* = 51.70; L.C. = 586.83; *M* = 48.90; *L* = 597.63.

4. *Given:* Same data as Problem 2, but use D_a. *Find: T, E,* L.C., *M*, and *L*. Compute by formulas, and check by tables.

5. *Given:* Sta. P.I. = 64+82.72; remaining data as in Problem 1. Set up a table of deflections to nearest $\frac{1}{2}$ minute for staking the curve by full stations. Determine the true subchords at the ends of the curve. *Partial answers:* T.C. = 61+72.38; C.T. = 67+70.01; first subdeflection = 0°52$\frac{1}{2}$′; true subchords = 27.63 and 70.03.

6. *Given:* Sta. P.I. = 21+25.18; remaining data as in Problem 2. Set up a table of deflections for staking the curve by half-stations. Determine the true half-station chord and the true subchords at the ends of the curve.

7. If the curve in Problem 5 had $D_a = 6°20′$, by how much (to nearest $\frac{1}{10}$ minute) would the first subdeflection be changed? Determine also the true full-station chord and the true subchords at the ends of the curve. *Answers:* Change = 0.3′; true chord = 99.95; true subchords = 27.46 and 70.15.

8. If the curve in Problem 6 had $D_a = 15°$, by how much (to nearest $\frac{1}{10}$ minute) would the first subdeflection be changed? Determine also the true full-station chord and the true subchords at the ends of the curve.

9. *Given: I* = 42°18′. Determine D_a to nearest $\frac{1}{2}$° for a curve passing approximately 15 feet inside the vertex. Find exact *E* for the selected curve. *Answers:* $D_a = 27\frac{1}{2}$°; *E* = 15.05.

10. *Given: I* = 52°49′., Determine D_c to nearest 10′ for a curve passing approximately 20 feet inside the vertex. Find exact *E* for the selected curve.

11. *Given: I* = 78°35′. Determine D_c to nearest $\frac{1}{2}$° for a curve for which *T* is approximately 500 feet. Find exact *T* (to tenths) for the selected curve. *Answers:* $D_c = 9°30′$; *T* = 494.1.

12. *Given:* $I = 84°16'$. Determine D_a to nearest degree for a curve for which T is approximately 250 feet. Find exact T (to tenths) for the selected curve.

13. *Given:* Sta. P.I. $= 27 + 81.73$; $I = 52°17'$; $R = 1,000$ feet. *Find:* Sta. of T.C. and C.T. (Determine L from Table VI.) *Answers:* T.C. $= 22 + 90.93$; C.T. $= 32 + 03.45$.

14. *Given:* Sta. P.I. $= 36 + 24.18$; $I = 13°40'30''$; $R = 3,000$ feet. Set up a table of deflections to nearest 30'' for staking curve by half-stations. (Use Tables V and VI.)

15. *Given:* A metric curve with sta. P.I. $18 + 4.23$; $I = 21°10'$; $D_m = 8°$ (arc def.). *Find:* Sta. of T.C. and C.T. What is the corresponding value of D_a? (Use Table VIII for T.) *Answers:* T.C. $= 17 + 0.85$; C.T. $= 19 + 7.31$; $D_a = 24°23'$.

16. *Given:* A metric curve with sta. P.I. $= 174 + 1.68$; $I = 37°29'$; $D_m = 5°$ (arc def.). *Find:* Sta. of T.C. and C.T. What is the corresponding value of D_a? (Use Table VIII for T.)

17. Find the tangent offsets for the full stations either side of the T.C. in Problem 5. *Answers:* t_1 (back sta.) $= 2.89$; $t_2 = 0.42$.

18. Find the tangent offsets for the regular half-stations either side of the T.C. in Problem 6.

19. In fitting a curve to a side-hill location, the P.I. is inaccessible. The back tangent has been stationed to a point selected for the T.C. Find D to the nearest $\frac{1}{4}°$ for a curve which will pass close to a point 30 feet inside the tangent and 235 feet beyond the T.C. *Answer:* $D = 6\frac{1}{4}°$.

20. Derive relation 2–30.

21. Prove relation 2–31.

22. Derive relation 2–32.

CHAPTER 3

COMPOUND AND REVERSE CURVES

3–1. Definitions.—Stated generally, a compound curve consists of two or more consecutive curves that are tangential. In the terminology of route surveying, however, a *compound curve* is a two-arc simple curve having its centers on the same side of the common tangent at the junction; whereas a *reverse curve* is one having its centers on opposite sides. A *multi-compound curve* has three or more centers on the same side of the curve.

COMPOUND CURVES

3–2. Use.—Owing to the inequality of their tangent distances, compound curves permit the fitting of a location to the topography with much greater refinement than do simple curves. Conditions often occur in railroad and highway location where the changes in direction between established tangents can only be accomplished economically by compound curves. This is true in mountainous terrain or along a large river winding close to a rock bluff.

The flexibility of compound curves may tempt the locating engineer to use them merely to reduce grading quantities or to expedite the field work (as in Art. 3–14). This is not good practice, as it complicates design details related to superelevation and introduces certain permanent operating disadvantages. A compound curve should not be used where a simple curve is practicable.

3–3. Requirements for a Rigid Solution.—Fig. 3–1 shows a compound curve, the notation for which is self-explanatory. The layout has *seven* important *parts*: T_S, T_L, R_S, R_L, I_S, I_L, and I. However, since $I = I_S + I_L$, there are only *six independent variables*, namely, the four lengths and any two angles. Trial with compass and ruler will show that:

> *For a rigid solution four parts must be known, including at least one angle and at least two lengths.*

Of the many possible combinations of four known parts giving a rigid solution, some are more readily solved than others. In practice the more difficult problems may often be converted to simpler cases by measuring one more angle or distance. Certain combinations rarely occur in the field.

The treatment which follows is not exhaustive; yet it is complete enough to serve as a basis for solving any compound-curve problem.

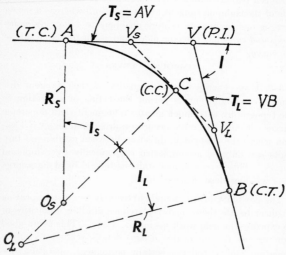

Fig. 3–1. Compound-curve layout

3–4. Solution Through Vertex Triangle.—The most obvious method of solving a compound-curve problem is by means of the triangle VV_SV_L, Fig. 3–1, formed by lines joining the P.I. and the vertices of the two simple curves. (The base of the triangle is the common tangent at the C.C.) If this vertex triangle can be solved, all unknown parts of the layout are easily determined. For example, if I_S, I_L, R_S, and R_L are known, solve first for the tangent distances of the individual simple curves. Their sum equals the base of the vertex triangle. Solve that triangle for the other sides by two applications of the sine law. Then find the missing compound-curve tangents, T_S and T_L, by adding those sides to the proper individual tangent distances. Of course, $I = I_S + I_L$.

It should be emphasized that the vertex-triangle method of solution is possible only if at least two of the known compound-curve parts are angles (fixing its shape), and then only if one side of the triangle can be found (fixing its size). The method is *not* applicable if, along with any two angles, the following parts are known: T_S and T_L, R_S and T_L, or R_L and T_S.

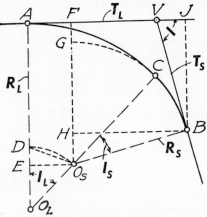

Fig. 3–2. Solution by construction

3–5. Solution by Special Construction.—One of the most useful cases occurs when I has been measured, and topographical conditions fix the T.C. and the C.T. within narrow limits at unequal distances from the P.I. If one more variable is assumed, the layout is fixed, but the problem may not be solved easily. Should the assumed variable be the degree of the sharper curve (a practical situation, since D is often limited by specifications), then R_S is the fourth known part, and solution through the vertex triangle is impossible.

Several methods of solving the foregoing problem by geometric construction have been used. One of the least complicated is shown in Fig. 3–2.

$$\tan DO_S E = \frac{DE}{EO_S} = \frac{FG}{AF} = \frac{JB - GH}{AV + VJ - BH}$$

Since angle $DO_S E = \frac{1}{2} I_L$,

$$\tan \tfrac{1}{2} I_L = \frac{T_S \sin I - R_S \text{ vers } I}{T_L + T_S \cos I - R_S \sin I} \qquad (3\text{--}1)$$

Also, $I_S = I - I_L$

The missing unknown R_L may be obtained either by the vertex-triangle method of Art. 3–4 or directly from Fig. 3–2. Thus,

$$EO_S = AF = AV + VJ - BH$$

or $(R_L - R_S) \sin I_L = T_L + T_S \cos I - R_S \sin I$

from which $(R_L - R_S) = \dfrac{T_L + T_S \cos I - R_S \sin I}{\sin I_L} \qquad (3\text{--}2)$

Or else $DE = FG = JB - GH$

or $(R_L - R_S) \text{ vers } I_L = T_S \sin I - R_S \text{ vers } I$

from which $(R_L - R_S) = \dfrac{T_S \sin I - R_S \text{ vers } I}{\text{vers } I_L} \qquad (3\text{--}3)$

When I_L is small, relation 3–3 is preferable to 3–2. For moderate angles either formula is satisfactory. Though the formulas look complicated, actual computation is simple because the numerators of formulas 3–2 and 3–3 appear in formula 3–1.

Fig. 3–2 applies to any rigid case in which *both* T_S *and* R_S *are known.* At least two of the three general relations, 3–1, 3–2, and 3–3, are needed; the particular unknowns determine the choice of relations, as well as their form and order of use.

If both T_L and R_L are known, the diagram for direct solution results from drawing the construction lines in a reverse way. However, the correct formulas may also be obtained by merely changing the subscripts in formulas 3–1, 3–2, and 3–3.

3–6. Solution by Traverse.—The general relations developed in Art. 3–5 are used too infrequently to justify memorizing them. Moreover, if the textbook is not available, it may be difficult to derive them when needed, owing to the complicated geometric construction. Fortunately, the same formulas may be derived by a method which requires no construction lines and involves only the elementary truth that the algebraic sum of the latitudes and the algebraic sum of the departures of a closed traverse must each equal zero.

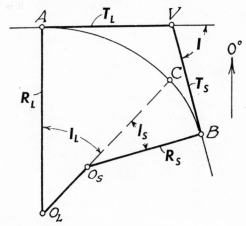

Fig. 3–3. Solution by traverse

Fig. 3–3 is the same as Fig. 3–2 except that construction lines have been omitted. Proceed clockwise around the selected closed traverse, assuming 0° azimuth in the direction $O_L A$. Consider that $I < 90°$; recall that *latitude = length × cosine of azimuth* and *departure = length × sine of azimuth*.

Side	Length	Azimuth	Latitude	Departure
$O_L A$	R_L	0°	R_L	0
AV	T_L	90°	0	T_L
VB	T_S	90°+I	$-T_S \sin I$	$T_S \cos I$
BO_S	R_S	180°+I	$-R_S \cos I$	$-R_S \sin I$
$O_S O_L$	$R_L - R_S$	180°+I_L	$-(R_L - R_S)\cos I_L$	$-(R_L - R_S)\sin I_L$

Then, from Σ *latitudes,*

$$R_L - T_S \sin I - R_S \cos I - (R_L - R_S)\cos I_L = 0$$

or
$$\cos I_L = \frac{R_L - T_S \sin I - R_S \cos I}{R_L - R_S} \qquad (3\text{–}4)$$

The term R_L in the numerator may be eliminated and the relation may be converted to formula 3–3 by subtracting both sides from 1, canceling R_L, and converting cosines to versines. The result is

$$\text{vers } I_L = \frac{T_S \sin I - R_S \text{ vers } I}{R_L - R_S} \tag{3-3}$$

From Σ *departures*,

$$T_L + T_S \cos I - R_S \sin I - (R_L - R_S) \sin I_L = 0$$

or

$$\sin I_L = \frac{T_L + T_S \cos I - R_S \sin I}{R_L - R_S} \tag{3-2}$$

But $\dfrac{\text{vers } A}{\sin A} = \tan \frac{1}{2}A$ (from formula 36 in Table XXVI). Therefore, if formula 3–3 is divided by 3–2, the result is

$$\tan \tfrac{1}{2} I_L = \frac{T_S \sin I - R_S \text{ vers } I}{T_L + T_S \cos I - R_S \sin I} \tag{3-1}$$

In applying the traverse method for solving any problem, it should be obvious that the traverse must be drawn so as to include all six independent variables (four lengths and any two angles). Moreover, any direction may be taken as 0° azimuth;

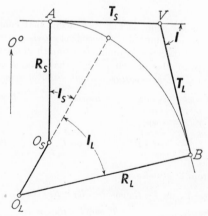

Fig. 3–3R

but, in order to obtain workable relations directly, the axes must be assumed parallel and perpendicular to an *unknown* length. Summarizing, the general rules of procedure are:

1. *Draw traverse to include all independent variables.*
2. *Take 0° azimuth parallel or perpendicular to an unknown length and proceed clockwise around traverse.*
3. *Set Σ latitudes and Σ departures equal to zero, obtaining two equations.*
4. *Solve the equation containing one unknown. If both equations have two unknowns, divide one by the other in such a way as to eliminate an unknown.*

To illustrate the directness and simplicity of the traverse method, Fig. 3–3R shows another compound curve in which the layout starts (for variety) with the shorter-radius arc. Another set of general equations will be developed by taking 0° azimuth in the direction $O_S A$.

Side	Length	Azimuth	Latitude	Departure
$O_S A$	R_S	$0°$	R_S	0
AV	T_S	$90°$	0	T_S
VB	T_L	$90°+I$	$-T_L \sin I$	$T_L \cos I$
BO_L	R_L	$180°+I$	$-R_L \cos I$	$-R_L \sin I$
$O_L O_S$	$R_L - R_S$	I_S	$(R_L - R_S) \cos I_S$	$(R_L - R_S) \sin I_S$

Then, from Σ *latitudes*,

$$R_S - T_L \sin I - R_L \cos I + (R_L - R_S) \cos I_S = 0$$

or
$$\cos I_S = \frac{T_L \sin I + R_L \cos I - R_S}{R_L - R_S} \qquad \textbf{(3–4R)}$$

The term R_S in the numerator may be eliminated by subtracting both sides from 1, canceling R_S, and converting cosines to versines. The result is

$$\text{vers } I_S = \frac{R_L \text{ vers } I - T_L \sin I}{R_L - R_S} \qquad \textbf{(3–3R)}$$

From Σ *departures*,

$$T_S + T_L \cos I - R_L \sin I + (R_L - R_S) \sin I_S = 0$$

or
$$\sin I_S = \frac{R_L \sin I - T_L \cos I - T_S}{R_L - R_S} \qquad \textbf{(3–2R)}$$

But $\dfrac{\text{vers } A}{\sin A} = \tan \frac{1}{2}A$ (from formula 36 in Table XXVI).

Thus, if formula 3–3R is divided by 3–2R, the result is

$$\tan \tfrac{1}{2} I_S = \frac{R_L \text{ vers } I - T_L \sin I}{R_L \sin I - T_L \cos I - T_S} \qquad \text{(3–1R)}$$

Inspection of the four formulas just derived shows that they are the reversed forms of 3–1 through 3–4; that is, they may be derived by changing the subscripts in the first set of formulas. Thus the statement made at the end of Art. 3–5 is verified.

The traverse method is valuable not only in the "standard" compound-curve problems just described but also in any special-curve problem which must otherwise be solved by means of complicated geometric construction. (Chapter 7 contains some practical examples.)

3–7. Summary of Compound Curves.—In a practical problem in which only one of the four known independent variables is an angle, it will be the angle I. If *any* two angles are known, the first step will always be to compute the dependent angle from $I = I_S + I_L$. After this the method of solution will depend on the particular combination of unknowns.

The following tabulation shows how to determine the fifth independent variable for the ten practical cases in which I is known, either directly or from given values of I_S and I_L.

Case No.	Given	Recommended Solution
1	2 angles, T_S, R_S	Vertex-triangle, or 3–3 for R_L
2	2 angles, T_L, R_L	Vertex-triangle, or 3–3R for R_S
3	2 angles, R_L, R_S	Vertex-triangle, or 3–3R for T_L
4	2 angles, T_S, R_L	3–3 or 3–4 for R_S
5	2 angles, T_L, R_S	3–3R or 3–4R for R_L
6	2 angles, T_L, T_S	3–1 for R_S, or 3–1R for R_L
7	I, T_L, T_S, R_S	3–1 for $\frac{1}{2} I_L$
8	I, T_L, T_S, R_L	3–1R for $\frac{1}{2} I_S$
9	I, T_S, R_L, R_S	3–3 or 3–4 for I_L
10	I, T_L, R_L, R_S	3–3R or 3–4R for I_S

After only one independent variable remains unknown, the solution can be performed either by the vertex-triangle method or by use of one of the eight general equations developed in Arts. 3–5 and 3–6.

3–8. Example of Calculation.—*Given:* $I = 75°21'$; $T_S = 1,175.42$; $T_L = 2,000$ (± 50 ft); $D_S = 6°$. Determine a convenient value for D_L which fits the conditions, and determine the exact values of I_L, I_S, and T_L for the selected D_L.

NOTE.—This problem illustrates the practical case noted in Art. 3–5. It also shows the utility of Table XX, which lists all needed natural functions in one table.

Find I_L by formula 3–1, which is

$$\tan \tfrac{1}{2}I_L = \frac{T_S \sin I - R_S \text{ vers } I}{T_L + T_S \cos I - R_S \sin I}$$

$$T_S \sin I = 1,175.42 \times 0.967489 = 1,137.21$$
$$R_S \text{ vers } I = 955.366 \times 0.747086 = \underline{\quad 713.74}$$
$$\text{Diff.} = \quad 423.47 = \text{Numerator, } N$$

$$T_L = 2,000.00$$
$$T_S \cos I = 1,175.42 \times 0.252914 = \quad 297.28$$
$$-R_S \sin I = 955.366 \times 0.967489 = \underline{-924.31}$$
$$\text{Alg. sum} = 1,372.97 = \text{Denominator, } D$$

$$\tan \tfrac{1}{2}I_L = \frac{N}{D} = 0.308434 \qquad \tfrac{1}{2}I_L = 17°08'30''$$
$$\text{Tentative } I_L = 34°17'$$

Now apply formula 3–3, which is

$$R_L - R_S = \frac{T_S \sin I - R_S \text{ vers } I}{\text{vers } I_L}$$

$$R_L - R_S = \frac{N}{0.173738} = 2,437.41$$

$$R_S = \quad 955.37$$
$$\text{Sum} = R_L = 3,392.78 \text{ and } D_L = 1°\ 41'+$$

Round off D_L to $1°40'$ for convenience in staking.

$$\text{Exact } R_L = 3,437.87$$
$$R_S = \underline{\quad 955.37}$$
$$R_L - R_S = 2,482.50$$

From 3–3,

$$\text{vers } I_L = \frac{N}{2,482.50} = 0.170582$$

and
$$I_L = 33°57'30''$$
$$I\ = 75°21'00''$$
$$I_S = 41°23'30''$$

By formula 3–2,
$$T_L = (R_L - R_S)\sin I_L + R_S \sin I - T_S \cos I$$
$$(R_L - R_S)\sin I_L = 2{,}482.50 \times 0.558590 = 1{,}386.70$$
$$R_S \sin I = \quad 924.31$$
$$-T_S \cos I = -297.28$$
$$T_L = \text{alg. sum} = \overline{2{,}013.73}$$

3–9. Multi-Compound Curves.—In especially difficult terrain, a compound curve may be made to fit the situation better by using more than two circular arcs. Such a multi-compound curve is located most simply by trial (see Art. 3–13). The layout is rarely symmetrical; practical examples are given in Art. 7–14.

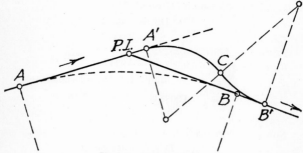

Fig. 3–4.   Reverse curve

Symmetrical multi-compound curves have many uses outside of route surveying, especially in architecture. The "three-centered" oval, or "basket-handle" arch, is a common form.

REVERSE CURVES

3–10. Limitations and Uses.—When conditions do not permit a simple curve AB inside the P.I. of established tangents (see Fig. 3–4), the change in direction may be accomplished by locating a reverse curve $A'CB'$ in the area beyond the P.I. Points A' and B' may lie on either side of the P.I. and point B, the positions depending on the radii.

On routes where speeds are high, reverse curves are inadmissible. This is particularly true on highways and railroads because opposite superelevation at the point of reversal cannot be provided. If the area beyond the P.I. must be used for the location, the two arcs of the reverse curve should be separated by a tangent long enough to permit proper operating conditions.

Reverse curves may be used to advantage on closed conduits such as aqueducts and pipe lines; on flumes and canals where erosion is no problem; and on local roads, in railroad yards, or in any similar location where speeds are low.

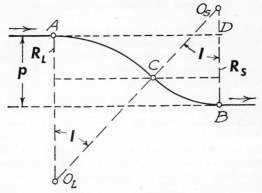

Fig. 3–5. Parallel tangents

3–11. Case of Parallel Tangents.—The simplest case of a reverse curve occurs when the tangents are parallel (see Fig. 3–5).

With the aid of the perpendicular dropped from C to the radii, the following relations may be written by inspection:

$$p = (R_L + R_S) \text{ vers } I \qquad (3\text{–}4)$$

$$AD = (R_L + R_S) \sin I \qquad (3\text{–}5)$$

Usually, p is known and two more variables must be assumed. More commonly, $R_L = R_S$, which reduces the number of variables to four, of which two must be known or assumed.

3–12. Case of Non-Parallel Tangents.—In essential theory, the general case of a reverse curve between non-parallel tangents is no different from a compound curve. The same seven parts are present, and the identical requirement for a rigid solution must be met (see Art. 3–3). The problem may be treated as two separate simple curves, provided sufficient data are available. More complicated cases may be solved by the construction method of Art. 3–5 or by the simpler traverse method described in Art. 3–6; the final relations resemble formulas 3–1, 3–2, and 3–3 closely. (See Art. 7–15.)

COMMENTS ON NOTES AND FIELD WORK

3–13. Notes.—Notes for staking compound and reverse curves by deflection angles are computed by treating the branches as separate simple curves, though they are set up in continuous stationing according to the form given in Art. 2–9. Owing to the change in curvature at the C.C. (or at the point of reversal in curvature, or C.R.C., on a reverse curve), that point must be occupied in moving up the transit from the T.C. The deflection angle would not be correct for a sight spanning the C.C. (or C.R.C.). Consequently, the safest form of notes is that in which the deflection at the C.C. (or C.R.C.) is 0° for starting the second arc. Some other method may be used, but it is likely to confuse the transitman.

3–14. Field Work.—*Set-ups and field checks* follow the general scheme outlined in Art. 2–11. If a set-up is made at the C.C. (or C.R.C.) and the deflections are recorded as just described, the transit is oriented so that the vernier will read 0° when the line of sight is along the common tangent. Generally, set-ups are best made at the T.C. and C.T., with the final check occurring at the C.C. (or C.R.C.).

Location by trial in the field often expedites fitting compound curves to particular situations. An example of an obstacle on the tangent is given in Art. 7–6.

Another use of the trial method is in running semi-final location in mountainous or otherwise difficult terrain not accurately mapped. Fig. 3–6 represents a situation in which the direction of the back tangent and the location of the T.C. at A have been fixed by the topography. The direction of the forward tangent is indefinite, though it should pass near a distant prominent point. The back tangent plunges into inaccessible territory toward the P.I

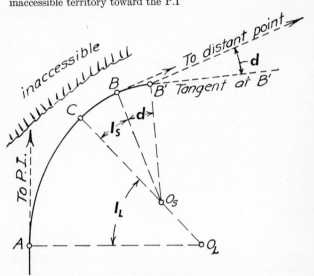

Fig. 3–6. Location by trial

The procedure is as follows: From the relation $t = \frac{7}{8} s^2 D$, select the degree of an initial curve fitting the conditions, as described in Art. 2–14. Continue this curve until it requires compounding (as at C) to fit the topography. Select the degree of the second arc by the same method, and repeat. Do this as many times as necessary. When the distant point is visible from a set-up on the last arc (as at B'), measure the angle d. To find the stationing of the C.T. at B, consider that the directions to the distant point from B and B' are parallel. Then, sta. $B =$ sta. $B' - \dfrac{100\,d}{D_S}$, where D_S is the degree of the final arc. Check the field work, if desired, by locating B and closing back to A by a convenient random traverse.

3–15. Problems

NOTE.—Certain of the practical problems in Art. 7–19 may also be assigned, particularly numbers 3 and 8.

1. Compound curve. *Given:* $I = 46°50'$; $I_L = 28°17'$; $D_L = 2°20'$; $D_S = 6°$ (both chord definition). *Find:* I_S, T_S, and T_L. *Answers:* $I_S = 18°33'$; $T_S = 659.33$; $T_L = 956.65$.

2. Compound curve. *Given:* $I_L = 32°10'$; $I_S = 34°24'$; $D_L = 10°30'$; $D_S = 20°$ (both arc definition). *Find:* I, T_L, and T_S. *Answers:* $I = 66°34'$; $T_L = 308.81$; $T_S = 231.42$.

3. Compound curve. *Given:* $I = 32°18'30''$; $T_L = 673.49$; $T_S = 418.02$; $D_S = 5°$ (chord definition). *Find:* I_L, I_S, and D_L. *Answers:* $I_L = 12°39'55''$; $I_S = 19°38'35''$; $D_L = 1°\ 53'+$.

4. Compound curve. *Given:* $I = 61°30'$; $T_L = 1,063.21$; $T_S = 731.83$; $D_L = 2°40'$ (chord definition). *Find:* I_L, I_S, and D_S. *Answers:* $I_L = 29°01'15''$; $I_S = 32°28'45''$; $D_S = 6°06'-$.

5. Compound curve. *Given:* $I = 58°41'$; $T_L = 460.27$; $D_L = 6°$; $D_S = 12°$ (both arc definition). *Find:* I_L, I_S, and T_S. *Answers:* $I_L = 28°20'50''$; $I_S = 30°20'10''$; $T_S = 335.42$.

6. Reverse curve. *Given:* $I_L = 26°44'$; $I_S = 65°13'$; $D_L = 8°30'$; $D_S = 16°$ (both arc definition). *Find:* T_L (T.C. to P.I.) and T_S (P.I. to C.T.). *Answers:* $T_L = 728.09$; $T_S = 52.30$ on same side of P.I. (See Art. 7–15 for sketch and extension of this problem.)

7. Reverse curve. *Given:* $I = 28°37'$; T_S (P.I. to T.C.) = 200, exactly; T_L (P.I. to C.T.) = 1,830, approx. *Find:* D_c (to nearest 10') for a common-radius reverse curve. *Answer:* $D_c = 4°40'$.

8. The tangents of a compound curve intersect in an inaccessible location (see Fig. 3–6). A point A is chosen as the T.C. and a distance AX of 1,200 ft is measured to a point on the forward tangent. Other measurements are: angle $VAX = 33°00'$ and angle $VXA = 32°00'$. Assume that the arc of shorter radius is to start at A; also that D_L (arc def.) = $2°30'$ and $I_L = 25°00'$. Determine D_S (arc def.) to the nearest minute and the distance from point X to the C.T. *Answers:* $D_S = 6°35'$; X to C.T. = 372.08 ft.

CHAPTER 4

PARABOLIC CURVES

4–1. Uses.—Parabolic, instead of circular, arcs may be used for horizontal curves. Where the curves are flat, there is no discernible difference between the two types. However, a parabola cannot be staked out readily by the deflection-angle method. Moreover, the determination of the radius of curvature at any point requires higher mathematics, thus complicating superelevation and related calculations. Also, parabolic alignment does not permit making simple right-of-way descriptions. For these reasons parabolic arcs on horizontal curves are restricted to such locations as park drives and walks, where they may be easily located by tape alone.

For curves in a vertical plane the situation is the reverse. Here, parabolic arcs are almost always used because elevations can be computed much more easily than on circular arcs. The parabola also has the incidental advantage of providing a smoother transition from the tangent grades. Vertical curves used in practice are surprisingly flat when converted to their equivalent circular arcs.

4–2. Equal-Tangent Vertical Curve.—The vertical parabola usually joins tangents having different gradients. Fig. 4–1 represents the usual form used on vertical curves. The parabola has a vertical axis, and it joins the tangent grades (also called "profile grades") G_1 and G_2 at points that are equidistant from the vertex, *measured horizontally*. (There is nothing to be gained by making the distance AV exactly equal to VB. On the contrary, simplicity is attained by making their horizontal projections equal, since calculations of stationing and field measurements of distance are made with respect to the horizontal.) Such a parabola is called an "equal-tangent" or "symmetrical" vertical curve. Actually the curve itself does not possess symmetry, though the offsets from AV and BV do.

The length L of a vertical curve is *not* the distance around the arc; it is the difference in stationing between the ends of the curve. Therefore, the length of a vertical parabolic curve,

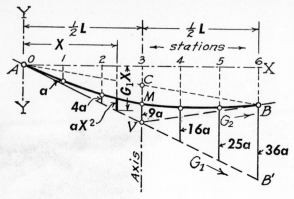

Fig. 4–1. Equal-tangent vertical curve

as the distance from point A to point B, is always equal to the horizontal projection of the curve, regardless of the directions or numerical values of the grades of the tangents. In Fig. 4–1 the length L of the vertical curve is 6 stations (600 feet).

A vertical curve may be treated as a parabola with the skewed axes YY and AV. However, it is more logical to use rectangular coordinate axes, since field measurements of elevations and stationing are made vertically and horizontally. Therefore, the reference axes are taken as the horizontal line AX and the vertical line YY. Also, the offsets from a tangent to the curve are measured along vertical lines.

From analytic geometry the general equation of a vertical parabola with respect to rectangular coordinate axes is $y = a x^2 + b x + c$. When a is positive, the parabola is turned upward; when negative, downward   If the origin is taken at A, the equation reduces to $y = a x^2 + b x$. The slope $\frac{dy}{dx}$ of a tangent is $2 a x + b$. At the origin, $x = 0$; consequently, the slope equals b. However, the slope at the origin is also measured by the tangent grade G_1. Hence, the working relation for the ordinates to an equal-tangent vertical curve is

$$y = aX^2 + G_1X \qquad (4-1)$$

where y is in feet, X is in stations, G_1 is in per cent, and a is in units of per cent per station. The usual algebraic signs apply to the coordinates. Grades rising in the direction of stationing are positive; falling grades are negative.

The terms in formula 4–1 have the graphical significance shown in Fig. 4–1. The *rule of offsets* (coming from the term aX^2) is particularly important:

Vertical offsets from a tangent to a parabola are proportional to the squares of the distances from the point of tangency.

For the 600-foot curve in Fig. 4–1, the offsets from the initial tangent to the curve are obviously a, $4a$, $9a$, $16a$, $25a$, and $36a$; those from the second tangent are the same, in the reverse order.

In Fig. 4–1, $VC = \frac{1}{2}B'B$ (from similar triangles). From the rule of offsets, $VM = \frac{1}{4}B'B$. Consequently, $VM = MC$. Thus, a parabola has the important characteristic that the external distance and the middle ordinate are equal. (This is not quite true for a circular arc. See Fig. 2–1.)

The term $G_2 - G_1$ is the rate, in per cent, at which the tangent grades diverge. It is analogous to the angle I of a simple curve. Some formulas are simplified by replacing $G_2 - G_1$ by the term A, defined as the algebraic difference in grades. In Fig. 4–1, $B'B$ equals the divergence in the distance $\frac{1}{2}L$, or $B'B = \left(\dfrac{L}{2}\right)\left(\dfrac{G_2 - G_1}{100}\right)$, L *always being in foot units.* Since $VM = \frac{1}{4}B'B$, the external distance, designated as E, is

$$E = \left(\frac{L}{800}\right)(G_2 - G_1) = \frac{AL}{800} \qquad (4-2)$$

The term a is useful in computations. In general, the second derivative of $y = ax^2 + bx + c$ equals the constant $2a$. This means that a tangent to a vertical-axis parabola changes direction a constant amount for equal increments of horizontal distance. (By analogy, a tangent to a circular arc changes direction a constant amount for equal increments of distance along the arc.) Therefore, *the rate of change of grade on an equal-tangent vertical curve is constant, and equals 2a per cent per station.*

On a vertical curve the total change in direction between the profile grades is $G_2 - G_1$ (or A) per cent. If this change is accomplished on a curve L feet long, the constant rate of change must be

$$2a = \frac{100(G_2 - G_1)}{L} = \frac{100A}{L} \qquad (4\text{--}3)$$

It is convenient to think of $2a$ as a measure of the sharpness of a vertical curve. In this respect it is analogous to D for a circular curve. Another measure of curvature that is used in sight-distance calculations (see Chapter 8) is the term K, which equals $L \div A$. This is the horizontal distance in feet required to effect a 1% change in gradient on a vertical curve. Therefore

$$a = \frac{50}{K} \qquad (4\text{--}4)$$

4–3. Methods of Calculation of Vertical Curves.—The object of vertical-curve calculations is to determine the elevations at specified stations on the designed grade line. These elevations are needed for cross-sectioning prior to grading and for setting construction grade stakes.

The calculation is simpler than for horizontal circular curves; no trigonometric formulas or special curve tables are needed. Either *chord gradients* or *tangent offsets* may be used. The method of chord gradients (or "chord offsets") is based upon the *rate-of-change principle*; it is a "self-checking" method. The tangent-offset method utilizes the *rule of offsets.*

4–4. Chord-Gradient Method.—Chords between full stations on a curve such as that in Fig. 4–1 must have the successive gradients $G_1 + a$, $G_1 + 3a$, $G_1 + 5a$ . . . , differing (algebraically) by $2a$. Since the offsets to the curve from BV are the same as those from AV, the calculated chord gradients are correct if the last chord gradient plus a equals G_2. For the 600-foot curve in Fig. 4–1, for example, $G_1 + 12a$ should equal G_2; it does when $L = 600$ in formula 4–3. If the calculations are started with the known elevation of A, the successive

Example.—*Special case—railroad type*

Given: Sta. $V = 18+00$; Elev. $V = 624.25$; $G_1 = -0.15\%$; $G_2 = +0.09\%$; $L = 600$ feet.

Station	Chord Gradient		Curve Elev.	Preliminary Calculations
On tang.				
(A) 15	$G_1 =$	-0.15	624.70	$2a = \dfrac{0.09 - (-0.15)}{6}$
	$a =$	$+0.02$	-0.13	$= +0.04\%$ per sta.
	$\overline{G_1 + a} =$	$\overline{-0.13}$	$\overline{624.57}$	
16	$2a =$	$+0.04$	-0.09	
	$\overline{G_1 + 3a} =$	$\overline{-0.09}$	$\overline{624.48}$	$G_2 = G_1 + \dfrac{2aL}{100}$
17	$2a =$	$+0.04$	-0.05	$= G_1 + 12a$
	$\overline{G_1 + 5a} =$	$\overline{-0.05}$	$\overline{624.43}$	
18	$2a =$	$+0.04$	-0.01	Elev. $A = 624.25$
	$\overline{G_1 + 7a} =$	$\overline{-0.01}$	$\overline{624.42}$	$+3 \times 0.15 = 624.70$
19	$2a =$	$+0.03$	$+0.03$	
	$\overline{G_1 + 9a} =$	$\overline{+0.03}$	$\overline{624.45}$	Elev. $B = 624.25$
20	$2a =$	$+0.04$	$+0.07$	$+3 \times 0.09 = 624.52$
	$\overline{G_1 + 11a} =$	$\overline{+0.07}$	$\overline{624.52} = B$ (check)	
(B) 21	$a =$	$+0.02$		
On tang.	$\overline{G_1 + 12a} =$	$\overline{+0.09} = G_2$ (check)		

addition of chord gradients gives the elevations of the full stations on the curve. All elevations are checked if the elevation at B equals its value as computed around the tangent grades AVB. This method has two pronounced advantages: simple theory and automatic checks.

On railroads, grades are so slight that it is common practice to place the vertex at a full station and use an even number of stations in the curve. (On high-speed main tracks, the A.R.E.A.* recommends that $2a$ should not exceed 0.05 in sags nor 0.10 on summits.) Consequently, the calculation is simple and requires no elaborate form; it may even be done mentally. See example on page 57.

Elevations at plus points on vertical curves are frequently needed for controlling cross-sections or for locating culverts and other construction details. Moreover, an even-length curve with the vertex at a full station does not always conform well with the topography, particularly in hilly country where grades are steep. In consequence, vertical curves must often have odd lengths with vertices at plus points, especially in highway work. (See Chapter 8 for considerations affecting lengths of vertical curves on highways.) The tangent-offset method has usually been used in such situations. However, the chord-gradient method can also be made to apply by calculating the gradients of the end subchords according to the following principles:

1. *The change in gradient between a tangent and a chord equals "a" times the station length of the chord.*

2. *The change in gradient between two adjacent chords equals "a" times the sum of their station lengths.*

An application of these principles is given on page 59.

The foregoing relations may be easily remembered by noting the analogy to a horizontal circular curve. The change in direction per station (D) corresponds to the change in grade per station ($2a$). On a circular arc the first subdeflection equals $\frac{1}{2}D$ times the nominal subchord length, and the deflection from any backsight chord to a foresight chord equals $\frac{1}{2}D$ times the sum of their nominal lengths (in stations).

*American Railway Engineering Association.

Example.—*General case—highway type*

Given: Sta. $V = 73+40$; Elev. $V = 254.16$; $G_1 = +5.2\%$; $G_2 = +0.8\%$; $L = 550$ feet.

Station	Chord Gradient	Chord in Stations	Curve Elev.	Preliminary Calculations
On tang.	$G_1 = +5.20$			$2a = \dfrac{0.8-5.2}{5.5}$
(A) 70+65	$0.35a = -0.14$		239.86	$= -0.8\%$ per sta.
	$\overline{G_1+0.35a = +5.06}$	0.35	$+1.77$	
	$1.35a = -0.54$		$\overline{241.63}$	
71	$\overline{G_1+1.7a = +4.52}$	1	$+4.52$	$G_2 = G_1 + \dfrac{2aL}{100}$
	$2a = -0.80$		$\overline{246.15}$	$= G_1 + 11a$
72	$\overline{G_1+3.7a = +3.72}$	1	$+3.72$	
	$2a = -0.80$		$\overline{249.87}$	
73	$\overline{G_1+5.7a = +2.92}$	1	$+2.92$	Elev. $A = 254.16$
	$2a = -0.80$		$\overline{252.79}$	$-2.75 \times 5.2 = 239.86$
74	$\overline{G_1+7.7a = +2.12}$	1	$+2.12$	
	$2a = -0.80$		$\overline{254.91}$	Elev. $B = 254.16$
75	$\overline{G_1+9.7a = +1.32}$	1	$+1.32$	$+2.75 \times 0.8 = 256.36$
	$1.15a = -0.46$		$\overline{256.23}$	
76	$\overline{G_1+10.85a = +0.86}$		$+0.13$	
	$0.15a = -0.06$	0.15	$\overline{256.36}$ = B (check)	
(B) 76+15	$\overline{G_1+11a = +0.80}$ = G_2 (check)			
On tang.				

The curve elevation at any plus point may also be found by the chord-gradient method. The procedure is to find the gradient of the subchord to the plus point (by principle 2), and then to calculate the elevation to the required plus point. As an illustration, the calculations to find the curve elevation at sta. 74+30 in the foregoing example are as follows:

$$
\begin{array}{ll}
\text{Chord gradient sta. 73 to 74} & = +2.92\% \\
\text{Change in gradient at } 74 = 1.30a & = -0.52 \\
\hline
\text{Subchord gradient 74 to } 74+30 & = +2.40\%
\end{array}
$$

$$
\begin{array}{ll}
\text{Elevation at sta. 74} & = \quad 252.79 \\
\text{Change in elevation} = +2.40 \times 0.30 = + & 0.72 \\
\hline
\text{Required elevation at sta. } 74+30 & = \quad 253.51
\end{array}
$$

It is not essential to compute the complete vertical curve in order to find the elevation at any plus point. *Principle 1* (page 58) can be used in this same example as follows:

$$
\begin{array}{ll}
\text{Gradient at } 70+65 = G_1 & = +5.20\% \\
\text{Change in gradient } 70+65 \text{ to } 74+30 = 3.65a = -1.46 \\
\hline
\text{Chord gradient } 70+65 \text{ to } 74+30 & = +3.74\%
\end{array}
$$

$$
\begin{array}{ll}
\text{Elevation at } 70+65 & = \quad 239.86 \\
\text{Change in elevation} = +3.74 \times 3.65 & = +13.65 \\
\hline
\text{Elevation at } 74+30 & = \quad 253.51
\end{array}
$$

4–5. Tangent-Offset Method.—The tangent-offset method is based upon the rule of offsets. For a special case, such as that in Fig. 4–1, VM is first computed from the external formula 4–2. Then the elevations at full stations along the tangent grades AV and VB are computed, and the symmetrical offsets—simple multiples of a—are applied to those elevations to give the curve elevations.

To show the application of this method to a general case, the problem worked on page 59 is set up as on page 61.

Though the foregoing method is perfectly general, it is not inherently self-checking, as is the chord-gradient method. This defect may be remedied partially by testing the second differences between elevations at equidistant points along the curve. Theoretically the second differences must be constant; they equal $2a$ for points 100 feet apart.

Station	Tangent Elev. = G_1X	Offsets from $AV = aX^2$	Curve Elev.	1st Diff.	2nd Diff.	Preliminary Calculations
						$a = \dfrac{100(G_2 - G_1)}{2L}$
(A) 70+65	239.86		239.86			$a = -0.4$
(5.2×0.35) =	+1.82					
71	241.68	$-0.4 \times 0.35^2 = -0.05$	241.63			
	+5.20			-4.52		
72	246.88	$-0.4 \times 1.35^2 = -0.73$	246.15		-0.8	From page 59
	+5.20			-3.72		
73	252.08	$-0.4 \times 2.35^2 = -2.21$	249.87		-0.8	
	+5.20			-2.92		
74	257.28	$-0.4 \times 3.35^2 = -4.49$	252.79		-0.8	Elev. $A = 239.86$
	+5.20			-2.12		
75	262.48	$-0.4 \times 4.35^2 = -7.57$	254.91		-0.8	Elev. $B = 256.36$
	+5.20			-1.32		
76	267.68	$-0.4 \times 5.35^2 = -11.45$	256.23			
(5.2×0.15)	+0.78					
(B) 76+15 =	268.46	$-0.4 \times 5.50^2 = -12.10$	356.36 = B (check)			

4–6. Unequal-Tangent Vertical Curve.—A vertical parabola having tangent grades of unequal station lengths is analogous to a compound curve (Chapter 3). It consists of two (or more) equal-tangent vertical curves having a common tangent where they join; and it is used where a single equal-tangent vertical curve cannot be made to fit imposed conditions so well.

Fig. 4–2 shows an unequal-tangent vertical curve. It approximates a parabola having an inclined axis. However, for ease in calculating elevations, it is best treated as two consecutive equal-tangent vertical curves AM and MB. Since the vertices V_1 and V_2 of the separate parabolas are at the midpoints of AV and VB, it follows that $VM = MC$.

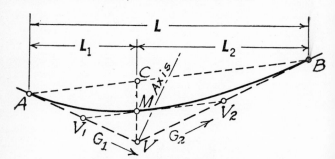

Fig. 4–2. Unequal-tangent vertical curve

The gradients of AB and of the parallel tangent V_1V_2 are both equal to $\dfrac{G_1L_1 + G_2L_2}{L_1 + L_2}$. Consequently, V_1M and V_1V diverge at the rate of $\dfrac{G_1L_1 + G_2L_2}{L_1 + L_2} - G_1$; and VM, the divergence in the distance $\frac{1}{2}L_1$, equals $\dfrac{L_1}{200}\left(\dfrac{G_1L_1 + G_2L_2}{L_1 + L_2} - G_1\right)$, which reduces to

$$E = \frac{L_1L_2A}{200L} = \frac{L_1L_2}{200K} \qquad (4\text{–}5)$$

In the preceding formula the lengths are in feet, gradients always being in per cent.

Either chord gradients or tangent offsets may be used to

calculate elevations. The curve must be treated as two separate parabolas having different values of $2a$. Tangent offsets, if used, are calculated from AV for the first parabola and from BV for the second; they are not symmetrical as in an equal-tangent vertical curve.

4-7. Lowest or Highest Point on Vertical Curve.—The lowest or highest point on a vertical curve is sometimes needed. (This point is sometimes called the turning point on the curve.) For installing a culvert at the low point, the approximate stationing may be determined quickly by interpolating between calculated elevations. The stationing of a high point or low point may be computed more accurately either by applying the chord-gradient principle or from specific formulas.

From the definition of K, the distance X_t in feet from the beginning of a vertical curve to the turning point (where the gradient is zero) must be KG_1. This may be derived mathematically by setting $\dfrac{dy}{dX}$ equal to zero in the expression $y = aX^2 + G_1X$. Thus, $2aX + G_1 = 0$ at the turning point. The result of solving this equation and expressing X in foot units is $X_t = \dfrac{-100G_1}{2a}$, which reduces to

$$X_t = \frac{LG_1}{G_1 - G_2} = KG_1 \tag{4-6}$$

After X_t has been computed, the elevation of the turning point may be found from the fact that *the gradients from the ends of the curve to the turning point are exactly one-half the gradients on the tangents.* This comes from *Principle 1*, which requires the gradient from A to the turning point to be $G_1 + \dfrac{aX_t}{100}$ (algebraically). This is equivalent to

$$G_1 + \left[\frac{100(G_2 - G_1)}{2L}\right]\left[\frac{LG_1}{100(G_1 - G_2)}\right]$$

which reduces to $\frac{1}{2}G_1$. From the turning point to B the gradient is $\frac{1}{2}G_2$.

On an unequal-tangent vertical curve the turning point may occur on either of the two parabolas, its position depending on the tangent grades. The final relations are:

$$X_1 = KG_1 \frac{L_1}{L_2} \tag{4-7}$$

and

$$X_2 = KG_2 \frac{L_2}{L_1} \tag{4-8}$$

where X_1 and X_2 are the distances (in feet) to the right and left from A and B; they cannot exceed L_1 and L_2, respectively.

4-8. Vertical Curve to Pass Through Fixed Point.—In the office work of grade-line design it is often necessary to find the length of a vertical curve that will join given tangents and will pass through a fixed point. The fixed point P may be a road intersection or the minimum clearance over a culvert or rock outcrop. Given values will usually be the gradients G_1 and G_2, the elevation and stationing of the fixed point P, and the elevation and stationing either of the beginning of the vertical curve or of the vertex.

In either case the unknown length of curve is found by substituting known values in formula 4-1. Careful attention must be paid to algebraic signs.

Example.—*Given:* $G_1 = -4.2\%$; $G_2 = +1.6\%$; Sta. $P = 17+00$; Elev. $P = 614.00$.

Case A—Beginning of curve known: Sta. $= 13+00$; Elev. $= 624.53$.

$$y = aX^2 + G_1 X, \text{ where } a = \frac{100(G_2 - G_1)}{2L}$$

Substituting, $-10.53 = \left(\frac{580}{2L}\right)(4)^2 - (4.2)(4)$

from which $6.27L = 4,640$

and $L = 740$ feet

Case B—Vertex of curve known: Sta. $= 16+70$; Elev. $= 608.99$. Substituting as in Case A gives

$$\frac{-4.2L}{200} + 5.01 = \left(\frac{580}{2L}\right)\left(\frac{L}{200} + 0.3\right)^2 - (4.2)\left(\frac{L}{200} + 0.3\right)$$

which reduces to $L^2 - 744.83L + 3,600 = 0$

A rapid slide-rule solution for L is performed by first converting the quadratic to the form $L(L - 744.83) = -3,600$. Then, by trial, $L = 740$. (This is the same curve as in Case A.)

Case C—Fixed point is highest or lowest point: In this practical case the elevation of the turning point (such as the clearance over the invert of a culvert) and the vertex of the curve are known. Although the stationing of the turning point can be scaled approximately from the profile, it is assumed to be unknown and is not used in finding the required curve.

If the position of the vertex is the same as in Case B and the turning point is at elevation 613.28, then in $y = aX^2 + G_1X$ the value of X is $\dfrac{LG_1}{G_1-G_2}$ (formula 4–6). By substitution,

$$\frac{-4.2L}{200} + 4.29 = \left(\frac{580}{2L}\right)\left(\frac{-4.2L}{-580}\right)^2 - (4.2)\left(\frac{-4.2L}{-580}\right)$$

which reduces to $0.0058\,L = 4.29$

and $L = 740$ feet

4–9. Reversed Vertical Curve.—In highway location where the terrain is rolling, and also on interchange ramps, it is often necessary to insert reversed vertical curves. Fig. 4–3 shows a simple example of this problem.

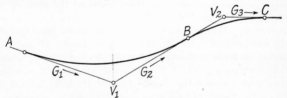

Fig. 4–3. Reversed vertical curve

A large number of cases are possible, the conditions depending on the particular combination of given values. Some cases have little practical value. However, all of them may be solved by proper use of formula 4–3. In one practical situation the given values will be the gradient G_1 and the elevation and stationing of points A, B, and C. A numerical example of this case is given in Art. 4–11, Problem 7.

4–10. Laying Out Parabola by Taping.—Though it is inconvenient to stake a horizontal parabola by the deflection-angle method, laying out such a curve by tape alone is very simple.

Fig. 4–4 shows two taping methods applied to the general case of an unequal-tangent parabola. The "middle-ordinate" method (shown by solid lines) is the simpler in field work and arithmetic; it requires only division by 2. The "tangent-offset" method (shown dotted) is based upon the rule of offsets.

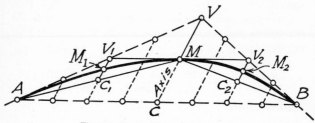

Fig. 4–4. Horizontal parabola by taping

One variation of the middle-ordinate method follows: Set stakes at the desired controlling points A, V, and B. Measure AV and VB; divide by 2 and set the mid-points V_1 and V_2. Measure V_1V_2; divide by 2 and set the point M on the axis of the parabola (VM may be measured, but it is not essential). Then measure AM and MB; divide by 2 and set the mid-points C_1 and C_2. Set two more points, M_1 and M_2, on the parabola at the mid-points of C_1V_1 and C_2V_2 (C_1V_1 and C_2V_2 both equal $\frac{1}{2}MV$). If more points are required to define the curve, measure the chords AM_1, M_1M, MM_2, and M_2B; divide by 2 and set four more points by middle ordinates as before. When conditions make the long chord AB inaccessible, the middle-ordinate method is particularly suitable.

In the tangent-offset method the long chord AB is divided into an even number of equal parts. The tangents AV and VB are also divided into equal parts, their number being the same as on the long chord. Then CV is measured and bisected, and the point M on the axis of the parabola is thus located. Offsets to the parabola from the points on the tangents are measured in the direction of the corresponding points on the long chord; the distances are simple fractions of VM, computed according to the rule of offsets (see Art. 4–2). In approximate work, points on the long chord may be dispensed with, except for C; the offsets from the tangents are computed as before, but are aligned by eye.

4-11. Problems

1. Equal-tangent vertical curve—railroad type. *Given:* Sta. $V = 70+00$; Elev. $V = 680.00$; $G_1 = +0.30\%$; $G_2 = -0.55\%$; $L = 1,000$ feet. Calculate the grade elevations to the nearest hundredth at full stations on the curve. (Note: It is necessary to carry gradients to thousandths.)

2. Equal-tangent vertical curve—highway type. *Given:* Sta. $V = 34+70$; Elev. $V = 874.21$; $G_1 = -4.5\%$; $G_2 = +2.5\%$; $L = 500$ feet. Calculate the grade elevations to the nearest hundredth at full stations on the curve. (Compute by chord gradients, and check by tangent offsets.)

3. Unequal-tangent vertical curve. *Given:* Sta. $V = 42+00$; Elev. $V = 316.52$; $G_1 = -6\%$; $G_2 = +4\%$; $L_1 = 400$ feet; $L_2 = 800$ feet. *Find:* the external VM and the values of $2a$ for the separate parabolas. *Answers:* $VM = 13\frac{1}{3}$ ft; $2a = 1.67\%$ and 0.42% per sta. (Calculate elevations on curve if specified.)

4. Calculate the station and elevation of the high point or low point on each of the curves in Problems 1 and 2. *Answers:* Prob. 1: $68+53$; 679.03. Prob. 2: $35+41$; 878.23.

5. Equal-tangent vertical curve to pass through turning point. *Given:* Sta. $V = 46+50$; Elev. $V = 375.00$; Elev. $P_t = 366.47$; $G_1 = +5.0\%$; $G_2 = -3.0\%$. *Find:* the length of curve and sta. of P_t. *Answers:* $L = 909$ feet; sta. $P_t = 47+63.6$.

6. Equal-tangent vertical curve to pass through fixed point. *Given:* Sta. $V = 27+50$; Elev. $V = 520.00$; Sta. $P = 26+00$; Elev. $P = 511.40$; $G_1 = +5.0\%$; $G_2 = +1.0\%$. Find the length of curve. *Answer:* $L = 690$ feet.

7. Reversed vertical curve. *Given:* Sta. and elev. of A, B, and C are, respectively, $27+00$, and 127.50, $37+00$ and 114.50, and $43+00$ and 116.30; $G_1 = -4.2\%$. *Find:* G_2, G_3, and the value of $2a$ of each curve. *Answers:* $G_2 = +1.6\%$; $G_3 = -1.0\%$; $2a$ of first curve $= 0.58\%$ per sta.; $2a$ of second curve $= 0.433\%$ per sta.

CHAPTER 5

SPIRALS

5-1. Foreword.—In high-speed operation over alignment on which the curves are circular arcs, an abrupt change from a straight path to a circular path is required at the T.C. of the curve. It is obviously impossible to make this change instantaneously. Smooth, safe operation around railroad and highway curves requires a *gradual transition* between the uniform operating conditions on tangents and the different (but also uniform) operating conditions on circular curves. Any curve inserted to provide such a transition is called an "easement" curve.

Fig. 5-1 shows a simple curve $A'E'B'$. The only way in which easement curves can be inserted at the tangents, while still preserving the radius R, is to shift the curve inward to a position represented by the parallel curve KEK'. It is impossible, however, to use a circular arc having the same length as the original circular arc. The portions KC and $C'K'$ must be deducted in order to provide room for the easement curves AC and $C'B$.

The easement curve AC is tangent to the initial tangent at A, at which point its radius of curvature is infinite. (The tangent may also be thought of as a curve of infinite radius.) At successive points along AC, the radius of curvature decreases until it becomes equal to R at point C, where the easement AC and the circular arc CC' have a common center at O. Thus, instead of abrupt changes in direction at A' and B' on the original simple curve, there are now gradual transitions between the tangents and the simple curve CC' by means of the easement curves AC and $C'B$.

In Fig. 5-1 the curved layout starts at the T.S. (tangent to spiral) and ends at the S.T. (spiral to tangent). The *approach spiral AC* joins the circular arc at the S.C. (spiral to curve), and the circular arc joins the *leaving spiral C'B* at the C.S. (curve to spiral). It should be observed that the total central angle I is unchanged. However, the central

68

angle of the circular arc is less than that of the original simple curve $A'B'$ by the amount used up by the two spirals. Thus, the central angle I_c of the arc CC' equals $I - 2\Delta$. Obviously the spiraled curve layout AB is appreciably longer than the original simple curve $A'B'$.

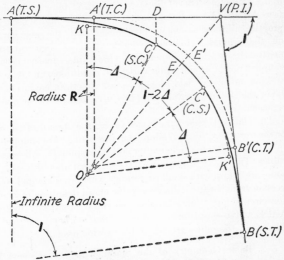

Fig. 5-1. Simple curve with spirals

The effect of an easement curve is to introduce centrifugal force gradually, thus reducing shock to track and equipment on railroads and making high-speed "streamliner" operation attractive to passengers. Moreover, the easement curve tends to "build safety into the highways" by following the natural path of the vehicle between tangent and circular arc, in that way reducing the tendency to veer from the traffic lane.

An easement curve serves several incidental purposes, the most important of which is to provide a logical place for accomplishing the gradual change from zero to full superelevation. It also simplifies, on highway curves, the addition of the extra pavement width found to be needed on curves for mechanical and psychological reasons.

Finding a suitable easement curve is not difficult. On

the contrary, the problem confronting engineers has been to decide which of several available forms should be selected. Many forms have been used. Some, including the cubic parabola, the lemniscate, and the clothoid, have definite mathematical equations; others, such as the Searles spiral (a multi-compound curve) and the A.R.E.A. ten-chord spiral (see Art. 5–13), are empirical. Within the limits used in practice, all these easements give substantially the same curve on the ground. However, consideration of their relative merits from three important viewpoints—mathematical simplicity, adaptability to a variety of conditions, and ease of staking out in the field—has led most American engineers to favor the clothoid, or the spiral first investigated by the Swiss mathematician, Leonard Euler.

The clothoid (called the *Euler spiral*, the *American spiral*, or the *transition spiral*) is adopted in this book. For simplicity it will be referred to hereafter as "the spiral." All spiral tables (Tables XI through XVI–C) are based upon this spiral; some are set up with small corrections which enable rapid conversion from the arc definition to the chord definition of D on the circular arc, thus changing the spiral practically to the A.R.E.A. ten-chord form used in the past on many railroads. Therefore, the tables are adaptable to wide usage.

5–2. Basic Geometry of the Spiral.—The spiral obeys a simple, exact law:

> *The radius of the spiral at any point is inversely proportional to its length.*

Although the spiral is a mathematically rich curve with applications in other fields of pure and applied science, its use in route surveying involves spiral parts which have clear graphical significance, simple formulas, and easily remembered analogies to the parts of a simple curve. Only a few relations require use of calculus in their derivations; tabulations for these and others are given so completely in Part III that the actual calculation and staking of a spiral-curve layout requires only slightly more trigonometry and very little more field work than are needed for a simple curve. On the other hand, it is possible to compute a satisfactory transition spiral without referring to special tables of any kind (see Art. 5–12).

All the relations needed for computing and staking a spiraled curve stem from Fig. 5–1 and the law of the spiral. In contrast to a circular arc, the spiral is a curve of variable radius, or variable degree of curve. At any point on the spiral, however, the inverse relationship between R and D is still correctly represented by equation 2–10. Since the radius of the spiral is infinite at the T.S., its degree of curve at that point must be zero. But the law of the spiral shows an inverse relationship between the radius at any point and the distance to that point from the T.S. The following statement is therefore true:

The degree of curve of the spiral increases at a uniform rate from zero at the T.S. to the degree D of the circular arc at the S.C.

The constant rate of increase in degree of curve per station along a spiral is represented by k. The basic formula for k is derived from its definition by dividing the total change in degree of curve, D, by the length of the spiral in stations. Since this length is $\dfrac{L_s}{100}$,

$$k = \frac{100D}{L_s} \qquad (5\text{--}1)$$

The constant k is useful in a variety of problems. As an illustration, suppose a spiral is required in making the transition between arcs of a compound curve on which $D_L = 3°$ and $D_S = 9°$. In such a case a limitation would be placed on the sharpness of the transition by specifying, for example, that the value of k should not exceed $2°$ per station. This condition would be met by a 300-ft spiral $(k = 2°)$ or by a 400-ft spiral $(k = 1\frac{1}{2}°)$. These lengths are the latter portions of complete spirals that are 450 ft and 600 ft long.

An extremely important element of a spiral is its central angle, or *spiral angle*, Δ. For a curve of *constant* radius (a circular arc), equation 2–14 shows that the central angle equals the length of curve in stations times the degree of curve, or $I = \dfrac{LD}{100}$. Since the spiral is a curve of *uniformly changing* degree of curve, it follows that its central angle equals the length of spiral in stations times the *average* degree of curve, or

$$\Delta = \frac{L_s D}{200} \qquad (5\text{-}2)$$

The foregoing central angle is exactly half that of a simple curve of the same length and degree (see formula 2–14).

The S.C. and the C.S. are comparable to the C.C. of a compound curve; at least one of them must be occupied by the transit in staking the layout by deflection angles. In consequence, the coordinates of the S.C. are two of the most important spiral parts. Their values, which are $X = AD$ and $Y = DC$, have been computed from exact relations derived in Appendix A and tabulated in the spiral tables of Part III; it is never necessary for the surveyor to compute them from their theoretical formulas.

Fig. 5–2 is a sketch of the first part of Fig. 5–1. The original simple curve has been omitted, however, and certain construction lines have been added to aid in deriving necessary formulas.

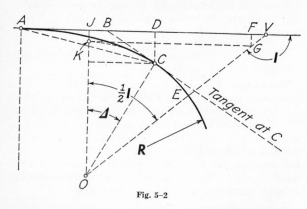

Fig. 5–2

The point K (the theoretical point where a tangent to the circular curve produced backward becomes parallel to the tangent AV) is known as the *offset T.C.* It is sometimes needed in the field; but is used more often in computations. If a perpendicular is dropped from C to OK, the coordinates of the offset T.C., which are $X_0 = AJ$ and $o = JK$, may be written by inspection. Thus,

$$X_0 = X - R \sin \Delta \qquad (5\text{-}3)$$

$$o = Y - R \text{ vers } \Delta \qquad (5\text{-}4)$$

The distance o is often called the "throw" (in Great Britain, the "shift"). It is the distance through which the circular curve must be moved inward in order to provide clearance for inserting the spiral. The shift $E'E$ at the middle of the curve (Fig. 5-1) is also called the throw. Obviously, $E'E = o \sec \frac{1}{2}I$. In any problem the particular distance referred to as the throw will be clear from the context.

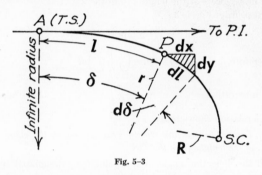

Fig. 5–3

Fig. 5–3 represents a spiral on which P is any point located by the spiral angle δ, the radius r, and the length l. Differentials being used,

$$d\delta = \frac{dl}{r}$$

However, from the law of the spiral,

$$r : R = L_s : l$$

Consequently,

$$d\delta = \frac{l \, dl}{R \, L_s}$$

By integration,

$$\delta = \frac{l^2}{2 \, R \, L_s} \qquad (5\text{-}5)$$

and

$$\Delta = \frac{L_s}{2 \, R} \qquad (5\text{-}6)$$

in which the angles are in radians.

When 5–5 is divided by 5–6 and the resulting equation is solved for δ, it is found that

$$\delta = \left(\frac{l}{L_s}\right)^2 \Delta \qquad (5\text{–}7)$$

which expresses the following important property:

> Spiral angles are directly proportional to the squares of the lengths from the T.S.

(On a simple curve, central angles are directly proportional to the first powers of the lengths from the T.C.)

Also, from Fig. 5–3,

$$\sin \delta = \frac{dy}{dl} = \delta \text{ (approximately)}$$

Therefore, $$dy = \delta \, dl = \left(\frac{l^2}{2 R L_s}\right) dl$$

By integration, $$y = \frac{l^3}{6 R L_s} \qquad (5\text{–}8) \text{ Approx.}$$

This relation shows that:

> Tangent offsets are closely proportional to the cubes of the lengths from the T.S.

If the deflection angle to any point P be designated by a,

$$\sin a = \frac{y}{l} = a \text{ (approximately)}$$

When the value in 5–8 is substituted for y,

$$a = \frac{l^2}{6 R L_s} \qquad (5\text{–}9) \text{ Approx.}$$

Hence, A, the deflection angle to the S.C., is

$$A = \frac{L_s}{6 R} \qquad (5\text{–}10) \text{ Approx.}$$

If relation 5–9 is divided by 5–10 and the resulting equation is solved for a,

$$a = \left(\frac{l}{L_s}\right)^2 A \qquad (5\text{–}11) \text{ Approx.}$$

This equation expresses another important property:

> Deflection angles are closely proportional to the squares of the lengths from the T.S.

(On a simple curve, deflection angles are exactly proportional to the first powers of the lengths from the T.C.)

It follows from the foregoing that

$$a = \tfrac{1}{3}\,\delta \qquad\qquad \textbf{(5–12) Approx.}$$

and

$$A = \tfrac{1}{3}\,\Delta \qquad\qquad \textbf{(5–13) Approx.}$$

Relations 5–12 and 5–13 are correct for most practical purposes. Theoretically, the relations produce values which are slightly too large. Should exact deflection angles be needed (as on a very long, sharp spiral), they are given in Table XV for any ten-chord spiral, and may be obtained quickly from Tables XVI and XVI–C for a spiral staked with any number of chords up to twenty. The derivation of the small correction which, if subtracted, would make equations 5–12 and 5–13 exact, is given in Appendix A.

The triangle ABC in Fig. 5–2 is analogous to that formed by the vertex and tangent points of a simple curve. The simple curve has equal tangents and equal angles at the long chord; the spiral, on the contrary, cannot have equal local tangents or equal angles. From formula 5–13, the angle BCA must be almost exactly equal to $\tfrac{2}{3}\,\Delta$.

The three lengths AC, AB, and BC are occasionally useful in field work; they are called the *long chord* (*L.C.*), *long tangent* (*L T.*), and *short tangent* (*S.T.*) of the spiral. When needed, their values are taken from tables, though they may readily be computed when X, Y, and Δ are known. For the flat spirals used on modern alignment, the L.T. and the S.T. are approximately in a 2:1 ratio.

5–3. Simple Curve with Spirals.—*Theoretical relations* for laying out any spiral, once the T.S. has been located, were given in Art. 5–2. The T.S. is usually staked, as in a simple curve, by measuring the calculated tangent distance T_s from the P.I. The tangent distances will be equal in the usual case of equal spirals at the tangents. There is rarely any justification for using unequal spirals, except in realigning existing railroad track.

If equal spirals are assumed in Fig. 5–2 and a line is drawn parallel to AV from K to G, T_s is made up of the three segments AJ, KG, and FV, which are X_0, R tan $\frac{1}{2}I$, and o tan $\frac{1}{2}I$. Therefore,

$$T_s = (R+o) \tan \tfrac{1}{2}I + X_0 \qquad (5\text{-}14)$$

or $$T_s = T + X_0 + o \tan \tfrac{1}{2}I \qquad (5\text{-}15)$$

By the same construction, the external distance E_s (VE) may be divided into the two segments EG and GV, which are R exsec $\frac{1}{2}I$ and o sec $\frac{1}{2}I$. Therefore,

$$E_s = E + o \sec \tfrac{1}{2}I \qquad (5\text{-}16)$$

By means of a trigonometric conversion, this equation may be written in the form

$$E_s = (R+o) \text{ exsec } \tfrac{1}{2}I + o \qquad (5\text{-}17)$$

Similar construction for the rare case of unequal spirals would result in formulas for the two tangent distances.

Calculations and field work for a spiral follow the general pattern described in Chapter 2 for a simple curve; the variations are in details only. In the usual case, sta. P.I., I, and D are known. Briefly, the sequence of the remaining work is as follows:

(a) Select L_s to fit the imposed conditions (Art. 5–14 contains reference to the choice of L_s).

(b) Calculate Δ from formula 5–2.

(c) Take X and Y from tables, and calculate X_0 and o from formulas 5–3 and 5–4. (This is theoretical; in practice, X_0 and o also may be taken from tables.)

(d) Calculate T_s from formula 5–14 or formula 5–15.

(e) Calculate the stationing of the T.S., which is sta. P.I.$-T_s$; the stationing of the S.C., which is sta. T.S.$+L_s$; the stationing of the C.S., which is sta. S.C.$+\dfrac{100\,(I-2\,\Delta)}{D}$; and the stationing of the S.T., which is sta. C.S.$+L_s$.

(f) Calculate deflection angles at selected points on the approach spiral, using formulas 5–13 and 5–11. (This is theoretical; for regularly spaced points on the spiral, tables or abbreviated relations may be used.)

(g) Set hubs at the T.S. and the S.T. by measuring T_s from the P.I.

(*h*) Occupy the T.S. and stake the approach spiral to the S.C. by deflection angles. (*L*$_s$ ordinarily equals the sum of the chords used to lay it out; corrections to chords are necessary only for fairly long chords near the end of long, sharp spirals.)

(*i*) Occupy the S.C. and backsight to the T.S. with $(\Delta - A)$ set off on the proper side of $0°$; $\Delta - A$ is almost exactly equal to $2\,A$. Then, plunge the telescope and stake the simple curve to the chosen check point by the usual methods. (The check point may be the C.S. or any point on the simple curve.)

(*j*) Occupy the S.T. and run in the leaving spiral to the C.S. (For regularly spaced points, the deflections are the same as those on the approach spiral.)

(*k*) Make the final check at the selected check point, which should preferably be near the middle of the simple curve. A set-up at the C.S. is required if this is done, but on final location the resulting smooth junction at the C.S. justifies this method.

Conditions frequently warrant varying the foregoing procedure. For example, instead of following steps (*h*) and (*j*), the S.C. and the C.S. may be located (or checked) by any one of three other methods: (1) by measuring the X and Y coordinates; (2) by measuring the long tangent (L.T.), the angle Δ, and the short tangent (S.T.) of the spiral; (3) by measuring $\frac{1}{3}\,\Delta$ and the long chord (L.C.).

Tables may be used to expedite some of the operations just described.

Table XI: See explanation on page 44 of Part III.

Table XII: See explanation on page 44 of Part III.

Table XIII: This table is explained in Art. 5–10.

Table XIV: This table is explained in Art. 5–11.

Table XV: This table gives exact deflection angles for any spiral up to $\Delta = 27°$ staked with ten equal chords.

If a table such as Table XV is not available, it is not necessary to use formulas 5–13 and 5–11 when points are spaced regularly. The following method is quicker:

Let $a_1 =$ the deflection angle (in minutes) to the *first regular point*. Then

$$a_1 \text{ (in min.)} = \frac{20 \, \Delta \text{(in degrees)}}{n^2} \qquad (5\text{–}18)$$

where $n =$ the number of equal chords on the spiral.

Calculate a_1 for given values of Δ and n. Then, to find the remaining deflection angles, simply multiply a_1 by the squares of the chord-point numbers. Thus, if Δ were 6° and n were 10, $a_1 = 1.2$ min. The remaining deflections are $4 \, a_1$, $9 \, a_1$, $16 \, a_1$, $25 \, a_1$, etc. (The student should check these against Table XV.)

Table XVI: This table is an extension of the principle just described (see examples on pages 70 and 71 of Part III). The "corrections" mentioned are the result of the slight approximation in the relation $a = \frac{1}{3} \, \delta$; their source is explained in Appendix A. The theory underlying deflections for a set-up on the spiral is outlined in Art. 5–6.

5–4. Locating Any Intermediate Point on Spiral.—Though the spiral is usually laid out with equal chords, the number commonly being ten, such a process does not serve all purposes. For example, on location prior to grading, earthwork estimates are made more rapidly if cross-sections are taken at regular full stations and possibly half-stations. Furthermore, important "breaks" requiring cross-sectioning may fall between regularly spaced points. During construction it may be necessary to set points on a spiral at trestle bents or on bridge piers. For these reasons it is convenient to have a simple formula for determining the deflection angle to any point at a distance l feet beyond the beginning of a spiral. The following relation serves this purpose:

$$a \text{ (in min.)} = \frac{k \, l^2}{1,000} \qquad (5\text{–}19)$$

The constant k may be computed from formula 5–1. It is recommended that an integral value of k be chosen in order to simplify the computation.

5–5. Field Notes.—Notes for staking a spiraled curve are set up in continuous stationing according to a modification of the form in Art. 2–9. Deflection angles for the spirals

should start with 0° at the T.S. and S.T. The comments in
Art. 3–13 are pertinent.

In the accompanying form, the columns for calculated and
magnetic bearings have been omitted in order to insert
explanatory notes. Otherwise the form is a typical example
of the left-hand page of a field book. Distances are here computed to tenths of a foot, and deflection angles are taken to the
nearest minute. In final location a higher degree of precision
would be required.

Form of Notes for Spiraled Curve

Sta.	Point	Total Defl.	Field Procedure	Curve Data
47+15.8	⊙S.T.	0°00′	At S.T., orient by	$I = 14°\ 10′$
46+55.8		0°04′	sighting to P.I.	$D = 3°$
45+95.8		0°14′	with 0°00′ on	P.I. $= 43+31.1$
45+35.8		0°32′	vernier. Make	$T_s = 387.5$
44+75.8		0°58′	final check at	$L_s = 300$
44+15.8	C.S.	1°30′	C.S.	
44+15.8	C.S.	2°35′	At S.C., orient by	
44+00		2°21′	sighting to T.S.	
43+50		1°36′	with 3°00′ on	
43+00		0°51′	proper side of	
42+50		0°06′	vernier.	
42+43.6	⊙S.C.	0°00′		
42+43.6	S.C.	1°30′	At T.S., orient by	
41+83.6		0°58′	sighting to P.I.	
41+23.6		0°32′	with 0°00′ on	
40+63.6		0°14′	vernier.	
40+03.6		0°04′		
39+43.6	⊙T.S.	0°00′		

In the foregoing example both spirals were run as five-
chord spirals. The deflection angles could be computed by

finding a_1 from formula 5–18 and multiplying by the squares of the chord-point numbers; or they could be taken directly from Table XV for every other chord point of the ten-chord spiral.

To illustrate how easily spiral deflections may be computed to fit any desired conditions, the following alternate notes are given for staking the approach spiral.

Alternate Notes for Approach Spiral

Case A: 4-chord spiral. Use formula 5–18 and Table XVI.			*Case B:* stakes at regular full stations. Use formula 5–19.		
Sta.	Point	Total Defl.	Sta.	Point	Total Defl.
42+43.6	S.C.	1°30'	42+43.6	S.C.	1°30'
41+68.6		0°51'	42+00		1°06'
40+93.6		0°22'	41+00		0°24'
40+18.6		0°06'	40+00		0°03'
39+43.6	T.S.	0°00'	39+43.6	T.S.	0°00'

5–6. Transit Set-ups on Spiral.—Field conditions sometimes require a set-up on the spiral. It is easy enough to place the line of sight on the local tangent at any point on a spiral by backsighting to the T.S. and deflecting twice the forward deflection from the T.S. to the point occupied. But the deflections as calculated from the T.S. cannot be used thereafter; in this respect a spiral differs from a simple curve.

In Fig. 5–4, P is any point on a spiral, just as in Fig. 5–3. The radius of curvature r of the spiral at P shows on a portion of the tangent circle, known as the *osculating circle*. The ocsulating circle at any point must lie inside the spiral toward the T.S. and outside the spiral toward the S.C.

Any circle has a constant degree of curve, whereas a spiral is a curve of uniformly changing degree. Since the tangent at the T.S. is a circle of infinite radius with D equal to zero, it follows that:

> *A spiral departs in both directions from any osculating circle at the same rate as from the tangent at the T.S.*

It follows from the principle of the osculating circle that the spiral is approximately bisected by the throw o, and vice versa. That is, line JK and spiral AC (Fig. 5–2) bisect each other. Since tangent offsets are proportional to the cubes of the spiral lengths, this means that

$$o = \frac{Y}{4} \qquad \text{(5–20) Approx.}$$

Since Y is approximately equal to $\dfrac{L_s^2}{6R}$ (from equation 5–8), it follows that

$$o = \frac{L_s^2}{24R} \qquad \text{(5–21) Approx.}$$

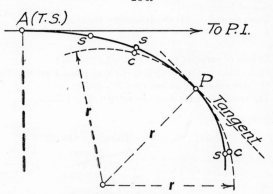

Fig. 5–4. Osculating circle

By means of the osculating-circle principle, the deflection to any point on a spiral from a set-up at any other point may be readily calculated. Theoretically it is only necessary to compute the deflection for a circular arc of degree d at the spiral point occupied and to add algebraically the spiral deflection computed (for the corresponding length) as though for a set-up at the T.S. For example, if three random points s on the spiral in Fig. 5–4 are located to give equal lengths l from the T.S. and in either direction from P, the points c being the same distance from P on the osculating circle, then the deflection from the tangent at P to the *forward point* s equals the deflection from the tangent to c *plus* the deflection from c to s; the deflection from the tangent at P to the *backward point s* equals the deflection from the tangent to c *minus* the deflection from c to s. Both deflections to c are equal. Those from c to s are also equal, and are the same as the deflection at the T.S. for the first point s.

Example.—*Given:* $D = 4°30'$; $L_s = 300$ ft. It is desired to stake the spiral by using six 50-ft chords. Owing to limited visibility, the last two chords must be located by means of a set-up at chord point 4.

$$\Delta = \frac{L_s D}{200} = \frac{300 \times 4.5}{200} = 6°45' \text{ and } A = \tfrac{1}{3} \Delta = 2°15'$$

From formula 5–11, the deflections to the spiral are $\dfrac{A}{36}$, $\dfrac{4 A}{36}$, $\dfrac{9 A}{36}$, etc.

Degree of curve at point 4 is $d_4 = \tfrac{4}{6} D = 3°00'$.

Deflections to the osculating circle at point 4 are multiples of the deflections for 50 feet on a 3° circular curve.

The resulting deflections are tabulated as follows:

Transit at T.S.

POINT	DEFL. TO SPIRAL
0	$0°00'$
1	$\dfrac{A}{36} = 0°03.8'$
2	$\dfrac{A}{9} = 0°15'$
3	$\dfrac{A}{4} = 0°33.8'$
4	$\dfrac{4 A}{9} = 1°00'$

Transit at Point 4

(Orient by sighting to T.S. with 2°00' on vernier)

POINT	DEFL. TO OSC. ⊙	DEFL. OSC. ⊙ TO SPIRAL	DEFL. TO SPIRAL
5	$0°45'$	$0°03.8'$	$0°48.8'$
6 (S.C.)	$1°30'$	$0°15'$	$1°45'$

Table XVI provides a rapid method of obtaining the deflection to any chord point from a set-up at any other point, without making the calculations just described. For example, the final deflections in the preceding problem may be found by first computing $a_1 = 3.75'$ (from formula 5–18) and then multiplying a_1 by the coefficients 1, 4, 9, 16, 13, and 28.

5–7. Spiral Between Arcs of Compound Curve.—If either arc of a compound curve is sharp enough to require insertion of a spiral at the main tangent, a spiral between the two arcs may also be justified.

Fig. 5–5 shows a spiral AC inserted between the arcs of a compound curve (the main tangents are omitted to simplify the sketch). The radius of the spiral at A equals R_L, instead of infinity as in Fig. 5–1; that at C equals R_S. In other words, AC is a portion of a spiral cut to fit between curves of degree D_L and D_S. An additional value—usually the length AC but sometimes the offset JK—must be assumed. The problem is then determinate; only one spiral will satisfy the given conditions.

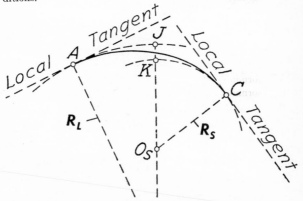

Fig. 5–5. Spiral between arcs of compound curve

From the principle of the osculating circle, the offset or "throw" JK is the value of o for a spiral of length AC and terminal degree $D_S - D_L$. It also follows that, for all practical purposes, JK and AC bisect each other. Accordingly, the problem of calculating deflections for running in the spiral AC is identical with that of calculating the deflections for staking the remainder of a spiral from a set-up at any point, as explained in Art. 5–6.

If the length of the spiral AC be designated by l_s, its *true* central angle equals the sum of the central angles for the simple curves produced, that is, for the arcs AJ and KC. From formula 2–14,

$$\text{true } \Delta = \left(\frac{l_s}{2}\right)\left(\frac{D_L}{100}\right) + \left(\frac{l_s}{2}\right)\left(\frac{D_S}{100}\right)$$

which reduces to $\text{true } \Delta = \left(\dfrac{l_s}{200}\right)(D_L + D_S)$ (5–22)

For computing the spiral deflections from the local tangent at A or C, the *nominal* value of Δ is used. This is defined as the difference between the true central angle of the connecting spiral and that of the osculating circle at either end. Since the osculating circle at A has a central angle of $\dfrac{l_s D_L}{100}$ in the distance l_s,

$$\text{nominal } \Delta = \text{true } \Delta - \frac{l_s D_L}{100}$$

which reduces to $\text{nominal } \Delta = \dfrac{l_s}{200}(D_S - D_L)$ (5–23)

(The nominal Δ may be taken from Table XI if the table is entered with l_s as L_s and with $D_S - D_L$ as D.)

Example.—*Given:* $D_L = 2°$; $D_S = 7°$; $AC = l_s = 300$ ft.

Here $D_S - D_L = 5°$; consequently, $o = 3.27$ (Table XI).

From formula 5–1 the value of k for this spiral is $\dfrac{100\,(7° - 2°)}{300} = 1\frac{2}{3}°$ per station, which means that l_s is the last 300 ft of a complete spiral that is $\dfrac{7°}{k} \times 100 = 420$ ft long.

From formula 5–22, true $\Delta = 13°20'$.

From formula 5–23 (or Table XI), nominal $\Delta = 7°30'$.

To compute spiral deflections, use the nominal Δ in formula 5–18. Thus, if the spiral AC were to be divided into four equal parts,

$$a_1 = \frac{20 \times 7.5°}{4^2} = 9.375'$$

and the deflections to the spiral from the osculating circle at A are a_1, $4\,a_1$, $9\,a_1$, and $16\,a_1$. These are added to the deflections from the tangent to the corresponding points on the osculating circle, namely, $0°45'$, $1°30'$, $2°15'$, and $3°00'$. The final deflections are: $0°54'$, $2°08'$, $3°39'$, and $5°30'$. For running in the spiral from the sharper arc (set-up at C), the required deflections from the tangent would be $2°28'$, $4°38'$, $6°28'$, and $8°00'$.

5–8. Completely Spiraled Compound Curve.—The basic parts of a completely spiraled compound curve are shown in Fig. 5–6. Arc ACB represents the nonspiraled compound curve. After insertion of the three spirals (which are omitted in the sketch for purposes of clarity), the layout starts at TS_1 and ends at S_3T. Point a is the offset T.C. for the first spiral; point b is the offset C.T. for the third spiral. The throws, o_1 and o_3, of these spirals are the distances Aa and $B'b$. The throw, o_2, of the second spiral is JK (see also Fig. 5–5).

The traverse method of Art. 3–6 provides the best solution for this problem. As an illustration, assume the given values to be sta. V, I, I_L, R_L, R_S, and the k-values of the spirals.

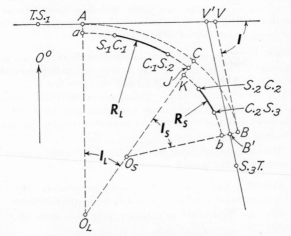

Fig. 5–6. Completely-spiraled compound curve

The problem is to find the stationing of all curve points (TS_1, S_1C_1, C_1S_2, etc.) so that the layout can be computed and staked. The data for the traverse are shown in Table 5–1.

Solve for $V'B'$. From Σ *latitudes*,

$$V'B' = \frac{(R_L + o_1) - (R_S + o_3) \cos I - (R_L - R_S - o_2) \cos I_L}{\sin I}$$

Then from Σ *departures*,

$$AV' = (R_S + o_3) \sin I + (R_L - R_S - o_2) \sin I_L - V'B' \cos I$$

As the next step, $V'V = \dfrac{(o_1 + o_2 - o_3)}{\sin I}$, and sta. $V' = $ sta. $V - V'V$. (If the sign of $o_1 + o_2 - o_3$ is negative, VB lies inside $V'B'$ and the stationing of V' will be greater than that of V.)

Finally, the tangent distances T_{sL} and T_{sS} are $X_{o1} + AV'$ and $X_{o3} + V'B'$. The stations of the curve points are then found in the usual way by subtracting T_{sL} from sta. V' to obtain sta. TS_1 and adding successive spiral and arc lengths to sta. TS_1. It will be necessary to use the principles brought out in Art. 5–7 in computing the true central angles of the circular arcs.

If the layout starts with the sharper curve, or if other combinations of values are given, the same basic traverse method will provide the solution. Numerical examples will be found in Art. 5–16, Problems 14 and 15.

5–9. Fitting Spiraled Curve to Specified E_s or T_s.—As in the case of a simple curve, it may be necessary to fit a spiraled curve to definite field conditions such as a specified E_s or T_s. There are voluminous tables* giving convenient combinations of D and L_s which approximate a specified value for E_s or T_s; the exact values of E_s and T_s for a selected combination are obtained by interpolation.

The tables in this book may also be used to select a spiral-curve layout fitting given conditions.

Example.—*Given:* $I = 27°00'$; $E_s = $approximately 34 ft. Determine suitable values of D and L_s (slide-rule calculation).

First use Table VIII to obtain a fairly close value of D.

---

* Barnett, Joseph, *Transition Curves for Highways.* Washington, D. C.: U. S. Govt. Printing Office, 1938.

TABLE 5-1

DATA FOR PROBLEM IN ART. 5-8

Line	Distance	Azimuth	Latitude	Departure
$O_L A$	$R_L + o_1$	$0°$	$R_L + o_1$	0
AV'	AV'	$90°$	0	AV'
$V'B'$	$V'B'$	$90° + I$	$-V'B' \sin I$	$V'B' \cos I$
$B'O_S$	$R_S + o_3$	$180° + I$	$-(R_S + o_3) \cos I$	$-(R_S + o_3) \sin I$
$O_S O_L$	$R_L - R_S - o_2$	$180° + I_L$	$-(R_L - R_S - o_2) \cos I_L$	$-(R_L - R_S - o_2) \sin I_L$

Thus,

$$D = \frac{163}{34} = 4.8° \text{ (roughly)}$$

Consideration of the relation $\Delta = \dfrac{L_s D}{200}$ shows two unknowns. Consequently, there are any number of combinations of Δ and L_s which will fit the conditions. A glance at Table XI might suggest a suitable combination.

Suppose that L_s is assumed to be 250 ft. Then

$$\Delta = \frac{250}{200} \times 4.8° = 6.0° \text{ (tentatively)}$$

From Table XII, $o = 0.00872 \times 250 = 2.2$ (approx.).

A closer value of R is then found from the relation

$$R + o = \frac{E_s - o}{\text{exsec } \frac{1}{2}I}$$

Thus, $\qquad R + o = \dfrac{34 - 2.2}{0.02842} = 1,119$

Therefore, $R = 1,117$ and $D = 5°08'$ (approx.).

If D were chosen to be 5°, the 250-ft spiral is one listed in "selected spirals" of Table XI. For this combination, E_s would differ slightly from 34 ft, but a rigid requirement permitting no deviation from a fixed E_s is rarely met (it would require an odd value of either D or L_s). The exact values would be $E_s = 34.9$ and $T_s = 400.6$.

If the approximate value of T_s were fixed, the first trial calculation may also be made by using Table VIII. This will give a rough value of D, but will allow selection of a suitable value for L_s. Since o is very small in comparison with R, formula 5–14 can be expressed approximately as $T_s = R \tan \frac{1}{2}I + \frac{1}{2}L_s$, thus giving a means of finding R.

If, in the preceding example, T_s is fixed at approximately 401 ft,

$$D = \frac{1,376}{401} = 3.4° \text{ (roughly)}$$

For the assumption that $L_s = 250$ ft,

$$R = \frac{T_s - \frac{1}{2}L_s}{\tan \frac{1}{2}I} = \frac{276}{0.240} = 1,150 \text{ (approx.)}$$

and $D = 5°00'$ as before.

5-10. Spiraled-Curve Formulas with Radius as Parameter.

In connection with the use of even-radius curves (Art. 2–12) it is convenient, though not essential, to express formulas for needed spiraled-curve parts in terms of the radius of the circular arc.

In Fig. 5–2, certain of the distances may be related to R by means of coefficients N, P, M, and S, which have the following significance:

$$N\,R = \text{the distance } AD = X$$

$$P\,R = \text{the distance } DC = Y$$

$$M\,R = \text{the distance } OJ = R + o$$

$$S\,R = \text{the distance } AJ = X_0$$

Values of these coefficients for $R = 1$ have been computed for various values of Δ (see Table XIII). When these values are substituted in the following relations, parts needed for computing and staking the layout result:

$$X = R\,N \qquad\qquad (5\text{–}24)$$

$$Y = R\,P \qquad\qquad (5\text{–}25)$$

$$T_s = R(M \tan \tfrac{1}{2}I + S) \qquad\qquad (5\text{–}26)$$

$$E_s = R(M \sec \tfrac{1}{2}I - 1) = R[M \operatorname{exsec} \tfrac{1}{2}I + (M-1)] \quad (5\text{–}27)$$

$$L_s = 2\,R\,\Delta \text{ (radians)} \qquad\qquad (5\text{–}6)$$

In applying this procedure to practical problems in the highway field, the "proportion rule" has been suggested for choosing L_s. The "proportion of transition" p is the ratio of the length of the two spirals to the total length of the spiraled curve. It may be proved that

$$\Delta = \left[\frac{p}{2(2-p)}\right]I \qquad\qquad (5\text{–}28)$$

It is not possible (except by coincidence) to have integral values of R, L_s, and Δ (in degrees); one, at least, must be an odd value. When it is desired to use Table XIII without interpolation or calculation of additional values, the odd variable is L_s.

As an illustration the example of Art. 5–9 is solved by this method. For a trial, assume that p = about 0.6 (evidence shows that the natural value of p ranges between 0.4 and 0.7 for high-speed operation on highways). Then

$$\Delta = \left[\frac{0.6}{2(2-0.6)} \right] \times 27° = 5.8°$$

Round off to 6° for convenience in using Table XIII.

From formula 5–27, $R = 1,130$ (approx.). Use $R = 1,100$, which is listed in Table V.

Finally, 2 $\Delta = 12° = 0.20944$ radians (Table VI) and $L_s = 0.20944 \times 1,100 = 230.4$ ft.

If L_s were rounded to a convenient value (say 250 ft), then Δ would be the odd value, but the circular arc could still be staked readily by means of the deflections listed in Table V. When the chord definition of D is used, Δ is obtained from 5–28; R_c, from 5–27; D_c, from Table I; and L_s, from 5–2.

The coefficients in formulas 5–24 through 5–27 apply whether or not a central circular arc is present; that is, they also can be used for the double-spiral curve described in the next article.

5–11. Double-Spiral Curve.—Some engineers advocate making curves transitional throughout by using a double spiral, which consists of two equal spirals placed end to end with the curvature changing from increasing to decreasing at the middle of the layout. This simplifies the selection of a curve that will have a specified value of E_s or T_s; since $\Delta = \frac{1}{2}I$, it follows that $T_s = X + Y \tan \frac{1}{2}I$ and $E_s = Y \sec \frac{1}{2}I$.

Table XIV gives values of T_s and E_s for $L_s = 1$. Multiplying the proper tabulated values by the actual length L_s gives T_s and E_s for a double-spiral curve having the given value of I.

Obviously, a double-spiral curve of given I is longer than a spiraled simple curve having the same D; hence there is a much greater length over which operating conditions—centrifugal force and superelevation, in particular—are variable. For this reason, the all-transitional curve should be used only in exceptional cases, at least on highway work.

5–12. Calculating Spiral Without Special Tables.—It is possible to compute a spiral without reference to special tables (if the engineer will do this occasionally, he will understand the spiral better). The method suggested is based upon certain approximations the significance of which may be seen by examining Fig. 5-2 in connection with Table XI. All calculations may be made by slide rule.

Procedure for Flat Spirals (up to $\Delta = 5°$)

(a) Compute from $Y = L_s \sin \frac{1}{3}\Delta$

(b) Compute X from $X = L_s - \dfrac{Y^2}{2\,L_s}$

(c) Compute o from $o = \frac{1}{4}\,Y$

(d) Compute X_0 from $X_0 = \frac{1}{2}\,X$

(e) Compute deflections by applying the principle that deflections are proportional to the squares of the distances.

If the foregoing method is applied to a 200-ft spiral joining a 3° curve, the computed values are: $Y = 3.49$, $X = 199.97$, $o = 0.87$, and $X_0 = 99.98$. For all practical purposes these are the same as the values listed in Table XI.

As Δ increases beyond 5°, more significant differences arise between the exact and approximate values of these four spiral parts. The greatest difference will be found in the value of X. However, X is not often needed in the field. The values of o and X_0 are of more practical use, for they are needed in obtaining T_s by formula 5-15. The following table shows that a relatively small error in T_s would result from using the approximate method when $\Delta = 15°$.

Given		Values by Approx. Method	Exact Values from Table XI	
			$D_a = 10°$	$D_c = 10°$
$L_s = 300$	$Y =$	26.1	26.05	26.05
$D = 10°$	$X =$	298.86	297.95	297.95
$(\Delta = 15°)$	$o =$	6.52	6.53	6.51
	$X_0 =$	149.43	149.66	149.47

5-13. The A.R.E.A. Ten-Chord Spiral.—The ten-chord spiral of the American Railway Engineering Association has been used by many American railroads since about 1912. This spiral is an approximation of equation 5-8 in which L_s is measured by ten equal chords instead of around the spiral itself. It is commonly used in connection with the chord definition of D.

The spiral in this book may be converted practically to the A.R.E.A. spiral by applying the corrections marked with an asterisk, as explained in Part III on page 44. (See Appendix A for the source of those corrections.) Consequently, there is no need to master the details of the A.R.E.A. spiral or to use tables prepared for it alone, as demonstrated by the following comparison in the case of an exceptionally sharp railroad curve:

	D_c	L_s	X	Y	X_0	o	A
Spiral in this book	10°	300	297.95	26.05	149.47	6.51	4°59.8'
A.R.E.A. spiral	10°	300	297.96	26.05	149.48	6.51	4°59.8'

5–14. Laying Out Spiral by Taping.—A spiral may be staked by using tangent offsets, chord offsets, or middle ordinates. The operations in the field are similar to those described in Art. 2–14. However, the calculations differ slightly from those for a simple curve owing to the variable curvature on a spiral.

Tangent offsets for selected points on the spiral are computed from the cube law (Art. 5–2). It is sufficiently accurate for the flat spirals used on modern highway and railroad alignment to assume that the spiral and the throw o bisect each other, and that $o = \dfrac{Y}{4}$ (equation 5–20). The throw is computed from the relation $\dfrac{L_s^2}{24\,R}$ (equation 5–21) or is taken from tables, after which the offsets from the tangent to the midpoint of the spiral (at equidistant points) are found from the principle that offsets are proportional to the cubes of the distances. The same offsets are then used to locate the second half of the spiral by measuring them radially from the circular arc (osculating circle) produced backward from the S.C. For example, the five offsets required to locate a ten-chord spiral are found by multiplying the throw by 0.004, 0.032, 0.108, 0.256, and 0.500. The advantage of this method, in comparison with measuring all offsets from the tangent, is that the measurements usually come well within the limits of the graded roadbed.

Chord offsets and middle ordinates are approximately proportional to the lengths from the T.S. Needed values

may.be obtained by substituting $\dfrac{D_1+D_2}{2}$ for D in the various
simple-curve offset formulas, D_1 and D_2 being the degrees of
curve of a spiral at the ends of a particular chord. The
values of C.O. and M.O. in Table I facilitate the computation.

5–15. Length of Spirals.—A spiral need not have a particular length, but it should be at least long enough for the
transition to be made safely and comfortably. Design speed
and the rate of attaining superelevation are controlling factors
in this respect.

On railroads, practice has been fairly well standardized
for a number of years, though the operation of high-speed
streamliners is adding new problems. Chapter 9 contains
examples and recommendations.

Practice on highways is not so definite as is that on railroads.
Lack of standardization is due to the later adoption of spirals,
the more diverse operating conditions, and the greater number
of administrative units involved. Recent practice is outlined
in Chapter 8.

5–16. Problems

1. Derive formula 5–18 from the basic formulas of Art. 5–2.

2. Derive formula 5–19 from the basic formulas of Art. 5–2.

3. Check the deflections given at the end of Art. 5–7.

4. Derive formulas 5–26 and 5–27.

5. Derive formula 5–28.

6. Derive the approximate relations listed in Art. 5–12.

7. *Given:* $D_c = 6°20'$; $L_s = 240$ ft. *Find:* X, Y, X_0, and o
by Table XII. *Answers:* $X = 239.58$; $Y = 10.60$; $X_0 = 119.87$;
$o = 2.65$.

8. Solve Problem 7 without tables of any kind, using slide
rule calculation. Compare answers with those given.

9. *Given:* sta. P.I. $= 64 + 82.72$; $I = 37°51'$; $D_c = 6°20'$; $L_s = $
240. Using answers in Problem 7, find the stationing of the
T.S., S.C., C.S., and S.T. *Answers:* T.S. $= 60 + 51.60$; S.C. $=$
$62 + 91.60$; C.S. $= 66 + 49.23$; S.T. $= 68 + 89.23$.

10. How much longer is the total layout in Problem 9 and how much further inside the P.I. is it than the same unspiraled curve in Art. 2–15, Problem 1? *Answers:* 240.00 and 2.80.

11. *Given:* sta. P.I. = 27+16.52; $I = 20°36'$; $D_a = 7°$; $L_s = 150$. Prepare a set of field notes for staking the curve as follows: (*a*) transit at T.S. and five-chord approach spiral; (*b*) transit at S.C. with full and half stations to C.S.; (*c*) transit at S.T. with full and half stations on leaving spiral.

12. Set up optional deflections for staking the approach spiral in Problem 11 as a six-chord spiral. The transit is to be at the T.S. for staking to the mid-point, and it is to be at the mid-point for staking the remainder of the spiral. Determine deflections by the theory of Art. 5–6, and check results by Table XVI.

13. It is required to run in a 240-ft spiral from point X on a 10° curve to point Y on a 4° curve. *Find:* (*a*) the deflection angle from the tangent at X to the mid-point of the spiral; (*b*) the deflection angle from the tangent at Y to the mid-point of the spiral; (*c*) the true central angle of the spiral; (*d*) the length of the complete spiral of which XY is a 240-ft portion. *Answers:* (*a*) 5°24'; (*b*) 3°00'; (*c*) 16°48'; (*d*) 400 ft.

14. Completely spiraled compound curve. *Given:* sta. P.I. = 34+42.70; $I_L = 21°14'$; $I_S = 34°28'$; $D_L = 2°$ and $D_S = 5°$ (both chord definition); the 2° curve occurs first (at the back tangent); the k-value of all three spirals is to be $1\frac{2}{3}°$ per sta. *Find:* the stationing of all curve points. *Answers:* T.S.$_1$ = 22+31.10; S.$_1$C.$_1$ = 23+51.10; C.$_1$S.$_2$ = 32+62.77; S.$_2$C.$_2$ = 34+42.77; C.$_2$S.$_3$ = 38+92.10; S.$_3$T. = 41+92.10.

15. Completely spiraled compound curve. *Given:* sta. P.I. = 62+44.27; $I_L = 18°26'$; $I_S = 43°57'$; $D_L = 5°$ and $D_S = 12°$ (both arc definition); the 12° curve occurs first (at the back tangent); each of the three spirals is to be 150 ft long. *Find:* stationing of T.S.$_1$, S.$_1$C.$_1$, C.$_1$S.$_2$, S.$_2$C.$_2$, C.$_2$S.$_3$, and S.$_3$T. *Answers:* T.S.$_1$ = 58+40.42; S.$_1$C.$_1$ = 59+90.42; C.$_1$S.$_2$ = 62+06.67; S.$_2$C.$_2$ = 63+56.67; C.$_2$S.$_3$ = 65+75.34; S.$_3$T. = 67+25.34.

16. *Given:* $I = 37°12'$; $T_s = 700 \pm 25$ ft; k for each of two equal spirals can range between $1\frac{1}{2}°$ and $2\frac{1}{2}°$ per sta. *Find:*

combinations of D and L_s (listed in Table XI) which fit the conditions closely.   *Answer: $D = 3°00'$, $L_s = 125$ or 150.*

17. Find a suitable spiral for the even-radius curve of Problem 13, Art. 2–15.   The proportion p should be about 0.5.

18. If a double-spiral curve having the same radius R_c at the mid-point were substituted for the spiraled curve in Problem 9, how much longer would the curved layout be?   *Answer: 358.24 ft.*

CHAPTER 6

EARTHWORK

6-1. Foreword.—On route-surveying projects the *basis of payment* for grading is usually *excavation as measured in place* and computed from the survey notes. Except as may be specified otherwise, the unit price for excavation also includes: hauling excavated material (*cut*) from within the limits of the roadway or moving in other material (*borrow*) from outside areas; building the embankments (*fill*) to specified form; disposing of surplus material (*waste*); and performing such operations as forming earth shoulders, trimming slopes, and preparing the subgrade for ballast or pavement.

Consequently, excavation quantities (the customary unit of volume is the *cubic yard*) must be determined carefully and accurately. Fill quantities are important in the office work of grade-line design. However, the final fill quantities are incidental; they do not affect the payments in the usual contract. Rarely, both excavation and embankment are paid for at separate unit prices. On projects consisting almost wholly of embankment—such as levees—the basis of payment is fill as measured in place.

Operations included under the general heading of *earthwork* are (see relation to Art. 1–8):

(*a*) Office work of making preliminary estimate of grading quantities by scaling depths of cut and fill at regular intervals along one or more paper locations.

(*b*) Field work of taking *cross-sections* along located line prior to construction.

(*c*) Office work of calculating volumes more accurately than in (*a*) from data obtained in (*b*) and, possibly, of making a distribution analysis (economical grading schedule) based upon a *mass diagram*.

(*d*) Field work of setting stakes for controlling the construction and of making measurements needed for computing partial and final payments.

(*e*) Office work of calculating all final quantities.

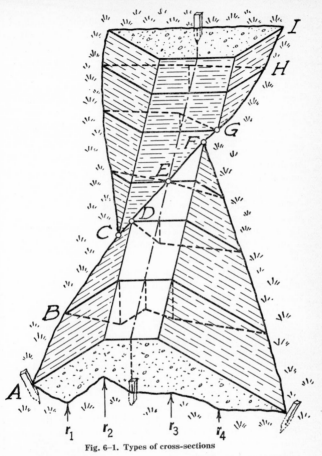

Fig. 6–1. Types of cross-sections

The same principles apply to computing volumes of materials other than earthwork, such as riprap and concrete built into structures, material stock piles, and reservoir volumes.

6–2. Types of Cross-Sections.—The exact determination of earthwork quantities is usually based upon field cross-sections taken in a specified manner before and after grading.

On highway and railroad work, cross-sections are vertical and at right angles to the survey center-line. Every section is an area formed by the subgrade (or *base*), the *side slopes*, and the original ground surface. Except as noted in Art. 6–5, the base is flat and level, and the side slopes at a section are uniform from the edge of the base to the ground surface. The base is usually wider in cuts than on fills, to provide room for side ditches.

Fig. 6–1 shows a portion of a graded roadbed passing from fill to cut (side ditches are omitted for simplicity). The sketch illustrates several cross-sections, the types depending on their shape and the number of rod readings used to determine them.

At any cross-section a rod reading is always taken at the center-line stake. Two additional readings are usually taken at the intersections of the side slopes and the ground surface; if stakes are driven at these points they are called *slope stakes*. Additional rod readings are taken where conditions require them.

The section at *H* is a regular *three-level section* in cut, so named because three rod readings are used to fix it—one at the center stake and the others at the slope-stake locations. This type (in cut or fill) occurs more often than any other.

The sections at *D* and *G* are special cases of a three-level section, each having a *grade point* (point *D* or *G*) at one corner.

The section at *B* is a *five-level section* in fill. This is a modification of a three-level section in which two additional readings are taken directly below (or above) the edges of the base.

The section at *A* is an *irregular section* in fill. A large number of rod readings are required to fix it—in the case shown, there are four readings at points *r* in addition to the three at the slope stakes and center stake.

The section at *E* is a *side-hill section*, having cut on one side and fill on the other side of a grade point at *E*. In the case illustrated the grade point is on the center line, but in general it may fall anywhere between the edges of the base.

The section at *I* is a *level section*, so designated because the ground is level transversely and only one rod reading at the center line is sufficient.

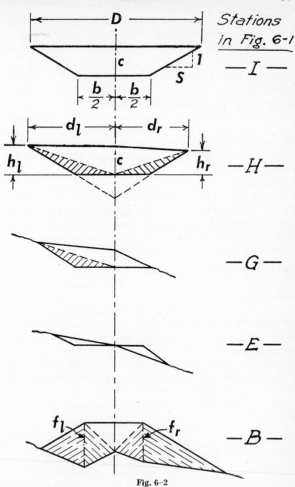

Fig. 6-2

6-3. Location of Cross-Sections.—For convenience in calculations and field work, cross-sections are usually taken at each full-station (or half-station) stake on the survey center-line. They are also taken at curve points and at additional plus-points where important "breaks" in the topography occur. Where grading is very heavy or where unit costs are high, as in rock excavation, cross-sections are taken at closer intervals.

If the transition between cut and fill occurs on a side hill, as many as five cross-sections may be needed. In Fig. 6–1 these sections are located at C, D, E, F, and G. Theoretically, complete cross-sections are not necessary at C and F, but their stationing is needed to locate the apexes of the pyramids having triangular end bases at E. Thus, the cross-sections at the transition are reduced to three: (1) at the fill-base grade point D, (2) at the center-line grade point E, and (3) at the cut-base grade point G. The points C and F are often so close to D and G that they are omitted from the notes and the apexes of the transition pyramids are assumed to fall at D and G. Where the three sections at the transition are very close together, the grade contour DEG is assumed to be at right angles to the center line; there are then wedged-shaped solids on either side of the grade contour. See page 110.

6–4. Formulas for End Areas.—Fig. 6–2 shows the areas at certain cross-sections in Fig. 6–1. The common notation is spread among the several sketches. The distance c is always the vertical distance (cut or fill) between ground and grade at the center line, and h_l (or h_r) is the vertical distance between ground and grade at the slope stake. Distances between ground and grade at other points are denoted by c_l and c_r in cut, and by f_l and f_r in fill (as at section B). The inclination s of the side slopes is expressed by the ratio of horizontal distance to vertical distance (as unity).

The horizontal distance from the survey center-line to any slope stake is

$$d_l \text{ (or } d_r) = \tfrac{1}{2}b + s\,h_l \text{ (or } s\,h_r) \tag{6–1}$$

The area of a *level section* (as at I) is

$$A_L = c\left(\frac{b+D}{2}\right) \tag{6–2}$$

or
$$A_L = c\,(b + c\,s) \tag{6–3}$$

The area of a *regular three-level section* (as at H) is found by adding the areas of the two cross-hatched triangles to the areas of the two triangles having the common altitude c. Thus,

$$A_3 = \tfrac{1}{2} c (d_l + d_r) + \tfrac{1}{4} b (h_l + h_r)$$

Substitution of H for $h_l + h_r$ and D for $d_l + d_r$ reduces the relation to

$$A_3 = \frac{c D}{2} + \frac{b H}{4} \qquad (6\text{--}4)$$

Another convenient formula for the area of a *regular three-level section* is found by extending the side slopes to an intersection at the center line so as to form a triangle, called the *grade triangle*, below (or above) the base. The dimensions of the grade triangle are constant until the base or slope changes; its fixed area is $\dfrac{b^2}{4 s}$. Consequently, the "grade-triangle formula" is

$$A_3 = \frac{D}{2} \left(c + \frac{b}{2 s} \right) - \frac{b^2}{4 s} \qquad (6\text{--}5)$$

Formula 6–5 is slightly more convenient than 6–4 for computing a long series of regular three-level sections in cut or fill, owing to the constant terms $\dfrac{b}{2 s}$ and $\dfrac{b^2}{4 s}$.

The *special three-level section* having a grade point at the ground surface (as at D or G, Fig. 6–1) is also determined by formula 6–4. One of the four triangles disappears; therefore, $D = d_l$ (or d_r) $+\tfrac{1}{2}b$, and $H = h_l$ or h_r. The grade-triangle formula also applies if properly modified, but its use is not recommended at the transition between cut and fill.

At a *side-hill section* (as at E) the end areas for cut and fill are kept separate. Obviously, both are triangles. In the general case, with the grade point not at the center line, each area is

$$A_T = \tfrac{1}{2} w h \qquad (6\text{--}6)$$

where w is the actual base width of the triangle. At section E in Fig. 6–2, $w = \dfrac{b}{2}$.

The area of a *five-level section* (as at B) is found by combining the indicated triangles having common bases. The final relation is

$$A_5 = \tfrac{1}{2} (c b + f_l d_l + f_r d_r) \qquad (6\text{--}7)$$

If the section is in cut, c_l and c_r are substituted for f_l and f_r.

Ordinate $\dfrac{-h_1}{-d_1}$ $\times$ $\dfrac{0}{-\frac{1}{2}b}$ $\times$ $\dfrac{-h_1}{+\frac{1}{2}b}$ $\times$ $\dfrac{-f_4}{+d_4}$ $\times$ $\dfrac{-f_3}{+d_3}$ $\times$ $\dfrac{-c}{0}$ $\times$ $\dfrac{-f_2}{-d_2}$ $\times$ $\dfrac{-f_1}{-d_1}$ $\times$ $\dfrac{-h_2}{-d_1}$

Abscissa

Double Area by Coordinates—First Form

$\dfrac{0}{0}$ $\times$ $\dfrac{c}{0}$ $\times$ $\dfrac{f_2}{d_2}$ $\times$ $\dfrac{f_1}{d_1}$ $\times$ $\dfrac{h_1}{0}$ $\times$ $\dfrac{0}{\frac{b}{2}}$ —℄— $\dfrac{0}{0}$ $\times$ $\dfrac{c}{0}$ $\times$ $\dfrac{f_3}{d_3}$ $\times$ $\dfrac{f_4}{d_4}$ $\times$ $\dfrac{h_1}{d_1}$ $\times$ $\dfrac{0}{\frac{b}{2}}$

Double Area by Coordinates—Second Form

The area of an *irregular section* (as at A, Fig. 6–1) is best found by a coordinate method. Thus, the coordinates of the corners of the area—the origin being taken at the center of the base and the order of the coordinates being determined by progressing clockwise from A and repeating those at A—are arranged as in the first form on page 102.

It will be recalled from plane surveying that the area of a closed figure whose coordinates are set up in the preceding form is equal to one-half the difference between the algebraic sums of the products indicated by the full diagonal lines and those indicated by the dotted diagonal lines.

A method of making the foregoing calculations in such a way as to reduce chances of errors in signs is to set up the coordinates as in the second form on page 102.

The coordinates start at the center of the base as origin, and then proceed *clockwise around the left portion* of the section and *counter-clockwise around the right portion* in the form of a figure 8 on its side. *Algebraic signs are omitted.* All products indicated by the solid diagonal lines have the same sign; all those indicated by the dotted diagonal lines have the opposite sign. As before, the end area is one-half the difference between the sums of the two sets of products.

This arrangement of coordinates is especially recommended for calculating-machine work. In using the machine, multiply the figures connected by the solid diagonal lines, accumulating the products on the proper dial. Then reverse-multiply the figures connected by the dotted diagonal lines, thus subtracting those products. The final result remaining on the dial is the *double area*. For cut areas, the sum of the products indicated by dotted diagonal lines is larger than the sum of the products indicated by full diagonal lines; for fill areas, the reverse is true. When using the calculating machine the products making up the larger sum are set up first.

Some computers prefer to use machine calculation for all areas, even the standard types represented by formulas 6–2 through 6–7. This is done by a generalization of the method just described. In all cases omit algebraic signs. For areas lying entirely to the left of the survey center-line, use the coordinates in clockwise order; for areas to the right, use counter-clockwise order of the coordinates. It makes no dif-

ference which coordinate is used first, so long as it is repeated
at the end, *i.e.*, so long as the traverse is closed. For areas
cut by the survey center-line, use the figure-8 construction
described for section *A*, starting at a point on the center
line.

After a little practice it will be found unnecessary actually
to write down the coordinates. The proper order may be
visualized and used directly from the field notes.

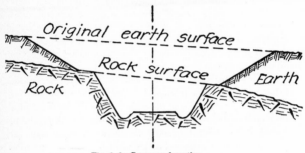

Fig. 6–3. Compound section

6–5. Compound and Other Irregular Sections.—In locations
where rock lies between ground and grade, a *compound section*
occurs, as in Fig. 6–3. Since the unit prices for rock and for
earth excavation usually differ, it is necessary to determine
the quantities of each material. This is done by first cross-
sectioning the original surface, and then doing the same to the
rock surface after stripping. Owing to the irregularity of the
earth section, a mathematical expression for its area is cumbersome. Though the area may be found by coordinates, the
planimeter method (Art. 6–6) is probably better.

Railroad roadbeds on curves are not usually crowned or
banked; the superelevation is adjusted in the rock ballast.
Earthwork quantities in the drainage ditches are usually computed as a separate item.

On highway roadbeds the subgrade may be crowned on
tangents and is usually banked parallel to the surface on
curves. Moreover, the drainage ditches and earth shoulders
are usually considered part of the cross-sectional area. (See

Fig. 6–4.) The resulting irregular areas do not permit the use of simple mathematical formulas. Two methods of determination are in common use: (1) conversion to an equivalent "balanced flat-top section" by means of transparent templates, and (2) graphical methods.

6–6. End Areas by Graphical Methods.—End areas, no matter how irregular, are easily found by plotting them to scale and running a planimeter around the boundaries. This method is widely used in highway work, especially if ditches and shoulders are part of the cross-section proper. It is particularly adapted to projects on which a permanent graphical record of the cross-sections is desired, as in tunnel construction through rock. Another distinct advantage of plotted sections is their value in studying the effects of minor changes in alignment or grade elevation. (See Chapter 10.)

In order to obtain precision consistent with the field work, areas are plotted to a fairly large scale, usually 1 inch = 10 feet or larger; consequently, the file of cross-section sheets is voluminous.

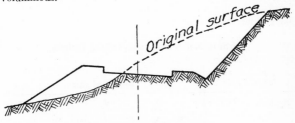

Fig. 6–4. Side-hill section on curve

Another graphical method, which is especially useful for shallow irregular areas plotted accurately to scale, is to mark off on the edge of a paper strip the continuous summation of verticals at 1-foot intervals across the area. Each vertical is the area of a trapezoidal strip 1 foot wide; the total length, applied against the scale of the cross-section, is the desired end area.

6–7. Methods of Cross-Sectioning.—The term *cross-sectioning* is loosely used to include any vertical and horizontal

measurements made on a transverse section. On routes such
as railroads, highways, and canals, two methods of cross-
sectioning are in use: (1) cross-section leveling, and (2) slope
staking.

Cross-section leveling is used when end areas are to be
determined graphically, as by planimeter. It is also the
method which must be used to obtain whatever cross-profiles
are needed in the office work of grade-line design. The field
process is essentially that of profile leveling, the difference
being that intermediate foresights are taken at breaks in the
transverse profile in addition to breaks along the survey
center-line. The left-hand page of the notes is similar to
a page in differential leveling, but the notes run up the page.
On the right-hand page the cross-section notes are entered in
the form of fractions, the numerator of each fraction indicating
the rod reading (intermediate foresight) and the denominator
indicating the transverse distance to the rod from the survey
center-line.

The hand level is a useful supplement to the engineer's
level, especially on steep transverse slopes. Rod readings
on ground higher than the H.I. are recorded as negative;

Form of Notes for Cross-Section Leveling

Portion of left-hand page		Right-hand page							
Station	H.I.	**L**			**℄**		**R**		
(T.C.) 71+76.2	....	$\frac{-0.8}{40}$ 473.4	$\frac{3.0}{26}$ 469.6	$\frac{4.2}{12}$ 468.4	$\frac{4.7}{0}$ 467.9	$\frac{5.3}{12}$ 467.3	$\frac{5.4}{18}$ 467.2	$\frac{7.5}{32}$ 465.1	$\frac{8.1}{40}$ 464.5
71+00	472.58	$\frac{2.1}{40}$ 470.5	$\frac{4.3}{20}$ 468.3	$\frac{5.7}{12}$ 466.9	$\frac{6.2}{0}$ 466.4	$\frac{6.8}{12}$ 465.8	$\frac{7.0}{16}$ 465.6	$\frac{8.5}{24}$ 464.1	$\frac{9.8}{40}$ 462.8
					(472.6)				

they must be *added* to the H.I. elevation (see the extreme left
reading at sta. 71+76.2 in the notes on page 106).

The form on page 106 represents a portion of the left-
hand page and complete notes for two cross-sections on the
right-hand page.   The sections are plotted and used in office
studies as explained further in Art. 10–6.

Slope staking* is a special form of leveling used only after
the grade line and the form of cross-section have been decided
upon.   The cross-sections are not usually plotted; either areas
or volumes are computed directly from the field notes.

This method may be used solely for the purpose of obtaining
data for calculating volumes without actually setting slope-
stakes.   It is also used preceding construction where grading
is heavy and slope stakes are needed to control the work.

The process of slope staking at any cross-section consists
of finding and recording the positions where the designed
side slopes will intersect the ground surface and of recording
breaks in the transverse ground profile between slope stakes.
The work may be done in connection with profile leveling over
the located line or as a separate process after profile leveling.
The latter is the simpler and speedier method.

When profile levels have already been run, the slope-
staking party is provided with the ground and subgrade elevations at each station stake.   Leveling is done with an engineer's level, a hand level, a level board, or a combination of
these instruments.   The form of notes resembles that used
in cross-section leveling.   But the numerator of the fraction,
instead of being the rod reading, is the difference between the
ground-surface elevation and the center-line grade elevation
at the particular station.   Cuts are designated C or $+$; fills,
F or $-$.   No record is kept of the actual rod readings used in
the process.   Also, the extreme left-hand and right-hand
entries in the notes are for the slope-stake locations.

The form on page 108 is a record of slope-staking notes
for the sections illustrated in Fig. 6–1.

In the example illustrated, elevations will have been
supplied for the full stations only, since the exact location of
the grade points is not known in advance.   Grade points are

---

* See traverse method of slope staking in Art. 10–7.

Slope-Staking Notes—First Example

Bases: 40 ft in cut; 30 ft in fill.
Side slopes: $1\frac{1}{2}$:1; Gradient: $+1.2\%$.

Sta.	Surface Elev.	Grade Elev.	L	℄	R
(I) ⁻63+00	570.3	562.84	C7.5 / 31.3	C7.5	C7.5 / 31.3
(H) 62+00	568.4	561.64	C7.1 / 30.7	C6.8	C6.4 / 29.6
(G) 61+48	565.1	561.02	C4.8 / 27.2	C4.1	0 / 20
(E) 61+36	560.9	560.87	C2.6 / 23.9	0	F2.0 / 18.0
(D) 61+25	557.1	560.74	0 / 15	F3.6	F5.8 / 23.7
(B) 61+00	554.6	560.44	F5.4 / 23.1 F6.9 / 15.0	F5.8	F6.7 / 15.0 F8.2 / 27.3
(A) 60+00	551.2	559.24	F7.2 / 25.8 F8.8 / 20.0 F7.0 / 14.7	F8.0	F8.1 / 18.0 F9.3 / 24.0 F9.4 / 29.1

found by trial in the field, their grade elevations are computed, and their surface elevations are obtained by leveling from any convenient known point. It will be noted that the stations at C and F were omitted. These points are assumed to fall at D and G, as explained in Art. 6–3.

In the field the process of finding the slope-stake locations is a matter of trial and error. It is one of those procedures in which a detailed numerical illustration of the method appears more complicated than it actually is. Briefly, the process follows:

(1) Record the cut or fill at the center, found by taking the difference between the given elevations.

(2) Observe whether the ground slopes up or down, *estimate* the cut or fill h at the probable slope-stake location, and calculate the corresponding distance d from the center line by the relation $d = \frac{1}{2}b + s\,h$.

(3) Take a rod reading at the computed distance and find the *actual h*

(4) If the actual and estimated values of h differ by more than 0.1 foot, make a new estimate, being guided by the first result; then repeat the process until d and h satisfy formula 6–1. Distances and depths are determined to the nearest tenth.

Slope staking is done rapidly by the foregoing method. With a little experience many of the points are located close enough for the purpose on the first trial. More than two trials are seldom needed.

Slope stakes, if set, are driven aslant. The cut or fill is marked on the side facing the center line, and the stationing is marked on the back.

If profile levels have not been run or if it is desired to verify them in slope staking, the engineer's level is used to carry continuous elevations along the line by usual leveling methods. In this case it is convenient to use a device known as the *grade rod*, which is the imaginary reading on a rod held on the finished subgrade. If the line of sight is below subgrade elevation, the rod is assumed to be read downward and the grade rod is given a negative sign. Various combinations are possible, the sign of the result depending on the type of section (cut or fill) and the relative elevations of instrument and subgrade. The following rules always give correct results if algebraic signs are strictly observed:

(1) *H.I. minus grade elevation equals grade rod.*

(2) *Grade rod minus ground rod equals cut or fill at the center line (the sign + signifies cut; the sign − indicates fill).*

If desired, grade-rod readings may be entered in a separate column in the leveling notes on the left-hand page of the field book, with slope-staking notes on the right-hand page. Once the center cut or fill has been determined, the slope-staking process is the same as that previously described.

In brush or on steep slopes the field work may be expedited by using a hand level or a level board to supplement the engineer's level.

Slope-Staking Notes—Second Example

Bases: 20 ft in cut; 16 ft in fill.
Side slopes: $1\frac{1}{2}$:1; Gradient: -0.75%.

Sta.	Surface Elev.	Grade Elev.	L	℄	R
20+15	662.4	675.6	$\dfrac{F11.5}{25.3}$	F13.2	$\dfrac{F12.3}{26.5}$
19+81	675.9	675.9	$\dfrac{0 \quad 0}{10 \quad 8}$	0	$\dfrac{0 \quad 0}{8 \quad 10}$
19+65	681.9	676.0	$\dfrac{C8.9}{23.4}$	C5.9	$\dfrac{C2.7}{14.1}$
19+00	688.3	676.5	$\dfrac{C13.0}{29.5}$	C11.8	$\dfrac{C8.6}{22.9}$
18+47	677.8	676.9	$\dfrac{C2.7}{14.1}$	C0.9	$\dfrac{0}{10}$
18+37	677.0	677.0	$\dfrac{C1.5}{12.3}$	0	$\dfrac{F0.6}{8.9}$
18+28	676.2	677.0	$\dfrac{C1.2}{11.8} \quad \dfrac{0}{6}$	F0.8	$\dfrac{F1.4}{10.1}$
17+98	677.3	677.3	$\dfrac{C1.8}{12.7}$	0	$\dfrac{F1.1}{9.7}$
17+83	678.0	677.4	$\dfrac{C2.3}{13.5}$	C0.6	$\dfrac{0}{10}$
17+05	678.0	678.0	$\dfrac{C1.8}{12.7}$	0	$\dfrac{F1.2}{9.8}$
16+48	677.6	678.4	$\dfrac{0}{8}$	F0.8	$\dfrac{F3.0}{12.5}$

The second example of slope-staking notes shows irregular ground with more-complex transitions between excavation and embankment. Included also is an example of the grade contour at right angles to the center line. This case was referred to on page 100.

6–8. Volume by Average End Areas.*—Except where the solid between cross-sections is a pyramid (as between E and F in Fig. 6–1), it is usually considered a prism whose right cross-sectional area is the average of the end areas. For sections having areas of A_1 and A_2 square feet and L feet apart, the average-end-area formula for volume in cubic yards is

$$V_e = \frac{L}{27}\left(\frac{A_1 + A_2}{2}\right) \tag{6-8}$$

This formula is exact only when the end areas are equal. For other cases it usually gives volumes slightly larger than their true values. If it were to be applied to a pyramid, for example, the error would be the maximum and would be equal to 50 per cent of the correct volume. In practice, however, the total error in a long line is rarely more than 2 per cent. Also, calculation of the errors or corrections (see Art. 6–11) is much more complicated than determining the average-end-area volumes themselves. In consequence, the average-end-area method is almost always used; it is invariably ruled to apply in the absence of specifications to the contrary.

In applying the average-end-area formula the simplest method is to add the end areas (determined by calculation or by planimeter) and multiply their sum by $\frac{L}{54}$. Table XIX facilitates the process.

6–9. Example of Earthwork Calculation.—The tabulation on page 112 gives the results of earthwork calculations for the notes in Art. 6–7 (Fig. 6–1). Areas were computed from formulas given in Art. 6–4; and volumes from the average-end-area formula (except for the two pyramids).

6–10. Earthwork Tables.—Table XIX is especially adapted to highway work or other projects on which cross-sectional areas are obtained graphically. Two other tables in Part III are useful in earthwork computations:

Table XVII gives cubic yards per 100 feet for level sections having various base widths and side-slope ratios. It is very useful in making preliminary estimates of grading quantities

---

* See "contour grading" in Art. 10–7.

Sta.	End Areas		Volumes, Cu Yd	
	Formula	Sq Ft	Cut	Fill
63+00	6–3	384.4		
			1,341.4	
62+00	6–4	340.0		
			466.9	
61+48	6–4	144.8		
			38.0	2.2
61+36	6–6	C 26.0 F 15.0		
			3.5	26.1
61+25	6–4	113.2		
				171.9
61+00	6–7	258.2		
				1,104.4
60+00	coordinates	338.2		
		Totals =	1,849.8	1,304.6

by scaling center cuts and fills from a projected paper location. (See Art. 9–11.)

Table XVIII gives cubic yards per 50 feet for triangular prisms having various widths and heights. It is the most useful earthwork table for general purposes, since practically all solids met in route surveying may be broken up into constituent triangular prisms.

If w is the width (base) of any triangle and h is the height (altitude), the volume in cubic yards for a triangular prism 50 feet long is

$$V_{50'} = \frac{50}{54}\, w\, h \qquad (6\text{–}9)$$

Comparison with the average-end-area formula shows that the volume between two end sections with areas A_1 and A_2 and spaced 100 feet apart is equal to the sum of the volumes of two 50-ft prisms having the given right cross-sectional areas.

Even more generally, if the area of any type of section is converted into the form $A = \frac{1}{2} \times$ (the product of two quantities), the volume in cubic yards between sections 100 feet apart may be found simply by adding two values taken from Table XVIII, each one found by entering the table with the proper given quantities. If the distance between the stations is less than 100 feet, the sum of the tabulated quantities is multiplied by the ratio of the actual spacing to 100. By means of this principle, volumes may be computed directly from slope-staking notes without separate computation of areas.

The following computations show the use of Table XVIII in determining three of the volumes previously found (Art. 6–9) by the average-end-area method.

| Sta. | Formula Converted to Form $\frac{1}{2} w h$ | Table XVIII | | Cu Yd Cut Between Stations |
		Entries	Cu Yd per 50 Ft	
63+00	$\frac{1}{2}(2c)(b+cs)$	$w = 2c = 15.0$ $h = b + cs = 51.25$	711.8	
				1,341.5
62+00	$\frac{1}{2}cD+\frac{1}{2}\left(\frac{b}{2}\right)(H)$	$w = c = 6.8$ $h = D = 60.3$ $w = \frac{b}{2} = 20$ $h = H = 13.5$	629.7	
				466.9
61+48	$\frac{1}{2}cD+\frac{1}{2}\left(\frac{b}{2}\right)(h_l)$	$w = c = 4.1$ $h = D = 47.2$ $w = \frac{b}{2} = 20$ $h = h_l = 4.8$	268.1	
				38.0
61+36	$\frac{1}{2}w h_l$	$w = \frac{b}{2} = 20$ $h = h_l = 2.6$	48.1	

In entering Table XVIII either of the given quantities may be taken as the height. By proper shifting of the decimal point all the separate values making up a given product may be taken from the same line in the table. For example, at sta. 63 the given quantities are 15.0 and 51.25.

Enter left-hand column with 15.0

Take out under 5 ($\times$10)	694.4
Take out under 1	13.9
Take out under 2 ($\times$0.1)	2.8
Take out under 5 ($\times$0.01)	0.7

Sum = cu yd per 50 ft = 711.8

At sta. 62 the given quantities for the second part of the converted formula are 20.0 and 13.5. Instead of entering the left-hand column with 20.0 and taking out three values under 1, 3, and 5, as before, it is quicker to enter with 13.5 and take out the final result in one operation under 2($\times$10).

6–11. Prismoidal Volumes and Corrections.—As noted in Art. 6–8, the average-end-area formula usually gives volumes slightly larger than their true values. When a precise value is necessary—and the field measurements are refined enough to warrant it—the solid between cross-sections is considered to be a *prismoid* rather than an average-end-area prism.

The prismoidal formula for volume in cubic yards is

$$V_p = \frac{L}{27}\left(\frac{A_1 + 4\,A_m + A_2}{6}\right) \qquad (6\text{–}10)$$

where A_m is the area of a section midway between A_1 and A_2 and the other terms have the same meanings as in formula 6–8.

In route surveying the prismoidal formula applies to any solid generated by a straight line passing around the sides of plane parallel end-bases. Accordingly, it fits warped-surface solids as well as plane-surface solids, provided that the warp is continuous between the ends. The formula also applies to a wide variety of solids seldom found in earthwork calculations, such as the frustums of prisms, cylinders, and cones.

Owing to the need for computing the area of the mid-section A_m, direct determination of volumes from the basic prismoidal formula is inconvenient. It is easier to apply a *prismoidal correction* C_p to the average-end-area volume. By definition,

$$C_p = V_e - V_p \qquad (6\text{–}11)$$

When the values given by formulas 6–8 and 6–10 are substituted in formula 6–11 and the resulting formula is reduced, the general prismoidal-correction formula is

$$C_p = \frac{L}{3 \times 27} (A_1 - 2 A_m + A_2) \qquad \textbf{(6-12)}$$

More convenient working formulas for solids commonly met in practice are found by calculating A_m in terms of the given dimensions of A_1 and A_2 and substituting in formula 6-12. (*Note:* A_m is not the mean of A_1 and A_2, but its dimensions are the means of corresponding dimensions at the end sections.) For a solid having triangular end areas the result is

$$C_T = \frac{L}{12 \times 27} (w_1 - w_2)(h_1 - h_2) \qquad \textbf{(6-13)}$$

Formula 6-13 can be made to fit any type of end area by dividing the area into triangles. However, the prevalence of three-level sections makes the following formula valuable:

$$C_3 = \frac{L}{12 \times 27} (D_1 - D_2)(c_1 - c_2) \qquad \textbf{(6-14)}$$

Although formula 6-14 is derived from the dimensions of three-level sections, it also fits a solid having level-section end areas and a solid having a triangular section at one end.

The prismoidal correction is applied with the sign indicated in formula 6-11; that is, it is normally *subtracted* from the average-end-area volume. In case the sign of C_T or C_3 should happen to be negative (rare, but possible), the prismoidal correction is added.

The corrections to the three volumes computed in Art. 6-10, in cubic yards, are:

Sta. $62+00$ to $63+00$: $C_3 = \dfrac{100}{12 \times 27} (62.6 - 60.3)(7.5 - 6.8) = 0.5$

Sta. $61+48$ to $62+00$: $C_3 = \dfrac{52}{12 \times 27} (60.3 - 47.2)(6.8 - 4.1) = 5.7$

Sta. $61+36$ to $61+48$: $C_3 = \dfrac{12}{12 \times 27} (47.2 - 23.9)(4.1 - 0.0) = 3.5$

Prismoidal corrections may also be determined by means of Table XVIII. The tabulated values come from formula 6-9, which may be written in the following general form:

$$V_{50'} = \frac{50}{54} \times (\text{product of two quantities})$$

When $L = 100$ the prismoidal-correction formulas 6–13 and
6–14 may also be written as follows:

$$C_p = (\tfrac{1}{3})(\tfrac{50}{54}) \times (\text{product of two quantities})$$

Consequently, the prismoidal correction for sections 100
feet apart is one-third the value found by entering Table
XVIII with $(w_1 - w_2)$ and $(h_1 - h_2)$, or $(D_1 - D_2)$ and $(c_1 - c_2)$, as
the given height and width.   The three corrections previously
computed are verified by Table XVIII to be:

$$\tfrac{1}{3} \times 1.49 \qquad = 0.5$$
$$\tfrac{1}{3} \times 0.52 \times 32.8 = 5.7$$
$$\tfrac{1}{3} \times 0.12 \times 88.5 = 3.5$$

The foregoing corrections are 0.04 per cent, 1.2 per cent,
and 9.2 per cent of the respective average-end-area volumes.
It is evident that prismoidal corrections are insignificant,
except at transitions between cut and fill.   Since, normally,
these locations account for only a small percentage of the total
yardage, it is obvious that volumes determined by the average-
end-area method are adequate for all but rare situations.

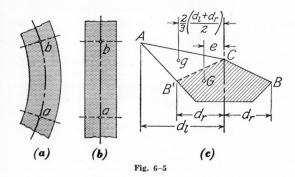

Fig. 6–5

6–12. Correction for Curvature.—Where conditions warrant
calculation of prismoidal corrections, they may also justify
correcting the prismoidal volumes on curves for the slight
error involved in assuming the center line to be straight.
On curves, cross-sections are taken radially, as in Fig. 6–5 (a);

but when curvature is ignored, the volume between the sections indicated in Fig. 6–5 (b) is computed. Obviously, the computed volume is too great by two wedge-shaped masses on the inside of the curve and is too small by similar masses on the outside. *The curvature correction is the difference between the volumes of these wedges.*

Fig. 6–5 (c) represents a three-level section in cut with the higher slope stake at A on the inside of the curve. If B' is located at the same height as B, the cross-hatched area is symmetrical about the survey center-line; therefore, there is no curvature correction for that portion of the total section. The remaining triangular area AB'C has its center of gravity at g, which is located $\frac{1}{3}$ (d_l+d_r) feet inside the center line.

Suppose that two cross-sections similar to Fig. 6–5 (c) are 1 station apart on a curve of degree D. Then the angle between the faces of the excess wedge at one section is $\frac{1}{2}D°$. From mechanics, the volume of the wedge formed by revolving triangle AB'C about a vertical axis at C is the product of the area and the length of the path described by its center of gravity.

$$\text{Area } AB'C = \tfrac{1}{2}\left(\frac{b}{2}+s\,c\right)(h_l-h_r) \text{ sq ft}$$

and the length of the path described by g is

$$\tfrac{1}{3}\,(d_l+d_r)\times\frac{\pi}{180}\times\frac{D°}{2} \text{ ft}$$

The product of these terms is the curvature correction in cubic feet per *half-station*. Multiplying by 2 and converting to cubic yards gives

$$C_c=\left(\frac{b}{2}+s\,c\right)(h_l-h_r)(d_l+d_r)\left(\frac{D°}{9,300}\right) \text{ cu yd per sta.} \quad \textbf{(6–15)}$$

For irregular sections, C_c may be found by plotting the sections to scale, drawing for each an equivalent three-level section by estimation, and scaling the values needed in formula 6–15. If this method is not considered accurate enough (as it may not be for highly-eccentric sections in rock), the following procedure may be applied: An irregular section may be divided into triangles; each triangular area may be multiplied by the distance from its center of gravity to a vertical axis at the survey center-line; and the algebraic sum of the products may be divided by the total area of the irregular section. The result is the *eccentricity e* of the total cross-section, or the distance from the survey center-line to the center of gravity G (see Fig. 6–5). This is the familiar method of moments.

For a length of 1 station on a curve of degree D, the curvature correction for an irregular area of A square feet is

$$C_c = \frac{A\,e\,D^\circ}{1,550} \text{ cu yd per sta.} \qquad (6\text{--}16)$$

In applying either of the preceding formulas to find the curvature correction for a solid between two different cross-sections L feet apart, the results are averaged and multiplied by the ratio of L to 100. For example, if a $10°$ curve to the left is assumed, calculations for the curvature correction between stations $61+48$ and $62+00$ in the notes in Art. 6–7 give:

$$\text{Sta. } 62+00 \ldots C_c = 1.37 \text{ cu yd per sta.}$$
$$\text{Sta. } 61+48 \ldots C_c = \underline{6.37}$$

$$\text{Sum} = 7.74 \text{ cu yd per sta.}$$
$$\text{Avg} = 3.87 \text{ cu yd per sta.}$$

$$C_c = 0.52 \times 3.87 = 2.0 \text{ cu yd}$$

The final corrected volume equals 459.2 cu yd, found as follows:

$$V_e = 466.9 \text{ cu yd (Art. 6–10)}$$
$$-C_p = -5.7 \qquad \text{(Art. 6–11)}$$
$$-C_c = \underline{-2.0}$$
$$V = 459.2 \text{ cu yd}$$

6–13. Borrow Pits.—When the quantity of material within the theoretical limits of excavation is not enough to make the fills, it is necessary to provide additional material, termed *borrow*. It is most convenient to obtain borrow by widening the cuts adjacent to the fills where the material is needed. When this can be done within the right-of-way limits (and without interfering with existing or planned structures), it has the added advantages of permitting wider shoulders (on highways), of "daylighting" curves, of reducing slope erosion, and of minimizing snow drifting on the traveled way.

Material taken from borrow pits adjacent to the main construction may be measured by extending the regular cross-sections and adding intermediate ones where necessary. The work is conveniently done by the cross-section-leveling method (see Art. 6–7).

Borrow pits located away from the route are cross-sectioned independently of the survey stationing. A convenient method is to stake out over the area a system of rectangles referenced to points outside the limits of the work. By leveling at the stakes before and after excavation, data are obtained from which to compute the volume of borrow taken from the pit.

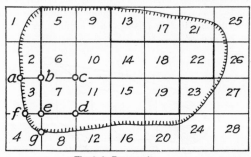

Fig. 6–6. Borrow pit

Fig. 6–6 shows a borrow-pit area over which 28 squares were originally staked out. The cross-hatched line represents the limits of the excavation. Squares are of such size that no important breaks, either in the original ground surface or in the pit floor, are assumed to lie between the corners of squares or between the edge of the excavation and the nearest interior corner. Those squares falling completely within the excavation are outlined by a heavy line. Within that line each square excavated to the pit floor is the volume of a truncated square prism. Square 7, for example, has the surface corner points b, c, d, and e; after excavation, corresponding points on the pit floor are b', c', d', and e' (see Fig. 6–7). The volume of the resulting prism is the product of the right cross-sectional area A and the average of the four corner heights bb', cc', dd' and ee'. In cubic yards,

$$V_7 = \frac{A}{4 \times 27} \; (bb' + cc' + dd' + ee') \qquad \textbf{exactly}$$

Each similar complete prism might be computed by the preceding method. However, when a number of such prisms adjoin one another, it is quicker to use the following relation which gives the total volume of *any number* of complete prisms:

$$V = \frac{A}{4 \times 27} \; (\Sigma h_1 + 2 \; \Sigma h_2 + 3 \; \Sigma h_3 + 4 \; \Sigma h_4) \qquad \textbf{(6–17)}$$

In formula 6–17, A is the right cross-sectional area of the unit rectangular prism, *not* the total area of all the complete prisms; h_1 is a corner height found in only one prism; h_2 is one common to two prisms; h_3 is one common to three prisms; and h_4 is one common to four prisms. For example, ee' is an h_1, dd' is an h_2, and cc' is an h_4.

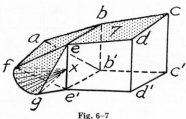

Fig. 6–7

The total borrow-pit quantity also includes the wedge-shaped volumes lying between the complete prisms and the limits of the excavation.

The portion of square 3, Fig. 6–6, excavated to the near face of prism 7 is shown in Fig. 6–7 to be a wedge-shaped mass with the cutting edge fa and the trapezoidal base $ebb'e'$. For all practical purposes its volume is one-half the product of the area of the base and the average of the horizontal distances ab and fe.

At a corner the portion of the square excavated is composed approximately of two quarter-cones, base to base. For example, as shown in Fig. 6–7, the mass in square 4 has one quarter-cone with base fxg and altitude xe, and another quarter-cone with the same base but with altitude xe'. The radius r

of the circular base may be taken as the average of fx and gx
Consequently, the volume at the corner equals $\frac{1}{3}\left(\dfrac{\pi\, r^2}{4}\right)\times ee'$
cu ft.   If the height ee' is designated by h, the volume reduces
to approximately $\dfrac{r^2\, h}{103}$ cu yd.

6–14. Shrinkage, Swell, and Settlement.—On many routes,
one object of the paper-location study is to design the grade
line so that total cut within the limits of the work will equal
total fill.   If it is assumed economical to haul all excavated
material to the embankments, the result is that borrow and
waste are eliminated.   Attainment of this ideal is prevented
by many factors, one of which is the uncertainty regarding
shrinkage or swell of the material.

Shrinkage denotes the fact—commonly noticed—that 1
cubic yard of earth as measured by cross-sectioning before
excavation will occupy less than a cubic yard of space when
excavated, hauled to an embankment, and compacted in place.
This difference is due principally to the combined effects of loss
of material during hauling and compaction to a greater than
original density by the heavy equipment used in making the
embankment.   Shrinkage is small in the case of granular
materials such as sand and gravel; larger in ordinary earth
containing appreciable percentages of silt, loam, or clay;
and very high (possibly as much as 30 per cent) for shallow
cuts containing humus which is discarded as being unsuitable
for building embankments.

Since payment for grading is usually based upon excavation
quantities (see Art. 6–1), the shrinkage allowance in grade-
line design is made by adding a percentage to the calculated
fill quantities.

Swell is the term used in referring to a condition which is
the reverse of shrinkage.   It occurs rarely, and then usually
in the case of broken rock blasted from solid beds and mixed
with little, if any, earth in making embankments.

Swell is apt to be fairly uniform for a given material.
Shrinkage, however, varies not only with changes in the soil
constituents but also with fluctuations in moisture content
when compacted and with the type of construction equipment

used. Consequently, a percentage allowance assumed in design may eventually prove to be 5 per cent or more in error. A common shrinkage allowance is 10 to 15 per cent for ordinary earth having little material unsuitable for fills.

The term *settlement* refers to subsidence of the completed embankment. It is due to slow additional compaction under traffic and to gradual plastic flow of the foundation material beneath the embankment. On railroad fills, small settlement can be corrected by tamping more ballast beneath the ties as routine maintenance work. In highway construction, new fills are sometimes built higher than the designed subgrade elevation and the placing of permanent pavement is deferred until most of the settlement has taken place. With modern construction methods, however, involving good foundations and compaction at optimum moisture content, settlement of fills is rarely serious.

DISTRIBUTION ANALYSIS

On projects in which embankments are built from material excavated and hauled from cuts within the limits of the right-of-way, mere calculation of separate cut and fill quantities does not provide enough information. The distribution of the earthwork, which involves the quantity, direction, and distance hauled, is also important both in planning the work and in computing extra payment in case the contract contains an overhaul clause.

6–15. Haul, Free Haul, and Overhaul.—The word *haul* has several definitions. In earthwork analyses, however, it means either the distance over which material is moved or (in a more technical sense) the product of volume and distance moved, the units being station-yards.

The contract sometimes contains a clause providing extra payment for hauling material a distance greater than a specified amount, known as the *limit of free haul*. In this case there is one unit price, *per cubic yard*, for earth excavation and another unit price, *per station-yard*, for *overhaul*. The former price includes hauling within the free-haul limit and forming the embankments either inside or outside that limit (see Art. 6–1). Short hauls are never averaged with those longer than the free-haul limit; therefore, there is no need to calculate the station-yards of *free haul*.

6-16. Limit of Economic Haul.—With an overhaul clause in effect, there is obviously a certain distance beyond which the cost of overhaul exceeds the cost of excavation without overhaul. This *limit of economic haul* equals the limit of free haul plus the quotient found by dividing the unit price for borrow (or for excavation, if there is no separate price for borrow) by the unit price for overhaul. Thus, if the free-haul limit were 1,000 feet and unit prices for excavation and over-haul were $0.60 per cu yd and $0.05 per sta.-yd, respectively, the limit of economic haul would be $10 + \frac{60}{5} = 22$ stations.

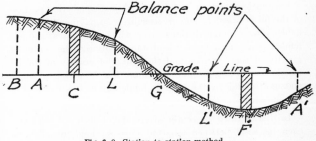

Fig. 6-8. Station-to-station method

6-17. Balance Points.—The principal problem in making a distribution analysis is locating the stationing of *balance points* between which excavation equals fill plus shrinkage allowance. On a small job the primary balance points may be found by making separate sub-totals of the cuts and corrected fills, balance points being located where the two sub-totals are equal. On important work this method is inadequate. It does not fix intermediate balance points; neither does it give data for computing overhaul, nor show how to schedule the work. More detailed analyses may be made by the *station-to-station method* or by the *mass-diagram method*.

Regardless of how complete an analysis is made, it is fairly common practice to show balance points on the plans, together with estimated quantities of cut, fill, borrow, and waste. It is advisable to label such balance points as "approximate," in order to avoid controversy with the contractor in case the balance points should prove to be in error because of variable shrinkage.

6–18. Station-to-Station Method.—Making a distribution analysis by the station-to-station method is a numerical process. The steps are illustrated by Fig. 6–8 which shows a portion of the profile along a route center-line. A grade point G is first located in the notes. Then balance points A and A', a distance apart equal to the limit of economic haul, are found by adding computed cuts and fills (plus shrinkage allowance) in opposite directions from G. Balance points L and L', spaced at the limit of free haul, are located similarly.

Excavation between A and L, which just equals that portion of the fill between L' and A', is subject to payment for overhaul. The average distance over which that excavation is hauled is assumed to be the distance between the center of gravity of the cut mass and the center of gravity of the fill mass. Deducting the free-haul limit LL' from that distance and multiplying by the yardage hauled gives the overhaul in station-yards

In this method the center of gravity of each cut solid and each fill solid between adjacent cross-sections (usually one station apart) is assumed to lie midway between the sections. Overhaul on each solid is the product of its volume and the distance between its center of gravity and the beginning of the free-haul limit. Thus, in Fig. 6–8, C is at the center of gravity of the individual cross-hatched cut volume and F is at the center of gravity of the indicated fill volume. The overhaul on the cut is its volume times CL; the overhaul on the fill is its volume times $L'F$. The total overhaul is the sum of the products found by multiplying each volume of cut between A and L by the distance between its center of gravity and station L, plus those products found by multiplying each volume of fill (plus shrinkage) between L' and A' by the distance between its center of gravity and station L'.

If B is an economic balance point following an earlier grade point, the quantity of excavation between B and A is not used in making embankment; it represents *waste.*

6–19. Mass-Diagram Method.—Though the numerical method just described is quite simple and rapid, it is not adapted to making a broad study of grading operations by analyzing the effects upon the over-all economy produced by various shifts in balance points. This is best done by a semigraphic method in which the *mass diagram* is used.

The earthwork mass-diagram is a continuous graph of net cumulative yardage. It is plotted with stations as abscissas and algebraic sums of cut and fill as ordinates. Customarily, a cut volume is given as a plus sign; a fill volume (plus shrinkage allowance) is given a minus sign.

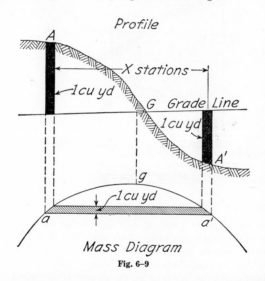

Fig. 6–9

Haul in station-yards is measured by areas on the mass diagram. In Fig. 6–9, suppose 1 cu yd of excavation at A on the profile is moved X stations to A' in the embankment. The haul is obviously X station-yards, which is shown graphically on the mass diagram by the cross-hatched trapezoidal area. If the remaining excavation between A and G were to be moved to the embankment between G and A', the haul for each cubic yard would be shown on the mass diagram as a stack of trapezoidal areas above the one indicated. The total haul in station-yards between A and A' would be the area aga'.

The profile illustrated in Fig. 6–8 is repeated (to reduced scale) in the upper sketch of Fig. 6–10. Directly below is a representation of the corresponding mass diagram.

By reference to Fig. 6–10 the following characteristics of a mass diagram are apparent:

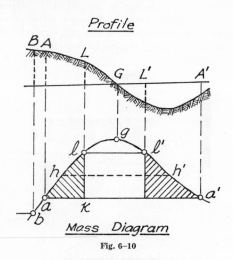

Fig. 6–10

(a) Any horizontal line (as aa') intersecting the mass diagram at two points is a *balance line*; total cut and total fill are equal between the stations at the intersections (as A and A').

(b) Any ordinate between two balance lines (as kl) is a measure of the yardage between the stations at the extremities of the balance lines (as between A and L or between L' and A'). Stated more generally, the vertical distance between two points on the diagram (as a and b) is a measure of the yardage between the corresponding stations.

(c) The highest point of a loop (as at g) indicates a change from cut to fill (in the direction of the stationing); conversely, the lowest point represents a change from fill to cut. Such points may not fall exactly at the stationing of center-line grade points if there is a side-hill transition (as at sta. E in Fig. 6–1).

(*d*) The area between the diagram and any balance line is a measure of the haul in station-yards between the stations at the extremities of the balance line. If this area were divided by the maximum ordinate between the balance line and the mass diagram, the result would be the average haul in stations. In Fig. 6–10 the area bounded by aga' measures the total haul between A and A'; that bounded by lgl' measures the total haul between L and L'. Since the latter is free haul, as is also the station-yards represented by the rectangle kl', the difference between total haul and free haul is the *overhaul* between A and A'. This overhaul is represented by the two cross-hatched areas.

When the portions of a mass diagram on the sides of two related overhaul areas are fairly smooth (as al and $l'a'$), even though not straight, the sum of the two areas may be found by drawing a horizontal line midway between the two balance lines, deducting the free-haul distance from its length, and multiplying the difference by the ordinate between the balance lines. For example, hh' bisects kl. The points h and h' are approximately at the centers of gravity of the volumes between A and L and between L' and A'. Consequently, the overhaul between A and A' is $(hh'-ll')\times kl$.

In case the mass diagram is very irregular between balance lines, the overhaul may be determined either by planimeter or by the method of moments. In the first of these methods the overhaul is found directly by planimetering the areas representing overhaul and applying the necessary scale factors to convert areas to station-yards. If needed, the distance to the center of mass of the yardage overhauled could be found by dividing the overhaul by the volume. Thus, in Fig. 6–10, the station of the center of mass of the yardage between A and L is sta. $A + \dfrac{\text{area } alk}{kl}$.

In the method of moments each separate volume is multiplied by its distance from a selected station, and the sum of the products is divided by the sum of the volumes. The result is the distance from the selected station to the center of mass.

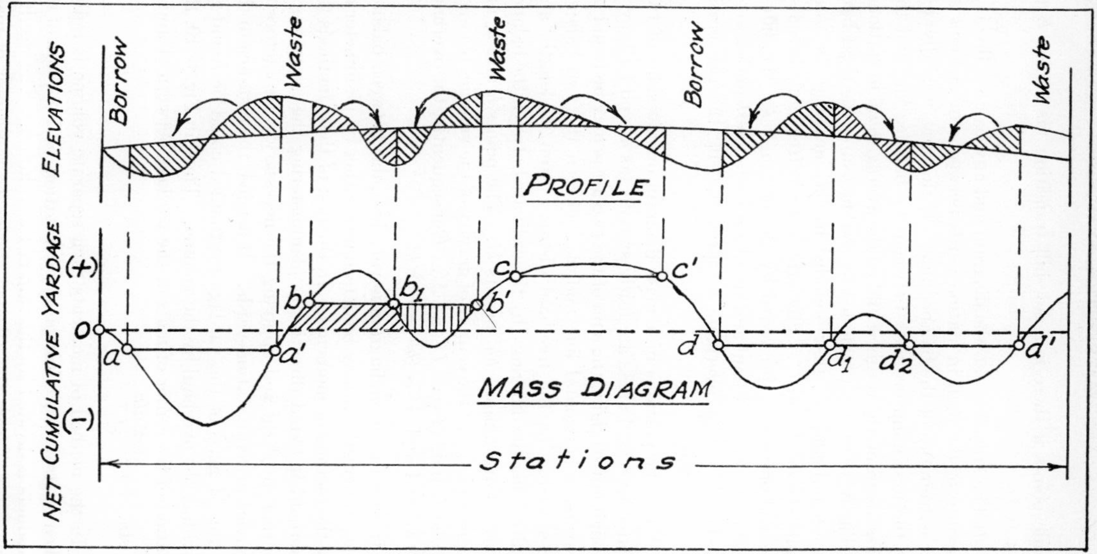

Fig. 6-11

ELEVATIONS

Borrow   Waste   Waste   Borrow   Waste

PROFILE

MASS DIAGRAM

NET CUMULATIVE YARDAGE

Stations

128

As in any other method, *overhaul = yardage × (distance between centers of mass — free-haul distance)*.

Other useful principles in making a distribution analysis by mass diagram are illustrated by Fig. 6–11, which represents the profile and mass diagram of a continuous section of line.

Balance lines equal in length to the limit of economic haul (as aa' and cc') are first drawn in the larger loops.

Between a' and c the most economical position of the balance line is at bb', which is drawn so that $bb_1 = b_1b'$ with neither segment longer than the limit of economic haul. That this is the best position may be shown by imagining bb' lowered to coincide with the horizontal plotting axis. There would be no change in the total waste; the waste at b would be decreased by the increase at b'. However, the total haul would be increased by the area shown cross-hatched diagonally and would be decreased by the area cross-hatched vertically. Since these areas have equal bases bb_1 and b_1b', there is a net increase in area, or haul. Shifting the balance line higher than bb' would obviously have the same effect.

The balance line dd' is adjusted so that $(dd_1 + d_2d' - d_1d_2)$ is equal to the limit of economic haul and no segment is greater than that limit. An analysis similar to that made for bb' would prove that raising or lowering dd' from the position shown also increases the cost.

In general, the most economical position for a balance line cutting *any even number of loops* is that in which the sum of the segments cutting convex loops equals the sum of the segments cutting concave loops, no segment being longer than the limit of economic haul. The most economical position for a balance line cutting *any odd number of loops* is that in which the sum of the segments cutting convex (or concave) loops less the sum of the segments in loops of opposite form equals the limit of economic haul, no segment being longer than that limit.

Theoretically, the foregoing principles are unaffected by the length of free haul. For example, if the alternate positions of balance line bb' produced segments longer than the free-haul limit, overhaul would be increased with consequent increase in the payment to the contractor. If the balance lines were shorter than the free-haul limit, there would be no actual payment for overhaul in either case. Nevertheless, the total haul in station-yards would be increased, thus adding to the contractor's cost of doing the work and, possibly, influencing him to submit slightly higher bid prices.

In drawing balance lines, one note of caution should be mentioned: *adjacent balance lines must not overlap.* The effect is to use part of the mass diagram twice—an obvious impossibility except by borrowing an extra mass of earthwork measured by the distance between the overlapping balance lines.

Figs. 6–12 and 6–13 show two solutions for a case not found in Fig. 6–11. This is the case in which there is an intermediate loop that is not cut by a balance line equal in length to the limit of economic haul.

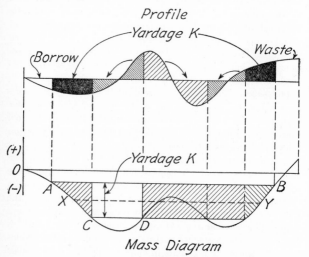

Fig. 6–12. **Two-way hauling from intermediate cut**

In both solutions, AB is the limit of economic haul and CD is the free-haul distance. The overhaul in Fig. 6–12 is the sum of the cross-hatched areas on the mass diagram. By the graphical method, this overhaul is $(XY-CD) \times K$ station-yards.

In the solution shown by Fig. 6–13, the overhaul is also

the sum of the cross-hatched areas on the mass diagram. By the graphical method the overhaul in this case is the sum of the areas of the four numbered triangular portions (found in the usual way) *plus* $(X'Y'-CD) \times K'$ station-yards.

Theoretically, the solution in Fig. 6–13 is the more economical one because it has less overhaul, more free haul, and the same amounts of borrow and waste. Yet, in practice, the solution in Fig. 6–12 might be preferred because of the two-way hauling and the shorter haul distances.

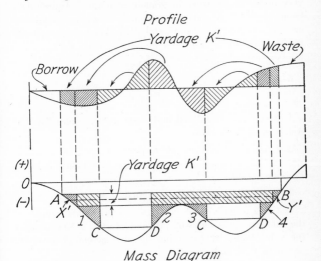

Fig. 6–13. Uni-directional hauling

Making a distribution analysis by mass diagram is not the purely mechanical process implied in the preceding discussion. Factors other than obtaining theoretical maximum economy enter into the planning of grading operations. For example, on steep grades the contractor prefers loaded hauls to be down hill. Moreover, he may prefer to haul more of a particular cut in a certain direction than is indicated on the plans. Again, there may be one fill which acts as a bottle-neck. Building it ahead of schedule, possibly by using extra borrow or longer hauls than those theoretically needed, may save time and money. These preferences may be realized by exercising good judgment in altering the theoretical balance lines. The result may be submission of lower bid prices. Even if the bid is not lower, the contractor is better satisfied—a condition which should produce a better job and friendlier relations with the owners.

Even if a grading contract contains no overhaul clause (this practice is becoming more common), the mass diagram is still very useful in the work of grade-line design. Approximate balance points are shown on the final plans to indicate the grading schedule to the contractor. It is then his responsibility to calculate or estimate the hauls and to adjust his bid prices for excavation to cover their cost.

6–20. Problems

(NOTE.—Problems 1 through 6 refer to the first example of slope-staking notes given in Art. 6–7.)

1. Verify the calculated end areas and volumes listed in Art. 6–9.

2. Using the grade-triangle formula, compute the areas at stations 62+00 and 63+00 and check with values found in Problem 1.

3. Verify the calculations tabulated in Art. 6–10.

4. Using formula 6–10, compute the prismoidal volume of the cut between stations 62+00 and 63+00. Compare with the value found by correcting the average-end-area volume (see Arts. 6–10 and 6–11).

5. Compute the prismoidal correction for the fill volume between stations 61+25 and 61+36. *Answer:* 2.5 cu yd.

6. Compute the curvature correction for the fill volume in Problem 5, assuming that $D = 10°$ to the left. (Be careful about the sign of the correction.) *Answer:* 0.3 cu yd to be added.

(NOTE.—Problems 7 through 11 refer to the second example of slope-staking notes given in Art. 6–7.)

7. Compute the yardages of the wedge-shaped volumes either side of station 19+81. *Answers:* Fill = 81.5 cu yd; Cut = 50.0 cu yd.

8. Compute the volumes of excavation and embankment between stations 18+28 and 18+37.

9. By inspection, state whether formula 6–13 or formula 6–14 should be used to find the prismoidal correction for each volume in the notes. Would any of the corrections have to be added?

10. Assuming a curve to the right, determine by inspection the sign of the curvature correction for each volume in the notes.

11. Compute the volumes, prismoidal corrections, or curvature corrections between any other sections assigned by the instructor. (Assume that $D = 12°$ to the right.)

12. Compute the yardage taken from the borrow pit shown in Fig. 6–6. (Values of A and h are to be assigned by the instructor.)

13. Plot a mass diagram from the accompanying notes, using a horizontal scale of $1'' = 5$ sta. and a vertical scale of $1'' =$

Sta.	Net Cumulative Yardage	Sta.	Net Cumulative Yardage	Sta.	Net Cumulative Yardage
0	0	15	8400	31	−550
1	320	16	7480	32	−400
2	660	17	6230	33	−540
3	1050	18	4250	34	−1160
4	1670	19	2100	35	−3600
5	2500	20	0	36	−5180
6	3100	21	−1370	37	−5650
7	4050	22	−4100	38	−5900
8	5160	23	−5350	39	−5580
9	6420	24	−6030	40	−4950
10	7750	25	−6200	41	−4160
11	9100	26	−6050	42	−3100
12	9380	27	−5600	43	−1900
12+70	9500	28	−4900	44	0
13	9400	29	−3680	45	2100
14	9120	30	−2150	46	3800

5,000 cu yd. (An $8\frac{1}{2} \times 11$ inch sheet of cross-section paper will suffice.) Show a hypothetical profile above the diagram, as in Fig. 6–11. Assume the following data: free-haul limit = 800 ft; cost of excavation = \$1.00 per cu yd; borrow = \$0.80 per cu yd; overhaul = \$0.10 per sta.-yd. Establish suitable balance points and make an estimate of the cost of grading (the pay quantities are excavation, borrow, and overhaul). Show by arrows on the profile the separate amounts of waste, borrow, and yardage hauled.

PART II
PRACTICAL APPLICATIONS

CHAPTER 7

SPECIAL CURVE PROBLEMS

7-1. Foreword.—In a subject as utilitarian as route surveying, there is hardly a strict division between basic principles
and practical applications. Though these headings are used
in this book, many practical features have already been referred to in Part I; moreover, some problems involving additional theory will be found in Part II. Nevertheless, Part I
is complete in itself; it does not require this additional material
in order to understand and apply the theory to any practical
problem met in route surveying.

Part II contains specific applications of basic theory to
some of the common problems and survey procedures found
in practice. It is not a detailed compilation of instructions
covering field and office work; such instructions are well taken
care of in the manuals published by most state highway departments and various other organizations for the guidance
of their chiefs of party. Part II is in the nature of a supplement to such manuals. Technical knowledge of route surveying being assumed, the explanations are briefer than those
given in Part I and the simpler proofs are omitted.

In practice, special curve problems occur in such great
variety that it is not possible to include a large number of
them in the space allotted to this chapter. Doing so, if
possible, would have questionable merit, since the "textbook
type" of problem is less apt to occur than some perplexing
variation of it. To serve the purpose, a few of the more
common problems will be described and general methods of
approach will be outlined. These, combined with a thorough
grounding in the basic principles of Part I, should enable the
engineer to develop the skill needed for solving any special
curve problem.

7-2. Methods of Solution.—In solving special curve problems there are four general methods of approach: (1) an exact
geometric or trigonometric solution, (2) a cut-and-try calcula-

tion method, (3) a graphical method, and (4) a cut-and-try field method.

Generally the first method is preferred. However, if the solution cannot be found or is very complicated, cut-and-try calculation often provides a fairly quick solution. In case a problem is not readily solvable by either of these methods, the unknowns may sometimes be scaled from a careful drawing; the scale must be fairly large to give adequate precision. Some problems are adaptable to cut-and-try solution in the field (see Art. 3–14 for an example previously described). Additional examples of these methods of solution follow.

OBSTACLE PROBLEMS

7–3. P.I. Inaccessible.—*Simple Curve:* This problem is of frequent occurrence. Conditions are shown in Fig. 7–1. The problem is to locate the curve points A and B.

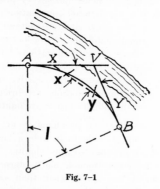

Fig. 7–1

Find any convenient line XY cutting the established tangents.

Measure distance XY and deflection angles x and y. Angle $I = x + y$.

Calculate XV and VY by using the sine law. Subtract their values from T (or T_s), giving the required distances to the beginning and end of the curve.

Compound Curve, Fig. 7–2: In this case the cut-off line is chosen so as to establish the T.C. and C.T. at X and Y. One more variable must be known. Assume R_S, since the maximum D is often fixed by specifications. Thus, the four known values are XY, R_S, and the angles x and y.

Use the closed traverse shown by heavy lines and solve by the traverse method described in Art. 3–6.

$$\text{Angle } I = x + y$$

From Σ *latitudes*:

$$R_L - XY \sin x - R_S \cos I - (R_L - R_S) \cos I_L = 0$$

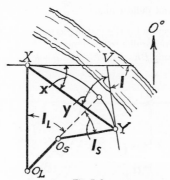

Fig. 7–2

If the hint preceding equation 3–3 in Art. 3–6 is used, this relation reduces to

$$\text{vers } I_L = \frac{XY \sin x - R_S \text{ vers } I}{R_L - R_S} \tag{7-1}$$

Similarly, the relation based on Σ *departures* reduces to

$$\sin I_L = \frac{XY \cos x - R_S \sin I}{R_L - R_S} \tag{7-2}$$

When equation 7–1 is divided by 7–2, the result is

$$\tan \tfrac{1}{2} I_L = \frac{XY \sin x - R_S \text{ vers } I}{XY \cos x - R_S \sin I} \tag{7-3}$$

Solve equation 7–3 for I_L. Then obtain $R_L - R_S$ from equation 7–1 (or 7–2). Finally, $I_S = I - I_L$.

Use the same method if R_L were assumed; the final relations differ only in signs and subscripts.

7–4. T.C. or C.T. Inaccessible.—In Fig. 7–3, assume B to be the C.T. The problem is to stake the computed curve and to check the work for alignment and stationing.

Set a check point F on the forward tangent by measuring VF, using right-angle offsets to get around the obstacle. Sta. F=Sta. C.T.$+VF-T$.

Stake the curve from A to a station (as P) from which a sight parallel to the forward tangent would clear the obstacle.

Occupy P and deflect angle $I-\dfrac{a}{2}$ (*i.e.*, angle I minus the tabulated deflection for the station occupied), thereby placing the line of sight parallel to the tangent. Set point E on this line by measuring PE=Sta. F−Sta. $B+R \sin (I-a)$.

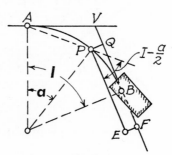

Fig. 7–3

Occupy E, turn 90° from EP, and check the distance and direction to F. The offset EF should equal R vers $(I-a)$. (If EF is small, it may be computed by slide rule from formula 2–30, in which arc PB is used for s.)

While the transit is at A (or P), set stakes on the curve for cross-sectioning between P and the obstacle, leaving one stake at the plus point marking the beginning of the obstacle.

If B were the T.C., run in the part AP of the curve backward from the C.T. The rest of the process is similar in principle to that just described.

If the curve is spiraled and the S.T. or T.S. is made inaccessible, such as by the obstacle at *position 1* in Fig. 7–4, the field procedure is the same but the computations differ somewhat.

In the general case, assume that the line of sight from the C.S., pointed parallel to the forward tangent, would be cut off by the obstacle at the S.T.   As before, run in the layout to a station P on the circular arc, a being the central angle (twice the deflection difference) between P and the C.S. at C.

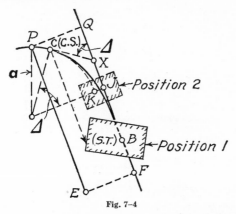

Fig. 7–4

Occupy P, turn the line of sight parallel to the forward tangent, and measure the distance PE to any convenient point beyond the obstacle.

Point K is the *offset C.T.* ($KJ = o$; $BJ = X_0$).

The offset PQ ($= EF$) $= o + \frac{7}{8} (PK)^2 D$, the value for PK being taken equal to the difference in stationing between P and C plus $\frac{1}{2} L_s$. If the offset is large, compute it from the relation $PQ = o + R$ vers $(a + \Delta)$.

For checking out on the tangent, the relation is:

$$\text{sta. } F = \text{sta. } P + PC + CB + BF$$

or $\text{sta. } F = \text{sta. } P + \dfrac{100\,a}{D} + L_s + [PE - X_0 - R \sin(a + \Delta)]$

If both the P.I. and the T.C. (or C.T.) are inaccessible, a combination of the foregoing procedures will provide the solution.

7-5. Obstacle on Curve.—For methods of by-passing obstacles preventing sights to curve points or obstacles on the curve itself, see Arts. 2–11 and 2–14 along with Figs. 2–8 and 2–11.

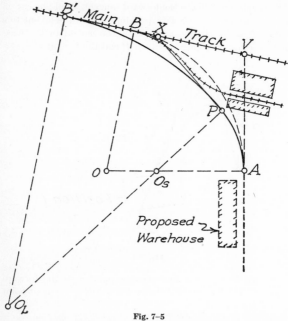

Fig. 7-5

If the obstacle cuts the spiral and the tangent but does not obstruct the S.T. (or T.S.), as at *position 2* in Fig. 7–4, first run in the layout to the C.S. (or S.C.). Then set up at the C.S. (or S.C.) and locate stakes on the spiral which are needed for cross-sectioning between the set-up and the obstacle. Finally, check the position of the S.T. (or T.S.) and the direction of the main tangent, by measuring the spiral coordinates X and Y and turning the necessary right angles.

An alternate procedure, which may be used if the obstacle interferes with the sight from C pointed parallel to the main tangent, is to place the line of sight on the local tangent at C

and to measure the spiral short tangent to a point x on the main tangent. The field work may then be checked by occupying point x, deflecting angle Δ from a backsight to point C, and measuring (possibly using right-angle offsets around the obstacle) the spiral long tangent to a check at the S.T. (or T.S.) of the layout. See also Art. 5–2 and Fig. 5–2.

7–6. Obstacle on Tangent.—For the general method of by-passing an obstacle on a tangent at a point unaffected by a curve, see Art. 9–13.

Examples of obstacles spanning both a tangent and a curve are given in Arts. 7–4 and 7–5.

Special problems affecting tangent distances of curves have infinite variety. Fig. 7–5 represents a case in which it was required to run a spur track to a proposed warehouse. Conditions (not shown) fixed the warehouse location as indicated. It was impossible to run in a simple curve AB without interfering with existing buildings and a turnout track. The solution was a compound curve APB'. See Problem 4, Art. 7–19, for the numerical values involved.

CHANGE-OF-LOCATION PROBLEMS

After part of the paper-location alignment has been staked, desirable minor adjustments often become apparent (see Art. 1–12). Frequently the data obtained and the stakes already set for the original curve can be used to advantage in making the revision. A few common cases coming under this heading are outlined in the following articles. More extensive adjustments are best made by locating the new P.I. and staking the revised curve irrespective of the original layout.

If the line has been staked and cross-sectioned beyond a location change, it is necessary to determine and mark clearly the *station equation* at the point common to both layouts.

7–7. Practical Suggestions.—Skill in solving change-of-location problems does not come from memorizing certain "textbook solutions" but is developed by identifying the key steps in those solutions and applying them to the unusual problems that arise in practice. The following practical hints, numbered for ease of reference, are helpful.

Hint 1:   Draw a careful sketch, which is not necessarily to scale.   Exaggerate small distances to make their effects clear. Preserve right angles.   Do not make other angles close to 90°; otherwise, a special case might result.   If only one graphical solution is possible when the known data are used, the problem is definite and determinate.

Hint 2:   If the problem involves a revision of some kind, such as the shift of a tangent, the solution must contain that known revision.   Try to connect known revisions to known points on the original layout by simple geometric construction, especially by triangles.   Considering a triangle containing curve centers or vertices often leads to the solution.

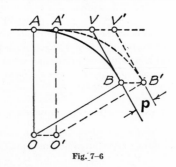

Fig. 7–6

Hint 3:   A known linear revision may often be expressed as the difference between a known part of the original layout and a similar unknown part of the revised scheme.   Also, an unknown linear revision may equal the difference between similar known parts of the two layouts.

Hint 4:   If a point is common to both layouts, perpendiculars dropped from that point to tangents or radii frequently disclose the key to the solution.

Hint 5:   Although there is only one correct set of numerical answers to a definite problem, there may be several correct geometric solutions.   If a certain solution cannot produce adequate precision, determine the reason for the lack of precision and search for a better solution.

Hint 6: If a solution by means of simple construction cannot be found, recall that a solution by traverse is usually applicable. (See Art. 3–6.)

7–8. Simple Curve; New Parallel Tangent; Same D. Assume that the forward tangent is to be shifted outward parallel to itself a small distance p in order to reduce grading or to improve the approach to the next curve.

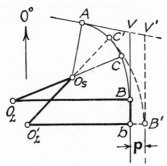

Fig. 7–7

In Fig. 7–6, the skew shift obviously equals $AA' = OO' = VV' = BB'$. From a triangle at any one of these positions (see Hint 2, Art. 7–7),

$$\text{skew shift} = \frac{p}{\sin I} \qquad (7\text{–}4)$$

Tape the skew shift from A and B to locate hubs at the new curve points A' and B'.

For a tangent shifted inward, use $A'B'$ as the original curve.

7–9. Compound Curve; New Parallel Tangent; Same D's. This is the same problem as the one in Art. 7–8, except that the curves are compounded at C and C' (Fig. 7–7).

Although a solution by construction is possible (Hints 3 and 4 being used), it may not be readily apparent. Therefore, use the traverse method (see Hint 6).

In the closed traverse $bBO_LO_SO'_Lb$,

$$\Sigma \; departures = -R_L + (R_L - R_S) \cos I_L$$
$$- (R_L - R_S) \cos I'_L + (R_L - p) = 0$$

from which

$$\cos I'_L = \cos I_L - \frac{p}{R_L - R_S} \qquad (7\text{-}5)$$

The distance bB needed for locating the new C.T. at B' is found by setting Σ *latitudes* equal to zero and reducing. The result is

$$bB = (R_L - R_S)(\sin I'_L - \sin I_L) \qquad (7\text{-}6)$$

(Observe that equation 7-6 also comes directly from Hints 3 and 4 by dropping perpendiculars from O_S to the radii.)

There are four variations of this problem, the solution depending on whether the layout starts with the sharper or flatter arc and on the direction (outward or inward) of the tangent shift. The final relations contain different signs and subscripts.

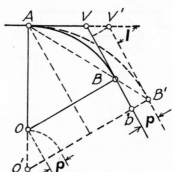

Fig. 7-8

7-10. Simple Curve; Parallel Tangent; Same T.C.—In contrast to the situation in Art. 7-8, assume that the original T.C. must be preserved, thereby requiring a curve of new D, as indicated in Fig. 7-8.

From the triangle at the vertex (Hint 2), VV' = the skew shift = $\dfrac{p}{\sin I'}$, and the new tangent distance T' equals $T + VV'$.

Then D' is found from Table VIII, or, if preferred (Hints 4 and 3), from

$$R' = R + \frac{p}{\text{vers } I} \qquad (7\text{-}7)$$

For setting the new C.T. at B', notice that B' must lie on AB produced. Since angle bBB' equals $\frac{1}{2}I$,

$$BB' = \frac{p}{\sin \frac{1}{2}I} \tag{7-8}$$

When the tangent is shifted inward, use AB' as the original curve.

7-11. Simple Curve; New C.T. Opposite Original C.T.—If conditions do not permit moving the C.T. forward (as in Fig. 7-8), it may be kept on the same radial line opposite the original position, as in Fig. 7-9.

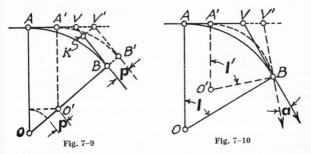

Fig. 7-9   Fig. 7-10

For the triangle at the vertex (Hint 2), $VK = p \cot I$, and the new tangent distance T' equals $T - VK$.

Then D' is found from Table VIII, or, if preferred (from Hint 3),

$$R' = R - \frac{p}{\text{exsec } I} \tag{7-9}$$

For setting the new T.C. at A', notice that AA' *does not* equal VV'. Find AA' from the triangle at the centers (Hint 2). This triangle gives

$$AA' = (R - R') \tan I \tag{7-10}$$

When the tangent is shifted inward, use $A'B'$ as the original curve.

7-12. Simple Curve; New Direction From C.T.—Changing the direction of the forward tangent after a curve has been staked may place the alignment on more favorable ground than by shifting the tangent parallel to its original position. Fig. 7–10 represents a case in which the tangent is swung inward through a measured angle a, the C.T. at B being preserved. The new central angle I' equals $I+a$.

Using Hint 4, drop perpendiculars (not shown) from B to the tangent AV produced and to the radii OA and $O'A'$. Then, by inspection, R' vers $I' = R$ vers I, and

$$R' = \frac{R \text{ vers } I}{\text{vers } I'} \qquad (7\text{–}11)$$

Also, from Hint 3,

$$AA' = R \sin I - R' \sin I' \qquad (7\text{–}12)$$

If preferred, solve triangle VBV' (Hint 2) for T'. Thus,

$$T' = \frac{T \sin I}{\sin I'} \qquad (7\text{–}13)$$

Then, obtain D' from Table VIII.

7–13. Modification for Spiraled Curve.—In the preceding examples illustrating change-of-location problems, the curves were not spiraled. Spiraling complicates field adjustments to a certain extent. The best general method is to locate on the ground the positions of the offset T.C.'s and the offset P.I., thereby converting the problem to one involving unspiraled curves.

In a simple problem it may not be necessary actually to stake the offset T.C.; but the calculations must then take the spiral into account. (See Fig. 7–4 for an example.)

RELOCATION PROBLEMS

Major relocations of existing highways are continually being made in order to bring them into conformity with modern standards. To a lesser extent, some large sections of railroad line are being relocated, especially in mountainous terrain where the amount of traffic originally expected did not warrant low grades and expensive alignment. In such work little, if any, use is made of the existing alignment records.

Minor relocations, both on highways and railroads, are even more common; they will probably continue to outrank major relocation projects in total mileage and construction cost. The shorter the relocation the more convenient it becomes to tie the survey work closely to the original alignment. Survey and design problems are closely related to those having to do with obtaining new right-of-way and abandoning old right-of-way.

Two typical minor relocation problems are outlined in the following articles. References to some major projects are given in Chapters 9 and 10.

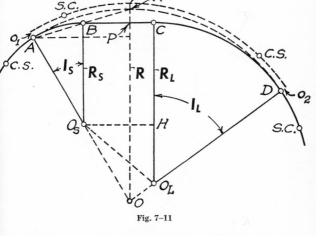

Fig. 7–11

7–14. Replacement of Broken-Back Curve.—A "broken-back" curve consists of two curves in the same direction separated by a tangent shorter than the sum of the distances needed to run out the superelevation. Formerly, such alignment was often used for reasons of economy, but present standards rarely justify the practice. When the entire layout is visible, it is very unsightly; even though obscured, it is apt to be dangerous (on highways).

Replacement of the tangent between the curves is a common relocation problem. Occasionally it can be done by inserting a spiral between points on the existing curves.

A more general method is illustrated in Fig. 7–11, which shows the original tangent BC separating curves with centers at O_S and O_L. A new curve with its center at O is sprung between points A and D on the existing curves, thus forming a three-centered compound curve (Art. 3–9). The problem is to locate points A and D.

If a value is assumed for the radius R of the new curve, the positions of A and D can be found by solving the right triangle O_SHO_L and the triangle O_SOO_L, and then calculating the angles I_S and I_L, which locate A and D.

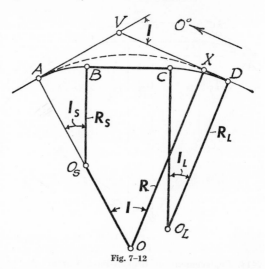

Fig. 7–12

If point K were fixed by topography, measured distances BP and PK being used, then R is unknown. First find I_S from $\tan \frac{1}{2}I_S = \dfrac{PK}{BP}$, after which R may be found from

$$(R - R_S) \text{ vers } I_S = PK \qquad (7\text{–}14)$$

If spirals are required between the curves, the problem then becomes a special case of inserting spirals between arcs of a compound curve. The center O is preserved and the radius of the new curve is increased to $R + KJ$, where $KJ = o_1 = o_2$. The two spirals usually have different lengths, since the differences between the degrees of the new and original curves will rarely be the same. The theory of the process is outlined in Arts. 5–7 and 5–8.

Fig. 7–12 illustrates how a change in specifications sometimes complicates a problem. The existing layout is a broken-back curve similar to that in Fig. 7–11, but field conditions require that the new curve start at A (the T.C. of the original shorter-radius curve) and end on the existing forward tangent at an unknown point X. The problem is to find the new radius R and the distance DX. No solution is possible by merely solving two triangles, as was the case in Fig. 7–11. To avoid more-intricate construction, the traverse method is used. (Hint 6, Art. 7–7).

The closed traverse $DXOO_SBCO_LD$ is imagined to be oriented so that direction DX is $0°$ azimuth (Rule 2, Art. 3–6). The data for the traverse are then as follows:

Side	Length	Azimuth
DX	DX	$0°$
XO	R	$270°$
OO_S	$R-R_S$	$90°-I$
O_SB	R_S	$90°-I_L$
BC	BC	$180°-I_L$
CO_L	R_L	$270°-I_L$
O_LD	R_L	$90°$

Setting Σ *departures* equal to 0 and reducing gives

$$R = \frac{R_S (\cos I_L - \cos I) + BC \sin I_L + R_L \text{ vers } I_L}{\text{vers } I} \quad (7\text{–}15)$$

Similarly, setting Σ *latitudes* equal to 0 gives

$$DX = (R_L - R_S) \sin I_L - (R - R_S) \sin I + BC \cos I_L \quad (7\text{–}16)$$

As in Fig. 7–11, the maximum offset is expressed by formula 7–14.

The foregoing formulas are solved quickly by calculating machine and Table XX, in which all needed natural functions appear in the same table. (See Problem 7, Art. 7–19.)

7–15. Replacement of Reverse Curve.—Fig. 7–13 shows an existing reverse curve ACB which is to be replaced by a new simple curve starting at the same T.C. at A. The problem is to find the new radius R and distance XB. The following solution is by the traverse method employed in Fig. 7–12, 0° azimuth being taken parallel to OX in the closed traverse $OXBO_SO_LO$. Angle $I = I_S - I_L$.

Setting Σ *latitudes* equal to 0 and reducing gives

$$R = \frac{R_L \,(\cos I - \cos I_S) + R_S \text{ vers } I_S}{\text{vers } I} \qquad (7\text{--}17)$$

Setting Σ *departures* equal to 0 and reducing gives

$$XB = (R_L + R) \sin I - (R_L + R_S) \sin I_S \qquad (7\text{--}18)$$

To find the maximum offset PK, first calculate angle a from the relation

$$\tan a = \frac{BX}{R - R_S} \qquad (7\text{--}19)$$

Then, $\qquad$ Offset $PK = (R - R_S) \text{ exsec } a \qquad (7\text{--}20)$

(See Problem 8, Art. 7–19.)

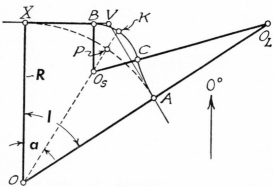

Fig. 7–13

7–16. General Method for Major Relocation.—Even in the case of a long relocation supplanting several curves and their intervening tangents, it is useful to tie the survey to the existing alignment and to compute the resulting closed traverse by means of the old alignment data on file. This not only gives a check on the field work without extra surveying but also provides the coordinates needed for drawing a map of the two layouts.

Relocations often result in surprisingly simple alignment. Fig. 7–14* shows a case in which a single 1° curve and two tangents replaced seventeen curves having total central angles of more than 900°.

MISCELLANEOUS PROBLEMS

7–17. Curve Through Fixed Point.—A curve may be made to pass through (or close to) a fixed point either by trial methods or by an exact geometric solution.

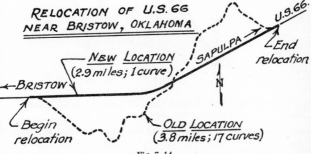

Fig. 7–14

A method of accomplishing the result by a trial field method from a selected T.C. was described in Art. 2–14 under the heading of *chord offsets*.

This problem is more intricate where the P.I. and the directions of the tangents have been established. In this situation a trial field method is apt to be unduly time-consuming. Either a trial calculation or an exact geometric method is better. Fig. 7–15 shows this situation, P being the point fixed by ties to the P.I. The tie measurements may be the distances VP' and $P'P$ or the distance VP and the angle a. Either pair of values may be obtained from the other by computation. The problem is to find the unknown radius R, after which all remaining data are easily computed.

Concrete Highways, Vol. XX, No. 1, Jan.-Feb., 1939.

The key to the trigonometric solution is the triangle OPV (the interior angles of which are denoted by o, p, and v). Although only one side (PV) and one angle (v) are known, the relation between the two unknown sides is known; therefore, the triangle can be solved.

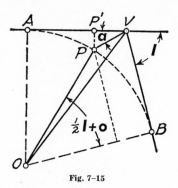

Fig. 7–15

The ratio of the unknown sides OP and OV is $R : R \sec \frac{1}{2}I$, which equals $\cos \frac{1}{2}I$. Therefore, the law of sines can be used in the key triangle, giving $\sin p : \sin v = OV : OP$, from which

$$\sin p = \frac{\sin v}{\cos \frac{1}{2}I} \qquad (7\text{–}21)$$

Since all angles of the triangle are now known, R may be found from the sine law. However, if angles v and o are very small, R may not be calculable to sufficient precision owing to the rapid variation in the sines of the angles (see Hint 5, Art. 7–7). In this case, solve for R from the relation

$$R = \frac{PV \sin (I+a)}{\text{vers} (\frac{1}{2}I+o)} \qquad (7\text{–}22)$$

The problem just described may be used to illustrate how a quick slide-rule solution by a trial calculation method often gives results close enough for the purpose. For example, suppose that $I = 28°16'$, $VP' = 150$ ft, and $P'P = 20$ ft. It is required to find D to the nearest 10 minutes.

$T_{1}°$ (Table VIII) $= 1{,}442.7$

Try D=3°

$$AV = \frac{1,442.7}{3} = 481$$
$$VP' \qquad = 150$$
$$AP' = \text{diff.} \quad = \overline{331}$$

$$\text{T.O.}_{3°} \text{ (Table I)} = 2.62$$
$$PP'_{3°} = 3.31^2 \times 2.62 = 28.7$$

Therefore, the curve is too flat.

Try D=4°

From a similar process, $PP'_{4°} = 15.4$

Hence, by interpolation, the required value of D is approximately equal to $3° + \dfrac{8.7}{13.3} \times 60' = 3°39'$ (say $3°40'$).

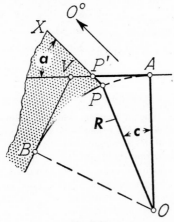

Fig. 7–16

The 3°40′ curve will not pass exactly through point P. If a closer value of D is required, interpolation between another pair of values for $D = 3°30'$ and $3°40'$ should give D to the nearest minute.

7–18. Intersection of Straight Line and Curve.—Fig. 7–16 represents a more general case of Fig. 7–15 in which a straight line XP' cuts the tangent AV of a given curve. The problem is to locate the intersection of the line and the curve at P. Among other places this problem occurs in right-of-way work, as in defining the corner of the piece of property shown shaded.

All curve data are known and the survey notes also provide the angle a and the distance AP' (or $P'V$).

This information being given, the problem could be converted to the preceding one by drawing another tangent (not shown) from P' to the curve, thereby making P' correspond to point V in Fig. 7–15. The problem could also be converted to one in analytic geometry by finding the equations of the line and of the circle and solving them simultaneously. However, the following solution is shorter and more direct.

If $0°$ azimuth is assumed in the direction PP', setting Σ *departures* equal to 0 in the traverse $PP'AOP$ gives

$$\cos (a+c) = \frac{R \cos a - P'A \sin a}{R} \qquad (7\text{–}23)$$

from which the central angle c and the stationing of P may be computed.

From Σ *latitudes* $= 0$,

$$PP' = R \sin a + P'A \cos a - R \sin (a+c) \qquad (7\text{–}24)$$

This is the type of problem which is solved readily by graphical methods. For example, if AP' is known, the exact tangent offset at P' is computed and laid off at right angles to a line representing the tangent AV. A large scale should be used (say 1 inch = 1 foot). Then, at a point 10 feet closer to A, another tangent offset is computed and laid off parallel to the previous one and 10 inches away. A spline fitted to three such points is used for drawing in the curve, and the line XP' is then drawn to the intersection at P. Finally, the required distance $P'P$ is scaled to the nearest 0.01 inch, the ground distance thus being determined with an error hardly greater than 0.01 foot.

In the case of a field problem, rather than one met in the office, the point P may be found by setting two points close together on the curve either side of where the straight line comes through. Point P is then located by "string intersection."

7–19. Problems

1. Simple curve with P.I. inaccessible (Fig. 7–1). *Given:* $XY = 421.60$; $x = 27°42'$; $y = 13°29'$; $D_c = 3°40'$. *Find:* XA and YB for setting the T.C. and C.T. *Answers:* $XA = 437.90$; $YB = 289.56$.

2. A traverse along an existing highway is as follows:

Line	Length	Bearing
AB	649.71	S78°41'E
BC	750.18	N80°56'E
CD	1451.32	S43°02'E

It was decided to replace the crooked alignment by a simple curve, which is tangent to AB and CD, in such a way as to have the new C.T. close to point D. Draw a sketch of the layout and determine D_a to the nearest 5 minutes. Then compute the distances and directions from B to the T.C. and from D to the C.T. *Answers:* $D_a = 1°50'$; B to T.C. = 62.60, direction S78°41'E; D to C.T. = 1.89, direction S43°02'E.

3. Compound curve with P.I. inaccessible (Fig. 7–2). *Given:* $XY = 698.27$; $x = 24°42'$; $y = 33°59'$; $D_S = 12°$ (arc def.). *Find:* D_L (arc def.), I_L, and I_S. *Answers:* $D_L = 6°14'$; $I_L = 30°51'$; $I_S = 27°50'$.

4. Compound curve (Fig. 7–5). *Given:* Arc AP consisted of 4 stations of a 10° curve (chord def.); distance $PX = 580.34$; angle $VXP = 40°02'$. *Find:* D_L (chord def.). *Answer:* $D_L = 3°35'50''$.

5. Change of location. *Given:* A simple curve AB has $I = 27°30'$ and $D_c = 4°10'$. It is necessary to move the forward tangent exactly 40 feet outward parallel to its original position. Conditions require preserving the original T.C. and also the original curve for a length of approximately 285 feet. *Find:* D_c for the second arc of a suitable compound curve, the distance Bb to a point opposite the new C.T., and the exact length of original curve used. (Note: This is an original problem not described in Chapter 7. The conditions are similar to those in Fig. 7–8, but the new curve is compounded.) *Answers:* $D_c = 2°20'$; $Bb = 291.25$; length of original curve used in new layout = 284.63.

6. Broken-back curve (Fig. 7–11). *Given: $D_S = 4°$ and $D_L = 2°30'$ (both chord definition); $BC = 257.80$.* It is required to replace the tangent BC by converting the layout to a three-centered compound curve in which the central $D_C = 1°20'$. *Find: I_S, I_L, the maximum offset PK, and the increased length of the relocation. Answers: $I_S = 2°48'30''$; $I_L = 3°21'28''$; offset $PK = 3.44$; increased length $= 0.14$.*

7. Broken-back curve (Fig. 7–12). *Given: $D_S = 20°$ and $D_L = 10°30'$ (both arc definition); $I_S = 34°24'$; $I_L = 32°10'$; $BC = 350.25$.* It is required to replace the tangent BC by a simple curve starting at A. *Find: D_a for the new simple curve; the distance DX between the original C.T. and the new C.T.; the maximum offset; and the increased length of the relocation. Answers: $D_a = 8°39'12''$; $DX = 89.82$; max. offset $= 65.69$; increased length $= 30.47$.*

8. Replacement of reverse curve (Fig. 7–13). *Given: $D_S = 16°$ and $D_L = 8°30'$ (both arc definition); $I_S = 65°13'$; $I_L = 26°44'$.* It is required to replace the layout by a simple curve starting at A. *Find: D_a for the new simple curve; distance BX between the original C.T. and the new C.T.; the maximum offset PK; and the saving in distance on the relocation. Answers: $D_a = 2°44'48''$; $BX = 780.39$; offset $PK = 168.06$; saving in distance $= 101.48$.* (NOTE: This is the same reverse curve as that in Problem 6, Art. 3–15. Compare answers for that problem with Fig. 7–13 and observe that V lies between X and B.)

9. Curve through fixed point (Fig. 7–15). *Given: $I = 43°23'$; $VP' = 186.5$; $P'P = 53.2$. Find: D_c (to nearest minute) for a simple curve passing through point P.* Check answer by the trial calculation method outlined in Art. 7–17. *Answer: $D_c = 3°58'$.*

10. Intersection of line and curve (Fig. 7–16). *Given: $D_a = 3°10'$; $AP' = 365.96$; angle $a = 59°27'$; sta. T.C. (at A) $= 37 + 48.26$. Find: sta. P and distance $P'P$. Answers: sta. $P = 40 + 96.64$; $P'P = 38.82$.*

CHAPTER 8

CURVE PROBLEMS IN HIGHWAY DESIGN

8–1. Foreword.—Because of the public nature of highway traffic, highway curves have a greater effect upon safety of operation than do curves on railroad lines. Railways, operating over fixed track on private right-of-way, are able to control the volume and spacing of traffic and to enforce slow orders on dangerous curves. Such restrictions are not practicable on the public highway. Consequently, it is necessary to "build safety into the highways" by proper location and design. It would be difficult enough to meet this requirement if conditions were static, but the continuous improvements in vehicle design and in highway construction, both of which encourage ever-increasing speeds, make safety the highway designer's paramount engineering problem—as yet unsolved in several important respects.

The importance and variety of curve problems in highway design warrant devoting a separate chapter to aspects of these problems not fully covered in the preceding chapters. Though certain physical and geometric principles are reasonably well established, the numerical recommendations controlling design are in many cases only tentative. Illustrative examples are taken from recent research or from current design "policies" or "standards." Revision of policies and standards can be expected as conditions change and as research discloses facts not yet known.

Until recently the various elements entering into highway-alignment design had been fixed largely by rule-of-thumb methods, and there was little agreement among State highway departments. This difference in practice was partly due to the mushroom growth of traffic, which forced the highway engineer to concentrate upon meeting the resulting demands quickly by any methods that seemed adequate at the time. However, the principal reason was lack of basic research concerning the human and mechanical factors which contribute to safe operation at high speeds. Research during the decade preceding World War II supplied much of the missing information; from time to time additional research continues to reveal new facts needed to bring all design elements into harmony with a chosen design speed.

C. M. Noble has listed[1] the design elements affected by speed as follows:

(1) Over-all Width of Highway
    (a) Median strip, width and treatment
    (b) Shoulders, width and treatment
    (c) Paved lane width

(2) Sight Distance
    (a) Vertically
    (b) Horizontally
    (c) Determination of proper friction factor and reaction time

(3) Minimum Radius for Horizontal Curvature

(4) Rates of Superelevation for Horizontal Curves
    (a) Determination of proper friction factor (unbalanced centrifugal ratio)
    (b) Correlation of superelevation rate with requirements of slow and fast vehicles

(5) Length of Spiral Curves

(6) Length of Superelevation Runout Beyond Spiral

(7) Length of Profile Tangents

(8) Distance Between Horizontal Curves
    (a) Same direction
    (b) Reverse direction

(9) Spacing of Points of Access and Exit

(10) Length of Acceleration and Deceleration Lanes at Points of Access and Exit

(11) Design of Turnouts at Points of Exit

(12) Signs
    (a) Size of letters
    (b) Maximum number of words in sign message

---

[1] See bibliography at end of this chapter.

(c) Reflectorization

(d) Position

(13) Type of Pavement

Of the items in the foregoing list, those from (2) to (8) inclusive come logically within the scope of this chapter; the others belong more properly to the field of highway construction and design.

An important step toward the incorporation in practice of design features which will result in the maximum degree of safety and utility was taken in 1937 by the American Association of State Highway Officials with the organization of a "Special Committee on Administrative Design Policies." Since that year several brochures have been approved by the States after thoughtful research, discussion, criticism, and final revision. One of the most useful was "A Policy on Sight Distance for Highways," approved in 1940. This policy, along with six others on various aspects of geometric design, played an important role in the gradual replacement of rule-of-thumb methods by scientific design based on research. Later, the material in these seven policies was revised, expanded, and brought up to date in the form of a single volume[2] entitled "A Policy on Geometric Design of Rural Highways." This latest policy, adopted May 3, 1954, is a monumental work which is bound to have a good influence on geometric highway design for many years. In the following articles, references to this publication are denoted, for brevity, by *AASHO Policy*.

SIGHT DISTANCE

8–2. Speeds.—Speed and sight distance are closely related. Several definitions of speed are used in the *AASHO Policy*. *Over-all travel speed* is the speed over a specified section of highway, being the distance divided by the over-all travel time. The term *running speed* refers to the distance divided by the time the vehicle is in motion. In either case, the *average speed* for all traffic, or component thereof, is the summation of distances divided by the summation of running (or over-all travel) times. The most useful concept of speed is *design speed*, which is the maximum safe speed that can be maintained over a specified section of highway when conditions are so favorable that the design features of the highway govern.

8–3. Definitions.—Two definitions of sight distance are in use, known as "stopping" and "passing."

Stopping sight distance should be long enough to permit a vehicle traveling at the assumed design speed to stop safely before reaching a stationary object in its path. At horizontal curves and at crest vertical curves, the height of the driver's eye is assumed to be 4.5 feet, and the height of the object is taken as 4 inches (*AASHO Policy*). At no point on a highway should the sight distance be less than the stopping value.

Passing sight distance on a tangent is the shortest distance required for a vehicle safely to pull out of a traffic lane, pass a vehicle traveling in the same direction, and return to the correct lane without interfering either with the overtaken vehicle or with opposing traffic. At horizontal curves and at crest vertical curves, passing sight distance is the length of road that must visibly be free of obstructions in order to permit a vehicle moving at the design speed to pass a slower-moving vehicle. For these cases the height of both eye and object is taken to be 4.5 feet (*AASHO Policy*). Highways on which passing must be accomplished on lanes that may be occupied by opposing traffic should be provided with frequent safe passing sections on which the sight distance is not less than the passing value for the assumed design speed.

Sight distances on overlapping horizontal and vertical curves are determined independently for each type of curvature. The critical sight distance at any point is then taken as the smaller of the two.

8–4. Stopping Sight Distance.—Stopping sight distance is the sum of two distances: (1) that traversed during perception plus brake reaction time; (2) that required for stopping after brakes are applied.

Numerous scientifically controlled tests have been made to determine perception time and brake reaction time. As might be expected, the results vary according to vehicle speed, age and natural aptitude of the driver, and the conditions accompanying the test. Brake reaction time is assumed to be 1 second, this having been found to be the value sufficient for most drivers; perception time is selected as slightly greater than that required by most drivers, and is assumed to be 1.5 seconds (*AASHO Policy*).

For a speed of V miles per hour and perception plus brake reaction time of t seconds, the total reaction distance in feet is

$$D_r = 1.47 \, V \, t \qquad (8-1)$$

(The conversion factor 1.47 may be recalled more readily by means of the exact relation: 60 mph = 88 ft per sec.)

Braking distance may be determined from fundamental principles of mechanics. The force causing a vehicle to stop after application of the brakes equals *mass times deceleration*, or

$$= M \, a = \frac{W}{g} \, a$$

If the coefficient of friction f is assumed to be uniform during deceleration, $F = W f$; hence, $a = f g$. Since the distance traversed in decelerating from a velocity v to rest is $\frac{v^2}{2 \, a}$, the braking distance is $\frac{v^2}{2 \, f \, g}$. When g is taken as 32.2 ft per sec², and the speed is converted to V in miles per hour, the braking distance in feet reduces to

$$D_b = \frac{V^2}{30 f} \qquad (8-2)$$

Actually the coefficient of friction is not constant during deceleration, but assuming it to be constant introduces no error so long as the proper equivalent uniform value is assumed to fit the speed in effect at the beginning of the operation. The coefficients of friction used in the *AASHO Policy* apply to normal clean wet pavements that are free of mud, snow, or ice.

In Table 8–1, values from 30 to 70 mph, inclusive, are from the *AASHO Policy*; others are obtained by extrapolation. The speed for wet conditions is taken to be slightly less than the design speed so that the greater proportion of traffic, traveling at yet lower speeds, will enjoy an additional safety factor. If the full design speed were used along with the coefficients of friction for dry pavements (almost double the tabulated values), the required stopping sight distances would be somewhat less than those for the assumed wet conditions. Therefore, the critical design values are those in Table 8–1.

TABLE 8–1

MINIMUM STOPPING SIGHT DISTANCE—WET PAVEMENTS

Design Speed	Assumed Speed for Condition	Perception plus Reaction		Coefficient of Friction	Braking Distance on Level	Stopping Sight Distance	
		Time	Dist.			Computed	Rounded for Design
mph	mph	sec	ft		ft	ft	ft
	V	t	D_r	f	D_b	$D_r + D_b$	
30	28	2.5	103	0.36	73	176	200
40	36	2.5	132	0.33	131	263	275
50	44	2.5	161	0.31	208	369	350
60	52	2.5	191	0.30	301	492	475
70	59	2.5	216	0.29	400	616	600
80	67	2.5	245	0.28	535	780	775
90	75	2.5	275	0.28	670	945	950
100	82	2.5	300	0.27	830	1,130	1,150

Theoretically, stopping distances are affected slightly by grades. If G is the per cent grade divided by 100, the formula for braking distance becomes

$$D_b = \frac{V^2}{30 \ (f \pm G)} \tag{8-3}$$

In practice the sight distance is usually longer on downgrades than on upgrades, a fact that automatically compensates for the greater braking distances on downgrades required by formula 8–3. Exceptions would be one-way lanes on divided highways having independent profiles for the two roadways.

8–5. Passing Sight Distance.—In the *AASHO Policy* the minimum passing sight distance for *two-lane highways* is the

sum of the following four distances which are shown in Fig.
8–1:

d_1 = distance traversed during the preliminary delay period
(the distance traveled during perception and reaction
time and during the initial acceleration to the point
of encroachment on the left lane).

d_2 = distance traveled while the passing vehicle occupies any
part of the left lane.

d_3 = distance between the passing vehicle at the end of its
maneuver and the opposing vehicle.

d_4 = distance traversed by an opposing vehicle for two-thirds
of the time the passing vehicle occupies the left lane,
or $\frac{2}{3}d_2$.

The preliminary delay period d_1 is a complex one. For
purposes of analysis it may be broken into two components:
(1) time for perception and reaction, and (2) an interval during which the driver accelerates his vehicle from the trailing
speed $V - m$ to the passing speed V at the point of encroachment on the left lane. The distance traversed is expressed as

$$d_1 = 1.47\, t_1 \left(V - m + \frac{at_1}{2} \right) \tag{8–4}$$

The distance traveled while the passing vehicle occupies the
left lane is

$$d_2 = 1.47\, V t_2 \tag{8–5}$$

Reference to Fig. 8–1 shows that during the first part of
the passing maneuver the driver can still return to the right
lane if he sees an opposing vehicle. From experience, this
"uncommitted" distance is about $\frac{1}{3}d_2$. Since the opposing
and passing vehicles are assumed to be traveling at the same
speed, $d_4 = \frac{2}{3}d_2$.

Basic data used in establishing the design curves in Fig.
8–1 are summarized in Table 8–2. The values of a, t_1, t_2, d_3, and
average passing speed come from a report[3] on extensive field
observations of driver behavior during passing maneuvers.
The average value of m is taken as 10 mph.

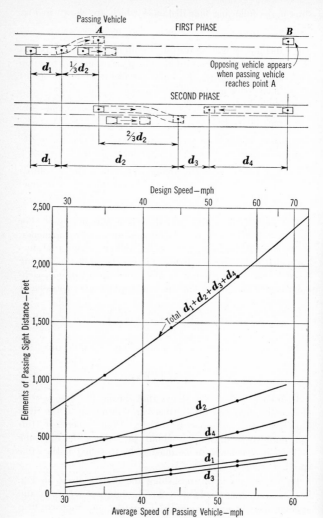

Fig. 8-1. Passing sight distance (2-lane highways)

TABLE 8–2

**ELEMENTS OF SAFE PASSING SIGHT DISTANCE—
2-LANE HIGHWAYS**

Speed group, mph Average passing speed, mph	30–40 34.9	40–50 43.8	50–60 52.6
Preliminary delay: a = avg. acceleration, mph per second	1.40	1.43	1.47
t_1 = time, seconds	3.6	4.0	4.3
d_1 = distance traveled, feet	145	215	290
Occupation of left lane: t_2 = time, seconds	9.3	10.0	10.7
d_2 = distance traveled, feet	475	640	825
Clearance length: d_3 = distance traveled, feet	100	180	250
Opposing vehicle: d_4 = distance traveled, feet	315	425	550
Total distance, $d_1+d_2+d_3+d_4$, feet	1,035	1,460	1,915

Table 8–3 contains a summary of passing sight distances determined from the foregoing analysis. Also included are values tentatively suggested in the *AASHO Policy* for the case of 3-lane highways. However, these values are not based on actual field observations and cannot be considered so reliable as those for 2-lane highways. The 3-lane values come from computation by omitting the distance d_4.

HORIZONTAL ALIGNMENT

8–6. Superelevation Theory.—Fig. 8–2 shows the forces W (weight of vehicle) and F (centrifugal force) acting through the center of gravity c of a vehicle traveling at a speed v around a curve of radius R, when the pavement is super-elevated at an angle θ with the horizontal ($\theta = \tan^{-1} e$).

TABLE 8-3

MINIMUM PASSING SIGHT DISTANCE

Design speed, mph	30	40	50	60	70
Passing speed, mph	30	40	48	55	60
Minimum passing sight distance, feet:					
		2-Lane Highways			
Fig. 8–1	810	1,265	1,675	2,040	2,310
Rounded	800	1,300	1,700	2,000	2,300
		3-Lane Highways			
Calculated			1,190	1,450	1,650
Rounded			1,200	1,400	1,600

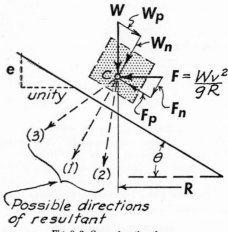

Fig. 8–2. Superelevation theory

In order to simplify the analysis, the two forces are resolved into their components normal and parallel to the pavement. The resultant of the forces must take one of three possible general directions:

(1) When $W_p = F_p$, the resultant is perpendicular to the pavement and no centrifugal sensation is felt by the occupants of the vehicle. The speed which produces this effect is called "equilibrium speed."

(2) When $W_p > F_p$, the resultant is inclined to the pavement down the slope. Consequently, there is a tendency for the vehicle to slide inward, and this tendency is resisted by a lateral force acting up the slope at the contact between the wheels and the road surface. Obviously, there is also a clockwise overturning moment causing the vehicle to tilt inward.

(3) When $W_p < F_p$, the resultant is inclined to the pavement up the slope. The effects are then opposite to those in (2); the resisting lateral force acts down the slope and the tilt is outward.

At equilibrium speed, $W_p = F_p$, or

$$W \sin \theta = \frac{W v^2}{g R} \cos \theta$$

Solving for θ gives the following basic equilibrium formula:

$$\tan \theta = e = \frac{v^2}{g R} \qquad (8\text{--}6)$$

The equilibrium formula is expressed in more usable form by replacing v in feet per second by V in miles per hour and by substituting 32.16 ft per sec^2 for g. The result is

$$e = \frac{0.067 \, V^2}{R} = \frac{V^2}{15 \, R} \qquad (8\text{--}7)$$

or

$$e = \frac{V^2 D_a}{85,700} \qquad (8\text{--}8)$$

When $W_p \neq F_p$, the magnitude of the tendency for the vehicle to move laterally may be denoted by the term f, which is the ratio of the lateral component of the resultant to its normal component. If all forces are assumed to have positive signs, the value of f is

$$f = \frac{F_p - W_p}{F_n + W_n} = \frac{F \cos \theta - W \sin \theta}{F \sin \theta + W \cos \theta}$$

Since the superelevation angles used in practice are small (θ is rarely permitted to exceed 7°), it is sufficiently accurate to assume that $F \sin \theta = 0$, this term being very small in comparison with $W \cos \theta$. Therefore, f is approximately equal to $\dfrac{F \cos \theta - W \sin \theta}{W \cos \theta} = \dfrac{F}{W} - \tan \theta$, which reduces to

$$f = \frac{v^2}{g R} - e \qquad (8\text{--}9)$$

The resulting working relations are:
When $W_p > F_p$ (or V is less than equilibrium speed),

$$e - f = \frac{V^2}{15 R} = \frac{V^2 D_a}{85,700} \qquad (8\text{--}10)$$

When $W_p < F_p$ (or V exceeds equilibrium speed),

$$e + f = \frac{V^2}{15 R} = \frac{V^2 D_a}{85,700} \qquad (8\text{--}11)$$

It should be observed that f is necessarily proportional to, and opposite in direction to, the resisting side friction which automatically comes into action at other than equilibrium speed.

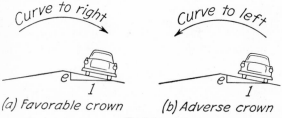

(a) Favorable crown   (b) Adverse crown

Fig. 8–3

In solving problems for various operating conditions, confusion in signs may be avoided by considering the terms in the foregoing equations to be positive quantities that are proportional to the actual forces acting on the vehicle. Since the forces themselves act in definite directions, these same directions may be given to the terms e, f, and $\dfrac{V^2}{15 R}$. Fig. 8–3 and the accompanying analysis illustrate this procedure.

Fig. 8–3(a)—Favorable crown (1) V = Equilibrium speed Superelevation counterbalances the centrifugal force. There is no side friction.	$$\frac{V^2}{15\,R} = e$$ $\longleftarrow \qquad \longrightarrow$ (Formula 8–7)
(2) V < Equilibrium speed Side friction and centrifugal force assist each other in counterbalancing excessive superelevation.	$$f + \frac{V^2}{15\,R} = e$$ $\longleftarrow \quad \longleftarrow \quad \longrightarrow$ (Formula 8–10)
(3) V > Equilibrium speed Side friction and superelevation assist each other in counterbalancing centrifugal force.	$$\frac{V^2}{15\,R} = e + f$$ $\longleftarrow \quad \longrightarrow \quad \longrightarrow$ (Formula 8–11)
Fig. 8–3 (b)—Adverse crown Only one possible case regardless of speed. Side friction alone holds car on road.	$$f = e + \frac{V^2}{15\,R}$$ $\longleftarrow \quad \longrightarrow \quad \longrightarrow$

The term f has been called the "lateral ratio" in research done by Leeming[1] in Great Britain, and this appears to be the most logical expression. In the United States, f has been termed "unbalanced centrifugal ratio," "cornering ratio" (at General Motors Proving Ground), "unbalanced side friction," and "side friction factor." Because of the widespread use of the last expression, it will be adopted in this book—with the warning that it should not be confused with the "coefficient of friction" as understood in dynamics.

8–7. Dynamics of Vehicle Operation on Curves.—On a curve having accurately built constant superelevation, there is a particular speed, known as the *equilibrium speed* or "hands-off" speed, at which a car steers itself around the curve. At this speed $W_p = F_p$, and the value of f is zero.

At other than equilibrium speed, equations 8–10 and 8–11 seem to indicate that safe operation around a given curve is entirely within the control of the driver. He has only to adopt any desired speed and rely upon the automatic development of whatever value of f is needed to make up for the lack of balance between e and $\dfrac{V^2}{15\,R}$. However, the matter is not so simple as this. On the contrary, it is very complex; and further research is required before curve design for high-speed operation can be placed upon a sound scientific basis.

When $W_p \neq F_p$, the car tends to creep out of the traffic lane. To offset this tendency the driver must exert force at the steering wheel and must steer slightly toward or away from the center of curvature, the direction depending on whether V is greater or less than equilibrium speed. As a result, each pair of tires must "slip" across the surface at a definite angle between the path of travel and the longitudinal axis of the wheels. Fig. 8–4 illustrates the normal condition when $W_p < F_p$.

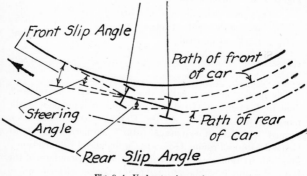

Fig. 8–4. Understeering action

Front and rear slip angles are rarely equal. When the front slip angle is greater than the rear slip angle, the car is said to be "understeering," as in Fig. 8–4; when the reverse is true, the car is "oversteering." Whether a car understeers or oversteers depends principally on its design and partly on factors within the control of the operator. For example, research at the General Motors Proving Ground[5] shows that it is possible to make a car either highly oversteering or highly understeering by merely varying front and rear tire pressures within certain limits.

The understeering car is somewhat more stable and susceptible to control than the oversteering type. Perhaps this is true because an increase in speed on a curve requires an *increase* in the steering angle of the understeering car (an operation that is instinctively natural), whereas a *decrease* in the steering angle is necessary in the case of the oversteering car. Above a certain critical speed the front wheels of the understeering car start to slide off the road, but by careful braking the driver can generally regain control and return to a fairly fixed course at a speed below the critical value. It is more difficult to hold an oversteering car on a fixed path even at moderate speeds. Above a certain critical speed the rear end of the car starts to slide off the road, and any slight application of brakes is apt to put the car into a spin.

At the same time at which a car develops certain slip angles in rounding a curve, there is some tilt or "body roll." The roll angle is a linear function of f, at least up to the limits of f considered safe. Roll angles are not large. Tests show that, when $f = 0.20$, body-roll angles vary between $1.8°$ and $3.5°$, the value depending on the make and model year of the car. Though body roll has less effect upon a car's general "roadability" than do the slip angles, it is a factor that must be allowed for in the accurate use of the ball bank indicator (see Art. 8–8).

Valuable research on correlation of slip angles, steering angles, body roll, and related factors with safe speed on curves has been published by Fox[6] (low-speed tests) and by Stonex and Noble[7] (high-speed tests on the Pennsylvania Turnpike). The facts brought out account for the common observation that all cars do not handle alike on the same curves.

8–8. Side Friction Factors.—The value of f at which side skidding is imminent depends principally upon the speed of the vehicle, the condition of the tires, and the characteristics of the roadway surface. Moyer's work[8] indicated maximum values of f of about 0.50 at relatively low speeds, with a reduction to approximately 0.35 at high speeds. The tests at very high speed on the Pennsylvania Turnpike[7] (speeds up to 105 mph) showed maximum values as low as 0.30, even though the cars were driven by skilled test drivers.

An important problem in curve design—especially on curves to be marked with safe-speed signs—is to determine the percentage of the maximum side friction that can be utilized safely by the average driver. The resulting values of f used in design should give posted speeds that have an ample margin of safety even when the pavement is wet. Furthermore, when the posted speed is exceeded, the added unbalanced centrifugal force should be enough to produce an uncomfortable sensation and an instinctive reduction in speed.

The simplest device yet developed for determining maximum safe speeds and their relation to side friction factors is the ball bank indicator, apparently first used by the Missouri State Highway Department in 1937. It consists of a sealed curved glass tube containing liquid and a steel ball slightly smaller than the bore of the tube. When the indicator is mounted on the dash by means of rubber suction cups, the ball is free to roll transversely under the influence of the forces acting upon it. The liquid produces enough damping effect to hold the ball fairly steady, even when the car is driven around a curve at high speed on a slightly rough surface. Readings are taken on a scale graduated in degrees with the 0° mark at the center of the tube.

Where the ball bank indicator is to be used, it is first mounted on the dash with the ball at the 0° reading when the car is in a stationary level position. Obviously, all observers who are to be in the car during the test run must be in their assigned positions when the indicator is set in place.

The indicator is used for two purposes: (1) to determine the ball bank angle and side friction factor at the maximum comfortable speed on a particular curve, and (2) to determine the speed on a curve required to produce a specified ball bank angle.

In the first use, the body roll ρ of the test car is determined by stopping the car on the curve and reading the ball bank angle β. When the car is stationary, $\rho = \beta - \theta$, as shown in Fig. 8–5. (Obviously the superelevation θ must be measured.) Then trial runs are made around the curve at various constant speeds until that speed is reached which first produces an uncomfortable centrifugal sensation. Simultaneous readings of speed and ball bank angle are then made, and the averages are taken. Thus, one of the desired values, β, is measured by direct observation.

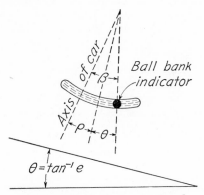

Fig. 8–5. Ball bank indicator—car stopped

To find the desired side friction factor f, the following analysis, based on Fig. 8–6, is made:

When a car rounds a superelevated curve at equilibrium speed, the resultant of the forces is perpendicular to the pavement surface; there is no body roll and the ball bank indicator reads $0°$. At a speed greater than equilibrium speed, side friction comes into play, acting inward. Were it not for the body roll, the ball bank angle would be practically a direct function of this side friction. However, the outward body roll tilts the car toward the horizontal, thereby increasing the reading of the ball bank indicator. The condition is shown in Fig. 8–6, from which

$$\beta - \rho = \tan^{-1} \frac{V^2}{g\,R} - \theta \qquad (8\text{–}12)$$

But equation 8–9 shows that

$$f = \frac{V^2}{g\,R} - e$$

or

$$\tan^{-1} f = \tan^{-1}\left(\frac{v^2}{g\,R} - e\right)$$

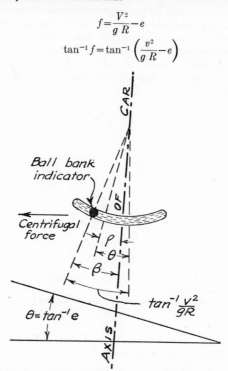

Fig. 8–6. Ball bank indicator when $V >$ equilibrium speed

Because of the small angles involved, it is sufficiently accurate to assume that

$$\tan^{-1} f = \tan^{-1}\frac{v^2}{g\,R} - \tan^{-1} e = \tan^{-1}\frac{v^2}{g\,R} - \theta$$

Substituting from equation 8–12 gives

$$\tan^{-1} f = \beta - \rho \qquad \text{(8–13) Approx.}$$

The work may be checked by assuming that ρ is zero and solving equation 8–12 for β, thus obtaining the theoretical ball bank angle on the assumption of zero body roll. The differnce between the calculated and observed ball bank angles is the body roll, which should agree with the value measured while the car is stationary on the superelevated curve. For any one test car there should be a linear relation between the values ρ and f.

This first use of the ball bank indicator represents its application in research. After the ball bank angle corresponding to the maximum safe speed has been determined, the second use of the indicator is in connection with establishing posted speeds on curves. In this application it is not necessary to measure the radius or the superelevation. The speed of the test car is gradually increased until the specified ball bank angle is reached, and this maximum speed is recorded.

The practical value of the ball bank indicator rests in its simplicity and in the fact that there is a surprisingly close agreement among the various States using it in regard to the numerical value, 10°, most widely adopted to indicate maximum safe speed. A canvass made by Moyer and Berry[9] showed that, after curves were first marked with safe-speed indications in Missouri in 1937, the plan was quickly adopted in 25 States and the ball bank indicator was the device most commonly used for determining posted speeds. As a result of this study, which also included an analysis of driver reaction to posted speeds, the authors arrived at the following conclusions:

> To obtain the driver's respect for the speed on the sign over a wide range of speed, the following ball bank angles are recommended: 14° for speeds below 20 mph, 12° for speeds of 25 and 30 mph, and 10° for speeds of 35 mph and higher.
>
> For speeds up to 50 or even 60 mph, a ball bank angle of 10° has been found to be quite satisfactory but for speeds above 60 mph a lower value should be used.

If the foregoing recommendations are converted into side friction factors by means of equation 8–13 (in which average values of body roll reported by the General Motors Proving Ground are used), the resulting values of f range from about 0.21 at 20 mph to 0.14 at 50 mph.

In earlier tests reported by Barnett[10] a safe side friction factor of 0.16 had been recommended for speeds up to 60 mph, with a reduction of 0.01 in f for each 5 mph increase in speed above 60 mph. However, of the 900 tests involved in this research only a few were made at speeds of 60 or more mph.

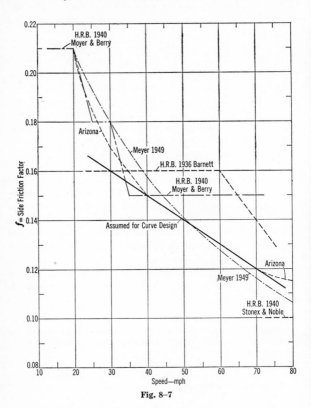

Fig. 8-7

As a result of the high-speed tests on the Pennsylvania Turnpike, Stonex and Noble[7] concluded: "$f=0.10$ is the maximum that should be utilized in curve design on public highways at speeds of 70 mph and higher."

The slight inconsistencies in the recommended values of f noted in the preceding paragraphs merely reflect the dif-

ferences in judgment as to what constitutes incipient insta-
bility or uncomfortable centrifugal sensation. Further
research and a more scientific means of measuring discomfort
should narrow the range of disagreement.

For reasons to be explained in Art. 8–9, it is not practicable
to use sufficient superelevation to counteract centrifugal force
completely, except possibly on sharp curves designed for low-
speed operation. On flat curves on which vehicles are operated
at high speeds, drivers place more reliance upon side friction
than upon superelevation. It is therefore logical to design
with a greater margin of safety at high speeds, owing to the
greater difficulty in steering a true course and to the longer
stopping distance required in case of an emergency. The
practice may be stated differently as follows: A smaller
percentage of the available side friction should be used at
high speeds than at low values.

TABLE 8–4

RECOMMENDED VALUES FOR USE IN DESIGN

Design Speed V mph	Side Friction Factor f	$\tan^{-1} f$ or $(\beta - \rho)^\circ$	Body Roll Angle ρ°	Ball Bank Angle β°
20	0.17	9.6	3.0	12.6
25	0.165	9.4	2.7	12.1
30	0.16	9.1	2.5	11.6
35	0.155	8.8	2.4	11.2
40	0.15	8.5	2.2	10.7
45	0.145	8.3	2.1	10.4
50	0.14	8.0	2.0	10.0
55	0.135	7.7	1.9	9.6
60	0.13	7.4	1.8	9.2
65	0.125	7.1	1.7	8.8
70	0.12	6.8	1.6	8.4
80	0.11	6.3	1.5	7.8
90	0.10	5.7	1.4	7.1
100	0.09	5.2	1.3	6.5

In view of the maximum values of f noted in the first paragraph of this article, it will be observed that the values of f summarized in Fig. 8–7 (from *AASHO Policy*) embody this principle of a greater safety factor at high speeds. The straight-line relation assumed for curve design represents a reasonable compromise based on the safe values recommended by various investigators; it was purposely kept lower at the low design speeds in order to compensate for the tendency of drivers to overdrive on highways with low design speeds.

Table 8–4 gives recommended side friction factors corresponding to the straight-line relation in Fig. 8–7. The ball bank angles were found by calculation, average body roll angles reported by General Motors Proving Ground being used. The final ball bank angles were accurate enough for determining posted speeds on curves, even though test-car roll angles differ somewhat from those listed. In the range of speeds—45 to 55 mph—within which the safe-speed signs are most frequently used, the recommended side friction factors give ball bank angles very close to the value 10° used by most States.

8–9. Maximum Superelevation Rates.—Because of the presence of both slow-moving and fast traffic, and the variations in weather conditions over the seasons, it is impossible to design a highway so that the superelevation is ideal for all traffic at all times. Safety is the paramount consideration. This requires a fairly low superelevation rate, with the result that road speeds are usually greater than the equilibrium speed.

When the speed is less than the equilibrium value, the resultant (Fig. 8–2) acts inward and the driver must steer slightly away from the center of curvature in order to maintain a true course in the traffic lane. The effect is somewhat like the action of an oversteering car. Since steering outward on a curve is not a natural operation, there is a tendency for slow-moving vehicles to "edge in" toward the shoulder or toward the inner traffic lane. Moreover, if the side friction factor is greater than about 0.05 when the road is icy, vehicles may slide inward despite the driver's efforts to steer a true course. On the other hand, if the superelevation rate is too low, design speeds on curves are limited by the safe side friction factors to values less than considered practicable in modern design. Therefore, a compromise between these conflicting requirements is necessary.

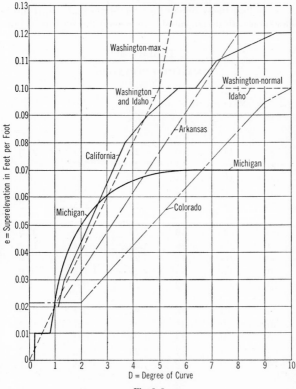

Fig. 8-8

There is fairly general agreement that a superelevation rate of 0.10 (approximately $1\frac{1}{4}$ inches per foot) is about the maximum that should be used in regions where snow and ice are encountered. Where exceptionally adverse winter conditions are likely to prevail for several months, a maximum super-

elevation rate of 0.07 or 0.08 is recommended.   A maximum
as high as 0.13 is used in localities free from snow or ice.

Figure 8–8 shows the practice in a number of States using
superelevation controls that do not vary with design speed.
This is the more traditional method.

As of 1954 there were at least ten States that varied superelevation with design speed.   In general the same maximum

TABLE 8–5

MAXIMUM CURVATURE

Design Speed mph	Maximum e	Maximum f	Total $e+f$	Minimum R Ft	Maximum D Deg
30	.06	.16	.22	273	21.0
40	.06	.15	.21	508	11.3
50	.06	.14	.20	833	6.9
60	.06	.13	.19	1,263	4.5
70	.06	.12	.18	1,815	3.2
30	.08	.16	.24	250	22.9
40	.08	.15	.23	464	12.4
50	.08	.14	.22	758	7.6
60	.08	.13	.21	1,143	5.0
70	.08	.12	.20	1,633	3.5
30	.10	.16	.26	231	24.8
40	.10	.15	.25	427	13.4
50	.10	.14	.24	694	8.3
60	.10	.13	.23	1,043	5.5
70	.10	.12	.22	1,485	3.9
30	.12	.16	.28	214	26.7
40	.12	.15	.27	395	14.5
50	.12	.14	.26	641	8.9
60	.12	.13	.25	960	6.0
70	.12	.12	.24	1,361	4.2

superelevation was used at all speeds, but at the higher design speeds the maximum was reached on flatter curves.

In the *AASHO Policy* it is "concluded that (*a*) several rates rather than a single rate of maximum superelevation should be

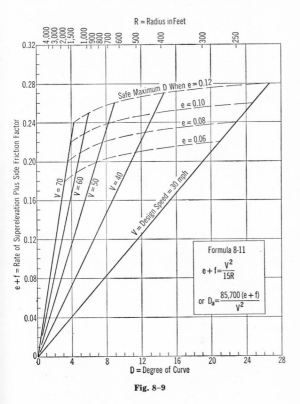

Fig. 8–9

recognized in establishing design controls for highway curves, (*b*) a rate of 0.12 should not be exceeded, and (*c*) at the other extreme a rate of 0.06 is applicable for urban design. Consistent with current practice, values for the 0.10 rate are referred to as generally desirable or nationally representative."

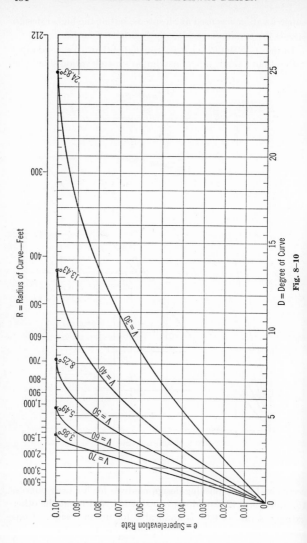

Fig. 8-10

8–10. Maximum Degree of Curve.—The use of any recommended maximum rate of superelevation in combination with a particular design speed results in a maximum degree (or minimum radius) of curve. If sharper curvature were used with the stated design speed, either the superelevation rate or the side friction factor would have to be increased beyond recommended safe limits. Thus, this maximum degree of curve is a significant value in alignment design.

Table 8–5 (from *AASHO Policy*) lists limiting values of curvature for four maximum rates of superelevation. The final values are consistent with formula 8–11 in which are substituted the safe side friction factors from Table 8–4.

The relationships given by formula 8–11 are shown graphically in Fig. 8–9 (from *AASHO Policy*) by the straight lines for each design speed. Superimposed on the graph are the values of maximum curvature, as taken from Table 8–5.

8–11. Superelevation Rate Over Range of Curvature.—It is not necessary to superelevate very flat curves; the normal crown is carried around the curve unchanged. (This matter is treated in Art. 8–12.) However, it is not logical to change abruptly from zero superelevation on a very flat curve to maximum superelevation at some arbitrary value of D or R. There should be a transition range of curvature within which maximum superelevation increases in a rational manner from zero to the full value permitted by climatic conditions. Fig. 8–8 indicates how some States have handled this matter.

As a result of careful analysis of the dynamic factors involved in four different methods of approach to this problem, "it was concluded (*AASHO Policy*) that a parabolic form, with the horizontal distance governing, represents a practical distribution [of superelevation] over the range of curvature." This is the type of relationship that was proposed in the first edition of this textbook as "a rational suggestion for general design."

8–12. Superelevation Rates for Design.—Fig. 8–10 (*AASHO Policy*) shows recommended design superelevation rates for the case where the maximum rate of superelevation equals 0.10. The maximum values of curvature at $e = 0.10$ correspond to those in Table 8–5. On curves flatter than the

maximum, the superelevation rates lie on parabolic curves of
the form recommended in Art. 8–11. In practice similar
design curves could be constructed for other maximum superelevation rates, such as those given in Table 8–5.

On two-lane highways, if the pavement cross-section
normally used on tangents is carried around a horizontal curve
unchanged, traffic entering a curve to the right has the benefit
of some favorable superelevation from the crowned pavement.
On the other hand, traffic entering a curve to the left meets an
adverse crown, as in Fig. 8–3 (b). This leads to a consideration of the maximum curvature for which the normal crowned
cross-section is suitable.

As a general rule, it is recommended that the minimum rate
of superelevation on any curve (except at a reverse transition)
should be about 0.012 and that the particular value should
correspond to the average rate of cross slope used on tangents.

With an average adverse cross slope of 0.012, the corresponding degree of curve (rounded) for each design speed in Fig.
8–10 is shown in the third column of Table 8–6 (from *AASHO
Policy*). It should be observed that the resulting side friction
required to counteract both adverse superelevation and centrifugal force is very small. Obviously, if the curves were
made sharper, the required side friction factors would increase,

TABLE 8–6

MAXIMUM CURVATURE FOR NORMAL CROWN SECTION

Design Speed mph	Average Running Speed mph	Maximum D	Minimum R ft	Resulting Side Friction Factor f When Adverse Crown $e = 0.012$	
				At Design Speed	At Running Speed
30	27	1°30′	3,800	.028	.025
40	34	0°45′	7,600	.026	.023
50	40	0°30′	11,450	.027	.022
60	45	0°20′	17,200	.026	.020
70	49	0°15′	22,900	.027	.019

and a point would be reached where a favorable slope across the entire pavement would be desirable.

In the *AASHO Policy* it is recommended that a plane slope across the pavement should be used wherever a curve is sharp enough to require a superelevation rate in excess of about 0.02. This practical limit corresponds to degrees of curve ranging from 2°30' at 30 mph to 0°45' at 70 mph. For curves between these values and those in Table 8–6 a compromise could be made, in the interest of construction economy, by rotating the normal crown slightly toward the inside of the curve. However, a change to a plane slope across both lanes would be preferable, at least at the higher design speeds.

Table 8–7 shows the resulting design superelevation rates for the case in which $e = 0.10$; it is the tabular form of Fig. 8–10. Similar tables for three other values of maximum e are found in the *AASHO Policy*. The basis for selecting the tabulated runoff or spiral lengths is discussed in Arts. 8–13 and 8–15.

8–13. Length of Spiral.—The purposes served by an easement curve and the reasons for choosing the spiral as the easement were stated succinctly in Art. 5–1.

Safe operation at high speeds requires that curves be designed to fit natural driver-vehicle behavior. It is obviously impossible, when traveling at any appreciable speed, to change instantaneously from a straight to a circular path at the T.C. of an unspiraled curve. On such alignment the driver makes his own transition as a matter of necessity, usually by starting to steer toward the curve in advance of the T.C. In so doing, there is bound to be some deviation from the traffic lane. If the curve is sharp or if the speed is high, the deviation may result in dangerous encroachment on the shoulder or on the adjacent traffic lane (see Fig. 8–11).

Though the operational and aesthetic advantages of spirals are generally recognized, their adoption in the United States (since about 1925) has been very gradual; as of 1955 only about one-half of the State highway departments used them. Among the reasons for this are the cumbersome, highly-mathematical treatments often presented, which result in the belief that tedious computations and awkward field work are inherent in the use of the spiral; the mistaken belief that a spiral of

e. max. = 0.10

D	R	V = 30 e	V = 30 L 2-lane	V = 30 L 4-lane	V = 40 e	V = 40 L 2-lane	V = 40 L 4-lane	V = 50 e	V = 50 L 2-lane	V = 50 L 4-lane	V = 60 e	V = 60 L 2-lane	V = 60 L 4-lane	V = 70 e	V = 70 L 2-lane	V = 70 L 4-lane
0° 15'	22918'	NC	0	0	NC	0	0	NC	0	0	NC	0	0	RC	200	200
0° 30'	11459'	NC	0	0	NC	0	0	NC	0	0	RC	175	175	RC	200	200
0° 45'	7639'	NC	0	0	RC	125	125	RC	150	150	.018	175	175	.020	200	200
1° 00'	5730'	NC	0	0	RC	125	125	.018	150	150	.022	175	175	.028	200	200
1° 30'	3820'	RC	100	100	.020	125	125	.027	150	150	.034	175	175	.042	200	200
2° 00'	2865'	RC	100	100	.027	125	125	.036	150	150	.046	175	190	.055	200	250
2° 30'	2292'	.020	100	100	.033	125	125	.045	150	150	.059	175	240	.069	210	310
3° 00'	1910'	.024	100	100	.038	125	125	.054	150	190	.070	190	280	.083	250	370
3° 30'	1637'	.027	100	100	.045	125	140	.063	150	230	.081	220	330	.096	290	430
4° 00'	1432'	.030	100	100	.050	125	160	.070	170	250	.090	240	360	.100	300	450
5° 00'	1146'	.038	100	100	.060	130	190	.083	200	300	.099	270	400	D max = 3.9°		
6° 00'	955'	.044	100	120	.068	140	210	.093	220	330	.100	270	400			
7° 00'	819'	.050	100	140	.076	160	240	.097	230	350	D max = 5.5°					
8° 00'	716'	.055	100	150	.084	180	260	.100	240	360						
9° 00'	637'	.061	110	160	.089	190	280	D max = 8.3°								
10° 00'	573'	.065	120	180	.093	200	290									
11° 00'	521'	.070	130	190	.096	200	300									
12° 00'	477'	.074	130	200	.098	210	310									
13° 00'	441'	.078	140	210	.099	210	310									
14° 00'	409'	.082	150	220	.100	210	320									
16° 00'	358'	.087	160	240	D max = 13.4°											
18° 00'	318'	.093	170	250												
20° 00'	286'	.096	170	260												
22° 00'	260'	.099	180	270												
24° 00'	239'	.100	180	270												
24.8°	231'	D max = 24.8°														

Notes. NC = normal crown section. RC = remove crown slope. NC = normal crown, superelevate at normal adverse crown. Spirals desirable but not as essential above heavy line. Lengths rounded in multiples of 25 or 50 feet permit simpler calculations.

TABLE 8-7.—DESIGN VALUES FOR RATE OF ELEVATION (e) AND MINIMUM LENGTH OF RUNOFF OR SPIRAL CURVE (L IN FEET)

particular length is required for each different value of curve radius or of design speed; and inertia—a reluctance to change existing rule-of-thumb practices.

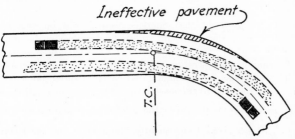

Fig. 8–11. Vehicle paths on unspiraled curve

It is hoped that the simple presentation of the basic geometry of the spiral in Chapter 5, in which easily remembered analogies to the corresponding parts of a circular curve are emphasized, will assist in dispelling the bugaboo of mathematical complexity. Moreover, the various spiral tables in Part III are so complete and so readily adapted to basing the circular arc either upon the radius or upon the chord or the arc definition of degree of curve that the required trigonometry and field work are no more complicated for the calculation and staking of a spiral-curve layout than for an unspiraled curve. (As a matter of interest, it is the author's practice to require that students be able to compute and stake an acceptable spiral without referring to tables of any kind. The method—given in Art. 5–12—is based upon a sketch showing the basic geometry of the spiral, from which all needed approximate relations may be derived by inspection; slide-rule calculation is adequate.)

The belief that the proper length of spiral is closely calculable adds to the impression of mathematical complexity. This belief is probably based upon early research done by Shortt[11] in the field of railroad practice. Later, the Shortt formula was applied to highways by Royal-Dawson[12] and others, although the physical conditions differed in some important respects. Until recently, no proof of the correctness of this transfer existed, although observation of highway driving practices led many engineers to doubt its validity. Fortunately, certain fallacies have been disclosed by recent research, the outcome of which promises to be a simpler method of selecting spirals.

It is significant that Shortt's research was on *unsuperelevated* transition curves on *railway track*. Briefly, the result of his work seemed to indicate that the length of transition for comfortable operation was a definitely calculable variable. The reasoning was as follows: At constant speed, the length of time required to traverse an easement curve of length L_s is $\frac{L_s}{v}$ seconds. On the curve, the acceleration toward the center is $\frac{v^2}{R}$ ft per sec². Consequently, the average (assumed constant) rate of change in centripetal acceleration is $\frac{v^3}{R\,L_s}$ ft per sec.³ Shortt denoted this constant rate by C. Converting v to V in miles per hour and solving for L_s gives the basic Shortt formula, which is

$$L_s = \frac{3.15\ V^3}{R\,C} \tag{8-14}$$

Shortt concluded from these experiments on unsuperelevated railroad track that a value for C of 1 ft per sec³ was the maximum that would go unnoticed.

In transplanting the Shortt formula to highway practice, it has been customary to overlook the possible effect of superelevation and also to use a larger value of C. Tentative suggestions that 2 might be a suitable value of C for highways led to the following version of the Shortt formula:

$$L_s = \frac{1.58\ V^3}{R} \tag{8-15}$$

Unfortunately, equation 8-15 has sometimes been used quite literally, as though to deviate from it would represent a departure from correct spiral theory as applied to highways. Arbitrary use of this equation involves two fallacies. One is neglect of the superelevation. Actually, the presence of superelevation cancels out part or all of the centrifugal force (as far as its effect upon comfort is concerned), thereby invalidating any mathematical relation that is based upon *unsuperelevated* curves. Review of the geometry of the spiral shows that it is a curve of *uniformly increasing degree.* If superelevation on a curve were *increased uniformly,* it follows from basic superelevation theory (Art. 8–6) that the side friction factor f would be zero when traversing the spiral at the so-called equilibrium speed for the circular arc. In other words, it would be theoretically possible for a car to steer itself on a true course around the complete spiral-curve layout without the driver touching the wheel.

It may be shown that the correct form of the Shortt formula for *superelevated* curves is

$$L_s = \frac{1}{C}\left(\frac{v^3}{R}\cos\theta - v\,g\,\sin\theta\right) \tag{8-16}$$

Since the values of θ used in practice are small, it is close enough to assume that $\cos\theta = 1$ and that $\sin\theta = \tan\theta = e$. When these substitutions are made and v is converted to V in miles per hour, equation 8–16 becomes[13]

$$L_s = \frac{3.15\,V}{C}\left(\frac{V^2}{R} - 15\,e\right) \tag{8-17}$$

When $e = 0$, formula 8–17 reduces to the Shortt formula for unsuperelevated curves; for this reason it has been called[2] the "modified Shortt formula."

In practice the speed on the circular arc is usually greater than the equilibrium value, resulting in a uniform value of f that must fit equation 8–11. Both comfort and safety at high speed make it desirable to approach f at a *uniform* rate along some form of easement curve. The spiral, when banked at a uniformly increasing rate, produces this condition.

A simpler form of equation 8–17 for the case in which V is greater than the equilibrium value is found by substituting $15(e+f)$ for $\frac{V^2}{R}$. The result is

$$L_s = \frac{47\,V\,f}{C} \tag{8-18}$$

A relation of this basic form was given by Haile,[14] though he recommended that it should not be used because of the short spiral lengths produced when f is small. There is no need to discard the theoretically correct relation represented by equation 8–18 solely for this reason. It is important, however, to consider the rotational effect. Though an extremely short spiral to a superelevated curve will result in no centrifugal sensation (if traversed at equilibrium speed), yet the rotational change about the axis of the car may be too rapid for comfort or safety.

Long years of operating experience on spiraled superelevated railroad track have led the American Railway Engineering Association to recommend that minimum spiral lengths be based upon attaining superelevation across standard-gage track at a desirable maximum rate of $1\frac{1}{4}$ inches per second of time. Highway and railroad operation are by no means analogous; but, in the absence of research on the motor-vehicle rotational rate at which discomfort begins, there is logic in tentative adoption of the same rate used successfully on railroads. (Haile[14] and other engineers advocated consideration of the rotational effect as early as 1936.)

A rise of 1.25 inches per second across the track gage of 4 ft $8\frac{1}{2}$ in. is equivalent to about 0.022 ft per ft per sec. Consequently, $L_s = 1.47\ V\left(\dfrac{e}{0.022}\right)$, or

$$L_s = 67\ e\ V \tag{8–19}$$

The two formulas for minimum desirable spiral length are separately inconsistent for certain conditions. Equation 8–18 gives values which are too short when f is small ($L_s = 0$ at equilibrium speed), whereas equation 8–19 gives values which are too short when e is small ($L_s = 0$ for unsuperelevated curves). However, by using each formula within its proper range, the resulting minimum spiral lengths will produce neither unsafe values of f nor an uncomfortable rate of angular rotation.

The spiral length at which the change from equation 8–18 to 8–19 occurs is found by equating the two values of L_s. Thus,

$$\frac{47\ V f}{C}\ \text{governs choice of minimum } L_s \text{ when } e < 0.7\ \frac{f}{C}$$

67 $e\,V$ governs choice of minimum L_s when $e > 0.7\dfrac{f}{C}$

The value of e is found from the relation $\dfrac{V^2\,D_a}{85{,}700} - f$ (or $\dfrac{V^2}{15\,R} - f$).

Rotational change, rather than side friction and centripetal acceleration, is likely to govern minimum spiral lengths on the open highway. This is because e will exceed $0.7\dfrac{f}{C}$ wherever the actual superelevation rate is greater than about 60 per cent of the recommended maximum for the given degree of curve and design speed.

Table 8–8 (from *AASHO Policy*) shows values of spiral length on the sharpest curves recommended when $e = 0.10$, as determined from the several formulas just described. The variations serve to emphasize that there is no basis for insisting on great precision in calculating lengths of spirals for design.

The practical value of the rotational-change method of choosing minimum spiral lengths is well-illustrated in the case of the Pennsylvania Turnpike. The spirals on this highway (Table 8–10) were designed on the basis of a rotational change of about 0.02 ft per ft per second—practically the value

TABLE 8–8

CALCULATED LENGTHS OF SPIRAL FOR MAXIMUM CURVATURE

Basis $e = 0.10$	L_s = Minimum length of spiral in feet for design speed, mph, of:				
	30	40	50	60	70
Shortt formula, $C = 1$	370	470	570	650	730
Shortt formula, $C = 2$	185	235	285	325	365
Modified Shortt formula, $C = 1$	230	285	330	370	400
Modified Shortt formula, $C = 1.35$	170	210	250	275	295
Meyer, $L_s = 67\,e\,V$	200	270	335	400	470

used in deriving equation 8–19. The generally favorable operating characteristics of these spirals, as observed on high-speed tests,[7] are undoubtedly due in no small measure to the constant (and comfortable) rate of rotational change experienced on successive curves.

Until recently, valid objection to this method of selecting spiral lengths might have been made on the grounds that it does not necessarily produce a constant value of C. The impression that C must be constant on a highway spiral— as it must of necessity be in the case of a spiral on railroad track—is another fallacy which has been disclosed by research. This assumption is equivalent to stating that the driver of a motor vehicle who is free to choose his own path in making the transition from a tangent to a circular curve always turns his wheel (1) at a constant rate on any given transition and (2) at the same rate on all transitions.

The careful field tests and statistical analyses made by Leeming and Black,[15] summarized and amplified in Leeming's later report,[16] verify the first part of this assumption. (This, in effect, validates the spiral as a curve of suitable shape but does not involve any condition as to its length.) However, the research, made with a recording accelerometer on more than 2,000 curves, shows that C varies between such wide limits that there is no "natural rate of turning" the wheel, such as is represented by $C = 2$ or by any other constant value. Though these investigators found no correlation between C and V nor between C and R, there was a definite tendency for C to *increase* as the value of f reached on any curve becomes greater. Since the higher values of f were recorded on the sharper curves, this trend is equivalent to stating that a driver turns his wheel faster upon entering a sharp curve than upon entering a flat one. Though contrary to the Shortt formula, this conclusion is in accordance with observation of general driver behavior, and has been verified in tests by Warren[17] and by Welty.[18]

From Leeming's experiments it appears that safety and comfort depend mainly on the value of f; and that a driver slows down to reduce f, not to reduce C. Relatively large values of C (far in excess of 2 ft per sec[3]) were frequently recorded as producing an "imperceptible" degree of discomfort, as long as the accompanying values of f were moderate (in the neighborhood of the design values suggested in Fig. 8–7).

The length of spiral may also be made equal to the length required for superelevation runoff. Runoff length is determined by the rate at which the pavement cross slope is changed, or rotated, subject to some modification on the basis of appearance as viewed by the driver. Thus, the resulting formula for runoff (and spiral) length would have the same general form as 8–19. This subject is treated in greater detail in Art. 8–15.

8–14. Minimum Curvature for Use of Spirals.—Neither superelevation nor spirals are required on extremely flat curves. It would appear logical to use spirals approaching all curves on which a plane cross slope is used across the entire pavement. In Art. 8–12 the superelevation requiring such design was fixed (*AASHO Policy*) at the rate $e = 0.02$ or greater. However, at this limiting rate a selected spiral would have such a small o-distance (offset, or throw, at the offset T.C.) that the spiral would have little significance. It could be omitted without hampering the ability of the driver to keep well within the traffic lane; if used, it would serve principally as a graceful method of changing from the normal crown to the superelevated cross-section.

In view of the fact that minimum curvature for use of spirals

TABLE 8–9

MINIMUM DEGREE OF CURVE FOR USE OF SPIRALS

Design Speed mph	Minimum Curvature	Assumed Minimum Length of Spiral ft	Calculated o-Distance ft
30	3°30′	100	.25
40	2°15′	125	.26
50	1°45′	150	.29
60	1°15′	175	.26
70	1°15′	200	.36

must be set arbitrarily, the control values selected in the
AASHO Policy were taken as rounded values obtained from
Fig. 8–10 at the points where $e = 0.03$, approximately. The
resulting recommendations are given in Table 8–9, the throws
in the last column being obtainable from Table XI. Minimum lengths of spirals approximate the distances traveled in
2 seconds at the design speeds.

8–15. Length of Superelevation Runoff.—Superelevation
runoff is the general term denoting the transition from the
normal crown section on a tangent to the fully superelevated
section on a curve. The runoff should be pleasing in appearance to the driver and effected smoothly over a length that is
safe and comfortable when the vehicle is operated at design
speed.

There is no completely rational method of determining
length of runoff. It has been made equal to the length of
spiral, as calculated from one of the formulas in Art. 8–13. If
this method is used, the most logical formula would be one
having the same general form as 8–19, since this formula is
based on restricting the rate of angular change in superelevation.

To possess a pleasing appearance as viewed by the driver,
the edge profiles should not appear to be distorted. Control
of runoff length from this standpoint has also been used; the
numerical controls must, of course, be empirical. In the
AASHO Policy the values suggested are as follows:

Design speed, mph.......	30	40	50	60	70
Max. relative slope in % gradient between edges of 2-lane pavement..........	1.33	1.14	1.00	0.89	0.80

On spiraled curves there is no sound basis for using different lengths of spiral and runoff. Simplicity in construction
is gained by using identical lengths. Since length of runoff is
applicable to all superelevated curves, whether spiraled or not,
it is concluded (*AASHO Policy*) that runoff lengths, as determined from the foregoing appearance controls, should also be
used for minimum lengths of spirals. On 4-lane highways the
runoff lengths are taken to be 1.5 times the lengths for 2-lane
highways, purely on an empirical basis. The resulting spiral

and runoff lengths are listed in Table 8–7. It should be emphasized that these are *minimum* values; high-type alignment or the attainment of proper pavement drainage may justify the use of greater lengths.

8–16. Methods of Attaining Superelevation.—The transition from the normal crowned section on a tangent to the fully superelevated section on a curve should be pleasing in appearance and inherently safe and comfortable for the operation of vehicles at the highway design speed. In addition, it should be relatively simple to calculate and stake out the transition.

Spiraled curves may be superelevated by the method shown in Fig. 8–12. In this method the normal profile grade of the center line is unchanged. The outer lane between sections *a-a* and *b-b* is gradually warped from the normal crowned section to a straight *level* section at the T.S.; beyond the T.S. the section is rotated at a uniform rate about the survey centerline until it reaches full superelevation at the S.C. (section *d-d*). The normal profile grade of the inner edge of the pavement is continued as far as section *c-c*. Between sections *b-b* and *c-c* the normal convex crown (if any) on the inner lane is gradually converted to a straight *inclined* section at *c-c*, where the rate of superelevation equals that on the outside lane. (The pavement areas over which the crown is taken out are shown crosshatched in the plan view.) Between sections *c-c* and *d-d* there is a uniformly increasing one-way bank across both lanes. The same method is used on a curve to the left and on the leaving spiral.

In Fig. 8–12 the edge profiles are shown as straight lines merely to illustrate the basic design; the edge breaks would actually be rounded in construction. Some agencies obtain the effect of short vertical curves by eye adjustments of the stakes or forms; others insert true vertical curves at the breaks; and a few States use reversed vertical curves. Graphical determination of edge profiles by means of splines is an excellent and economical method in office design.

The preceding method of rotating a section about the center line should not be adhered to rigidly. Practical considerations, as well as aesthetics, are poorly served by such stereotyped design. Drainage conditions, for example, may not permit depressing the inside edge of the pavement by the amount required by this method. In such a case the pavement can be rotated about the normal profile grade of the inside edge or about a line a short distance from that edge and parallel to it. Where summit vertical curves and horizontal curves overlap,

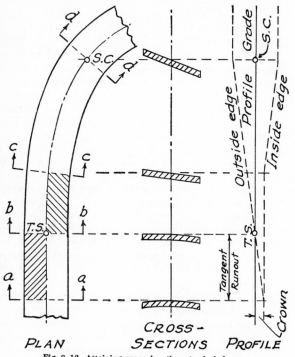

Fig. 8–12. Attaining superelevation at spiraled curve

rotation about the normal profile grade of the outside edge may be the obvious method of reducing the unsightly hump produced along that edge by either of the preceding methods. No one method is best for all situations; each case should be studied individually.

Multi-lane highways having a median strip present an

especially difficult problem in runoff design. Here, consideration of all important factors—aesthetics, drainage conditions, economics of grading, riding comfort, and safety—is necessary in arriving at a harmonious solution.

The design finally adopted on the original section of the Pennsylvania Turnpike is especially instructive in these respects. On this highway the rather narrow median strip (10 ft wide) and frequent curves—aggregating 50½ miles in the 160-mile distance—were principally responsible for the decision to keep the edges of the paved roadway nearest the median strip in the same horizontal plane at all times. Each 24-ft roadway slopes away from these edges at a rate of ⅛ in. per ft. Consequently, on tangents there is surface drainage over the roadways from the median strip. This disadvantage, however, is offset by the simpler method of runoff design made possible. The method is essentially that of Fig. 8–12, adapted to rotation about the edges closest to the median strip. Fig. 8–13 shows the runoff details for a curve to the left; specific curve data are given in Table 8–10.

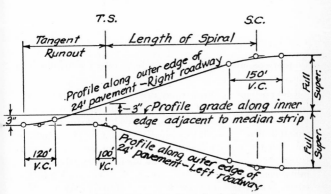

Fig. 8–13. Runoff design on Pennsylvania Turnpike

It should be observed that the level-inclined section, corresponding to *b-b* in Fig. 8–12, occurs in advance of the T.S. in Fig. 8–13, and that the inclined section corresponding to *c-c* in Fig. 8–12 occurs at the T.S. in Fig. 8–13. These modifica-

TABLE 8–10

PENNSYLVANIA TURNPIKE SPIRALS

Degree of Curve	Rate of Superelevation per Foot of Width Inches	Length of Spiral Feet	Tangent Runout Feet
1°45′	$\frac{5}{16}$	150	260
2°00′	$\frac{3}{8}$	150	210
2°15′	$\frac{7}{16}$	200	210
2°30′	$\frac{9}{16}$	200	164
2°45′	$\frac{11}{16}$	250	162
3°00′	$\frac{3}{4}$	250	160
3°15′	$\frac{13}{16}$	280	158
3°30′	$\frac{7}{8}$	300	157
4°00′	1	350	154
4°30′	$1\frac{1}{16}$	370	148
5°00′	$1\frac{3}{16}$	410	146
5°15′	$1\frac{3}{16}$	400	145
5°30′	$1\frac{3}{16}$	400	141

tions are required by the one-way bank over the roadways on tangents.

Observations of high-speed driving over spiraled curves built with and without a tangent runout on the outer lane indicate that the runout is a desirable feature of superelevation runoff design. Used in combination with a suitable length of spiral, it is[7] "a pronounced aid in entering horizontal curvature. This is quite noticeable at night during adverse visibility conditions. The car appears to steer itself into the curve before the operator is aware of its presence. This quality of self-steering eliminates the element of surprise when entering curves travelling at speeds in excess of visibility requirements during adverse weather."

Unspiraled circular curves are superelevated by various rule-of-thumb methods. Obviously, no method can be completely rational, since it is impossible to have full superelevation between the T.C. and the C.T. (where it belongs) without placing the runoff entirely on the tangent (where it does not belong). On the other hand, the runoff cannot be accomplished completely on the curve without having inadequate and variable superelevation over a substantial portion of the distance. No agencies are known to follow the latter procedure, although several States (Massachusetts among them) place all the runoff on the tangent. The method adopted is usually a compromise, in which the runoff starts on the tangent and ends at a point some distance beyond the T.C.

In the foregoing method there is invariably a section of tangent at each end of the curve over which the cross-section varies from the normal crown on tangents to a one-way bank at the T.C. and C.T., where the rate is between seven-tenths and nine-tenths of the full superelevation value. There is no standard practice as to details. For example, some State highway departments provide full superelevation a fixed distance beyond the T.C., regardless of the length of runoff (Washington, 50 feet). The distance may or may not coincide with the point at which full widening (Art. 8–18) is attained. Other States provide full superelevation beyond the T.C. at a variable distance equal to a certain fraction of the length of runoff. In Michigan and California the fraction is one-third. Rotation may be about the center-line or about any other line parallel to the center-line; the modifying circumstances that need to be considered are the same as those in the case of spiraled curves.

The objection inherent in all methods of designing superelevation runoff for unspiraled curves is the inevitable violation of sound dynamic principles. In traversing that portion of the runoff on the entering tangent, the driver—if he is to maintain a straight course—must steer against the gradually increasing superelevation. However, as soon as he reaches the T.C. of a curve involving the usual combination of an understeering car and a speed greater than the equilibrium value, he must steer toward the center of curvature (see Art. 8–7). This reversal in steering direction is neither natural nor obtainable instantaneously. Consequently, during the approach to the T.C., the vehicle usually creeps toward the shoulder or toward the inner lane. Near the T.C. it traverses a reverse curve in getting back into the traffic lane. Upon leaving the curve similar effects are produced.

The effects just described are not particularly important where vehicles are operated at low speeds. But at high design speeds they may have consequences serious enough to justify universal adoption of center-line spiraling. In fact, one of the conclusions of Stonex and Noble as a result of the carefully-instrumented high-speed tests on the Pennsylvania Turnpike[7] was: "the use of spirals in modern highway design is imperative if inherent safety is to be provided."

8–17. Pavement Widening on Curves.—The practice of widening pavements on sharp curves is well established, although there is little uniformity among State highway departments as to the amount of widening required.

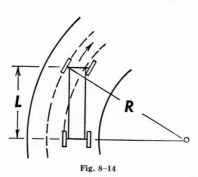

Fig. 8–14

When a vehicle travels at equilibrium speed around a curve, the rear wheels track inside the front wheels by an amount equal to $R - \sqrt{R^2 - L^2}$ (see Fig. 8–14). At other than equilibrium speed, the rear wheels track further in or out, the positions depending on whether the speed is less or greater than the equilibrium value. When the speed is high, though still within safe limits, the rear wheels may even track outside the front wheels (see Fig. 8–4). There is no way of determining the exact amount of extra lane widening required to compensate for the non-tracking effect, except at equilibrium speed, since it depends on the particular slip angles developed by each vehicle. However, measurements of actual wheel paths on two-lane highways show that drivers sense the need for greater clearance between opposing traffic, and that they instinctively increase the clearance when the speed is higher or the curvature is sharper.

One of the earliest formulas giving the recommended total extra width for a two-lane highway was that suggested by Voshell.[19] This formula is

$$w = 2\left[R - \sqrt{R^2 - L^2}\right] + \frac{35}{R} \qquad (8\text{--}20)$$

Formula 8–20, with L taken as 20 ft, has been used by several agencies. The expression is not entirely rational, however, since the first term applies only at equilibrium speed and the second term is purely empirical. Other simpler empirical formulas give results fully as satisfactory. Among these are: $w = \sqrt[3]{D}$, $w = \frac{D}{10} + 1$, and $w = \frac{D}{5}$.

It is customary to limit the widening for a 2-lane pavement to between 1.5 and 6.0 feet, approximately, there being no widening on curves flatter than 5° or 6°. There are many exceptions to these values, however. Some States determine the widening only to the nearest foot; others work as close as the nearest 0.1 foot.

In an attempt to rationalize the subject, the *AASHO Policy* contains an analysis in which four factors enter into the formula for widening. These are (1) the track width of the design vehicle (a single-unit truck or bus); (2) the lateral clearance per vehicle; (3) the width of front overhang of the vehicle on the inner lane; and (4) an extra width allowance that depends on the sharpness of the curve and the design speed. Accompanying the analysis is the recommendation that design values for widening should be multiples of $\frac{1}{2}$ foot and the minimum value should be 2 feet. On this basis no widening is required on 2-lane pavements that are normally 24 feet wide or greater.

Table 8–11 contains a summary of values for widening obtained by three representative methods. The term W is the normal width of the 2-lane pavement.

Widening is no longer the important subject that it was when sharp curves and 8-foot or 9-foot lane widths were preva-

TABLE 8–11

WIDENING ON CURVES—TWO-LANE PAVEMENTS

Degree of Curve D	Formula 8–20 L=20	$\frac{D}{10}+1$	AASHO Policy, W=20 ft Design Speed, mph				
			30	40	50	60	70
4	1.2	1.4				2	2
5	1.4	1.5			2	2	
6	1.6	1.6		2	2	AASHO W=22 ft Speed, mph	
7	1.7	1.7		2	2.5		
8	1.9	1.8	2	2	2.5		
10	2.2	2.0	2	2		30	40
13	2.6	2.3	2.5	3			2
16	3.0	2.6	3			2	
20	3.5	3.0	3.5			2.5	
24	4.0	3.4	4			3	

lent. In much modern alignment design no extra widening is used, since high design speeds limit curvature to 5° or 6° and traffic lanes are commonly 11 and 12 feet wide.

8–18. Transition to Widened Section.—Theoretically, the full extra widening should continue for the whole length of a circular arc. It is relatively easy to do this with spiraled curves. When curves are not spiraled, however, it is impossible to carry the full widening from the T.C. to the C.T. without introducing undesirable kinks in the edge of the pavement.

Spiraled curves may be widened by the methods shown in Figs. 8–15 and 8–16. In Fig. 8–15 the total widening is placed on the inside of the curve. Widening begins at the T.S., reaches the full amount at the S.C., and tapers off from the C.S. to the S.T. in like manner. At intermediate points on the transition the *widenings are proportional to the distances from the T.S.* Forms for the curve at the inside edge of the roadway are located on radial offsets from the survey center-line at

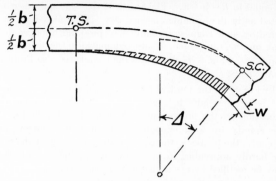

Fig. 8–15. Inside widening on spiraled curve

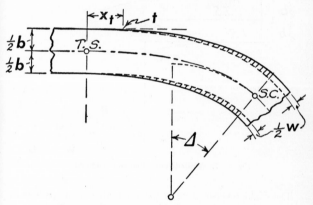

Fig. 8–16. Equal lane widening on spiraled curve

distances equal to $\frac{1}{2}b$ plus the proportional amounts of the widening.

In this method the curve of the inside edge is not a true spiral. However, the transition is smooth except at the S.C., where the slight break may be remedied by eye adjustment of the stakes or forms. The alternative would be to calculate a separate spiral for the inside edge having a throw equal to w plus the throw of the center-line spiral, and having a radius

R' equal to $R - \frac{1}{2}b - w$. The length of the edge spiral is computed as in the example on page 208. This procedure, preferred by some engineers, results in a spiral much longer than that on the center-line; it also complicates the field work somewhat. Fig. 8–17 illustrates the layout; see also Problem 8, Art. 8–28.

In Fig. 8–16 the total widening is divided equally between the inside and outside edges, and is distributed along the transition by the proportion method used in Fig. 8–15. If the spirals are long enough to attain the superelevation properly, the breaks in the edges of the pavement at the S.C. are hardly noticeable; in case they are apparent at all, they may be rectified by eye adjustment of the forms.

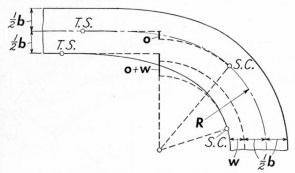

Fig. 8–17. Spiraled center-line and inside edge

The slight reverse curve in the outer edge of the pavement near the T.S. may be avoided by starting the outside widening at the point where the tangent produced intersects the widened pavement, as point t in Fig. 8–16. The distance from the T.S. to t is approximately equal to

$$x_t = L_s \sqrt{\frac{w}{2\,Y}} \qquad (8\text{–}21)$$

Theoretically, there is a slight break at point t, but it is imperceptible. Moreover, the small loss in widening between t and the T.S. is negligible. For example, on a 10°

curve for which $L_s = 400$ ft and $w = 2$ ft, $x_t = 59$ ft and the widening at point t is only 0.15 ft.

When curves are spiraled, the method of Fig. 8–16 has considerable justification, particularly in the case of a 2-lane concrete pavement having a longitudinal joint on the survey center-line. For one thing, staking is simplified. In addition, traffic on the outside lane is provided with the same extra widening that is given to the inner lane, and the tendency to edge across the longitudinal joint is thereby reduced. On sharp curves requiring center striping, there is no unsightly and confusing deviation between the striping and the center joint.

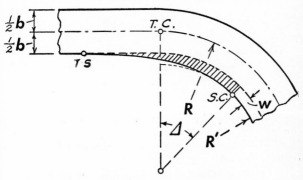

Fig. 8–18. Inside widening on unspiraled curve

Unspiraled circular curves are widened at the inside edge of the pavement and approached by some sort of easement curve, such as a spiral (Fig. 8–18). Theoretically, a perfectly smooth transition will result by using a spiral which has a throw equal to w and which terminates in a circular curve having a radius R' equal to $R - \frac{1}{2}b - w$. There are several methods of determining the value of L_s. The simplest is to assume that $Y = 4$ times the throw (equation 5–20). Then,

$$L_s = \sqrt{6\,R'\,Y} \qquad \text{(from equation 5–8)}$$

after which $$\Delta \text{ (in radians)} = \frac{L_s}{2\,R'} \text{ (from equation 5–6)}$$

Example.—*Given:* $D_a = 10°$; $\frac{1}{2}b = 12$ ft; $w = 2$ ft.

$$L_s = \sqrt{6 \times 559 \times 8} = 164 \text{ ft, and } \Delta = 8.4°$$

On a very sharp curve having a large value of w, the approximation $Y = 4\,o$ may not give sufficient accuracy. In this case, calculate the coefficient M (Art. 5–10) and determine Δ from Table XIII. Thus, in the preceding example,

$$M = \frac{R' + w}{R'} = \frac{560.96}{558.96} = 1.00358$$

From Table XIII, by interpolation, $\Delta = 8.4°$, as before. (In this example the first method is obviously satisfactory.) Then, $L_s = 164$ ft, from equation 5–6; or, from Table XII,

$$L_s = \frac{2.0}{0.01221} = 164 \text{ ft}$$

The method of Fig. 8–18 leaves a strip of ineffective pavement at the outside edge near the T.C. (see Fig. 8–11). In order to compensate for this, the outside edge may be independently spiraled. This produces a layout in which the survey center-line is a simple curve but the edges of the pavement are true spirals. (The State of Indiana used this practice for many years on curves having $D = 5°$ and greater.) One method of selecting the spirals is by using the following procedure, illustrated with the aid of Fig. 8–19:

1. Choose a value for the throw o of the outside spiral. In practice, o is usually about $\frac{1}{2}w$.

2. Calculate L_s (and Δ) for the outside spiral, as previously described, using $R' = R + \frac{1}{2}b - o$.

3. Calculate L_s (and Δ) for the inside spiral, using a throw equal to $o + w$ and a radius $R' = R - \frac{1}{2}b - o - w$.

4. Examine the two spiral lengths and, if necessary, adjust the value of o (and possibly of w) to give more suitable spirals.

When the inner and outer edges are separately spiraled, the S.C.'s of the two spirals will not be opposite each other. Moreover, the inside spiral must be longer than that on the outside edge, because of the greater throw (see Art. 8–28, Problem 10).

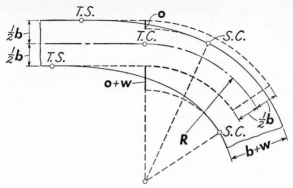

Fig. 8–19. True edge spirals on unspiraled curve

An objection to using a spiral for the widening transition to unspiraled curves—aside from the fact that each combination of R, b, and w requires a different spiral—is that only one-half the desired widening is attained at the T.C. of the circular arc. Furthermore, if the circular curve is short, there may not be distance enough beyond the T.C. in which to reach full widening unless an exceedingly short spiral is used. Accordingly, most State highway departments that have not yet adopted center-line spiraling use transitions which reach full widening on the inside edge at some relatively small fixed distance beyond the T.C., regardless of the values of R, b, and w. The length of the transition is also a fixed distance, although some States vary the length with the degree of curve according to a rule-of-thumb procedure. The edge transition itself cannot be a spiral; usually it is a curve approximating a parabola. On pavement work, the eye adjustment of the forms required to produce a smooth curve near the point of maximum widening is likely to be quite extensive. This matter is treated in greater detail in Art. 8–20.

The voluminous tables worked up by some State highway departments for staking widening transitions and superelevation runoffs on unspiraled curves—in contrast to the simple procedures based upon Figs. 8–12, 8–15, and 8–16—are themselves strong arguments for adoption of center-line spiraling.

8–19. Sight Distances on Horizontal Curves.—Where a building, wall, cut slope, or other obstruction is located at the inside of a curve, the designer must consider the possible effect of the obstruction on the sight distance.   Fig. 8–20 shows this situation for the case in which the sight line AB is shorter than the curve.   The driver's eye at A is assumed to be at the center of the inside lane.   Although the chord AB is the actual line of sight, the stopping sight distance S_H is taken as the arc AB because this is the travel distance available for stopping in order to avoid hitting an object at B.

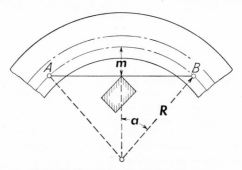

Fig. 8–20. Sight distance on horizontal curve

In the following analysis, R, D, and L refer to the center of the inside lane, not to the survey center-line.   If the notation on Fig. 8–20 is used, $m = R$ vers a.   But $a : D = \frac{1}{2} S_H : 100$, and R is approximately equivalent to $\dfrac{5,730}{D}$.   Hence

$$m = \frac{5,730}{D} \text{ vers } \frac{S_H D}{200} \qquad (8\text{–}22)$$

Also,
$$S_H = \frac{R}{28.65} \cos^{-1} \frac{R-m}{R} \qquad (8\text{–}23)$$

Fig. 8–21 is a design chart (*AASHO Policy*) showing the required middle ordinates, at various degrees of curve, needed to satisfy the stopping sight distances given in Table 8–1. Where the obstruction is a cut slope, the criteria for height of

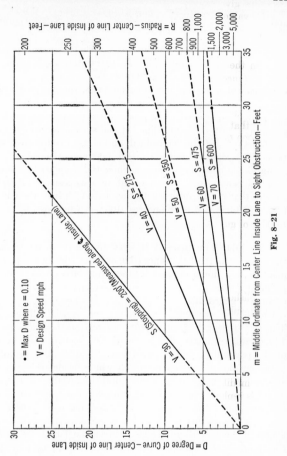

Fig. 8–21

eye and object (Art. 8–3) can be approximated by using a height of 2.5 feet at the point where m is measured.

In case the sight distance is longer than the curve, the following approximate formulas may be used:

$$M = \frac{L(2S_H - L)}{8R} \qquad \text{(8–24) Approx.}$$

and
$$S_H = \frac{4\,R\,m}{L} + \frac{L}{2} \qquad \text{(8–25) Approx.}$$

These formulas may also be used with the passing sight distances given in Table 8–3. However, this application is of little value except on long flat curves.

Instead of using the foregoing methods, the designer may prefer to scale sight distances from the plans. Since high precision is unnecessary, the procedure is to place a straight-edge on the survey center-line (at the station for which the sight distance is to be determined) and tangent to the obstruction. The sight distance is then taken as the difference in stationing between the points where the straightedge intersects the center line. When scaled, it is suggested (*AASHO Policy*) that S_H be recorded to the nearest 50 feet when less than 1,000 feet and to the nearest 100 feet when greater than 1,000 feet.

8–20. Edge Lengths.—It is often necessary to determine the curved length of the inner edge or outer edge of the pavement or of a line a certain distance from either edge. This problem occurs in connection with estimating the length of curb or of guard rail.

Unwidened circular arcs present no special difficulty. The desired length is found from the relation $L = IR$, where I is in radians (degrees divided by 57.296), and R is the radius of the particular edge or offset line. (Table VI is useful.)

In the case of a circular arc on which inside widening is accomplished by means of a true spiral (Fig. 8–18), the length of each spiraled edge is found from the basic spiral-length formula, $L_s = 2\,\Delta\,R'$ (equation 5–6), Δ being in radians and R' being the radius of the fully widened edge. The total length of the curved inside edge between the T.S. and S.T. of the spirals is $(I + 2\,\Delta)\,(R - \tfrac{1}{2}b - w)$, whereas the length of the curved outside edge is $I(R + \tfrac{1}{2}b)$.

The modification of the preceding case, in which the true spiral is replaced by a rule-of-thumb transition reaching full widening a short distance beyond the T.C., does not admit of any mathematically simple method of calculating edge lengths accurately. Since high precision is rarely required, approximate methods usually suffice. Thus, in Fig. 8–22, full widening is attained at C, the distances a, d, h, and w being given. The length of the curved edge AB is approximately equal to the chord distance, or

$$AB = a + \frac{h^2}{2\,a} \text{ (approx.)}$$

Also, the curve BC is approximately equal to the arc BC', or

$$BC = BC' = \left(\frac{R - \frac{1}{2}b - h}{R}\right) d \text{ (approx.)}$$

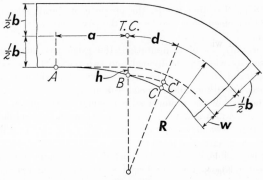

Fig. 8–22

When center-line spiraling is practiced, unwidened pavements usually have a uniform width along the spiral. That is, the edges of the pavement are on radial offsets from the center line at distances of $\frac{1}{2}b$. In this method the edge curves are not true spirals. However, their lengths (from points opposite the T.S. to points opposite the S.C.) are found accurately from

$$L' = L_s \pm \frac{1}{2}b\,\Delta \qquad (8\text{–}26)$$

in which L_s is the length of the center-line spiral and Δ is in radians.

If the pavement is widened, as in Fig. 8–15, the length of the inside edge is given by the relation

$$L' = L_s - \Delta\,(\tfrac{1}{2}b + \tfrac{2}{3}w) \qquad (8\text{–}27)$$

When the widening is divided equally between the inside and outside lanes, as in Fig. 8–16, the edge lengths are given by the relations

$$L' = L_s \pm \Delta \left(\tfrac{1}{2}b + \tfrac{1}{3}w\right) \tag{8-28}$$

(The foregoing formulas are derived by the Calculus.)

8–21. Pavement Areas on Curves.—The area of pavement on an unwidened curve is found from the relation A (sq yd) $= \dfrac{b\,L}{9}$. The distance L is the total arc length along the center-line between the T.C. and the C.T. or between the T.S. and the S.T. In other words, the presence of spirals does not affect pavement areas, so long as the pavement width is uniform.

For purposes of computation, the extra pavement area caused by widening is divided into two parts: (1) the strip of uniform width; (2) the strips of variable width at the approaches to the fully-widened section.

The area of the uniform strip is equal to the product of the extra width and the length of arc through the middle of the strip. On curves spiraled as in Fig. 8–15, this length is equal to $(I - 2\Delta)(R - \tfrac{1}{2}b - \tfrac{1}{2}w)$.

It is possible, by use of the Calculus, to derive theoretically correct relations for the curved strips along the approach transitions. For example, the extra area of the cross-hatched portion in Fig. 8–15 is

$$A = \tfrac{1}{2} L_s\, w - \Delta \left(\tfrac{1}{3}\, wb + \tfrac{1}{4}\, w^2\right) \tag{8-29}$$

An even more complicated relation is needed to express correctly the comparable area in Fig. 8–18.

The small size of the variable-width strip, in comparison with the total pavement area on a curve, hardly justifies the use of intricate—though mathematically correct—formulas. The following approximations give adequate results more quickly.

Consider the variable-width curved strip to be a triangle having a base w and altitude L. Then the area is $\tfrac{1}{2}\, wL$. For flat curves (say 6° and under), take L equal to L_s, the center-line distance to the point where full widening occurs. When D is between 6° and about 15°, take L equal to the length of the *unwidened edge*; when D is greater than $15°$, use the length of the *widened edge*.

Example 1.—*Given:* $D_a = 6°$; $b = 22$ ft; $w = 1.5$ ft; $L_s = 300$ ft; $\Delta = 9°$.

By the approximate method, the extra pavement area at one spiral is

$$A = \tfrac{1}{2} \times 1.5 \times \frac{300}{9} = 25.0 \text{ sq yd}$$

whereas the theoretically correct area, found by equation 8–29, is 24.8 sq yd.

Example 2.—*Given:* $D_a = 15°$; $b = 22$ ft; $w = 3$ ft; $L_s = 250$ ft; $\Delta = 18°45'$.

By the approximate method,

$$L' = 250 - \tfrac{1}{2} \times 22 \times \frac{18.75}{57.3} = 246.4 \quad \text{(equation 8–26)}$$

and
$$A = \tfrac{1}{2} \times 3.0 \times \frac{246.4}{9} = 41.1 \text{ sq yd}$$

whereas, by equation 8–29, $A = 40.9$ sq yd.

VERTICAL ALIGNMENT

8–22. Sight Distances at Crest Vertical Curves.—At a crest vertical curve the sight distance is considered to be the horizontal projection of the line of sight for the assumed conditions.   Fig. 8–23 shows the situation where the sight distance S is less than the length L of the vertical curve, or $S < L$.   The distances h_1 and h_2, representing the height of the driver's eye

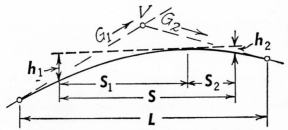

Fig. 8–23. Sight distance on vertical curve, where S<L

and the height of the object, respectively, are vertical offsets to the tangent sight line. In the general case, $h_1 \neq h_2$, and the sight line is not parallel to the chord joining the ends of the parabola.

From the *rule of offsets* in Art. 4–2 and formula 4–2,

$$h_1 : \frac{AL}{800} = S_1^2 : \left(\frac{L}{2}\right)^2$$

(It should be recalled that A is the difference between the gradients G_1 and G_2.) Therefore,

$$S_1 = \sqrt{\frac{200\,L\,h_1}{A}}$$

Similarly,

$$S_2 = \sqrt{\frac{200\,L\,h_2}{A}}$$

The result obtained by substituting S for $S_1 + S_2$ and solving for L is the following general relation:

When $S < L$,
$$L = \frac{A\,S^2}{200(\sqrt{h_1} + \sqrt{h_2})^2} \qquad (8\text{–}30)$$

In the *AASHO Policy* the values in the case of *stopping sight distance* are $h_1 = 4.5$ feet and $h_2 = 4$ inches. In the case of *passing sight distance*, $h_1 = h_2 = 4.5$ feet. (See Art. 8–3.) Substituting these values in formula 8–30 gives the following practical relations:

When $S < L$,

(*non-passing conditions*) $L = \dfrac{A\,S^2}{1,457} \qquad (8\text{–}31)$

(*passing conditions*) $L = \dfrac{A\,S^2}{3,600} \qquad (8\text{–}32)$

Figure 8–24 shows the situation where $S > L$. In the general case $h_1 \neq h_2$ and the sight line ad is not parallel to the chord joining the ends of the parabola.

The problem is to find the slope of the sight line that will make the distance ad a minimum. Let g represent the difference between the gradient of the sight line and the gradient G_1. Then $A - g$ will be the difference between the gradient of the sight line and the gradient G_2. Use is also made of the following property of the parabola: If a tangent to the parabola is drawn between the main tangents, the horizontal projection of the intercept cut off on this new tangent by the main tangents is equal to one-half the horizontal projection of the long chord of the parabola; that is, the horizontal projection of bc is equal to $\frac{1}{2}L$.

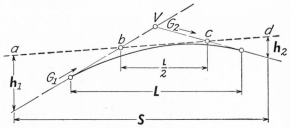

Fig. 8–24. Sight distance on vertical curve, where S<L

By definition, S equals the sum of the horizontal projections of the distances ab, bc, and cd. Consequently, the general expression for sight distance where $S > L$ is

$$S = \frac{100\, h_1}{g} + \frac{L}{2} + \frac{100\, h_2}{A - g} \tag{A}$$

For the sight distance to be a minimum, $\dfrac{dS}{dg} = 0$, or

$$\frac{dS}{dg} = \frac{-100\, h_1}{g^2} + \frac{100\, h_2}{(A - g)^2} = 0$$

Thus, the relation for the critical condition is

$$g = \frac{A\sqrt{h_1 h_2} - h_1 A}{h_2 - h_1} \tag{B}$$

The result of substituting the value of g from equation B in equation A and solving for L is the following general relation:

When $S > L$, $$L = 2S - \frac{200(\sqrt{h_1} + \sqrt{h_2})^2}{A} \tag{8-33}$$

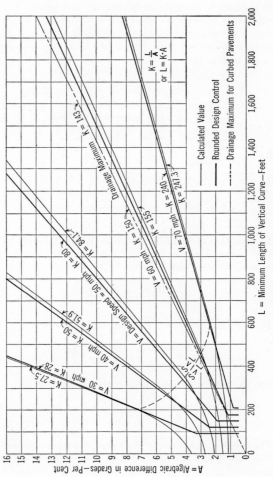

Fig. 8-25. Design controls for crest vertical curves

For the values of h_1 and h_2 in the *AASHO Policy* the practical relations are:

When $S > L$,

(*non-passing conditions*) $L = 2S - \dfrac{1,457}{A}$ **(8–34)**

(*passing conditions*) $L = 2S - \dfrac{3,600}{A}$ **(8–35)**

The light solid lines in Fig. 8–25 (*AASHO Policy*) show minimum lengths of crest vertical curves needed to provide stopping sight distances at various design speeds. The value of K, or the length of curve required to effect a 1% change in A (Art. 4–2), is a simple expression of the design control. For convenience, the theoretical values of K required to fit the stopping distances in Table 8–1 have been rounded to integral values; lengths of vertical curves computed from the rounded values of K are plotted as the heavy solid lines in Fig. 8–25.

Where $S > L$ the theoretical minimum lengths become zero for small values of A because the sight line passes over the crest of the vertical curve. However, good practice in design calls for inserting a vertical curve at all changes in vertical alignment. As an approximation of current practice, the minimum length of vertical curve is taken as about 3 times the design speed. This approximation is represented by the heavy vertical lines at the lower left of Fig. 8–25.

Drainage requirements may affect the maximum lengths of vertical curves. If pavements are curbed, experience indicates the desirability of attaining a minimum longitudinal grade of 0.35% at a point about 50 feet from the crest. This corresponds to a K-value of 143 feet for a change of 1 per cent in A; the resulting line is plotted in Fig. 8–25 as the *drainage maximum*. Special attention to drainage should be given for combinations below and to the right of this line.

Some attempts have been made to introduce headlight sight distance as a design control for stopping sight distance at crest vertical curves, the height of headlight h_1 being taken as 2.5 feet and the height of object h_2 as 4 inches or more. Obviously these conditions would demand much longer vertical curves, but this requirement is considered to be unnecessary in view of the lower running speeds used in night driving.

Although formulas 8–32 and 8–35 for passing sight distance are contained in the *AASHO Policy*, there is no design chart comparable to Fig. 8–25. (This is in contrast to the original 1940 Policy.[20]) Because of the high construction cost where crest cuts are made, it is ordinarily impracticable to provide the much longer vertical curves needed for passing.

8–23. Sight Distances at Sag Vertical Curves.—There is no generally accepted basis for establishing the lengths of sag vertical curves. Four criteria have been used: (1) headlight-beam distance, (2) rider comfort, (3) drainage control, and (4) general appearance.

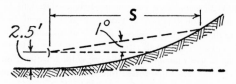

Fig. 8–26. Headlight beam. distance, where S<L

Headlight-beam distance, as used by the Pennsylvania Turnpike Commission[1], is represented by Figs. 8–26 and 8–27. With the aid of these figures it is not difficult to derive the practical relations, which are:

When S<L, $$L = \frac{A\,S^2}{500 + 3.5\,S}$$ (8–36)

When S>L, $$L = 2\,S - \frac{500 + 3.5\,S}{A}$$ (8–37)

The light solid lines in Fig. 8–28 (*AASHO Policy*) show lengths of sag vertical curves conforming to the preceding

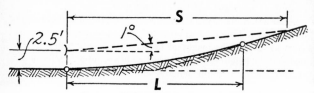

Fig. 8–27. Headlight beam distance, where S>L

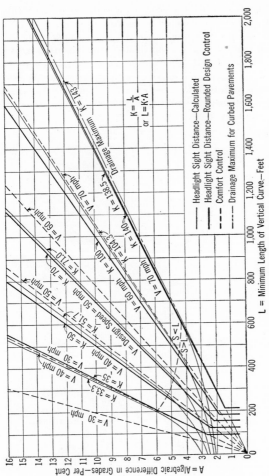

Fig. 8-28. Design controls for sag vertical curves.

formulas, in which values of S are the stopping distances in Table 8–1.

When a vehicle is traversing a sag vertical curve, centrifugal and gravitational force act in the same direction. As a result there is some discomfort when the speed is high. The effect is not easily evaluated, but limited attempts at its measurement have led to the general conclusion (*ASSHO Policy*) that riding on sag vertical curves is comfortable when the centripetal acceleration does not exceed 1 ft per sec². A mathematical approximation of this criterion can be derived with the aid of Fig. 8–29.

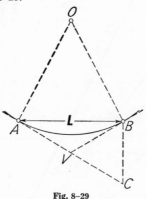

Fig. 8–29

Because of the small gradients used in practice, the curve AB may be taken as a circular arc and the distance VB as approximately $\frac{1}{2}L$. In the similar triangles AOB and CVB,

$$AB : OA = BC : VB \quad \text{or} \quad L : R = \frac{A\,L}{200} : \frac{L}{2} \text{ (approximately)}$$

Thus, $L = \dfrac{A\,R}{100}$. But $\dfrac{v^2}{R} = 1$ ft per sec². Substituting for R and converting v to V in mph gives

$$L = \frac{A\,V^2}{46.5} \tag{8–38}$$

Lengths of sag vertical curves satisfying this comfort factor are shown in Fig. 8–28 by the lines composed of short dashes.

The criterion for drainage is the same as on a crest vertical curve; *i.e.*, K should not exceed 143 feet for a change of 1 per cent in A. This criterion is plotted in Fig. 8–28 as the *drainage maximum*. It should be observed that the maximum length for drainage on a sag curve exceeds the minimum lengths set by the other criteria—a fortunate circumstance.

Several rule-of-thumb relationships have been used to insure that a sag curve will have satisfactory appearance. One of the simplest requires that L be at least 100 A. In Fig. 8–28 this corresponds to a design speed of 60 mph, based on headlight-beam distance.

Of the four criteria for the minimum length of a sag vertical curve, that based on headlight-beam distance appears to be the most logical. This is the conclusion in the *AASHO Policy*, in which the K-values have been rounded off for convenience in design, as represented by the heavy solid lines in Fig. 8–28.

8–24. Sight Distances at Interchanges.—Sight distances at interchanges should be at least as long as the stopping distances listed in Table 8–1. When a sag vertical curve occurs at an underpass, the overhead structure may shorten the sight distance otherwise obtainable. However, if the length of the sag curve conforms with that in Fig. 8–28, the structure does not shorten the sight distance below the minimum required for stopping. This is true even though the sight distance is measured from a height of eye of 6 feet (truck driver) to a height of object of 1.5 feet (tail light) and the vertical clearance is the recommended minimum of 14 feet. The practical relations (*AASHO Policy*) corresponding to these conditions are:

When $S < L$,
$$L = \frac{A\,S^2}{8,200} \tag{8–39}$$

When $S > L$,
$$L = 2\,S - \frac{8,200}{A} \tag{8–40}$$

In the case of dual highways it may be desirable to check the distance available for *passing* at an undercrossing without ramps. This can be done either by using the preceding formulas or by scaling from the profile.

Limited sight distance is more likely to occur where an interchange is located at a horizontal curve. Ordinarily, the lateral clearance to bridge rails at an overpass or to abutments at an underpass is not enough to permit use of maximum curvature for the design speed. The formulas for S_H in Art. 8–19 can be used in analyzing this situation.

DESIGN PRINCIPLES

Exact adherence to the specific controls outlined in the foregoing articles will not guarantee attainment of the best location. Experience, judgment, and the observance of recognized principles of good design are also necessary. When the geometric controls are applied, certain general principles should also be observed.

8–25. General Controls for Horizontal Alignment.—Important principles relating to horizontal alignment are as follows:

1. Alignment between the location control points (see Art. 9–3) should be as directional as possible. Long, flowing curves fitted to the topography are better than long tangents that slash through the terrain in an artificial manner.

2. Closely spaced short curves should be avoided. Such unsightly kinks as broken-back and reverse curves may be converted into more pleasing alignment in several ways. (See Arts. 7–14 and 7–15.)

3. Small changes in direction should not be accomplished by means of the sharpest curve permitted by the design speed. The maximum degree of curve should only be used with large central angles and at critical locations in general.

4. Curves, unless very flat, should be avoided on long, high embankments.

5. Consistent alignment design should be attained (see Art. 1–5). In case the topography requires a reduction in design speed, the change—reflected in reduced sight distances, increased curvature, and shorter distances between curves—should be made gradually over a distance of several miles. Moreover, there should be conspicuous warning signs to show that such a change is in progress.

6. Horizontal and vertical alignment should be studied together. Some general design controls for such study are outlined in Art. 8–27.

8–26. General Controls for Vertical Alignment.—When considering vertical alignment, some important principles are the following:

1. A smooth-flowing profile with long vertical curves is preferable to a profile with numerous breaks and short grades.

2. Care should be taken to avoid sag vertical curves on comparatively straight horizontal alignment. These produce "hidden dips" and are serious hazards, especially during passing maneuvers.

3. In general, long steep grades may be broken to the advantage of traffic by placing the steepest grade at the bottom of the ascent.

4. Steep grades should be reduced through important intersections at grade, in order to minimize hazards to turning traffic.

5. Unnatural and unsightly design should be avoided. Among these defects are crest vertical curves on embankments and sag vertical curves in cuts; broken-back vertical curves; and the presence of numerous minor undulations in grade line so located that they are visible to the driver.

6. On important highways carrying a large percentage of commercial traffic, economic studies of motor-truck performance relative to grades should accompany the office work of grade-line design. Some references [21,22,23] are included in the bibliography at the end of this chapter.

8–27. Combination of Horizontal and Vertical Alignment. Where there is a combination of horizontal and vertical curvature the following principles should be kept in mind.

1. It is not essential to separate horizontal and vertical curves; in general, the alignment is more natural and more pleasing in appearance if they are combined—subject to the limitations which follow in 2 and 3.

2. A change in horizontal alignment should preferably be made at a sag vertical curve where the change in direction is readily apparent to the driver. However, the horizontal curve should be flat, in order to avoid the distorted appearance caused by foreshortening.

3. If horizontal curvature at a crest vertical curve cannot be avoided, the change in direction should precede the change in profile.

4. Relatively small savings in cost of right-of-way or of grading should not be an excuse for the insertion of short sections of sub-standard design. On most locations in rural areas the cost of these relatively permanent elements of the highway is less than that of the pavement and other shorter-lived appurtenances. Therefore, it is unwise to reduce the built-in safety of some sections of a highway, and to invite almost certain early obsolescence, for the sole purpose of reducing the cost by a small percentage.

5. As noted in Art. 1–5, "the aim of good location should be the attainment of consistent conditions with a proper balance between curvature and grade." Balanced design, everywhere consistent with the chosen design speed, is the ideal to be constantly sought. Straight alignment obtained at the expense of long, steep grades, or excessive curvature inserted to follow the grade contour closely, are both poor designs. The best design is a compromise in which safety, economics, and aesthetics are sensibly blended.

8–28. Problems

1. Using the basic data of Art. 8–5, verify selected values of passing sight distance (assigned by the instructor) shown in Table 8–3 and Fig. 8–1.

2. A curve with a radius of 1,000 ft is superelevated at the rate of 1 in. per ft. (a) What value of the side friction factor f would be developed by a vehicle rounding the curve at 60 mph? Would the value be within the recommended safe limit for clean wet pavements? Would side skidding occur, or be imminent? (Justify your answers by specific references in Art. 8–8.) (b) If this curve were icy, giving an ultimate f of 0.05, at what minimum speed would the vehicle have to operate in order not to slide inward? *Answer:* 22 mph.

3. On the New York State Thruway the degree of the sharpest horizontal curve is 2°. (NOTE: In this problem use recommended values of f found in Table 8–4.) (a) At what rate would a 2° curve have to be superelevated to be safe for a speed

of 80 mph?   *Answer:* 0.039 ft per ft.   (*b*) On tangents the inner lane slopes toward the median at a rate of $\frac{3}{16}$ in. per ft. If this cross-section were continued around a 2° curve to the right, without rotating the pavement, for what maximum speeds would the two lanes be safe?   *Answers* (to nearest $\frac{1}{2}$ mph):   For inner lane, 75 mph; for outer lane adjacent to median, $67\frac{1}{2}$ mph.

4. Verify selected values of R and D shown in Table 8–5 and Fig. 8–9.

5. Verify selected values of f shown in Table 8–6.

6. For any selected value of V, verify the fact that the design superelevation rates in Table 8–7 and Fig. 8–10 lie on parabolic curves.

7. For any selected value of V, verify the several values of L_s listed in Table 8–8.

8. *Given:* a 10° spiraled curve; two 11-ft lanes, with 2 feet of widening as in Fig. 8–17.   On the center-line $L_s = 200$ ft. Compute the length of a true spiral on the inside edge. *Answer:* 257 ft.

9. *Given:* a 10° unspiraled curve; two 11-ft lanes, with 2 feet of widening as in Fig. 8–18.   Compute the length of a true spiral on the inside edge.   *Answer:* 164 ft. (Compare with Problem 8.)

10. *Given:* a 10° unspiraled curve; two 11-ft lanes, with 2 feet of widening as in Fig. 8–19.   Compute the lengths of separate inside-edge and outside-edge spirals, assuming the throw of the outer spiral to be 1 ft.   *Answers:*   Inside, 201 ft; outside, 118 ft.   (Compare with Problem 9.)

11. What horizontal sight distance would be provided on the curve in Problem 9 if the offset m to an obstruction were 20 ft?   *Answer:*   About 300 ft.

12. On an unspiraled curve with 500-ft radius and two 11-ft lanes, highways in Massachusetts are widened by the method in Fig. 8–22.   Standard values are as follows: $a = 90$ ft; $d = 25$ ft; $h = 2.22$ ft; $w = 3$ ft.   Compute the edge length of the transition to the widened section.   *Answer:* 114.4 ft.

13. *Given:* the same curve as in Problem 8, except that the widening is applied as in Fig. 8–15.   Compute the length of the inside-edge curve.   *Answer:* 197.85 ft.   (Compare with Problem 8.)

14. *Given:* a 15° spiraled curve; two 11-ft lanes, with 3 feet of widening as in Fig. 8–15; on the center-line $L_s = 250$ ft; total central angle $I = 62°17'$.   Compute the total number of square yards of pavement between the T.S. and the S.T. *Answer:* $1,761\frac{1}{2}$ sq yd.

15. Starting with equation A in Art. 8–22, verify the derivation of equation 8–33.

16. At a crest vertical curve the algebraic difference in grades is 6% and the design speed is 50 mph.   (*a*) What are the recommended minimum length of vertical curve and the actual sight distance which it provides?   *Answers:* $L = 480$ ft; $S = 341$ ft.   (*b*) Approximately what length of curve would be required to permit a design speed of 55 mph?   *Answer:* about 750 ft.

17. At a sag vertical curve the algebraic difference in grades is 6% and the design speed is 50 mph.   The design is based on headlight-beam distance: (*a*) What are the recommended minimum length of vertical curve and the actual sight distance which it provides?   *Answers:* $L = 420$ ft; $S = 346$ ft.   (*b*) Approximately what length of curve would be required to permit a design speed of 55 mph?   *Answer:* about 550 ft.

18. Suppose that the sag vertical curve in Problem 17 (*a*) occurs at an underpass.   Assuming heights and clearance as in Art. 8–24, what sight distance is provided?   *Answer:* 893 ft.

BIBLIOGRAPHY

1. Noble, C.M., "Engineering Design of Superhighways," *Proceedings, American Road Builders' Association*, 1941, pp. 183-217.

2. "A Policy on Geometric Design of Rural Highways," *American Association of State Highway Officials*, 1954.

3. Prisk, C.W., "Passing Practices on Rural Highways," *Proceedings, Highway Research Board*, 1941, pp. 366-378.

4. Leeming, J.J., "Road Curvature and Superelevation," *Road Paper No. 7*, Inst. C.E., Oct., 1942.

5. Stonex, K.A., "Car Control Factors and Their Measurement," *S.A.E. Journal*, March, 1941.

6. Fox, M.L., "Relations Between Curvature and Speed," *Proceedings, Highway Research Board*, 1937, pp. 202-211.

7. Stonex, K.A., and Noble, C.M., "Curve Design and Tests on the Pennsylvania Turnpike," *Proceedings, Highway Research Board*, 1940, pp. 429-451.

8. Moyer, R.A., *Bulletin 120*, Iowa Engineering Experiment Station, 1934.

9. Moyer, R.A., and Berry, D.S., "Marking Highway Curves with Safe Speed Indications," *Proceedings, Highway Research Board*, 1940, pp. 399-428.

10. Barnett, J., "Safe Side Friction Factors and Super-elevation Design," *Proceedings, Highway Research Board*, 1936, pp. 69-76.

11. Shortt, W.H., "A Practical Method for the Improvement of Existing Railway-Curves," *Proceedings*, Inst. C.E., Vol. 176, 1909, pp. 97 ff.

12. Royal-Dawson, F.G., *Elements of Curve Design*, E.& F.N. Spon, Ltd., London, 1932.

13. Smirnoff, M.V., "Analytical Method of Determining the Length of Transition Spiral," *Transactions, ASCE*, Vol. 116, 1951, pp. 155-185.

14. Haile, E.R., Discussion on "The Modern Express Highway," *Transactions, ASCE*, Vol. 102, 1937, pp. 1091-1099.

15. Leeming, J.J., and Black, A.N., "Road Curvature and Superelevation: Experiments on Comfort and Driving Practice," *Journal, Inst. Municipal and County Engineers*, Vol. LXXI, No. 5, Dec., 1944, pp. 137 ff.

16. Leeming, J.J., "The General Principles of Highway Transition Curve Design," *Transactions, ASCE*, Vol. 113, 1948, pp. 868-896.

17. Warren, H.A., and Hazeldine, E.R., "Experimental Transition Curves," *Journal, Inst. Municipal and County Engineers*, Vol. LXV, No. 21, March, 1939, pp. 1012 ff.

18. Welty, W.R., "A Method for Studying the Paths of Motor Vehicles on Curves," Bureau of Highway Traffic, Yale University, New Haven, Conn., 1947.

19. Bruce, A.G., and Brown, R.D., "The Trend of Highway Design," *Public Roads*, Vol. 8, No. 1, March, 1927, p. 8.

20. "A Policy on Sight Distance for Highways," *American Association of State Highway Officials*, 1940.

21. Saal, C.C., "Hill Climbing Ability of Motor Trucks," *Public Roads*, Vol. 23, No. 3, May, 1942, pp. 33-54.

22. Taragin, A., "Effect of Length of Grade on Speed of Motor Vehicles," *Proceedings, Highway Research Board*, 1945, pp. 342-353.

23. "Time and Gasoline Consumption in Motor Truck Operation," *Research Report No. 9-A, Highway Research Board*, 1950.

CHAPTER 9

RAILROAD SURVEYS

9–1. Foreword.—The purpose of this chapter is to present a few examples of curve and earthwork theory and surveying procedures applied to the field of railway surveying. More detailed descriptions of some of the subjects, particularly track layout and maintenance (turnouts, connecting tracks, string lining, etc.), will be found in railway surveying handbooks, notably *Railroad Curves and Earthwork*, by Allen, or *Field Engineering*, by Searles, Ives, and Kissam.

It is essential that Chapter 1 be restudied in connection with the following description of survey methods and paper-location procedure. Otherwise, much of the material in that chapter—consisting of basic considerations more important than the technical details to be presented—would have to be repeated.

Fig. 9–1 shows an example of railroad location in the Rocky Mountains near Blacktail, Montana. The pictured alignment includes a simple 8° curve with a total central angle of 152°40′ and a total length, including two 180-foot spirals, of 2,088 feet. On the adjoining tangents the grade is 1.80%; on the curve it is compensated 0.04% per degree, and the actual grade is 1.48%. Shown is a 106-car freight train powered by a 5,400-horsepower diesel locomotive at the head and a 4,050-horsepower helper at the rear.

9–2. Reconnaissance.—Typically, the conception of a project is followed first by a careful study of the best available maps and then by field reconnaissance of the terrain between the proposed termini. In the early years of railroad expansion in the United States, it was often necessary to reconnoiter relatively unexplored regions without the aid of maps. Directions were determined by pocket compass; elevations, by barometer; slopes, by clinometer; and distances, by pedometer or by timing the gait of saddle horses. Though such devices are still useful at times, they have been made nearly obsolete by the growing file of good maps and by improvements in

(Courtesy Great Northern Railway)

Fig. 9–1

the science of photogrammetry. In fact, it is becoming increasingly apparent that, except for minor projects, aerial-surveying methods may almost entirely supplant the older methods of field reconnaissance, and perhaps of the preliminary survey as well. Several particularly valuable types of information that may be obtained more readily from aerial photographs than from former ground methods are noted in Chapter 12.

9–3. Location Controls.—The proposed railway must pass through or near certain controlling points. Some of the primary controls will have been fixed in the conception of the project; others, including most of the secondary ones, will be revealed by office studies of the maps and by whatever field reconnaissance is needed to verify questionable points. Typical location controls include:

Primary Controls

> The termini.
>
> Important intermediate traffic centers.
>
> Unique mountain passes, tunnel sites, or major stream crossings.

Secondary Controls

> Minor intermediate markets or production centers.
>
> Water courses.
>
> Crossings of existing railroads or important highways.
>
> Swampy areas.
>
> Areas subject to snow or rock slides.
>
> Areas involving costly land damages.
>
> Topography in general, as it affects the economical attainment of desirable grades and curvature.

9–4. Organizing the Field Work.—Prior to starting extensive field work, the locating engineer preferably should make a field examination of the general route recommended in the reconnaissance report. Before going into the field, he must become acquainted with the general objectives of the project. Moreover, he should be informed as to how much information he may divulge to curious property owners along the route.

A great variety of useful purposes may be accomplished in this preliminary field examination. Among these are:

Arrangements for temporary office quarters, and for housing and boarding the men.

Hiring of local help for axemen or other positions.

Permission to trespass on private property for survey purposes, with whatever qualifications are imposed by the owner.

Identification of convenient bench marks described in Federal or State publications.

Determination of best access to the work by automobile or other means of transportation.

Making of special notes regarding secondary controls.

Taken together, the information acquired should enable the locating engineer to select the needed field and office personnel and to determine the most efficient methods of performing the various surveying operations.

9–5. Stadia Traverse.—In remote regions that are inadequately mapped and on projects for which aerial-surveying methods are not justified, the reconnaissance may not definitely disclose the best general route. In such cases it is wise to run a stadia traverse along each of the possible locations.

Needed measurements are made as rapidly as possible, consistent with the required accuracy. Transit stations are far apart. Single deflection angles need be read no closer than the nearest 10 minutes, though it is advisable to check the resulting bearings by compass in order to guard against blunders. A few intermediate shots along the traverse line may be needed to give data for plotting a profile of the traverse. Only enough side shots (supplemented by sketches) need be taken to give the approximate positions and elevations of the secondary controls.

Especially good judgment is needed in conducting this type of stadia survey; if the survey is intrusted to inexperienced personnel, it usually reverts to an unnecessarily detailed and time-consuming topographical survey.

The resulting maps, plotted by protractor and scale, really serve as high-grade reconnaissance; if the work is well done, they permit the definite discard of certain routes and go far toward fixing closely the best general route to be followed in the more precise preliminary surveys.

9–6. Transit-and-Tape Traverse.—Whenever the reconnaissance narrows the location down to a fairly definite route, it is good practice to run a careful transit-and-tape traverse, called the "base line" or "P-line," joining the various location controls. This traverse then serves not only as an accurate framework for plotting the topographic details but also as a convenient means of transferring the paper location to the ground and checking its accuracy.

The P-line is a continuous deflection-angle traverse located as close as convenient to the expected position of the final location. Transit stations are marked by substantial tacked hubs, which are driven flush, carefully referenced, and identified by guard stakes. Deflection angles are at least doubled, the telescope being reversed on the second angle in order to eliminate instrumental errors. To guard against blunders in reading angles the magnetic bearing of the forward line should be compared with the calculated bearing before leaving any transit station. If the survey is a long one, a traverse bearing should be checked independently every 10 miles or so by means of a sun or star observation for azimuth.

Horizontal distances are measured with a 100-foot (or longer) steel tape, usually being recorded to the nearest tenth of a foot, but sometimes to hundredths. Station stakes are set at regular 100-ft stations, at intermediate plus points where profile breaks occur, and, possibly, at fence lines and highways crossing the center line. It is not necessary to center all station stakes, since they serve only for profile leveling and cross-sectioning. The method described in Art. 2–11 is invariably close enough for the purpose. However, chaining from pin to pin, not from stake to stake, is always advisable.

9–7. Levels.—If the survey is over terrain permitting the transit party to make rapid progress, it is often worth while to start two two-man level parties at the time at which the transit party begins its work. One, the *bench level party*, carries the elevations from the nearest bench mark and sets additional bench marks every 1,000 feet or so along the general route. It is not necessary for this party to follow the exact path taken by the transit party; swampy areas and steep slopes, for example, should be by-passed wherever possible. In fact, the best plan is for the bench level party to work ahead of the transit party along a general route specified by the locating engineer. This party can then close its levels back to the starting point each half-day without falling behind the transit party.

The second level party, the *profile level party*, takes its initial backsight on a bench mark established near station P 0+00 by the bench level party. It follows immediately behind the transit party, taking rod readings to tenths of a foot on the ground at every station stake and intermediate plus point. Elevations are carried along through turning points on which readings are made to hundredths. In proceeding along the line, a check is made on bench marks previously set by the bench level party. Thus, there is no need for the profile level party to close its levels back; the party is always close to the transit party, where the locating engineer frequently needs the information on elevations in planning the position of forward transit stations.

In following the dual leveling-party scheme, it is advisable to alternate rodmen every half-day; this practice reduces delays to the profile leveling party in searching for bench marks established by the bench level party.

Bench-mark elevations should be adjusted as required by the closing errors. Closures of bench levels should be less than $0.05\sqrt{M}$, where M is the distance between bench marks in miles. Another criterion sometimes used is $0.01\sqrt{S}$, where S is the total number of set-ups in a closed circuit between bench marks.

Bench-mark elevations as determined by the profile level party should be compared with their adjusted values each day. The adjusted elevations should be noted in the field book and used on all subsequent work.

9–8. Topography by Stadia.—The method to be used for taking topography depends on the character of the terrain, the scale of the map, and the selected contour interval. A scale of 1 in. = 400 ft, with 10-ft contours, is about the smallest useful combination. A better general combination is 1 in. = 200 ft, with 5-ft contours; a scale of 1 in. = 100 ft, with 5-ft contours, is also popular.

Under some circumstances the stadia method of taking topography is the most efficient one. This may be the case in open regions permitting unobscured sights, especially if a wide strip of topography is required. In this method, no station stakes are set between traverse stations, and profile leveling is unnecessary. All field work (except bench leveling) is done by one large party. It is good practice to have a separate computer and field draftsman in the party, in order that the notes may be reduced and plotted as the field work progresses. This method requires skilled personnel and careful supervision by the locating engineer.

9-9. Topography by Hand Level.—Wherever a narrow strip of accurate topography is required through a region covered with brush or timber, the "standard" railway-surveying method of taking topography with hand level, rod, and tape is almost essential. In this method the topography party is supplied with the ground elevation at each station stake, as determined by the profile leveling. The locations of contours on lines at right angles to the survey center-line are then determined by the following method:

A perpendicular to the traverse is first established at each station either by estimation or with the aid of a pocket compass, an optical square, or a cross staff. In timber or brush the transverse lines are kept reasonably straight by ranging through with three flags or range poles.

The location of the first regular contour on a transverse line is determined by hand leveling from the known ground elevation at the station stake. A forked stick cut for a 5-ft height of eye is a convenient support for the hand level. To illustrate the process, assume that the center-line ground elevation is 673.2 and that the locations of 5-ft contours are required along rising ground to one side of the center line. The levelman, resting the hand level in the fork of the 5-ft stick, directs the rodman out until the hand level reads 3.2 on the rod. This reading locates the 675-ft contour, the distance to which, say 36 ft, is measured with a metallic tape. If notes are kept (somewhat similar to cross-section leveling, Art. 6–7), the entry is recorded as $\frac{6.7.5}{3.6}$. The levelman then continues out past the rodman until he reads 10.0 on the rod, and the distance beyond the previous point, say 42 ft, is measured. The corresponding entry would be $\frac{6.8.0}{7.8}$. If the distances between contours are too great for hand-level readings, intermediate readings are taken at shorter distances by the same step-by-step process until the desired contour is reached.

The hand-level method is surprisingly accurate. With a little experience, levels may be carried 400 ft from the center line and checked back with an error of less than 0.5 ft. Since each new cross line starts with a correct center-line elevation, there is no cumulative error.

In wooded terrain the speed in taking topography is greater by hand leveling than by any other method giving comparable accuracy. Only a thin gap need be cut through brush. Trees never need be cut, for the tape and sight line may be offset around them by eye without introducing serious error, the scale of the map being considered.

In addition to locating contours, the topography party locates all buildings, property lines, highways, streams, rock outcrops, and other physical features likely to affect the location of the railroad.

Though some engineers prefer to record notes of contour locations (supplemented by sketches in the field book), a method which is usually more accurate and much faster is to plot the topography in the field at once on special field sheets. These are usually strips of cross-section drawing paper mounted on a topographer's sketch board about $12'' \times 18''$ in size. The sheets are prepared in advance by drawing the survey center-line straight and continuous through traverse stations, provided the angles are small (possibly less than 5°). Where the deflection angles are larger, distortion of the plotted topography is reduced by repeating the traverse station after leaving a 1-inch gap in the center line. A still better method —one that eliminates all distortion at large horizontal angles— is to cut adjoining sheets on the proper bevel through the plotted position of the transit station and mount them on the sketch board so that the center line is an exact reproduction of the traverse line. The lines on the cross-section paper are thus parallel and perpendicular to the center line, thereby being more convenient for plotting in the field. The final step in preparing the field sheets is to record the stations and elevations along one edge.

The particular advantage of the preceding method, aside from eliminating voluminous notes, is that contours and all other topographic details are plotted immediately in the field, where the faithfulness of the reproduction is readily apparent. Moreover, field plotting to the scale that is to be used on the subsequent map gives the topographer a clear idea of the degree of precision needed in the field work. He is better able to decide whether cross lines at some stations might logically be omitted, and whether contours along additional lines (such as on lines parallel to the center line or on ridge lines and valley lines making an angle with the center line) are necessary in order to complete the topography of difficult sections.

9–10. Plotting the Preliminary Map.—If the map is to serve most efficiently for paper-location purposes, the control traverse should be plotted by coordinates. The survey should be tied, if convenient, to a State-plane-coordinate system or to some other official system having coordinated monuments; otherwise, an origin of coordinates may be assumed arbitrarily.

Stadia topography is plotted in the usual manner by protractor angles and distances scaled from the plotted transit stations.

Hand-level topography taken on special field sheets may be transferred to the map by scale or dividers. However, this is a time-consuming method. When the field sheets are to the scale of the preliminary map—a relation strongly recommended—a much better way is to fit each section of field sheet to the corresponding traverse line and to transfer the plotted topography to the map directly through thin carbon paper, using a well-sharpened, very hard pencil or a slightly-rounded stylus. This process is rapid, inexpensive, and accurate; it results in the exact reproduction of the field sheets, free from the possibility of drafting-room errors.

9–11. Paper-Location Procedure.—The preliminary surveys and subsequent office work result in a topographic map
of a strip of territory, varying possibly from 400 to 1,000 feet
in width, in which the ultimate location is expected to lie.

Finding a satisfactory location having suitable curves
and grades is not usually a difficult task; it is largely a technical
process involving patience and quite a bit of routine scaling
and calculation. But finding the *best* location requires some-
thing more than drafting-room technique. As stated in
Art. 1–5, "To produce a harmonious balance between curvature and grade, and to do it economically, requires that the
engineer possess broad experience, mature judgment, and a
thorough knowledge of the objectives of the project."

It is obviously impossible to write a set of rules which, if
followed, will inevitably produce the best location. The set
which follows is merely a suggested office procedure that will
be principally of value to the novice; the intangible ingredients,
skill and judgment, grow with the locator's experience.

(NOTE: In the technique to be described, splines may be
substituted for thread and curve templates.)

1. Using the preliminary map, set small pins at the termini
   and also near the intermediate controls. Stretch a fine
   thread around the pins.

2. Examine the terrain along the thread line, and set additional pins (angle points) where they apparently are
   needed between location controls.

3. Scale the elevations at the pins and the distances between
   them, thus giving the approximate grades.

4. Place transparent circular-curve templates tangent to
   the thread, allowing enough room between curves for
   subsequent insertion of spirals. Shift pins and change
   templates until a trial alignment is obtained which fits
   the alignment specifications and appears to be reasonable
   in so far as gradients and probable earthwork quantities
   are concerned. It may be helpful to use the grade contour as a guide (see Art. 11-5).

5. Pencil the trial alignment lightly but precisely, and
   station it continuously along the tangents and curves
   by stepping around it with dividers.

6. Plot the ground profile of the trial alignment to an exaggerated vertical scale.

7. Using pins and thread, establish a tentative grade line on the profile which fits the specifications for grades and appears to produce a reasonable balance of earthwork. The circular-curve templates may be used for vertical curves. In estimating earthwork balance from center cuts and fills, make approximate allowance for the fact that the graded roadbed is wider in cuts than on fills and that a certain percentage will be added to the fill quantities for shrinkage (see Art. 6–14).

8. Examine the trial alignment and grade line together. Go over the alignment station by station, visualizing the finished roadbed if built as indicated. The need for drainage structures and the probable maintenance difficulties dealing with drainage, slides, and snow drifting should be examined. Then make whatever changes will obviously improve operating and maintenance characteristics without changing earthwork quantities appreciably.

9. Make an earthwork estimate, using the following column headings:

Station	Center Height	Cubic Yards	
		Cut	Fill+*%

(*Insert suitable shrinkage factor—possibly from 10 to 15% for purposes of estimate)

In the station column, enter in proper order each 100-ft station, the station and plus of each high or low point, and the station and plus of each grade point. Scale center heights from the profile at positions midway between the points entered in the station column; designate the values C or F. Take earthwork quantities from the proper table of *level sections* (Table XVII, Part III). Do not forget to reduce tabulated quantities for fractional distances or to add the shrinkage percentage to the fill quantities.

10. Enter the sub-totals for each increment of cut and fill. If conditions appear to warrant striving for an approximate balance of quantities along certain grading sec-

tions, see how close the balance comes. Observe also the relative sizes of adjoining cuts and fills and the approximate distances between their centers of gravity. For convenience, note these numerical values on the profile.

11. Re-examine the tentative alignment and grade line in the light of the numerical values obtained in the first earthwork estimate. Make any minor changes in the alignment or the grade line, or both, which will reduce the pay quantities and improve the balance and distribution of earthwork. Do not erase the first trial; merely use a different style of line for the revised portions. Scale new center heights along the revised portions and determine the new quantities. Preserve all discarded tabulations, but identify them and mark them "void."

12. Repeat step 11 until the location appears to be the best one possible.

The paper location finally established by the foregoing process should not be accepted rigidly as final; the remarks contained in Arts. 1–11 and 1–12 are pertinent in this respect. Though the earthwork estimate is based upon level sections, the errors introduced by transverse slopes tend to cancel. In a long line, level-section quantities will usually be within 5 per cent of the true values found later by cross-sectioning.

9–12. The Location Survey.—The principal purpose of the location survey is to transfer the paper location, called the "L-line," to the ground. This may be done quite accurately if the preliminary map is based upon a transit-tape traverse plotted by coordinates.

The first step is to scale the coordinates of the P.I.'s of the L-line and from them to compute the bearings of the tangents and the distances between P.I.'s. If the map is carefully drawn to a scale of 1 in. = 100 ft, these computed bearings and lengths are usually reliable to the nearest minute and foot. The bearings and lengths are useful not only in making ties to the P-line but also in checking the location field work.

The L-line should never be run by turning the calculated angles and measuring the calculated distances continuously from beginning to end. Instead, each L-line tangent should be tied independently to the P-line and run to a string intersection with the adjacent L-line tangent, at which point the exact central angle of the curve is then measured.

An excellent tie exists wherever an L-line tangent crosses the P-line. The P-line stationing of the crossing can be scaled close enough for the purpose if the angle of intersection is large; otherwise, it may be computed by coordinates. A hub at the intersection is then located by sighting and measuring from the most convenient P-line hub, after which the L-line tangent is projected in both directions by setting up at the intersection hub and turning off the calculated angle.

L-line tangents may sometimes be tied to the P-line by right-angle offsets. Another method is to produce a P-line course for a scaled or calculated distance to an intersection with the L-line. Considerable ingenuity and field experience are needed in establishing ties rapidly and accurately.

Great care should be taken to insure the straightness of the L-line tangents. The lines should always be produced forward through P.O.T.'s by double centering. Obstacles on the tangents may be by-passed by the method described in Art. 9–13.

After the P.I.'s have been located and the central angles have been measured, the curves and spirals are run in as described in Part I. Stationing is continuous along the tangents and curves. Some minor adjustments in alignment are usually made during or following the staking of the curves (see Art. 1–12). These adjustments may involve some of the special curve problems described in Chapter 7.

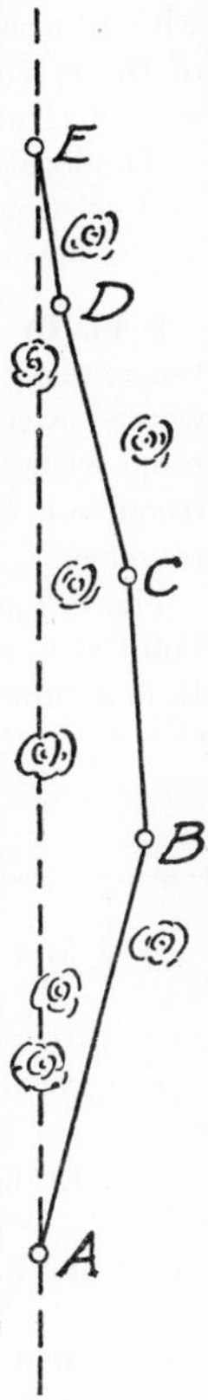

It is a good plan to run profile levels over the staked L-line in order to compare the actual ground profile with the paper-location ground profile. The degree of "fit" is a measure of the accuracy of the topography.

Fig. 9–2

If it is suspected that the earthwork estimate may be in error, owing possibly to the prevalence of side-hill sections, the line may be cross-sectioned by the slope-staking method described in Art. 6–7. The more accurate earthwork quantities may then justify some slight revisions in the grade line without necessarily changing the alignment. Further analysis of the earthwork distribution may be made by means of a mass diagram (see Art. 6–19).

The location survey also includes ties to property lines and existing improvements, as well as a variety of measurements needed for the design of miscellaneous structures.

9–13. By-Passing Obstacles on Tangents.—Where location tangents (or other straight survey lines) are produced through woods, large trees often obstruct the line. To avoid felling them without authorization, and also to save time, the best recourse is to by-pass them by a small-angle deflection-angle traverse.

Fig. 9–2 and the accompanying notes illustrate the process. Point A is a transit station (P.O.T.) on the location tangent. It is assumed that large trees obstruct the line beyond A. Consequently, a small deflection angle is turned to the right

Notes for Fig. 9–2

Sta.	Defl.	Angle with Tangent	Dist.	Products		Offset from Tangent
				Angle × Dist.	Alg. Sum	
A	35′ R					zero
		35′ R	640	+22,400		
B	42′ L				+22,400	6.5 R
		7′ L	400	−2,800		
C	30′ L				+19,600	5.7 R
		37′ L	420	−15,540		
D	20′ R				+4,060	1.2 R
		17′ L	238.82	−4,060		
E	17′ R				zero	zero
		zero				
Tang.						

and a hub B is set at any convenient distance. At B it does not prove possible to get back on the tangent; therefore, the auxiliary traverse is continued through convenient openings between the trees until point D is reached, after which the tangent is resumed at E.

It is convenient to adopt a systematic form of notes which will indicate the distance from the tangent as well as the measurements needed to get back on line. In the form suggested, for example, the algebraic sum of the products of distances and angles in minutes must be zero up to a point on the tangent. Moreover, since the reciprocal of the sine of 1 minute is 3,440, the offset at any point is found by dividing the proper algebraic sum by that constant. The sign of any product is determined by the angle that the course makes with the tangent. An angle to the right gives a plus product; one to the left, minus.

In the example given, it is assumed that a deflection angle of 20′ R at D is a convenient direction toward the tangent. The required distance to a P.O.T. at E is, therefore, $4,060 \div 17$ $=238.82$ ft. At E the deflection required to place the line of sight on the correct tangent produced is obviously 17′ R.

If the angle between any auxiliary course and the tangent is kept below 1 or 2 degrees, a negligible error results from assuming that the length along the auxiliary traverse is the same as the distance along the tangent. In the foregoing example the true tangent distance between A and E is only 0.06 ft shorter than the traverse distance of 1,698.82 ft. This small correction is found quickly by slide rule, if required, by summing the products of the distances and the versines of the angles with the tangent.

It is not usual to move station stakes back on the correct tangent. However, if required, it may be done by eye with the aid of the offsets in the last column of the notes.

9–14. Construction Surveys.—It is not considered necessary in a book of this kind to give detailed examples of the great variety of measurements required on railroad construction. These are best covered by reference to instructions and forms supplied by railroads to their resident engineers. Briefly, the principal survey work related to new construction includes the following operations:

1. Re-Establishing the Final Location

Checking and referencing key points, such as P.I.'s, T.S.'s, S.T.'s, and occasional intermediate points on long tangents, so that they are quickly available during construction.

Resetting enough station stakes on curves to control clearing of the right-of-way.

Checking the bench-mark elevations and setting convenient new bench marks in locations in which they are not likely to be disturbed during construction.

2. Setting Construction Stakes

Cross-sectioning the line after clearing (and just ahead of grading operations), together with setting slope stakes wherever needed.

Line and grade stakes (and in some cases, batter boards) for appurtenant structures, such as buildings, bridge piers, culverts, and trestles.

Finishing stakes for completing cuts and fills to exact grade; center stakes for track laying; grade stakes for ballast and final rail profile.

Stakes for borrow pits; also cross-sectioning borrow pits after stripping.
Stakes for right-of-way fences.

3. Making Periodic Quantity Measurements

Measurements, calculations, and estimates of work done to serve as basis of monthly payments to contractor, as well as for progress reports to headquarters.

4. Final Measurements

Final cross-sections for calculation of total grading pay quantities.
"As-built" measurements of all work to serve as basis for final payment, as well as for preparation of "record" plans.
Monumenting curve points.

5. *Property Surveys*

Making all measurements needed for preparing legal descriptions of easements and of land acquired by purchase or through condemnation proceedings.

Setting right-of-way monuments.

9–15. Superelevation.—Fundamentally, superelevation theory is the same on railways as on highways. Fig. 8–2 and the equations developed in Art. 8–6 are valid for both types of operation.

The equilibrium formula for superelevation of railroad track* is

$$E = 0.00066 \; DS_E^2 \qquad (9\text{–}1)$$

in which E is the superelevation, in inches, of the outer rail at the gage line, and S_E is the equilibrium speed in mph. This relation corresponds to equation 8–8, and is found by substituting $\dfrac{E}{56.5}$ for e (the "standard" gage of track is 56.5 inches).

The following quotations are also taken from the A.R.E.A. Manual:

"If it were possible to operate all classes of traffic at the same speed around a curve, the ideal condition of smooth riding and minimum rail wear could be obtained by elevating for equilibrium. However, a section of curve track must usually handle several classes of traffic operating at different speeds. A slow train passing over a curve that is elevated for a much higher speed tends to throw the track out of surface and to cause excessive wear on the inside rail.

"Safety and comfort limit the speed at which a passenger train may negotiate a curve. Any speed that gives comfortable riding on a curve is well within the limits of safety. Experience has shown that the usual passenger coach, pullman car or light-weight equipment will ride comfortably around a curve at a speed which would require an elevation about three inches higher for equilibrium. As far as speed traffic is concerned, it may therefore be said that passenger comfort governs train speed on curves and that trains may be operated over curves at speeds somewhat greater than equilibrium speed. Advantage is taken of this condition in operating high-speed trains on track that must also carry slower traffic.

"Since the elevation required is a function of the train speed, this speed is the first element to be determined.

---

*1947 *Manual*, American Railway Engineering Association.

TABLE 9-1

ELEVATIONS AND SPEEDS FOR CURVES

Se = Speed at equilibrium elevation, in miles per hour.
Sp = Speed at 3" unbalanced elevation, in miles per hour.

Curves		1/4"	1/2"	3/4"	1"	1 1/4"	1 1/2"	1 3/4"	2"	2 1/4"	2 1/2"	2 3/4"	3"	3 1/4"	3 1/2"	3 3/4"	4"	4 1/4"	4 1/2"	4 3/4"	5"	5 1/4"	5 1/2"	5 3/4"	6"	6 1/4"	6 1/2"	6 3/4"	7"	Curves
0°30'	Se	30	40	50	55	60	65	70	75	80	85	90	95	100	105	110														Se
	Sp	100	110																						95				100	Sp
1°00'	Se	20			45					60	65		70		75		80	85			110				95					Se
	Sp	70	85		80					90			100		105		105				70									Sp
1°30'	Se				40	35					50										90		75		95	80			100	Se
	Sp	55			85	65		75			70		80				65	85			70				95	85				Sp
2°00'	Se		20			30					40		50			80							65		60	70				Se
	Sp					65							45		70		55				60		80			85				Sp
2°30'	Se				30						35			40		70		50			55				60					Se
	Sp	50			60			55						45		45						70			55					Sp
3°00'	Se								35				40						60		50						70			Se
	Sp	45						55			35							55	45											Sp
3°30'	Se						25					30						40			45			60						Se
	Sp				50			45							50															Sp
4°00'	Se					20					30					35			55											Se
	Sp	40			40								55		60				50						60				55	Sp
4°30'	Se										30									45										Se
	Sp	35			35				25				45					50			40	50			55					Sp
5°00'	Se						20								30				35							50				Se
	Sp						35											45	45			40			55				55	Sp
5°30'	Se							20			25																			Se
	Sp						35									35					40				50					Sp
6°00'	Se																30													Se
	Sp								25				30				40								40				50	Sp
7°00'	Se											20							30					35						Se
	Sp						35	20					40													45				Sp
8°00'	Se							20										35		30										Se
	Sp			30									25				25	25								35				Sp
9°00'	Se						25			20																	40			Se
	Sp																								30					Sp
10°00'	Se					25															35									Se
	Sp	20									20												35							Sp
11°00'	Se						25																		35		30			Se
	Sp												30																	Sp
12°00'	Se								25												25								35	Se
	Sp	20																												Sp

248

"Ordinarily an elevation of 6 inches should not be exceeded for a track carrying both fast and slow traffic; and an elevation of 7 inches where one class of traffic is carried exclusively.

"The inner rail should preferably be maintained at grade."

Using these recommendations, the A.R.E.A. formula for superelevation based on permissible speed becomes:

$$E = 0.00066 \ DS_P^2 - 3 \qquad (9\text{--}2)$$

Equation 9–2 is analogous to 8–11.

Table 9–1 gives the speeds in mph for equilibrium and for 3 inches of unbalanced superelevation. The 5-mph increments represent general practice for use on speed-limit signs.

9–16. Spirals.—In contrast to the situation with regard to the use of spirals on highways (Art. 8–13), spirals have been used on railroad track since about 1880. (A concise history of the use of spirals is given in *Proceedings, A.R.E.A.,* Vol. 40, 1939, pp. 172–174.)

As a result of long years of experience in operating over spiraled superelevated curves, American railroads almost invariably base minimum spiral length upon the rate of rotational change. For many years it has been the recommendation of the A.R.E.A. that spiral length be based upon attaining superelevation across standard-gage track at a desirable maximum rate of 1.25 inches per second when trains are operated at maximum speed.

In a committee report* on "Spirals Required for High Speed Operation," it was found that some American railroads operating high-speed passenger trains used values higher than 1.25 inches per second, and other railroads used lower values. However, this value was substantially verified by modern practice, and it was concluded that there should be no change in the recommendation. (This report also contains an interesting tabulation of spiral practice on European high-speed lines.)

Based upon attaining superelevation at a rate of 1.25 inches per second, the equation for desirable minimum spiral length is

$$L_s = 1.17 \ ES_P \quad (\text{or } L_s = \tfrac{88}{75} \ ES_P) \qquad (9\text{--}3)$$

_____

*Proceedings, *A.R.E.A.,* Vol. 39, 1938, pp. 497–507.

This equation is the same as 8–19, except for slightly different notation.

As in the case of highways, the superelevation is run out uniformly over the spiral. The slight vertical curves in the outer rail at the beginning and end of the spiral are taken care of automatically by the flexibility of the rail.

Track spirals are staked either by deflection angles or by offsets. The basic theory is fully covered in Chapter 5. Art. 5–14 contains practical suggestions for applying the offset methods.

9–17. String Lining.—In spite of ballast and rail braces, tracks on curves tend to creep slowly out of line. This creeping is due principally to the unbalanced lateral forces caused by operation at other than equilibrium speed. Other contributing factors are rapid deceleration during emergency stops and, possibly, temperature expansion and contraction. Track once irregularly out of line becomes progressively worse, owing to the variable impact produced by moving trains.

The trend toward higher train speeds in both freight and passenger operation makes it more important than ever to maintain curved track continuously in good alignment. This can be done either by the deflection-angle method or by *string lining*. The latter method has so many obvious advantages that it is rapidly superseding the former method.

Briefly, string lining consists in shifting the track in or out along the circular curve until equal middle ordinates are obtained at equal chords. Theoretically, the chord used may be of any length; but to obtain good control on main-line track it should be between 50 and 80 feet. Many engineers use a 62-ft chord. This is the value recommended by the A.R.E.A.; it is a convenient length, and also produces the useful relation that the degree of curve is numerically equal to the middle ordinate in inches (see equation 2–31).

Equipment consists simply of a tape, a strong fish line or a fine wire, and a scale for measuring the middle ordinates. Some engineers use wooden or metal templates which are held against the rail head; the string passes through holes or slots a fixed distance from the rail. With such devices, it is necessary to deduct the fixed distance from the measured middle ordinates, or to use a special scale with an offset zero point.

The procedure involves (1) preliminary field work, (2) calculation, and (3) track shifting in accordance with the approved calculations.

Preliminary field work

1. Locate the T.C. by sighting along the gage side of the outer rail. Make a keel mark on the inside of the rail head at this point and mark it sta. 0 on the web.

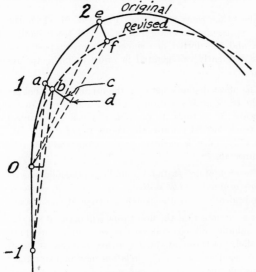

Fig. 9–3

2. Mark sta. −1 similarly, 31 feet back from sta. 0 on the tangent. Then mark stations, 1, 2, 3, etc. at 31-ft intervals along the outer rail until the last station is beyond the end of the curve.

3. Stretch the line taut between the keel marks at stations −1 and 1. Measure and record the middle ordinate at sta. 0. In similar manner, stretch the cord between

stations 0 and 2 and measure the middle ordinate at sta. 1. Continue this process until the middle ordinates become zero.

Calculation is based upon four simple rules. The first comes from the fact that the middle ordinate m is proportional to D. Since $D = \dfrac{100 \, I}{L}$, it follows that $\Sigma m \propto I$. This relation may be expressed by the following rule:

> **Rule 1.** *For any chord length the sum of the middle ordinates on a curve between given tangents is constant.*

The other rules come from Fig. 9–3, in which the solid line represents the outer rail of curved track badly out of line, and the dotted line shows the correct position. (The scale is greatly exaggerated in order to make the relations clear.)

The offset distance between the original and final positions of the track at any station is called the *throw*. Track moved outward in revising its position is given a positive throw; for track moved inward, the throw is negative. Thus, the throw at sta. 1 is negative and is numerically equal to the distance *ab*.

The *error* at any station is found from the following relation: *error = original middle ordinate minus revised middle ordinate* (algebraically). In the sketch the error at sta. 1 is $ac - bd$.

It is obvious that the first throw will occur at sta. 1. Since the middle ordinates at successive stations are practically parallel, the throw at sta. 1 is twice the error at sta. 0; both have negative signs. This relation may be expressed by the following rule:

> **Rule 2.** *At the first station at which a throw occurs, the half-throw $(\frac{1}{2} t)$ equals the error at the preceding station.*

The throw at sta. 2 is *ef* (negative sign); and for all practical purposes *ef* = twice *cd*. The length *cd* may be written in the following form:

$$-cd = \underset{(1)}{(-\tfrac{1}{2} \, ab)} + \underset{(2)}{(-\tfrac{1}{2} \, ab)} + \underset{(4)}{\underbrace{[(ab + bc) - bd]}} \quad {\scriptstyle (3)}$$

Term (1) is the half-throw at sta. 2.

Term (2) is the half-throw at sta. 1.

Term (3) is the error at sta. 0.

Term (4) is the error at sta. 1.

From the foregoing relation, the following rule may be stated:

> *Rule 3.* *The half-throw at any station equals the half-throw at the preceding station plus the algebraic sum of the errors up to and including the preceding station.*

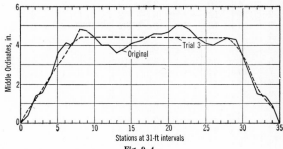

Fig. 9–4

In solving a string-lining problem, it is helpful to plot a graph of the measured middle ordinates. Fig. 9–4 shows such a graph for a spiraled curve very badly out of line. The curve is too flat near sta. 13 and too sharp near sta. 22. The original middle ordinates were measured to tenths of inches at stations 31 feet apart; their values (with the decimal point omitted for simplicity) are given in Table 9–2, col. (2).

For perfect alignment the middle ordinates on the circular curve must be constant, and those on the spirals must change uniformly. Moreover, the half-throw at the final station must be zero; otherwise, the forward tangent will be shifted parallel to itself by an amount equal to the full throw.

Trial 1 is shown in Table 9–2; it approximates trial 3, shown in Fig. 9–4. The middle ordinate for a 4.4° curve between stations 7 and 28 was assumed to be the average of the existing middle ordinates on the circular arc.

Col. (3) contains the revised middle ordinates. The middle ordinates on the spirals were adjusted so that the sum of the

TABLE 9–2

STRING-LINING CALCULATIONS

Station	Original m								
		TRIAL 1				TRIAL 2			
		Revised m	Error	Sum of Errors	Half-Throw	Revised m	Error	Sum of Errors	Half-Throw
(1)	(2)	(3)	(4)	(5)	(6)	(7)	(8)	(9)	(10)
−1	0	0	0	0	0	0	0	0	0
0	0	0	0	0	0	0	0	0	0
1	4	6	−2	−2	0	5	−1	−1	0
2	14	12	+2	0	−2	11	+3	+2	−1
3	16	19	−3	−3	−2	18	−2	0	+1
4	23	25	−2	−5	−5	24	−1	−1	+1
5	36	31	+5	0	−10	30	+6	+5	0
6	41	38	+3	+3	−10	37	+4	+9	+5
7	40	44	−4	−1	−7	44	−4	+5	+14
8	48	44	+4	+3	−8	44	+4	+9	+19
9	47	44	+3	+6	−5	44	+3	+12	+28
10	44	44	0	+6	+1	44	0	+12	+40
11	40	44	−4	+2	+7	44	−4	+8	+52
12	40	44	−4	−2	+9	44	−4	+4	+60
13	36	44	−8	−10	+7	44	−8	−4	+64
14	38	44	−6	−16	−3	44	−6	−10	+60
15	41	44	−3	−19	−19	44	−3	−13	+50
16	42	44	−2	−21	−38	44	−2	−15	+37
17	44	44	0	−21	−59	44	0	−15	+22
18	46	44	+2	−19	−80	44	+2	−13	+7
19	46	44	+2	−17	−99	44	+2	−11	−6
20	47	44	+3	−14	−116	44	+3	−8	−17
21	50	44	+6	−8	−130	44	+6	−2	−25
22	50	44	+6	−2	−138	44	+6	+4	−27
23	48	44	+4	+2	−140	44	+4	+8	−23
24	44	44	0	+2	−138	44	0	+8	−15
25	41	44	−3	−1	−136	44	−3	+5	−7
26	40	44	−4	−5	−137	44	−4	+1	−2
27	42	44	−2	−7	−142	44	−2	−1	−1
28	44	44	0	−7	−149	44	0	−1	−2
29	43	38	+5	−2	−156	39	+4	+3	−3
30	34	32	+2	0	−158	33	+1	+4	0
31	24	25	−1	−1	−158	26	−2	+2	+4
32	15	19	−4	−5	−159	21	−6	−4	+6
33	14	12	+2	−3	−164	12	+2	−2	+2
34	9	6	+3	0	−167	7	+2	0	0
35	0	0	0	0	−167	0	0	0	0
Sum	1231	1231				1231			

TABLE 9–2—(*Continued*)

Station	Revised m	Error	Sum of Errors	Half-Throw
(11)	(12)	(13)	(14)	(15)
-1	0	0	0	0
0	0	0	0	0
1	7	-3	-3	0
2	13	+1	-2	-3
3	18	-2	-4	-5
4	24	-1	-5	-9
5	30	+6	+1	-14
6	35	+6	+7	-13
7	41	-1	+6	-6
8	44	+4	+10	0
9	44	+3	+13	+10
10	44	0	+13	+23
11	44	-4	+9	+36
12	44	-4	+5	+45
13	44	-8	-3	+50
14	44	-6	-9	+47
15	44	-3	-12	+38
16	44	-2	-14	+26
17	44	0	-14	+12
18	44	+2	-12	-2
19	44	+2	-10	-14
20	44	+3	-7	-24
21	44	+6	-1	-31
22	44	+6	+5	-32
23	44	+4	+9	-27
24	44	0	+9	-18
25	44	-3	+6	-9
26	44	-4	+2	-3
27	44	-2	0	-1
28	44	0	0	-1
29	40	+3	+3	-1
30	35	-1	+2	+2
31	26	-2	0	+4
32	18	-3	-3	+4
33	12	+2	-1	+1
34	8	+1	0	0
35	0	0	0	0
Sum	1231			

Revision—Trial 1 to 2

Sta.	Change in m	Change in $\frac{1}{2} t$ at sta. 35
1	-1	+34
2	-1	+33
3	-1	+32
4	-1	+31
5	-1	+30
6	-1	+29
Sum	-6	+189
29	+1	-6
30	+1	-5
31	+1	-4
32	+2	-6
33	0	0
34	+1	-1
Sum	+6	-22
Net	0	+167

Revision—Trial 2 to 3

Sta.	Change in m	Change in $\frac{1}{2} t$ at sta. 35	13	22
1	+2	-68	-24	-42
2	+2	-66	-22	-40
6	-2	+58	+14	+32
7	-3	+84	+18	+45
Sum	-1	+8	-14	-5
29	+1	-6		
30	+2	-10		
32	-3	+9		
34	+1	-1		
Sum	+1	-8		
Net	0	0		

revised middle ordinates is equal to the original sum. Rule 1 requires this relation.

The errors and their algebraic sums were next calculated; the arithmetic was automatically checked by the zero value at the foot of col. (5).

Then the half-throws were calculated from Rules 2 and 3 and entered in col. (6). Arrows indicate the additions.

Up to about sta. 17, it appeared that a fairly close solution might be found on the first trial. After that, however, the half-throws became excessive. Instead of starting over when this happens, it is a good plan to continue col. (6) to completion; otherwise, a large number of trials might have to be made before finding a solution giving zero half-throw at the final station.

In the illustrative example the result of the first trial was modified by a method which guarantees a check on the second trial. The method is based upon the following rule:

> *Rule 4.* *The effect upon the half-throw at any station caused by a change in middle ordinate at any preceding station equals the product of the change in middle ordinate and the difference in stationing; the sign of the product is opposite to the sign of the change in the middle ordinate.*

The modification of trial 1 is shown at the top of the page to the right of trial 3. It should be observed that the small changes were made entirely on the spirals. The middle ordinates were adjusted in such a way as to make their net change zero (Rule 1) and at the same time to produce the required change of +167 units in the half-throw at sta. 35. The resulting half-throws are given in col. (10).

Trial 2 might be considered an acceptable solution, provided that there are no objects which might interfere with the fairly large throws between stations 10 and 15.

There are any number of solutions which will give zero throw at the end of the curve. The best solution is the one having the smallest intermediate throws, consistent with specified clearances and smooth curvature.

Trial 3 shows a second solution to the illustrative example. In revising trial 2, an attempt was made to decrease the throws near sta. 13 without increasing those near sta. 22 too much. The tabulation at the bottom of the page to the right of trial 3 shows how this was done and the zero throw at the end checked before the detailed calculations for trial 3 were performed. The resulting half-throws are given in col. (15). By using trial 3 instead of trial 2, the full throw is reduced from a maximum of 12.8 inches to 10.0 inches.

It is possible to obtain further improvement in this example by continuing the foregoing process, especially if the middle ordinates are expressed to the nearest 0.05 inch. (This is suggested as a profitable exercise for the student.)

String-lining problems are more complicated if it is necessary to hold the track fixed at certain points, such as at frogs, bridges, or station platforms. In such cases, zero throws are entered at the proper stations and the middle ordinates are adjusted so as to produce the required result. Numerous restrictions on throws make it difficult to obtain perfectly smooth track.

Track shifting in conformity with the throws finally approved is controlled by setting suitable line (and, possibly, grade) stakes.

Stout tacked line stakes are driven between the ties opposite each station, or as close thereto as permitted by the position of the ties. It is usually necessary to remove some of the ballast from around the stakes to prevent their being disturbed in shifting the track.

Some engineers prefer to set the line stakes on the revised center line. Track in the shifted position is then checked by means of the usual track gage. Instead of being centered, the line stakes may be set flush with the base of the rail at a distance such that, when the track is shifted, the base of the rail will be a constant distance (such as exactly 1 foot) from the tack. The final data for setting the line stakes require additional calculations not shown in Table 9–2.

On a long curve requiring considerable throwing, it may be necessary to set grade stakes for adjusting the rails to proper superelevation.

Track shifting is accomplished by moving the track and ties to their new positions with the aid of lining bars or jacks. To facilitate the process, some ballast is temporarily removed.

9–18. Spiraling Existing Curves.—In earlier years of railway surveying a variety of track realignment problems arose in connection with spiraling existing track originally laid out as simple curves. Since such problems are much less common now, only one typical case will be illustrated.

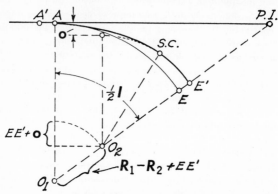

Fig. 9–5. Spiraling an existing curve

Fig. 9–5 shows half of an existing circular curve, AE. It is necessary to introduce spirals in such a way as to minimize shifting of the track and at the same time to keep the new and old track lengths practically the same. So doing facilitates shifting the track to its new position. The spiraled half-curve is shown at $A'E'$. The throw EE' at the center of the curve is usually restricted to a maximum value of 10 to 12 inches.

Obviously, the new simple curve, with radius R_2, must be somewhat sharper than the original one. The selected value of L_s and the final value of R_2 must fit the following relation:

$$(R_1 - R_2 + EE') \text{ vers } \tfrac{1}{2}I = EE' + o \qquad (9\text{–}4)$$

Any number of combinations of R_2 and L_s may be found. A suggested procedure follows:

1. Select a trial value of D_2 slightly greater than the original degree of curve.

2. Select a practical spiral length not less than that required by equation 9–3; and calculate the resulting value of o from the relation $\dfrac{L_s^2}{24\,R_2}$ (equation 5–21).

3. By a trial slide-rule calculation, determine the value of EE' needed to balance equation 9–4. If EE' is greater than the permitted maximum, go through the same process with new values of D_2 and L_s properly chosen to bring EE' within the required limit.

4. After satisfactory values of D_2 and L_s have been obtained, calculate the difference in length between the original and revised alignments. This difference should be figured between points common to both layouts, namely, the T.S. and the S.T. of the new alignment.

See Art. 9–21, Problem 5, for a practical example of the preceding case.

In other problems, it may be necessary to hold a certain portion of the circular curve in its original position, such as on a bridge, trestle, or high embankment. In this case, it is necessary to compound the curve with slightly sharper arcs in order to obtain the needed clearance for inserting the spirals. As in the previous case, any number of combinations of R_2 and L_s will fit the conditions. A practical example of this type of problem is given in Art. 9–21, Problem 6.

9–19. Track Layouts.—Railway track layouts involving surveying operations in their location are exceedingly complex. Included under this heading are:

1. *Turnouts*
   - (a) Simple *split-switch* turnouts from straight track
   - (b) Turnouts from curved track
   - (c) Double turnouts, involving *three-throw* and *tandem* split switches

2. *Crossovers*
   - (a) Between parallel straight tracks (see Fig. 9–6)
   - (b) Between parallel curved tracks

3. *Crossings*
   - (a) Straight or curved track
   - (b) Combination crossings, or *slip switches*

4. *Connecting tracks* from turnout to:

    (*a*) Diverging track

    (*b*) Another turnout, such as at *wye tracks*

    (*c*) Parallel siding

5. *Yard Layouts*

    (*a*) Complex combinations of the foregoing

    (*b*) Various arrangements of *ladder tracks*

Each of these layouts involves a multitude of features, including switches, frogs, guard rails, operating devices, rail braces, and fasteners of various kinds.

One of the layouts most frequently used is a crossover between parallel straight tracks, a simplified diagram of which is shown in Fig. 9–6.

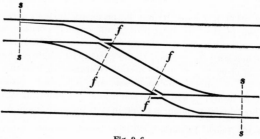

Fig. 9–6

The layout involves two turnouts, each of which includes the two switch rails, the frog, and the sections of curved and straight track shown located between lines *s-s* and *f-f*. The crossover tracks are straight between lines *f-f*, which are located at the heels of the frogs.

The best general source of information concerning track details is the portfolio of *Trackwork Plans of the A.R.E.A.* These have been undergoing extensive revision since 1940. Plans 910–41, and 911–41, covering *straight* split switches, are given in Table XXV, Part III (the data, occupying two sheets in the A.R.E.A. portfolio, have been rearranged slightly to fit the pages of this book).

The sketch on Plan No. 910–41 shows in outline form the principal features of a straight split-switch turnout and crossover. The data given on this plan are used in conjunction with Plan No. 911–41. Corresponding plans covering *curved* split switches (not included here) are numbers 920–51 and 921–51.

The following definitions are taken from the 1947 *Manual* of the A.R.E.A.:

Curved Lead—The distance between the actual point of switch and the half-inch point of the frog measured on the outside gage line of the turnout.

Frog—A track structure used at the intersection of two running rails to provide support for wheels and passageways for their flanges, thus permitting wheels on either rail to cross the other.

Frog Angle—The angle formed by the intersecting gage lines of a frog.

Frog Number—One-half the cotangent of one-half the frog angle, or the number of units of center line length in which the spread is one unit.

Gage (of Track)—The distance between the gage lines, measured at right angles thereto. (The standard gage is 4 ft $8\frac{1}{2}$ in.)

Guard Rail—A rail or other structure laid parallel with the running rails of a track to prevent wheels from being derailed; or to hold wheels in correct alinement to prevent their flanges from striking the points of turnout or crossing frogs or the points of switches.

Lead (Actual)—The length between the actual point of the switch and the half-inch point of the frog measured on the line of the parent track.

Stock Rail—A running rail against which the switch rail operates.

Stock Rail Bend—The bend or set which must be given the stock rail at the vertex of a switch to allow it to follow the gage line of the turnout.

Turnout—An arrangement of a switch and a frog with closure rails, by means of which rolling stock may be diverted from one track to another.

Turnout Number—The number corresponding to the frog number of the frog used in the turnout.

The values most useful to the surveyor are the frog number and the lead; these determine the distance occupied by the turnout and the angle to whatever connection is to be made beyond the frog.

The field work for ordinary problems, such as locating a turnout from straight track, follows a simple routine:

(*a*) Selecting the position for the frog.

(*b*) Choosing (tentatively) a standard combination of the switch rail and the frog number.

(*c*) Measuring the lead to see where the point of switch comes.

(*d*) Modifying the position of the frog (or changing the frog number) so as to bring the switch point the proper distance from the joints in the stock rails. (Recommended distances are given in Plan No. 911–41.)

(*e*) Setting a tacked hub on the turnout opposite the actual point of frog at a distance equal to half the gage distance from the gage line of the main track.

(*f*) Laying out the turnout with the aid of the dimensions and gage line offsets given in Plan No. 910–41.

Data for staking connections to track layouts beyond the frog must be calculated from certain key measurements controlling the individual problems. The great variety of such problems precludes their inclusion in this textbook.

9–20. Relocations.—Though the principal trunk railroad lines in the United States that can be justified in the foreseeable future have already been located, relocations are continually being made in order to bring sub-standard sections of line into conformity with modern requirements.

A typical relocation problem takes the form of flattening a single sharp curve formerly requiring operation under a slow order. If economic considerations do not eventually force the relocation, a serious wreck of a fast passenger train usually does. The elimination (in 1947) of the "Gulf curve" at Little Falls, N. Y.,* is an example.

Major relocations are invariably made for economic reasons. The changes include (either separately or in combination) reduction in distance, in grade, or in rate of curvature. The objectives generally sought are: (1) increased speed, in order to reduce running time; (2) greater riding comfort for passengers; (3) operating savings; (4) increased train tonnage, either as a result of grade reduction or from conservation of momentum formerly wasted through braking at the approach to slow-order curves.

A complete treatment of the economics of railway location and operation is beyond the scope of a *Route Surveying* textbook. Excellent analyses of these subjects will be found in *Proceedings, A.R.E.A.*, Vol. 39 (1938), pp. 439–560, and in *Proceedings, A.R.E.A.*, Vol. 45 (1944), pp. 25–44.

Major relocations involve surveying operations fully as complex and interesting as those met in the original location of trunk lines. In view of the existence of thousands of miles of track having curvature and grades which limit economical operation at high speeds, there is every reason to believe that such major relocations will continue to be made for many years. The railroads—stimulated by competition from other forms of transportation, as well as by competition from each other—are apparently aware of the necessity for making many improvements in the alignment of main-line track.

References to a few examples of relocation follow (it is suggested that they be made required reading assignments for students):

1. "The Eight-Mile Cascade Tunnel, Great Northern Railway," *Transactions, ASCE*, Vol. 96 (1932), pp. 915–1004.

2. "Two Important Tunnels Built in 1945."

   (1) The 3,015-Foot Bozeman Pass Tunnel in Montana (Northern Pacific), *Railway Age*, Vol. 120, No. 19, May 11, 1946, pp. 952–955.

Railway Age, Vol. 122, No. 1, Jan. 4, 1947, p. 118. Also *Highway Magazine*, March, 1948, p. 71.

(2) The 2,550-Foot Tennessee Pass Tunnel in Colorado (Denver & Rio Grande Western), *Railway Age*, Vol. 120, No. 21, May 25, 1946, pp. 1056–1058.

3. "Frisco Line Changes Improve Operation" (12-mile relocation in Missouri, involving grade reduction from 2.3 to 1.27% and curvature reduction amounting to more than 1,046 degrees), *Railway Age*, Vol. 121, No. 7, Aug. 17, 1946, pp. 281–284.

4. "Rock Island Completes Relocation in Iowa" (about 88 miles of relocation, involving elimination of 1,020 feet of rise and fall, and curvature reduction of 2,900 degrees), *Engineering News-Record*, Vol. 139, No. 22, Nov. 27, 1947, pp. 726–730.

5. "Grade and Line Revisions Lower Operating Costs on Missouri Pacific" (two relocations involving grade reduction from maximum of 2.45% to 1.25% compensated, distance saving of 3 miles, and curvature reduction of almost 900 degrees), *Civil Engineering*, March, 1949.

6. "Short-cut Through Missouri" (71-mile relocation on C.B. & Q. reduces Chicago-Kansas City run by 22 miles and passenger schedules by 5 hours. Has high design standards, such as maximum grade of 0.8% and maximum curvature of 1°. Aerial photographs used in planning the location). *Engineering New-Record*, Vol. 145, No. 19, Nov. 9, 1950, pp. 32–35.

9–21. Problems

1. If the course in route surveying does not include field practice at a summer camp, project a railroad paper location on a topograhic map supplied by the instructor. Follow the procedure given in Art. 9–11. Complete the work by making a mass diagram and an estimate of the grading cost.

2. In Fig. 9–2, assume that it is possible to get back on line from station C by deflecting 60' L from the backsight to B. Determine the required distance and final deflection angle. *Answers:* 292.54 ft and 67' R.

3. In projecting a location tangent through heavy woods, points A, B, and C were on line, whereas points X, Y, and Z

were offset in order to miss large trees. The survey data follow:

> *At B:* Backsight to A; deflect left $0°18'$ to X; measure BX = 300 ft.
>
> *At X:* Backsight to B; deflect right $0°34'$ to Y; measure $XY = 400$ ft.
>
> *At Y:* Backsight to X; deflect right $0°10'$ to Z; measure $YZ = 300$ ft.

(a) How far off line is point Z? (b) If the tangent were resumed by measuring $ZC = 400$ ft, what deflection (amount and direction) was made at point Z after backsighting to Y? (c) What deflection (amount and direction) was made at point C, after backsighting to Z, in order to resume the tangent?

4. Try to improve upon the trial-3 result in the string-lining problem of Art. 9–17.

5. In the string-lining problem of Art. 9–17, assume that physical limitations restrict *full* throws to a maximum of 3 inches between stations 21 and 23. Determine satisfactory half-throws to fit this specification.

6. *Given:* An unspiraled curve on existing track; $I = 24°18'$; $D_c = 4°30'$; speed on division = 50 mph; it is necessary to throw the curve outward to provide clearance for spirals. *Required:* A satisfactory combination of spiral length and new degree of curve, keeping the maximum throw less than 10 inches. *Answer* (one of several possible combinations): New $D_c = 5°20'$; $L_s = 320$ ft; throw $EE' = 0.50$ ft; new length 0.07 ft shorter than old.

7. *Given:* An unspiraled curve on existing track; $I = 16°14'$; $D_c = 3°40'$; speed on division = 45 mph; the existing curve has 100 feet of its central portion on a trestle; superelevation on trestle = 3 in. *Required:* A satisfactory compounded and spiraled curve which will not disturb the portion on the trestle. *Answer* (one of several possible combinations): $L_s = 160$ ft; D_c of new sharper arcs = $4°00'$; $L_c = 72.81$ ft each; L of present $3°40'$ curve unchanged = 100.21 ft.

8. Using the standard dimensions of switch and frog given in Plan No. 910–41, check the tabulated values of the lead and crossover distances (columns 4, 23, and 24) for a turnout number specified by the instructor.

CHAPTER 10

HIGHWAY SURVEYS

10–1. Foreword.—As a separate subject, adequate treatment of *Highway Surveys* would require many pages of detailed description. In this chapter, however, the subject is presented briefly in order to avoid repeating material already covered in this book in previous chapters. One referring directly to this chapter for information about highway surveys should not fail to note the discussion in Chapter 1 of the basic considerations affecting route location; the details of curve and earthwork theory given in Chapters 2, 3, 4, 5, and 6; and, in particular, the practical treatment of curve problems in highway design found in Chapter 8. Moreover, much of the material on *Railroad Surveys*, described in Chapter 9, applies equally to highway location.

Purposely omitted are samples of field notes and examples of the various maps and profiles needed for location and construction. Typical curve notes are given in Arts. 2–9 and 5–5; notes for cross-sectioning and slope staking, in Art. 6–7. Generally, the best sources of information for practical forms of notes are the instruction manuals issued to their engineers by State highway departments. Highway drawings, especially plan-profile sheets and "vicinity maps" for railroad crossings or bridge sites, suffer so much by reduction to book-page size as to be practically worthless for illustration. For instruction of students, reference to a set of full-scale highway plans (obtainable from most State highway departments) is strongly recommended.

Continued improvements in survey methods and in standards of alignment design are due not alone to the progressive policies of numerous State highway departments but also to the activities of certain other organizations. Among these are the *Bureau of Public Roads* (formerly the *Public Roads Administration*), whose original research and whose insistence upon high standards of design and construction in administering the provisions of the *Federal-Aid Highway Act* are perpetual stimuli to progress; the *American Association of State Highway Officials*, whose close cooperation with the B.P.R. in developing modern "design policies" (Art. 8–1) is only one of its many valuable activities; the *American Road Builders' Association* (the oldest highway organization in the United States), pre-eminent in highway public relations, early sponsor of improved alignment standards, and recently active in attracting better trained engineering personnel to the highway profession; and the *Highway Research Board*, whose outstanding work in basic highway research—organizing, correlating, disseminating information—has been largely responsible for supplanting rule-of-thumb methods with scientific design.

10–2. The Scope of a Modern Highway Project.—The definition of *Route Surveying* given in Art. 1–2 suggested the broad economic aspects of the subject. Modern highway planning illustrates the economic relationships particularly well, for in highway construction the taxpayer's dollar is spent, in competition with countless other demands for public services, upon projects which return to him only the intangible benefits of improved transportation.

Though many phases of highway planning and design are not properly a part of route surveying, it is felt that an illustration of their interrelationship would be valuable—at least to students. For this reason, there is included the following outline taken directly from the *Manual for Chiefs of Party* issued by the New Jersey State Highway Department.

PROCEDURES FOR PLANS PREPARATION FOR STATE HIGHWAY PROJECTS

FIRST STEP

(Responsibility of Division of Planning and Economics)

1. Prepare brief report on purpose of highway, giving its functions:

   (a) To serve through traffic
   (b) To serve local traffic predominantly
   (c) To develop recreational, industrial, residential and agricultural areas.

2. Recommend classification of highway:
   - (a) Density of traffic (30th peak hour, 30 years hence)
   - (b) Passenger cars (P), Mixed traffic (M), Trucks (T)
   - (c) Design speed.

3. Recommend type of highway:
   - (a) Two lane
   - (b) Three lane (not normally recommended)
   - (c) Four lane undivided (not normally recommended)
   - (d) Four or more lanes divided (not more than four lanes normally recommended)
   - (e) At grade "land service highway"
   - (f) At grade with major intersections separated (either initially or eventually)
   - (g) Freeway
   - (h) Parkway.

4. Recommend location of termini.

5. Recommend general area of location and reasons therefor.

6. Preliminary recommendations on traffic
   Interchange locations.

7. Justification:
   - (a) Traffic
   - (b) Economic factors
   - (c) Benefit-cost ratio
   - (d) Priority
   - (e) Place in comprehensive plan.

8. Review of report by Department of Design and Construction.

After approval (or modification) of above report by the State Highway Engineer he will transmit to the Chief, Department of Design and Construction, for progressing Surveys and Plans. (Copies of this report shall be sent to Bureau of Public Roads if participation in financing is expected.)

SECOND STEP

(Responsibility of Department of Design and Construction)

1. Reconnaissance surveys and proposed typical cross-sections.

2. After approval by the State Highway Engineer of Item 1, prepare "Hearing Map" precedent to line adoption. After line has been adopted by the State Highway Commissioner, design shall proceed.

3. Develop typical main roadway cross-sections (including right-of-way width) based on satisfactory maximum roadway capacity for the 30th peak hour, thirty years hence. (In some cases this may be desirable, tolerable, or maximum roadway capacity, in which case it will be the subject of individual decision of the State Highway Engineer with review by the State Highway Commissioner.)

4. Develop geometric design standards for approved design speed.

5. Field reports on Interchange locations as outlined in Memo of State Highway Engineer dated October 3, 1946, shall be submitted.

6. Detailed traffic and economic data relating to Interchange sites shall be obtained from Planning and Economics and transmitted to field.

7. Preliminary sketch designs of Interchanges based on data included in (6) above shall be submitted by field for approval.

8. Submission of a general plan (generally $1'' = 200'$) and profile showing widths, alignment, grades, and tentative Interchanges to State Highway Engineer for approval. (After approval, prints of this plan shall be submitted to Bureau of Public Roads.)

9. On approval of Interchange sketches and alignment and grades, an accurate layout of Interchange design shall be submitted for approval before being tied down mathematically.

10. Submission of proposal for developing order and extent of construction contracts shall be submitted to the State Highway Engineer for approval, plus special or unusual specification provisions.

11. Approval of construction plans and specifications by State Highway Engineer and State Highway Commissioner.

In developing plans it is expected that Planning and Economics and Department of Design and Construction will cooperate closely and draw freely on information and techniques each from the other, and that the Maintenance Division and Parkway Engineer will be consulted freely on matters of mutual concern.

10–3. Similarity to Railroad Surveys on New Locations.
Surveys for major rural highways on new locations may follow identically the same procedure as those on railroad location. For this reason, the descriptive material in Arts. 9–2 to 9–14 should also be considered as part of this chapter.

The principal differences in highway survey methods are caused by the somewhat greater latitude with respect to profile grades and especially by problems of highway interchange design. Generally, these differences require a wider strip of topography than on railroad location. Perhaps this is the reason why aerial survey methods—rarely used by railroads—are supplanting field reconnaissance, and even preliminary surveys, on important new highway location. (Some examples are given in Chapter 12.)

Aside from the use of aerial survey methods, the greatest difference in technique on new locations is in the method of cross-sectioning, which is usually done by cross-section leveling rather than by slope staking (see Art. 6–7). The reason for this is that the exact profile grades are not designed until after the alignment is fixed. The cross-sections, plotted to scale, aid in selecting the grades and in designing drainage facilities.

10–4. Modifications of Railroad Methods on Relocations.
Most new highway construction is in the form of improvements of existing highways. The changes usually involve widening of pavements, increasing the number of traffic lanes, reduction of grades, and flattening of curves to increase sight distances and safe speeds. Frequently, most of the existing right-of-way can be utilized, but minor relocations or "cut-

offs" over new right-of-way are often required when sub-standard sections cannot be improved without incurring excessive land damages. A closely related problem is the location of by-passes around congested areas, with the accompanying problems of grade separation and interchange design.

Surveys for relocations involve numerous modifications of the usual railroad survey methods. A few of the common modifications are described in the following paragraphs.

For one thing, reconnaissance is more localized. The reason is that the need for possible relocation is usually disclosed by accident statistics or by obvious traffic bottle-necks. Reconnaissance is often simplified by reference to the original construction plans, to tax maps, and—in increasing instances—to aerial photographs (in New Jersey, for example, photographs are available for the entire State and can be ordered to any scale). Alignment closely approximating the final location can usually be selected from a study of the reconnaissance information.

The proposed alignment, complete with curves, is very carefully staked, since it serves as one of the "base lines" for design and construction. In case it is not possible to fix the alignment in advance, the base line may follow the center line of the old road; all drawings and designs are simplified, however, if it follows the center line of the proposed road. In the case of dual highways, it is advisable to use two base lines, one at the crown line (the profile grade line) of each roadway. Additional construction base lines are needed at interchanges; in most cases the center lines of ramps or connections serve best.

Ordinarily the alignment is staked at full stations and at half-stations. Station stakes are centered and tacked; on a pavement each exact point is chiseled or marked by a nail driven through a washer or a square of red cloth. Angles are determined at least to the nearest 30 seconds; distances, to the nearest 0.01 foot. On important surveys through congested areas, temperature corrections are applied to the taped distances, and tape tension is estimated carefully and checked occasionally with a spring balance. Check chaining or calculated traverse closures are required to have a precision of from 1 in 5,000 to 1 in 10,000.

In comparison with surveys for new locations, those for relocations cover a relatively narrow strip of territory. But it is necessary to measure and record many more topographic details. Among these are present paving, curbs, sidewalks, trees, guard rails, drainage structures, fences, walls, property lines, public utilities, buildings, land usage, intersecting highways, streams, railroads, and—in general— all features which might affect the grade-line design or which might have to be removed and relocated.

Measurements for topography and right-of-way data are customarily made by the transit party and recorded in the field book. Details are tied to the base line by "plus and offset," supplemented by range ties. Intersecting railroads, pole lines, etc. are located by stationing and angle of intersection. Contours are not located in this form of topographic survey. Some highway departments use the "field-sheet" method described in Art. 9–9.

Cross-sectioning differs from railroad practice in that the process of cross-section leveling is used instead of slope staking. The usual method is that given in Art. 6–7, though some engineers prefer to run profile levels first and then to do cross-sectioning by recording rod readings as plus or minus from the given center-line elevations. Since no elevations are determined in taking topography, the cross-sections must give the needed information concerning elevations of existing curbs, walls, drainage structures, utilities, and building foundations. Other special methods are found in Art. 10–7.

Though ground cross-sections are used principally for determining earthwork end areas, they sometimes serve the purpose of plotting contours to assist in the design of ramps and grade separations.

10–5. Soil Surveys.—Comprehensive soil surveys, rarely needed in railroad location, have become standard practice among progressive State highway departments. Such surveys are superseding the former types of soil surveys which were often restricted to borings at bridge sites and cursory examination of the route for surface indications of snow slides or unstable side slopes.

Modern alignment standards often require that routes traverse topographic features formerly avoided; as a result, long heavy fills and deep cuts—sometimes through bedrock—are frequently necessary. Since the cost of a modern highway may exceed one-half million dollars per mile, possible savings in construction and maintenance costs justify using fairly expensive methods of determining pertinent information about surface and subsurface soil conditions.

Soils investigations for highways continue to grow more comprehensive in scope. This phase of highway engineering requires close cooperation with the soil physicist, the geologist, and even the seismologist. The modern tendency is to go beyond merely making auger borings along the proposed route and classifying the soil samples in the laboratory. Instead, the past geologic history of the area is investigated. From these studies, area soil maps are prepared which show the soil "pattern"—land forms, types of soil deposits, swamp areas, drainage conditions, and related information. A proposed route traversing the region covered by an area soil map is then the subject of a preliminary soil report which shows the relationship of the soils to the engineering considerations of alignment, grade, drainage, and grading and compaction processes. The availability of materials for borrow, for subbase, or for concrete aggregates is also indicated. The report may suggest alignment changes; it also contains specific recommendations regarding the extent of subsurface exploration needed to answer detailed questions for design and construction.

In glaciated regions, erratic depths to bedrock may justify the use of seismic methods of subsurface exploration. Massachusetts, for example, has developed a procedure in which a geologic "strip" map is prepared and the locations where seismic studies are recommended, such as at deep cuts and bridge sites, are shown on this map. Seismological field work has been done under a cooperative program of the Massachusetts Department of Public Works and the U.S. Geological Survey.

Complete treatment of the subject of modern highway soil surveys is beyond the scope of a text on *Route Surveying*. For detailed information, see any modern text on *Highway Engineering*. Broader aspects of the subject are described in

Bulletin 13, Highway Research Board (1948), entitled "The Appraisal of Terrain Conditions for Highway Engineering Purposes."

10–6. Preparation of Plans.—Office procedure in design and preparation of plans for a major highway project involves a multitude of operations. Some of these are quite routine and may be done by the sub-professional members of the surveying crews during rainy weather; others require specialized training and experience.

State highway departments usually follow certain "standards" with regard to methods of design, sizes of drawing sheets, arrangement of work, and forms for estimating quantities. No one scheme is best for all projects; a great deal depends on the size and type of the project and on the personnel available. However, on Federal-Aid projects certain specifications of the B.P.R. relative to size of drawing sheet and form of layout must be followed.

The final objective of the office work is to prepare a cost estimate and a complete set of plans showing clearly all information needed (1) by the engineers in laying out the lines and grades to be used by the contractor in building the project, (2) by the contractor in estimating the nature and extent of all work to be performed, in order that he may prepare his bid, and (3) by the legal agents to assist in preparing the right-of-way descriptions and other data connected with land takings and easements.

A detailed description of office design methods not only would be too voluminous for inclusion in this book but also would encroach upon subjects more properly treated in a study of highway engineering. Consequently, only a bare outline of typical office routine follows to serve in illustrating the relation between survey work and design.

Supplied with the reconnaissance report and all the data from the field surveys, the designers carry out the following steps of the project:

1. Design of typical sections: These are dimensioned drawings showing the proposed roadway cross-sections of the standard portions of the project. Shown are width, thickness, and crown of pavements; shoulder widths and slopes;

positions of ditches, side slopes, curbs, median strips, guard rails, and other construction details.

2. Preparation of location map: Usually done on a series of 22″×36″ *Federal Aid Sheets*, which show the profile as well as the plan. Common scales are 1″ = 100′ horizontally; 1″ = 10′ vertically. Plan shows survey base lines, topographic details, and all alignment and right-of-way data. Profile (sometimes drawn on separate sheets) shows the ground line, grade line as finally designed, drainage structures, and estimated earthwork quantities and balance points.

3. Plotting of cross-sections: Ground cross-sections, used for earthwork calculation and in grade-line design, are plotted directly from the cross-section leveling notes. A common scale is 1″ = 10′. Scale may be larger when end areas are to be determined by the "strip" method (Art. 6–6); smaller when found by calculating machine (Art. 6–4).

4. Establishing of profile grades: Grade line designed with regard to relative importance of economy of construction, balance of earthwork quantities, property damage, sight distances, safety of operation, drainage and soil conditions, aesthetics, and adaptability to future property development and to future highway or railroad grade separations. Frequent reference to plotted ground cross-sections is helpful in design.

5. Drawing of cross-section plans: Proposed roadway cross-sections drawn on ground cross-section sheets in conformity with the designed profile grades. These sections show the pay lines for excavation. Widening and superelevation are allowed for.

6. Making of special detail drawings: Includes detail drawings of all types of drainage structures; of retaining walls, curbs, guard rails, and other appurtenances; and of complicated interchanges and intersections. In connection with the latter problems, standards often followed are those given in the *AASHO Policy on Geometric Highway Design.*[2]

7. Preparation of right-of-way plans: Property maps of all parcels to be acquired or conveyed, showing locations, owners' names, and ties to existing and proposed right-of-ways.

[2] See bibliography at the end of Chapter **8**.

8. *Estimate of quantities:* Detailed estimate of quantities of grading, paving, and other construction work, prepared systematically with the aid of special "take-off sheets." Summary of results, to serve as basis for engineer's cost estimate and to aid contractors in preparing bids.

9. *Preparation of specifications:* Detailed general and special provisions relating to proposal conditions, submission of bids, prosecution of work, construction details, and methods of measurement and payment.

10–7. Construction Surveys.—Generally, the types of surveying operations needed on highway construction are the same as those outlined for railroad construction in Art. 9–14; therefore, the descriptions will not be repeated here.

In general, field layout and staking are somewhat more complex in highway work, owing to the multiplicity of lanes and the many ramps and intersections. Staking practices vary with the type of highway, the nature of the terrain, the magnitude and the cuts and fills, and the preferences of the particular organization.

In the conventional method, tacked line stakes, marked with station and offset, are set no more than 50 feet apart on offset lines from the construction base lines. Their elevations are determined and recorded for future use in setting grade stakes. After the right-of-way has been cleared, a double line of slope stakes or "rough grading" stakes is set at 50-foot intervals. Finishing stakes are necessary for the final operations of side-slope trimming, subgrade preparation, and setting of forms for paving. After the grading has been completed, "blue-topped" line and grade stakes are set on the subgrade near enough to the work to permit forms to be set truly by means of a short grade board.

In mountainous terrain, where grading is very heavy and there are complications in the form of variable slopes and benches, the customary method of setting construction slope stakes is very clumsy. Instead, a "traverse method" may be used to great advantage. Because of its specialized application, the traverse method will not be described in detail. However, an engineer having to solve this problem should consult the reference in the footnote.[1]

---

[1] *Construction Manual*, State of California, Dept. of Public Works, Div. of Highways.

The use of freeway design, in which double roadways are often at different levels separated by a median of varying width, complicates not only the construction staking but also the calculation of grading quantities. Good results can be obtained by substituting a contour grading plan for the usual voluminous set of cross-section sheets. In essence, "contour grading" consists in superimposing contour lines of the proposed construction on the existing contour map, thereby forming a series of areas bounded by closed contours. The areas are planimetered, and the volumes of the horizontal slices of earthwork are determined by the average-end-area method. This method is subject to further refinement and greater accuracy if partial contour intervals are taken into account. As a result of some time studies, it is estimated that earthwork calculations, together with the drafting and survey operations, can save about 40 per cent in man-hours. The reference in the footnote[2] contains detailed examples of contour grading.

Warped surfaces at intersections require specially worked out staking arrangements in order to produce smooth riding surfaces.

Record plans of all work "as built" are worked up as construction proceeds. Since pavement is usually paid for on the basis of surface area, the final measurement of the length of the project is somewhat greater than the horizontal survey measurement.

10–8. Examples of Modern Practice.—Examples of good practice in highway location and interchange design are too numerous to permit reference to any but a very few. The following examples are noted because they illustrate various types of problems.

1. "Difficult Location Problems on 476-Mile Blue Ridge Parkway." (Shows application of railway surveying methods to new highway location in mountainous terrain. Alignment includes spirals and double spirals, eleven tunnels, grade separations, and grade compensation for curvature.) *Civil Engineering*, Vol. 17, No. 7, July, 1947, pp. 378 ff.

2. "North Santiam Highway Follows Difficult Route Near Cascade Summit." (Costly 15.6-mile Oregon highway in-

---

[2] C. V. Kane, "Contour Grading," *California Highways and Public Works*, Sept.–Oct., 1952.

volves heavy cuts and fills; stability of fills affected by possible sudden drawdown of flood-control reservoir.) *Civil Engineering*, Vol. 18, No. 8, August, 1948, pp. 507 ff.

3. "Application of Coordinate Methods to Freeway Planning and Construction." (Describes precise surveying methods used to solve complex design and right-of-way problems on freeway construction in urban areas.) *California Highways and Public Works*, Nov.–Dec., 1946.

4. "New Jersey Turnpike." (A group of articles covering the planning, financing, design, and construction of this 118-mile expressway.) *Civil Engineering*, Vol. 22, No. 1, January, 1952, pp. 1–69.

5. "New York State Thruway." (A group of articles covering the planning, financing, and design of the first 427-mile section of this modern toll highway.) *Civil Engineering*, Vol. 23, No. 11, November, 1953, pp. 735–752.

6. "Tough Terrain Conquered by Builders of West Virginia Turnpike." (Describes a difficult location problem in which a modern 88-mile highway, having geometric design standards suited to speeds of 60 mph or higher, replaced a tortuous route 107 miles long that had some grades of 9% and some curves of 50-ft radius.) *Civil Engineering*, Vol. 24, No. 2, February, 1954, pp. 74–80.

10–9. Use of Aerial Surveys.—It is noteworthy that highway engineers have been active in adapting aerial surveys to ever-widening fields of usefulness in the planning, location, and design of highways. In fact, the science has progressed to such a point that E. T. Gawkins, commenting upon the results of experience in New York State, wrote:[18]

> . . . aerial surveying . . . will in most cases obviate the need for one or more reconnaissance surveys and all the labor required for preliminary estimates of several alternate routes. Once the line has been selected from the use of aerial surveys, field surveying can be reduced to include only those necessary steps such as laying out of base line, setting of stakes, determination of right-of-way limits on the ground, and taking of sections for earthwork estimates prior to the award of the contract—the steps that will always be required for the construction of a highway.

---

[18] See bibliography at the end of Chapter 12.

The most suitable relationship between ground-survey and aerial-survey methods has yet to be worked out. Possible combinations of these two methods are suggested in Chapter 12. Their relative use is largely an economic question involving the size of the project, the character of the terrain, and the availability of existing photographs to suitable scale.

Most of the United States has been photographed from the air at least once. The work has been done by several agencies and for a variety of purposes. Consequently, not all the photographs are suitable for highway-location purposes. Up-to-date information on the existence and nature of available aerial photographs may be obtained from the Map Information Office of the United States Geological Survey.

The Bureau of Public Roads lists the six stages of highway location as follows:[19]

First Stage—Reconnaissance survey of the entire area between terminal points.

Second Stage—Reconnaissance survey of all feasible route bands.

Third Stage—Preliminary survey of the best route.

Fourth Stage—Location of the highway on the ground.

Fifth Stage—Construction of the highway.

Sixth Stage—Operation and maintenance of the highway.

The earliest use of aerial photography in highway location was as a supplement to the usual ground reconnaissance surveys. Improvements in the art have now enabled photogrammetry to supplant ground methods for reconnaissance studies of large areas.

The first stage, according to present practice, consists of stereoscopic examination of small-scale aerial photographs covering a broad area between the terminal points. Intermediate controls related to topography and land-use are disclosed and broadly considered. The result of these studies is the determination of all bands within the area which might contain a feasible location for the highway.

In the second stage, large-scale aerial photographs are taken along each of the feasible route bands. The photographs

---

[19] See bibliography at the end of Chapter 12.

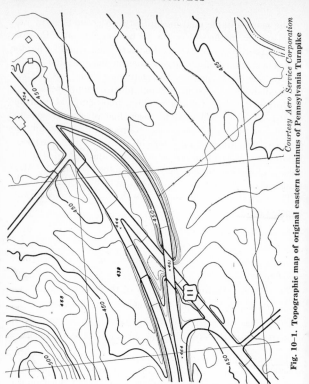

Fig. 10–1. Topographic map of original eastern terminus of Pennsylvania Turnpike

Courtesy Aero Service Corporation

are examined stereoscopically, as before, but their larger scale permits the controls of topography and land-use to be given special scrutiny. All possible route bands are compared, after evaluating the several controls, and the best one is chosen for more-detailed surveys. Thus, the use of aerial photographs in two stages of reconnaissance will have disclosed the best route without costly ground surveys of several alternate routes.

The third stage of location includes the making of a topographic map of the selected route band, and the projection of a geometric location by the familiar paper-location method (see Art. 9–11). As indicated in the quotation on page 278, photogrammetric methods are being used to an increasing degree in studies following reconnaissance, especially in the preparation of topographic maps. Fig. 10–1 shows an example of a map on which contours were drawn by a photogrammetric process. The map also contains all the important planimetric detail appearing on the aerial photograph. A reproduction of an original aerial photograph, and the resulting topographic map, are shown on pages 296 and 297.

The fourth stage will always be done by ground surveying, since aerial methods cannot conceivably be extended to the processes of running in curves or setting stakes for grading and other construction operations. Information of great value in connection with the fifth and sixth stages can also be obtained from aerial photographs.

In the over-all problem of route location, both photogrammetric and ground surveying methods will be used. For practical examples of their interrelationships the engineer should study the up-to-date practices described in Chapter 12

CHAPTER 11

SURVEYS FOR OTHER ROUTES

11–1. Foreword.—Reference to the broad definition of *transportation* stated in Art. 1–2 suggests that the following additional types of transportation may involve surveying operations similar to those already described for railroads and highways:

1. Transportation (transmission) of power and messages by means of overhead tower or pole lines, or by lines in underground conduits.

2. Transportation of liquids and gases through closed conduits under pressure, such as pipe lines for water, gasoline, oil, and natural gas; through closed conduits by means of gravity, such as sewers and aqueducts; and through open channels, such as canals and flumes.

3. Transportation of materials (sand, gravel, stone, or selected borrow) to the site of large construction projects, by means of cableways and belt conveyors.

Whenever any of the foregoing are projects of considerable magnitude and involve termini a fairly long distance apart, the required surveying operations may properly be included in the term *route surveying*.

Special types of surveys are necessary in the case of tunnel location and construction. These are noted briefly in Art. 11–6.

11–2. Similarity to Railroad and Highway Surveys.—Surveys for all routes of transportation and communication are similar in general respects to those described in Chapters 9 and 10 for railroads and highways. This is because all routes have certain location controls (Art. 9–3); in fitting the line to those controls the natural sequence of field and office work approximates that outlined in Art. 1–8. The particular differences that do occur are caused by requirements peculiar to a specific type of route. The engineer acquainted with railroad or highway surveying should have no difficulty in adapting his knowledge to surveys for other routes, once the uses to which the surveys are to be put are known. Surveys for some other routes are described briefly in the succeeding articles.

11–3. Transmission-Line Surveys.—The location of a power transmission line is controlled less by topography than is the location of other types of routes. Power loss due to voltage drop is proportional to the length of the conductor; consequently, high-tension transmission lines run as directly as possible from generating station to substation. Changes in direction, where required by intermediate controls, are made at angle towers instead of along curves. A trunk telephone or telegraph line is usually located within the right-of-way of a highway or of a railroad, in which case the curves of the right-of-way must be followed.

Unless aerial photographs are used, the field and office work for transmission-line location involves, after a study of available maps, the following operations:

1. Reconnaissance for the location of intermediate features to be avoided, such as buildings, cemeteries, extensive swamps, stands of heavy timber, and particularly valuable improved land; and for the location of intermediate controls fixing points on the line, such as the most advantageous crossings of important highways, railroads, and streams.

2. A transit-and-tape (or a stadia) traverse. The traverse may be either a preliminary line or the final center line, the selection depending on the difficulty of the problem. In staking the long straight sections between intermediate controls, the deflection-angle method of by-passing obstacles on tangents (described in Art. 9–13) is particularly useful. Contours are not located; however, all topographic features and right-of-way data are measured with respect to the traverse, as described in Art. 10–4.

3. Levels sufficient in extent to aid in locating the towers. These may be merely "spot" elevations or those for a complete profile along the traverse line. On final location in difficult terrain, it is advisable to take levels along two lines, one on each side of the center line, in order to obtain proper conductor clearance when spotting the positions of the towers.

4. Office studies, including the features common to all route location: drawing of the map, description of right-of-way easements, estimate of quantities and cost, and preparation of specifications. A special problem in transmission-line design is the location of the towers. This location work may be done with the aid of special transparent templates, as described after step 5.

5. Construction surveys. These are relatively simple on transmission-line construction, since there is practically no grading. Stakes are needed only for clearing the right-of-way and for building tower footings. However, the surveyor's assistance is also valuable in planning other details related to construction, such as in spotting cable reels and locating suitable dead-end and pulling points.

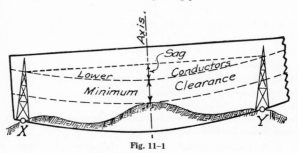

Fig. 11–1

A convenient method of spotting tower locations on the profile is to use a transparent template, the lower edge of which is cut to the curve (approximately a parabola) that will be taken by the conductor cables. Obviously the curve must be modified to fit the scale of the profile. Two other curves are inscribed on the template parallel to the curve of the lower edge. The axial distance from the lower edge to the middle curve equals the maximum cable sag for a particular span; that from the middle curve to the upper curve equals the specified minimum ground clearance.

The template is used as shown in Fig. 11–1. First a point X is located at a suitable position for a tower; then the lower edge of the template is placed on this point and the template is moved until the middle curve touches the ground line.   The other point Y at which the lower edge of the template intersects the ground line is the possible location of the next tower.   One template fits a considerable range of spans with sufficient accuracy.

After the towers at certain controlling points have been located, the location of the intermediate towers is a matter of cut and try; the object is to cover the greatest length of line with the least number of towers.

On important new transmission-line work, aerial photographs are now commonly used, at least for reconnaissance, and they are sometimes used for all phases of the survey work except final staking.   The growing file of available aerial photographs (Art. 10–9) often makes this method feasible where it was formerly prevented by economic considerations.

11–4. Surveys for Pressure Pipe Lines and Underground Conduits.

—Surveys for the location of long pressure pipe lines are almost as simple as those for transmission lines.   In fact, the descriptions contained in steps 1 and 2 in Art. 11–3 apply also to pipe-line surveys.   However, since pressure pipe lines are usually located underground, greater attention is paid to foundation conditions and especially to avoiding costly rock excavation and frequent stream crossings.   Accessibility to power for operating booster pumping stations is also an important intermediate control.

Grades and undulations in the profile are relatively unimportant, especially on small-diameter steel pipe lines; consequently, detailed profile levels may be omitted and replaced by spot elevations at proposed pumping stations and at the high and low points along the line.

On construction, line stakes are more important than grade stakes.   In fact, grade stakes for steel pipe lines may be needed only at pumping stations and at crossings of highways, railroads, and streams.   Along intervening sections, at least in easy terrain, several sections of pipe are welded together on the ground before being laid in the relatively uniform trench dug by the trenching machine.

Large reinforced-concrete pipe lines require much more careful attention to undulations in the profile, since there is a practical limit to the change in direction possible at each joint, and beyond that limit special pipe sections are necessary.

As in the case of transmission lines, right-of-way for a pressure pipe line usually takes the form of easements for its construction and operation.

Aerial surveys are particularly useful in the location of long pipe lines. Only mosaics are used, since contours are not essential. As a rule, a stereoscopic study of the photographs will give enough information for the preliminary location. After this the line may be "walked over" prior to deciding upon the final location. It is possible, however, to rely upon aerial photographs to an even greater extent. For example, in building one of the longest pipe lines from the southwestern part of the United States to the industrial middle west, no surveyor went on the job until the sections of pipe were ready to be laid; yet, the right-of-way agents completed much of their work before that time.

Surveys for underground conduits containing power lines on private right-of-way are much the same as those for pressure pipe lines.

Underground communication circuits are commonly placed in conduits located beneath the highway pavement. Access for maintenance is by means of manholes. Coaxial cables used for telephone, broadcast, and television circuits may be drawn through existing conduits. However, they are also placed directly in a shallow ploughed trench beside the highway. In neither case is any extensive survey work required.

11–5. Surveys for Construction at the Hydraulic Gradient.
Surveys for hydraulic construction in which flow is by gravity require very careful attention to elevations, owing to the flat grades used. If the flow is in an open channel, as in a canal, the alignment may have to be circuitous in order to obtain proper velocity and to avoid costly grading. A more direct alignment is possible if the construction is below the ground surface, such as in the case of a grade-line tunnel, aqueduct, or sewer.

Surveys for surface construction may be identical with those for railroad location, the principal modification being that a narrower strip of topography will suffice. This condition is caused by the necessity for keeping the gradients between relatively narrow limits.

Stations on the preliminary traverse are kept close to the final location by setting them near the "grade contour." The grade contour is the line on the ground (starting at a controlling point) along which the grade changes at the rate best suited to the construction. In locating the stations, it is obviously necessary that the leveling be kept up with the transit work. In simple irrigation-ditch construction in easy terrain, a line may be located on the grade contour in the field by tape and level, without need for the transit.

On a contour map the grade contour is found by starting at a controlling point and stepping from contour to contour with dividers set at a distance equal to the contour interval divided by the desired rate of grade. The closer the final alignment follows the grade contour, the lower will be the grading quantities.

Since economy of grading is an important factor in canal construction, careful cross-sections are taken at short intervals. Construction surveys for canals are very similar to those for highways, but all stakes must be set on offset lines.

There are cases in which aerial surveys have been used in studies for canal location—for example, on the proposed Florida Barge Canal. They have also been used in studies for levees and dikes to control meandering rivers. Difficulty of access for ground-survey parties is an important consideration favoring the use of aerial-survey methods. However, the small contour interval needed on maps for canal studies does not ordinarily permit the location of contours by photogrammetric methods. Mosaics are useful for general studies; but for detailed location the best method probably is to make an accurate planimetric map from the aerial photographs and then to add the contours by the plane-table method.

For gravity-flow structures below the ground surface, it is entirely suitable to use railroad surveying methods, supplemented by adequate subsurface exploration. A most important aspect of the office studies for such construction is to decide whether cut-and-cover construction or tunnel construction is the better. Often a combination of the two provides the most economical solution.

11–6. Tunnel Surveys.—In mountainous terrain, it is sometimes necessary to use tunnels on route alignment. Surveying operations for locating tunnels vary greatly in complexity. For short tunnels, it may be possible to locate a transit line on the ground directly over the tunnel. As a rule, however, an indirect precise traverse is necessary. In the case of subaqueous tunnels or long tunnels to be driven through rugged mountain ranges, triangulation control must be used. This is a subject outside the scope of route surveying.

The traverse or triangulation control provides only the data for calculating the tunnel alignment; elevations must be determined by careful spirit leveling between the proposed portals.

Locating the portals, adits, and shafts by means of the accurate control surveys is only one of the surveyor's important tasks. His work in controlling the accuracy of the tunnel driving is fully as important; it must be done with the highest precision, for it cannot be verified conclusively until the headings are holed through—and then it is too late to make adjustments.

Surveying for tunnels driven through rock involves specialized operations not found in other types of route surveying. Among these are:

1. Carrying the alignment down shafts by means of heavy bobs damped in oil and suspended from piano wires. The equipment also includes lateral adjusting devices for the sheaves and scales for measuring the swing of the wires.

2. Transferring the alignment from the wires to plumb bobs suspended from riders, or "skyhooks," mounted on scales attached to the roof of the tunnel.

3. Extending the alignment into the tunnel on "spads" driven in plugged holes in the roof. The transitman usually works on a suspended platform, out of the way of the muck cars.

4. Carrying the alignment to the working face, or "painting the heading," for locating the drill holes.

5. Transferring grade down shafts by means of weighted tapes or by taping down elevator guides.

6. Carrying temporary grade into the tunnel by means of inverted rod readings on the wood plugs in which the spads are driven.

7. Cross-sectioning twice; first for locating points needing trimming, and finally for obtaining permanent graphical records of the sections and for computing pay yardage and overbreak.

Several ingenious devices for cross-sectioning have been used, such as pantographs and "sunflowers." The latter are designed to locate breaks in the tunnel cross-section by polar coordinates. A unique adaptation of the sunflower was used in cross-sectioning the tunnels on the Pennsylvania Turnpike.*

Numerous other special procedures are necessary in surveying for shield-driven tunnels and for those driven by the compressed-air method.

---

*"Evolution of the Pennsylvania Superhighway," *Roads and Streets*, Vol. 82, No. 10, October, 1939, p. 77.

CHAPTER 12

AERIAL PHOTOGRAPHY IN ROUTE SURVEYING

12-1. Foreword.—The uses of aerial photographs in route surveying have now become important enough to justify devoting a separate chapter to aspects of the subject not covered in textbooks on photogrammetry. Aside from a brief review of certain definitions and mapping processes, this chapter avoids repeating the technical principles of photogrammetric mapping as described in recent books on the subject.[1] Instead, the emphasis is on the special applications of this new science to route location, and on the advantages, limitations, and economic value of such applications.

12-2. Definitions.—Definitions of photogrammetric terms to be used in this chapter are given in this article. For a more comprehensive list the engineer is referred to the *Manual of Photogrammetry* of the American Society of Photogrammetry.[2]

Photogrammetry is the science or art of obtaining reliable measurements by means of photography. The subject is subdivided into *terrestrial photogrammetry* and *aerial photogrammetry*. In terrestrial photogrammetry the photographs are taken from one or more ground stations; in aerial photogrammetry, from an aeroplane in flight. Terrestrial photogrammetry utilizes *horizontal photographs* or *oblique photographs*, whereas aerial photogrammetry utilizes *vertical photographs* or *oblique photographs*. Since oblique photographs are used only for special purposes (see Art. 12–11), the aerial photographs referred to in this chapter are considered to have been made with the camera axis vertical, or as nearly vertical as practicable in an aircraft.

The photographs used may be *contact prints*, made with the negatives in contact with sensitized photographic paper; *ratio prints*, the scales of which have been changed from those of the negatives by enlargement or reduction; or *stereoscopic pairs* (stereo-pairs), in which two photographs of the same area are taken in such a manner as to afford stereoscopic vision.

---

[1] See bibliography at end of this chapter.

An important property of a photograph is its scale, which is the ratio of a distance on the photograph to a corresponding distance on the ground. The scale of a photograph varies from point to point because of *displacements* caused by camera *tilt* and topographic *relief*. These displacements must be corrected for, if the photograph is to be used for precise measurements.

A *flight strip* is a succession of overlapping aerial photographs taken along a single course. The *overlap* is necessary for stereoscopic examination and for the construction of mosaics.

A *mosaic* is an assemblage of aerial photographs the edges of which have been trimmed and matched to form a continuous photographic representation of a portion of the earth's surface. If the photographs are matched without reference to ground control points, the resulting map is an *uncontrolled mosaic*; if they have first been brought to a uniform scale and fitted to ground control stations, the map is a *controlled mosaic*.

A *planimetric map* is one which shows the horizontal positions of selected natural and cultural features, whereas a *topographic map* also shows relief in measurable form, usually by contours. The term *base map* is used to define a large-scale planimetric map compiled from aerial photographs. A copy of the base map may be used for the addition of contours and other data located by means of the plane table and/or photogrammetric methods.

12–3. Uncontrolled Mosaics.—In making an uncontrolled mosaic, contact prints covering the area to be studied are trimmed and assembled by matching like images and are then fastened to a rigid or flexible backing. If the mosaic is for temporary use in the field, the prints are mounted on linen or other material that will permit the map to be rolled up. For this purpose semi-matte prints are preferred because they take pencil lines readily and are not scratched as easily as glossy prints. For more permanent use, properly matched glossy prints may be stapled or pasted to a rigid backing. If desired, the assembly may be photographed to preserve one or more copies of the complete map, after which the mosaic is dismantled so that the contact prints may be used for stereoscopic study.

Such a mosaic is relatively inexpensive and, though subject to errors because of scale variations and displacements, it is extremely valuable for reconnaissance (Art. 12–8) and miscellaneous uses (Art. 12–11).

12–4. Importance of Stereoscopic Vision.—Most aerial photography is done by flying parallel flights across an area. During the flights, photographs are taken at intervals such that adjacent photographs will overlap approximately 30 per cent at the sides and 60 per cent in the direction of flight. This insures that the center (*principal point*) in each photograph will appear in the adjacent picture taken in the line of flight, thus providing what is called "stereoscopic overlap." By properly orienting the overlapping photographs (stereopairs) and viewing them through a stereoscope, the process known as "stereoscopic fusion" takes place. In this process there is a vivid mental impression of the terrain in three dimensions. (A simple demonstration of stereoscopic fusion is shown on page 294.) In effect, two positions of the camera lens several thousand feet apart are substituted for the observer's eyes. In the resulting image, relative heights of hills and structures, depths of canyons, and slopes of terrain are determinable. Used in this way, the old principle of stereoscopic vision has become probably the most important basic tool for studying the manifold problems of route-location.

12–5. Controlled Mosaics.—The utility of a mosaic may be greatly increased by bringing the photographs to a uniform scale, correcting them for tilt, and fitting them in their correct relative positions. This procedure requires the location of *control points* by ground surveying methods.

Control stations, properly distributed over the area, are first selected with the aid of the stereoscope. They should be definite points easily recognized on the photographs and accessible on the ground. Buildings, fence corners, or road intersections usually serve this purpose. Preparatory to planning the ground control surveys, the selected control points are marked on each photograph by a circled prick point.

The ground control consists of suitable triangulation, traverse, and level circuits from which the coordinates and elevations of the control points may be computed. Ground control is costly and should therefore be no more precise or extensive than is required for the purpose. In research aimed at reducing the cost of ground control for surveys of very large areas, some progress in use of air-borne radar, and shoran techniques, has been made.[3,4,5]

In making the finished mosaic, the contact prints are ratioed (brought to the same predetermined scale), rectified (corrected for tilt), and fitted on a base board to the plotted ground control points. There are several methods of doing this, all of which are highly technical and require special equipment. Only the central part of each photograph is used in compiling the mosaic, and the trimmed edges are feathered on the underside. In addition, prints having the same tone, or degree of exposure, are selected. The finished mosaic then has the appearance of a single large photograph.

12–6. Planimetric Maps.—A planimetric map, on which are shown the accurate positions of such natural and cultural features as watercourses, forests, highways, and buildings, may be constructed from aerial photographs which are tied to adequate ground control. The first step is to make a control plot on which the ground control points are located from their computed coordinates. Photographic control points ("picture points") must also be located on the plot to permit proper matching of the photographs. These are points that are clearly visible on two or more photographs but are not tied in by the ground surveys. They are usually located on the control plot by an analytic or graphical method of *radial triangulation*.

The positions of details may be transferred from the photographs to the plot either by a relatively simple tracing method or by a stereographic method that employs special plotting instruments. The tracing method yields good results only if the photographs are relatively free from relief or tilt displacements. In this method each photograph is fitted as closely as possible to the plotted control points, and the selected details are traced onto the plot. The positions of details which show on two photographs may have to be adjusted to compensate for slight differences in their traced locations.

A more accurate map, free from the effects of tilt displacement, may be constructed with the aid of complicated optical and mechanical instruments. The principal types of such instruments are the *stereocomparator* (and related instruments such as the *stereo-planigraph* and *aero-cartograph*), the *multiplex aero-projector*, and the Kelsh plotter.

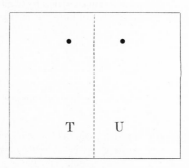

Hold a card between the letters and along the dotted line. Closing one eye at a time, adjust the head so the letter T (but not U) can be seen with the left eye, and conversely with the right eye. Then open both eyes. The two dots above the letters will fuse together and appear as one. To prove that two dots are actually being seen, notice that the letters T and U appear to be superimposed. Moreover, a slight rotation of the head will cause the dots and letters to separate vertically.

Fig. 12-1. Stereoscopic fusion

These instruments utilize the principle of the *floating mark*. The photographs of a stereo-pair are viewed through two movable eyepieces, each having a small dot or mark etched on a lens of the optical system. When the photographs are viewed, the two marks will appear to fuse to form a single mark apparently floating in space above or below the terrain in the stereoscopic view. A simple demonstration of stereoscopic fusion is shown in Fig. 12–1. By proper manipulation of the instrument the floating mark can be made to rise or sink vertically. In planimetric mapping by use of the stereo-comparator, the general procedure is to operate the device so that the floating mark appears to be touching the surface of the ground (or other feature to be mapped) in the stereoscopic image, and then to read scales from which the coordinates of the point viewed may be determined. Points so located are eventually plotted on the map. In more-complex instruments of this type a special arrangement of levers, gears, and shafts permits the path of the floating mark to be plotted directly.

Many details appearing on the aerial photographs may be transferred to the planimetric map without commensurate increase in cost—in contrast to the situation in ground survey-ing. Moreover, only the relevant details need be transferred. Thus, several different planimetric maps may be constructed from the same photographs, the features shown on a map depending on the use to be made of the map.

12–7. Topographic Maps by Photogrammetric Methods. A stereoscopic plotting instrument of the type just described may also be manipulated in such a way as to measure the dif-ferences in elevation between points on the stereo-pairs. In principle, the first step in doing this is to adjust the instru-ment until the floating mark rests on a control point of known elevation. The frame carrying the two eyepieces is then moved in the x- and y-directions until the mark is at the detail being measured but is apparently floating in space above or below it. The mark is then made to rise or sink until it is at the same elevation as the detail. This is done by narrowing or increasing the distance between the eyepieces. Scale read-ings made during the procedure can be converted to give the x- and y-coordinates of the particular detail viewed and its elevation with respect to the control point. The principle can be extended to the drawing of contours, thus converting the planimetric map into a complete topographic representation.

As instruments and techniques have been improved, the accuracy of topographic maps made by photogrammetric methods now approaches that attainable by ground surveys.

(a)

Fig. 12–2. Reproduction of an aerial photograph, and a photogrammetric map. (Courtesy Jack Ammann Photogrammetric Engineers, Inc.)

For example, the National Map Accuracy Standards require that 90 per cent of all elevations be correct within one-half the contour interval and that the remaining 10 per cent not be in error by more than the contour interval. In addition, these standards require that 90 per cent of well-defined map features be within $\frac{1}{50}$ in. (map scale) of their true coordinate positions

That such standards are realistic and attainable was demonstrated by their use in planning the Pennsylvania Turn-

CITY OF KEOKUK, IOWA

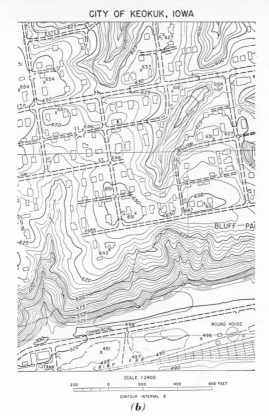

SCALE 1:2400

CONTOUR INTERVAL 5'

(b)

Fig. 12-2—*Continued*

pike extensions,[6,7] which utilized photogrammetric maps made
to a scale of 1 in. = 200 ft, showing planimetric details, spot
elevations, and 5-ft contours.   Even more-rigid requirements
are sometimes specified.   For example, topographic maps with
a contour interval of 1 ft, at a scale of 1 in. = 40 ft, have been
prepared for the highway commission of one eastern state.
The accuracy required was that 90 per cent of the contours be
dependable within $\frac{1}{2}$ ft.[8,9]   A reproduction of a portion of an

aerial photograph is shown in Fig. 12–2(a), and a photogrammetric map of the area covered by the photograph is shown in Fig. 12–2(b).

12–8. Photogrammetry for Reconnaissance.—Before making the detailed projection of a route between selected termini, there must be general studies dealing with intermediate controls and interpretation of terrain. These studies may be summarized in the one word *reconnaissance*. If the controls usually present are examined (see Art. 9–3), they will be seen to fall into two principal types: (1) land usage and (2) topography. Both types of controls are recorded in great detail on aerial photographs. In fact, it is now generally agreed that such photographs provide the best means of making the type of careful reconnaissance so aptly emphasized by Wellington (Art. 1–9).

For the first stage of reconnaissance, as described in Art. 10–9, small-scale photographs of the region between the termini will enable the designer to select the important controls and locate all feasible route bands. The scale of these photographs will depend on the distance between the termini and the importance of the intervening terrain. In practice, scales as small as 1 in. = 2,000 ft (1 : 24,000) are quite suitable. The best procedure is to lay up an uncontrolled mosaic and to study it in conjunction with stereoscopic examination of stereo-pairs. The result will be the selection of several bands of terrain between the termini within each of which lies an apparently feasible location. These bands may be from 1,800 feet to 1 mile or more in width.

The second stage of reconnaissance has for its purpose the comparison of the route bands and the selection of the most promising one. In some instances the choice will become apparent during the first stage, but in more-difficult cases it may first be necessary to study larger-scale photographs. These may be prepared with little extra cost by enlarging the original photographs up to a practical maximum of about four diameters. Even when the original photographs are taken in the summer, these enlargements are usable, since heavy foliage does not detract seriously from their value in reconnaissance studies.

In both stages of reconnaissance the aerial photographs should be supplemented by other available maps. One ingenious method is to make photographic enlargements of U.S.G.S. sheets on a transparent-film base, to serve as an overlay at the same scale as the mosaic.[10] Used in conjunction with the stereo-pairs, this method adds a quantitative factor to the study. Inaccuracies in the maps or scale distortions in the photographs affect all route bands equally and are not large enough to invalidate this procedure. Many of the miscellaneous values disclosed by aerial photographs (Art. 12-11) will become apparent in these studies and will also contribute toward the selection of the best route band. Field inspection at critical locations may be needed to resolve some difficulties.

12-9. Photogrammetry for Detailed Location Studies.—The type of photogrammetric application used for detailed location depends on the type of transportation route involved. It is possible to establish the location of a transmission line or a long pressure pipe line simply from the study of mosaics and stereo-pairs. However, the accurate location of a highway, a railroad, or other route on which grades and right-of-way costs are more important requires either a planimetric map or a topographic map.

It should be recalled that both planimetric and topographic maps, when made by photogrammetric methods, necessitate careful ground control and specialized mapping techniques. Their cost calls for keeping ground control and plotted detail to the minimum required for the purpose. Consequently the planimetric map need only show relevant details. To locate some types of routes, spot elevations at critical points may be the only data needed to indicate relief. For superhighway location, however, a complete topographic map showing contours at not more than 5-ft intervals is almost a necessity.

In some instances contours may be drawn by stereoscopic plotting only on certain portions of the planimetric map, the remaining contours being fixed by plane-table or other ground-survey methods. This might be true, for example, in extremely flat areas or where dense ground cover prevents obtaining the specified accuracy of contour location from photographs.

Complete topographic maps, made as outlined in Art. 12–7, vary in scale from 1 in. = 200 ft, with a 5-ft or 10-ft contour interval, to 1 in. = 40 ft, with 1-ft contours. To meet the National Map Accuracy Standards the scale of the contact prints cannot ordinarily exceed four times the map scale, although the maps to a scale of 1 in. = 200 ft prepared for the Pennsylvania Turnpike extensions[6,7] were made from prints having a taking scale of about 1 in. = 1,000 ft. (The selected route band in these examples was 1 mile wide.)

Other practical examples from states that have used photogrammetric maps on highway projects are:

California[11]—Taking scale 200 ft per inch. Map scale 1 in. = 50 ft, with 2-ft contours.

Connecticut[12]—Taking scales 500, 200, and 100 ft per inch. Corresponding map scales 1 in. = 200 ft (5-ft contours), 1 in. = 100 ft (2-ft contours), 1 in. = 40 ft (1-ft contours).

Massachusetts[4,12]—Taking scale 600 ft per inch for rural locations; 400 ft per inch for urban work. Map scales 1 in. = 200 ft (5-ft contours) and 1 in. = 100 ft (2-ft contours).

Ohio[10]—Taking scale 200 ft per inch. Map scale 1 in. = 50 ft, with 2-ft contours.

Once the topographic maps are prepared, trial lines are laid down on them with a spline, and the best route is chosen by following the usual paper-location procedure, as outlined in Art. 9–11.

An important feature of the paper-location study is the estimate of grading quantities. If topographic maps made from aerial photographs actually meet the National Map Accuracy Standards, there is no reason why adequate quantity estimates cannot be prepared from them. Recently, highway engineers are finding that this is true. For example, in Massachusetts on a 2-mile relocation the difference between quantities computed from surveyed cross sections and from sections plotted from aerial topographic maps was only 2.6 per cent in embankment and 3.3 per cent in excavation.[13] A similar comparison on a 7,600-ft project in Connecticut[12] showed discrepancies of 1.4 per cent in cut and 1.2 per cent in fill.   On a 30-mile project in California[11] the variation in the excavation quantities was less than 2.5 per cent.

The foregoing results lead to the belief that in highway construction we may eventually make contract payment for excavation on the basis of quantities derived from photogrammetric studies.   A step in this direction was taken in Ohio[10] on a 4.12-mile relocation for which a complete set of construction plans was prepared by photogrammetric studies and these plans were used immediately for award of the construction contract by the usual competitive method.

12–10. Costs of Photogrammetric Mapping.—In addition to possessing many other advantages, photogrammetric maps can often be prepared at far less cost than maps made by conventional ground survey methods.   The tabulation on page 302 is instructive in this regard.

In preparing the tabulation, the cost data for projects not listed in the bibliography were obtained from commercial organizations specializing in photogrammetric mapping.   It is important to observe that unit costs of photogrammetric maps depend principally on the scale and the contour interval. The length of the project—for given specifications—has practically no effect on unit costs.

On a cost-per-mile basis, comparable maps made by ground survey methods will rarely cost less, and will usually cost much more, than photogrammetric maps.   However, a fairer comparison of costs should take into account the fact that maps compiled from ground surveys rarely cover as wide a strip of topography as those made photogrammetrically.   On recent work in Massachusetts, for example, the average cost of aerial topographic maps was $680 per mile for a strip 6,000 ft wide; whereas costs for ground surveys and plotting were about $1,500 per mile for a strip only 500 ft wide.[13]

Regardless of whether photogrammetry produces savings in mapping costs, it is likely to yield substantial savings in construction costs.   These savings accrue not only from time savings but also from reduction in grading quantities and construction difficulties because the wider strip of topography and the astute use of stereo-pairs may result in the projection of a better location than is possible by former methods.

Cost Data on Photogrammetric Maps for Highway-Route Location

Year	State	Mileage	Cost per Mile	Cost per Acre	Special Notes
		Specification:	40-ft Scale—1-ft Contours—1,000 ft Wide		
1948	Conn.	4	$3,000	$25	Ref. No. 8, p. 307
1950	Conn.	3.8	1,950	16	Ref. No. 8, p. 307
		Specification:	100-ft Scale—2-ft Contours—½ Mile Wide		
1950	Conn.	7.7	$1,020	$3.19	Ref. No. 8, p. 307
1952	Mass.	15	1,033	4.27	Strip 1,200 ft wide
		Specification:	200-ft Scale—5-ft Contours—1 Mile Wide		
1944	N.Y.-N.J.	31	$ 570	$0.79	6,000-ft strip. Ref. 20, p. 308
1944	Mass.	20.5	629	0.86	6,000-ft strip. Ref. 21, p. 308
1947	Pa.	140	586	0.92	Ref. No. 6, p. 307
1947	Pa.	68	825	1.29	Ref. No. 6, p. 307
1950	Conn.	7.1	610	0.96	Ref. No. 8, p. 307
1952	Mass.	60	958	1.50	
1953	Pa.	150	953	1.49	
1954	Mass.	11	1,091	1.71	
1954	Pa.	44	1,023	1.60	
1954	N.Y.	100	820	1.28	
1954	Ill.*	450	348	1.43	2,000-ft strip.

* This project was unusual in that the entire 450 miles of mapping was delivered within 90 days after signing of the contract. In order to attain this speed, the usual field control was omitted. The control consisted of spot elevations and horizontal positions taken from available Federal maps and surveys of the area. Tolerance on vertical accuracy was a full contour interval rather than the customary half contour interval.

As an example, on a highway project in rugged terrain in Mississippi, excavation quantities averaged 42,872 cu yd per mile as determined from a ground survey location, whereas another location, worked out later with the aid of aerial photographs, was selected with excavation quantities averaging only 27,536 cu yd per mile.[14]   A similar comparison on a recent 16-mile highway in Georgia[15] showed that photogrammetric location cut mapping costs in half and also produced construction-cost savings of $200,000.

The comments made in Art. 1–13 relative to costs and ultimate accuracies are especially pertinent in aerial photography and mapping.   Photographs should be taken at a scale suited to resolving the smallest detail that must actually be shown on the map; otherwise additional field surveys will be needed and costs will mount.   The topographic map itself should be drawn with the smallest horizontal scale and largest contour interval that will serve the requirements.   Greater accuracy and larger scales than are needed are wasteful and costly.

12–11. Miscellaneous Uses of Aerial Photographs.—The technical utility and economic advantages of aerial photographs, as described in the preceding articles, carry enough weight to justify their employment on all important route-location projects.   However, it is worth emphasizing that aerial photographs possess other inherent values which may result as by-products from their primary uses.   Often, these miscellaneous uses will require little additional cost or effort.

The auxiliary uses of aerial photographs are many and varied.   They may be found in any stage of route location, from the preliminary planning to studies made after the route is in operation.   The following valuable uses have been reported:

For Preliminary Planning

   Interpretation of terrain.   Drainage patterns.   Soil types.   Land use as affecting costs of right-of-way. Location and extent of wooded areas, swamps, rock outcrops, snow-slide and erosion scars, and borrow material and granular deposits for use in construction.

For Detailed Studies

Size of drainage areas for culvert determination. Planning of interchanges, using oblique photographs. Large-scale site maps for bridges, intersections, and other detailed studies, prepared from one pair of photographs with a stereoscopic plotting instrument.[10]

For Construction

Determination of best means of access. Type of clearing. Possible effect of terrain and climatic conditions on choice of construction equipment. Progress reports, using series of oblique photographs taken in sequence along route at convenient time intervals.[7]

After Construction

Traffic studies, including traffic counts, speeds, and densities, congestion, railroad grade-crossing elimination, efficiency of existing parking facilities, and location of new parking areas. Road-inventory studies, including changes in use of abutting land and pavement-condition surveys.[16]

General

Public-relations purposes in general, such as illustrations at public hearings and legislative reviews pertaining to proposed route location and land takings, using oblique photographs that are easier for the layman to understand (see the Frontispiece).

12-12. Limitations of Photogrammetry.—Photogrammetry for purposes of route location is not without its limitations. Clarity in photographs requires good atmospheric conditions—freedom from clouds, mist, smoke, or severe haze. In some parts of the world such ideal conditions may occur only one or two days in the year.[17]

The interrrelationship between aerial photographs and ground control requires careful planning as to their timing. A hasty decision to take aerial photographs, solely in the belief that they always save time, invites inefficiency and may raise costs.

It is virtually impossible to determine precise elevations from photographs taken when there is heavy snow cover or dense vegetation. Consequently, for contour mapping the photographs should be taken when the ground is bare and the trees are defoliated. Regions having dense forests of different types and heights of evergreens obviously present a difficult problem.

Photogrammetric methods should not usually be used for maps requiring elevations with an error of less than 1 ft. For example, contour mapping by photogrammetry is questionable for canal location in areas when contours are widely spaced and where high precision is needed. In such circumstances is would be better to draw a planimetric map by photogrammetric methods and then add contours and spot elevations by appropriate ground surveying methods.

If the area to be mapped is small or if only a narrow strip of topography is needed, photogrammetry may then be restricted by economics rather than by technical limitations.

Finally, projects such as highway relocation require additional data about details that can only be obtained by ground methods. Among these are: precise location of hydrants, water gates, and property-line markers; utility-pole numbers; type, critical elevation, and house number of buildings; size and invert elevation of culverts; and all the information regarding existing subsurface installations that are needed for design drawings and construction planning.

12–13. Summary of Advantages of Aerial Photography in Route Surveying.—To summarize the information in this chapter, it is apparent that the salient advantages of aerial photography in route surveying are:

1. The larger area and wider route bands covered by the photographs give greater flexibility in route location and practically insure that no better location has been overlooked.

2. Practically all the studies preceding construction can be made without encroaching on private property or arousing premature fears in regard to the extent of property damage. Land speculation is thereby reduced. Moreover, the eventual acquiring of right-of-way is expedited

because property owners can see clearly on the photographs the effects of the takings.

3. On a large project the elapsed time between starting the survey work and construction can be greatly shortened. Should weather conditions provide only a short field season, ground control and photography can be done then, the map compilation being left for indoor work during the winter months. In contrast to plane-table work, the stereoscopic plotting of contours is independent of weather and can be done on a day-and-night schedule if necessary.

4. Over-all survey and mapping costs may be considerably less than by ground methods.

5. Maps made by photogrammetric methods possess a more uniform accuracy than is usually found in those compiled from ground surveys.

6. What was formerly thought to be the ultimate goal of aerial photography—the compilation of detailed topographic maps—is being extended to even more useful purposes, such as quantity estimates and complete construction plans.

7. Photogrammetry is of direct value in reducing the shortage of engineering services by releasing engineering personnel from routine survey work for more-advanced employment in design.

8. Aerial photographs have many auxiliary uses and contain more information about a variety of significant features than the engineer can obtain by ground methods except at greatly increased cost.

BIBLIOGRAPHY

1. Whitmore, G.D., *Advanced Surveying and Mapping*, Scranton: International Textbook Company, 1949.

2. *Manual of Photogrammetry*, 2d ed., American Society of Photogrammetry, Washington, D.C., 1952.

3. Hoover, C.R., "Development of an Optical Radar System for Surveying Purposes," *Transactions, American Geophysical Union*, Vol. 31, No. 4, August, 1950, pp. 518-524.

4. Ross, J.E.R., "Shoran, Application to Geodetic Triangulation," *The Canadian Surveyor*, Vol. 10, No. 3, January, 1950, pp. 9-18.

5. Aslakson, C.I., "The Use of Electronics in Surveying and Mapping," *Proceedings of The Third National Surveying-Teachers' Conference*, American Society for Engineering Education, 1952, pp. 198-217.

6. Williams, F.J., "Photogrammetry Locates 208 Miles of Pennsylvania Turnpike Extensions," *Civil Engineering*, Vol. 20, No. 12, December, 1950, pp. 761-763.

7. Gilbert, G.B., "Photogrammetry Aids the Pennsylvania Turnpike," *Proceedings ASCE*, Vol. 80, Separate No. 577, December, 1954.

8. Hooper, C.J., "Photogrammetry and Its Uses in Highway Planning and Design," *Photogrammetric Engineering*, Vol. XVII, No. 1, March, 1951, pp. 133-137.

9. Quinn, A.O., "Photogrammetry Aids Highway Engineers," *Photogrammetric Engineering*, Vol. XVIII, No. 5, December, 1952, pp. 787-790.

10. Meyer, R.W., "Aerial Photography Streamlines Ohio's Highway Program," *Photogrammetric Engineering*, Vol. XIX, No. 5, December, 1953, pp. 771-776.

11. Telford, E.T., "Photogrammetry as Applied to Highway Engineering," *Photogrammetric Engineering*, Vol. XVII, No. 1, March, 1951, pp. 175-180.

12. Perkins, E.T., "Use of Aerial Surveys in Highway Location," *Proceedings of Conference on Modern Highways*, Massachusetts Institute of Technology, June, 1953, pp. 70-77.

13. Houdlette, E.C., "Photogrammetry as Applied to Highway Engineering in Massachusetts," *Photogrammetric Engineering*, Vol. XVII, No. 1, March, 1951, pp. 138-143.

14. Brown, I.W., "Photogrammetry as Applied To Highway Engineering in Mississippi," *Photogrammetric Engineering*, Vol. XVII, No. 1, March, 1951, pp. 151-160.

15. Norton, E.A., Panel: "Photogrammetry Saves Dollars," *Photogrammetric Engineering*, Vol. XX, No. 3, June, 1954, pp. 467-486.

16. McMaster, H.M., and Legault, A.R., "Pavement Condition Surveys by Means of Aerial Photographs," Univ. of Nebraska, Eng. Exp. Sta., *Bulletin No. 1*, April, 1952.

17. Cottrell, C.M., Panel: "Engineering Applications of Photogrammetry," *Photogrammetric Engineering*, Vol. XX, No. 3, June, 1954, pp. 516-520.

18. Gawkins, E.T., "Aerial Mapping Cuts Cost of Highway Location in New York," *Civil Engineering*, Vol. 17, No. 2, February, 1947, pp. 80-82.

19. Pryor, W.T., "Photogrammetry as Applied to Highway Engineering," *Photogrammetric Engineering*, Vol. 17, No. 1, March, 1951, pp. 111-125.

20. Nelson, S., "Aerial Surveys Expedite Highway Planning," *1944 Group Meeting Book*, American Association of State Highway Officials.

21. Houdlette, E.C., "Massachusetts Adapts Aerial Photography to Highway Location," *Civil Engineering*, Vol. 17, No. 2, February, 1947, pp. 85 ff.

APPENDIX

PARTIAL THEORY OF THE SPIRAL

APPENDIX

PARTIAL THEORY OF THE SPIRAL

Derivation of Coordinates X and Y.—From Fig. 5–3, $dx = dl \cos \delta$ and $dy = dl \sin \delta$. When the cosine and the sine are expressed as infinite series,

$$dx = dl \left[1 - \frac{\delta^2}{2!} + \frac{\delta^4}{4!} - \frac{\delta^6}{6!} + \ldots \right]$$

and

$$dy = dl \left[\delta - \frac{\delta^3}{3!} + \frac{\delta^5}{5!} - \frac{\delta^7}{7!} + \ldots \right]$$

But $d\delta = \dfrac{dl}{r}$, $r = \dfrac{5,729.58}{d}$, and $d = \dfrac{k\,l}{100}$. Substituting and integrating gives:

$$\delta = \frac{k\,l^2}{1,145,916} = \text{(for simplicity) } \alpha\,l^2$$

Therefore, $dx = dl \left[1 - \dfrac{\alpha^2\,l^4}{2!} + \dfrac{\alpha^4\,l^8}{4!} - \dfrac{\alpha^6\,l^{12}}{6!} + \ldots \right]$

and

$$dy = dl \left[\alpha\,l^2 - \frac{\alpha^3\,l^6}{3!} + \frac{\alpha^5\,l^{10}}{5!} - \frac{\alpha^7\,l^{14}}{7!} + \ldots \right]$$

The result obtained by integrating and substituting δ for $\alpha\,l^2$ is

$$x = l \left[1 - \frac{\delta^2}{5(2!)} + \frac{\delta^4}{9(4!)} - \frac{\delta^6}{13(6!)} + \ldots \right] \tag{A–1}$$

and

$$y = l \left[\frac{\delta}{3} - \frac{\delta^3}{7(3!)} + \frac{\delta^5}{11(5!)} - \frac{\delta^7}{15(7!)} + \ldots \right] \tag{A·2}$$

Equations A–1 and A–2, in which Δ is substituted for δ, are used in calculating X and Y for insertion in spiral tables, such as Tables XI and XII in Part III.

Derivation of Correction C in $a = \frac{1}{3}\delta - C$.—Dividing equation A–2 by equation A–1 gives:

$$\tan a = \frac{y}{x} = \frac{\delta}{3} + \frac{\delta^3}{105} + \frac{26\,\delta^5}{155,925} - \frac{17\,\delta^7}{3,378,375} - \ldots \tag{A–3}$$

But

$$a = \tan a - \tfrac{1}{3} \tan^3 a + \tfrac{1}{5} \tan^5 a - \ldots \tag{A–4}$$

311

When the value of tan a from equation A-3 is substituted in equation A-4 and like terms are collected, the result is

$$a = \frac{\delta}{3} - \frac{8\,\delta^3}{2,835} - \frac{32\,\delta^5}{467,775} - \frac{128\,\delta^7}{83,284,288} - \ldots \quad (A-5)$$

or
$$a = \tfrac{1}{3}\,\delta - \text{a small correction } C$$

Radians being converted to minutes, the value of the correction C is:

C (in minutes) $= 516\ (10)^{-7}\,\delta^3 + 381\ (10)^{-12}\,\delta^5 + \ldots \quad (A-6)$

The corrections in Table XVI-C were computed from equation A-6.

Source of the Corrections Marked * for Conversion to A.R.E.A. Spiral.—In the case of a spiraled curve, changing the definition of the degree of the simple curve from D_a to D_c affects only the coordinates of the offset T.C.

In Table XI the * corrections to be subtracted from the coordinates of the offset T.C. based upon D_a, in order to obtain those based upon D_c, are:

$$(X - R_a \sin \Delta) - (X - R_c \sin \Delta) = (R_c - R_a) \sin \Delta \quad (A-7)$$

and $\quad (Y - R_a \text{ vers } \Delta) - (Y - R_c \text{ vers } \Delta) = (R_c - R_a) \text{ vers } \Delta \ (A-8)$

In Table XII the * coefficients come from the following relations:

Total correction to $X_o = (R_c - R_a) \sin \Delta = {}^*$ times D

Total correction to $o = (R_c - R_a) \text{ vers } \Delta = {}^*$ times D

LIST OF TABLES

I.	Radii, Deflections, Offsets, etc.	2
II.	Lengths of Arcs and True Chords	14
III.	Correction Coefficients for Subchords. Chord Definition of D	15
IV.	Correction Coefficients for Subchords. Arc Definition of D	15
V.	Even-Radius Curves. Deflections and Chords	16
VI.	Lengths of Circular Arcs; Radius $=1$	18
VII.	Minutes and Seconds in Decimals of a Degree	19
VIII.	Tangents and Externals for a 1° Curve	20
IX.	Corrections for Tangents. Chord Def. of D	43
X.	Corrections for Externals. Chord Def. of D	43
XI.	Selected Spirals	45
XII.	Spiral Functions for $L_s = 1$	54
XIII.	Coefficients for Curve with Equal Spirals	63
XIV.	Tangents and Externals for Unit Double-Spiral Curve	64
XV.	Deflection Angles for 10-Chord Spiral	66
XVI.	Coefficients of a_1 for Deflections to any Chord Point on Spiral	70
XVI–C.	Corrections to Table XVI for Large Deflections	71
XVII.	Level Sections	72
XVII–A.	Corrections to Table XVII for Transverse Ground Slopes	79
XVII–B.	Corrections to Table XVII for Transverse Ground Slopes	79
XVIII.	Triangular Prisms. Cubic Yards per 50 feet	80
XIX.	Cubic Yards per 100-Foot Station	90
XX.	Natural Trigonometric Functions	92
XXI.	Logarithms of Numbers	183
XXI–A.	7-Place Logarithms of Numbers from 1 to 100	207
XXI–B.	7-Place Logarithms of Useful Constants	207
XXII.	Logarithmic Sin, Cos, Tan, and Cot	208
XXIII.	Logarithmic Versines	254
XXIV.	Stadia Reductions	278
XXV.	Turnout and Crossover Data	286
XXVI.	Trigonometric Formulas	292
XXVII.	Squares, Cubes, Square Roots, Cube Roots, and Reciprocals	295

TABLE I.—RADII, DEFLECTIONS, OFFSETS, ETC.

Chord Definition of Degree of Curve* (D_c)	Arc Definition of Degree of Curve* (D_a)
MATHEMATICAL RELATIONS	MATHEMATICAL RELATIONS
1. $\sin \frac{1}{2} D_c = \dfrac{50}{R}$ .... exactly	1. $D_a = \dfrac{5{,}729.58}{R}$ .... exactly
2. C.O. $= \dfrac{100^2}{R} = 200 \sin \frac{1}{2} D_c$ exactly	2. C.O. $= 4\,R \sin^2 \frac{1}{2} D_a$ exactly
3. T.O. $= \frac{1}{2}$C.O. ..... exactly	3. T.O. $= \frac{1}{2}$C.O. ..... exactly
4. M.O. $= \frac{1}{8}$C.O. .... approx.	4. M.O. $= \frac{1}{8}$C.O. .... approx.

Notes

1) For values of D_a less than 12°, the C.O. (not tabulated) may be taken equal to the tabulated C.O. for the corresponding value of D_c. Exact values of C.O. are tabulated for both definitions of D, where D equals or exceeds 12°.

2) For values of D_c and D_a less than 12°, relation 4 will give M.O. without perceptible error. Beyond $D_c = 12°$, the exact values of M.O. are tabulated.

3) For any value of D, the ratio $\dfrac{\text{M.O.}}{\text{C.O.}}$ is numerically the same for both definitions of D. Thus, if D_a were 52°, the M.O. equals $\dfrac{11.54}{87.67}$ (84.69), which is 11.17.

4) To obtain *c.o.*, *t*, and *m.o.* for a chord or arc shorter than 100 ft, multiply C.O., T.O., and M.O. by $\left(\dfrac{\text{chord or arc}}{100}\right)^2$.

* See Arts. 2–4 and 2–14.

TABLE I.—RADII, DEFLECTIONS, OFFSETS, ETC.

Degree of Curve D	Defl. Per Ft of Sta. (Min)	Chord Definition			Arc Definition	
		Radius R	log R	C.O. 1 Sta.	Radius R	log R
0° 0'		Infinite	Infin.		Infinite	Infin.
1'	0.005	343775.	5.536274	0.03	343775.	5.536274
2'	0.01	171887.	5.235244	0.06	171887.	5.235244
3'	0.015	114592.	5.059153	0.09	114592.	5.059153
4'	0.02	85943.7	4.934214	0.12	85943.7	4.934214
5'	0.025	68754.9	4.837304	0.15	68754.9	4.837304
6'	0.03	57295.8	4.758123	0.17	57295.8	4.758123
7'	0.035	49110.7	4.691176	0.20	49110.7	4.691176
8'	0.04	42971.8	4.633184	0.23	42971.8	4.633184
9'	0.045	38197.2	4.582031	0.26	38197.2	4.582031
10'	0.05	34377.5	4.536274	0.29	34377.5	4.536274
11'	0.055	31252.3	4.494881	0.32	31252.3	4.494881
12'	0.06	28647.8	4.457093	0.35	28647.8	4.457093
13'	0.065	26444.2	4.422331	0.38	26444.2	4.422331
14'	0.07	24555.4	4.390146	0.41	24555.3	4.390146
15'	0.075	22918.3	4.360183	0.44	22918.3	4.360183
16'	0.08	21485.9	4.332154	0.47	21485.9	4.332154
17'	0.085	20222.1	4.305825	0.49	20222.0	4.305825
18'	0.09	19098.6	4.281002	0.52	19098.6	4.281001
19'	0.095	18093.4	4.257521	0.55	18093.4	4.257520
20'	0.1	17188.8	4.235244	0.58	17188.7	4.235244
21'	0.105	16370.2	4.214055	0.61	16370.2	4.214055
22'	0.11	15626.1	4.193852	0.64	15626.1	4.193851
23'	0.115	14946.8	4.174547	0.67	14946.7	4.174546
24'	0.12	14324.0	4.156064	0.70	14323.9	4.156063
25'	0.125	13751.0	4.138335	0.73	13751.0	4.138334
26'	0.13	13222.1	4.121302	0.76	13222.1	4.121300
27'	0.135	12732.4	4.104911	0.79	12732.4	4.104910
28'	0.14	12277.7	4.089117	0.81	12277.7	4.089116
29'	0.145	11854.3	4.073877	0.84	11854.3	4.073876
30'	0.15	11459.2	4.059153	0.87	11459.2	4.059153
31'	0.155	11089.6	4.044914	0.90	11089.5	4.044912
32'	0.16	10743.0	4.031125	0.93	10743.0	4.031124
33'	0.165	10417.5	4.017762	0.96	10417.4	4.017760
34'	0.17	10111.1	4.004797	0.99	10111.0	4.004795
35'	0.175	9822.18	3.992208	1.02	9822.13	3.992206
36'	0.18	9549.34	3.979973	1.05	9549.29	3.979971
37'	0.185	9291.25	3.968074	1.07	9291.21	3.968072
38'	0.19	9046.75	3.956493	1.11	9046.70	3.956490
39'	0.195	8814.78	3.945212	1.13	8814.73	3.945209
40'	0.2	8594.42	3.934216	1.16	8594.37	3.934214
41'	0.205	8384.80	3.923493	1.19	8384.75	3.923490
42'	0.21	8185.16	3.913027	1.21	8185.11	3.913025
43'	0.215	7994.81	3.902808	1.25	7994.76	3.902805
44'	0.22	7813.11	3.892824	1.28	7813.06	3.892821
45'	0.225	7639.49	3.883065	1.31	7639.44	3.883061
46'	0.23	7473.42	3.873519	1.34	7473.36	3.873516
47'	0.235	7314.41	3.864179	1.37	7314.35	3.864176
48'	0.24	7162.03	3.855036	1.39	7161.97	3.855033
49'	0.245	7015.87	3.846082	1.43	7015.81	3.846078
50'	0.25	6875.55	3.837308	1.45	6875.49	3.837304
51'	0.255	6740.74	3.828708	1.48	6740.68	3.828704
52'	0.26	6611.12	3.820275	1.51	6611.05	3.820270
53'	0.265	6486.38	3.812002	1.54	6486.31	3.811998
54'	0.27	6366.26	3.803885	1.57	6366.20	3.803880
55'	0.275	6250.51	3.795916	1.60	6250.45	3.795911
56'	0.28	6138.90	3.788091	1.63	6138.83	3.788086
57'	0.285	6031.20	3.780404	1.66	6031.14	3.780399
58'	0.29	5927.22	3.772851	1.69	5927.15	3.772846
59'	0.295	5826.76	3.765427	1.72	5826.69	3.765422

3

TABLE I.—RADII, DEFLECTIONS, OFFSETS, ETC.

Degree of Curve D	Defl. Per Ft of Sta. (Min)	Chord Definition			Arc Definition	
		Radius R	log R	C.O. 1 Sta.	Radius R	log R
1° 0'	0.3	5729.65	3.758128	1.75	5729.58	3.758123
1'	0.305	5635.72	3.750950	1.77	5635.65	3.750944
2'	0.31	5544.83	3.743888	1.80	5544.75	3.743882
3'	0.315	5456.82	3.736939	1.83	5456.74	3.736933
4'	0.32	5371.56	3.730100	1.86	5371.48	3.730094
5'	0.325	5288.92	3.723367	1.89	5288.84	3.723360
6'	0.33	5208.79	3.716737	1.92	5208.71	3.716730
7'	0.335	5131.05	3.710206	1.95	5130.97	3.710199
8'	0.34	5055.59	3.703772	1.98	5055.51	3.703765
9'	0.345	4982.33	3.697432	2.01	4982.24	3.697425
10'	0.35	4911.15	3.691183	2.03	4911.07	3.691176
11'	0.355	4841.98	3.685023	2.07	4841.90	3.685015
12'	0.36	4774.74	3.678949	2.09	4774.65	3.678941
13'	0.365	4709.33	3.672959	2.12	4709.24	3.672951
14'	0.37	4645.69	3.667051	2.15	4645.60	3.667042
15'	0.375	4583.75	3.661221	2.18	4583.66	3.661213
16'	0.38	4523.44	3.655469	2.21	4523.35	3.655460
17'	0.385	4464.70	3.649792	2.24	4464.61	3.649783
18'	0.39	4407.46	3.644189	2.27	4407.37	3.644179
19'	0.395	4351.67	3.638656	2.30	4351.58	3.638647
20'	0.4	4297.28	3.633194	2.33	4297.18	3.633184
21'	0.405	4244.23	3.627799	2.35	4244.13	3.627789
22'	0.41	4192.47	3.622470	2.39	4192.37	3.622460
23'	0.415	4141.96	3.617206	2.41	4141.86	3.617196
24'	0.42	4092.66	3.612005	2.44	4092.56	3.611995
25'	0.425	4044.51	3.606866	2.47	4044.41	3.606855
26'	0.43	3997.49	3.601787	2.50	3997.38	3.601775
27'	0.435	3951.54	3.596766	2.53	3951.43	3.596755
28'	0.44	3906.64	3.591803	2.56	3906.53	3.591791
29'	0.445	3862.74	3.586896	2.59	3862.64	3.586884
30'	0.45	3819.83	3.582044	2.62	3819.71	3.582031
31'	0.455	3777.85	3.577245	2.65	3777.74	3.577232
32'	0.46	3736.79	3.572499	2.68	3736.68	3.572486
33'	0.465	3696.61	3.567804	2.71	3696.50	3.567791
34'	0.47	3657.29	3.563160	2.73	3657.18	3.563146
35'	0.475	3618.80	3.558564	2.76	3618.68	3.558550
36'	0.48	3581.10	3.554017	2.79	3580.99	3.554003
37'	0.485	3544.19	3.549517	2.82	3544.07	3.549502
38'	0.49	3508.02	3.545063	2.85	3507.91	3.545048
39'	0.495	3472.59	3.540654	2.88	3472.47	3.540638
40'	0.5	3437.87	3.536289	2.91	3437.75	3.536274
41'	0.505	3403.83	3.531968	2.94	3403.71	3.531952
42'	0.51	3370.46	3.527690	2.97	3370.34	3.527673
43'	0.515	3337.74	3.523453	3.00	3337.62	3.523437
44'	0.52	3305.65	3.519257	3.03	3305.53	3.519241
45'	0.525	3274.17	3.515101	3.05	3274.04	3.515085
46'	0.53	3243.29	3.510985	3.08	3243.16	3.510968
47'	0.535	3212.98	3.506908	3.11	3212.85	3.506890
48'	0.54	3183.23	3.502868	3.14	3183.10	3.502850
49'	0.545	3154.03	3.498866	3.17	3153.90	3.498847
50'	0.55	3125.36	3.494900	3.20	3125.22	3.494881
51'	0.555	3097.20	3.490970	3.23	3097.07	3.490951
52'	0.56	3069.55	3.487075	3.26	3069.42	3.487056
53'	0.565	3042.39	3.483215	3.29	3042.25	3.483195
54'	0.57	3015.71	3.479389	3.32	3015.57	3.479369
55'	0.575	2989.48	3.475596	3.35	2989.34	3.475576
56'	0.58	2963.72	3.471836	3.37	2963.58	3.471816
57'	0.585	2938.39	3.468109	3.40	2938.25	3.468087
58'	0.59	2913.49	3.464413	3.43	2913.34	3.464392
59'	0.595	2889.01	3.460749	3.46	2888.86	3.460727

TABLE I.—RADII, DEFLECTIONS, OFFSETS, ETC.

Degree of Curve D	Defl. Per Ft of Sta. (Min)	Chord Definition			Arc Definition	
		Radius R	log R	C.O. 1 Sta.	Radius R	log R
2° 0'	0.6	2864.93	3.457115	3.49	2864.79	3.457093
1'	0.605	2841.26	3.453511	3.52	2841.11	3.453488
2'	0.61	2817.97	3.449937	3.55	2817.83	3.449914
3'	0.615	2795.06	3.446392	3.58	2794.92	3.446369
4'	0.62	2772.53	3.442876	3.61	2772.38	3.442852
5'	0.625	2750.35	3.439388	3.64	2750.20	3.439364
6'	0.63	2728.52	3.435928	3.66	2728.37	3.435903
7'	0.635	2707.04	3.432495	3.69	2706.89	3.432470
8'	0.64	2685.89	3.429089	3.72	2685.74	3.429064
9'	0.645	2665.08	3.425710	3.75	2664.92	3.425684
10'	0.65	2644.58	3.422356	3.78	2644.42	3.422330
11'	0.655	2624.39	3.419029	3.81	2624.23	3.419002
12'	0.66	2604.51	3.415727	3.84	2604.35	3.415700
13'	0.665	2584.93	3.412449	3.87	2584.77	3.412422
14'	0.67	2565.65	3.409197	3.90	2565.48	3.409169
15'	0.675	2546.64	3.405968	3.93	2546.48	3.405940
16'	0.68	2527.92	3.402763	3.96	2527.75	3.402735
17'	0.685	2509.47	3.399582	3.98	2509.30	3.399553
18'	0.69	2491.29	3.396424	4.01	2491.12	3.396395
19'	0.695	2473.37	3.393289	4.04	2473.20	3.393259
20'	0.7	2455.70	3.390176	4.07	2455.53	3.390145
21'	0.705	2438.29	3.387085	4.10	2438.12	3.387055
22'	0.71	2421.12	3.384016	4.13	2420.95	3.383985
23'	0.715	2404.19	3.380969	4.16	2404.02	3.380938
24'	0.72	2387.50	3.377943	4.19	2387.32	3.377911
25'	0.725	2371.04	3.374938	4.22	2370.86	3.374905
26'	0.73	2354.80	3.371954	4.25	2354.62	3.371921
27'	0.735	2338.78	3.368990	4.28	2338.60	3.368956
28'	0.74	2322.98	3.366046	4.30	2322.80	3.366012
29'	0.745	2307.39	3.363122	4.33	2307.21	3.363087
30'	0.75	2292.01	3.360217	4.36	2291.83	3.360183
31'	0.755	2276.84	3.357332	4.39	2276.65	3.357297
32'	0.76	2261.86	3.354466	4.42	2261.68	3.354430
33'	0.765	2247.08	3.351618	4.45	2246.89	3.351582
34'	0.77	2232.49	3.348789	4.48	2232.30	3.348753
35'	0.775	2218.09	3.345797	4.51	2217.90	3.345942
36'	0.78	2203.87	3.343187	4.54	2203.68	3.343149
37'	0.785	2189.84	3.340412	4.57	2189.65	3.340374
38'	0.79	2175.98	3.337655	4.60	2175.79	3.337617
39'	0.795	2162.30	3.334916	4.62	2162.10	3.334877
40'	0.8	2148.79	3.332193	4.65	2148.59	3.332154
41'	0.805	2135.44	3.329488	4.68	2135.25	3.329448
42'	0.81	2122.26	3.326799	4.71	2122.07	3.326759
43'	0.815	2109.24	3.324127	4.74	2109.05	3.324086
44'	0.82	2096.39	3.321471	4.77	2096.19	3.321430
45'	0.825	2083.68	3.318832	4.80	2083.48	3.318790
46'	0.83	2071.13	3.316208	4.83	2070.93	3.316166
47'	0.835	2058.73	3.313600	4.86	2058.53	3.313557
48'	0.84	2046.48	3.311008	4.89	2046.28	3.310964
49'	0.845	2034.37	3.308431	4.92	2034.17	3.308387
50'	0.85	2022.41	3.305869	4.94	2022.20	3.305825
51'	0.855	2010.59	3.303323	4.97	2010.38	3.303278
52'	0.86	1998.90	3.300791	5.00	1998.69	3.300745
53'	0.865	1987.35	3.298274	5.03	1987.14	3.298228
54'	0.87	1975.93	3.295771	5.06	1975.72	3.295725
55'	0.875	1964.64	3.293283	5.09	1964.43	3.293236
56'	0.88	1953.48	3.290809	5.12	1953.27	3.290761
57'	0.885	1942.44	3.288349	5.15	1942.23	3.288301
58'	0.89	1931.53	3.285902	5.18	1931.32	3.285854
59'	0.895	1920.75	3.283470	5.21	1920.53	3.283421

5

TABLE I.—RADII, DEFLECTIONS, OFFSETS, ETC.

Degree of Curve D	Defl. Per Ft of Sta. (Min)	Chord Definition			Arc Definition	
		Radius R	log R	C.O. 1 Sta.	Radius R	log R
3° 0'	0.9	1910.08	3.281051	5.24	1909.86	3.281001
1'	0.905	1899.53	3.278646	5.26	1899.31	3.278595
2'	0.91	1889.09	3.276253	5.29	1888.87	3.276203
3'	0.915	1878.77	3.273874	5.32	1878.55	3.273823
4'	0.92	1868.56	3.271508	5.35	1868.34	3.271456
5'	0.925	1858.47	3.269155	5.38	1858.24	3.269105
6'	0.93	1848.48	3.266814	5.41	1848.25	3.266761
7'	0.935	1838.59	3.264486	5.44	1838.37	3.264432
8'	0.94	1828.82	3.262170	5.47	1828.59	3.262116
9'	0.945	1819.14	3.259867	5.50	1818.91	3.259812
10'	0.95	1809.57	3.257576	5.53	1809.34	3.257520
11'	0.955	1800.10	3.255296	5.56	1799.87	3.255240
12'	0.96	1790.73	3.253029	5.58	1790.49	3.252973
13'	0.965	1781.45	3.250774	5.61	1781.22	3.250716
14'	0.97	1772.27	3.248530	5.64	1772.03	3.248472
15'	0.975	1763.18	3.246297	5.67	1762.95	3.246239
16'	0.98	1754.19	3.244077	5.70	1753.95	3.244018
17'	0.985	1745.29	3.241867	5.73	1745.05	3.241808
18'	0.99	1736.48	3.239669	5.76	1736.24	3.239609
19'	0.995	1727.75	3.237481	5.79	1727.51	3.237421
20'	1.0	1719.12	3.235305	5.82	1718.87	3.235244
21'	1.005	1710.57	3.233140	5.85	1710.32	3.233078
22'	1.01	1702.10	3.230985	5.88	1701.85	3.230922
23'	1.015	1693.72	3.228841	5.90	1693.47	3.228778
24'	1.02	1685.42	3.226707	5.93	1685.17	3.226644
25'	1.025	1677.20	3.224584	5.96	1676.95	3.224520
26'	1.03	1669.06	3.222472	5.99	1668.81	3.222407
27'	1.035	1661.00	3.220369	6.02	1660.75	3.220303
28'	1.04	1653.01	3.218277	6.05	1652.76	3.218210
29'	1.045	1645.11	3.216195	6.08	1644.85	3.216128
30'	1.05	1637.28	3.214122	6.11	1637.02	3.214055
31'	1.055	1629.52	3.212060	6.14	1629.26	3.211991
32'	1.06	1621.84	3.210007	6.17	1621.58	3.209938
33'	1.065	1614.22	3.207964	6.19	1613.96	3.207894
34'	1.07	1606.68	3.205930	6.22	1606.42	3.205860
35'	1.075	1599.21	3.203906	6.25	1598.95	3.203835
36'	1.08	1591.81	3.201892	6.28	1591.55	3.201820
37'	1.085	1584.48	3.199886	6.31	1584.21	3.199814
38'	1.09	1577.21	3.197890	6.34	1576.95	3.197817
39'	1.095	1570.01	3.195903	6.37	1569.75	3.195830
40'	1.1	1562.88	3.193925	6.40	1562.61	3.193851
41'	1.105	1555.81	3.191956	6.43	1555.54	3.191881
42'	1.11	1548.80	3.189996	6.46	1548.53	3.189921
43'	1.115	1541.86	3.188045	6.49	1541.59	3.187969
44'	1.12	1534.98	3.186103	6.51	1534.71	3.186026
45'	1.125	1528.16	3.184169	6.54	1527.89	3.184091
46'	1.13	1521.40	3.182244	6.57	1521.13	3.182165
47'	1.135	1514.17	3.180327	6.60	1514.43	3.180248
48'	1.14	1508.06	3.178419	6.63	1507.78	3.178339
49'	1.145	1501.48	3.176519	6.66	1501.20	3.176438
50'	1.15	1494.95	3.174627	6.69	1494.67	3.174546
51'	1.155	1488.48	3.172744	6.72	1488.20	3.172661
52'	1.16	1482.07	3.170868	6.75	1481.79	3.170786
53'	1.165	1475.71	3.169001	6.78	1475.43	3.168918
54'	1.17	1469.41	3.167142	6.81	1469.12	3.167058
55'	1.175	1463.16	3.165291	6.83	1462.87	3.165206
56'	1.18	1456.96	3.163447	6.86	1456.67	3.163362
57'	1.185	1450.81	3.161612	6.89	1450.53	3.161526
58'	1.19	1444.72	3.159784	6.92	1444.43	3.159697
59'	1.195	1438.68	3.157963	6.95	1438.39	3.157876

TABLE I.—RADII, DEFLECTIONS, OFFSETS, ETC.

Degree of Curve D	Defl. Per Ft of Sta. (Min)	Chord Definition			Arc Definition	
		Radius R	log R	C.O. 1 Sta.	Radius R	log R
4° 0'	1.2	1432.69	3.156151	6.98	1432.39	3.156063
1'	1.205	1426.74	3.154346	7.01	1426.45	3.154257
2'	1.21	1420.85	3.152548	7.04	1420.56	3.152458
3'	1.215	1415.01	3.150758	7.07	1414.71	3.150667
4'	1.22	1409.21	3.148975	7.10	1408.91	3.148884
5'	1.225	1403.46	3.147200	7.13	1403.16	3.147108
6'	1.23	1397.76	3.145431	7.15	1397.46	3.145339
7'	1.235	1392.10	3.143670	7.18	1391.80	3.143577
8'	1.24	1386.49	3.141916	7.21	1386.19	3.141822
9'	1.245	1380.92	3.140170	7.24	1380.62	3.140074
10'	1.25	1375.40	3.138430	7.27	1375.10	3.138334
11'	1.255	1369.92	3.136697	7.30	1369.62	3.136600
12'	1.26	1364.49	3.134971	7.33	1364.19	3.134873
13'	1.265	1359.10	3.133251	7.36	1358.79	3.133153
14'	1.27	1353.75	3.131539	7.39	1353.44	3.131440
15'	1.275	1348.45	3.129833	7.42	1348.14	3.129734
16'	1.28	1343.18	3.128134	7.45	1342.87	3.128034
17'	1.285	1337.96	3.126442	7.47	1337.64	3.126341
18'	1.29	1332.77	3.124756	7.50	1332.46	3.124654
19'	1.295	1327.63	3.123077	7.53	1327.32	3.122974
20'	1.3	1322.53	3.121404	7.56	1322.21	3.121300
21'	1.305	1317.46	3.119738	7.59	1317.14	3.119633
22'	1.31	1312.43	3.118078	7.62	1312.12	3.117972
23'	1.315	1307.45	3.116424	7.65	1307.13	3.116318
24'	1.32	1302.50	3.114777	7.68	1302.18	3.114669
25'	1.325	1297.58	3.113136	7.71	1297.26	3.113028
26'	1.33	1292.71	3.111501	7.74	1292.39	3.111392
27'	1.335	1287.87	3.109872	7.76	1287.55	3.109762
28'	1.34	1283.07	3.108249	7.79	1282.74	3.108139
29'	1.345	1278.30	3.106632	7.82	1277.97	3.106521
30'	1.35	1273.57	3.105022	7.85	1273.24	3.104910
31'	1.355	1268.87	3.103417	7.88	1268.54	3.103304
32'	1.36	1264.21	3.101818	7.91	1263.88	3.101705
33'	1.365	1259.58	3.100225	7.94	1259.25	3.100111
34'	1.37	1254.98	3.098638	7.97	1254.65	3.098523
35'	1.375	1250.42	3.097057	8.00	1250.09	3.096941
36'	1.38	1245.89	3.095481	8.03	1245.56	3.095365
37'	1.385	1241.40	3.093912	8.06	1241.06	3.093974
38'	1.39	1236.94	3.092347	8.08	1236.60	3.092229
39'	1.395	1232.51	3.090789	8.11	1232.17	3.090670
40'	1.4	1228.11	3.089236	8.14	1227.77	3.089116
41'	1.405	1223.74	3.087689	8.17	1223.40	3.087566
42'	1.41	1219.40	3.086147	8.20	1219.06	3.086025
43'	1.415	1215.09	3.084610	8.23	1214.75	3.084487
44'	1.42	1210.82	3.083079	8.26	1210.47	3.082955
45'	1.425	1206.57	3.081553	8.29	1206.23	3.081429
46'	1.43	1202.36	3.080033	8.32	1202.01	3.079908
47'	1.435	1198.17	3.078518	8.35	1197.82	3.078392
48'	1.44	1194.01	3.077008	8.38	1193.66	3.076881
49'	1.445	1189.88	3.075504	8.40	1189.53	3.075376
50'	1.45	1185.78	3.074005	8.43	1185.43	3.073876
51'	1.455	1181.71	3.072511	8.46	1181.36	3.072381
52'	1.46	1177.66	3.071022	8.49	1177.31	3.070891
53'	1.465	1173.65	3.069538	8.52	1173.29	3.069406
54'	1.47	1169.66	3.068059	8.55	1169.30	3.067927
55'	1.475	1165.70	3.066585	8.58	1165.34	3.066452
56'	1.48	1161.76	3.065116	8.61	1161.40	3.064982
57'	1.485	1157.85	3.063653	8.64	1157.49	3.063517
58'	1.49	1153.97	3.062194	8.67	1153.61	3.062057
59'	1.495	1150.11	3.060740	8.69	1149.75	3.060603

7

TABLE I.—RADII, DEFLECTIONS, OFFSETS, ETC.

Degree of Curve D	Defl. Per Ft of Sta. (Min)	Chord Definition			Arc Definition	
		Radius R	log R	C.O. 1 Sta.	Radius R	log R
5° 0'	1.5	1146.28	3.059290	8.72	1145.92	3.059153
1'	1.505	1142.47	3.057707	8.75	1142.11	3.057707
2'	1.51	1138.69	3.056407	8.78	1138.33	3.056267
3'	1.515	1134.94	3.054972	8.81	1134.57	3.054831
4'	1.52	1131.21	3.053542	8.84	1130.84	3.053400
5'	1.525	1127.50	3.052116	8.87	1127.13	3.051974
6'	1.53	1123.82	3.050696	8.90	1123.45	3.050553
7'	1.535	1120.16	3.049280	8.93	1119.79	3.049135
8'	1.54	1116.52	3.047868	8.96	1116.15	3.047723
9'	1.545	1112.91	3.046462	8.99	1112.54	3.046315
10'	1.55	1109.33	3.045059	9.01	1108.95	3.044912
11'	1.555	1105.76	3.043662	9.04	1105.38	3.043514
12'	1.56	1102.22	3.042268	9.07	1101.84	3.042119
13'	1.565	1098.70	3.040880	9.10	1098.32	3.040729
14'	1.57	1095.20	3.039495	9.13	1094.82	3.039343
15'	1.575	1091.73	3.038115	9.16	1091.35	3.037963
16'	1.58	1088.28	3.036740	9.19	1087.89	3.036587
17'	1.585	1084.85	3.035368	9.22	1084.46	3.035215
18'	1.59	1081.44	3.034002	9.25	1081.05	3.033847
19'	1.595	1078.05	3.032639	9.28	1077.66	3.032483
20'	1.6	1074.68	3.031281	9.31	1074.30	3.031124
21'	1.605	1071.34	3.029927	9.33	1070.95	3.029769
22'	1.61	1068.01	3.028577	9.36	1067.62	3.028418
23'	1.615	1064.71	3.027231	9.39	1064.32	3.027071
24'	1.62	1061.43	3.025890	9.42	1061.03	3.025729
25'	1.625	1058.16	3.024552	9.45	1057.77	3.024390
26'	1.63	1054.92	3.023219	9.48	1054.52	3.023056
27'	1.635	1051.70	3.021890	9.51	1051.30	3.021726
28'	1.64	1048.49	3.020565	9.54	1048.09	3.020400
29'	1.645	1045.31	3.019244	9.57	1044.91	3.019078
30'	1.65	1042.14	3.017927	9.60	1041.74	3.017760
31'	1.655	1039.00	3.016614	9.62	1038.59	3.016446
32'	1.66	1035.87	3.015305	9.65	1035.47	3.015136
33'	1.665	1032.76	3.013999	9.68	1032.36	3.013829
34'	1.67	1029.67	3.012698	9.71	1029.27	3.012527
35'	1.675	1026.60	3.011401	9.74	1026.19	3.011229
36'	1.68	1023.55	3.010107	9.77	1023.14	3.009935
37'	1.685	1020.51	3.008818	9.80	1020.10	3.008644
38'	1.69	1017.49	3.007532	9.83	1017.08	3.007357
39'	1.695	1014.50	3.006250	9.86	1014.08	3.006074
40'	1.7	1011.51	3.004972	9.89	1011.10	3.004795
41'	1.705	1008.55	3.003698	9.92	1008.14	3.003520
42'	1.71	1005.60	3.002427	9.94	1005.19	3.002248
43'	1.715	1002.67	3.001160	9.97	1002.26	3.000980
44'	1.72	999.762	2.999897	10.00	999.345	2.999715
45'	1.725	996.867	2.998637	10.03	996.448	2.998455
46'	1.73	993.988	2.997381	10.06	993.568	2.997198
47'	1.735	991.126	2.996129	10.09	990.705	2.995944
48'	1.74	988.280	2.994880	10.12	987.858	2.994695
49'	1.745	985.451	2.993635	10.15	985.028	2.993448
50'	1.75	982.638	2.992393	10.18	982.213	2.992206
51'	1.755	979.840	2.991155	10.21	979.415	2.990967
52'	1.76	977.060	2.989921	10.23	976.632	2.989731
53'	1.765	974.294	2.988690	10.26	973.866	2.988499
54'	1.77	971.544	2.987463	10.29	971.115	2.987271
55'	1.775	968.810	2.986239	10.32	968.379	2.986045
56'	1.78	966.091	2.985018	10.35	965.659	2.984824
57'	1.785	963.387	2.983801	10.38	962.954	2.983606
58'	1.79	960.698	2.982587	10.41	960.264	2.982391
59'	1.795	958.025	2.981377	10.44	957.590	2.981179

8

TABLE I.—RADII, DEFLECTIONS, OFFSETS, ETC.

Degree of Curve D	Defl. Per Ft of Sta. (Min)	Chord Definition			Arc Definition	
		Radius R	log R	C.O. 1 Sta.	Radius R	log R
6° 0'	1.8	955.366	2.980170	10.47	954.930	2.979971
2'	1.81	950.093	2.977766	10.53	949.654	2.977565
4'	1.82	944.877	2.975375	10.58	944.436	2.975173
6'	1.83	939.719	2.972998	10.64	939.275	2.972793
8'	1.84	934.616	2.970633	10.70	934.170	2.970426
10'	1.85	929.569	2.968282	10.76	929.121	2.968072
12'	1.86	924.576	2.965943	10.82	924.126	2.965731
14'	1.87	919.637	2.963616	10.87	919.184	2.963402
16'	1.88	914.750	2.961303	10.93	914.294	2.961086
18'	1.89	909.915	2.959001	10.99	909.457	2.958783
20'	1.9	905.131	2.956711	11.05	904.670	2.956490
22'	1.91	900.397	2.954434	11.11	899.934	2.954211
24'	1.92	895.712	2.952168	11.16	895.247	2.951943
26'	1.93	891.076	2.949915	11.22	890.608	2.949687
28'	1.94	886.488	2.947673	11.28	886.017	2.947442
30'	1.95	881.946	2.945442	11.34	881.474	2.945209
32'	1.96	877.451	2.943223	11.40	876.976	2.942988
34'	1.97	873.002	2.941015	11.45	872.525	2.940778
36'	1.98	868.598	2.938819	11.51	868.118	2.938579
38'	1.99	864.238	2.936633	11.57	863.756	2.936391
40'	2.0	859.922	2.934459	11.63	859.437	2.934214
42'	2.01	855.648	2.932295	11.69	855.161	2.932048
44'	2.02	851.417	2.930142	11.75	850.927	2.929892
46'	2.03	847.228	2.928000	11.80	846.736	2.927748
48'	2.04	843.080	2.925869	11.86	842.585	2.925616
50'	2.05	838.972	2.923747	11.92	838.475	2.923490
52'	2.06	834.904	2.921637	11.98	834.405	2.921377
54'	2.07	830.876	2.919536	12.04	830.374	2.919274
56'	2.08	826.886	2.917446	12.09	826.381	2.917181
58'	2.09	822.934	2.915365	12.15	822.427	2.915098
7° 0'	2.1	819.020	2.913295	12.21	818.511	2.913025
2'	2.11	815.144	2.911234	12.27	814.632	2.910961
4'	2.12	811.303	2.909183	12.33	810.789	2.908908
6'	2.13	807.499	2.907142	12.38	806.983	2.906864
8'	2.14	803.731	2.905111	12.44	803.212	2.904830
10'	2.15	799.997	2.903089	12.50	799.476	2.902805
12'	2.16	796.299	2.901076	12.56	795.775	2.900790
14'	2.17	792.634	2.899073	12.62	792.108	2.898784
16'	2.18	789.003	2.897079	12.67	788.474	2.896787
18'	2.19	785.405	2.895094	12.73	784.874	2.894800
20'	2.2	781.840	2.893118	12.79	781.306	2.892821
22'	2.21	778.307	2.891151	12.85	777.771	2.890852
24'	2.22	774.806	2.889193	12.91	774.267	2.888891
26'	2.23	771.336	2.887244	12.96	770.795	2.886939
28'	2.24	767.897	2.885303	13.02	767.354	2.884996
30'	2.25	764.489	2.883371	13.08	763.944	2.883061
32'	2.26	761.112	2.881448	13.14	760.563	2.881135
34'	2.27	757.764	2.879534	13.20	757.213	2.879218
36'	2.28	754.445	2.877627	13.25	753.892	2.877309
38'	2.29	751.155	2.875730	13.31	750.600	2.875408
40'	2.3	747.894	2.873840	13.37	747.336	2.873516
42'	2.31	744.661	2.871959	13.43	744.101	2.871631
44'	2.32	741.456	2.870086	13.49	740.894	2.869756
46'	2.33	738.279	2.868221	13.55	737.714	2.867888
48'	2.34	735.129	2.866363	13.60	734.561	2.866028
50'	2.35	732.005	2.864514	13.66	731.436	2.864176
52'	2.36	728.909	2.862673	13.72	728.336	2.862332
54'	2.37	725.838	2.860840	13.78	725.263	2.860496
56'	2.38	722.793	2.859014	13.84	722.216	2.858667
58'	2.39	719.774	2.857196	13.89	719.194	2.856846

TABLE I.—RADII, DEFLECTIONS, OFFSETS, ETC.

Degree of Curve D	Defl. Per Ft of Sta. (Min)	Chord Definition			Arc Definition	
		Radius R	log R	C.O. 1 Sta.	Radius R	log R
8° 0'	2.4	716.779	2.855385	13.95	716.197	2.855033
2'	2.41	713.810	2.853583	14.01	713.226	2.853227
4'	2.42	710.865	2.851787	14.07	710.278	2.851428
6'	2.43	707.945	2.849999	14.13	707.355	2.849638
8'	2.44	705.048	2.848219	14.18	704.456	2.847854
10'	2.45	702.175	2.846446	14.24	701.581	2.846078
12'	2.46	699.326	2.844679	14.30	698.729	2.844309
14'	2.47	696.499	2.842921	14.36	695.900	2.842547
16'	2.48	693.696	2.841169	14.42	693.094	2.840792
18'	2.49	690.914	2.839424	14.47	690.311	2.839045
20'	2.5	688.156	2.837687	14.53	687.549	2.837304
22'	2.51	685.419	2.835956	14.59	684.810	2.835570
24'	2.52	682.704	2.834232	14.65	682.093	2.833843
26'	2.53	680.010	2.832515	14.71	679.397	2.832123
28'	2.54	677.338	2.830805	14.76	676.722	2.830410
30'	2.55	674.686	2.829102	14.82	674.068	2.828704
32'	2.56	672.056	2.827405	14.88	671.435	2.827004
34'	2.57	669.446	2.825715	14.94	668.822	2.825311
36'	2.58	666.856	2.824032	15.00	666.230	2.823624
38'	2.59	664.286	2.822355	15.05	663.658	2.821944
40'	2.6	661.736	2.820685	15.11	661.105	2.820270
42'	2.61	659.205	2.819021	15.17	658.572	2.818603
44'	2.62	656.694	2.817363	15.23	656.059	2.816941
46'	2.63	654.202	2.815712	15.29	653.564	2.815288
48'	2.64	651.729	2.814067	15.34	651.088	2.814640
50'	2.65	649.274	2.812428	15.40	648.632	2.811998
52'	2.66	646.838	2.810796	15.46	646.193	2.810362
54'	2.67	644.420	2.809169	15.52	643.773	2.808732
56'	2.68	642.021	2.807549	15.58	641.371	2.807109
58'	2.69	639.639	2.805935	15.63	638.986	2.805492
9° 0'	2.7	637.275	2.804327	15.69	636.620	2.803880
2'	2.71	634.928	2.802724	15.75	634.271	2.802275
4'	2.72	632.599	2.801128	15.81	631.939	2.800675
6'	2.73	630.286	2.799538	15.87	629.624	2.799081
8'	2.74	627.991	2.797953	15.92	627.326	2.797494
10'	2.75	625.712	2.796374	15.98	625.045	2.795911
12'	2.76	623.450	2.794801	16.04	622.780	2.794335
14'	2.77	621.203	2.793234	16.10	620.532	2.792764
16'	2.78	618.974	2.791673	16.16	618.300	2.791199
18'	2.79	616.760	2.790117	16.21	616.084	2.789640
20'	2.8	614.563	2.788566	16.27	613.883	2.788086
22'	2.81	612.380	2.787021	16.33	611.699	2.786538
24'	2.82	610.214	2.785482	16.39	609.530	2.784995
26'	2.83	608.062	2.783948	16.45	607.376	2.783457
28'	2.84	605.926	2.782420	16.50	605.237	2.781926
30'	2.85	603.805	2.780897	16.56	603.114	2.780399
32'	2.86	601.698	2.779379	16.62	601.005	2.778878
34'	2.87	599.607	2.777867	16.68	598.911	2.777362
36'	2.88	597.530	2.776360	16.74	596.831	2.775851
38'	2.89	595.467	2.774858	16.79	594.766	2.774346
40'	2.9	593.419	2.773361	16.85	592.715	2.772846
42'	2.91	591.384	2.771870	16.91	590.678	2.771351
44'	2.92	589.364	2.770383	16.97	588.655	2.769861
46'	2.93	587.357	2.768902	17.03	586.646	2.768376
48'	2.94	585.364	2.767426	17.08	584.651	2.766897
50'	2.95	583.385	2.765955	17.14	582.669	2.765422
52'	2.96	581.419	2.764489	17.20	580.700	2.763952
54'	2.97	579.466	2.763028	17.26	578.745	2.762487
56'	2.98	577.526	2.761572	17.32	576.803	2.761028
58'	2.99	575.599	2.760120	17.37	574.874	2.759573

TABLE I.—RADII, DEFLECTIONS, OFFSETS, ETC.

Degree of Curve D	Defl. Per Ft of Sta. (Min)	Chord Definition			Arc Definition	
		Radius R	log R	C.O. 1 Sta.	Radius R	log R
10° 0'	3.0	573.686	2.758674	17.43	572.958	2.758123
2'	3.01	571.784	2.757232	17.49	571.054	2.756667
4'	3.02	569.896	2.755796	17.55	569.163	2.755237
6'	3.03	568.020	2.754364	17.61	567.285	2.753801
8'	3.04	566.156	2.752937	17.66	565.419	2.752370
10'	3.05	564.305	2.751514	17.72	563.565	2.750944
12'	3.06	562.466	2.750096	17.78	561.723	2.749522
14'	3.07	560.638	2.748683	17.84	559.894	2.748106
16'	3.08	558.823	2.747274	17.89	558.076	2.746693
18'	3.09	557.019	2.745870	17.95	556.270	2.745285
20'	3.1	555.227	2.744471	18.01	554.475	2.743882
22'	3.11	553.447	2.743076	18.07	552.692	2.742483
24'	3.12	551.678	2.741686	18.13	550.921	2.741089
26'	3.13	549.920	2.740300	18.18	549.161	2.739700
28'	3.14	548.174	2.738918	18.24	547.412	2.738314
30'	3.15	546.438	2.737541	18.30	545.674	2.736933
32'	3.16	544.714	2.736169	18.36	543.947	2.735557
34'	3.17	543.001	2.734800	18.42	542.231	2.734185
36'	3.18	541.298	2.733436	18.47	540.526	2.732817
38'	3.19	539.606	2.732077	18.53	538.832	2.731453
40'	3.2	537.924	2.730721	18.59	537.148	2.730094
42'	3.21	536.253	2.729370	18.65	535.475	2.728739
44'	3.22	534.593	2.728023	18.71	533.812	2.727388
46'	3.23	532.943	2.726681	18.76	532.159	2.726041
48'	3.24	531.303	2.725342	18.82	530.516	2.724699
50'	3.25	529.673	2.724008	18.88	528.884	2.723360
52'	3.26	528.053	2.722677	18.94	527.262	2.722026
54'	3.27	526.443	2.721351	19.00	525.649	2.720696
56'	3.28	524.843	2.720029	19.05	524.047	2.719370
58'	3.29	523.252	2.718711	19.11	522.454	2.718048
11° 0'	3.3	521.671	2.717397	19.17	520.871	2.716730
2'	3.31	520.100	2.716087	19.23	519.297	2.715417
4'	3.32	518.539	2.714781	19.28	517.733	2.714106
6'	3.33	516.986	2.713479	19.34	516.178	2.712799
8'	3.34	515.443	2.712181	19.40	514.633	2.711497
10'	3.35	513.909	2.710887	19.46	513.097	2.710199
12'	3.36	512.385	2.709596	19.52	511.569	2.708905
14'	3.37	510.869	2.708310	19.57	510.051	2.707614
16'	3.38	509.363	2.707027	19.63	508.542	2.706327
18'	3.39	507.865	2.705748	19.69	507.042	2.705044
20'	3.4	506.376	2.704473	19.75	505.551	2.703765
22'	3.41	504.896	2.703202	19.81	504.068	2.702490
24'	3.42	503.425	2.701934	19.86	502.595	2.701218
26'	3.43	501.962	2.700671	19.92	501.129	2.699950
28'	3.44	500.507	2.699410	19.98	499.672	2.698685
30'	3.45	499.061	2.698154	20.04	498.224	2.697425
32'	3.46	497.624	2.696901	20.10	496.784	2.696168
34'	3.47	496.195	2.695652	20.15	495.353	2.694914
36'	3.48	494.774	2.694407	20.21	493.929	2.693665
38'	3.49	493.361	2.693165	20.27	492.514	2.692418
40'	3.5	491.956	2.691926	20.33	491.107	2.691176
42'	3.51	490.559	2.690692	20.38	489.708	2.689937
44'	3.52	489.171	2.689460	20.44	488.316	2.688701
46'	3.53	487.790	2.688233	20.50	486.933	2.687469
48'	3.54	486.417	2.687008	20.56	485.557	2.686241
50'	3.55	485.051	2.685788	20.62	484.190	2.685015
52'	3.56	483.694	2.684570	20.67	482.830	2.683974
54'	3.57	482.344	2.683357	20.73	481.477	2.682576
56'	3.58	481.001	2.682146	20.79	480.132	2.681361
58'	3.59	479.666	2.680939	20.85	478.795	2.680149

TABLE I.—RADII, DEFLECTIONS, OFFSETS, ETC.

Degree of Curve D	Defl. Per Ft of Sta. (Min)	Chord Definition				Arc Definition		
		Radius R	log R	C.O. 1 Sta.	M.O. 1 Sta.	Radius R	log R	C.O. 1 Sta.
12° 0'	3.6	478.339	2.679735	20.91	2.62	477.465	2.678941	20.87
10'	3.65	471.810	2.673767	21.19	2.66	470.924	2.672951	21.15
20'	3.7	465.459	2.667881	21.48	2.69	464.560	2.667042	21.44
30'	3.75	459.276	2.662074	21.77	2.73	458.366	2.661213	21.73
40'	3.8	453.259	2.656345	22.06	2.77	452.335	2.655460	22.02
50'	3.85	447.395	2.650691	22.35	2.80	446.461	2.649783	22.30
13° 0'	3.9	441.684	2.645111	22.64	2.84	440.737	2.644179	22.59
10'	3.95	436.117	2.639603	22.93	2.88	435.158	2.638647	22.88
20'	4.0	430.690	2.634164	23.22	2.91	429.718	2.633184	23.16
30'	4.05	425.396	2.628794	23.51	2.95	424.413	2.627789	23.45
40'	4.1	420.233	2.623490	23.80	2.99	419.237	2.622460	23.74
50'	4.15	415.194	2.618251	24.09	3.02	414.186	2.617196	24.03
14° 0'	4.2	410.275	2.613075	24.37	3.06	409.256	2.611995	24.31
10'	4.25	405.473	2.607962	24.66	3.10	404.441	2.606855	24.60
20'	4.3	400.782	2.602908	24.95	3.13	399.738	2.601775	24.89
30'	4.35	396.200	2.597914	25.24	3.17	395.143	2.596755	25.17
40'	4.4	391.722	2.592978	25.53	3.20	390.653	2.591791	25.46
50'	4.45	387.345	2.588097	25.82	3.24	386.264	2.586884	25.74
15° 0'	4.5	383.065	2.583272	26.11	3.28	381.972	2.582031	26.03
10'	4.55	378.880	2.578501	26.39	3.31	377.774	2.577232	26.32
20'	4.6	374.786	2.573783	26.68	3.35	373.668	2.572486	26.60
30'	4.65	370.780	2.569116	26.97	3.39	369.650	2.567791	26.89
40'	4.7	366.859	2.564500	27.26	3.42	365.718	2.563146	27.17
50'	4.75	363.022	2.559933	27.55	3.46	361.868	2.558550	27.46
16° 0'	4.8	359.265	2.555415	27.83	3.50	358.099	2.554003	27.74
10'	4.85	355.585	2.550944	28.12	3.53	354.407	2.549502	28.03
20'	4.9	351.981	2.546519	28.41	3.57	350.790	2.545048	28.31
30'	4.95	348.450	2.542140	28.70	3.61	347.247	2.540638	28.60
40'	5.0	344.990	2.537806	28.99	3.64	343.775	2.536274	28.89
50'	5.05	341.598	2.533516	29.27	3.68	340.371	2.531952	29.16
17° 0'	5.1	338.273	2.529268	29.56	3.72	337.034	2.527673	29.45
10'	5.15	335.013	2.525062	29.85	3.75	333.762	2.523437	29.73
20'	5.2	331.816	2.520898	30.14	3.79	330.553	2.519241	30.02
30'	5.25	328.689	2.516774	30.42	3.82	327.404	2.515085	30.31
40'	5.3	325.604	2.512690	30.71	3.86	324.316	2.510968	30.59
50'	5.35	322.585	2.508645	31.00	3.90	321.285	2.506890	30.87
18° 0'	5.4	319.623	2.504638	31.29	3.94	318.310	2.502850	31.16
10'	5.45	316.715	2.500668	31.57	3.97	315.390	2.498847	31.44
20'	5.5	313.860	2.496736	31.86	4.01	312.522	2.494881	31.72
30'	5.55	311.056	2.492839	32.15	4.04	309.707	2.490951	32.00
40'	5.6	308.303	2.488978	32.44	4.08	306.942	2.487056	32.29
50'	5.65	305.599	2.485152	32.72	4.12	304.225	2.483195	32.58
19° 0'	5.7	302.943	2.481361	33.01	4.16	301.557	2.479369	32.86
10'	5.75	300.333	2.477603	33.30	4.19	298.934	2.475576	33.14
20'	5.8	297.768	2.473878	33.58	4.23	296.357	2.471816	33.42
30'	5.85	295.247	2.470186	33.87	4.26	293.825	2.468087	33.71
40'	5.9	292.770	2.466526	34.16	4.30	291.334	2.464392	33.99
50'	5.95	290.334	2.462897	34.44	4.34	289.866	2.460727	34.27
20° 0'	6.0	287.939	2.459300	34.73	4.37	286.479	2.457093	34.55
10'	6.05	285.583	2.455733	35.02	4.41	284.111	2.453488	34.83
20'	6.1	283.267	2.452195	35.30	4.45	281.783	2.449914	35.12
30'	6.15	280.988	2.448688	35.59	4.48	279.492	2.446369	35.40
40'	6.2	278.746	2.445209	35.87	4.52	277.238	2.442852	35.68
50'	6.25	276.541	2.441759	36.16	4.56	275.020	2.439364	35.96
21° 0'	6.3	274.370	2.438337	36.45	4.59	272.837	2.435903	36.24
10'	6.35	272.234	2.434943	36.73	4.63	270.689	2.432470	36.52
20'	6.4	270.132	2.431576	37.02	4.67	268.574	2.429064	36.80
30'	6.45	268.062	2.428235	37.30	4.70	266.492	2.425684	37.08
40'	6.5	266.024	2.424921	37.59	4.74	264.442	2.422330	37.37
50'	6.55	264.018	2.421633	37.88	4.78	262.423	2.419002	37.65

TABLE I.—RADII, DEFLECTIONS, OFFSETS, ETC.

Degree of Curve D	Defl. Per Ft of Sta. (Min)	Chord Definition				Arc Definition		
		Radius R	log R	C.O. 1 Sta.	M.O. 1 Sta.	Radius R	log R	C.O. 1 Sta.
22° 0'	6.6	262.042	2.418371	38.16	4.81	260.435	2.415700	37.93
10'	6.65	260.098	2.415134	38.45	4.85	258.477	2.412422	38.21
20'	6.7	258.180	2.411922	38.73	4.89	256.548	2.409169	38.49
30'	6.75	256.292	2.408734	39.02	4.92	254.648	2.405940	38.77
40'	6.8	254.431	2.405571	39.30	4.96	252.775	2.402735	39.05
50'	6.85	252.599	2.402431	39.59	5.00	250.930	2.399553	39.33
23° 0'	6.9	250.793	2.399315	39.87	5.04	249.112	2.396395	39.61
10'	6.95	249.013	2.396222	40.16	5.07	247.320	2.393259	39.89
20'	7.0	247.258	2.393151	40.44	5.11	245.553	2.390145	40.16
30'	7.05	245.529	2.390103	40.73	5.14	243.812	2.387055	40.44
40'	7.1	243.825	2.387077	41.01	5.18	242.095	2.383985	40.72
50'	7.15	242.144	2.384074	41.30	5.22	240.402	2.380938	41.00
24° 0'	7.2	240.487	2.381091	41.58	5.26	238.732	2.377911	41.28
10'	7.25	238.853	2.378130	41.87	5.29	237.086	2.374905	41.56
20'	7.3	237.241	2.375190	42.15	5.33	235.462	2.371921	41.84
30'	7.35	235.652	2.372270	42.44	5.37	233.860	2.368956	42.11
40'	7.4	234.084	2.369371	42.72	5.40	232.280	2.336012	42.39
50'	7.45	232.537	2.366492	43.00	5.44	230.721	2.363087	42.67
25° 0'	7.5	231.011	2.363633	43.28	5.48	229.183	2.360183	42.95
10'	7.55	229.506	2.360794	43.57	5.51	227.665	2.357279	43.23
20'	7.6	228.020	2.357974	43.86	5.55	226.168	2.354430	43.50
30'	7.65	226.555	2.355173	44.14	5.59	224.689	2.351582	43.78
40'	7.7	225.108	2.352391	44.42	5.62	223.230	2.348753	44.06
50'	7.75	223.680	2.349627	44.71	5.66	221.790	2.345942	44.33
26° 0'	7.8	222.271	2.346882	44.99	5.70	220.368	2.343149	44.60
30'	7.95	218.150	2.338755	45.84	5.81	216.210	2.334877	45.43
27° 0'	8.1	214.183	2.330785	46.69	5.92	212.207	2.326759	46.26
30'	8.25	210.362	2.322967	47.54	6.03	208.348	2.318790	47.08
28° 0'	8.4	206.678	2.315295	48.38	6.14	204.628	2.310964	47.91
30'	8.55	203.125	2.307764	49.23	6.25	201.038	2.303278	48.72
29° 0'	8.7	199.696	2.300370	50.08	6.36	197.572	2.295725	49.55
30'	8.85	196.385	2.293108	50.92	6.47	194.223	2.288301	50.36
30° 0'	9.0	193.185	2.285974	51.76	6.58	190.986	2.281001	51.18
32° 0'	9.6	181.398	2.258632	55.13	7.03	179.049	2.252973	54.42
34° 0'	10.2	171.015	2.233035	58.47	7.47	168.517	2.226644	57.62
36° 0'	10.8	161.803	2.208988	61.80	7.92	159.155	2.201820	60.79
38° 0'	11.4	153.578	2.186328	65.11	8.37	150.778	2.178339	63.93
41° 0'	12.3	142.773	2.154645	70.04	9.04	139.746	2.145339	68.55
44° 0'	13.2	133.473	2.125395	74.92	9.72	130.218	2.114669	73.09
48° 0'	14.4	122.930	2.089657	81.35	10.63	119.366	2.076881	78.98
52° 0'	15.6	114.058	2.057128	87.67	11.54	110.184	2.042119	84.69
57° 0'	17.1	104.787	2.020307	95.43	12.70	100.519	2.002248	91.55
64° 0'	19.2	94.354	1.974760	106.0	14.34	89.525	1.951943	100.6
72° 0'	21.6	85.065	1.929751	117.6	16.25	79.577	1.900790	110.0
82° 0'	24.6	76.213	1.882027	131.8	18.69	69.873	1.844309	120.3
95° 0'	28.5	67.817	1.831339	147.5	22.00	60.311	1.780399	131.1
115° 0'	34.5	59.284	1.772941	168.7	27.43	49.822	1.697425	141.8

NOTE. The odd values of *D* between 30° and 115° are those whose arc-definition radii vary approximately from 190 feet to 50 feet by 10-ft intervals. For curves having exactly these radii, see Table V.

TABLE II.—LENGTHS OF ARCS AND TRUE CHORDS

D	Chord Definition of D				Arc Definition of D		
	Arc for 1 Sta.	True Chords			True Chords		
		1/10 Sta.	1/4 Sta.	1/2 Sta.	1/4 Sta.	1/2 Sta	1 Sta.
1°	100.001	10	25	50	25	50	100
2°	100.005	10	25	50	25	50	100
3°	100.011	10	25	50	25	50	99.99
4°	100.020	10	25	50	25	50	99.98
5°	100.032	10	25	50.01	25	50	99.97
6°	100.046	10.01	25.01	50.02	25	50	99.95
7°	100.062	10.01	25.02	50.02	25	50	99.94
8°	100.081	10.01	25.02	50.03	25	49.99	99.92
9°	100.103	10.01	25.02	50.04	25	49.99	99.90
10°	100.127	10.01	25.03	50.05	25	49.98	99.88
11°	100.154	10.02	25.04	50.06	25	49.98	99.85
12°	100.183	10.02	25.04	50.07	25	49.98	99.82
13°	100.215	10.02	25.05	50.08	25	49.97	99.79
14°	100.249	10.02	25.06	50.09	25	49.97	99.75
15°	100.286	10.03	25.07	50.11	25	49.96	99.72
16°	100.326	10.03	25.08	50.12	25	49.96	99.68
17°	100.368	10.04	25.09	50.14	25	49.95	99.63
18°	100.412	10.04	25.10	50.16	24.99	49.95	99.59
19°	100.460	10.04	25.11	50.17	24.99	49.94	99.54
20°	100.510	10.05	25.12	50.19	24.99	49.94	99.49
21°	100.562	10.06	25.13	50.21	24.99	49.93	99.44
22°	100.617	10.06	25.14	50.23	24.99	49.92	99.39
23°	100.675	10.07	25.16	50.25	24.99	49.92	99.33
24°	100.735	10.07	25.17	50.27	24.99	49.91	99.27
25°	100.798	10.08	25.19	50.30	24.99	49.90	99.21
26°	100.863	10.08	25.20	50.32	24.99	49.89	99.14
27°	100.931	10.09	25.22	50.35	24.99	49.88	99.08
28°	101.002	10.10	25.23	50.38	24.98	49.88	99.01
29°	101.075	10.11	25.25	50.40	24.98	49.87	98.94
30°	101.152	10.11	25.27	50.43	24.98	49.86	98.86
32°	101.312	10.13	25.31	50.49	24.98	49.84	98.71
34°	101.482	10.15	25.35	50.56	24.98	49.82	98.54
36°	101.664	10.16	25.39	50.62	24.97	49.79	98.36
38°	101.857	10.18	25.43	50.69	24.97	49.77	98.18
41°	102.166	10.21	25.51	50.81	24.97	49.73	97.88
44°	102.500	10.25	25.59	50.94	24.96	49.69	97.56
48°	102.986	10.30	25.70	51.12	24.95	49.63	97.10
52°	103.516	10.35	25.82	51.31	24.95	49.57	96.60
57°	104.246	10.42	25.98	51.59	24.94	49.49	95.93
64°	105.394	10.53	26.26	52.01	24.92	49.35	94.88
72°	106.896	10.68	26.61	52.57	24.90	49.18	93.55
82°	109.073	10.90	27.12	53.38	24.87	48.94	91.68
95°	112.445	11.23	27.91	54.63	24.82	48.58	88.93
115°	118.992	11.88	29.44	57.03	24.74	47.93	84.04

Chord Definition of D

For degrees of curve not listed obtain excess arc per station approximately by interpolation, or exactly to 3 decimal places (up to D = 15°) from:

$$\text{Excess} = 0.00127 \, D^2$$

Arc Definition of D

For degrees of curve not listed obtain chord deficiency per station approximately by interpolation, or exactly to 2 decimal places (up to D = 30°) from:

$$\text{Deficiency} = 0.00127 \, D^2$$

14

TABLES III & IV.—CORRECTION COEFFICIENTS FOR SUBCHORDS

Chord Definition of D

The following table may be used to obtain true lengths of subchords not listed in Table II.

For any degree of curve the small correction to be added to the nominal length in order to obtain the true length is almost a constant percentage of the excess of arc for 1 station on a curve of that degree. The maximum correction is required for a nominal subchord about 57.5 feet long.

Nominal Subchord	Ratio of Chord Correction to Excess Arc per Station
5	.050
10	.099
15	.147
20	.192
25	.234
30	.273
35	.307
40	.336
45	.359
50	.375
55	.383
60	.384
65	.375
70	.357
75	.328
80	.288
85	.236
90	.171
95	.093
100	0

EXAMPLE. Given: a 20° curve. Required: true subchord for 75-ft nominal length.

Solution: Excess arc per sta. = 0.510 (from Table II). Corr. = 0.510 × 0.328 = 0.17. *Add corr. to nominal length* giving true subchord = 75.17.

For subchords not listed, interpolate for correction coefficients.

Arc Definition of D

The following table may be used to obtain true lengths of subchords not listed in Table II.

For any degree of curve the small correction to be subtracted from an arc length in order to obtain the true chord length is almost a constant percentage of the chord deficiency for a 100-foot arc on a curve of that degree. These percentages vary approximately as the cubes of the arc lengths.

Length of Arc	Ratio of Chord Correction to Chord Deficiency for 100-ft Arc
5	.0001
10	.0010
15	.0034
20	.0080
25	.016
30	.027
35	.043
40	.064
45	.091
50	.125
55	.166
60	.216
65	.275
70	.343
75	.422
80	.512
85	.614
90	.729
95	.857
100	1

EXAMPLE. Given: a 25° curve. Required: true subchord for 75-ft arc.

Solution: Chord def. per sta. = 0.79 (from Table II). Corr. = 0.79 × 0.422 = 0.33. *Subtract corr. from arc* giving true subchord = 74.67.

For arcs not listed, note that correction coefficients are proportional to the cubes of the arcs.

15

TABLE V.—EVEN-RADIUS CURVES. DEFLECTIONS AND CHORDS

Radius Ft	Defl. Min per Ft of Arc	Deflections for Arcs of			Chords for Arcs of		
		10 Ft	25 Ft	100 Ft	10 Ft	25 Ft	100 Ft
50	34.377	5°43.78'	14°19.44'	57°17.75'	9.98	24.74	84.15
60	28.648	4°46.48'	11°56.20'	47°44.79'	9.99	24.82	88.82
70	24.555	4°05.55'	10°13.88'	40°55.53'	9.99	24.87	91.73
80	21.486	3°34.86'	8°57.15'	35°48.59'	10	24.90	93.62
90	19.099	3°10.99'	7°57.46'	31°49.86'	10	24.92	94.94
100	17.189	2°51.89'	7°09.72'	28°38.87'	10	24.93	95.89
110	15.626	2°36.26'	6°30.65'	26°02.61'	10	24.95	96.59
120	14.324	2°23.24'	5°58.10'	23°52.39'	10	24.96	97.13
130	13.222	2°12.22'	5°30.55'	22°02.21'	10	24.96	97.55
140	12.278	2°02.78'	5°06.94'	20°27.77'	10	24.96	97.88
150	11.459	1°54.59'	4°46.48'	19°05.92'	10	24.97	98.16
160	10.743	1°47.43'	4°28.58'	17°54.30'	10	24.97	98.38
170	10.111	1°41.11'	4°12.77'	16°51.10'	10	24.97	98.57
180	9.549	1°35.49'	3°58.73'	15°54.93'	10	24.98	98.72
190	9.047	1°30.47'	3°46.17'	15°04.67'	10	24.98	98.85
		25 Ft	50 Ft		25 Ft	50 Ft	
200	8.594	3°34.86'	7°09.72'	14°19.44'	24.98	49.87	98.96
225	7.639	3°10.99'	6°21.97'	12°43.94'	24.99	49.90	99.18
250	6.875	2°51.89'	5°43.78'	11°27.55'	24.99	49.92	99.34
275	6.250	2°36.26'	5°12.52'	10°25.05'	24.99	49.93	99.45
300	5.730	2°23.24'	4°46.48'	9°32.96'	24.99	49.94	99.54
325	5.289	2°12.22'	4°24.44'	8°48.88'	24.99	49.95	99.61
350	4.911	2°02.78'	4°05.55'	8°11.11'	25	49.96	99.66
375	4.584	1°54.59'	3°49.18'	7°38.37'	25	49.96	99.70
400	4.297	1°47.43'	3°34.86'	7°09.72'	25	49.97	99.74
425	4.044	1°41.11'	3°22.22'	6°44.44'	25	49.97	99.77
450	3.820	1°35.49'	3°10.99'	6°21.97'	25	49.97	99.79
475	3.619	1°30.47'	3°00.93'	6°01.87'	25	49.98	99.82
500	3.438	1°25.94'	2°51.89'	5°43.77'	25	49.98	99.83
550	3.235	1°18.13'	2°36.26'	5°12.52'	25	49.98	99.86
600	2.865	1°11.62'	2°23.24'	4°46.48'	25	49.99	99.89
650	2.644	1°06.11'	2°12.22'	4°24.44'	25	49.99	99.90
700	2.455	1°01.39'	2°02.78'	4°05.55'	25	49.99	99.92
750	2.292	0°57.30'	1°54.59'	3°49.18'	25	50	99.93
800	2.149	0°53.71'	1°47.43'	3°34.86'	25	50	99.93
850	2.022	0°50.56'	1°41.11'	3°22.22'	25	50	99.94
900	1.910	0°47.75'	1°35.49'	3°10.99'	25	50	99.95
950	1.809	0°45.23'	1°30.47'	3°00.93'	25	50	99.95
1000	1.719	0°42.97'	1°25.94'	2°51.89'	25	50	99.96
1050	1.637	0°40.93'	1°21.85'	2°43.70'	25	50	99.96
1100	1.563	0°39.07'	1°18.13'	2°36.26'	25	50	99.96
1200	1.432	0°35.81'	1°11.62'	2°23.24'	25	50	99.97
1300	1.322	0°33.06'	1°06.11'	2°12.22'	25	50	99.97
1400	1.228	0°30.69'	1°01.39'	2°02.78'	25	50	99.98
1500	1.146	0°28.65'	0°57.30'	1°54.59'	25	50	99.98
1600	1.074	0°26.86'	0°53.72'	1°47.43'	25	50	99.98
1700	1.011	0°25.28'	0°50.56'	1°41.11'	25	50	99.99
1800	0.955	0°23.87'	0°47.75'	1°35.49'	25	50	99.99
1900	0.905	0°22.62'	0°45.23'	1°30.47'	25	50	100
2000	0.859	0°21.49'	0°42.97'	1°25.94'	25	50	100
2100	0.819	0°20.46'	0°40.93'	1°21.85'	25	50	100
2200	0.781	0°19.53'	0°39.07'	1°18.13'	25	50	100
2300	0.747	0°18.68'	0°37.37'	1°14.73'	25	50	100
2400	0.716	0°17.91'	0°35.81'	1°11.62'	25	50	100
2500	0.688	0°17.19'	0°34.38'	1°08.75'	25	50	100
2600	0.661	0°16.53'	0°33.06'	1°06.11'	25	50	100

TABLE V.—EVEN-RADIUS CURVES. DEFLECTIONS AND CHORDS

Radius Ft	Defl. Min per Ft of Arc	Deflections for Arcs of			Chords for Arcs of		
		25 Ft	50 Ft	100 Ft	25 Ft	50 Ft	100 Ft
2700	0.637	0°15.91'	0°31.83'	1°03.66'	25	50	100
2800	0.614	0°15.35'	0°30.69'	1°01.39'	25	50	100
2900	0.593	0°14.82'	0°29.64'	0°59.27'	25	50	100
3000	0.573	0°14.32'	0°28.65'	0°57.30'	25	50	100
3100	0.555	0°13.86'	0°27.72'	0°55.45'	25	50	100
3200	0.537	0°13.43'	0°26.86'	0°53.71'	25	50	100
3300	0.521	0°13.02'	0°26.04'	0°52.09'	25	50	100
3400	0.506	0°12.64'	0°25.28'	0°50.55'	25	50	100
3500	0.491	0°12.26'	0°24.56'	0°49.11'	25	50	100
3600	0.477	0°11.94'	0°23.87'	0°47.75'	25	50	100
3700	0.465	0°11.61'	0°23.23'	0°46.46'	25	50	100
3800	0.452	0°11.31'	0°22.62'	0°45.23'	25	50	100
3900	0.441	0°11.02'	0°22.04'	0°44.07'	25	50	100
4000	0.430	0°10.74'	0°21.49'	0°42.97'	25	50	100
4100	0.419	0°10.48'	0°20.96'	0°41.92'	25	50	100
4500	0.382	0°09.55'	0°19.10'	0°38.20'	25	50	100
5000	0.344	0°08.59'	0°17.19'	0°34.38'	25	50	100
5500	0.313	0°07.81'	0°15.63'	0°31.25'	25	50	100
6000	0.286	0°07.16'	0°14.32'	0°28.65'	25	50	100
6500	0.264	0°06.61'	0°13.22'	0°26.44'	25	50	100
7000	0.246	0°06.14'	0°12.28'	0°24.56'	25	50	100
7500	0.229	0°05.73'	0°11.46'	0°22.92'	25	50	100
8000	0.215	0°05.37'	0°10.74'	0°21.49'	25	50	100
9000	0.191	0°04.77'	0°09.55'	0°19.10'	25	50	100
10000	0.172	0°04.30'	0°08.59'	0°17.19'	25	50	100

NOTES. Degree of Curve (arc definition) = twice the deflection for a 100-ft arc = defl. per 100 ft on a curve having one-half the given value of R.

Deflections for even-radius curves or arcs not listed may be computed from:

$$\text{Defl. (in minutes)} = \frac{1718.873}{R} \times \text{arc length}$$

Chords not listed may be obtained by interpolation or computed from:
Chord = $2R \sin$ defl.

Total length of curve may be determined by use of Table VI. See Art. 5-10 for selection of spirals for even-radius curves.

Deg	Length	Deg	Length	Min	Length	Sec	Length
1	0.017 45 329	61	1.064 65 084	1	.000 29 089	1	.000 00 485
2	.034 90 659	62	.082 10 414	2	0 58 178	2	00 970
3	.052 35 988	63	.099 55 743	3	0 87 266	3	01 454
4	.069 81 317	64	.117 01 072	4	1 16 355	4	01 939
5	0.087 26 646	65	1.134 46 401	5	.001 45 444	5	.000 02 424
6	.104 71 976	66	.151 91 731	6	1 74 533	6	02 909
7	.122 17 305	67	.169 37 060	7	2 03 622	7	03 394
8	.139 62 634	68	.186 82 389	8	2 32 711	8	03 879
9	.157 07 963	69	.204 27 718	9	2 61 799	9	04 363
10	0.174 53 293	70	1.221 73 048	10	.002 90 888	10	.000 04 848
11	.191 98 622	71	.239 18 377	11	3 19 977	11	05 333
12	.209 43 951	72	.256 63 706	12	3 49 066	12	05 818
13	.226 89 280	73	.274 09 035	13	3 78 155	13	06 303
14	.244 34 610	74	.291 54 365	14	4 07 243	14	06 787
15	0.261 79 939	75	1.308 99 694	15	.004 36 332	15	.000 07 272
16	.279 25 268	76	.326 45 023	16	4 65 421	16	07 757
17	.296 70 597	77	.343 90 352	17	4 94 510	17	08 242
18	.314 15 927	78	.361 35 682	18	5 23 599	18	08 727
19	.331 61 256	79	.378 81 011	19	5 52 688	19	09 211
20	0.349 06 585	80	1.396 26 340	20	.005 81 776	20	.000 09 696
21	.366 51 914	81	.413 71 669	21	6 10 865	21	10 181
22	.383 97 244	82	.431 16 999	22	6 39 954	22	10 666
23	.401 42 573	83	.448 62 328	23	6 69 043	23	11 151
24	.418 87 902	84	.466 07 657	24	6 98 132	24	11 636
25	0.436 33 231	85	1.483 52 986	25	.007 27 221	25	.000 12 120
26	.453 78 561	86	.500 98 316	26	7 56 309	26	12 605
27	.471 23 890	87	.518 43 645	27	7 85 398	27	13 090
28	.488 69 219	88	.535 88 974	28	8 14 487	28	13 575
29	.506 14 548	89	.553 34 303	29	8 43 576	29	14 060
30	0.523 59 878	90	1.570 79 633	30	..008 72 665	30	.000 14 544
31	.541 05 207	91	.588 24 962	31	9 01 753	31	15 029
32	.558 50 536	92	.605 70 291	32	9 30 842	32	15 514
33	.575 95 865	93	.623 15 620	33	9 59 931	33	15 999
34	.593 41 195	94	.640 60 950	34	9 89 020	34	16 484
35	0.610 86 524	95	1.658 06 279	35	.010 18 109	35	.000 16 969
36	.628 31 853	96	.675 51 608	36	10 47 198	36	17 453
37	.645 77 182	97	.692 96 937	37	10 76 286	37	17 938
38	.663 22 512	98	.710 42 267	38	11 05 375	38	18 423
39	.680 67 841	99	.727 87 596	39	11 34 464	39	18 908
40	0.698 13 170	100	1.745 32 925	40	.011 63 553	40	.000 19 393
41	.715 58 499	101	.762 78 254	41	11 92 642	41	19 877
42	.733 03 829	102	.780 23 584	42	12 21 730	42	20 362
43	.750 49 158	103	.797 68 913	43	12 50 819	43	20 847
44	.767 94 487	104	.815 14 242	44	12 79 908	44	21 332
45	0.785 39 816	105	1.832 59 571	45	.013 08 997	45	.000 21 817
46	.802 85 146	106	.850 04 901	46	13 38 086	46	22 301
47	.820 30 475	107	.867 50 230	47	13 67 175	47	22 786
48	.837 75 804	108	.884 95 559	48	13 96 263	48	23 271
49	.855 21 133	109	.902 40 888	49	14 25 352	49	23 756
50	0.872 66 463	110	1.919 86 218	50	.014 54 441	50	.000 24 241
51	.890 11 792	111	.937 31 547	51	14 83 530	51	24 726
52	.907 57 121	112	.954 76 876	52	15 12 619	52	25 210
53	.925 02 450	113	.972 22 205	53	·15 41 708	53	25 695
54	.942 47 780	114	.989 67 535	54	15 70 796	54	26 180
55	0.959 93 109	115	2.007 12 864	55	.015 99 885	55	.000 26 665
56	.977 38 438	116	.024 58 193	56	16 28 974	56	27 150
57	.994 83 767	117	.042 03 522	57	16 58 063	57	27 634
58	1.012 29 097	118	.059 48 852	58	16 87 152	58	28 119
59	1.029 74 426	119	.076 94 181	59	17 16 240	59	28 604
60	1.047 19 755	120	.094 39 510	60	17 45 329	60	29 089

TABLE VII.—MINUTES AND SECONDS IN DECIMALS OF A DEGREE

Min	Seconds							
	0	10	15	20	30	40	45	50
0	.0000	.0028	.0042	.0056	.0083	.0111	.0125	.0139
1	.0167	.0194	.0208	.0222	.0250	.0278	.0292	.0306
2	.0333	.0361	.0375	.0389	.0417	.0444	.0458	.0472
3	.0500	.0528	.0542	.0556	.0583	.0611	.0625	.0639
4	.0667	.0694	.0708	.0722	.0750	.0778	.0792	.0806
5	.0833	.0861	.0875	.0889	.0917	.0944	.0958	.0972
6	.1000	.1028	.1042	.1056	.1083	.1111	.1125	.1139
7	.1167	.1194	.1208	.1222	.1250	.1278	.1292	.1306
8	.1333	.1361	.1375	.1389	.1417	.1444	.1458	.1472
9	.1500	.1528	.1542	.1556	.1583	.1611	.1625	.1639
10	.1667	.1694	.1708	.1722	.1750	.1778	.1792	.1806
11	.1833	.1861	.1875	.1889	.1917	.1944	.1958	.1972
12	.2000	.2028	.2042	.2056	.2083	.2111	.2125	.2139
13	.2167	.2194	.2208	.2222	.2250	.2278	.2292	.2306
14	.2333	.2361	.2375	.2389	.2417	.2444	.2458	.2472
15	.2500	.2528	.2542	.2556	.2583	.2611	.2625	.2639
16	.2667	.2694	.2708	.2722	.2750	.2778	.2792	.2806
17	.2833	.2861	.2875	.2889	.2917	.2944	.2958	.2972
18	.3000	.3028	.3042	.3056	.3083	.3111	.3125	.3139
19	.3167	.3194	.3208	.3222	.3250	.3278	.3292	.3306
20	.3333	.3361	.3375	.3389	.3417	.3444	.3458	.3472
21	.3500	.3528	.3542	.3556	.3583	.3611	.3625	.3639
22	.3667	.3694	.3708	.3722	.3750	.3778	.3792	.3806
23	.3833	.3861	.3875	.3889	.3917	.3944	.3958	.3972
24	.4000	.4028	.4042	.4056	.4083	.4111	.4125	.4139
25	.4167	.4194	.4208	.4222	.4250	.4278	.4292	.4306
26	.4333	.4361	.4375	.4389	.4417	.4444	.4458	.4472
27	.4500	.4528	.4542	.4556	.4583	.4611	.4625	.4639
28	.4667	.4694	.4708	.4722	.4750	.4778	.4792	.4806
29	.4833	.4861	.4875	.4889	.4917	.4944	.4958	.4972
30	.5000	.5028	.5042	.5056	.5083	.5111	.5125	.5139
31	.5167	.5194	.5208	.5222	.5250	.5278	.5292	.5306
32	.5333	.5361	.5375	.5389	.5417	.5444	.5458	.5472
33	.5500	.5528	.5542	.5556	.5583	.5611	.5625	.5639
34	.5667	.5694	.5708	.5722	.5750	.5778	.5792	.5806
35	.5833	.5861	.5875	.5889	.5917	.5944	.5958	.5972
36	.6000	.6028	.6042	.6056	.6083	.6111	.6125	.6139
37	.6167	.6194	.6208	.6222	.6250	.6278	.6292	.6306
38	.6333	.6361	.6375	.6389	.6417	.6444	.6458	.6472
39	.6500	.6528	.6542	.6556	.6583	.6611	.6625	.6639
40	.6667	.6694	.6708	.6722	.6750	.6778	.6792	.6806
41	.6833	.6861	.6875	.6889	.6917	.6944	.6958	.6972
42	.7000	.7028	.7042	.7056	.7083	.7111	.7125	.7139
43	.7167	.7194	.7208	.7222	.7250	.7278	.7292	.7306
44	.7333	.7361	.7375	.7389	.7417	.7444	.7458	.7472
45	.7500	.7528	.7542	.7556	.7583	.7611	.7625	.7639
46	.7667	.7694	.7708	.7722	.7750	.7778	.7792	.7806
47	.7833	.7861	.7875	.7889	.7917	.7944	.7958	.7972
48	.8000	.8028	.8042	.8056	.8083	.8111	.8125	.8139
49	.8167	.8194	.8208	.8222	.8250	.8278	.8292	.8306
50	.8333	.8361	.8375	.8389	.8417	.8444	.8458	.8472
51	.8500	.8528	.8542	.8556	.8583	.8611	.8625	.8639
52	.8667	.8694	.8708	.8722	.8750	.8778	.8792	.8806
53	.8833	.8861	.8875	.8889	.8917	.8944	.8958	.8972
54	.9000	.9028	.9042	.9056	.9083	.9111	.9125	.9139
55	.9167	.9194	.9208	.9222	.9250	.9278	.9292	.9306
56	.9333	.9361	.9375	.9389	.9417	.9444	.9458	.9472
57	.9500	.9528	.9542	.9556	.9583	.9611	.9625	.9639
58	.9667	.9694	.9708	.9722	.9750	.9778	.9792	.9806
59	.9833	.9861	.9875	.9889	.9917	.9944	.9958	.9972

TABLE VIII.—TANGENTS AND EXTERNALS FOR A 1° CURVE
(Chord or Arc Definition)

Explanation

Chord Definition of Degree of Curve (D_c)	Arc Definition of Degree of Curve (D_a)
MATHEMATICAL RELATIONS	MATHEMATICAL RELATIONS

1. $\sin \frac{1}{2}D_c = \frac{50}{R}$ .... exactly

1a. $D_c = \frac{5,729.65}{R}$ ... approx.

2. $T = R \tan \frac{1}{2}I$ ... exactly

2a. $T = \frac{T_{1^\circ}}{D_c}$ .... approx.

3. $E = R$ exsec $\frac{1}{2}I$ .. exactly

3a. $E = \frac{E_{1^\circ}}{D_c}$ .... approx.

1. $D_a = \frac{5,729.58}{R}$ ... exactly

2. $T = R \tan \frac{1}{2}I$ ... exactly

2a. $T = \frac{T_{1^\circ}}{D_a}$ .... exactly

3. $E = R$ exsec $\frac{1}{2}I$ .. exactly

3a. $E = \frac{E_{1^\circ}}{D_a}$ .... exactly

Table VIII gives values of T and E for a 1° curve having various central angles. The values may be considered correct for both the chord definition and the arc definition of D, since the difference in R for $D = 1°$ is only seven units in the sixth significant figure. To find T and E for any given values of I and D, use relations 2a and 3a, as in the following example:

EXAMPLE. *Given:* $I = 68°45'$, $D = 8°40'$. (*Note:* To avoid lack of precision in calculation, use D as $8\frac{2}{3} = \frac{26}{3}$, instead of 8.666 . . .)

For Arc Definition of D,

$$T = 3,919.5 \times \frac{3}{26} = 452.25$$

$$E = 1,212.3 \times \frac{3}{26} = 139.88$$

For Chord Definition of D,

T = Arc-definition value plus correction of 0.43 found
from Table IX by interpolation; or $T = 452.68$
E = Arc-definition value plus correction of 0.14 found
from Table X by interpolation; or $E = 140.02$

20

'	I = 0°		I = 1°		I = 2°		I = 3°		I = 4°		'
	T	E	T	E	T	E	T	E	T	E	
0	0.0	0.0	50.0	0.2	100.0	0.9	150.0	2.0	200.1	3.5	0
1	0.8	0.0	50.8	0.2	100.8	0.9	150.9	2.0	200.9	3.5	1
2	1.7	0.0	51.7	0.2	101.7	0.9	151.7	2.0	201.8	3.6	2
3	2.5	0.0	52.5	0.2	102.5	0.9	152.5	2.0	202.6	3.6	3
4	3.3	0.0	53.3	0.2	103.3	0.9	153.4	2.1	203.4	3.6	4
5	4.2	0.0	54.2	0.3	104.2	0.9	154.2	2.1	204.3	3.7	5
6	5.0	0.0	55.0	0.3	105.0	1.0	155.0	2.1	205.1	3.7	6
7	5.8	0.0	55.8	0.3	105.8	1.0	155.9	2.1	205.9	3.7	7
8	6.7	0.0	56.7	0.3	106.7	1.0	156.7	2.1	206.8	3.7	8
9	7.5	0.0	57.5	0.3	107.5	1.0	157.5	2.2	207.6	3.8	9
10	8.3	0.0	58.3	0.3	108.3	1.0	158.4	2.2	208.4	3.8	10
11	9.2	0.0	59.2	0.3	109.2	1.0	159.2	2.2	209.3	3.8	11
12	10.0	0.0	60.0	0.3	110.0	1.1	160.0	2.2	210.1	3.9	12
13	10.8	0.0	60.8	0.3	110.8	1.1	160.9	2.3	210.9	3.9	13
14	11.7	0.0	61.7	0.3	111.7	1.1	161.7	2.3	211.8	3.9	14
15	12.5	0.0	62.5	0.3	112.5	1.1	162.5	2.3	212.6	3.9	15
16	13.3	0.0	63.3	0.3	113.3	1.1	163.4	2.3	213.4	4.0	16
17	14.2	0.0	64.2	0.4	114.2	1.1	164.2	2.4	214.3	4.0	17
18	15.0	0.0	65.0	0.4	115.0	1.2	165.0	2.4	215.1	4.0	18
19	15.8	0.0	65.8	0.4	115.9	1.2	165.9	2.4	215.9	4.1	19
20	16.7	0.0	66.7	0.4	116.7	1.2	166.7	2.4	216.8	4.1	20
21	17.5	0.0	67.5	0.4	117.5	1.2	167.6	2.4	217.6	4.1	21
22	18.3	0.0	68.3	0.4	118.4	1.2	168.4	2.5	218.4	4.2	22
23	19.2	0.0	69.2	0.4	119.2	1.2	169.2	2.5	219.3	4.2	23
24	20.0	0.0	70.0	0.4	120.0	1.3	170.1	2.5	220.1	4.2	24
25	20.8	0.0	70.8	0.4	120.9	1.3	170.9	2.5	220.9	4.3	25
26	21.7	0.0	71.7	0.4	121.7	1.3	171.7	2.6	221.8	4.3	26
27	22.5	0.0	72.5	0.5	122.5	1.3	172.6	2.6	222.6	4.3	27
28	23.3	0.0	73.3	0.5	123.4	1.3	173.4	2.6	223.4	4.4	28
29	24.2	0.1	74.2	0.5	124.2	1.3	174.2	2.6	224.3	4.4	29
30	25.0	0.1	75.0	0.5	125.0	1.4	175.1	2.7	225.1	4.4	30
31	25.8	0.1	75.8	0.5	125.9	1.4	175.9	2.7	226.0	4.5	31
32	26.7	0.1	76.7	0.5	126.7	1.4	176.7	2.7	226.8	4.5	32
33	27.5	0.1	77.5	0.5	127.5	1.4	177.6	2.8	227.6	4.5	33
34	28.3	0.1	78.3	0.5	128.4	1.4	178.4	2.8	228.5	4.6	34
35	29.2	0.1	79.2	0.5	129.2	1.5	179.2	2.8	229.3	4.6	35
36	30.0	0.1	80.0	0.6	130.0	1.5	180.1	2.8	230.1	4.6	36
37	30.8	0.1	80.8	0.6	130.9	1.5	180.9	2.9	231.0	4.7	37
38	31.7	0.1	81.7	0.6	131.7	1.5	181.7	2.9	231.8	4.7	38
39	32.5	0.1	82.5	0.6	132.5	1.5	182.6	2.9	232.6	4.7	39
40	33.3	0.1	83.3	0.6	133.4	1.6	183.4	2.9	233.5	4.8	40
41	34.2	0.1	84.2	0.6	134.2	1.6	184.2	3.0	234.3	4.8	41
42	35.0	0.1	85.0	0.6	135.0	1.6	185.1	3.0	235.1	4.8	42
43	35.8	0.1	85.8	0.6	135.9	1.6	185.9	3.0	236.0	4.9	43
44	36.7	0.1	86.7	0.7	136.7	1.6	186.7	3.0	236.8	4.9	44
45	37.5	0.1	87.5	0.7	137.5	1.7	187.6	3.1	237.6	4.9	45
46	38.3	0.1	88.3	0.7	138.4	1.7	188.4	3.1	238.5	5.0	46
47	39.2	0.1	89.2	0.7	139.2	1.7	189.2	3.1	239.3	5.0	47
48	40.0	0.1	90.0	0.7	140.0	1.7	190.1	3.2	240.1	5.0	48
49	40.8	0.1	90.8	0.7	140.9	1.7	190.9	3.2	241.0	5.1	49
50	41.7	0.2	91.7	0.7	141.7	1.8	191.7	3.2	241.8	5.1	50
51	42.5	0.2	92.5	0.7	142.5	1.8	192.6	3.2	242.6	5.1	51
52	43.3	0.2	93.3	0.8	143.4	1.8	193.4	3.3	243.5	5.2	52
53	44.2	0.2	94.2	0.8	144.2	1.8	194.2	3.3	244.3	5.2	53
54	45.0	0.2	95.0	0.8	145.0	1.8	195.1	3.3	245.2	5.2	54
55	45.8	0.2	95.8	0.8	145.9	1.9	195.9	3.3	246.0	5.3	55
56	46.7	0.2	96.7	0.8	146.7	1.9	196.7	3.4	246.8	5.3	56
57	47.5	0.2	97.5	0.8	147.5	1.9	197.6	3.4	247.7	5.3	57
58	48.3	0.2	98.3	0.8	148.4	1.9	198.4	3.4	248.5	5.4	58
59	49.2	0.2	99.2	0.9	149.2	1.9	199.2	3.5	249.3	5.4	59

21

TABLE VIII.—TANGENTS AND EXTERNALS FOR A 1° CURVE
(Chord or Arc Definition)

'	I = 5°		I = 6°		I = 7°		I = 8°		I = 9°		'
	T	E	T	E	T	E	T	E	T	E	
0	250.2	5.5	300.3	7.9	350.4	10.7	400.7	14.0	450.9	17.7	0
1	251.0	5.5	301.1	7.9	351.3	10.8	401.5	14.1	451.8	17.8	1
2	251.8	5.5	301.9	8.0	352.1	10.8	402.3	14.1	452.6	17.8	2
3	252.7	5.6	302.8	8.0	352.9	10.9	403.2	14.2	453.4	17.9	3
4	253.5	5.6	303.6	8.0	353.8	11.0	404.0	14.2	454.3	18.0	4
5	254.3	5.6	304.5	8.1	354.6	11.0	404.8	14.3	455.1	18.0	5
6	255.2	5.7	305.3	8.1	355.5	11.0	405.7	14.3	456.0	18.1	6
7	256.0	5.7	306.1	8.2	346.3	11.1	406.5	14.4	456.8	18.2	7
8	256.8	5.8	307.0	8.2	357.1	11.1	407.4	14.5	457.6	18.2	8
9	257.7	5.8	307.8	8.3	358.0	11.2	408.2	14.5	458.5	18.3	9
10	258.5	5.8	308.6	8.3	358.8	11.2	409.0	14.6	459.3	18.4	10
11	259.3	5.9	309.5	8.4	359.6	11.3	409.9	14.6	460.2	18.4	11
12	260.2	5.9	310.3	8.4	360.5	11.3	410.7	14.7	461.0	18.5	12
13	261.0	5.9	311.1	8.4	361.3	11.4	411.5	14.8	461.8	18.6	13
14	261.9	6.0	312.0	8.5	362.2	11.4	412.4	14.8	462.7	18.7	14
15	262.7	6.0	312.8	8.5	363.0	11.5	413.2	14.9	463.5	18.7	15
16	263.5	6.1	313.7	8.6	363.8	11.5	414.1	14.9	464.4	18.8	16
17	264.4	6.1	314.5	8.6	364.7	11.6	414.9	15.0	465.2	18.9	17
18	265.2	6.1	315.3	8.7	365.5	11.6	415.7	15.1	466.0	18.9	18
19	266.0	6.2	316.2	8.7	366.3	11.7	416.6	15.1	466.9	19.0	19
20	266.9	6.2	317.0	8.8	367.2	11.8	417.4	15.2	467.7	19.1	20
21	267.7	6.3	317.8	8.8	368.0	11.8	418.2	15.2	468.5	19.1	21
22	268.5	6.3	318.7	8.9	368.8	11.9	419.1	15.3	469.4	19.2	22
23	269.4	6.3	319.5	8.9	369.7	11.9	419.9	15.4	470.2	19.3	23
24	270.2	6.4	320.3	8.9	370.5	12.0	420.8	15.4	471.1	19.3	24
25	271.0	6.4	321.2	9.0	371.4	12.0	421.6	15.5	471.9	19.4	25
26	271.9	6.4	322.0	9.0	372.2	12.1	422.4	15.6	472.7	19.5	26
27	272.7	6.5	322.8	9.1	373.0	12.1	423.3	15.6	473.6	19.5	27
28	273.5	6.5	323.7	9.1	373.9	12.2	424.1	15.7	474.4	19.6	28
29	274.4	6.6	324.5	9.2	374.7	12.2	424.9	15.7	475.3	19.7	29
30	275.2	6.6	325.4	9.2	375.5	12.3	425.8	15.8	476.1	19.7	30
31	276.1	6.6	326.2	9.3	376.4	12.3	426.6	15.9	476.9	19.8	31
32	276.9	6.7	327.0	9.3	377.2	12.4	427.5	15.9	477.8	19.9	32
33	277.7	6.7	327.9	9.4	378.1	12.5	428.3	16.0	478.6	20.0	33
34	278.6	6.8	328.7	9.4	378.9	12.5	429.1	16.0	479.5	20.0	34
35	279.4	6.8	329.5	9.5	379.7	12.6	430.0	16.1	480.3	20.1	35
36	280.2	6.9	330.4	9.5	380.6	12.6	430.8	16.2	481.1	20.2	36
37	281.1	6.9	331.2	9.6	381.4	12.7	431.7	16.2	482.0	20.2	37
38	281.9	6.9	332.0	9.6	382.2	12.7	432.5	16.3	482.8	20.3	38
39	282.7	7.0	332.9	9.7	383.1	12.8	433.3	16.4	483.6	20.4	39
40	283.6	7.0	333.7	9.7	383.9	12.8	434.2	16.4	484.5	20.4	40
41	284.4	7.1	334.6	9.8	384.7	12.9	435.0	16.5	485.3	20.5	41
42	285.2	7.1	335.4	9.8	385.6	13.0	435.8	16.6	486.2	20.6	42
43	286.1	7.1	336.2	9.9	386.4	13.0	436.7	16.6	487.0	20.7	43
44	286.9	7.2	337.1	9.9	387.3	13.1	437.5	16.7	487.8	20.7	44
45	287.7	7.2	337.9	10.0	388.1	13.1	438.4	16.7	488.7	20.8	45
46	288.6	7.3	338.7	10.0	388.9	13.2	439.2	16.8	489.5	20.9	46
47	289.4	7.3	339.6	10.1	389.8	13.2	440.0	16.9	490.4	20.9	47
48	290.3	7.3	340.4	10.1	390.6	13.3	440.9	17.0	491.2	21.0	48
49	291.1	7.4	341.2	10.2	391.4	13.4	441.7	17.0	492.0	21.1	49
50	291.9	7.4	342.1	10.2	392.3	13.4	442.5	17.1	492.9	21.2	50
51	292.8	7.5	342.9	10.3	393.1	13.5	443.4	17.1	493.7	21.2	51
52	293.6	7.5	343.7	10.3	394.0	13.5	444.2	17.2	494.6	21.3	52
53	294.4	7.6	344.6	10.4	394.8	13.6	445.1	17.3	495.4	21.4	53
54	295.3	7.6	345.4	10.4	395.6	13.6	445.9	17.3	496.2	21.5	54
55	296.1	7.6	346.3	10.5	396.5	13.7	446.7	17.4	497.1	21.5	55
56	296.9	7.7	347.1	10.5	397.3	13.8	447.6	17.5	497.9	21.6	56
57	297.8	7.7	347.9	10.6	398.1	13.8	448.4	17.5	498.8	21.7	57
58	298.6	7.8	348.8	10.6	399.0	13.9	449.3	17.6	499.6	21.7	58
59	299.4	7.8	349.6	10.7	399.8	13.9	450.1	17.7	500.4	21.8	59

TABLE VIII.—TANGENTS AND EXTERNALS FOR A 1° CURVE
(Chord or Arc Definition)

I = 10°		I = 11°		I = 12°		I = 13°		I = 14°		'
T	E	T	E	T	E	T	E	T	E	
501.3	21.9	551.7	26.5	602.2	31.6	652.8	37.1	703.5	43.0	0
502.1	22.0	552.5	26.6	603.1	31.6	653.7	37.2	704.4	43.1	1
503.0	22.0	553.4	26.7	603.9	31.7	654.5	37.3	705.2	43.2	2
503.8	22.1	554.2	26.7	604.7	31.8	655.3	37.4	706.1	43.3	3
504.6	22.2	555.1	26.8	605.6	31.9	656.2	37.5	706.9	43.4	4
505.5	22.3	555.9	26.9	606.4	32.0	657.0	37.6	707.7	43.5	5
506.3	22.3	556.7	27.0	607.3	32.1	657.9	37.6	708.6	43.7	6
507.2	22.4	557.6	27.1	608.1	32.2	658.7	37.7	709.4	43.8	7
508.0	22.5	558.4	27.2	609.0	32.3	659.6	37.8	710.3	43.9	8
508.8	22.6	559.3	27.2	609.8	32.4	660.4	37.9	711.1	44.0	9
509.7	22.6	560.1	27.3	610.6	32.4	661.3	38.0	712.0	44.1	10
510.5	22.7	561.0	27.4	611.5	32.5	662.1	38.1	712.8	44.2	11
511.4	22.8	561.8	27.5	612.3	32.6	662.9	38.2	713.7	44.3	12
512.2	22.8	562.6	27.6	613.2	32.7	663.8	38.3	714.5	44.4	13
513.0	22.9	563.5	27.6	614.0	32.8	664.6	38.4	715.4	44.5	14
513.9	23.0	564.3	27.7	614.9	32.9	665.5	38.5	716.2	44.6	15
514.7	23.1	565.2	27.8	615.7	33.0	666.3	38.6	717.1	44.7	16
515.6	23.1	566.0	27.9	616.5	33.1	667.2	38.7	717.9	44.8	17
516.4	23.2	566.8	28.0	617.4	33.2	668.0	38.8	718.7	44.9	18
517.2	23.3	567.7	28.1	618.2	33.3	668.9	38.9	719.6	45.0	19
518.1	23.4	568.5	28.1	619.1	33.3	669.7	39.0	720.4	45.1	20
518.9	23.5	569.4	28.2	619.9	33.4	670.5	39.1	721.3	45.2	21
519.8	23.5	570.2	28.3	620.8	33.5	671.4	39.2	722.1	45.3	22
520.6	23.6	571.1	28.4	621.6	33.6	672.2	39.3	723.0	45.4	23
521.4	23.7	571.9	28.5	622.4	33.7	673.1	39.4	723.8	45.5	24
522.3	23.8	572.7	28.6	623.3	33.8	673.9	39.5	724.7	45.6	25
523.1	23.8	573.6	28.6	624.1	33.9	674.8	39.6	725.5	45.8	26
524.0	23.9	574.4	28.7	625.0	34.0	675.6	39.7	726.4	45.9	27
524.8	24.0	575.3	28.8	625.8	34.1	676.5	39.8	727.2	46.0	28
525.6	24.1	576.1	28.9	626.7	34.2	677.3	39.9	728.1	46.1	29
526.5	24.1	576.9	29.0	627.5	34.3	678.1	40.0	728.9	46.2	30
527.3	24.2	577.8	29.1	628.3	34.4	679.0	40.1	729.8	46.3	31
528.2	24.3	578.6	29.1	629.2	34.4	679.8	40.2	730.6	46.4	32
529.0	24.4	579.5	29.2	630.0	34.5	680.7	40.3	731.4	46.5	33
529.8	24.4	580.3	29.3	630.9	34.6	681.5	40.4	732.3	46.6	34
530.7	24.5	581.2	29.4	631.7	34.7	682.4	40.5	733.1	46.7	35
531.5	24.6	582.0	29.5	632.6	34.8	683.2	40.6	734.0	46.8	36
532.4	24.7	582.8	29.6	633.4	34.9	684.1	40.7	734.8	46.9	37
533.2	24.8	583.7	29.7	634.2	35.0	684.9	40.8	735.7	47.0	38
534.0	24.8	584.5	29.7	635.1	35.1	685.8	40.9	736.5	47.1	39
534.9	24.9	585.4	29.8	635.9	35.2	686.6	41.0	737.4	47.3	40
535.7	25.0	586.2	29.9	636.8	35.3	687.4	41.1	738.2	47.4	41
536.6	25.1	587.0	30.0	637.6	35.4	688.3	41.2	739.1	47.5	42
537.4	25.1	587.9	30.1	638.5	35.5	689.1	41.3	739.9	47.6	43
538.2	25.2	588.7	30.2	639.3	35.6	690.0	41.4	740.8	47.7	44
539.1	25.3	589.6	30.3	640.2	35.7	690.8	41.5	741.6	47.8	45
539.9	25.4	590.4	30.3	641.0	35.7	691.7	41.6	742.5	47.9	46
540.8	25.5	591.3	30.4	641.8	35.8	692.5	41.7	743.3	48.0	47
541.6	25.5	592.1	30.5	642.7	35.9	693.4	41.8	744.2	48.1	48
542.5	25.6	592.9	30.6	643.5	36.0	694.2	41.9	745.0	48.2	49
543.3	25.7	593.8	30.7	644.4	36.1	695.1	42.0	745.8	48.3	50
544.1	25.8	594.6	30.8	645.2	36.2	695.9	42.1	746.7	48.5	51
545.0	25.9	595.5	30.9	646.1	36.3	696.7	42.2	747.5	48.6	52
545.8	25.9	596.3	30.9	646.9	36.4	697.6	42.3	748.4	48.7	53
546.7	26.0	597.2	31.0	647.7	36.5	698.4	42.4	749.2	48.8	54
547.5	26.1	598.0	31.1	648.6	36.6	699.3	42.5	750.1	48.9	55
548.3	26.2	598.8	31.2	649.4	36.7	700.1	42.6	750.9	49.0	56
549.2	26.3	599.7	31.3	650.3	36.8	701.0	42.7	751.8	49.1	57
550.0	26.3	600.5	31.4	651.1	36.9	701.8	42.8	752.6	49.2	58
550.9	26.4	601.4	31.5	652.0	37.0	702.7	42.9	753.5	49.3	59

TABLE VIII.—TANGENTS AND EXTERNALS FOR A 1° CURVE
(Chord or Arc Definition)

'	I = 15°		I = 16°		I = 17°		I = 18°		I = 19°		'
	T	E	T	E	T	E	T	E	T	E	
0	754.3	49.4	805.2	56.3	856.3	63.6	907.5	71.4	958.8	79.7	0
1	755.2	49.6	806.1	56.4	857.2	63.8	908.3	71.6	959.7	79.8	1
2	756.0	49.7	806.9	56.5	858.0	63.9	909.2	71.7	960.5	80.0	2
3	756.9	49.8	807.8	56.7	858.9	64.0	910.1	71.8	961.4	80.1	3
4	757.7	49.9	808.6	56.8	859.7	64.1	910.9	72.0	962.2	80.2	4
5	758.6	50.0	809.5	56.9	860.6	64.3	911.8	72.1	963.1	80.4	5
6	759.4	50.1	810.3	57.0	861.4	64.4	912.6	72.2	964.0	80.5	6
7	760.3	50.2	811.2	57.1	862.3	64.5	913.5	72.4	964.8	80.7	7
8	761.1	50.3	812.0	57.3	863.1	64.6	914.3	72.5	965.7	80.8	8
9	762.0	50.4	812.9	57.4	864.0	64.8	915.2	72.6	966.5	80.9	9
10	762.8	50.6	813.7	57.5	864.8	64.9	916.0	72.8	967.4	81.1	10
11	763.7	50.7	814.6	57.6	865.7	65.0	916.9	72.9	968.2	81.2	11
12	764.5	50.8	815.5	57.7	866.5	65.2	917.7	73.0	969.1	81.4	12
13	765.3	50.9	816.3	57.9	867.4	65.3	918.6	73.2	970.0	81.5	13
14	766.2	51.0	817.2	58.0	868.2	65.4	919.5	73.3	970.8	81.7	14
15	767.0	51.1	818.0	58.1	869.1	65.5	920.3	73.4	971.7	81.8	15
16	767.9	51.2	818.9	58.2	869.9	65.7	921.2	73.6	972.5	82.0	16
17	768.7	51.3	819.7	58.3	870.8	65.8	922.0	73.7	973.4	82.1	17
18	769.6	51.5	820.6	58.5	871.6	65.9	922.9	73.8	974.2	82.2	18
19	770.4	51.6	821.4	58.6	872.5	66.1	923.7	74.0	975.1	82.4	19
20	771.3	51.7	822.3	58.7	873.3	66.2	924.6	74.1	976.0	82.5	20
21	772.1	51.8	823.1	58.8	874.2	66.3	925.4	74.3	976.8	82.7	21
22	773.0	51.9	824.0	58.9	875.1	66.4	926.3	74.4	977.7	82.8	22
23	773.8	52.0	824.8	59.1	875.9	66.6	927.1	74.5	978.5	83.0	23
24	774.7	52.1	825.7	59.2	876.8	66.7	928.0	74.7	979.4	83.1	24
25	775.5	52.2	826.5	59.3	877.6	66.8	928.9	74.8	980.2	83.2	25
26	776.4	52.4	827.4	59.4	878.5	67.0	929.7	74.9	981.1	83.4	26
27	777.2	52.5	828.2	59.5	879.3	67.1	930.6	75.1	982.0	83.5	27
28	778.1	52.6	829.1	59.7	880.2	67.2	931.4	75.2	982.8	83.7	28
29	778.9	52.7	829.9	59.8	881.0	67.3	932.3	75.4	983.7	83.8	29
30	779.8	52.8	830.8	59.9	881.9	67.5	933.1	75.5	984.5	84.0	30
31	780.6	52.9	831.6	60.0	882.7	67.6	934.0	75.6	985.4	84.1	31
32	781.5	53.0	832.5	60.2	883.6	67.7	934.8	75.8	986.3	84.3	32
33	782.3	53.2	833.3	60.3	884.4	67.9	935.7	75.9	987.1	84.4	33
34	783.2	53.3	834.2	60.4	885.3	68.0	936.6	76.0	988.0	84.6	34
35	784.0	53.4	835.0	60.5	886.1	68.1	937.4	76.2	988.8	84.7	35
36	784.9	53.5	835.9	60.7	887.0	68.3	938.3	76.3	989.7	84.8	36
37	785.7	53.6	836.7	60.8	887.9	68.4	939.1	76.5	990.5	85.0	37
38	786.6	53.7	837.6	60.9	888.7	68.5	940.0	76.6	991.4	85.1	38
39	787.4	53.9	838.4	61.0	889.6	68.6	940.8	76.7	992.3	85.3	39
40	788.3	54.0	839.3	61.1	890.4	68.8	941.7	76.9	993.1	85.4	40
41	789.1	54.1	840.1	61.3	891.3	68.9	942.5	77.0	994.0	85.6	41
42	790.0	54.2	841.0	61.4	892.1	69.0	943.4	77.1	994.8	85.7	42
43	790.8	54.3	841.8	61.5	893.0	69.2	944.3	77.3	995.7	85.9	43
44	791.7	54.4	842.7	61.6	893.8	69.3	945.1	77.4	996.5	86.0	44
45	792.5	54.6	843.5	61.8	894.7	69.4	946.0	77.6	997.4	86.2	45
46	793.4	54.7	844.4	61.9	895.5	69.6	946.8	77.7	998.3	86.3	46
47	794.2	54.8	845.2	62.0	896.4	69.7	947.7	77.8	999.1	86.5	47
48	795.1	54.9	846.1	62.1	897.2	69.8	948.5	78.0	1000.0	86.6	48
49	795.9	55.0	846.9	62.3	898.1	70.0	949.4	78.1	1000.8	86.8	49
50	796.8	55.1	847.8	62.4	898.9	70.1	950.2	78.3	1001.7	86.9	50
51	797.6	55.2	848.6	62.5	899.8	70.2	951.1	78.4	1002.6	87.1	51
52	798.5	55.4	849.5	62.6	900.7	70.4	952.0	78.5	1003.4	87.2	52
53	799.3	55.5	850.3	62.8	901.5	70.5	952.8	78.7	1004.3	87.3	53
54	800.2	55.6	851.2	62.9	902.4	70.6	953.7	78.8	1005.1	87.5	54
55	801.0	55.7	852.0	63.0	903.2	70.8	954.5	79.0	1006.0	87.6	55
56	801.9	55.8	852.9	63.1	904.1	70.9	955.4	79.1	1006.9	87.8	56
57	802.7	56.0	853.7	63.3	904.9	71.0	956.2	79.2	1007.7	87.9	57
58	803.6	56.1	854.6	63.4	905.8	71.2	957.1	79.4	1008.6	88.1	58
59	804.4	56.2	855.5	63.5	906.6	71.3	958.0	79.5	1009.4	88.2	59

'	I = 20°		I = 21°		I = 22°		I = 23°		'
	T	E	T	E	T	E	T	E	
0	1010.3	88.4	1061.9	97.6	1113.7	107.2	1165.7	117.4	0
1	1011.2	88.5	1062.8	97.7	1114.6	107.4	1166.6	117.6	1
2	1012.0	88.7	1063.7	97.9	1115.5	107.6	1167.4	117.7	2
3	1012.9	88.8	1064.5	98.0	1116.3	107.7	1168.3	117.9	3
4	1013.7	89.0	1065.4	98.2	1117.2	107.9	1169.2	118.1	4
5	1014.6	89.1	1066.2	98.4	1118.1	108.1	1170.1	118.3	5
6	1015.4	89.3	1067.1	98.5	1118.9	108.2	1170.9	118.4	6
7	1016.3	89.4	1068.0	98.7	1119.8	108.4	1171.8	118.6	7
8	1017.2	89.6	1068.8	98.8	1120.7	108.6	1172.7	118.8	8
9	1018.0	89.7	1069.7	99.0	1121.5	108.7	1173.5	118.9	9
10	1018.9	89.9	1070.6	99.2	1122.4	108.9	1174.4	119.1	10
11	1019.8	90.0	1071.4	99.3	1123.2	109.1	1175.3	119.3	11
12	1020.6	90.2	1072.3	99.5	1124.1	109.2	1176.1	119.5	12
13	1021.5	90.3	1073.1	99.6	1125.0	109.4	1177.0	119.6	13
14	1022.3	90.5	1074.0	99.8	1125.8	109.6	1177.9	119.8	14
15	1023.2	90.6	1074.9	100.0	1126.7	109.7	1178.7	120.0	15
16	1024.0	90.8	1075.7	100.1	1127.6	109.9	1179.6	120.2	16
17	1024.9	90.9	1076.6	100.3	1128.4	110.1	1180.5	120.3	17
18	1025.8	91.1	1077.5	100.4	1129.3	110.2	1181.3	120.5	18
19	1026.6	91.2	1078.3	100.6	1130.2	110.4	1182.2	120.7	19
20	1027.5	91.4	1079.2	100.7	1131.0	110.6	1183.1	120.9	20
21	1028.3	91.6	1080.0	100.9	1131.9	110.7	1183.9	121.0	21
22	1029.2	91.7	1080.9	101.1	1132.8	110.9	1184.8	121.2	22
23	1030.1	91.9	1081.8	101.2	1133.6	111.1	1185.7	121.4	23
24	1030.9	92.0	1082.6	101.4	1134.5	111.2	1186.6	121.6	24
25	1031.8	92.2	1083.5	101.6	1135.4	111.4	1187.4	121.8	25
26	1032.6	92.3	1084.4	101.7	1136.2	111.6	1188.3	121.9	26
27	1033.5	92.5	1085.2	101.9	1137.1	111.8	1189.2	122.1	27
28	1034.4	92.6	1086.1	102.0	1138.0	111.9	1190.0	122.3	28
29	1035.2	92.8	1086.9	102.2	1138.8	112.1	1190.9	122.5	29
30	1036.1	92.9	1087.8	102.3	1139.7	112.3	1191.8	122.6	30
31	1037.0	93.1	1088.7	102.5	1140.6	112.4	1192.6	122.8	31
32	1037.8	93.2	1089.5	102.7	1141.4	112.6	1193.5	123.0	32
33	1038.7	93.4	1090.4	102.8	1142.3	112.8	1194.4	123.2	33
34	1039.5	93.5	1091.3	103.0	1143.2	112.9	1195.2	123.3	34
35	1040.4	93.7	1092.1	103.2	1144.0	113.1	1196.1	123.5	35
36	1041.3	93.8	1093.0	103.3	1144.9	113.3	1197 0	123.7	36
37	1042.1	94.0	1093.9	103.5	1145.8	113.4	1197.9	123.9	37
38	1043.0	94.2	1094.7	103.6	1146.6	113.6	1198.7	124.1	38
39	1043.8	94.3	1095.6	103.8	1147.5	113.8	1199.6	124.2	39
40	1044.7	94.5	1096.4	104.0	1148.4	113.9	1200.5	124.4	40
41	1045.6	94.6	1097.3	104.1	1149.2	114.1	1201.3	124.6	41
42	1046.4	94.8	1098.2	104.3	1150.1	114.3	1202.2	124.8	42
43	1047.3	94.9	1099.0	104.5	1151.0	114.4	1203.1	124.9	43
44	1048.1	95.1	1099.9	104.6	1151.8	114.6	1203.9	125.1	44
45	1049.0	95.2	1100.8	104.8	1152.7	114.8	1204.8	125.3	45
46	1049.9	95.4	1101.6	104.9	1153.6	115.0	1205.7	125.5	46
47	1050.7	95.5	1102.5	105.1	1154.4	115.1	1206.6	125.7	47
48	1051.6	95.7	1103.4	105.3	1155.3	115.3	1207.4	125.8	48
49	1052.4	95.9	1104.2	105.4	1156.2	115.5	1208.3	126.0	49
50	1053.3	96.0	1105.1	105.6	1157.0	115.7	1209.2	126.2	50
51	1054.2	96.2	1105.9	105.8	1157.9	115.8	1210.0	126.4	51
52	1055.0	96.3	1106.8	105.9	1158.8	116.0	1210.9	126.6	52
53	1055.9	96.5	1107.7	106.1	1159.6	116.2	1211.8	126.7	53
54	1056.8	96.6	1108.5	106.3	1160.5	116.3	1212.6	126.9	54
55	1057.6	96.8	1109.4	106.4	1161.4	116.5	1213.5	127.1	55
56	1058.5	97.0	1110.3	106.6	1162.2	116.7	1214.4	127.3	56
57	1059.3	97.1	1111.1	106.7	1163.1	116.9	1215.3	127.5	57
58	1060.2	97.3	1112.0	106.9	1164.0	117.0	1216.1	127.6	58
59	1061.1	97.4	1112.9	107.1	1164.8	117.2	1217.0	127.8	59

TABLE VIII.—TANGENTS AND EXTERNALS FOR A 1° CURVE
(Chord or Arc Definition)

'	I = 24°		I = 25°		I = 26°		I = 27°		'
	T	E	T	E	T	E	T	E	
0	1217.9	128.0	1270.2	139.1	1322.8	150.7	1375.6	162.8	0
1	1218.7	128.2	1271.1	139.3	1323.7	150.9	1376.4	163.0	1
2	1219.6	128.4	1272.0	139.5	1324.5	151.1	1377.3	163.2	2
3	1220.5	128.5	1272.9	139.7	1325.4	151.3	1378.2	163.4	3
4	1221.4	128.7	1273.7	139.9	1326.3	151.5	1379.1	163.6	4
5	1222.2	128.9	1274.6	140.1	1327.2	151.7	1380.0	163.8	5
6	1223.1	129.1	1275.5	140.3	1328.1	151.9	1380.9	164.0	6
7	1224.0	129.3	1276.4	140.4	1328.9	152.1	1381.7	164.2	7
8	1224.8	129.5	1277.2	140.6	1329.8	152.3	1382.6	164.5	8
9	1225.7	129.6	1278.1	140.8	1330.7	152.5	1383.5	164.7	9
10	1226.6	129.8	1279.0	141.0	1331.6	152.7	1384.4	164.9	10
11	1227.5	130.0	1279.9	141.2	1332.5	152.9	1385.3	165.1	11
12	1228.3	130.2	1280.7	141.4	1333.3	153.1	1386.1	165.3	12
13	1229.2	130.4	1281.6	141.6	1334.2	153.3	1387.0	165.5	13
14	1230.1	130.6	1282.5	141.8	1335.1	153.5	1387.9	165.7	14
15	1230.9	130.7	1283.4	142.0	1336.0	153.7	1388.8	165.9	15
16	1231.8	130.9	1284.2	142.2	1336.8	153.9	1389.7	166.1	16
17	1232.7	131.1	1285.1	142.4	1337.7	154.1	1390.6	166.3	17
18	1233.6	131.3	1286.0	142.5	1338.6	154.3	1391.4	166.5	18
19	1234.4	131.5	1286.9	142.7	1339.5	154.5	1392.3	166.7	19
20	1235.3	131.7	1287.7	142.9	1340.4	154.7	1393.2	167.0	20
21	1236.2	131.8	1288.6	143.1	1341.2	154.9	1394.1	167.2	21
22	1237.0	132.0	1289.5	143.3	1342.1	155.1	1395.0	167.4	22
23	1237.9	132.2	1290.4	143.5	1343.0	155.3	1395.9	167.6	23
24	1238.8	132.4	1291.2	143.7	1343.9	155.5	1396.7	167.8	24
25	1239.7	132.6	1292.1	143.9	1344.8	155.7	1397.6	168.0	25
26	1240.5	132.8	1293.0	144.1	1345.6	155.9	1398.5	168.2	26
27	1241.4	132.9	1293.9	144.3	1346.5	156.1	1399.4	168.4	27
28	1242.3	133.1	1294.7	144.5	1347.4	156.3	1400.3	168.6	28
29	1243.2	133.3	1295.6	144.7	1348.3	156.5	1401.2	168.8	29
30	1244.0	133.5	1296.5	144.9	1349.2	156.7	1402.0	169.0	30
31	1244.9	133.7	1297.4	145.0	1350.0	156.9	1402.9	169.3	31
32	1245.8	133.9	1298.2	145.2	1350.9	157.1	1403.8	169.5	32
33	1246.6	134.1	1299.1	145.4	1351.8	157.3	1404.7	169.7	33
34	1247.5	134.2	1300.0	145.6	1352.7	157.5	1405.6	169.9	34
35	1248.4	134.4	1300.9	145.8	1353.6	157.7	1406.5	170.1	35
36	1249.3	134.6	1301.7	146.0	1354.4	157.9	1407.3	170.3	36
37	1250.1	134.8	1302.6	146.2	1355.3	158.1	1408.2	170.5	37
38	1251.0	135.0	1303.5	146.4	1356.2	158.3	1409.1	170.7	38
39	1251.9	135.2	1304.4	146.6	1357.1	158.5	1410.0	170.9	39
40	1252.8	135.4	1305.3	146.8	1358.0	158.7	1410.9	171.2	40
41	1253.6	135.5	1306.1	147.0	1358.8	158.9	1411.8	171.4	41
42	1254.5	135.7	1307.0	147.2	1359.7	159.1	1412.6	171.6	42
43	1255.4	135.9	1307.9	147.4	1360.6	159.3	1413.5	171.8	43
44	1256.3	136.1	1308.8	147.6	1361.5	159.5	1414.4	172.0	44
45	1257.1	136.3	1309.6	147.8	1362.4	159.7	1415.3	172.2	45
46	1258.0	136.5	1310.5	148.0	1363.2	159.9	1416.2	172.4	46
47	1258.9	136.7	1311.4	148.2	1364.1	160.1	1417.1	172.6	47
48	1259.7	136.9	1312.3	148.4	1365.0	160.4	1417.9	172.8	48
49	1260.6	137.0	1313.1	148.6	1365.9	160.6	1418.8	173.1	49
50	1261.5	137.2	1314.0	148.7	1366.8	160.8	1419.7	173.3	50
51	1262.4	137.4	1314.9	148.9	1367.6	161.0	1420.6	173.5	51
52	1263.2	137.6	1315.8	149.1	1368.5	161.2	1421.5	173.7	52
53	1264.1	137.8	1316.7	149.3	1369.4	161.4	1422.4	173.9	53
54	1265.0	138.0	1317.5	149.5	1370.3	161.6	1423.3	174.1	54
55	1265.9	138.2	1318.4	149.7	1371.2	161.8	1424.1	174.3	55
56	1266.7	138.4	1319.3	149.9	1372.0	162.0	1425.0	174.6	56
57	1267.6	138.5	1320.2	150.1	1372.9	162.2	1425.9	174.8	57
58	1268.5	138.7	1321.0	150.3	1373.8	162.4	1426.8	175.0	58
59	1269.4	138.9	1321.9	150.5	1374.7	162.6	1427.7	175.2	59

TABLE VIII.—TANGENTS AND EXTERNALS FOR A 1° CURVE
(Chord or Arc Definition)

'	I = 28°		I = 29°		I = 30°		I = 31°		'
	T	E	T	E	T	E	T	E	
0	1428.6	175.4	1481.8	188.5	1535.3	.202.1	1589.0	216.2	0
1	1429.4	175.6	1482.7	188.7	1536.1	202.4	1589.9	216.5	1
2	1430.3	175.8	1483.6	189.0	1537.0	202.6	1590.8	216.7	2
3	1431.2	176.1	1484.5	189.2	1537.9	202.8	1591.7	217.0	3
4	1432.1	176.3	1485.3	189.4	1538.8	203.0	1592.6	217.2	4
5	1433.0	176.5	1486.2	189.6	1539.7	203.3	1593.5	217.5	5
6	1433.9	176.7	1487.1	189.8	1540.6	203.5	1594.4	217.7	6
7	1434.8	176.9	1488.0	190.1	1541.5	203.7	1595.3	217.9	7
8	1435.6	177.1	1488.9	190.3	1542.4	204.0	1596.2	218.2	8
9	1436.5	177.3	1489.8	190.5	1543.3	204.2	1597.1	218.4	9
10	1437.4	177.6	1490.7	190.7	1544.2	204.4	1598.0	218.7	10
11	1438.3	177.8	1491.6	191.0	1545.1	204.7	1598.8	218.9	11
12	1439.2	178.0	1492.5	191.2	1546.0	204.9	1599.7	219.1	12
13	1440.1	178.2	1493.4	191.4	1546.9	205.1	1600.6	219.4	13
14	1441.0	178.4	1494.2	191.6	1547.8	205.4	1601.5	219.6	14
15	1441.8	178.6	1495.1	191.9	1548.7	205.6	1602.4	219.9	15
16	1442.7	178.9	1496.0	192.1	1549.6	205.8	1603.3	220.1	16
17	1443.6	179.1	1496.9	192.3	1550.4	206.1	1604.2	220.4	17
18	1444.5	179.3	1497.8	192.5	1551.3	206.3	1605.1	220.6	18
19	1445.4	179.5	1498.7	192.8	1552.2	206.5	1606.0	220.8	19
20	1446.3	179.7	1499.6	193.0	1553.1	206.8	1606.9	221.1	20
21	1447.2	180.0	1500.5	193.2	1554.0	207.0	1607.8	221.3	21
22	1448.1	180.2	1501.4	193.4	1554.9	207.2	1608.7	221.6	22
23	1448.9	180.4	1502.3	193.7	1555.8	207.5	1609.6	221.8	23
24	1449.8	180.6	1503.1	193.9	1556.7	207.7	1610.5	222.1	24
25	1450.7	180.8	1504.0	194.1	1557.6	207.9	1611.4	222.3	25
26	1451.6	181.0	1504.9	194.3	1558.5	208.2	1612.3	222.5	26
27	1452.5	181.2	1505.8	194.6	1559.4	208.4	1613.2	222.8	27
28	1453.4	181.5	1506.7	194.8	1560.3	208.7	1614.1	223.0	28
29	1454.3	181.7	1507.6	195.0	1561.2	208.9	1615.0	223.3	29
30	1455.1	181.9	1508.5	195.2	1562.1	209.1	1615.9	223.5	30
31	1456.0	182.1	1509.4	195.5	1563.0	209.4	1616.8	223.8	31
32	1456.9	182.3	1510.3	195.7	1563.9	209.6	1617.7	224.0	32
33	1457.8	182.5	1511.2	195.9	1564.8	209.8	1618.6	224.2	33
34	1458.7	182.8	1512.1	196.2	1565.7	210.1	1619.5	224.5	34
35	1459.6	183.0	1512.9	196.4	1566.6	210.3	1620.4	224.7	35
36	1460.5	183.2	1513.8	196.6	1567.5	210.5	1621.3	225.0	36
37	1461.4	183.4	1514.7	196.8	1568.4	210.8	1622.2	225.2	37
38	1462.2	183.6	1515.6	197.1	1569.2	211.0	1623.1	225.5	38
39	1463.1	183.9	1516.5	197.3	1570.1	211.2	1624.0	225.7	39
40	1464.0	184.1	1517.4	197.5	1571.0	211.5	1624.9	226.0	40
41	1464.9	184.3	1518.3	197.8	1571.9	211.7	1625.8	226.2	41
42	1465.8	184.5	1519.2	198.0	1572.8	212.0	1626.7	226.5	42
43	1466.7	184.7	1520.1	198.2	1573.7	212.2	1627.6	226.7	43
44	1467.6	185.0	1521.0	198.4	1574.6	212.4	1628.5	226.9	44
45	1468.5	185.2	1521.9	198.7	1575.5	212.7	1629.4	227.2	45
46	1469.3	185.4	1522.8	198.9	1576.4	212.9	1630.3	227.4	46
47	1470.2	185.6	1523.6	199.1	1577.3	213.1	1631.2	227.7	47
48	1471.1	185.8	1524.5	199.4	1578.2	213.4	1632.1	227.9	48
49	1472.0	186.1	1525.4	199.6	1579.1	213.6	1633.0	228.2	49
50	1472.9	186.3	1526.3	199.8	1580.0	213.9	1633.9	228.4	50
51	1473.8	186.5	1527.2	200.1	1580.9	214.1	1634.8	228.7	51
52	1474.7	186.7	1528.1	200.3	1581.8	214.3	1635.7	228.9	52
53	1475.6	187.0	1529.0	200.5	1582.7	214.6	1636.6	229.2	53
54	1476.5	187.2	1529.9	200.7	1583.6	214.8	1637.5	229.4	54
55	1477.3	187.4	1530.8	201.0	1584.5	215.1	1638.4	229.7	55
56	1478.2	187.6	1531.7	201.2	1585.4	215.3	1639.3	229.9	56
57	1479.1	187.8	1532.6	201.4	1586.3	215.5	1640.2	230.2	57
58	1480.0	188.1	1533.5	201.7	1587.2	215.8	1641.1	230.4	58
59	1480.9	188.3	1534.4	201.9	1588.1	216.0	1642.0	230.7	59

TABLE VIII.—TANGENTS AND EXTERNALS FOR A 1° CURVE
(Chord or Arc Definition)

'	I = 32°		I = 33°		I = 34°		I = 35°		'
	T	E	T	E	T	E	T	E	
0	1643.0	230.9	1697.2	246.1	1751.7	261.8	1806.6	278.1	0
1	1643.9	231.1	1698.1	246.3	1752.6	262.1	1807.5	278.3	1
2	1644.8	231.4	1699.0	246.6	1753.6	262.3	1808.4	278.6	2
3	1645.7	231.6	1699.9	246.9	1754.5	262.6	1809.3	278.9	3
4	1646.6	231.9	1700.8	247.1	1755.4	262.9	1810.2	279.2	4
5	1647.5	232.1	1701.7	247.4	1756.3	263.1	1811.1	279.4	5
6	1648.4	232.4	1702.6	247.6	1757.2	263.4	1812.1	279.7	6
7	1649.3	232.6	1703.5	247.9	1758.1	263.7	1813.0	280.0	7
8	1650.2	232.9	1704.5	248.1	1759.0	263.9	1813.9	280.3	8
9	1651.1	233.1	1705.4	248.4	1759.9	264.4	1814.8	280.5	9
10	1652.0	233.4	1706.3	248.7	1760.8	264.5	1815.7	280.8	10
11	1652.9	233.6	1707.2	248.9	1761.8	264.7	1816.6	281.1	11
12	1653.8	233.9	1708.1	249.2	1762.7	265.0	1817.6	281.4	12
13	1654.7	234.1	1709.0	249.4	1763.6	265.3	1818.5	281.7	13
14	1655.6	234.4	1709.9	249.7	1764.5	265.5	1819.4	281.9	14
15	1656.5	234.6	1710.8	250.0	1765.4	265.8	1820.3	282.2	15
16	1657.4	234.9	1711.7	250.2	1766.3	266.1	1821.2	282.5	16
17	1658.3	235.1	1712.6	250.5	1767.2	266.4	1822.1	282.8	17
18	1659.2	235.4	1713.5	250.7	1768.1	266.6	1823.1	283.0	18
19	1660.1	235.6	1714.4	251.0	1769.1	266.9	1824.0	283.3	19
20	1661.0	235.9	1715.3	251.3	1770.0	267.2	1824.9	283.6	20
21	1661.9	236.2	1716.2	251.5	1770.9	267.4	1825.8	283.9	21
22	1662.8	236.4	1717.2	251.8	1771.8	267.7	1826.7	284.2	22
23	1663.7	236.7	1718.1	252.0	1772.7	268.0	1827.6	284.4	23
24	1664.6	236.9	1719.0	252.3	1773.6	268.2	1828.6	284.7	24
25	1665.5	237.2	1719.9	252.6	1774.5	268.5	1829.5	285.0	25
26	1666.4	237.4	1720.8	252.8	1775.4	268.8	1830.4	285.3	26
27	1667.3	237.7	1721.7	253.1	1776.4	269.1	1831.3	285.6	27
28	1668.2	237.9	1722.6	253.3	1777.3	269.3	1832.2	285.8	28
29	1669.1	238.2	1723.5	253.6	1778.2	269.6	1833.2	286.1	29
30	1670.0	238.4	1724.4	253.9	1779.1	269.9	1834.1	286.4	30
31	1670.9	238.7	1725.3	254.1	1780.0	270.1	1835.0	286.7	31
32	1671.8	238.9	1726.2	254.4	1780.9	270.4	1835.9	287.0	32
33	1672.8	239.2	1727.2	254.7	1781.8	270.7	1836.8	287.2	33
34	1673.7	239.4	1728.1	254.9	1782.8	270.9	1837.8	287.5	34
35	1674.6	239.7	1729.0	255.2	1783.7	271.2	1838.7	287.8	35
36	1675.5	239.9	1729.9	255.4	1784.6	271.5	1839.6	288.1	36
37	1676.4	240.2	1730.8	255.7	1785.5	271.8	1840.5	288.4	37
38	1677.3	240.5	1731.7	256.0	1786.4	272.0	1841.4	288.6	38
39	1678.2	240.7	1732.6	256.2	1787.3	272.3	1842.4	288.9	39
40	1679.1	241.0	1733.5	256.5	1788.2	272.6	1843.3	289.2	40
41	1680.0	241.2	1734.4	256.8	1789.2	272.9	1844.2	289.5	41
42	1680.9	241.5	1735.3	257.0	1790.1	273.1	1845.1	289.8	42
43	1681.8	241.7	1736.3	257.3	1791.0	273.4	1846.0	290.0	43
44	1682.7	242.0	1737.2	257.6	1791.9	273.7	1847.0	290.3	44
45	1683.6	242.2	1738.1	257.8	1792.8	273.9	1847.9	290.6	45
46	1684.5	242.5	1739.0	258.1	1793.7	274.2	1848.8	290.9	46
47	1685.4	242.8	1739.9	258.3	1794.6	274.5	1849.7	291.2	47
48	1686.3	243.0	1740.8	258.6	1795.6	274.8	1850.6	291.5	48
49	1687.2	243.3	1741.7	258.9	1796.5	275.0	1851.5	291.7	49
50	1688.1	243.5	1742.6	259.1	1797.4	275.3	1852.5	292.0	50
51	1689.0	243.8	1743.5	259.4	1798.3	275.6	1853.4	292.3	51
52	1690.0	244.0	1744.4	259.7	1799.2	275.9	1854.3	292.6	52
53	1690.9	244.3	1745.4	259.9	1800.1	276.1	1855.2	292.9	53
54	1691.8	244.5	1746.3	260.2	1801.1	276.4	1856.2	293.2	54
55	1692.7	244.8	1747.2	260.5	1802.0	276.7	1857.1	293.4	55
56	1693.6	245.1	1748.1	260.7	1802.9	277.0	1858.0	293.7	56
57	1694.5	245.3	1749.0	261.0	1803.8	277.2	1858.9	294.0	57
58	1695.4	245.6	1749.9	261.3	1804.7	277.5	1859.9	294.3	58
59	1696.3	245.8	1750.8	261.5	1805.6	277.8	1860.8	294.6	59

28

TABLE VIII.—TANGENTS AND EXTERNALS FOR A 1° CURVE
(Chord or Arc Definition)

'	I = 36°		I = 37°		I = 38°		I = 39°		'
	T	E	T	E	T	E	T	E	
0	1861.7	294.9	1917.1	312.2	1972.9	330.1	2029.0	348.6	0
1	1862.6	295.1	1918.0	312.5	1973.8	330.5	2029.9	349.0	1
2	1863.5	295.4	1919.0	312.8	1974.7	330.8	2030.9	349.3	2
3	1864.4	295.7	1919.9	313.1	1975.7	331.1	2031.8	349.6	3
4	1865.4	296.0	1920.8	313.4	1976.6	331.4	2032.7	349.9	4
5	1866.3	296.3	1921.7	313.7	1977.5	331.7	2033.7	350.2	5
6	1867.2	296.6	1922.7	314.0	1978.5	332.0	2034.6	350.5	6
7	1868.1	296.9	1923.6	314.3	1979.4	332.3	2035.5	350.8	7
8	1869.0	297.1	1924.5	314.6	1980.3	332.6	2036.5	351.2	8
9	1870.0	297.4	1925.5	314.9	1981.3	332.9	2037.4	351.5	9
10	1870.9	297.7	1926.4	315.2	1982.2	333.2	2038.4	351.8	10
11	1871.8	298.0	1927.3	315.5	1983.1	333.5	2039.3	352.1	11
12	1872.7	298.3	1928.2	315.8	1984.1	333.8	2040.2	352.4	12
13	1873.7	298.6	1929.2	316.1	1985.0	334.1	2041.2	352.7	13
14	1874.6	298.9	1930.1	316.4	1985.9	334.4	2042.1	353.0	14
15	1875.5	299.2	1931.0	316.7	1986.9	334.7	2043.1	353.4	15
16	1876.4	299.4	1932.0	316.9	1987.8	335.0	2044.0	353.7	16
17	1877.4	299.7	1932.9	317.2	1988.7	335.3	2044.9	354.0	17
18	1878.3	300.0	1933.8	317.5	1989.7	335.6	2045.9	354.3	18
19	1879.2	300.3	1934.7	317.8	1990.6	335.9	2046.8	354.6	19
20	1880.1	300.6	1935.7	318.1	1991.5	336.2	2047.8	354.9	20
21	1881.0	300.9	1936.6	318.4	1992.5	336.6	2048.7	355.3	21
22	1882.0	301.2	1937.5	318.7	1993.4	336.9	2049.6	355.6	22
23	1882.9	301.5	1938.5	319.0	1994.3	337.2	2050.6	355.9	23
24	1883.8	301.7	1939.4	319.3	1995.3	337.5	2051.5	356.2	24
25	1884.7	302.0	1940.3	319.6	1996.2	337.8	2052.5	356.5	25
26	1885.7	302.3	1941.2	319.9	1997.1	338.1	2053.4	356.8	26
27	1886.6	302.6	1942.2	320.2	1998.1	338.4	2054.3	357.2	27
28	1887.5	302.9	1943.1	320.5	1999.0	338.7	2055.3	357.5	28
29	1888.4	303.2	1944.0	320.8	1999.9	339.0	2056.2	357.8	29
30	1889.4	303.5	1945.0	321.1	2000.9	339.3	2057.2	358.1	30
31	1890.3	303.8	1945.9	321.4	2001.8	339.6	2058.1	358.4	31
32	1891.2	304.1	1946.8	321.7	2002.8	339.9	2059.0	358.7	32
33	1892.1	304.3	1947.7	322.0	2003.7	340.2	2060.0	359.1	33
34	1893.1	304.6	1948.7	322.3	2004.6	340.6	2060.9	359.4	34
35	1894.0	304.9	1949.6	322.6	2005.6	340.9	2061.9	359.7	35
36	1894.9	305.2	1950.5	322.9	2006.5	341.2	2062.8	360.0	36
37	1895.8	305.5	1951.5	323.2	2007.4	341.5	2063.7	360.3	37
38	1896.7	305.8	1952.4	323.5	2008.4	341.8	2064.7	360.7	38
39	1897.7	306.1	1953.3	323.8	2009.3	342.1	2065.6	361.0	39
40	1898.6	306.4	1954.3	324.1	2010.2	342.4	2066.6	361.3	40
41	1899.5	306.7	1955.2	324.4	2011.2	342.7	2067.5	361.6	41
42	1900.4	307.0	1956.1	324.7	2012.1	343.0	2068.5	361.9	42
43	1901.4	307.2	1957.0	325.0	2013.0	343.3	2069.4	362.3	43
44	1902.3	307.5	1958.0	325.3	2014.0	343.7	2070.3	362.6	44
45	1903.2	307.8	1958.9	325.6	2014.9	344.0	2071.3	362.9	45
46	1904.1	308.1	1959.8	325.9	2015.9	344.3	2072.2	363.2	46
47	1905.1	308.4	1960.8	326.2	2016.8	344.6	2073.2	363.5	47
48	1906.0	308.7	1961.7	326.5	2017.7	344.9	2074.1	363.9	48
49	1906.9	309.0	1962.6	326.8	2018.7	345.2	2075.0	364.2	49
50	1907.9	309.3	1963.6	327.1	2019.6	345.5	2076.0	364.5	50
51	1908.8	309.6	1964.5	327.4	2020.5	345.8	2076.9	364.8	51
52	1909.7	309.9	1965.4	327.7	2021.5	346.1	2077.9	365.1	52
53	1910.6	310.2	1966.4	328.0	2022.4	346.5	2078.8	365.5	53
54	1911.6	310.5	1967.3	328.3	2023.4	346.8	2079.8	365.8	54
55	1912.5	310.8	1968.2	328.6	2024.3	347.1	2080.7	366.1	55
56	1913.4	311.0	1969.1	328.9	2025.2	347.4	2081.6	366.4	56
57	1914.3	311.3	1970.1	329.2	2026.2	347.7	2082.6	366.8	57
58	1915.3	311.6	1971.0	329.5	2027.1	348.0	2083.5	367.1	58
59	1916.2	311.9	1971.9	329.8	2028.0	348.3	2084.5	367.4	59

TABLE VIII.—TANGENTS AND EXTERNALS FOR A 1° CURVE
(Chord or Arc Definition)

.	I = 40°		I = 41°		I = 42°		I = 43°		.
	T	E	T	E	T	E	T	E	
0	2085.4	367.7	2142.2	387.4	2199.4	407.6	2257.0	428.5	0
1	2086.4	368.0	2143.2	387.7	2200.4	408.0	2257.9	428.9	1
2	2087.3	368.4	2144.1	388.0	2201.3	408.3	2258.9	429.2	2
3	2088.3	368.7	2145.1	388.4	2202.3	408.7	2259.9	429.6	3
4	2089.2	369.0	2146.0	388.7	2203.2	409.0	2260.8	429.9	4
5	2090.1	369.3	2147.0	389.0	2204.2	409.4	2261.8	430.3	5
6	2091.1	369.7	2147.9	389.4	2205.1	409.7	2262.7	430.6	6
7	2092.0	370.0	2148.9	389.7	2206.1	410.0	2263.7	431.1	7
8	2093.0	370.3	2149.8	390.0	2207.1	410.4	2264.7	431.3	8
9	2093.9	370.6	2150.8	390.4	2208.0	410.7	2265.6	431.7	9
10	2094.9	371.0	2151.7	390.7	2209.0	411.1	2266.6	432.0	10
11	2095.8	371.3	2152.7	391.0	2209.9	411.4	2267.6	432.4	11
12	2096.8	371.6	2153.6	391.4	2210.9	411.8	2268.5	432.8	12
13	2097.7	371.9	2154.6	391.7	2211.8	412.1	2269.5	433.1	13
14	2098.6	372.3	2155.5	392.1	2212.8	412.5	2270.5	433.5	14
15	2099.6	372.6	2156.5	392.4	2213.8	412.8	2271.4	433.8	15
16	2100.5	372.9	2157.4	392.7	2214.7	413.1	2272.4	434.2	16
17	2101.5	373.2	2158.4	393.1	2215.7	413.5	2273.4	434.5	17
18	2102.4	373.6	2159.3	393.4	2216.6	413.8	2274.3	434.9	18
19	2103.4	373.9	2160.3	393.7	2217.6	414.2	2275.3	435.2	19
20	2104.3	374.2	2161.2	394.1	2218.6	414.5	2276.2	435.6	20
21	2105.3	374.5	2162.2	394.4	2219.5	414.9	2277.2	435.9	21
22	2106.2	374.9	2163.2	394.7	2220.5	415.2	2278.2	436.3	22
23	2107.2	375.2	2164.1	395.1	2221.4	415.6	2279.1	436.7	23
24	2108.1	375.5	2165.1	395.4	2222.4	415.9	2280.1	437.0	24
25	2109.0	375.8	2166.0	395.7	2223.3	416.3	2281.1	437.4	25
26	2110.0	376.2	2167.0	396.1	2224.3	416.6	2282.0	437.7	26
27	2110.9	376.5	2167.9	396.4	2225.3	416.9	2283.0	438.1	27
28	2111.9	376.8	2168.9	396.8	2226.2	417.3	2284.0	438.4	28
29	2112.8	377.1	2169.8	397.1	2227.2	417.6	2284.9	438.8	29
30	2113.8	377.5	2170.8	397.4	2228.1	418.0	2285.9	439.2	30
31	2114.7	377.8	2171.7	397.8	2229.1	418.3	2286.9	439.5	31
32	2115.7	378.1	2172.7	398.1	2230.1	418.7	2287.8	439.9	32
33	2116.6	378.5	2173.6	398.4	2231.0	419.0	2288.8	440.2	33
34	2117.6	378.8	2174.6	398.8	2232.0	419.4	2289.8	440.6	34
35	2118.5	379.1	2175.5	399.1	2232.9	419.7	2290.7	441.0	35
36	2119.5	379.4	2176.5	399.5	2233.9	420.1	2291.7	441.3	36
37	2120.4	379.8	2177.4	399.8	2234.9	420.4	2292.7	441.7	37
38	2121.4	380.1	2178.4	400.1	2235.8	420.8	2293.6	442.0	38
39	2122.3	380.4	2179.4	400.5	2236.8	421.1	2294.6	442.4	39
40	2123.3	380.8	2180.3	400.8	2237.7	421.5	2295.6	442.7	40
41	2124.2	381.1	2181.3	401.2	2238.7	421.8	2296.5	443.1	41
42	2125.1	381.4	2182.2	401.5	2239.7	422.2	2297.5	443.5	42
43	2126.1	381.8	2183.2	401.8	2240.6	422.5	2298.5	443.8	43
44	2127.0	382.1	2184.1	402.2	2241.6	422.9	2299.4	444.2	44
45	2128.0	382.4	2185.1	402.5	2242.5	423.2	2300.4	444.6	45
46	2128.9	382.7	2186.0	402.9	2243.5	423.6	2301.4	444.9	46
47	2129.9	383.1	2187.0	403.2	2244.5	423.9	2302.3	445.3	47
48	2130.8	383.4	2187.9	403.5	2245.4	424.3	2303.3	445.6	48
49	2131.8	383.7	2188.9	403.9	2246.4	424.6	2304.3	446.0	49
50	2132.7	384.1	2189.9	404.2	2247.3	425.0	2305.2	446.4	50
51	2133.7	384.4	2190.8	404.6	2248.3	425.3	2306.2	446.7	51
52	2134.6	384.8	2191.8	404.9	2249.3	425.7	2307.2	447.1	52
53	2135.6	385.1	2192.7	405.2	2250.2	426.0	2308.1	447.4	53
54	2136.5	385.4	2193.7	405.6	2251.2	426.4	2309.1	447.8	54
55	2137.5	385.7	2194.6	405.9	2252.2	426.7	2310.1	448.2	55
56	2138.4	386.1	2195.6	406.3	2253.1	427.1	2311.1	448.5	56
57	2139.4	386.4	2196.5	406.6	2254.1	427.4	2312.0	448.9	57
58	2140.3	386.7	2197.5	407.0	2255.0	427.8	2313.0	449.3	58
59	2141.3	387.0	2198.5	407.3	2256.0	428.1	2314.0	449.6	59

ABLE VIII.—TANGENTS AND EXTERNALS FOR A 1° CURVE
(Chord or Arc Definition)

′	I = 44°		I = 45°		I = 46°		I = 47°		′
	T	E	T	E	T	E	T	E	
0	2314.9	450.0	2373.3	472.1	2432.1	494.8	2491.3	518.2	0
1	2315.9	450.3	2374.3	472.5	2433.1	495.2	2492.3	518.6	1
2	2316.9	450.7	2375.3	472.8	2434.1	495.6	2493.3	519.0	2
3	2317.8	451.1	2376.2	473.2	2435.0	496.0	2494.3	519.4	3
4	2318.8	451.4	2377.2	473.6	2436.0	496.4	2495.3	519.8	4
5	2319.8	451.8	2378.2	474.0	2437.0	496.7	2496.3	520.2	5
6	2320.7	452.2	2379.2	474.3	2438.0	497.1	2497.3	520.6	6
7	2321.7	452.5	2380.1	474.7	2439.0	497.5	2498.3	521.0	7
8	2322.7	452.9	2381.1	475.1	2440.0	497.9	2499.3	521.4	8
9	2323.7	453.3	2382.1	475.4	2440.9	498.3	2500.2	521.8	9
10	2324.6	453.6	2383.1	475.8	2441.9	498.7	2501.2	522.2	10
11	2325.6	454.0	2384.0	476.2	2442.9	499.1	2502.2	522.6	11
12	2326.6	454.4	2385.0	476.6	2443.9	499.4	2503.2	523.0	12
13	2327.5	454.7	2386.0	477.0	2444.9	499.8	2504.2	523.4	13
14	2328.5	455.1	2387.0	477.3	2445.9	500.2	2505.2	523.7	14
15	2329.5	455.4	2388.0	477.7	2446.9	500.6	2506.2	524.1	15
16	2330.5	455.8	2388.9	478.1	2447.8	501.0	2507.2	524.5	16
17	2331.4	456.2	2389.9	478.5	2448.8	501.4	2508.2	524.9	17
18	2332.4	456.5	2390.9	478.8	2449.8	501.8	2509.2	525.3	18
19	2333.4	456.9	2391.9	479.2	2450.8	502.2	2510.2	525.7	19
20	2334.3	457.3	2392.8	479.6	2451.8	502.5	2511.2	526.1	20
21	2335.3	457.6	2393.8	480.0	2452.8	502.9	2512.2	526.5	21
22	2336.3	458.0	2394.8	480.3	2453.8	503.3	2513.2	526.9	22
23	2337.3	458.4	2395.8	480.7	2454.7	503.7	2514.1	527.3	23
24	2338.2	458.7	2396.8	481.1	2455.7	504.1	2515.1	527.7	24
25	2339.2	459.1	2397.7	481.5	2456.7	504.5	2516.1	528.1	25
26	2340.2	459.5	2398.7	481.9	2457.7	504.9	2517.1	528.5	26
27	2341.1	459.8	2399.7	482.2	2458.7	505.3	2518.1	528.9	27
28	2342.1	460.2	2400.7	482.6	2459.7	505.6	2519.1	529.3	28
29	2343.1	460.6	2401.7	483.0	2460.7	506.0	2520.1	529.7	29
30	2344.1	460.9	2402.6	483.4	2461.6	506.4	2521.1	530.1	30
31	2345.0	461.3	2403.6	483.8	2462.6	506.8	2522.1	530.5	31
32	2346.0	461.7	2404.6	484.1	2463.6	507.2	2523.1	530.9	32
33	2347.0	462.1	2405.6	484.5	2464.6	507.6	2524.1	531.3	33
34	2348.0	462.4	2406.6	484.9	2465.6	508.0	2525.1	531.7	34
35	2348.9	462.8	2407.5	485.3	2466.6	508.4	2526.1	532.1	35
36	2349.9	463.2	2408.5	485.7	2467.6	508.8	2527.1	532.5	36
37	2350.9	463.5	2409.5	486.0	2468.6	509.2	2528.1	532.9	37
38	2351.8	463.9	2410.5	486.4	2469.6	509.5	2529.1	533.3	38
39	2352.8	464.3	2411.5	486.8	2470.5	509.9	2530.1	533.7	39
40	2353.8	464.6	2412.4	487.2	2471.5	510.3	2531.1	534.1	40
41	2354.8	465.0	2413.4	487.6	2472.5	510.7	2532.1	534.6	41
42	2355.7	465.4	2414.4	487.9	2473.5	511.1	2533.1	535.0	42
43	2356.7	465.8	2415.4	488.3	2474.5	511.5	2534.1	535.4	43
44	2357.7	466.1	2416.4	488.7	2475.5	511.9	2535.0	535.8	44
45	2358.7	466.5	2417.4	489.1	2476.5	512.3	2536.0	536.2	45
46	2359.6	466.9	2418.3	489.5	2477.5	512.7	2537.0	536.6	46
47	2360.6	467.2	2419.3	489.8	2478.5	513.1	2538.0	537.0	47
48	2361.6	467.6	2420.3	490.2	2479.4	513.5	2539.0	537.4	48
49	2362.6	468.0	2421.3	490.6	2480.4	513.9	2540.0	537.8	49
50	2363.6	468.4	2422.3	491.0	2481.4	514.3	2541.0	538.2	50
51	2364.5	468.7	2423.2	491.4	2482.4	514.6	2542.0	538.6	51
52	2365.5	469.1	2424.2	491.7	2483.4	515.0	2543.0	539.0	52
53	2366.5	469.5	2425.2	492.1	2484.4	515.4	2544.0	539.4	53
54	2367.4	469.8	2426.2	492.5	2485.4	515.8	2545.0	539.8	54
55	2368.4	470.2	2427.2	492.9	2486.4	516.2	2546.0	540.2	55
56	2369.4	470.6	2428.2	493.3	2487.4	516.6	2547.0	540.6	56
57	2370.4	471.0	2429.1	493.7	2488.4	517.0	2548.0	541.0	57
58	2371.3	471.3	2430.1	494.1	2489.3	517.4	2549.0	541.4	58
59	2372.3	471.7	2431.1	494.4	2490.3	517.8	2550.0	541.8	59

TABLE VIII.—TANGENTS AND EXTERNALS FOR A 1° CURV
(Chord or Arc Definition)

'	I = 48°		I = 49°		I = 50°		I = 51°		'
	T	E	T	E	T	E	T	E	
0	2551.0	542.2	2611.2	566.9	2671.8	592.3	2732.9	618.4	0
1	2552.0	542.6	2612.2	567.4	2672.8	592.8	2733.9	618.8	1
2	2553.0	543.0	2613.2	567.8	2673.8	593.2	2734.9	619.3	2
3	2554.0	543.5	2614.2	568.2	2674.8	593.6	2736.0	619.7	3
4	2555.0	543.9	2615.2	568.6	2675.8	594.0	2737.0	620.2	4
5	2556.0	544.3	2616.2	569.0	2676.9	594.5	2738.0	620.6	5
6	2557.0	544.7	2617.2	569.4	2677.9	594.9	2739.0	621.0	6
7	2558.0	545.1	2618.2	569.9	2678.9	595.3	2740.1	621.5	7
8	2559.0	545.5	2619.2	570.3	2679.9	595.8	2741.1	621.9	8
9	2560.0	545.9	2620.2	570.7	2680.9	596.2	2742.1	622.4	9
10	2561.0	546.3	2621.2	571.1	2681.9	596.6	2743.1	622.8	10
11	2562.0	546.7	2622.2	571.5	2682.9	597.1	2744.2	623.3	11
12	2563.0	547.1	2623.2	572.0	2684.0	597.5	2745.2	623.7	12
13	2564.0	547.5	2624.2	572.4	2685.0	597.9	2746.2	624.1	13
14	2565.0	547.8	2625.3	572.8	2686.0	598.3	2747.2	624.6	14
15	2566.0	548.3	2626.3	573.2	2687.0	598.8	2748.3	625.0	15
16	2567.0	548.8	2627.3	573.6	2688.0	599.2	2749.3	625.4	16
17	2568.0	549.2	2628.3	574.1	2689.0	599.6	2750.3	625.9	17
18	2569.0	549.6	2629.3	574.5	2690.1	600.1	2751.3	626.4	18
19	2570.0	550.0	2630.3	574.9	2691.1	600.5	2752.4	626.8	19
20	2571.0	550.4	2631.3	575.3	2692.1	600.9	2753.4	627.2	20
21	2572.0	550.8	2632.3	575.7	2693.1	601.4	2754.4	627.7	21
22	2573.0	551.2	2633.3	576.2	2694.1	601.8	2755.4	628.1	22
23	2574.0	551.6	2634.3	576.6	2695.2	602.2	2756.5	628.6	23
24	2575.0	552.0	2635.3	577.0	2696.2	602.7	2757.5	629.0	24
25	2576.0	552.4	2636.4	577.4	2697.2	603.1	2758.5	629.5	25
26	2577.0	552.9	2637.4	577.9	2698.2	603.5	2759.5	629.9	26
27	2578.0	553.3	2638.4	578.3	2699.2	604.0	2760.6	630.4	27
28	2579.0	553.7	2639.4	578.7	2700.2	604.4	2761.6	630.8	28
29	2580.0	554.1	2640.4	579.1	2701.3	604.8	2762.6	531.2	29
30	2581.0	554.5	2641.4	579.5	2702.3	605.3	2763.7	631.7	30
31	2582.0	554.9	2642.4	580.0	2703.3	605.7	2764.7	632.1	31
32	2583.0	555.3	2643.4	580.4	2704.3	606.1	2765.7	632.6	32
33	2584.0	555.7	2644.4	580.8	2705.3	606.6	2766.7	633.0	33
34	2585.0	556.2	2645.4	581.2	2706.4	607.0	2767.8	633.5	34
35	2586.0	556.6	2646.5	581.7	2707.4	607.4	2768.8	633.9	35
36	2587.0	557.0	2647.5	582.1	2708.4	607.9	2769.8	634.4	36
37	2588.0	557.4	2648.5	582.5	2709.4	608.3	2770.8	634.8	37
38	2589.0	557.8	2649.5	582.9	2710.4	608.8	2771.9	635.3	38
39	2590.0	558.2	2650.5	583.4	2711.5	609.2	2772.9	635.7	39
40	2591.1	558.6	2651.5	583.8	2712.5	609.6	2773.9	636.2	40
41	2592.1	559.0	2652.5	584.2	2713.5	610.1	2775.0	636.6	41
42	2593.1	559.5	2653.5	584.6	2714.5	610.5	2776.0	637.1	42
43	2594.1	559.9	2654.6	585.1	2715.5	610.9	2777.0	637.5	43
44	2595.1	560.3	2655.6	585.5	2716.6	611.4	2778.1	638.0	44
45	2596.1	560.7	2656.6	585.9	2717.6	611.8	2779.1	638.4	45
46	2597.1	561.1	2657.6	586.3	2718.6	612.2	2780.1	638.9	46
47	2598.1	561.5	2658.6	586.8	2719.6	612.7	2781.1	639.3	47
48	2599.1	561.9	2659.6	587.2	2720.6	613.1	2782.2	639.8	48
49	2600.1	562.4	2660.6	587.6	2721.7	613.6	2783.2	640.2	49
50	2601.1	562.8	2661.6	588.0	2722.7	614.0	2784.2	640.7	50
51	2602.1	563.2	2662.7	588.5	2723.7	614.4	2785.3	641.1	51
52	2603.1	563.6	2663.7	588.9	2724.7	614.9	2786.3	641.6	52
53	2604.1	564.0	2664.7	589.3	2725.7	615.3	2787.3	642.0	53
54	2605.1	564.4	2665.7	589.8	2726.8	615.8	2788.4	642.5	54
55	2606.1	564.9	2666.7	590.2	2727.8	616.2	2789.4	642.9	55
56	2607.1	565.3	2667.7	590.6	2728.8	616.6	2790.4	643.4	56
57	2608.1	565.7	2668.7	591.0	2729.8	617.1	2791.4	643.8	57
58	2609.1	566.1	2669.8	591.5	2730.9	617.5	2792.5	644.3	58
59	2610.1	566.5	2670.8	591.9	2731.9	618.0	2793.5	644.7	59

TABLE VIII.—TANGENTS AND EXTERNALS FOR A 1° CURVE
(Chord or Arc Definition)

'	I = 52° T	I = 52° E	I = 53° T	I = 53° E	I = 54° T	I = 54° E	I = 55° T	I = 55° E	'
0	2794.5	645.2	2856.7	672.7	2919.4	700.9	2982.7	729.9	0
1	2795.6	645.6	2857.7	673.1	2920.5	701.4	2983.7	730.3	1
2	2796.6	646.1	2858.8	673.6	2921.5	701.8	2984.8	730.8	2
3	2797.6	646.5	2859.8	674.1	2922.6	702.3	2985.8	731.3	3
4	2798.7	647.0	2860.9	674.5	2923.6	702.8	2986.9	731.8	4
5	2799.7	647.4	2861.9	675.0	2924.7	703.3	2988.0	732.3	5
6	2800.7	647.9	2862.9	675.5	2925.7	703.8	2989.0	732.8	6
7	2801.8	648.3	2864.0	675.9	2926.8	704.2	2990.1	733.3	7
8	2802.8	648.8	2865.0	676.4	2927.8	704.7	2991.1	733.8	8
9	2803.8	649.2	2866.1	676.9	2928.9	705.2	2992.2	734.3	9
10	2804.9	649.7	2867.1	677.3	2929.9	705.7	2993.3	734.8	10
11	2805.9	650.2	2868.2	677.8	2931.0	706.1	2994.3	735.3	11
12	2806.9	650.6	2869.2	678.3	2932.0	706.6	2995.4	735.7	12
13	2808.0	651.1	2870.2	678.7	2933.1	707.1	2996.5	736.2	13
14	2809.0	651.5	2871.3	679.2	2934.1	707.6	2997.5	736.7	14
15	2810.0	652.0	2872.3	679.7	2935.2	708.1	2998.6	737.2	15
16	2811.1	652.4	2873.4	680.1	2936.2	708.6	2999.6	737.7	16
17	2812.1	652.9	2874.4	680.6	2937.3	709.0	3000.7	738.2	17
18	2813.1	653.3	2875.5	681.1	2938.3	709.5	3001.8	738.7	18
19	2814.2	653.8	2876.5	681.5	2939.4	710.0	3002.8	739.2	19
20	2815.2	654.3	2877.5	682.0	2940.4	710.5	3003.9	739.7	20
21	2816.2	654.7	2878.6	682.5	2941.5	710.9	3004.9	740.2	21
22	2817.3	655.2	2879.6	682.9	2942.5	711.4	3006.0	740.7	22
23	2818.3	655.6	2880.7	683.4	2943.6	711.9	3007.1	741.2	23
24	2819.3	656.1	2881.7	683.9	2944.6	712.4	3008.1	741.7	24
25	2820.4	656.5	2882.8	684.3	2945.7	712.9	3009.2	742.1	25
26	2821.4	657.0	2883.8	684.8	2946.7	713.4	3010.3	742.6	26
27	2822.4	657.5	2884.8	685.3	2947.8	713.8	3011.3	743.1	27
28	2823.5	657.9	2885.9	685.7	2948.9	714.3	3012.4	743.6	28
29	2824.5	658.4	2886.9	686.2	2949.9	714.8	3013.5	744.1	29
30	2825.6	658.8	2888.0	686.7	2951.0	715.3	3014.5	744.6	30
31	2826.6	659.3	2889.0	687.2	2952.0	715.8	3015.6	745.1	31
32	2827.6	659.7	2890.1	687.6	2953.1	716.2	3016.6	745.6	32
33	2828.7	660.2	2891.1	688.1	2954.1	716.7	3017.7	746.1	33
34	2829.7	660.7	2892.2	688.6	2955.2	717.2	3018.8	746.6	34
35	2830.7	661.1	2893.2	689.0	2956.2	717.8	3019.8	747.1	35
36	2831.8	661.6	2894.3	689.5	2957.3	718.2	3020.9	747.6	36
37	2832.8	662.1	2895.3	690.0	2958.3	718.7	3022.0	748.1	37
38	2833.8	662.5	2896.3	690.5	2959.4	719.1	3023.0	748.6	38
39	2834.9	663.0	2897.4	690.9	2960.5	719.6	3024.1	749.1	39
40	2835.9	663.4	2898.4	691.4	2961.5	720.1	3025.2	749.6	40
41	2837.0	663.9	2899.5	691.9	2962.6	720.6	3026.2	750.1	41
42	2838.0	664.3	2900.5	692.3	2963.6	721.1	3027.3	750.6	42
43	2839.0	664.8	2901.6	692.8	2964.7	721.6	3028.4	751.1	43
44	2840.1	665.3	2902.6	693.3	2965.7	722.1	3029.4	751.6	44
45	2841.1	665.7	2903.7	693.8	2966.8	722.5	3030.5	752.1	45
46	2842.1	666.2	2904.7	694.2	2967.9	723.0	3031.6	752.6	46
47	2843.2	666.6	2905.8	694.7	2968.9	723.5	3032.6	753.1	47
48	2844.2	667.1	2906.8	695.2	2970.0	724.0	3033.7	753.6	48
49	2845.3	667.6	2907.9	695.7	2971.0	724.5	3034.8	754.1	49
50	2846.3	668.0	2908.9	696.1	2972.1	725.0	3035.8	754.6	50
51	2847.3	668.5	2910.0	696.6	2973.1	725.5	3036.9	755.1	51
52	2848.4	668.9	2911.0	697.1	2974.2	725.9	3038.0	755.6	52
53	2849.4	669.4	2912.1	697.6	2975.3	726.4	3039.0	756.1	53
54	2850.5	669.9	2913.1	698.0	2976.3	726.9	3040.1	756.6	54
55	2851.5	670.3	2914.2	698.5	2977.4	727.4	3041.2	757.1	55
56	2852.5	670.8	2915.2	699.0	2978.4	727.9	3042.2	757.6	56
57	2853.6	671.3	2916.3	699.5	2979.5	728.4	3043.3	758.1	57
58	2854.6	671.7	2917.3	699.9	2980.5	728.9	3044.4	758.6	58
59	2855.7	672.2	2918.4	700.4	2981.6	729.4	3045.4	759.1	59

TABLE VIII.—TANGENTS AND EXTERNALS FOR A 1° CURVE
(Chord or Arc Definition)

'	I = 56°		I = 57°		I = 58°		I = 59°		'
	T	E	T	E	T	E	T	E	
0	3046.5	759.6	3110.9	790.1	3176.0	821.4	3241.7	853.5	0
1	3047.6	760.1	3112.0	790.6	3177.1	821.9	3242.8	854.0	1
2	3048.6	760.6	3113.1	791.1	3178.2	822.4	3243.9	854.5	2
3	3049.7	761.1	3114.2	791.6	3179.3	823.0	3245.0	855.1	3
4	3050.8	761.6	3115.3	792.1	3180.4	823.5	3246.1	855.6	4
5	3051.9	762.1	3116.3	792.7	3181.4	824.0	3247.2	856.2	5
6	3052.9	762.6	3117.4	793.2	3182.5	824.5	3248.3	856.7	6
7	3054.0	763.1	3118.5	793.7	3183.6	825.1	3249.4	857.3	7
8	3055.1	763.6	3119.6	794.2	3184.7	825.6	3250.5	857.8	8
9	3056.1	764.1	3120.7	794.7	3185.8	826.1	3251.6	858.3	9
10	3057.2	764.6	3121.7	795.2	3186.9	826.7	3252.7	858.9	10
11	3058.3	765.1	3122.8	795.8	3188.0	827.2	3253.8	859.4	11
12	3059.3	765.6	3123.9	796.3	3189.1	827.7	3254.9	860.0	12
13	3060.4	766.1	3125.0	796.8	3190.2	828.3	3256.0	860.5	13
14	3061.5	766.6	3126.1	797.3	3191.3	828.8	3257.1	861.1	14
15	3062.6	767.1	3127.2	797.8	3192.4	829.3	3258.2	861.6	15
16	3063.6	767.6	3128.2	798.3	3193.5	829.9	3259.3	862.2	16
17	3064.7	768.1	3129.3	798.9	3194.5	830.4	3260.4	862.7	17
18	3065.8	768.6	3130.4	799.4	3195.6	830.9	3261.5	863.2	18
19	3066.8	769.2	3131.5	799.9	3196.7	831.4	3262.6	863.8	19
20	3067.9	769.7	3132.6	800.4	3197.8	832.0	3263.7	864.3	20
21	3069.0	770.2	3133.6	800.9	3198.9	832.5	3264.8	864.9	21
22	3070.1	770.7	3134.7	801.5	3200.0	833.0	3265.9	865.4	22
23	3071.1	771.2	3135.8	802.0	3201.1	833.6	3267.0	866.0	23
24	3072.2	771.7	3136.9	802.5	3202.2	834.1	3268.1	866.5	24
25	3073.3	772.2	3138.0	803.0	3203.3	834.6	3269.2	867.1	25
26	3074.4	772.7	3139.1	803.5	3204.4	835.2	3270.3	867.6	26
27	3075.4	773.2	3140.1	804.1	3205.5	835.7	3271.4	868.2	27
28	3076.5	773.7	3141.2	804.6	3206.6	836.2	3272.6	868.7	28
29	3077.6	774.2	3142.3	805.1	3207.7	836.8	3273.7	869.3	29
30	3078.7	774.7	3143.4	805.6	3208.8	837.3	3274.8	869.8	30
31	3079.7	775.2	3144.5	806.1	3209.9	837.8	3275.9	870.4	31
32	3080.8	775.7	3145.6	806.7	3210.9	838.4	3277.0	870.9	32
33	3081.9	776.3	3146.6	807.2	3212.0	838.9	3278.1	871.5	33
34	3082.9	776.8	3147.7	807.7	3213.1	839.5	3279.2	872.0	34
35	3084.0	777.3	3148.8	808.2	3214.2	840.0	3280.3	872.6	35
36	3085.1	777.8	3149.9	808.8	3215.3	840.5	3281.4	873.1	36
37	3086.2	778.3	3151.0	809.3	3216.4	841.1	3282.5	873.7	37
38	3087.2	778.8	3152.1	809.8	3217.5	841.6	3283.6	874.2	38
39	3088.3	779.3	3153.2	810.3	3218.6	842.1	3284.7	874.8	39
40	3089.4	779.8	3154.2	810.9	3219.7	842.7	3285.8	875.3	40
41	3090.5	780.3	3155.3	811.4	3220.8	843.2	3286.9	875.9	41
42	3091.6	780.9	3156.4	811.9	3221.9	843.7	3288.0	876.4	42
43	3092.6	781.4	3157.5	812.4	3223.0	844.3	3289.2	877.0	43
44	3093.7	781.9	3158.6	812.9	3224.1	844.8	3290.3	877.5	44
45	3094.8	782.4	3159.7	813.5	3225.2	845.4	3291.4	878.1	45
46	3095.9	782.9	3160.8	814.0	3226.3	845.9	3292.5	878.6	46
47	3096.9	783.4	3161.8	814.5	3227.4	846.4	3293.6	879.2	47
48	3098.0	783.9	3162.9	815.0	3228.5	847.0	3294.7	879.7	48
49	3099.1	784.4	3164.0	815.6	3229.6	847.5	3295.8	880.3	49
50	3100.2	784.9	3165.1	816.1	3230.7	848.1	3296.9	880.8	50
51	3101.2	785.5	3166.2	816.6	3231.8	848.6	3298.0	881.4	51
52	3102.3	786.0	3167.3	817.2	3232.9	849.1	3299.1	881.9	52
53	3103.4	786.5	3168.4	817.7	3234.0	849.7	3300.2	882.5	53
54	3104.5	787.0	3169.5	818.2	3235.1	850.2	3301.4	883.1	54
55	3105.6	787.5	3170.6	818.7	3236.2	850.8	3302.5	883.6	55
56	3106.6	788.0	3171.6	819.3	3237.3	851.3	3303.6	884.2	56
57	3107.7	788.5	3172.7	819.8	3238.4	851.8	3304.7	884.7	57
58	3108.8	789.1	3173.8	820.3	3239.5	852.4	3305.8	885.3	58
59	3109.9	789.6	3174.9	820.8	3240.6	852.9	3306.9	885.8	59

TABLE VIII.—TANGENTS AND EXTERNALS FOR A 1° CURVE
(Chord or Arc Definition)

'	I = 60°		I = 61°		I = 62°		I = 63°		'
	T	E	T	E	T	E	T	E	
0	3308.0	886.4	3375.0	920.1	3442.7	954.8	3511.1	990.2	0
1	3309.1	886.9	3376.1	920.7	3443.9	955.3	3512.3	990.8	1
2	3310.2	887.5	3377.3	921.3	3445.0	955.9	3513.4	991.4	2
3	3311.3	888.1	3378.4	921.9	3446.1	956.5	3514.6	992.0	3
4	3312.5	888.6	3379.5	922.4	3447.3	957.1	3515.7	992.6	4
5	3313.6	889.2	3380.5	923.0	3448.4	957.7	3516.9	993.3	5
6	3314.7	889.7	3381.8	923.6	3449.5	958.3	3518.0	993.8	6
7	3315.8	890.3	3382.9	924.1	3450.7	958.8	3519.2	994.4	7
8	3316.9	890.8	3384.9	924.7	3451.8	959.4	3520.3	995.0	8
9	3318.0	891.4	3385.1	925.3	3452.9	960.0	3521.5	995.6	9
10	3319.1	891.9	3386.3	925.8	3454.1	960.6	3522.6	996.2	10
11	3320.2	892.5	3387.4	926.4	3455.2	961.2	3523.8	996.8	11
12	3321.4	893.1	3388.5	927.0	3456.3	961.8	3524.9	997.5	12
13	3322.5	893.6	3389.6	927.6	3457.5	962.4	3526.1	998.1	13
14	3323.6	894.2	3390.8	928.1	3458.6	963.0	3527.2	998.7	14
15	3324.7	894.7	3391.9	928.7	3459.8	963.5	3528.4	999.3	15
16	3325.8	895.3	3393.0	929.3	3460.9	964.1	3529.5	999.9	16
17	3326.9	895.9	3394.1	929.9	3462.0	964.7	3530.7	1000.5	17
18	3328.0	896.4	3395.3	930.4	3463.2	965.3	3531.8	1001.1	18
19	3329.2	897.0	3396.4	931.0	3464.3	965.9	3533.0	1001.7	19
20	3330.3	897.5	3397.5	931.6	3465.4	966.5	3534.1	1002.3	20
21	3331.4	898.1	3398.6	932.2	3466.6	967.1	3535.3	1002.9	21
22	3332.5	898.7	3399.8	932.7	3467.7	967.7	3536.4	1003.5	22
23	3333.6	899.2	3400.9	933.3	3468.9	968.2	3537.6	1004.1	23
24	3334.7	899.8	3402.0	933.9	3470.0	968.8	3538.7	1004.7	24
25	3335.9	900.3	3403.1	934.5	3471.1	969.4	3539.9	1005.3	25
26	3337.0	900.9	3404.3	935.0	3472.3	970.0	3541.0	1005.9	26
27	3338.1	901.5	3405.4	935.6	3473.4	970.6	3542.2	1006.5	27
28	3339.2	902.0	3406.5	936.2	3474.6	971.2	3543.3	1007.1	28
29	3340.3	902.6	3407.7	936.8	3475.7	971.8	3544.5	1007.7	29
30	3341.4	903.2	3408.8	937.3	3476.8	972.4	3545.6	1008.3	30
31	3342.6	903.7	3409.9	937.9	3478.0	973.0	3546.8	1008.9	31
32	3343.7	904.3	3411.0	938.5	3479.1	973.6	3547.9	1009.5	32
33	3344.8	904.8	3412.2	939.1	3480.3	974.2	3549.1	1010.1	33
34	3345.9	905.4	3413.3	939.7	3481.4	974.8	3550.2	1010.7	34
35	3347.0	906.0	3414.4	940.2	3482.5	975.3	3551.4	1011.3	35
36	3348.1	906.5	3415.6	940.8	3483.7	975.9	3552.5	1012.0	36
37	3349.3	907.1	3416.7	941.4	3484.8	976.5	3553.7	1012.6	37
38	3350.4	907.7	3417.8	942.0	3486.0	977.1	3554.8	1013.2	38
39	3351.5	908.2	3418.9	942.5	3487.1	977.7	3556.0	1013.8	39
40	3352.6	908.8	3420.1	943.1	3488.2	978.3	3557.2	1014.4	40
41	3353.7	909.4	3421.2	943.7	3489.4	978.9	3558.3	1015.0	41
42	3354.8	909.9	3422.3	944.3	3490.5	979.5	3559.5	1015.6	42
43	3356.0	910.5	3423.5	944.9	3491.7	980.1	3560.6	1016.2	43
44	3357.1	911.1	3424.6	945.4	3492.8	980.7	3561.8	1016.8	44
45	3358.2	911.6	3425.7	946.0	3494.0	981.3	3562.9	1017.4	45
46	3359.3	912.2	3426.9	946.6	3495.1	981.9	3564.1	1018.1	46
47	3360.4	912.8	3428.0	947.2	3496.2	982.5	3565.2	1018.7	47
48	3361.6	913.3	3429.1	947.8	3497.4	983.1	3566.4	1019.3	48
49	3362.7	913.9	3430.3	948.3	3498.5	983.7	3567.5	1019.9	49
50	3363.8	914.5	3431.4	948.9	3499.7	984.3	3568.7	1020.5	50
51	3364.9	915.0	3432.5	949.5	3500.8	984.9	3569.9	1021.1	51
52	3366.0	915.6	3433.7	950.1	3502.0	985.5	3571.0	1021.7	52
53	3367.2	916.2	3434.8	950.7	3503.1	986.1	3572.2	1022.3	53
54	3368.3	916.7	3435.9	951.3	3504.3	986.7	3573.3	1022.9	54
55	3369.4	917.3	3437.1	951.8	3505.4	987.3	3574.5	1023.5	55
56	3370.5	917.9	3438.2	952.4	3506.6	987.9	3575.6	1024.2	56
57	3371.7	918.4	3439.3	953.0	3507.7	988.4	3576.8	1024.8	57
58	3372.8	919.0	3440.5	953.6	3508.8	989.0	3578.0	1025.4	58
59	3373.9	919.6	3441.6	954.2	3510.8	989.6	3579.1	1026.0	59

TABLE VIII.—TANGENTS AND EXTERNALS FOR A 1° CURVE
(Chord or Arc Definition)

′	I = 64°		I = 65°		I = 66°		I = 67°		′
	T	E	T	E	T	E	T	E	
0	3580.3	1026.6	3650.2	1063.9	3720.9	1102.2	3792.4	1141.4	0
1	3581.4	1027.2	3651.4	1064.5	3722.1	1102.8	3793.6	1142.1	1
2	3582.6	1027.8	3652.5	1065.2	3723.2	1103.5	3794.8	1142.7	2
3	3583.8	1028.5	3653.7	1065.8	3724.4	1104.1	3796.0	1143.4	3
4	3584.9	1029.1	3654.9	1066.4	3725.6	1104.8	3797.2	1144.0	4
5	3586.1	1029.7	3656.1	1067.0	3726.8	1105.4	3798.4	1144.7	5
6	3587.2	1030.3	3657.2	1067.7	3728.0	1106.0	3799.6	1145.4	6
7	3588.4	1030.9	3658.4	1068.3	3729.2	1106.7	3800.8	1146.0	7
8	3589.6	1031.6	3659.6	1068.9	3730.4	1107.3	3802.0	1146.7	8
9	3590.7	1032.2	3660.7	1069.6	3731.6	1108.0	3803.2	1147.3	9
10	3591.9	1032.8	3661.9	1070.2	3732.7	1108.6	3804.4	1148.0	10
11	3593.0	1033.4	3663.1	1070.8	3733.9	1109.2	3805.6	1148.7	11
12	3594.2	1034.0	3664.3	1071.5	3735.1	1109.9	3806.8	1149.3	12
13	3595.4	1034.7	3665.4	1072.1	3736.3	1110.5	3808.0	1150.0	13
14	3596.5	1035.3	3666.6	1072.8	3737.5	1111.2	3809.2	1150.7	14
15	3597.7	1035.9	3667.8	1073.4	3738.7	1111.8	3810.4	1151.3	15
16	3598.8	1036.5	3669.0	1074.0	3739.9	1112.5	3811.6	1152.0	16
17	3600.0	1037.1	3670.1	1074.7	3741.1	1113.1	3812.8	1152.7	17
18	3601.2	1037.8	3671.3	1075.3	3742.2	1113.8	3814.0	1153.4	18
19	3602.3	1038.4	3672.5	1076.0	3743.4	1114.4	3815.2	1154.0	19
20	3603.5	1039.0	3673.7	1076.6	3744.6	1115.1	3816.4	1154.7	20
21	3604.7	1039.6	3674.8	1077.2	3745.8	1115.8	3817.6	1155.4	21
22	3605.8	1040.2	3676.0	1077.9	3747.0	1116.4	3818.8	1156.0	22
23	3607.0	1040.9	3677.2	1078.5	3748.2	1117.1	3820.0	1156.7	23
24	3608.2	1041.5	3678.4	1079.1	3749.4	1117.7	3821.2	1157.3	24
25	3609.3	1042.1	3679.5	1079.7	3750.6	1118.4	3822.4	1158.0	25
26	3610.5	1042.7	3680.7	1080.4	3751.8	1119.1	3823.6	1158.7	26
27	3611.6	1043.3	3681.9	1081.0	3752.9	1119.7	3824.8	1159.3	27
28	3612.8	1044.0	3683.1	1081.6	3754.1	1120.4	3826.0	1160.0	28
29	3614.0	1044.6	3684.3	1082.3	3755.3	1121.0	3827.2	1160.6	29
30	3615.1	1045.2	3685.4	1082.9	3756.5	1121.7	3828.4	1161.3	30
31	3616.3	1045.8	3686.6	1083.5	3757.7	1122.3	3829.6	1162.0	31
32	3617.5	1046.4	3687.8	1084.2	3758.9	1123.0	3830.8	1162.7	32
33	3617.6	1047.1	3689.0	1084.8	3760.1	1123.6	3832.0	1163.3	33
34	3619.8	1047.7	3690.1	1085.5	3761.3	1124.3	3833.3	1164.0	34
35	3621.0	1048.3	3691.3	1086.1	3762.5	1124.9	3834.5	1164.7	35
36	3622.1	1048.9	3692.5	1086.7	3763.7	1125.6	3835.7	1165.4	36
37	3623.3	1049.5	3693.7	1087.4	3764.9	1126.2	3836.9	1166.1	37
38	3624.5	1050.2	3694.9	1088.0	3766.1	1126.9	3838.1	1166.7	38
39	3625.6	1050.8	3696.0	1088.7	3767.3	1127.5	3839.3	1167.4	39
40	3626.8	1051.4	3697.2	1089.3	3768.5	1128.2	3840.5	1168.1	40
41	3628.0	1052.0	3698.4	1089.9	3769.6	1128.9	3841.7	1168.8	41
42	3629.1	1052.7	3699.6	1090.6	3770.8	1129.5	3842.9	1169.4	42
43	3630.3	1053.3	3700.8	1091.2	3772.0	1130.2	3844.1	1170.1	43
44	3631.5	1053.9	3702.0	1091.9	3773.2	1130.8	3845.3	1170.8	44
45	3632.6	1054.5	3703.1	1092.5	3774.4	1131.5	3846.5	1171.4	45
46	3633.8	1055.2	3704.3	1093.1	3775.6	1132.2	3847.7	1172.1	46
47	3635.0	1055.8	3705.5	1093.8	3776.8	1132.8	3849.0	1172.8	47
48	3636.1	1056.4	3706.7	1094.4	3778.0	1133.5	3850.2	1173.5	48
49	3637.3	1057.1	3707.9	1095.1	3779.2	1134.1	3851.4	1174.1	49
50	3638.5	1057.7	3709.0	1095.7	3780.4	1134.8	3852.6	1174.8	50
51	3639.7	1058.3	3710.2	1096.3	3781.6	1135.5	3853.8	1175.5	51
52	3640.8	1058.9	3711.4	1097.0	3782.8	1136.1	3855.0	1176.2	52
53	3642.0	1059.6	3712.6	1097.6	3784.0	1136.8	3856.2	1176.8	53
54	3643.2	1060.2	3713.8	1098.3	3785.2	1137.4	3857.4	1177.5	54
55	3644.3	1060.8	3715.0	1098.9	3786.4	1138.1	3858.6	1178.2	55
56	3645.5	1061.4	3716.1	1099.6	3787.6	1138.8	3859.8	1178.9	56
57	3646.7	1062.0	3717.3	1100.2	3788.8	1139.4	3861.1	1179.6	57
58	3647.8	1062.7	3718.5	1100.9	3790.0	1140.1	3862.3	1180.2	58
59	3649.0	1063.3	3719.7	1101.5	3791.2	1140.7	3863.5	1180.9	59

TABLE VIII.—TANGENTS AND EXTERNALS FOR A 1° CURVE
(Chord or Arc Definition)

'	I = 68° T	I = 68° E	I = 69° T	I = 69° E	I = 70° T	I = 70° E	I = 71° T	I = 71° E	'
0	3864.7	1181.6	3937.9	1222.7	4011.9	1265.0	4086.9	1308.2	0
1	3865.9	1182.3	3939.1	1223.4	4013.2	1265.7	4088.2	1308.9	1
2	3867.1	1183.0	3940.3	1224.1	4014.4	1266.4	4089.4	1309.7	2
3	3868.3	1183.6	3941.6	1224.8	4015.7	1267.1	4090.7	1310.4	3
4	3869.6	1184.3	3942.8	1225.5	4016.9	1267.8	4091.9	1311.2	4
5	3870.8	1185.0	3944.0	1226.2	4018.2	1268.5	4093.2	1311.9	5
6	3872.0	1185.7	3945.2	1226.9	4019.4	1269.3	4094.5	1312.6	6
7	3873.2	1186.4	3946.5	1227.6	4020.6	1270.0	4095.7	1313.4	7
8	3874.4	1187.0	3947.7	1228.3	4021.9	1270.7	4097.0	1314.1	8
9	3875.6	1187.7	3948.9	1229.0	4023.1	1271.4	4098.2	1314.9	9
10	3876.8	1188.4	3950.2	1229.7	4024.4	1272.1	4099.5	1315.5	10
11	3878.0	1189.1	3951.4	1230.4	4025.6	1272.8	4100.8	1316.3	11
12	3879.3	1189.8	3952.6	1231.1	4026.9	1273.5	4102.0	1317.1	12
13	3880.5	1190.4	3953.9	1231.8	4028.1	1274.3	4103.3	1317.8	13
14	3881.7	1191.1	3955.1	1232.5	4029.4	1275.0	4104.5	1318.5	14
15	3882.9	1191.8	3956.3	1233.2	4030.6	1275.7	4105.8	1319.2	15
16	3884.1	1192.5	3957.5	1233.9	4031.8	1276.4	4107.1	1320.0	16
17	3885.3	1193.2	3958.8	1234.6	4033.1	1277.1	4108.3	1320.7	17
18	3886.6	1193.8	3960.0	1235.3	4034.3	1277.9	4109.6	1321.4	18
19	3887.8	1194.5	3961.2	1236.0	4035.6	1278.6	4110.9	1322.2	19
20	3889.0	1195.2	3962.5	1236.7	4036.8	1279.3	4112.1	1322.9	20
21	3890.2	1195.9	3963.7	1237.4	4038.1	1280.0	4113.4	1323.6	21
22	3891.4	1196.6	3964.9	1238.1	4039.3	1280.7	4114.6	1324.4	22
23	3892.6	1197.2	3966.2	1238.8	4040.6	1281.5	4115.9	1325.1	23
24	3893.9	1197.9	3967.4	1239.5	4041.8	1282.2	4117.2	1325.9	24
25	3895.1	1198.6	3968.6	1240.2	4043.1	1282.9	4118.4	1326.6	25
26	3896.3	1199.3	3969.9	1240.9	4044.3	1283.6	4119.7	1327.3	26
27	3897.5	1200.0	3971.1	1241.6	4045.6	1284.3	4121.0	1328.1	27
28	3898.7	1200.6	3972.3	1242.3	4046.8	1285.1	4122.2	1328.8	28
29	3900.0	1201.3	3973.6	1243.0	4048.1	1285.8	4123.5	1329.6	29
30	3901.2	1202.0	3974.8	1243.7	4049.3	1286.5	4124.8	1330.3	30
31	3902.4	1202.7	3976.0	1244.4	4050.6	1287.2	4126.0	1331.0	31
32	3903.6	1203.4	3977.3	1245.1	4051.8	1287.9	4127.3	1331.8	32
33	3904.8	1204.1	3978.5	1245.8	4053.1	1288.6	4128.6	1332.5	33
34	3906.1	1204.8	3979.7	1246.5	4054.3	1289.3	4129.8	1333.3	34
35	3907.3	1205.4	3981.0	1247.2	4055.6	1290.0	4131.1	1334.0	35
36	3908.5	1206.1	3982.2	1248.0	4056.8	1290.8	4132.4	1334.7	36
37	3909.7	1206.8	3983.4	1248.7	4058.1	1291.5	4133.6	1335.5	37
38	3910.9	1207.5	3984.7	1249.4	4059.3	1292.2	4134.9	1336.2	38
39	3912.2	1208.2	3985.9	1250.1	4060.6	1292.9	4136.2	1337.0	39
40	3913.4	1208.9	3987.2	1250.8	4061.8	1293.7	4137.4	1337.7	40
41	3914.6	1209.6	3988.4	1251.5	4063.1	1294.3	4138.7	1338.4	41
42	3915.8	1210.3	3989.6	1252.2	4064.3	1295.1	4140.0	1339.2	42
43	3917.1	1211.0	3990.9	1252.9	4065.6	1295.8	4141.2	1339.9	43
44	3918.3	1211.7	3992.1	1253.6	4066.8	1296.5	4142.5	1340.7	44
45	3919.5	1212.3	3993.3	1254.3	4068.1	1297.2	4143.8	1341.4	45
46	3920.7	1213.0	3994.6	1255.1	4069.3	1298.0	4145.0	1342.1	46
47	3921.9	1213.7	3995.8	1255.8	4070.6	1298.7	4146.3	1342.9	47
48	3923.2	1214.4	3997.1	1256.5	4071.9	1299.4	4147.6	1343.6	48
49	3924.4	1215.1	3998.3	1257.2	4073.1	1300.2	4148.8	1344.4	49
50	3925.6	1215.8	3999.5	1257.9	4074.4	1300.9	4150.1	1345.1	50
51	3926.8	1216.5	4000.8	1258.6	4075.6	1301.6	4151.4	1345.8	51
52	3928.1	1217.2	4002.0	1259.3	4076.9	1302.4	4152.7	1346.6	52
53	3929.3	1217.9	4003.3	1260.0	4078.1	1303.1	4153.9	1347.3	53
54	3930.5	1218.6	4004.5	1260.7	4079.4	1303.8	4155.2	1348.1	54
55	3931.7	1219.2	4005.7	1261.4	4080.6	1304.5	4156.5	1348.8	55
56	3933.0	1219.9	4007.0	1262.2	4081.9	1305.3	4157.7	1349.6	56
57	3934.2	1220.6	4008.2	1262.9	4083.1	1306.0	4159.0	1350.3	57
58	3935.4	1221.3	4009.5	1263.6	4084.4	1306.7	4160.3	1351.1	58
59	3936.7	1222.0	4010.7	1264.3	4085.7	1307.5	4161.6	1351.8	59

TABLE VIII.—TANGENTS AND EXTERNALS FOR A 1° CURVE
(Chord or Arc Definition)

'	I = 72°		I = 73°		I = 74°		I = 75°		'
	T	E	T	E	T	E	T	E	
0	4162.8	1352.6	4239.7	1398.0	4317.6	1444.6	4396.5	1492.4	0
1	4164.1	1353.3	4241.0	1398.8	4318.9	1445.4	4397.8	1493.2	1
2	4165.4	1354.1	4242.3	1399.5	4320.2	1446.2	4399.2	1494.0	2
3	4166.7	1354.8	4243.6	1400.3	4321.5	1447.0	4400.5	1494.8	3
4	4167.9	1355.6	4244.9	1401.1	4322.8	1447.8	4401.8	1495.6	4
5	4169.2	1356.3	4246.2	1401.8	4324.1	1448.5	4403.1	1496.4	5
6	4170.5	1357.1	4247.5	1402.6	4325.4	1449.3	4404.5	1497.3	6
7	4171.8	1357.8	4248.8	1403.4	4326.8	1450.1	4405.8	1498.1	7
8	4173.0	1358.6	4250.0	1404.2	4328.1	1450.9	4407.1	1498.9	8
9	4174.3	1359.3	4251.3	1404.9	4329.4	1451.7	4408.4	1499.7	9
10	4175.6	1360.1	4252.6	1405.7	4330.7	1452.5	4409.8	1500.5	10
11	4176.9	1360.8	4253.9	1406.5	4332.0	1453.3	4411.1	1501.3	11
12	4178.1	1361.6	4255.2	1407.3	4333.3	1454.1	4412.4	1502.1	12
13	4179.4	1362.3	4256.5	1408.0	4334.6	1454.9	4413.8	1502.9	13
14	4180.7	1363.1	4257.8	1408.8	4335.9	1455.7	4415.1	1503.7	14
15	4182.0	1363.8	4259.1	1409.6	4337.2	1456.4	4416.4	1504.5	15
16	4183.2	1364.6	4260.4	1410.4	4338.5	1457.2	4417.7	1505.4	16
17	4184.5	1365.3	4261.7	1411.2	4339.9	1458.0	4419.1	1506.2	17
18	4185.8	1366.1	4263.0	1411.9	4341.2	1458.8	4420.4	1507.0	18
19	4187.1	1366.8	4264.3	1412.7	4342.5	1459.6	4421.7	1507.8	19
20	4188.4	1367.6	4265.6	1413.5	4343.8	1460.4	4423.1	1508.6	20
21	4189.6	1368.4	4266.9	1414.3	4345.1	1461.2	4424.4	1509.4	21
22	4190.9	1369.1	4268.2	1415.0	4346.4	1462.0	4425.7	1510.2	22
23	4192.2	1369.9	4269.5	1415.8	4347.7	1462.8	4427.0	1511.0	23
24	4193.5	1370.6	4270.7	1416.6	4349.0	1463.6	4428.4	1511.8	24
25	4194.8	1371.4	4272.0	1417.3	4350.4	1464.4	4429.7	1512.6	25
26	4196.0	1372.2	4273.3	1418.1	4351.7	1465.2	4431.0	1513.5	26
27	4197.3	1372.9	4274.6	1418.9	4353.0	1466.0	4432.4	1514.3	27
28	4198.6	1373.7	4275.9	1419.7	4354.3	1466.8	4433.7	1515.1	28
29	4199.9	1374.4	4277.2	1420.4	4355.6	1467.6	4435.0	1515.9	29
30	4201.2	1375.2	4278.5	1421.2	4356.9	1468.4	4436.4	1516.7	30
31	4202.4	1376.0	4279.8	1422.0	4358.2	1469.2	4437.7	1517.5	31
32	4203.7	1376.7	4281.1	1422.8	4359.6	1470.0	4439.0	1518.3	32
33	4205.0	1377.5	4282.4	1423.5	4360.9	1470.8	4440.4	1519.2	33
34	4206.3	1378.2	4283.7	1424.3	4362.2	1471.6	4441.7	1520.0	34
35	4207.6	1379.0	4285.0	1425.1	4363.5	1472.4	4443.0	1520.8	35
36	4208.8	1379.8	4286.3	1425.9	4364.8	1473.2	4444.4	1521.6	36
37	4210.1	1380.5	4287.6	1426.7	4366.1	1474.0	4445.7	1522.4	37
38	4211.4	1381.3	4288.9	1427.4	4367.5	1474.8	4447.0	1523.3	38
39	4212.7	1382.0	4290.2	1428.2	4368.8	1475.6	4448.4	1524.1	39
40	4214.0	1382.8	4291.5	1429.0	4370.1	1476.4	4449.7	1524.9	40
41	4215.3	1383.6	4292.8	1429.8	4371.4	1477.2	4451.1	1525.7	41
42	4216.5	1384.3	4294.1	1430.6	4372.7	1478.0	4452.4	1526.5	42
43	4217.8	1385.1	4295.4	1431.3	4374.1	1478.8	4453.7	1527.4	43
44	4219.1	1385.8	4296.7	1432.1	4375.4	1479.6	4455.1	1528.2	44
45	4220.4	1386.6	4298.0	1432.9	4376.7	1480.4	4456.4	1529.0	45
46	4221.7	1387.4	4299.3	1433.7	4378.0	1481.2	4457.7	1529.8	46
47	4223.0	1388.1	4300.6	1434.5	4379.3	1482.0	4459.1	1530.6	47
48	4224.3	1388.9	4301.9	1435.2	4380.6	1482.8	4460.4	1531.5	48
49	4225.5	1389.6	4303.2	1436.0	4382.0	1483.6	4461.7	1532.3	49
50	4226.8	1390.4	4304.6	1436.8	4383.3	1484.4	4463.1	1533.1	50
51	4228.1	1391.2	4305.9	1437.6	4384.6	1485.2	4464.4	1533.9	51
52	4229.4	1391.9	4307.2	1438.4	4385.9	1486.0	4465.8	1534.8	52
53	4230.7	1392.7	4308.5	1439.1	4387.3	1486.8	4467.1	1535.6	53
54	4232.0	1393.4	4309.8	1439.9	4388.6	1487.6	4468.4	1536.4	54
55	4233.3	1394.2	4311.1	1440.7	4389.9	1488.4	4469.8	1537.2	55
56	4234.6	1395.0	4312.4	1441.5	4391.2	1489.2	4471.1	1538.1	56
57	4235.9	1395.7	4313.7	1442.3	4392.5	1490.0	4472.5	1538.9	57
58	4237.1	1396.5	4315.0	1443.0	4393.9	1490.8	4473.8	1539.7	58
59	4238.4	1397.2	4316.3	1443.8	4395.2	1491.6	4475.2	1540.6	59

TABLE VIII.—TANGENTS AND EXTERNALS FOR A 1° CURVE
(Chord or Arc Definition)

′	I = 76°		I = 77°		I = 78°		I = 79°		′
	T	E	T	E	T	E	T	E	
0	4476.5	1541.4	4557.6	1591.6	4639.8	1643.0	4723.2	1695.8	0
1	4477.8	1542.2	4558.9	1592.4	4641.2	1643.9	4724.6	1696.7	1
2	4479.2	1543.1	4560.3	1593.3	4642.5	1644.7	4726.0	1697.6	2
3	4480.5	1543.9	4561.7	1594.1	4643.9	1645.6	4727.4	1698.5	3
4	4481.9	1544.7	4563.0	1595.0	4645.3	1646.5	4728.8	1699.4	4
5	4483.2	1545.5	4564.4	1595.8	4646.7	1647.3	4730.2	1700.2	5
6	4484.6	1546.4	4565.7	1596.7	4648.1	1648.2	4731.6	1701.1	6
7	4485.9	1547.2	4567.1	1597.5	4649.4	1649.1	4733.0	1702.0	7
8	4487.2	1548.0	4568.5	1598.4	4650.8	1650.0	4734.4	1702.9	8
9	4488.6	1548.9	4569.8	1599.2	4652.2	1650.8	4735.8	1703.8	9
10	4489.9	1549.7	4571.2	1600.1	4653.6	1651.7	4737.2	1704.7	10
11	4491.3	1550.5	4572.6	1600.9	4655.0	1652.6	4738.6	1705.6	11
12	4492.6	1551.4	4573.9	1601.8	4656.4	1653.5	4740.0	1706.5	12
13	4494.0	1552.2	4575.3	1602.6	4657.7	1654.3	4741.4	1707.4	13
14	4495.3	1553.0	4576.6	1603.5	4659.1	1655.2	4742.8	1708.3	14
15	4496.7	1553.8	4578.0	1604.3	4660.5	1656.1	4744.2	1709.2	15
16	4498.0	1554.7	4579.4	1605.2	4661.9	1657.0	4745.6	1710.1	16
17	4499.4	1555.5	4580.7	1606.0	4663.3	1657.9	4747.0	1711.0	17
18	4500.7	1556.3	4582.1	1606.9	4664.7	1658.7	4748.4	1711.9	18
19	4502.0	1557.2	4583.5	1607.7	4666.1	1659.6	4749.8	1712.8	19
20	4503.4	1558.0	4584.8	1608.6	4667.4	1660.5	4751.2	1713.7	20
21	4504.7	1558.8	4586.2	1609.4	4668.8	1661.4	4752.6	1714.6	21
22	4506.1	1559.7	4587.6	1610.3	4670.2	1662.2	4754.0	1715.5	22
23	4507.4	1560.5	4589.0	1611.1	4671.6	1663.1	4755.4	1716.4	23
24	4508.8	1561.3	4590.3	1612.0	4673.0	1664.0	4756.8	1717.3	24
25	4510.1	1562.1	4591.7	1612.8	4674.4	1664.8	4758.3	1718.2	25
26	4511.5	1563.0	4593.1	1613.7	4675.8	1665.7	4759.7	1719.1	26
27	4512.8	1563.8	4594.4	1614.5	4677.2	1666.6	4761.1	1720.0	27
28	4514.2	1564.6	4595.8	1615.4	4678.5	1667.5	4762.5	1720.9	28
29	4515.5	1565.5	4597.2	1616.2	4679.9	1668.3	4763.9	1721.8	29
30	4516.9	1566.3	4598.5	1617.1	4681.3	1669.2	4765.3	1722.7	30
31	4518.2	1567.1	4599.9	1618.0	4682.7	1670.1	4766.7	1723.6	31
32	4519.6	1568.0	4601.3	1618.8	4684.1	1671.0	4768.1	1724.5	32
33	4520.9	1568.8	4602.6	1619.7	4685.5	1671.9	4769.5	1725.4	33
34	4522.3	1569.7	4604.0	1620.5	4686.9	1672.8	4770.9	1726.3	34
35	4523.7	1570.5	4605.4	1621.4	4688.3	1673.6	4772.4	1727.2	35
36	4525.0	1571.3	4606.8	1622.3	4689.7	1674.5	4773.8	1728.1	36
37	4526.4	1572.2	4608.1	1623.1	4691.1	1675.4	4775.2	1729.0	37
38	4527.7	1573.0	4609.5	1624.0	4692.4	1676.3	4776.6	1729.9	38
39	4529.1	1573.9	4610.9	1624.8	4693.8	1677.2	4778.0	1730.8	39
40	4530.4	1574.7	4612.2	1625.7	4695.2	1678.1	4779.4	1731.7	40
41	4531.8	1575.5	4613.6	1626.6	4696.6	1679.0	4780.8	1732.6	41
42	4533.1	1576.4	4615.0	1627.4	4698.0	1679.9	4782.2	1733.5	42
43	4534.5	1577.2	4616.4	1628.3	4699.4	1680.7	4783.7	1734.4	43
44	4535.8	1578.1	4617.7	1629.2	4700.8	1681.6	4785.1	1735.3	44
45	4537.2	1578.9	4619.1	1630.0	4702.2	1682.5	4786.5	1736.2	45
46	4538.6	1579.7	4620.5	1630.9	4703.6	1683.4	4787.9	1737.2	46
47	4539.9	1580.6	4621.9	1631.8	4705.0	1684.3	4789.3	1738.1	47
48	4541.3	1581.4	4623.2	1632.7	4706.4	1685.1	4790.7	1739.0	48
49	4542.6	1582.3	4624.6	1633.5	4707.8	1686.0	4792.1	1739.9	49
50	4544.0	1583.1	4626.0	1634.4	4709.2	1686.9	4793.6	1740.8	50
51	4545.3	1583.9	4627.4	1635.3	4710.6	1687.8	4795.0	1741.7	51
52	4546.7	1584.8	4628.8	1636.1	4712.0	1688.7	4796.4	1742.6	52
53	4548.1	1585.6	4630.1	1637.0	4713.4	1689.6	4797.8	1743.5	53
54	4549.4	1586.5	4631.5	1637.8	4714.8	1690.5	4799.2	1744.4	54
55	4550.8	1587.3	4632.9	1638.7	4716.2	1691.3	4800.7	1745.3	55
56	4552.1	1588.2	4634.3	1639.6	4717.6	1692.2	4802.1	1746.3	56
57	4553.5	1589.0	4635.6	1640.4	4719.0	1693.1	4803.5	1747.2	57
58	4554.9	1589.9	4637.0	1641.3	4720.4	1694.0	4804.9	1748.1	58
59	4556.2	1590.7	4638.4	1642.1	4721.8	1694.9	4806.3	1749.0	59

TABLE VIII.—TANGENTS AND EXTERNALS FOR A 1° CURVE
(Chord or Arc Definition)

'	I = 80°		I = 81°		I = 82°		I = 83°		'
	T	E	T	E	T	E	T	E	
0	4807.7	1749.9	4893.6	1805.3	4980.7	1862.2	5069.2	1920.5	0
1	4809.2	1750.8	4895.0	1806.2	4982.2	1863.2	5070.7	1921.5	1
2	4810.6	1751.7	4896.5	1807.2	4983.6	1864.1	5072.1	1922.5	2
3	4812.0	1752.6	4897.9	1808.1	4985.1	1865.1	5073.6	1923.5	3
4	4813.4	1753.5	4899.4	1809.1	4986.6	1866.0	5075.1	1924.5	4
5	4814.9	1754.4	4900.8	1810.0	4988.0	1867.0	5076.6	1925.4	5
6	4816.3	1755.4	4902.2	1810.9	4989.5	1868.0	5078.1	1926.4	6
7	4817.7	1756.3	4903.7	1811.9	4991.0	1868.9	5079.6	1927.4	7
8	4819.1	1757.2	4905.1	1812.8	4992.4	1869.9	5081.1	1928.4	8
9	4820.5	1758.1	4906.6	1813.8	4993.9	1870.8	5082.6	1929.4	9
10	4822.0	1759.0	4908.0	1814.7	4995.4	1871.8	5084.0	1930.4	10
11	4823.4	1759.9	4909.5	1815.6	4996.8	1872.8	5085.5	1931.4	11
12	4824.8	1760.8	4910.9	1816.6	4998.3	1873.7	5087.0	1932.4	12
13	4826.2	1761.8	4912.4	1817.5	4999.8	1874.7	5088.5	1933.4	13
14	4827.7	1762.7	4913.8	1818.5	5001.3	1875.7	5090.0	1934.4	14
15	4829.1	1763.6	4915.2	1819.4	5002.7	1876.6	5091.5	1935.3	15
16	4830.5	1764.5	4916.7	1820.3	5004.2	1877.6	5093.0	1936.3	16
17	4831.9	1765.4	4918.1	1821.3	5005.6	1878.6	5094.5	1937.3	17
18	4833.4	1766.4	4919.6	1822.2	5007.1	1879.6	5096.0	1938.3	18
19	4834.8	1767.3	4921.0	1823.2	5008.6	1880.5	5097.5	1939.3	19
20	4836.2	1768.2	4922.5	1824.1	5010.0	1881.5	5099.0	1940.3	20
21	4837.6	1769.1	4923.9	1825.0	5011.5	1882.5	5100.4	1941.3	21
22	4839.1	1770.0	4925.4	1826.0	5013.0	1883.4	5101.9	1942.3	22
23	4840.5	1771.0	4926.8	1826.9	5014.5	1884.4	5103.4	1943.3	23
24	4841.9	1771.9	4928.3	1827.9	5015.9	1885.4	5104.9	1944.3	24
25	4843.4	1772.8	4929.7	1828.8	5017.4	1886.3	5106.4	1945.3	25
26	4844.8	1773.7	4931.2	1829.8	5018.9	1887.3	5107.9	1946.3	26
27	4846.2	1774.6	4932.6	1830.7	5020.3	1888.3	5109.4	1947.3	27
28	4847.6	1775.6	4934.1	1831.7	5021.8	1889.3	5110.9	1948.3	28
29	4849.1	1776.5	4935.5	1832.6	5023.3	1890.2	5112.4	1949.3	29
30	4850.5	1777.4	4937.0	1833.6	5024.8	1891.2	5113.9	1950.3	30
31	4851.9	1778.3	4938.4	1834.5	5026.2	1892.2	5115.4	1951.3	31
32	4853.4	1779.3	4939.9	1835.5	5027.7	1893.1	5116.9	1952.3	32
33	4854.8	1780.2	4941.3	1836.4	5029.2	1894.1	5118.4	1953.3	33
34	4856.2	1781.1	4942.8	1837.4	5030.7	1895.1	5119.9	1954.3	34
35	4857.7	1782.0	4944.2	1838.3	5032.1	1896.0	5121.4	1955.3	35
36	4859.1	1783.0	4945.7	1839.3	5033.6	1897.0	5122.9	1956.2	36
37	4860.5	1783.9	4947.2	1840.2	5035.1	1898.0	5124.4	1957.2	37
38	4862.0	1784.8	4948.6	1841.2	5036.6	1899.0	5125.9	1958.2	38
39	4863.4	1785.8	4950.1	1842.1	5038.1	1900.0	5127.4	1959.2	39
40	4864.8	1786.7	4951.5	1843.1	5039.5	1901.0	5128.9	1960.2	40
41	4866.3	1787.6	4953.0	1844.0	5041.0	1901.9	5130.4	1961.2	41
42	4867.7	1788.6	4954.4	1845.0	5042.5	1902.9	5131.9	1962.2	42
43	4869.1	1789.5	4955.9	1845.9	5044.0	1903.8	5133.4	1963.2	43
44	4870.6	1790.4	4957.3	1846.9	5045.4	1904.8	5134.9	1964.2	44
45	4872.0	1791.3	4958.8	1847.8	5046.9	1905.8	5136.4	1965.2	45
46	4873.4	1792.3	4960.3	1848.8	5048.4	1906.8	5137.9	1966.3	46
47	4874.9	1793.2	4961.7	1849.7	5049.9	1907.8	5139.4	1967.3	47
48	4876.3	1794.1	4963.2	1850.7	5051.4	1908.7	5140.9	1968.3	48
49	4877.8	1795.1	4964.6	1851.6	5052.8	1909.7	5142.4	1969.3	49
50	4879.2	1796.0	4966.1	1852.6	5054.3	1910.7	5143.9	1970.3	50
51	4880.6	1796.9	4967.6	1853.6	5055.8	1911.7	5145.4	1971.3	51
52	4882.1	1797.9	4969.0	1854.5	5057.3	1912.7	5146.9	1972.3	52
53	4883.5	1798.8	4970.5	1855.5	5058.8	1913.6	5148.4	1973.3	53
54	4884.9	1799.7	4971.9	1856.4	5060.3	1914.6	5150.0	1974.3	54
55	4886.4	1800.6	4973.4	1857.4	5061.7	1915.6	5151.5	1975.3	55
56	4887.8	1801.6	4974.9	1858.4	5063.2	1916.6	5153.0	1976.4	56
57	4889.3	1802.5	4976.3	1859.3	5064.7	1917.6	5154.5	1977.4	57
58	4890.7	1803.4	4977.8	1860.3	5066.2	1918.5	5156.0	1978.4	58
59	4892.1	1804.4	4979.2	1861.2	5067.7	1919.5	5157.5	1979.4	59

'	I = 84°		I = 85°		I = 86°		I = 87°		'
	T	E	T	E	T	E	T	E	
0	5159.0	1980.4	5250.3	2041.7	5343.0	2104.7	5437.2	2169.2	0
1	5160.5	1981.4	5251.8	2042.7	5344.5	2105.8	5438.8	2170.3	1
2	5162.0	1982.4	5253.3	2043.8	5346.1	2106.8	5440.4	2171.4	2
3	5163.5	1983.4	5254.9	2044.8	5347.7	2107.9	5442.0	2172.5	3
4	5165.0	1984.4	5256.4	2045.9	5349.2	2108.9	5443.6	2173.6	4
5	5166.6	1985.4	5257.9	2046.9	5350.8	2110.0	5445.2	2174.7	5
6	5168.1	1986.5	5259.5	2047.9	5352.3	2111.1	5446.7	2175.8	6
7	5169.6	1987.5	5261.0	2049.0	5353.9	2112.1	5448.3	2176.9	7
8	5171.1	1988.5	5262.5	2050.0	5355.5	2113.2	5449.9	2178.0	8
9	5172.6	1989.5	5264.1	2051.1	5357.5	2114.2	5451.5	2179.1	9
10	5174.1	1990.5	5265.6	2052.1	5358.6	2115.3	5453.1	2180.2	10
11	5175.6	1991.5	5267.1	2053.1	5360.1	2116.4	5454.7	2181.3	11
12	5177.1	1992.5	5268.7	2054.2	5361.7	2117.4	5456.3	2182.4	12
13	5178.7	1993.5	5270.2	2055.2	5363.3	2118.5	5457.9	2183.5	13
14	5180.2	1994.5	5271.8	2056.3	5364.8	2119.6	5459.5	2184.6	14
15	5181.7	1995.5	5273.3	2057.3	5366.4	2120.6	5461.0	2185.6	15
16	5183.2	1996.6	5274.8	2058.3	5368.0	2121.7	5462.6	2186.7	16
17	5184.7	1997.6	5276.4	2059.4	5369.5	2122.8	5464.2	2187.8	17
18	5186.2	1998.6	5277.9	2060.4	5371.1	2123.9	5465.8	2188.9	18
19	5187.7	1999.6	5279.5	2061.5	5372.7	2124.9	5467.4	2190.0	19
20	5189.3	2000.6	5281.0	2062.5	5374.2	2126.0	5469.0	2191.1	20
21	5190.8	2001.6	5282.5	2063.5	5375.8	2127.1	5470.6	2192.2	21
22	5192.3	2002.6	5284.1	2064.6	5377.4	2128.1	5472.2	2193.3	22
23	5193.8	2003.7	5285.6	2065.6	5378.9	2129.2	5473.8	2194.4	23
24	5195.3	2004.7	5287.2	2066.7	5380.5	2130.3	5475.4	2195.5	24
25	5196.8	2005.7	5288.7	2067.7	5382.1	2131.3	5477.0	2196.6	25
26	5198.4	2006.7	5290.3	2068.8	5383.6	2132.4	5478.6	2197.8	26
27	5199.9	2007.7	5291.8	2069.8	5385.2	2133.5	5480.2	2198.9	27
28	5201.4	2008.8	5293.3	2070.9	5386.8	2134.6	5481.8	2200.0	28
29	5202.9	2009.8	5294.9	2071.9	5388.3	2135.6	5483.4	2201.1	29
30	5204.5	2010.8	5296.4	2073.0	5389.9	2136.7	5484.9	2202.2	30
31	5206.0	2011.8	5298.0	2074.0	5391.5	2137.8	5486.5	2203.3	31
32	5207.5	2012.9	5299.5	2075.1	5393.1	2138.9	5488.1	2204.4	32
33	5209.0	2014.0	5301.1	2076.1	5394.6	2139.9	5489.7	2205.5	33
34	5210.5	2014.9	5302.6	2077.2	5396.2	2141.0	5491.3	2206.6	34
35	5212.1	2015.9	5304.2	2078.2	5397.8	2142.1	5492.9	2207.7	35
36	5213.6	2017.0	5305.7	2079.3	5399.3	2143.2	5494.5	2208.8	36
37	5215.1	2018.0	5307.3	2080.3	5400.9	2144.3	5496.1	2209.9	37
38	5216.6	2019.0	5308.8	2081.4	5402.5	2145.3	5497.7	2211.0	38
39	5218.2	2020.1	5310.4	2082.4	5404.1	2146.4	5499.3	2212.1	39
40	5219.7	2021.1	5311.9	2083.5	5405.6	2147.5	5500.9	2213.2	40
41	5221.2	2022.1	5313.5	2084.6	5407.2	2148.6	5502.5	2214.3	41
42	5222.7	2023.2	5315.0	2085.6	5408.8	2149.7	5504.1	2215.4	42
43	5224.3	2024.2	5316.6	2086.7	5410.4	2150.8	5505.7	2216.5	43
44	5225.8	2025.2	5318.1	2087.7	5412.0	2151.9	5507.3	2217.6	44
45	5227.3	2026.2	5319.7	2088.8	5413.5	2152.9	5509.0	2218.7	45
46	5228.8	2027.3	5321.2	2089.9	5415.1	2154.0	5510.6	2219.9	46
47	5230.4	2028.3	5322.8	2090.9	5416.7	2155.1	5512.2	2221.0	47
48	5231.9	2029.3	5324.3	2092.0	5418.3	2156.2	5513.8	2222.1	48
49	5233.4	2030.4	5325.9	2093.0	5419.8	2157.3	5515.4	2223.2	49
50	5234.9	2031.4	5327.4	2094.1	5421.4	2158.4	5517.0	2224.3	50
51	5236.5	2032.4	5329.0	2095.2	5423.0	2159.5	5518.6	2225.4	51
52	5238.0	2033.5	5330.5	2096.2	5424.6	2160.6	5520.2	2226.5	52
53	5239.5	2034.5	5332.1	2097.3	5426.2	2161.6	5521.8	2227.7	53
54	5241.1	2035.5	5333.6	2098.3	5427.7	2162.7	5523.4	2228.8	54
55	5242.6	2036.5	5335.2	2099.4	5429.3	2163.8	5525.0	2229.9	55
56	5244.1	2037.6	5336.8	2100.5	5430.9	2164.9	5526.6	2231.0	56
57	5245.7	2038.6	5338.3	2101.5	5432.5	2166.0	5528.2	2232.1	57
58	5247.2	2039.6	5339.9	2102.6	5434.1	2167.0	5529.8	2233.3	58
59	5248.7	2040.7	5341.4	2103.6	5435.7	2168.1	5531.4	2234.4	59

TABLE VIII.—TANGENTS AND EXTERNALS FOR A 1° CURVE
(Chord or Arc Definition)

.	I = 88°		I = 89°		I = 90°		I = 91°		.
	T	E	T	E	T	E	T	E	
0	5533.1	2235.5	5630.5	2303.5	5729.7	2373.3	5830.5	2444.9	0
1	5534.7	2236.6	5632.2	2304.6	5731.3	2374.5	5832.2	2446.1	1
2	5536.3	2237.7	5633.8	2305.8	5733.0	2375.7	5833.9	2447.3	2
3	5537.9	2238.9	5635.4	2306.9	5734.7	2376.8	5835.6	2448.6	3
4	5539.5	2240.0	5637.1	2308.1	5736.3	2378.0	5837.3	2449.8	4
5	5541.1	2241.1	5638.7	2309.2	5738.0	2379.2	5839.0	2451.0	5
6	5542.7	2242.2	5640.3	2310.4	5739.7	2380.4	5840.7	2452.2	6
7	5544.3	2243.3	5642.0	2311.5	5741.3	2381.6	5842.4	2453.4	7
8	5546.0	2244.5	5643.6	2312.7	5743.0	2382.7	5844.1	2454.7	8
9	5547.6	2245.6	5645.3	2313.8	5744.7	2383.9	5845.8	2455.9	9
10	5549.2	2246.7	5646.9	2315.0	5746.3	2385.1	5847.5	2457.1	10
11	5550.8	2247.8	5648.6	2316.2	5748.0	2386.3	5849.2	2458.3	11
12	5552.4	2249.0	5650.2	2317.3	5749.7	2387.5	5850.9	2459.5	12
13	5554.0	2250.1	5651.8	2318.5	5751.4	2388.7	5852.6	2460.8	13
14	5555.7	2251.2	5653.5	2319.6	5753.0	2389.9	5854.3	2462.0	14
15	5557.3	2252.3	5655.1	2320.8	5754.7	2391.0	5856.0	2463.2	15
16	5558.9	2253.5	5656.8	2322.0	5756.4	2392.2	5857.7	2464.4	16
17	5560.5	2254.6	5658.4	2323.1	5758.1	2393.4	5859.4	2465.6	17
18	5562.1	2255.7	5660.1	2324.3	5759.7	2394.6	5861.1	2466.9	18
19	5563.7	2256.9	5661.7	2325.4	5761.4	2395.8	5862.9	2468.1	19
20	5565.4	2258.0	5663.4	2326.6	5763.1	2397.0	5864.6	2469.3	20
21	5567.0	2259.1	5665.0	2327.8	5764.8	2398.2	5866.3	2470.5	21
22	5568.6	2260.3	5666.7	2328.9	5766.4	2399.4	5868.0	2471.7	22
23	5570.2	2261.4	5668.3	2330.1	5768.1	2400.6	5869.7	2473.0	23
24	5571.8	2262.5	5670.0	2331.2	5769.8	2401.8	5871.4	2474.2	24
25	5573.5	2263.6	5671.6	2332.4	5771.5	2402.9	5873.1	2475.4	25
26	5575.1	2264.8	5673.3	2333.6	5773.2	2404.1	5874.8	2476.6	26
27	5576.7	2265.9	5674.9	2334.7	5774.8	2405.3	5876.5	2477.8	27
28	5578.3	2267.0	5676.6	2335.9	5776.5	2406.5	5878.2	2479.1	28
29	5580.0	2268.2	5678.2	2337.0	5778.2	2407.7	5879.9	2480.3	29
30	5581.6	2269.3	5679.9	2338.2	5779.9	2408.9	5881.7	2481.5	30
31	5583.2	2270.4	5681.5	2339.4	5781.6	2410.1	5883.4	2482.7	31
32	5584.8	2271.6	5683.2	2340.5	5783.2	2411.3	5885.1	2484.0	32
33	5586.5	2272.7	5684.8	2341.7	5784.9	2412.5	5886.8	2485.2	33
34	5588.1	2273.8	5686.5	2342.8	5786.6	2413.7	5888.5	2486.4	34
35	5589.7	2274.9	5688.1	2344.0	5788.3	2414.9	5890.2	2487.6	35
36	5591.3	2276.1	5689.8	2345.2	5790.0	2416.1	5891.9	2488.9	36
37	5593.0	2277.2	5691.4	2346.3	5791.7	2417.3	5893.6	2490.1	37
38	5594.6	2278.3	5693.1	2347.5	5793.3	2418.5	5895.4	2491.3	38
39	5596.2	2279.5	5694.8	2348.6	5795.0	2419.7	5897.1	2492.6	39
40	5597.9	2280.6	5696.4	2349.8	5796.7	2420.9	5898.8	2493.8	40
41	5599.5	2281.7	5698.1	2351.0	5798.4	2422.1	5900.5	2495.0	41
42	5601.1	2282.9	5699.7	2352.1	5800.1	2423.3	5902.2	2496.3	42
43	5602.7	2284.0	5701.4	2353.3	5801.8	2424.5	5903.9	2497.5	43
44	5604.4	2285.2	5703.0	2354.5	5803.5	2425.7	5905.7	2498.7	44
45	5606.0	2286.3	5704.7	2355.6	5805.1	2426.9	5907.4	2499.9	45
46	5607.6	2287.4	5706.4	2356.8	5806.8	2428.1	5909.1	2501.2	46
47	5609.3	2288.6	5708.0	2358.0	5808.5	2429.3	5910.8	2502.4	47
48	5610.9	2289.7	5709.7	2359.2	5810.2	2430.5	5912.5	2503.6	48
49	5612.5	2290.9	5711.3	2360.3	5811.9	2431.7	5914.3	2504.9	49
50	5614.2	2292.0	5713.0	2361.5	5813.6	2432.9	5916.0	2506.1	50
51	5615.8	2293.1	5714.7	2362.7	5815.3	2434.1	5917.7	2507.3	51
52	5617.4	2294.3	5716.3	2363.9	5817.0	2435.3	5919.4	2508.6	52
53	5619.1	2295.4	5718.0	2365.0	5818.7	2436.5	5921.2	2509.8	53
54	5620.7	2296.6	5719.7	2366.2	5820.4	2437.7	5922.9	2511.1	54
55	5622.3	2297.7	5721.3	2367.4	5822.1	2438.9	5924.6	2512.3	55
56	5624.0	2298.9	5723.0	2368.6	5823.8	2440.1	5926.3	2513.5	56
57	5625.6	2300.0	5724.7	2369.8	5825.4	2441.3	5928.0	2514.8	57
58	5627.2	2301.2	5726.3	2370.9	5827.1	2442.5	5929.8	2516.0	58
59	5628.9	2302.3	5728.0	2372.1	5828.8	2443.7	5931.5	2517.3	59

TABLE IX. —CORRECTIONS FOR TANGENTS*
(Chord Definition of D)

After dividing T_1 (Table VIII) by D, add correction.

I	1°	2°	3°	4°	5°	6°	8°	10°	12°	14°	16°	I
					Degree of Curve (D_c)							
5°	.00	.01	.01	.01	.02	.02	.03	.03	.04	.04	.05	5°
10°	.01	.01	.02	.03	.03	.04	.05	.06	.08	.09	.10	10°
15°	.01	.02	.03	.04	.05	.06	.08	.10	.12	.13	.15	15°
20	.01	.02	.04	.05	.06	.08	.10	.13	.15	.18	.21	20
25°	.02	.03	.05	.07	.08	.10	.13	.16	.19	.23	.26	25°
30°	.02	.04	.06	.08	.10	.12	.16	.20	.23	.27	.31	30°
35°	.02	.04	.07	.09	.11	.14	.18	.23	.28	.32	.37	35°
40	.03	.05	.08	.11	.13	.16	.21	.26	.32	.37	.42	40
45°	.03	.06	.09	.12	.15	.18	.24	.30	.36	.42	.48	45°
50°	.03	.07	.10	.14	.17	.20	.27	.34	.41	.48	.54	50°
55°	.04	.07	.11	.16	.19	.23	.30	.38	.45	.53	.61	55°
60	.04	.08	.13	.17	.21	.25	.34	.42	.50	.59	.67	60
65°	.04	.09	.14	.19	.23	.28	.37	.46	.56	.65	.74	65°
70°	.05	.10	.15	.21	.25	.31	.41	.51	.61	.71	.82	70°
75°	.05	.11	.17	.23	.28	.33	.45	.56	.67	.78	.89	75°
80	.06	.12	.18	.25	.30	.37	.49	.61	.73	.86	.98	80
85°	.06	.13	.20	.27	.33	.40	.53	.67	.80	.93	1.07	85°
90°	.07	.14	.22	.30	.36	.44	.58	.73	.87	1.02	1.17	90°
95°	.08	.15	.24	.33	.39	.48	.63	.79	.95	1.11	1.27	95°
100	.08	.17	.26	.36	.43	.52	.69	.87	1.04	1.21	1.39	100
105°	.09	.18	.29	.39	.47	.57	.76	.95	1.14	1.33	1.52	105°
110°	.10	.20	.31	.43	.51	.62	.83	1.04	1.25	1.46	1.67	110°
115°	.11	.22	.35	.47	.57	.68	.91	1.14	1.37	1.60	1.83	115°
120	.12	.24	.38	.52	.62	.76	1.01	1.26	1.51	1.76	2.02	120

* See page 20 for explanation and example.

TABLE X.—CORRECTIONS FOR EXTERNALS*
(Chord Definition of D)

After dividing E_1 (Table VIII) by D, add correction.

I	1°	2°	3°	4°	5°	6°	8°	10°	12°	14°	16°	I
					Degree of Curve (D_c)							
10°	.00	.00	.00	.00	.00	.00	.00	.00	.00	.00	.00	10°
20°	.00	.00	.00	.00	.01	.01	.01	.01	.01	.02	.02	20°
30°	.00	.00	.01	.01	.01	.02	.02	.03	.03	.04	.04	30°
40°	.00	.01	.01	.02	.02	.03	.04	.05	.06	.07	.07	40°
50°	.01	.01	.02	.03	.04	.05	.06	.08	.09	.11	.12	50°
60	.01	.02	.03	.05	.06	.07	.09	.11	.14	.16	.18	60
65°	.01	.03	.04	.06	.07	.08	.11	.14	.16	.19	.22	65°
70°	.02	.03	.05	.07	.08	.10	.13	.16	.19	.22	.26	70°
75°	.02	.04	.06	.08	.09	.11	.15	.19	.23	.27	.30	75°
80°	.02	.04	.07	.09	.11	.13	.18	.22	.27	.31	.36	80°
85	.03	.05	.08	.11	.13	.16	.21	.26	.31	.36	.42	85°
90°	.03	.06	.09	.12	.15	.18	.24	.30	.36	.42	.48	90
95°	.03	.07	.11	.14	.17	.21	.28	.35	.42	.49	.56	95°
100°	.04	.08	.12	.17	.20	.24	.32	.40	.49	.57	.65	100°
105°	.04	.09	.14	.19	.23	.28	.37	.47	.56	.65	.75	105°
110°	.05	.10	.16	.22	.27	.32	.43	.54	.65	.76	.87	110°
115°	.06	.12	.19	.26	.31	.38	.50	.63	.75	.88	1.00	115°
120	.07	.14	.22	.30	.36	.44	.58	.73	.87	1.02	1.17	120

* See page 20 for explanation and example.

PARTIAL NOTATION

(See Chapter 5 for complete theory and notation)

D Degree of central circular curve (D_a=arc definition of D; D_c=chord definition of D).

L_s Length of spiral curve, in feet.

Δ Central angle of the spiral, or spiral angle.

X, Y Coordinates (abscissa and ordinate) of the S.C. referred to the T.S. as origin and to the initial tangent as X-axis.

X_0, o Coordinates (abscissa and ordinate) of the offset T.C., which is the point where a tangent to the circular curve produced backward becomes parallel to the tangent at the T.S.

L.T.   "Long tangent" of the spiral.

S.T.   "Short tangent" of the spiral.

L.C.   "Long chord" of the spiral.

Table XI. This table gives spiral parts for various selected values of D and L_s. *It may be used for both chord definition and arc definition of D.* The definition of D affects only the co-ordinates of the offset T.C.; correct values of these coordinates may be obtained by observing the following:

1. *When arc definition of D is used*, select values of o and X_0 from sub-columns headed D_a.
2. *When chord definition of D is used*, subtract the corrections in the columns headed * from the arc-definition values of o and X_0.

Table XII. This table may be used to obtain spiral parts for *any combination* of D and L_s up to $\Delta = 45$. Proceed as follows:

1. *When arc definition of D is used*, enter table with given value of Δ (interpolating if necessary) and multiply the tabulated coefficients by the value of L_s.
2. *When chord definition of D is used*, calculate spiral parts as above. Then, since only the coordinates of the offset T.C. are affected by the definition of D, correct the calculated values of o and X_0 by subtracting the products of D and the coefficients in the columns headed by an asterisk.

Example. $D = 12$; $L_s = 320$; $\Delta = 19.2$. For arc definition,

$$o = 320 \times .02781 = 8.90$$
$$X_0 = 320 \times .49813 = 159.40$$

For chord definition,

$$o = 8.90 - 12 \times .0041 = 8.85$$
$$X_0 = 159.40 - 12 \times .0240 = 159.11$$

TABLE XI.—SELECTED SPIRALS

L_s	Δ	o	X_0	X	Y	L.T.	S.T.	L.C.
				$D = 0°\ 30'$				
100	0°15.0′	0.03	50.00	100.00	0.14	66.67	33.33	100.00
125	0 18.8	0.06	62.50	125.00	0.23	83.33	41.67	125.00
150	0 22.5	0.08	75.00	150.00	0.33	100.00	50.00	150.00
200	0 30.0	0.15	100.00	200.00	0.58	133.33	66.67	200.00
250	0 37.5	0.23	125.00	250.00	0.91	166.67	83.33	250.00
300	0 45.0	0.31	150.00	299.99	1.31	200.00	100.00	300.00
350	0 52.5	0.44	175.00	349.99	1.78	233.34	116.67	350.00
400	1 00.0	0.58	200.00	399.99	2.33	266.67	133.34	399.99
450	1 07.5	0.74	225.00	449.98	2.95	300.01	150.01	449.99
500	1 15.0	0.91	250.00	499.98	3.64	333.34	166.67	499.99
550	1 22.5	1.10	274.99	549.97	4.40	366.68	183.34	549.99
600	1 30.0	1.31	299.99	599.96	5.24	400.01	200.01	599.98
700	1 45.0	1.78	349.99	699.93	7.13	466.69	233.35	699.97
800	2 00.0	2.33	399.98	799.90	9.31	533.37	266.70	799.96
900	2 15.0	2.94	449.98	899.86	11.78	600.05	300.05	899.94
1000	2 30.0	3.64	499.97	999.81	14.54	666.73	333.39	999.92
				$D = 0°\ 40'$				
100	0°20.0′	0.05	50.00	100.00	0.18	66.67	33.33	100.00
125	0 25.0	0.08	62.50	125.00	0.30	83.33	41.67	125.00
150	0 30.0	0.11	75.00	150.00	0.44	100.00	50.00	150.00
200	0 40.0	0.20	100.00	200.00	0.78	133.33	66.67	200.00
250	0 50.0	0.30	125.00	249.99	1.21	166.67	83.33	250.00
300	1 00.0	0.44	150.00	299.99	1.75	200.00	100.00	300.00
350	1 10.0	0.59	175.00	349.99	2.38	233.34	116.67	349.99
400	1 20.0	0.78	200.00	399.98	3.10	266.67	133.34	399.99
450	1 30.0	0.98	225.00	449.97	3.93	300.01	150.01	449.99
500	1 40.0	1.21	249.99	499.96	4.85	333.35	166.68	499.98
550	1 50.0	1.47	274.99	549.95	5.87	366.69	183.35	549.98
600	2 00.0	1.75	299.99	599.93	6.98	400.03	200.02	599.97
700	2 20.0	2.38	349.98	699.88	9.50	466.71	233.37	699.95
800	2 40.0	3.10	399.97	799.83	12.41	533.39	266.72	799.92
900	3 00.0	3.93	449.96	899.75	15.70	600.09	300.08	899.89
1000	3 20.0	4.85	499.94	999.66	19.39	666.79	333.44	999.85
				$D = 0°\ 50'$				
100	0°25.0′	0.06	50.00	100.00	0.24	66.67	33.33	100.00
125	0 31.3	0.09	62.50	125.00	0.38	83.33	41.67	125.00
150	0 37.5	0.14	75.00	150.00	0.55	100.00	50.00	150.00
200	0 50.0	0.24	100.00	200.00	0.97	133.33	66.67	200.00
250	1 02.5	0.38	125.00	249.99	1.52	166.67	83.34	250.00
300	1 15.0	0.55	150.00	299.99	2.18	200.00	100.00	299.99
350	1 27.5	0.74	175.00	349.98	2.97	233.34	116.67	349.99
400	1 40.0	0.97	199.99	399.97	3.88	266.68	133.34	399.99
450	1 52.5	1.23	224.99	449.95	4.91	300.02	150.02	449.98
500	2 05.0	1.51	249.99	499.93	6.06	333.36	166.69	499.97
550	2 17.5	1.83	274.99	549.91	7.33	366.70	183.36	549.96
600	2 30.0	2.18	299.98	599.89	8.73	400.04	200.04	599.95
700	2 55.0	2.97	349.97	699.82	11.88	466.73	233.39	699.92
800	3 20.0	3.88	399.95	799.73	15.51	533.43	266.75	799.88
900	3 45.0	4.91	449.93	899.63	19.63	600.14	300.12	899.83
1000	4 10.0	6.06	499.91	999.47	24.23	666.85	333.50	999.77

45

TABLE XI.—SELECTED SPIRALS

L_s	Δ	o	D_a	*	X	Y	L.T.	S.T.	L.C.
			X_0						

<table>
<tr><td colspan="10" align="center">D = 1°</td></tr>
<tr><td>100</td><td>0°30.0'</td><td>0.07</td><td>50.00</td><td>....</td><td>100.00</td><td>0.29</td><td>66.67</td><td>33.33</td><td>100.00</td></tr>
<tr><td>125</td><td>0 37.5</td><td>0.11</td><td>62.50</td><td>....</td><td>125.00</td><td>0.45</td><td>83.33</td><td>41.67</td><td>125.00</td></tr>
<tr><td>150</td><td>0 45.0</td><td>0.16</td><td>75.00</td><td>....</td><td>150.00</td><td>0.65</td><td>100.00</td><td>50.00</td><td>150.00</td></tr>
<tr><td>200</td><td>1 00.0</td><td>0.29</td><td>100.00</td><td>....</td><td>199.99</td><td>1.16</td><td>133.34</td><td>66.67</td><td>200.00</td></tr>
<tr><td>250</td><td>1 15.0</td><td>0.45</td><td>125.00</td><td>....</td><td>249.99</td><td>1.82</td><td>166.67</td><td>83.34</td><td>249.99</td></tr>
<tr><td>300</td><td>1 30.0</td><td>0.65</td><td>150.00</td><td>....</td><td>299.98</td><td>2.62</td><td>200.01</td><td>100.01</td><td>299.99</td></tr>
<tr><td>350</td><td>1 45.0</td><td>0.89</td><td>174.99</td><td>....</td><td>349.97</td><td>3.56</td><td>233.34</td><td>116.68</td><td>349.99</td></tr>
<tr><td>400</td><td>2 00.0</td><td>1.16</td><td>199.99</td><td>....</td><td>399.95</td><td>4.65</td><td>266.68</td><td>133.35</td><td>399.98</td></tr>
<tr><td>450</td><td>2 15.0</td><td>1.47</td><td>224.99</td><td>....</td><td>449.93</td><td>5.89</td><td>300.02</td><td>150.02</td><td>449.97</td></tr>
<tr><td>500</td><td>2 30.0</td><td>1.82</td><td>249.98</td><td>....</td><td>499.91</td><td>7.27</td><td>333.37</td><td>166.70</td><td>499.96</td></tr>
<tr><td>550</td><td>2 45.0</td><td>2.20</td><td>274.98</td><td>....</td><td>549.87</td><td>8.80</td><td>366.71</td><td>183.37</td><td>549.94</td></tr>
<tr><td>600</td><td>3 00.0</td><td>2.62</td><td>299.97</td><td>....</td><td>599.84</td><td>10.47</td><td>400.06</td><td>200.05</td><td>599.93</td></tr>
<tr><td>700</td><td>3 30.0</td><td>3.56</td><td>349.94</td><td>....</td><td>699.74</td><td>14.25</td><td>466.76</td><td>233.42</td><td>699.89</td></tr>
<tr><td>800</td><td>4 00.0</td><td>4.65</td><td>399.94</td><td>.01</td><td>799.61</td><td>18.61</td><td>533.47</td><td>266.79</td><td>799.82</td></tr>
<tr><td>900</td><td>4 30.0</td><td>5.89</td><td>449.91</td><td>.01</td><td>899.44</td><td>23.55</td><td>600.19</td><td>300.18</td><td>899.76</td></tr>
<tr><td>1000</td><td>5 00.0</td><td>7.27</td><td>499.87</td><td>.01</td><td>999.24</td><td>29.07</td><td>666.93</td><td>333.58</td><td>999.66</td></tr>

<tr><td colspan="10" align="center">D = 1° 15'</td></tr>
<tr><td>100</td><td>0°37.5'</td><td>0.09</td><td>50.00</td><td>....</td><td>100.00</td><td>0.36</td><td>66.67</td><td>33.33</td><td>100.00</td></tr>
<tr><td>125</td><td>0 46.9</td><td>0.14</td><td>62.50</td><td>....</td><td>125.00</td><td>0.57</td><td>83.33</td><td>41.67</td><td>125.00</td></tr>
<tr><td>150</td><td>0 56.2</td><td>0.20</td><td>75.00</td><td>....</td><td>150.00</td><td>0.82</td><td>100.00</td><td>50.00</td><td>150.00</td></tr>
<tr><td>200</td><td>1 15.0</td><td>0.36</td><td>100.00</td><td>....</td><td>199.99</td><td>1.45</td><td>133.34</td><td>66.67</td><td>200.00</td></tr>
<tr><td>250</td><td>1 33.8</td><td>0.57</td><td>124.99</td><td>....</td><td>249.98</td><td>2.27</td><td>166.67</td><td>83.34</td><td>244.99</td></tr>
<tr><td>300</td><td>1 52.5</td><td>0.82</td><td>149.99</td><td>....</td><td>299.97</td><td>3.27</td><td>200.01</td><td>100.01</td><td>299.99</td></tr>
<tr><td>350</td><td>2 11.3</td><td>1.11</td><td>174.99</td><td>....</td><td>349.95</td><td>4.45</td><td>233.35</td><td>116.68</td><td>349.98</td></tr>
<tr><td>400</td><td>2 30.0</td><td>1.45</td><td>199.99</td><td>....</td><td>399.92</td><td>5.82</td><td>266.69</td><td>133.36</td><td>399.97</td></tr>
<tr><td>450</td><td>2 48.8</td><td>1.84</td><td>224.98</td><td>....</td><td>449.89</td><td>7.36</td><td>300.04</td><td>150.03</td><td>449.95</td></tr>
<tr><td>500</td><td>3 07.5</td><td>2.27</td><td>249.97</td><td>....</td><td>499.85</td><td>9.09</td><td>333.39</td><td>166.71</td><td>499.93</td></tr>
<tr><td>550</td><td>3 26.3</td><td>2.75</td><td>274.97</td><td>.01</td><td>549.80</td><td>11.00</td><td>366.74</td><td>183.40</td><td>549.91</td></tr>
<tr><td>600</td><td>3 45.0</td><td>3.27</td><td>299.96</td><td>.01</td><td>599.74</td><td>13.09</td><td>400.09</td><td>200.08</td><td>599.89</td></tr>
<tr><td>700</td><td>4 22.5</td><td>4.45</td><td>349.93</td><td>.01</td><td>699.59</td><td>17.81</td><td>466.81</td><td>233.46</td><td>699.82</td></tr>
<tr><td>800</td><td>5 00.0</td><td>5.82</td><td>399.90</td><td>.01</td><td>799.39</td><td>23.26</td><td>533.54</td><td>266.86</td><td>799.73</td></tr>
<tr><td>900</td><td>5 37.5</td><td>7.36</td><td>449.86</td><td>.01</td><td>899.13</td><td>29.43</td><td>600.30</td><td>300.28</td><td>899.62</td></tr>
<tr><td>1000</td><td>6 15.0</td><td>9.08</td><td>499.80</td><td>.01</td><td>998.80</td><td>36.33</td><td>667.08</td><td>333.71</td><td>999.48</td></tr>

<tr><td colspan="10" align="center">D = 1° 30'</td></tr>
<tr><td>100</td><td>0°45.0'</td><td>0.11</td><td>50.00</td><td>....</td><td>100.00</td><td>0.44</td><td>66.67</td><td>33.33</td><td>100.00</td></tr>
<tr><td>125</td><td>0 56.2</td><td>0.17</td><td>62.50</td><td>....</td><td>125.00</td><td>0.68</td><td>83.33</td><td>41.67</td><td>125.00</td></tr>
<tr><td>150</td><td>1 07.5</td><td>0.25</td><td>75.00</td><td>....</td><td>149.99</td><td>0.98</td><td>100.00</td><td>50.00</td><td>150.00</td></tr>
<tr><td>200</td><td>1 30.0</td><td>0.44</td><td>100.00</td><td>....</td><td>199.99</td><td>1.75</td><td>133.34</td><td>66.67</td><td>199.99</td></tr>
<tr><td>250</td><td>1 52.5</td><td>0.68</td><td>124.99</td><td>....</td><td>249.97</td><td>2.73</td><td>166.68</td><td>83.34</td><td>249.99</td></tr>
<tr><td>300</td><td>2 15.0</td><td>0.98</td><td>149.99</td><td>....</td><td>299.95</td><td>3.93</td><td>200.02</td><td>100.01</td><td>299.98</td></tr>
<tr><td>350</td><td>2 37.5</td><td>1.33</td><td>174.99</td><td>....</td><td>349.93</td><td>5.34</td><td>233.36</td><td>116.69</td><td>349.97</td></tr>
<tr><td>400</td><td>3 00.0</td><td>1.74</td><td>199.98</td><td>....</td><td>399.89</td><td>6.98</td><td>266.71</td><td>133.37</td><td>399.95</td></tr>
<tr><td>450</td><td>3 22.5</td><td>2.20</td><td>224.97</td><td>.01</td><td>449.85</td><td>8.83</td><td>300.06</td><td>150.05</td><td>449.93</td></tr>
<tr><td>500</td><td>3 45.0</td><td>2.72</td><td>249.96</td><td>.01</td><td>499.78</td><td>10.90</td><td>333.41</td><td>166.74</td><td>499.90</td></tr>
<tr><td>550</td><td>4 07.5</td><td>3.30</td><td>274.95</td><td>.01</td><td>549.71</td><td>13.19</td><td>366.77</td><td>183.42</td><td>549.87</td></tr>
<tr><td>600</td><td>4 30.0</td><td>3.92</td><td>299.94</td><td>.01</td><td>599.63</td><td>15.70</td><td>400.13</td><td>200.12</td><td>599.84</td></tr>
<tr><td>700</td><td>5 15.0</td><td>5.35</td><td>349.90</td><td>.01</td><td>699.41</td><td>21.36</td><td>466.88</td><td>233.52</td><td>699.74</td></tr>
<tr><td>800</td><td>6 00.0</td><td>6.98</td><td>399.86</td><td>.01</td><td>799.12</td><td>27.90</td><td>533.64</td><td>266.94</td><td>799.61</td></tr>
<tr><td>900</td><td>6 45.0</td><td>8.83</td><td>449.79</td><td>.01</td><td>898.75</td><td>35.31</td><td>600.44</td><td>300.40</td><td>899.44</td></tr>
</table>

* Subtract from tabulated value for D_a when chord definition of D is used.

TABLE XI.—SELECTED SPIRALS

L_s	Δ	o	X_0		X	Y	L.T.	S.T.	L.C.
			D_a	*					
$D = 1° 45'$									
100	0°52.5′	0.13	50.00	....	100.00	0.51	66.67	33.33	100.00
125	1 05.6	0.20	62.50	....	125.00	0.80	83.33	41.67	125.00
150	1 18.8	0.29	75.00	....	149.99	1.15	100.00	50.00	150.00
200	1 45.0	0.51	100.00	....	199.98	2.36	133.34	66.67	199.99
250	2 11.3	0.80	124.99	....	249.96	3.18	166.68	83.35	249.98
300	2 37.5	1.15	149.99	.01	299.94	4.58	200.02	100.02	299.97
350	3 03.8	1.56	174.98	.01	349.90	6.23	233.37	116.70	349.96
400	3 30.0	2.03	199.98	.01	399.85	8.14	266.72	133.38	399.93
450	3 56.3	2.57	224.96	.01	449.79	10.30	300.07	150.07	449.91
500	4 22.5	3.18	249.95	.01	499.71	12.72	333.43	166.76	499.87
550	4 48.8	3.85	274.93	.01	549.61	15.39	366.80	183.46	549.83
600	5 15.0	4.58	299.92	.01	599.50	18.32	400.18	200.16	599.78
700	6 07.5	6.24	349.87	.01	699.20	24.92	466.95	233.59	699.65
800	7 00.0	8.14	399.80	.02	798.81	32.54	533.75	267.05	799.47
900	7 52.5	10.30	449.71	.02	898.31	41.18	600.60	300.55	899.25
$D = 2°$									
100	1°00.0′	0.15	50.00	....	100.00	0.58	66.67	33.33	100.00
125	1 15.0	0.23	62.50	....	124.99	0.91	83.34	41.67	125.00
150	1 30.0	0.33	75.00	....	149.99	1.31	100.00	50.00	150.00
200	2 00.0	0.58	100.00	.01	199.98	2.33	133.34	66.67	199.99
250	2 30.0	0.91	124.99	.01	249.95	3.64	166.68	83.35	249.98
300	3 00.0	1.30	149.99	.01	299.92	5.24	200.03	100.03	299.96
350	3 30.0	1.78	174.98	.01	349.88	7.13	233.38	116.71	349.94
400	4 00.0	2.32	199.97	.01	399.80	9.30	266.73	133.40	399.91
450	4 30.0	2.94	224.96	.01	449.72	11.78	300.10	150.09	449.88
500	5 00.0	3.64	249.94	.01	499.62	14.54	333.47	166.79	499.83
550	5 30.0	4.40	274.92	.01	549.49	17.59	366.84	183.50	549.77
600	6 00.0	5.23	299.89	.02	599.34	20.93	400.23	200.21	599.71
700	7 00.0	7.13	349.82	.02	698.96	28.48	467.03	233.67	699.54
800	8 00.0	9.30	399.74	.02	798.44	37.18	533.88	267.16	799.30
$D = 2° 15'$									
100	1°07.5′	0.16	50.00	....	100.00	0.65	66.67	33.33	100.00
125	1 24.4	0.26	62.50	....	124.99	1.02	83.34	41.67	125.00
150	1 41.2	0.37	74.99	....	149.99	1.47	100.00	50.00	149.99
200	2 15.0	0.65	99.99	.01	199.97	2.62	133.34	66.68	199.99
250	2 48.8	1.02	124.99	.01	249.94	4.09	166.69	83.35	249.97
300	3 22.5	1.47	149.98	.01	299.90	5.89	200.04	100.03	299.95
350	3 56.3	2.00	174.97	.01	349.83	8.02	233.39	116.72	349.93
400	4 30.0	2.62	199.96	.01	399.75	10.47	266.75	133.41	399.89
450	5 03.8	3.31	224.94	.01	449.65	13.24	300.12	150.11	449.84
500	5 37.5	4.09	249.92	.02	499.52	16.35	333.50	166.82	499.79
550	6 11.3	4.94	274.90	.02	549.36	19.78	366.89	183.54	549.72
600	6 45.0	5.89	299.86	.02	599.17	23.54	400.29	200.26	599.63
700	7 52.5	8.02	349.78	.03	698.69	32.03	467.13	233.75	699.42
800	9 00.0	10.46	399.67	.03	798.03	41.82	534.02	267.30	799.12

* Subtract from tabulated value for D_a when chord definition of D is used.

TABLE XI.—SELECTED SPIRALS

L_s	Δ	o	X_0		X	Y	L.T.	S.T.	L.C.
			D_a	*					
					$D = 2°\ 30'$				
100	1°15.0′	0.18	50.00	....	100.00	0.72	66.67	33.33	100.00
125	1 33.8	0.28	62.50	....	124.99	1.14	83.34	41.67	125.00
150	1 52.5	0.41	75.00	.01	149.98	1.64	100.01	50.01	149.99
200	2 30.0	0.73	99.99	.01	199.96	2.91	133.35	66.68	199.98
250	3 07.5	1.13	124.99	.01	249.93	4.54	166.69	83.36	249.97
300	3 45.0	1.63	149.98	.01	299.87	6.54	200.04	100.04	299.94
350	4 22.5	2.22	174.97	.01	349.80	8.91	233.40	116.73	349.91
400	5 00.0	2.91	199.95	.02	399.70	11.63	266.77	133.43	399.86
450	5 37.5	3.68	224.93	.02	449.56	14.72	300.15	150.14	449.81
500	6 15.0	4.54	249.90	.02	499.40	18.16	333.54	166.86	499.73
550	6 52.5	5.49	274.87	.02	549.21	21.98	366.94	183.59	549.65
600	7 30.0	6.55	299.83	.02	598.97	26.15	400.36	200.33	599.54
700	8 45.0	8.90	349.73	.03	698.37	35.57	467.24	233.86	699.27
800	10 00.0	11.62	399.59	.03	797.57	46.44	534.18	267.45	798.92
					$D = 2°\ 45'$				
100	1°22.5′	0.20	50.00	....	99.99	0.80	66.67	33.34	100.00
125	1 43.2	0.31	62.50	.01	124.99	1.25	83.34	41.67	125.00
150	2 03.8	0.45	75.00	.01	149.98	1.80	100.01	50.01	149.99
200	2 45.0	0.80	99.99	.01	199.95	3.20	133.35	66.68	199.98
250	3 26.3	1.25	124.98	.01	249.91	5.00	166.70	83.36	249.96
300	4 07.5	1.80	149.97	.01	299.85	7.20	200.06	100.05	299.93
350	4 48.8	2.45	174.96	.02	349.75	9.79	233.42	116.75	349.89
400	5 30.0	3.20	199.94	.02	399.56	12.79	266.80	133.45	399.84
450	6 11.3	4.05	224.91	.02	449.47	16.19	300.19	150.17	449.77
500	6 52.5	5.00	249.88	.02	499.28	19.98	333.58	166.90	499.68
550	7 33.8	6.04	274.84	.03	549.03	24.17	367.00	183.64	549.58
600	8 15.0	7.20	299.79	.03	598.76	28.76	400.43	200.40	599.45
700	9 37.5	9.80	349.67	.03	698.02	39.12	467.36	233.96	699.13
					$D = 3°$				
100	1°30.0′	0.22	50.00	.01	99.99	0.87	66.67	33.34	100.00
125	1 52.5	0.34	62.50	.01	124.99	1.36	83.34	41.67	124.99
150	2 15.0	0.49	75.00	.01	149.98	1.96	100.01	50.01	149.99]
200	3 00.0	0.87	99.99	.01	199.95	3.49	133.35	66.68	199.98
250	3 45.0	1.36	124.98	.01	249.89	5.45	166.70	83.37	249.95
300	4 30.0	1.96	149.97	.02	299.81	7.85	200.06	100.06	299.92
350	5 15.0	2.67	174.95	.02	349.71	10.68	233.44	116.76	349.87
400	6 00.0	3.49	199.93	.02	399.56	13.95	266.82	133.47	399.80
450	6 45.0	4.42	224.89	.03	449.37	17.65	300.22	150.20	449.72
500	7 30.0	5.46	249.86	.03	499.14	21.79	333.63	166.94	499.62
550	8 15.0	6.60	274.81	.03	548.86	26.36	367.06	183.70	549.49
600	9 00.0	7.85	299.75	.03	598.52	31.36	400.52	200.47	599.34]
700	10 30.0	10.68	349.61	.04	697.66	42.66	467.49	234.08	698.96]

* Subtract from tabulated value for D_a when chord definition of D is used.

48

TABLE XI.—SELECTED SPIRALS

L_s	Δ	o	X_0		X	Y	L.T.	S.T.	L.C.
			D_a	*					

					$D = 3°\ 30'$				
100	1°45.0′	0.25	50.00	.01	99.99	1.02	66.67	33.34	100.00
125	2 11.3	0.40	62.50	.01	124.98	1.59	83.34	41.67	124.99
150	2 37.5	0.57	74.99	.01	149.97	2.29	100.01	50.01	149.99
200	3 30.0	1.02	99.99	.02	199.93	4.07	133.36	66.69	199.97
250	4 22.5	1.59	124.98	.02	249.85	6.36	166.72	83.38	249.94
300	5 15.0	2.29	149.96	.02	299.75	9.16	200.09	100.08	299.89
350	6 07.5	3.12	174.93	.03	349.60	12.46	233.47	116.97	349.82
400	7 00.0	4.07	199.90	.03	399.40	16.27	266.88	133.52	399.73
450	7 52.5	5.15	224.86	.03	449.15	20.59	300.30	150.27	449.63
500	8 45.0	6.36	249.80	.04	498.84	25.41	333.74	167.04	499.48
550	9 37.5	7.69	274.74	.04	548.45	30.73	367.21	183.83	549.31
600	10 30.0	9.16	299.66	.05	597.99	36.56	400.71	200.64	599.10
700	12 15.0	12.45	349.46	.05	696.80	49.72	467.79	234.35	698.58

L_s	Δ	o		X_0		X	Y	L.T.	S.T.	L.C.
		D_a	*	D_a	*					

						$D = 4°$				
100	2°00.0′	0.29	....	50.00	.01	99.99	1.16	66.67	33.34	99.99
125	2 30.0	0.45	....	62.50	.01	124.98	1.82	83.34	41.67	124.99
150	3 00.0	0.65	....	74.99	.02	149.96	2.62	100.01	50.01	149.98
200	4 00.0	1.16	....	99.98	.02	199.90	4.65	133.37	66.70	199.96
250	5 00.0	1.82	....	124.97	.03	249.81	7.27	166.73	83.39	249.92
300	6 00.0	2.62	....	149.95	.03	299.67	10.46	200.11	100.10	299.85
350	7 00.0	3.56	....	174.91	.04	349.48	14.24	233.52	116.83	349.77
400	8 00.0	4.65	....	199.87	.04	399.22	18.59	266.94	133.58	399.65
450	9 00.0	5.89	....	224.82	.05	448.89	23.52	300.39	150.35	449.50
500	10 00.0	7.26	....	249.74	.05	498.48	29.02	333.87	167.15	499.32
550	11 00.0	8.79	.01	274.66	.06	547.98	35.11	367.38	183.98	549.10
600	12 00.0	10.46	.01	299.56	.06	597.37	41.75	400.92	200.84	598.83
650	13 00.0	12.27	.01	324.44	.07	646.66	48.98	434.51	217.74	648.51

						$D = 4°\ 30'$				
100	2°15.0′	0.33	....	50.00	.01	99.98	1.31	66.67	33.34	99.99
125	2 48.8	0.51	....	62.50	.02	124.97	2.04	83.34	41.67	124.99
150	3 22.5	0.74	....	74.99	.02	149.95	2.94	100.02	50.02	149.98
200	4 30.0	1.31	....	99.98	.03	199.88	5.23	133.38	66.71	199.95
250	5 37.5	2.04	....	124.96	.03	249.76	8.18	166.75	83.41	249.89
300	6 45.0	2.94	....	149.93	.04	299.58	11.77	200.15	100.13	299.81
350	7 52.5	4.01	....	174.89	.04	349.34	16.02	233.56	116.88	349.71
400	9 00.0	5.23	....	199.84	.05	399.02	20.91	267.01	133.65	399.56
450	10 07.5	6.62	.01	224.77	.06	448.60	26.45	300.49	150.45	449.37
500	11 15.0	8.17	.01	249.68	.06	498.08	32.64	334.01	167.28	499.14
550	12 22.5	9.88	.01	274.57	.07	547.44	39.47	367.57	184.15	548.86
600	13 30.0	11.76	.01	299.45	.08	596.68	46.94	401.17	201.07	598.52
650	14 37.5	13.79	.01	324.30	.08	645.78	55.05	434.82	218.02	648.12

* Subtract from tabulated value for D_a when chord definition of D is used.

TABLE XI.—SELECTED SPIRALS

L_s	Δ	o D_a	*	X_0 D_a	*	X	Y	L.T.	S.T.	L.C.
					$D = 5°$					
100	2°30.0′	0.36	....	50.00	.02	99.98	1.45	66.67	33.34	99.99
125	3 07.5	0.57	....	62.49	.02	124.96	2.27	83.35	41.68	124.98
150	3 45.0	0.82	....	74.99	.02	149.94	3.27	100.02	50.02	149.97
200	5 00.0	1.45	....	99.97	.03	199.85	5.81	133.39	66.72	199.93
250	6 15.0	2.27	....	124.95	.04	249.70	9.08	166.77	83.43	249.87
300	7 30.0	3.27	....	149.91	.05	299.49	13.07	200.18	100.16	299.77
350	8 45.0	4.45	....	174.86	.06	349.18	17.79	233.62	116.93	349.64
400	10 00.0	5.81	.01	199.80	.06	398.78	23.22	267.09	133.72	399.46
450	11 15.0	7.36	.01	224.71	.07	448.27	29.37	300.61	150.55	449.23
500	12 30.0	9.08	.01	249.60	.08	497.62	36.24	334.17	167.43	498.94
550	13 45.0	10.98	.01	274.47	.09	546.84	43.82	367.78	184.36	548.59
600	15 00.0	13.06	.01	299.32	.09	595.90	52.10	401.45	201.32	598.17
					$D = 5° 30′$					
100	2°45.0′	0.40	....	50.00	.02	99.98	1.60	66.67	33.34	99.99
125	3 26.3	0.62	....	62.49	.02	124.96	2.50	83.35	41.68	124.98
150	4 07.5	0.90	....	74.99	.03	149.92	3.60	100.03	50.02	149.97
200	5 30.0	1.60	....	99.97	.04	199.82	6.40	133.40	66.73	199.92
250	6 52.5	2.50	....	124.94	.05	249.64	9.99	166.79	83.45	249.84
300	8 15.0	3.60	....	149.90	.06	299.38	14.38	200.22	100.20	299.72
350	9 37.5	4.90	.01	174.84	.07	349.01	19.56	233.68	116.98	349.56
400	11 00.0	6.39	.01	199.76	.08	398.53	25.53	267.18	133.80	399.34
450	12 22.5	8.09	.01	224.65	.09	447.90	32.29	300.74	150.67	449.07
500	13 45.0	9.98	.01	249.52	.10	497.13	39.83	334.35	167.59	498.72
550	15 07.5	12.07	.01	274.36	.10	546.16	48.15	368.02	184.56	548.30
600	16 30.0	14.36	.02	299.17	.11	595.04	57.26	401.75	201.59	597.79
					$D = 6°$					
100	3°00.0′	0.44	....	50.00	.02	99.97	1.74	66.68	33.34	99.99
125	3 45.0	0.68	....	62.49	.03	124.95	2.73	83.35	41.68	124.98
150	4 30.0	0.98	....	74.98	.03	149.91	3.93	100.03	50.03	149.96
200	6 00.0	1.74	....	99.96	.05	199.78	6.98	133.41	66.74	199.90
250	7 30.0	2.73	....	124.93	.06	249.57	10.90	166.82	83.47	249.81
300	9 00.0	3.92	.01	149.88	.07	299.26	15.68	200.26	100.24	299.67
350	10 30.0	5.34	.01	174.80	.08	348.83	21.33	233.75	117.04	349.48
400	12 00.0	6.97	.01	199.71	.09	398.25	27.84	267.28	133.89	399.22
450	13 30.0	8.82	.01	224.59	.10	447.51	35.20	300.88	150.80	448.89
500	15 00.0	10.88	.01	249.43	.11	496.58	43.42	334.54	167.76	498.48
					$D = 6° 30′$					
100	3°15.0′	0.47	....	49.99	.03	99.97	1.89	66.68	33.34	99.99
125	4 03.8	0.74	....	62.49	.03	124.94	2.95	83.36	41.69	124.97
150	4 52.5	1.06	....	74.98	.04	149.89	4.25	100.04	50.04	149.95
200	6 30.0	1.89	....	99.96	.05	199.74	7.56	133.42	66.75	199.89
250	8 07.5	2.95	....	124.91	.07	249.50	11.80	166.84	83.49	249.78
300	9 45.0	4.25	.01	149.85	.08	299.13	16.98	200.30	100.28	299.61
350	11 22.5	5.78	.01	174.77	.09	348.62	23.10	233.82	117.11	349.39
400	13 00.0	7.55	.01	199.66	.11	397.94	30.14	267.39	133.99	399.08
450	14 37.5	9.55	.02	224.51	.12	447.08	38.11	301.03	150.94	448.70
500	16 15.0	11.78	.02	249.33	.13	495.99	47.00	334.75	167.96	498.22

* Subtract from tabulated value for D_a when chord definition of D is used.

TABLE XI.—SELECTED SPIRALS

L_s	Δ	o D_a	$*$	X_0 D_a	$*$	X	Y	L.T.	S.T.	L.C.
						D = 7°				
100	3°30.0'	0.51	....	49.99	.03	99.96	2.04	66.68	33.35	99.98
125	4 22.5	0.79	....	62.49	.04	124.93	3.18	83.36	41.69	124.97
150	5 15.0	1.15	....	74.98	.05	149.87	4.58	100.04	50.04	149.94
200	7 00.0	2.04	....	99.95	.06	199.70	8.14	133.44	66.76	199.87
250	8 45.0	3.18	.01	124.90	.08	249.42	12.70	166.87	83.52	249.74
300	10 30.0	4.58	.01	149.83	.09	298.99	18.28	200.35	100.32	299.55
350	12 15.0	6.23	.01	174.73	.11	348.40	24.86	233.89	117.18	349.29
400	14 00.0	8.13	.02	199.60	.12	397.62	32.44	267.51	134.10	398.94
450	15 45.0	10.28	.02	224.43	.14	446.61	41.01	301.20	151.09	448.49
500	17 30.0	12.68	.02	249.22	.15	495.36	50.56	334.98	168.16	497.93
						D = 8°				
100	4°00.0'	0.58	....	49.99	.04	99.95	2.33	66.68	33.35	99.98
125	5 00.0	0.91	....	62.48	.05	124.90	3.63	83.37	41.70	124.96
150	6 00.0	1.31	....	74.97	.06	149.83	5.23	100.06	50.05	149.93
200	8 00.0	2.33	.01	99.93	.08	199.61	9.30	133.47	66.79	199.83
250	10 00.0	3.63	.01	124.87	.10	249.24	14.51	166.93	83.58	249.66
300	12 00.0	5.23	.01	149.78	.12	298.69	20.88	200.46	100.42	299.42
350	14 00.0	7.11	.02	174.65	.14	347.92	28.38	234.07	117.33	349.07
400	16 00.0	9.28	.02	199.48	.16	396.89	37.03	267.76	134.33	398.62
450	18 00.0	11.74	.03	224.26	.18	445.58	46.79	301.57	151.42	448.03
500	20 00.0	14.48	.04	248.99	.20	493.94	57.68	335.49	168.63	497.30
						D = 9°				
100	4°30.0'	0.65	....	49.99	.05	99.94	2.62	66.69	33.35	99.97
125	5 37.5	1.02	....	62.48	.06	124.88	4.09	83.38	41.71	124.95
150	6 45.0	1.47	....	74.96	.08	149.79	5.88	100.07	50.07	149.91
200	9 00.0	2.62	.01	99.92	.10	199.51	10.45	133.51	66.82	199.78
250	11 15.0	4.09	.01	124.84	.13	249.04	16.32	167.00	83.64	249.57
300	13 30.0	5.88	.02	149.72	.15	298.34	23.47	200.58	100.53	299.26
350	15 45.0	7.99	.02	174.56	.18	347.36	31.90	234.26	117.51	348.83
400	18 00.0	10.43	.03	199.34	.20	396.07	41.59	268.06	134.60	398.25
450	20 15.0	13.19	.04	224.07	.23	444.41	52.54	301.99	151.81	447.51
500	22 30.0	16.27	.05	248.72	.25	492.34	64.73	336.07	169.15	496.58
						D = 10°				
100	5°00.0'	0.73	....	49.99	.06	99.92	2.91	66.69	33.36	99.97
125	6 15.0	1.14	....	62.48	.08	124.85	4.54	83.39	41.71	124.93
150	7 30.0	1.64	.01	74.96	.10	149.74	6.54	100.09	50.08	149.89
200	10 00.0	2.91	.01	99.90	.13	199.39	11.61	133.55	66.86	199.73
250	12 30.0	4.54	.02	124.80	.16	248.81	18.12	167.08	83.71	249.47
300	15 00.0	6.53	.02	149.66	.19	297.95	26.05	200.72	100.66	299.09
350	17 30.0	8.88	.03	174.46	.22	346.75	35.40	234.48	117.71	348.55
400	20 00.0	11.58	.04	199.19	.25	395.15	46.14	268.39	134.90	397.84
450	22 30.0	14.64	.06	223.85	.28	443.11	58.26	302.46	152.24	446.92
500	25 00.0	18.06	.07	248.42	.31	490.56	71.74	336.72	169.75	495.78

* Subtract from tabulated value for D_a when chord definition of D is used.

TABLE XI.—SELECTED SPIRALS

L_s	Δ	o		X_0		X	Y	L.T.	S.T.	L.C.
		D_a	*	D_a	*					
						D = 11°				
80	4°24.0'	0.51	....	39.99	.06	79.95	2.05	53.35	26.68	79.98
100	5 30.0	0.80	....	49.98	.08	99.91	3.20	66.70	33.36	99.96
125	6 52.5	1.25	.01	62.47	.10	124.82	5.00	83.40	41.72	124.92
150	8 15.0	1.80	.01	74.95	.12	149.69	7.19	100.11	50.10	149.86
200	11 00.0	3.20	.01	99.88	.15	199.26	12.77	133.59	66.90	199.67
250	13 45.0	4.99	.02	124.76	.19	248.56	19.92	167.17	83.79	249.36
300	16 30.0	7.18	.03	149.59	.23	297.52	28.63	200.88	100.80	298.90
350	19 15.0	9.76	.04	174.34	.26	346.07	38.88	234.73	117.94	348.25
400	22 00.0	12.73	.06	199.02	.30	394.14	50.66	268.76	135.23	397.39
500	27 30.0	19.84	.09	248.09	.37	488.60	78.69	337.45	170.41	494.90
						D = 12°				
80	4°48.0'	0.56	....	39.99	.07	79.94	2.23	53.35	26.68	79.98
100	6 00.0	0.87	....	49.98	.09	99.89	3.49	66.70	33.37	99.95
125	7 30.0	1.36	.01	62.46	.11	124.79	5.45	83.41	41.74	124.90
150	9 00.0	1.96	.01	74.94	.14	149.63	7.84	100.13	50.12	149.84
200	12 00.0	3.49	.02	99.85	.18	199.12	13.92	133.64	66.95	199.61
250	15 00.0	5.44	.03	124.72	.23	248.29	21.71	167.27	83.88	249.24
300	18 00.0	7.82	.04	149.51	.27	297.05	31.19	201.04	100.95	298.69
350	21 00.0	10.64	.06	174.22	.31	345.33	42.35	235.00	118.18	347.91
400	24 00.0	13.88	.08	198.84	.36	393.04	55.16	269.16	135.60	396.89
500	30 00.0	21.60	.12	247.73	.44	486.46	85.57	338.25	171.14	493.93
						D = 13°				
80	5°12.0'	0.60	....	39.99	.09	79.93	2.42	53.36	26.69	79.97
100	6 30.0	0.94	.01	49.98	.11	99.87	3.78	66.71	33.37	99.94
125	8 07.5	1.48	.01	62.45	.13	124.75	5.90	83.42	41.75	124.89
150	9 45.0	2.13	.01	74.93	.16	149.57	8.49	100.15	50.14	149.81
200	13 00.0	3.77	.02	99.83	.21	198.97	15.07	133.69	67.00	199.54
250	16 15.0	5.89	.04	124.67	.27	248.00	23.50	167.37	83.98	249.11
300	19 30.0	8.47	.05	149.42	.32	296.54	33.75	201.23	101.12	298.46
350	22 45.0	11.52	.07	174.09	.37	344.52	45.80	235.29	118.45	347.55
400	26 00.0	15.01	.10	198.63	.42	391.84	59.62	269.60	136.00	396.35
500	32 30.0	23.36	.15	247.34	.51	484.15	92.39	339.13	171.95	492.89
						D = 14°				
80	5°36.0'	0.64	....	39.99	.10	79.93	2.56	53.36	26.69	79.97
100	7 00.0	1.02	.01	49.98	.12	99.85	4.07	66.72	33.38	99.93
125	8 45.0	1.59	.01	62.45	.16	124.71	6.35	83.44	41.76	124.87
150	10 30.0	2.29	.02	74.92	.19	149.50	9.14	100.18	50.16	149.78
200	14 00.0	4.06	.03	99.80	.25	198.81	16.22	133.75	67.05	199.47
250	17 30.0	6.34	.05	124.61	.31	247.68	25.28	167.49	84.08	248.96
300	21 00.0	9.12	.07	149.33	.37	296.00	36.30	201.43	101.30	298.21
350	24 30.0	12.39	.09	173.94	.42	343.65	49.24	235.61	118.74	347.16
400	28 00.0	16.15	.12	198.42	.48	390.55	64.06	270.08	136.44	395.77
500	35 00.0	25.12	.18	246.92	.59	481.66	99.13	340.09	172.83	491.76

* Subtract from tabulated value for D_a when chord definition of D is used.

TABLE XI.—SELECTED SPIRALS

L_s	Δ	o D_a	*	X_0 D_a	*	X	Y	L.T.	S.T.	L.C.
						$D=15°$				
80	6°00.0'	0.70	.01	39.99	.11	79.91	2.79	53.36	26.69	79.96
100	7 30.0	1.09	.01	49.97	.14	99.83	4.36	66.73	33.39	99.92
125	9 22.5	1.70	.01	62.44	.18	124.67	6.80	83.45	41.77	124.85
150	11 15.0	2.45	.02	74.90	.21	149.42	9.79	100.20	50.18	149.74
200	15 00.0	4.35	.04	99.77	.28	198.63	17.37	133.82	67.11	199.39
250	18 45.0	6.79	.06	124.56	.35	247.34	27.06	167.61	84.19	248.81
300	22 30.0	9.76	.08	149.23	.42	295.41	38.84	201.64	101.49	297.95
350	26 15.0	13.26	.11	173.78	.48	342.72	52.65	235.95	119.05	346.75
400	30 00.0	17.28	.15	198.18	.55	389.17	68.46	270.60	136.92	395.15
500	37 30.0	26.86	.22	246.48	.67	479.00	105.79	341.14	173.78	490.55
						$D=16°$				
80	6°24.0'	0.74	.01	39.98	.13	79.90	2.98	53.37	26.70	79.96
100	8 00.0	1.16	.01	49.97	.16	99.80	4.65	66.74	33.40	99.91
125	10 00.0	1.82	.02	62.44	.20	124.62	7.26	83.47	41.79	124.83
150	12 00.0	2.61	.03	74.89	.24	149.34	10.44	100.23	50.21	149.71
200	16 00.0	4.64	.05	99.74	.32	198.45	18.51	133.88	67.17	199.31
250	20 00.0	7.24	.07	124.50	.40	246.97	28.84	167.74	84.31	248.65
300	24 00.0	10.41	.10	149.13	.48	294.78	41.37	201.87	101.70	297.67
350	28 00.0	14.13	.14	173.62	.55	341.73	56.05	236.32	119.39	346.30
400	32 00.0	18.41	.18	197.94	.62	387.70	72.82	271.16	137.43	394.48
500	40 00.0	28.59	.27	246.00	.75	476.18	112.36	342.26	174.81	489.25
						$D=18°$				
80	7°12.0'	0.84	.01	39.98	.15	79.87	3.48	53.38	26.71	79.94
100	9 00.0	1.31	.02	49.96	.21	99.75	5.23	66.75	33.41	99.89
125	11 15.0	2.04	.03	62.42	.26	124.52	8.16	83.50	41.82	124.79
150	13 30.0	2.94	.04	74.86	.31	149.17	11.73	100.29	50.27	149.63
200	18 00.0	5.22	.06	99.67	.41	198.04	20.80	134.03	67.30	199.12
250	22 30.0	8.14	.10	124.36	.50	246.17	32.36	168.03	84.58	248.29
300	27 00.0	11.69	.14	148.90	.60	293.41	46.38	202.38	102.16	297.05
350	31 30.0	15.86	.19	173.25	.69	339.57	62.77	237.14	120.13	345.32
400	36 00.0	20.65	.25	197.40	.77	384.50	81.44	272.40	138.56	393.03
500	45 00.0	32.02	.38	244.95	.93	470.02	125.24	344.78	177.12	486.43
						$D=20°$				
60	6°00.0'	0.52	.01	29.99	.15	59.93	2.09	40.02	20.02	59.97
80	8 00.0	0.93	.01	39.97	.20	79.84	3.72	53.39	26.72	79.93
100	10 00.0	1.45	.02	49.95	.25	99.70	5.80	66.77	33.43	99.86
125	12 30.0	2.27	.03	62.40	.31	124.41	9.06	83.54	41.86	124.74
150	15 00.0	3.26	.05	74.83	.38	148.98	13.03	100.36	50.33	149.54
200	20 00.0	5.79	.09	99.60	.50	197.58	23.07	134.19	67.45	198.92
250	25 00.0	9.03	.14	124.21	.62	245.28	35.87	168.36	84.87	247.89
300	30 00.0	12.96	.20	148.64	.73	291.88	51.34	202.95	102.69	296.36
350	35 00.0	17.58	.27	172.85	.84	337.16	69.39	238.06	120.98	344.23
400	40 00.0	22.87	.34	196.80	.94	380.94	89.89	273.81	139.85	391.40

* Subtract from tabulated value for D_a when chord definition of D is used.

53

TABLE XII.—SPIRAL FUNCTIONS FOR $L_s = 1$

$\Delta°$	o		X_0		X	Y	L.T.	S.T.	L.C.
	D_a	*	D_a	*					
0.0	.00000	.0000	.50000	.0000	1.00000	.00000	.66667	.33333	1.00000
.1	015	00	000	01	1.00000	058	667	333	1.00000
.2	029	00	000	03	1.00000	116	667	334	1.00000
.3	044	00	000	04	.99999	175	667	334	1.00000
.4	058	00	000	05	.99999	233	667	334	1.00000
0.5	.00073	.0000	.50000	.0006	.99999	.00291	.66667	.33334	1.00000
.6	088	00	000	08	9999	349	667	334	1.00000
.7	102	00	000	09	998	407	668	334	.99999
.8	117	00	000	10	998	465	668	334	999
.9	131	00	000	11	997	524	668	334	999
1.0	.00146	.0000	.49999	.0013	.99997	.00582	.66668	.33334	.99999
.1	161	00	999	14	996	640	668	335	998
.2	175	00	999	15	995	698	668	335	998
.3	190	00	999	17	995	756	669	335	998
.4	204	00	999	18	994	814	669	335	997
1.5	.00219	.0000	.49999	.0019	.99993	.00873	.66669	.33336	.99997
.6	233	00	999	20	992	931	669	336	997
.7	248	00	998	22	991	989	670	336	996
.8	262	00	998	23	990	.01047	670	337	996
.9	277	00	998	24	989	105	671	337	995
2.0	.00291	.0000	.49998	.0025	.99988	.01163	.66671	.33337	.99995
.1	305	00	998	27	987	222	671	338	994
.2	320	00	997	28	985	280	672	338	993
.3	334	01	997	29	984	338	672	339	993
.4	349	01	997	31	982	396	673	339	992
2.5	.00363	.0001	.49997	.0032	.99981	.01454	.66673	.33339	.99992
.6	377	01	996	33	979	512	674	340	991
.7	392	01	996	34	978	571	675	340	990
.8	406	01	996	36	976	629	675	341	990
.9	421	01	996	37	975	687	676	341	989
3.0	.00435	.0001	.49995	.0038	.99973	.01745	.66676	.33342	.99988
.1	450	01	995	39	971	803	677	343	987
.2	464	01	994	41	969	861	678	343	986
.3	479	01	994	42	967	919	678	344	985
.4	493	01	994	43	965	978	679	345	984
3.5	.00508	.0001	.49994	.0045	.99963	.02036	.66680	.33345	.99983
.6	523	01	993	46	961	094	681	346	962
.7	537	01	993	47	958	152	681	347	981
.8	552	02	993	48	956	210	682	347	980
.9	566	02	992	50	953	268	683	348	979
4.0	.00581	.0002	.49992	.0051	.99951	.02326	.66684	.33349	.99978
.1	596	02	991	52	948	384	685	350	977
.2	610	02	991	53	946	443	686	350	976
.3	625	02	991	55	943	501	686	351	975
.4	639	02	990	56	941	559	687	351	974
4.5	.00654	.0002	.49990	.0057	.99938	.02617	.66688	.33353	.99973
.6	669	02	989	59	935	675	689	354	971
.7	683	02	989	60	932	733	690	355	970
.8	698	03	988	61	930	791	691	356	969
.9	712	03	988	62	927	849	692	357	967
5.0	.00727	.0003	.49987	.0064	.99924	.02907	.66693	.33358	.99966

*Multiply functions (except * values) by the given value of L_s. When chord definition of degree of curve (D_c) is used, correct the calculated values of o or X_0 by subtracting the product of D_c and the * values. See page 44 for example.

TABLE XII.—SPIRAL FUNCTIONS FOR $L_s=1$

Δ°	o		X_o		X	Y	L.T.	S.T.	L.C.
	D_a	•	D_a	•					
5.0	.00727	.0003	.49987	.0064	.99924	.02907	.66693	.33358	.99966
.1	742	03	987	65	921	965	694	359	965
.2	756	03	986	66	918	.03023	696	360	963
.3	771	03	986	67	914	082	697	361	962
.4	785	03	985	69	911	140	698	362	961
5.5	.00800	.0003	.49985	.0070	.99908	.03198	.66699	.33363	.99959
.6	814	03	984	71	904	256	700	364	958
.7	829	04	984	73	901	314	701	365	956
.8	843	04	983	74	897	372	703	366	954
.9	858	04	983	75	894	430	704	367	953
6.0	.00872	.0004	.49982	.0076	.99890	.03488	.66705	.33368	.99951
.1	887	04	981	78	886	546	706	369	950
.2	901	04	981	79	882	604	708	371	948
.3	916	04	980	80	879	662	709	372	946
.4	930	05	979	81	875	720	710	373	944
6.5	.00945	.0005	.49979	.0083	.99871	.03778	.66712	.33374	.99943
.6	960	05	978	84	867	836	713	376	941
.7	974	05	977	85	863	894	715	377	939
.8	989	05	976	86	859	952	716	378	937
.9	.01003	05	976	88	855	.04010	717	380	936
7.0	.01018	.0005	.49975	.0089	.99851	.04068	.66719	.33381	.99934
.1	033	06	974	90	846	126	720	382	932
.2	047	06	973	91	842	184	722	384	930
.3	062	06	973	93	838	242	724	385	928
.4	076	06	972	94	833	300	725	386	926
7.5	.01091	.0006	.49971	.0095	.99829	.04358	.66727	.33388	.99924
.6	105	06	970	97	824	416	728	389	922
.7	120	07	969	98	819	474	730	391	920
.8	134	07	969	99	815	532	732	392	918
.9	149	07	968	.0100	810	590	733	394	916
8.0	.01163	.0007	.49967	.0102	.99805	.04648	.66735	.33395	.99913
.1	178	07	966	03	800	706	737	397	911
.2	192	07	965	04	795	764	738	399	909
.3	207	08	965	05	790	822	740	400	907
.4	221	08	964	07	785	879	742	402	904
8.5	.01236	.0008	.49963	.0108	.99780	.04937	.66744	.33403	.99902
.6	250	08	962	09	775	995	745	405	900
.7	265	08	961	10	770	.05053	747	407	897
.8	279	09	961	12	764	111	749	409	895
.9	294	09	960	13	759	169	751	410	893
9.0	.01308	.0009	.49959	.0114	.99754	.05227	.66753	.33412	.99890
.1	323	09	958	16	748	285	755	414	888
.2	337	09	957	17	742	342	757	416	885
.3	352	10	956	18	737	400	759	417	883
.4	366	10	955	19	731	458	761	419	880
9.5	.01381	.0010	.49954	.0120	.99725	.05516	.66763	.33421	.99878
.6	395	10	953	22	719	574	765	423	875
.7	410	10	952	23	713	632	767	425	873
.8	424	11	951	24	708	690	769	427	870
.9	439	11	950	26	702	747	771	428	867
10.0	.01453	.0011	.49949	.0127	.99696	.05805	.66773	.33430	.99865

• Use only with Chord Definition of D. See page 44.

TABLE XII.—SPIRAL FUNCTIONS FOR L$_s$=1

Δ°	o		X₀		X	Y	L.T.	S.T.	L.C.
	D$_a$	•	D$_a$	•					
10.0	.01453	.0011	.49949	.0127	.99696	.05805	.66773	.33430	.99865
.1	468	11	948	28	690	863	776	432	862
.2	482	12	947	29	684	921	778	434	859
.3	497	12	946	31	677	978	780	436	856
.4	511	12	945	32	671	.06036	782	438	854
10.5	.01526	.0012	.49944	.0133	.99665	.06094	.66784	.33440	.99851
.6	540	12	943	34	658	.152	787	442	848
.7	555	13	942	36	652	210	789	444	845
.8	569	13	941	37	645	267	791	447	842
.9	584	13	940	38	639	325	794	449	839
11.0	.01598	.0013	.49939	.0139	.99632	.06383	.66796	.33451	.99836
.1	613	14	938	41	625	440	798	453	833
.2	627	14	937	42	618	498	801	455	830
.3	642	14	935	43	612	556	803	457	827
.4	656	14	934	44	605	614	806	460	824
11.5	.01671	.0015	.49933	.0146	.99598	.06671	.66808	.33462	.99821
.6	685	15	932	47	591	729	811	464	818
.7	700	15	931	48	584	787	813	466	815
.8	714	15	929	49	576	844	816	469	812
.9	729	16	928	51	569	902	818	471	808
12.0	.01743	.0016	.49927	.0152	.99562	.06959	.66821	.33473	.99805
.1	757	16	926	53	555	.07017	823	476	802
.2	772	16	924	54	547	075	826	478	799
.3	786	17	923	56	540	132	828	480	795
.4	801	17	922	57	532	190	831	483	792
12.5	.01815	.0017	.49921	.0158	.99525	.07248	.66834	.33485	.99789
.6	829	18	919	59	517	305	836	488	785
.7	844	18	918	60	509	363	839	490	782
.8	858	18	917	62	502	420	842	493	778
.9	873	18	915	63	494	478	845	495	775
13.0	.01887	.0019	.49914	.0164	.99486	.07535	.66847	.33498	.99771
.1	902	19	913	65	478	593	850	500	768
.2	916	19	911	67	470	650	853	503	764
.3	931	20	910	68	462	708	856	505	761
.4	945	20	909	69	454	765	859	508	757
13.5	.01960	.0020	.49908	.0170	.99446	.07823	.66862	.33511	.99753
.6	974	20	906	72	438	880	865	513	750
.7	989	21	905	73	430	938	868	516	746
.8	.02003	21	904	74	421	995	871	519	742
.9	018	21	902	75	413	.08053	874	521	739
14.0	.02032	.0022	.49901	.0177	.99405	.08110	.66877	.33524	.99735
.1	046	22	900	78	396	168	880	527	731
.2	061	22	898	79	387	225	883	530	727
.3	075	23	897	80	379	282	886	532	723
.4	090	23	895	82	370	340	889	535	720
14.5	.02104	.0023	.49894	.0183	.99362	.08397	.66892	.33538	.99716
.6	118	24	892	84	353	455	895	541	712
.7	133	24	891	85	344	512	898	544	708
.8	147	24	889	86	335	569	901	547	704
.9	162	25	888	88	326	627	904	550	700
15.0	.02176	.0025	.49886	.0189	.99317	.08684	.66908	.33553	.99696

* Use only with Chord Definition of D. See page 44.

56

TABLE XII.—SPIRAL FUNCTIONS FOR $L_s=1$

$\Delta°$	o		X_o		X	Y	L.T.	S.T.	L.C.
	D_a	*	D_a	*					
15.0	.02176	.0025	.49886	.0189	.99317	.08684	.66908	.33553	.99696
.1	190	25	884	90	308	741	911	556	692
.2	205	26	883	91	299	799	914	559	688
.3	219	26	881	93	289	856	918	561	683
.4	234	26	880	94	280	913	921	564	679
15.5	.02248	.0026	.49878	.0195	.99271	.08970	.66924	.33567	.99675
.6	262	27	876	96	261	.09028	928	571	671
.7	277	27	875	98	252	085	931	574	667
.8	291	28	873	99	242	142	934	577	662
.9	306	28	872	.0200	233	200	938	580	658
16.0	.02320	.0028	.49870	.0201	.99223	.09257	.66941	.33583	.99654
.1	335	29	868	02	213	314	945	586	649
.2	349	29	867	04	203	371	948	589	645
.3	364	29	865	05	.194	428	952	593	641
.4	378	,30	864	06	184	485	955	596	636
16.5	.02393	.0030	.49862	.0207	.99174	.09543	.66959	.33599	.99632
.6	407	30	860	09	164	600	962	602	627
.7	422	31	859	10	154	657	966	606	623
.8	436	31	857	11	143	714	970	609	618
.9	451	32	856	12	133	771	973	612	614
17.0	.02465	.0032	.49854	.0213	.99123	.09828	.66977	.33615	.99609
.1	479	32	852	15	113	885	981	619	605
.2	494	33	850	16	102	942	984	622	600
.3	508	33	849	17	092	999	988	626	595
.4	522	33	847	18	081	.10056	992	629	591
17.5	.02537	.0034	.49845	.0220	.99071	.10113	.66995	.33632	.99586
.6	551	34	843	21	060	170	999	636	581
.7	565	35	841	22	050	227	.67003	639	576
.8	579	35	840	23	039	284	007	643	572
.9	594	35	838	24	029	341	011	646	567
18.0	.02608	.0036	.49836	.0226	.99018	.10398	.67015	.33650	.99562
.1	622	36	834	27	.007	455	019	654	557
.2	637	37	832	28	.98996	512	023	657	552
.3	651	37	830	29	985	569	027	661	547
.4	666	37	828	30	974	626	031	664	542
18.5	.02680	.0038	.49827	.0232	.98962	.10683	.67035	.33668	.99537
.6	694	38	825	33	951	740	039	672	532
.7	709	39	823	34	940	797	043	675	527
.8	723	39	821	35	929	854	047	679	522
.9	738	39	819	36	917	910	051	683	517
19.0	.02752	.0040	.49817	.0238	.98906	.10967	.67055	.33687	.99512
.1	766	40	815	39	894	.11024	059	690	507
.2	781	41	.813	40	883	081	063	694	502
.3	795	41	811	41	871	138	067	698	497
.4	810	41	809	42	860	194	072	702	.491
19.5	.02824	.0042	.49808	.0244	.98848	.11251	.67076	.33706	.99486
.6	838	42	806	45	836	308	080	709	481
.7	853	43	804	46	824	364	084	713	476
.8	867	43	802	47	812	421	089	717	470
.9	882	44	800	48	800	478	093	721	465
20.0	.02896	.0044	.49798	.0250	.98788	.11535	.67097	.33725	.99460

* Use only with Chord Definition of D. See page 44.

TABLE XII.—SPIRAL FUNCTIONS FOR $L_s=1$

$\Delta°$	o		Xo		X	Y	L.T.	S.T.	L.C.
	D_a	•	D_a	•					
20.0	.02896	.0044	.49798	.0250	.98788	.11535	.67097	.33725	.99460
.1	910	44	796	51	776	591	102	729	454
.2	925	45	794	52	764	648	106	733	449
.3	939	45	791	53	752	705	111	737	443
.4	954	46	789	54	740	761	115	741	438
20.5	.02968	.0046	.49787	.0256	.98728	.11818	.67119	.33745	.99432
.6	982	47	785	57	715	875	124	749	427
.7	997	47	783	58	703	931	128	753	421
.8	.03011	48	781	59	690	988	133	758	415
.9	026	48	779	60	678	.12044	137	762	410
21.0	.03040	.0048	.49777	.0262	.98665	.12101	.67142	.33766	.99404
.1	054	49	775	63	652	157	147	770	399
.2	068	49	773	64	639	214	151	774	393
.3	083	50	770	65	627	270	156	779	387
.4	097	50	768	66	614	327	161	783	381
21.5	.03111	.0051	.49766	.0267	.98601	.12383	.67165	.33787	.99376
.6	125	51	764	68	588	439	170	791	370
.7	140	52	762	70	575	496	175	796	364
.8	154	52	759	71	562	552	180	800	358
.9	169	53	757	72	549	609	184	804	352
22.0	.03183	.0053	.49755	.0273	.98536	.12665	.67189	.33809	.99346
.1	197	54	753	75	523	721	194	813	340
.2	211	54	751	76	509	777	199	818	334
.3	226	55	749	77	496	834	204	822	328
.4	240	55	747	78	482	890	208	826	322
22.5	.03254	.0056	.49745	.0279	.98469	.12946	.67213	.33831	.99316
.6	268	56	743	81	455	.13002	218	835	310
.7	283	57	740	82	442	059	223	840	304
.8	297	57	738	83	428	115	228	844	298
.9	312	58	735	84	415	172	233	849	292
23.0	.03326	.0058	.49733	.0285	.98401	.13228	.67238	.33854	.99286
.1	340	59	731	86	387	284	243	858	279
.2	354	59	728	88	373	340	248	863	273
.3	369	60	726	89	359	396	254	868	267
.4	383	60	723	90	345	452	259	872	261
23.5	.03397	.0061	.49721	.0291	.98331	.13508	.67264	.33877	.99254
.6	411	61	719	92	316	564	269	882	248
.7	426	62	716	93	302	621	274	886	242
.8	440	62	714	95	288	677	280	891	235
.9	455	63	711	96	274	733	285	896	229
24.0	.03469	.0063	.49709	.0297	.98260	.13789	.67290	.33901	.99222
.1	483	64	707	98	245	845	295	906	216
.2	497	64	704	99	231	901	301	910	209
.3	512	65	702	.0300	216	957	306	915	203
.4	526	65	699	02	202	.14012	311	920	196
24.5	.03540	.0066	.49697	.0303	.98187	.14068	.67317	.33925	.99190
.6	554	66	694	04	172	124	322	930	183
.7	568	67	692	05	157	180	328	935	177
.8	583	67	689	06	143	236	333	940	170
.9	597	68	687	07	128	292	339	945	163
25.0	.03611	.0068	.49684	.0309	.98113	.14348	.67344	.33950	.99157

* Use only with Chord Definition of D. See page 44.

TABLE XII.—SPIRAL FUNCTIONS FOR $L_s=1$

$\Delta°$	o		X_o		X	Y	L.T.	S.T.	L.C.
	D_a	•	D_a	•					
25.0	.03611	.0068	.49684	.0309	.98113	.14348	.67344	.33950	.99157
.1	625	69	681	10	098	404	350	955	150
.2	640	69	679	11	083	459	355	960	143
.3	654	70	676	12	068	515	361	965	136
.4	669	71	674	13	053	571	366	970	129
25.5	.03683	.0071	.49671	.0314	.98038	.14627	.67372	.33975	.99123
.6	697	72	668	15	022	682	378	981	116
.7	711	72	666	17	007	738	383	986	109
.8	725	73	663	18	.97991	794	389	991	102
.9	739	73	661	19	976	849	395	996	095
26.0	.03753	.0074	.49658	.0320	.97960	.14905	.67400	.34001	.99088
.1	767	74	656	21	945	961	406	007	081
.2	782	75	653	22	929	.15016	412	012	074
.3	796	76	651	23	913	072	418	017	067
.4	811	76	648	25	898	128	424	023	060
26.5	.03825	.0077	.49646	.0326	.97882	.15183	.67430	.34028	.99053
.6	839	77	643	27	866	239	435	033	046
.7	853	78	640	28	850	294	441	039	038
.8	868	78	638	29	834	350	447	044	031
.9	882	79	635	30	818	405	453	049	024
27.0	.03896	.0080	.49632	.0331	.97802	.15461	.67459	.34055	.99017
.1	910	80	629	33	786	516	465	060	009
.2	924	81	626	34	770	571	471	066	002
.3	939	81	624	35	753	627	477	071	.98995
.4	953	82	621	36	737	682	483	077	987
27.5	.03967	.0082	.49618	.0337	.97721	.15738	.67490	.34083	.98980
.6	981	83	615	38	704	793	496	088	973
.7	995	84	613	39	688	848	502	094	965
.8	.04009	84	610	40	671	903	508	099	958
.9	023	85	608	42	655	959	514	105	950
28.0	.04037	.0085	.49605	.0343	.97638	.16014	.67520	.34111	.98943
.1	051	86	602	44	621	069	527	116	935
.2	065	87	599	45	604	124	533	122	928
.3	080	87	596	46	588	180	539	128	920
.4	094	88	593	47	571	235	546	134	913
28.5	.04108	.0088	.49590	.0348	.97554	.16290	.67552	.34139	.98905
.6	122	89	587	49	537	345	558	145	897
.7	136	90	584	51	520	400	565	151	890
.8	151	90	582	52	503	455	571	157	882
.9	165	91	579	53	486	510	578	163	874
29.0	.04179	.0092	.49576	.0354	.97469	.16565	.67584	.34169	.98866
.1	193	92	573	55	452	620	591	175	859
.2	207	93	570	56	434	675	597	181	851
.3	222	93	567	57	417	730	604	187	843
.4	236	94	564	58	399	785	610	193	835
29.5	.04250	.0095	.49561	.0359	.97382	.16840	.67617	.34199	.98827
.6	264	95	558	61	364	895	623	205	819
.7	278	96	555	62	346	950	630	211	811
.8	293	97	552	63	329	.17005	637	217	803
.9	307	97	549	64	311	060	643	223	795
30.0	.04321	.0098	.49546	.0365	.97293	.17114	.67650	.34229	.98787

* Use only with Chord Definition of D. See page 44.

TABLE XII.—SPIRAL FUNCTIONS FOR Ls=1

Δ°	o		X_o		X	Y	L.T.	S.T.	L.C.
	D_a	*	D_a	*					
30.0	.04321	.0098	.49546	.0365	.97293	.17114	.67650	.34229	.98787
.1	335	98	543	66	275	169	657	235	779
.2	349	99	540	67	257	224	664	241	771
.3	363	.0100	537	68	239	279	670	248	763
.4	377	00	534	69	221	333	677	254	755
30.5	.04391	.0101	.49531	.0371	.97203	.17388	.67684	.34260	.98746
.6	405	01	528	-72	185	443	691	266	738
.7	419	02	525	73	167	498	698	273	730
.8	434	03	522	74	148	552	705	279	722
.9	448	04	519	75	130	607	712	285	713
31.0	.04462	.0104	.49516	.0376	.97112	.17661	.67719	.34292	.98705
.1	476	05	513	77	094	716	726	298	697
.2	490	06	510	78	075	770	733	304	688
.3	504	06	506	79	057	825	740	311	680
.4	518	07	503	80	038	879	747	317	672
31.5	.04532	.0108	.49500	.0381	.97020	.17934	.67754	.34324	.98663
.6	546	08	497	83	001	988	761	330	655
.7	560	09	494	84	.96982	.18043	768	337	646
.8	574	10	490	85	963	097	775	343	638
.9	588	10	487	86	944	152	783	350	629
32.0	.04602	.0111	.49484	.0387	.96926	.18206	.67790	.34356	.98621
.1	616	12	481	88	907	260	797	363	612
.2	630	12	478	89	887	315	804	370	603
.3	645	13	475	90	868	369	812	376	595
.4	659	14	472	91	849	424	819	383	586
32.5	.04673	.0114	.49469	.0392	.96830	.18478	.67826	.34390	.98577
.6	687	15	466	93	811	532	834	397	569
.7	701	16	462	94	791	586	841	403	560
.8	715	16	459	95	772	640	849	410	551
.9	729	17	455	97	752	694	856	417	542
33.0	.04743	.0118	.49452	.0398	.96733	.18748	.67863	.34424	.98534
.1	757	18	449	99	713	803	871	431	525
.2	771	19	445	.0400	694	857	878	438	516
.3	785	20	442	01	674	911	886	444	507
.4	799	21	438	02	655	965	894	451	498
33.5	.04813	.0121	.49435	.0403	.96635	.19019	.67901	.34458	.98489
.6	827	22	432	04	615	073	909	465	480
.7	841	23	429	05	595	127	916	472	471
.8	855	23	425	06	576	181	924	479	462
.9	869	24	422	07	556	234	932	486	453
34.0	.04883	.0125	.49419	.0408	.96536	.19288	.67939	.34493	.98444
.1	897	26	415	09	516	342	947	500	435
.2	911	26	412	10	496	396	955	508	425
.3	925	27	408	11	475	450	963	515	416
.4	939	28	405	12	455	504	971	522	407
34.5	.04953	.0128	.49401	.0413	.96435	.19557	.67979	.34529	.98398
.6	967	29	398	15	414	611	987	536	389
.7	981	30	395	16	394	665	994	544	379
.8	995	31	391	17	373	718	.68002	551	370
.9	.05009	31	388	18	353	772	010	558	361
35.0	.05023	.0132	.49385	.0419	.96332	.19826	.68018	.34565	.98351

* Use only with Chord Definition of D. See page 44.

60

TABLE XII.—SPIRAL FUNCTIONS FOR $L_s=1$

$\Delta°$	o		X_o		X	Y	L.T.	S.T.	L.C.
	D_a	•	D_a	•					
35.0	.05023	.0132	.49385	.0419	.96332	.19826	.68018	.34565	.98351
.1	037	33	381	20	311	879	026	573	342
.2	051	33	378	21	291	933	034	580	333
.3	065	34	374	22	270	987	042	587	323
.4	079	35	371	23	250	.20040	051	.595	314
35.5	.05093	.0136	.49367	.0424	.96229	.20094	.68059	.34602	.98304
.6	107	36	363	25	208	147	067	610	295
.7	121	37	360	26	187	201	075	617	285
.8	135	38	356	27	166	254	083	625	276
.9	149	39	353	28	145	307	092	632	266
36.0	.05163	.0139	.49349	.0429	.96124	.20361	.68100	.34640	.98257
.1	177	40	345	30	103	414	108	647	247
.2	191	41	342	31	081	467	116	655	237
.3	204	42	338	32	060	521	125	663	227
.4	218	42	335	33	038	574	133	670	218
36.5	.05232	.0143	.49331	.0434	.96017	.20627	.68141	.34678	.98208
.6	246	44	327	35	.95996	680	150	686	198
.7	260	45	324	36	974	734	158	693	188
.8	273	45	320	37	953	787	167	701	179
.9	287	46	317	38	931	840	175	709	169
37.0	.05301	.0147	.49313	.0439	.95910	.20893	.68184	.34717	.98159
.1	315	48	309	40	888	946	192	725	149
.2	329	49	306	41	866	999	201	732	139
.3	343	49	302	42	844	.21052	210	740	129
.4	357	50	299	43	822	105	218	748	119
37.5	.05371	.0151	.49295	.0444	.95800	.21158	.68227	.34756	.98109
.6	385	52	291	45	778	211	236	764	099
.7	399	52	287	46	756	264	244	772	089
.8	413	53	284	47	734	317	253	780	079
.9	427	54	280	48	712	370	262	788	069
38.0	.05441	.0155	.49276	.0449	.95690	.21423	.68271	.34796	.98059
.1	455	56	272	50	668	475	279	804	049
.2	469	56	268	51	645	528	288	812	038
.3	482	57	264	52	623	581	297	820	028
.4	496	58	260	53	601	634	306	829	018
38.5	.05510	.0159	.49256	.0454	.95578	.21686	.68315	.34837	.98008
.6	524	59	252	55	556	739	324	845	.97997
.7	538	60	249	56	533	792	333	853	987
.8	551	61	245	57	511	844	342	861	977
.9	565	62	242	58	488	897	351	870	967
39.0	.05579	.0163	.49238	.0459	.95466	.21949	.68360	.34878	.97956
.1	593	63	234	60	443	.22002	369	886	946
.2	607	64	230	61	420	054	379	895	935
.3	620	65	226	62	397	107	388	903	925
.4	634	66	222	63	374	159	397	911	914
39.5	.05648	.0167	.49218	.0464	.95351	.22212	.68406	.34920	.97904
.6	662	68	214	65	328	264	415	928	893
.7	676	68	210	66	305	316	424	937	883
.8	690	69	207	67	281	369	434	945	872
.9	704	70	203	68	258	421	443	954	861
40.0	.05718	.0171	.49199	.0469	.95235	.22473	.68452	.34962	.97851

* Use only with Chord Definition of D. See page 44.

TABLE XII.—SPIRAL FUNCTIONS FOR $L_s=1$

$\Delta°$	o		x_0		X	Y	L.T.	S.T.	L.C.
	D_a	•	D_a	•					
40.0	.05718	.0171	.49199	.0469	.95235	.22473	.68452	.34962	.97851
.1	732	72	195	70	212	526	462	971	840
.2	745	72	191	71	188	578	471	980	829
.3	759	73	187	72	165	630	481	988	819
.4	772	74	183	73	141	682	490	997	808
40.5	.05786	.0175	.49179	.0474	.95118	.22734	.68500	.35006	.97797
.6	800	76	175	75	094	786	509	014	786
.7	814	77	171	76	071	838	519	023	775
.8	827	77	167	77	047	890	528	032	765
.9	841	78	163	78	023	942	538	041	754
41.0	.05855	.0179	.49159	.0479	.95000	.22994	.68547	.35049	.97743
.1	869	80	155	80	.94976	.23046	557	058	732
.2	883	81	151	81	952	098	567	067	721
.3	896	82	146	82	928	150	577	076	710
.4	910	82	142	83	904	202	586	085	699
41.5	.05924	.0183	.49138	.0484	.94880	.23254	.68596	.35094	.97688
.6	938	84	134	85	856	306	606	103	677
.7	952	85	130	86	832	358	616	112	666
.8	965	86	126	87	807	409	626	121	655
.9	979	87	122	88	783	461	635	130	643
42.0	.05993	.0187	.49118	.0488	.94759	.23513	.68645	.35139	.97632
.1	.06007	88	114	89	734	564	655	148	621
.2	020	89	110	90	710	616	665	158	610
.3	034	90	105	91	685	667	675	167	599
.4	047	91	101	92	661	719	685	176	587
42.5	.06061	.0192	.49097	.0493	.94636	.23771	.68695	.35185	.97576
.6	075	93	093	94	612	822	706	194	565
.7	089	93	088	95	587	874	716	204	553
.8	102	94	084	96	562	925	726	213	542
.9	116	95	079	97	538	976	736	222	531
43.0	.06130	.0196	.49075	.0498	.94513	.24028	.68746	.35232	.97519
.1	144	97	071	99	488	079	756	241	508
.2	157	98	067	.0500	463	130	767	250	496
.3	171	99	062	01	438	182	777	260	485
.4	184	.0200	058	02	413	233	787	·269	473
43.5	.06198	.0200	.49054	.0503	.94388	.24284	.68798	.35279	.97462
.6	212	01	050	03	363	335	808	288	450
.7	226	02	045	04	337	387	818	298	438
.8	239	03	041	05	312	438	829	307	427
.9	253	04	036	06	287	489	839	317	415
44.0	.06267	.0205	.49032	.0507	.94262	.24540	.68850	.35327	.97404
.1	281	06	028	08	236	591	860	336	392
.2	294	07	024	09	211	642	871	346	380
.3	308	08	019	10	185	693	882	356	368
.4	321	08	015	11	160	744	892	365	357
44.5	.06335	.0209	.49011	.0512	.94134	.24795	.68903	.35375	.97345
.6	349	10	007	13	108	846	914	385	333
.7	362	11	003	14	082	896	924	395	321
.8	376	12	.48998	14	057	947	935	405	309
.9	389	13	994	15	031	998	946	415	297
45.0	.06403	.0214	.48990	.0516	.94005	.25049	.68957	.35424	.97285

* Use only with Chord Definition of D. See page 44.

TABLE XIII.—COEFFICIENTS FOR CURVE WITH
EQUAL SPIRALS*

Δ	N	P	M	S
0 30	.017453	.000051	1.000013	.008727
1 00	.034905	.000203	1.000051	.017453
1 30	.052356	.000457	1.000114	.026178
2 00	.069805	.000812	1.000203	.034905
2 30	.087250	.001269	1.000317	.043630
3 00	.104691	.001827	1.000457	.052355
3 30	.122127	.002487	1.000622	.061079
4 00	.139558	.003248	1.000812	.069802
4 30	.156983	.004110	1.001028	.078524
5 00	.174400	.005074	1.001269	.087244
5 30	.191809	.006139	1.001535	.095964
6 00	.209210	.007305	1.001827	.104682
6 30	.226601	.008572	1.002144	.113398
7 00	.243982	.009940	1.002486	.122112
7 30	.261351	.011409	1.002854	.130825
8 00	.278709	.012979	1.003247	.139537
8 30	.296054	.014649	1.003665	.148244
9 00	.313385	.016420	1.004109	.156950
9 30	.330702	.018292	1.004577	.165654
10 00	.348004	.020264	1.005071	.174356
10 30	.365290	.022336	1.005591	.183054
11 00	.382560	.024508	1.006135	.191751
11 30	.399812	.026780	1.006705	.200444
12 00	.417045	.029152	1.007299	.209134
12 30	.434260	.031623	1.007919	.217821
13 00	.451455	.034194	1.008564	.226504
13 30	.468629	.036865	1.009234	.235184
14 00	.485783	.039634	1.009930	.243861
14 30	.502913	.042502	1.010650	.252533
15 00	.520022	.045469	1.011395	.261203
15 30	.537106	.048535	1.012166	.269867
16 00	.554166	.051699	1.012961	.278528
16 30	.571200	.054961	1.013781	.287185
17 00	.588209	.058322	1.014626	.295837
17 30	.605191	.061780	1.015497	.304485
18 00	.622146	.065335	1.016392	.313129
18 30	.639072	.068988	1.017311	.321767
19 00	.655969	.072738	1.018256	.330401
19 30	.672836	.076584	1.019226	.339029
20 00	.689673	.080527	1.020220	.347653
20 30	.706479	.084566	1.021240	.356271
21 00	.723252	.088702	1.022282	.364884
21 30	.739993	.092933	1.023351	.373492
22 00	.756700	.097260	1.024444	.382093
22 30	.773373	.101682	1.025561	.390689
23 00	.790010	.106198	1.026703	.399279
23 30	.806612	.110810	1.027870	.407863
24 00	.823178	.115515	1.029061	.416441
24 30	.839706	.120315	1.030276	.425013
25 00	.856196	.125208	1.031516	.433578

Example

Formulas for Basic Parts of Spiraled Curve Based on the Radius of the Circular Arc.

(See Article 5-9)

$$\Delta = \left[\frac{p}{2(2-p)} \right] I, \text{ where}$$

p is the "proportion of transition," that is, the ratio of the length of the two spirals to the total length of curve and spirals.

$L_s = 2\Delta R$ (Δ being in radians)

$$T_s = R(M \tan \frac{I}{2} + S)$$

$$E_s = R(M \sec \frac{I}{2} - 1)$$

$$= R\left[M \text{ exsec } \frac{I}{2} + (M-1) \right]$$

$X = N R$

$Y = P R$

NOTE. The above relations are also valid for the all-transitional, or double-spiral, curve covered by Table XIV. In this special case, $p = 1$, or $\Delta = \frac{I}{2}$.

Example. *Given:* $I = 32°\ 14'$; E_s = exactly 75 feet—restriction imposed by topography. Assume $p = 0.6 \pm$ (for high-speed operation on highways, p will range between 0.4 and 0.7).

Then $\Delta = \dfrac{0.6}{2(2-0.6)} \times 32.233° = 7°00'$ (rounded off to nearest 30')

Whence, $R = \dfrac{75.00}{(1.002486)(.040909) + 0.002486} = 1724.26$.

Since $2\Delta = 0.244346$ radian (Table VI), $L_s = 1724.26 \times 0.244346 = 421.32$ ft.

If neither E_s nor T_s is fixed, a convenient value of D and an approximate value of p may be chosen, thus fixing the remaining parts of the curve-spiral layout.

*J. J. Leeming, "The General Principles of Highway Transition Curve Design," *Transactions ASCE*, Vol. 113 (1948), p. 877.

TABLE XIV.—TANGENTS AND EXTERNALS FOR
UNIT DOUBLE-SPIRAL CURVE

I°	T_s	E_s	I°	T_s	E_s	I°	T_s	E_s
4	1.00028	.01164	42.5	1.03394	.13135	57.0	1.06399	.18536
6	1.00064	.01747	43.0	1.03479	.13309	.2	1.06449	.18617
8	1.00114	.02332	43.5	1.03566	.13484	.4	1.06499	.18698
10	1.00178	.02918	44.0	1.03653	.13660	.6	1.06550	.18778
12	1.00257	.03507	44.5	1.03742	.13836	.8	1.06600	.18859
13	1.00302	.03802	45.0	1.03831	.14013	58.0	1.06651	.18940
14	1.00350	.04098	45.5	1.03922	.14191	.2	1.06703	.19021
15	1.00402	.04396	46.0	1.04015	.14370	.4	1.06754	.19103
16	1.00458	.04696	46.5	1.04109	.14550	.6	1.06806	.19184
17	1.00518	.04992	47.0	1.04204	.14730	.8	1.06857	.19266
18	1.00581	.05292	47.5	1.04301	.14912	59.0	1.06909	.19348
19	1.00648	.05593	48.0	1.04399	.15094	.2	1.06962	.19431
20	1.00719	.05895	48.5	1.04498	.15277	.4	1.07015	.19513
21	1.00794	.06198	49.0	1.04598	.15460	.6	1.07068	.19596
22	1.00873	.06502	49.5	1.04701	.15645	.8	1.07121	.19679
23	1.00955	.06808	50.0	1.04804	.15831	60.0	1.07174	.19762
24	1.01042	.07115	.2	1.04845	.15905	.2	1.07228	.19846
25	1.01132	.07424	.4	1.04887	.15980	.4	1.07282	.19929
26	1.01226	.07734	.6	1.04929	.16055	.6	1.07337	.20013
27	1.01324	.08045	.8	1.04971	.16130	.8	1.07391	.20097
27.5	1.01375	.08201	51.0	1.05014	.16206	61.0	1.07446	.20181
28.0	1.01427	.08358	.2	1.05057	.16281	.2	1.07501	.20266
28.5	1.01480	.08515	.4	1.05100	.16356	.4	1.07556	.20350
29.0	1.01533	.08674	.6	1.05143	.16432	.6	1.07612	.20435
29.5	1.01588	.08831	.8	1.05186	.16508	.8	1.07668	.20519
30.0	1.01644	.08990	52.0	1.05230	.16584	62.0	1.07724	.20604
30.5	1.01700	.09149	.2	1.05274	.16660	.2	1.07781	.20690
31.0	1.01758	.09309	.4	1.05318	.16736	.4	1.07838	.20775
31.5	1.01817	.09469	.6	1.05362	.16813	.6	1.07895	.20861
32.0	1.01877	.09630	.8	1.05407	.16889	.8	1.07953	.20947
32.5	1.01938	.09791	53.0	1.05452	.16966	63.0	1.08010	.21034
33.0	1.02000	.09952	.2	1.05497	.17043	.2	1.08068	.21120
33.5	1.02064	.10114	.4	1.05542	.17120	.4	1.08126	.21207
34.0	1.02128	.10277	.6	1.05588	.17197	.6	1.08184	.21294
34.5	1.02194	.10440	.8	1.05634	.17275	.8	1.08243	.21381
35.0	1.02260	.10604	54.0	1.05680	.17352	64.0	1.08302	.21468
35.5	1.02327	.10768	.2	1.05726	.17430	.2	1.08361	.21555
36.0	1.02396	.10933	.4	1.05772	.17508	.4	1.08421	.21643
36.5	1.02466	.11099	.6	1.05819	.17586	.6	1.08481	.21731
37.0	1.02537	.11265	.8	1.05866	.17664	.8	1.08541	.21820
37.5	1.02609	.11432	55.0	1.05913	.17742	65.0	1.08602	.21908
38.0	1.02682	.11599	.2	1.05961	.17820	.2	1.08663	.21997
38.5	1.02756	.11767	.4	1.06009	.17899	.4	1.08724	.22086
39.0	1.02832	.11936	.6	1.06057	.17979	.6	1.08785	.22175
39.5	1.02909	.12105	.8	1.06105	.18058	.8	1.08847	.22265
40.0	1.02987	.12275	56.0	1.06153	.18137	66.0	1.08909	.22355
40.5	1.03066	.12446	.2	1.06201	.18217	.2	1.08971	.22445
41.0	1.03146	.12617	.4	1.06250	.18296	.4	1.09034	.22535
41.5	1.03227	.12789	.6	1.06299	.18376	.6	1.09097	.22625
42.0	1.03310	.12962	.8	1.06349	.18456	.8	1.09160	.22716

TABLE XIV.—TANGENTS AND EXTERNALS FOR UNIT DOUBLE-SPIRAL CURVE

$I°$	T_s	E_s	$I°$	T_s	E_s	$I°$	T_s	E_s
67.0	1.09223	.22807	75.0	1.12036	.26669	83.0	1.15453	.31048
.2	1.09287	.22898	.2	1.12124	.26772	.2	1.15547	.31165
.4	1.09351	.22990	.4	1.12192	.26875	.4	1.15642	.31283
.6	1.09416	.23082	.6	1.12270	.26978	.6	1.15738	.31401
.8	1.09481	.23174	.8	1.12348	.27082	.8	1.15834	.31520
68.0	1.09546	.23266	76.0	1.12427	.27186	84.0	1.15930	.31639
.2	1.09612	.23358	.2	1.12507	.27290	.2	1.16027	.31759
.4	1.09678	.23451	.4	1.12587	.27394	.4	1.16124	.31879
.6	1.09744	.23544	.6	1.12667	.27499	.6	1.16222	.31999
.8	1.09810	.23637	.8	1.12747	.27604	.8	1.16320	.32120
69.0	1.09876	.23731	77.0	1.12828	.27710	85.0	1.16418	.32241
.2	1.09943	.23825	.2	1.12909	.27816	.2	1.16517	.32363
.4	1.10010	.23919	.4	1.12991	.27923	.4	1.16617	.32485
.6	1.10078	.24013	.6	1.13074	.28030	.6	1.16717	.32607
.8	1.10146	.24108	.8	1.13157	.28137	.8	1.16818	.32730
70.0	1.10214	.24203	78.0	1.13240	.28244	86.0	1.16919	.32854
.2	1.10283	.24298	.2	1.13323	.28352	.2	1.17021	.32978
.4	1.10352	.24393	.4	1.13407	.28460	.4	1.17123	.33102
.6	1.10421	.24489	.6	1.13491	.28568	.6	1.17226	.33227
.8	1.10491	.24585	.8	1.13576	.28677	.8	1.17329	.33352
71.0	1.10561	.24681	79.0	1.13661	.28786	87.0	1.17433	.33478
.2	1.10632	.24777	.2	1.13746	.28896	.2	1.17537	.33605
.4	1.10703	.24874	.4	1.13832	.29006	.4	1.17642	.33732
.6	1.10774	.24971	.6	1.13918	.29116	.6	1.17748	.33859
.8	1.10854	.25069	.8	1.14005	.29226	.8	1.17854	.33987
72.0	1.10917	.25167	80.0	1.14092	.29337	88.0	1.17960	.34115
.2	1.10989	.25265	.2	1.14179	.29449	.2	1.18067	.34244
.4	1.11062	.25363	.4	1.14267	.29561	.4	1.18174	.34373
.6	1.11135	.25462	.6	1.14356	.29673	.6	1.18282	.34503
.8	1.11208	.25561	.8	1.14445	.29785	.8	1.18391	.34633
73.0	1.11281	.25660	81.0	1.14535	.29898	89.0	1.18500	.34764
.2	1.11355	.25760	.2	1.14625	.30011	.2	1.18609	.34895
.4	1.11429	.25860	.4	1.14715	.30125	.4	1.18719	.35027
.6	1.11504	.25960	.6	1.14805	.30239	.6	1.18830	.35159
.8	1.11579	.26060	.8	1.14896	.30353	.8	1.18942	.35292
74.0	1.11654	.26161	82.0	1.14988	.30468	90.0	1.19054	.35425
.2	1.11730	.26262	.2	1.15080	.30583	.2	1.19167	.35559
.4	1.11806	.26363	.4	1.15173	.30699	.4	1.19280	.35693
.6	1.11882	.26465	.6	1.15266	.30815	.6	1.19394	.35828
.8	1.11959	.26567	.8	1.15359	.30931	.8	1.19508	.35963

NOTES. (1) For any given I and selected spiral length, T_s and E_s for the double-spiral, or all-transitional, curve may be found by multiplying the tabulated values by the length of spiral. (2) If the given I does not correspond to a tabulated value, T_s and E_s may be found by simple interpolation. (3) Deflection angles for staking the curve may be computed, as for any spiral, by using $\Delta = \dfrac{I}{2}$.

TABLE XV.—DEFLECTION ANGLES FOR 10-CHORD SPIRAL

Δ	1	2	3	4	5	6	7	8	9	10
°	° '	° '	° '	° '	° '	° '	° '	° '	° '	° '
0.0	0 00.00	0 00.0	0 00.0	0 00.0	0 00.0	0 00.0	0 00.0	0 00.0	0 00.0	0 00.0
.1	00.02	00.1	00.2	00.3	00.5	00.7	01.0	01.3	01.6	02.0
.2	00.04	00.2	00.4	00.6	01.0	01.4	02.0	02.6	03.2	04.0
.3	00.06	00.2	00.5	01.0	01.5	02.2	02.9	03.8	04.9	06.0
.4	00.08	00.3	00.7	01.3	02.0	02.9	03.9	05.1	06.5	08.0
0.5	0 00.10	0 00.4	0 00.9	0 01.6	0 02.5	0 03.6	0 04.9	0 06.4	0 08.1	0 10.0
.6	00.12	00.5	01.1	01.9	03.0	04.3	05.9	07.7	09.7	12.0
.7	00.14	00.6	01.3	02.2	03.5	05.0	06.9	09.0	11.3	14.0
.8	00.16	00.6	01.4	02.6	04.0	05.8	07.8	10.2	13.0	16.0
.9	00.18	00.7	01.6	02.9	04.5	06.5	08.8	11.5	14.6	18.0
1.0	0 00.20	0 00.8	0 01.8	0 03.2	0 05.0	0 07.2	0 09.8	0 12.8	0 16.2	0 20.0
.1	00.22	00.9	02.0	03.5	05.5	07.9	10.8	14.1	17.8	22.0
.2	00.24	01.0	02.2	03.8	06.0	08.6	11.8	15.4	19.4	24.0
.3	00.26	01.0	02.3	04.2	06.5	09.4	12.7	16.6	21.1	26.0
.4	00.28	01.1	02.5	04.5	07.0	10.1	13.7	17.9	22.7	28.0
1.5	0 00.30	0 01.2	0 02.7	0 04.8	0 07.5	0 10.8	0 14.7	0 19.2	0 24.3	0 30.0
.6	00.32	01.3	02.9	05.1	08.0	11.5	15.7	20.5	25.9	32.0
.7	00.34	01.4	03.1	05.4	08.5	12.2	16.7	21.8	27.5	34.0
.8	00.36	01.4	03.2	05.8	09.0	13.0	17.6	23.0	29.2	36.0
.9	00.38	01.5	03.4	06.1	09.5	13.7	18.6	24.3	30.8	38.0
2.0	0 00.40	0 01.6	0 03.6	0 06.4	0 10.0	0 14.4	0 19.6	0 25.6	0 32.4	0 40.0
.1	00.42	01.7	03.8	06.7	10.5	15.1	20.6	26.9	34.0	42.0
.2	00.44	01.8	04.0	07.0	11.0	15.8	21.6	28.2	35.6	44.0
.3	00.46	01.8	04.1	07.4	11.5	16.6	22.5	29.4	37.3	46.0
.4	00.48	01.9	04.3	07.7	12.0	17.3	23.5	30.7	38.9	48.0
2.5	0 00.50	0 02.0	0 04.5	0 08.0	0 12.5	0 18.0	0 24.5	0 32.0	0 40.5	0 50.0
.6	00.52	02.1	04.7	08.3	13.0	18.7	25.5	33.3	42.1	52.0
.7	00.54	02.2	04.9	08.6	13.5	19.4	26.5	34.6	43.7	54.0
.8	00.56	02.2	05.0	09.0	14.0	20.2	27.4	35.8	45.4	56.0
.9	00.58	02.3	05.2	09.3	14.5	20.9	28.4	37.1	47.0	58.0
3.0	0 00.60	0 02.4	0 05.4	0 09.6	0 15.0	0 21.6	0 29.4	0 38.4	0 48.6	1 00.0
.1	00.62	02.5	05.6	09.9	15.5	22.3	30.4	39.7	50.2	02.0
.2	00.64	02.6	05.8	10.2	16.0	23.0	31.4	41.0	51.8	04.0
.3	00.66	02.6	05.9	10.6	16.5	23.8	32.3	42.2	53.5	06.0
.4	00.68	02.7	06.1	10.9	17.0	24.5	33.3	43.5	55.1	08.0
3.5	0 00.70	0 02.8	0 06.3	0 11.2	0 17.5	0 25.2	0 34.3	0 44.8	0 56.7	1 10.0
.6	00.72	02.9	06.5	11.5	18.0	25.9	35.3	46.1	58.3	12.0
.7	00.74	03.0	06.7	11.8	18.5	26.6	36.3	47.4	59.9	14.0
.8	00.76	03.0	06.8	12.2	19.0	27.4	37.2	48.6	1 01.6	16.0
.9	00.78	03.1	07.0	12.5	19.5	28.1	38.2	49.9	03.2	18.0
4.0	0 00.80	0 03.2	0 07.2	0 12.8	0 20.0	0 28.8	0 39.2	0 51.2	1 04.8	1 20.0
.1	00.82	03.3	07.4	13.1	20.5	29.5	40.2	52.5	06.4	22.0
.2	00.84	03.4	07.6	13.4	21.0	30.2	41.2	53.8	08.0	24.0
.3	00.86	03.4	07.7	13.8	21.5	31.0	42.1	55.0	09.7	26.0
.4	00.88	03.5	07.9	14.1	22.0	31.7	43.1	56.3	11.3	28.0
4.5	0 00.90	0 03.6	0 08.1	0 14.4	0 22.5	0 32.4	0 44.1	0 57.6	1 12.9	1 30.0
.6	00.92	03.7	08.3	14.7	23.0	33.1	45.1	58.9	14.5	32.0
.7	00.94	03.8	08.5	15.0	23.5	33.8	46.1	1 00.2	16.1	34.0
.8	00.96	03.8	08.6	15.4	24.0	34.6	47.0	01.4	17.8	36.0
.9	00.98	03.9	08.8	15.7	24.5	35.3	48.0	02.7	19.4	38.0
5.0	0 01.00	0 04.0	0 09.0	0 16.0	0 25.0	0 36.0	0 49.0	1 04.0	1 21.0	1 40.0
.1	01.02	04.1	09.2	16.3	25.5	36.7	50.0	05.3	22.6	42.0
.2	01.04	04.2	09.4	16.6	26.0	37.4	51.0	06.6	24.2	44.0
.3	01.06	04.2	09.5	17.0	26.5	38.2	51.9	07.8	25.9	46.0
.4	01.08	04.3	09.7	17.3	27.0	38.9	52.9	09.1	27.5	48.0
5.5	0 01.10	0 04.4	0 09.9	0 17.6	0 27.5	0 39.6	0 53.9	1 10.4	1 29.1	1 50.0
.6	01.12	04.5	10.1	17.9	28.0	40.3	54.9	11.7	30.7	52.0
.7	01.14	04.6	10.3	18.2	28.5	41.0	55.9	13.0	32.3	54.0
.8	01.16	04.6	10.4	18.6	29.0	41.8	56.8	14.2	34.0	56.0
.9	01.18	04.7	10.6	18.9	29.5	42.5	57.8	15.5	35.6	58.0

TABLE XV.—DEFLECTION ANGLES FOR 10-CHORD SPIRAL

Δ	1	2	3	4	5	6	7	8	9	10
°	° ′	° ′	° ′	° ′	° ′	° ′	° ′	° ′	° ′	° ′
6.0	0 01.20	0 04.8	0 10.8	0 19.2	0 30.0	0 43.2	0 58.8	1 16.8	1 37.2	2 00.0
.1	01.22	04.9	11.0	19.5	30.5	43.9	59.8	18.1	38.8	02.0
.2	01.24	05.0	11.2	19.8	31.0	44.6	1 00.8	19.4	40.4	04.0
.3	01.26	05.0	11.3	20.2	31.5	45.4	01.7	20.6	42.1	06.0
.4	01.28	05.1	11.5	20.5	32.0	46.1	02.7	21.9	43.7	08.0
6.5	0 01.30	0 05.2	0 11.7	0 20.8	0 32.5	0 46.8	1 03.7	1 23.2	1 45.3	2 10.0
.6	01.32	05.3	11.9	21.1	33.0	47.5	04.7	24.5	46.9	12.0
.7	01.34	05.4	12.1	21.4	33.5	48.2	05.7	25.8	48.5	14.0
.8	01.36	05.4	12.2	21.8	34.0	49.0	06.6	27.0	50.2	16.0
.9	01.38	05.5	12.4	22.1	34.5	49.7	07.6	28.3	51.8	18.0
7.0	0 01.40	0 05.6	0 12.6	0 22.4	0 35.0	0 50.4	1 08.6	1 29.6	1 53.4	2 20.0
.1	01.42	05.7	12.8	22.7	35.5	51.1	09.6	30.9	55.0	22.0
.2	01.44	05.8	13.0	23.0	36.0	51.8	10.6	32.2	56.6	24.0
.3	01.46	05.8	13.1	23.4	36.5	52.6	11.5	33.4	58.3	26.0
.4	01.48	05.9	13.3	23.7	37.0	53.3	12.5	34.7	59.9	28.0
7.5	0 01.50	0 06.0	0 13.5	0 24.0	0 37.5	0 54.0	1 13.5	1 36.0	2 01.5	2 30.0
.6	01.52	06.1	13.7	24.3	38.0	54.7	14.5	37.3	03.1	32.0
.7	01.54	06.2	13.9	24.6	38.5	55.4	15.5	38.6	04.7	34.0
.8	01.56	06.2	14.0	25.0	39.0	56.2	16.4	39.8	06.4	36.0
.9	01.58	06.3	14.2	25.3	39.5	56.9	17.4	41.1	08.0	38.0
8.0	0 01.60	0 06.4	0 14.4	0 25.6	0 40.0	0 57.6	1 18.4	1 42.4	2 09.6	2 40.0
.1	01.62	06.5	14.6	25.9	40.5	58.3	19.4	43.7	11.2	42.0
.2	01.64	06.6	14.8	26.2	41.0	59.0	20.4	45.0	12.8	44.0
.3	01.66	06.6	14.9	26.6	41.5	59.8	21.3	46.2	14.5	46.0
.4	01.68	06.7	15.1	26.9	42.0	1 00.5	22.3	47.5	16.1	48.0
8.5	0 01.70	0 06.8	0 15.3	0 27.2	0 42.5	1 01.2	1 23.3	1 48.8	2 17.7	2 50.0
.6	01.72	06.9	15.5	27.5	43.0	01.9	24.3	50.1	19.3	52.0
.7	01.74	07.0	15.7	27.8	43.5	02.6	25.3	51.4	20.9	54.0
.8	01.76	07.0	15.8	28.2	44.0	03.4	26.2	52.6	22.6	56.0
.9	01.78	07.1	16.0	28.5	44.5	04.1	27.2	53.9	24.2	58.0
9.0	0 01.80	0 07.2	0 16.2	0 28.8	0 45.0	1 04.8	1 28.2	1 55.2	2 25.8	3 00.0
.1	01.82	07.3	16.4	29.1	45.5	05.5	29.2	56.5	27.4	02.0
.2	01.84	07.4	16.6	29.4	46.0	06.2	30.2	57.8	29.0	04.0
.3	01.86	07.4	16.7	29.8	46.5	07.0	31.1	59.0	30.7	06.0
.4	01.88	07.5	16.9	30.1	47.0	07.7	32.1	2 00.3	32.3	08.0
9.5	0 01.90	0 07.6	0 17.1	0 30.4	0 47.5	1 08.4	1 33.1	2 01.6	2 33.9	3 10.0
.6	01.92	07.7	17.3	30.7	48.0	09.1	34.1	02.9	35.5	12.0
.7	01.94	07.8	17.5	31.0	48.5	09.8	35.1	04.2	37.1	14.0
.8	01.96	07.8	17.6	31.4	49.0	10.6	36.0	05.4	38.8	16.0
.9	01.98	07.9	17.8	31.7	49.5	11.3	37.0	06.7	40.4	18.0
10.0	0 02.00	0 08.0	0 18.0	0 32.0	0 50.0	1 12.0	1 38.0	2 08.0	2 42.0	3 20.0
.1	02.02	08.1	18.2	32.3	50.5	12.7	39.0	09.3	43.6	21.9
.2	02.04	08.2	18.4	32.6	51.0	13.4	40.0	10.6	45.2	23.9
.3	02.06	08.2	18.5	33.0	51.5	14.2	40.9	11.8	46.8	25.9
.4	02.08	08.3	18.7	33.3	52.0	14.9	41.9	13.1	48.5	27.9
10.5	0 02.10	0 08.4	0 18.9	0 33.6	0 52.5	1 15.6	1 42.9	2 14.4	2 50.1	3 29.9
.6	02.12	08.5	19.1	33.9	53.0	16.3	43.9	15.7	51.7	31.9
.7	02.14	08.6	19.3	34.2	53.5	17.0	44.9	17.0	53.3	33.9
.8	02.16	08.6	19.4	34.6	54.0	17.8	45.8	18.2	54.9	35.9
.9	02.18	08.7	19.6	34.9	54.5	18.5	46.8	19.5	56.6	37.9
11.0	0 02.20	0 08.8	0 19.8	0 35.2	0 55.0	1 19.2	1 47.8	2 20.8	2 58.2	3 39.9
.1	02.22	08.9	20.0	35.5	55.5	19.9	48.8	22.1	59.8	41.9
.2	02.24	09.0	20.2	35.8	56.0	20.6	49.8	23.4	3 01.4	43.9
.3	02.26	09.0	20.3	36.2	56.5	21.4	50.7	24.6	03.0	45.9
.4	02.28	09.1	20.5	36.5	57.0	22.1	51.7	25.9	04.7	47.9
11.5	0 02.30	0 09.2	0 20.7	0 36.8	0 57.5	1 22.8	1 52.7	2 27.2	3 06.3	3 49.9
.6	02.32	09.3	20.9	37.1	58.0	23.5	53.7	28.5	07.9	51.9
.7	02.34	09.4	21.1	37.4	58.5	24.2	54.7	29.7	09.5	53.9
.8	02.36	09.4	21.2	37.8	59.0	25.0	55.6	31.0	11.1	55.9
.9	02.38	09.5	21.4	38.1	59.5	25.7	56.6	32.3	12.7	57.9

TABLE XV.—DEFLECTION ANGLES FOR 10-CHORD SPIRAL

Δ	1	2	3	4	5	6	7	8	9	10
°	° ′	° ′	° ′	° ′	° ′	° ′	° ′	° ′	° ′	° ′
12.0	0 02.40	0 09.6	0 21.6	0 38.4	1 00.0	1 26.4	1 57.6	2 33.6	3 14.4	3 59.9
.1	02.42	09.7	21.8	38.7	00.5	27.1	58.6	34.9	16.0	4 01.9
.2	02.44	09.8	22.0	39.0	01.0	27.8	59.5	36.1	17.6	03.9
.3	02.46	09.8	22.1	39.4	01.5	28.6	2 00.5	37.4	19.2	05.9
.4	02.48	09.9	22.3	39.7	02.0	29.3	01.5	38.7	20.8	07.9
12.5	0 02.50	0 10.0	0 22.5	0 40.0	1 02.5	1 30.0	2 02.5	2 40.0	3 22.5	4 09.9
.6	02.52	10.1	22.7	40.3	03.0	30.7	03.5	41.3	24.1	11.9
.7	02.54	10.2	22.9	40.6	03.5	31.4	04.4	42.5	25.7	13.9
.8	02.56	10.2	23.0	41.0	04.0	32.2	05.4	43.8	27.3	15.9
.9	02.58	10.3	23.2	41.3	04.5	32.9	06.4	45.1	28.9	17.9
13.0	0 02.60	0 10.4	0 23.4	0 41.6	1 05.0	1 33.6	2 07.4	2 46.4	3 30.5	4 19.9
.1	02.62	10.5	23.6	41.9	05.5	34.3	08.4	47.7	32.2	21.9
.2	02.64	10.6	23.8	42.2	06.0	35.0	09.3	48.9	33.8	23.9
.3	02.66	10.6	23.9	42.6	06.5	35.8	10.3	50.2	35.4	25.9
.4	02.68	10.7	24.1	42.9	07.0	36.5	11.3	51.5	37.0	27.9
13.5	0 02.70	0 10.8	0 24.3	0 43.2	1 07.5	1 37.2	2 12.3	2 52.8	3 38.6	4 29.9
.6	02.72	10.9	24.5	43.5	08.0	37.9	13.3	54.0	40.3	31.9
.7	02.74	11.0	24.7	43.8	08.5	38.6	14.2	55.3	41.9	33.9
.8	02.76	11.0	24.8	44.2	09.0	39.4	15.2	56.6	43.5	35.9
.9	02.78	11.1	25.0	44.5	09.5	40.1	16.2	57.9	45.1	37.9
14.0	0 02.80	0 11.2	0 25.2	0 44.8	1 10.0	1 40.8	2 17.2	2 59.2	3 46.7	4 39.9
.1	02.82	11.3	25.4	45.1	10.5	41.5	18.2	3 00.4	48.4	41.9
.2	02.84	11.4	25.6	45.4	11.0	42.2	19.1	01.7	50.0	43.9
.3	02.86	11.4	25.7	45.8	11.5	43.0	20.1	03.0	51.6	45.9
.4	02.88	11.5	25.9	46.1	12.0	43.7	21.1	04.3	53.2	47.9
14.5	0 02.90	0 11.6	0 26.1	0 46.4	1 12.5	1 44.4	2 22.1	3 05.6	3 54.8	4 49.9
.6	02.92	11.7	26.3	46.7	13.0	45.1	23.1	06.8	56.4	51.9
.7	02.94	11.8	26.5	47.0	13.5	45.8	24.0	08.1	58.1	53.9
.8	02.96	11.8	26.6	47.4	14.0	46.6	25.0	09.4	59.7	55.8
.9	02.98	11.9	26.8	47.7	14.5	47.3	26.0	10.7	4 01.3	57.8
15.0	0 03.00	0 12.0	0 27.0	0 48.0	1 15.0	1 48.0	2 27.0	3 12.0	4 02.9	4 59.8
.1	03.02	12.1	27.2	48.3	15.5	48.7	28.0	13.2	04.5	5 01.8
.2	03.04	12.2	27.4	48.6	16.0	49.4	28.9	14.5	06.1	03.8
.3	03.06	12.2	27.5	49.0	16.5	50.2	29.9	15.8	07.8	05.8
.4	03.08	12.3	27.7	49.3	17.0	50.9	30.9	17.1	09.4	07.8
15.5	0 03.10	0 12.4	0 27.9	0 49.6	1 17.5	1 51.6	2 31.9	3 18.4	4 11.0	5 09.8
.6	03.12	12.5	28.1	49.9	18.0	52.3	32.9	19.6	12.6	11.8
.7	03.14	12.6	28.3	50.2	18.5	53.0	33.8	20.9	14.2	13.8
.8	02.16	12.6	28.4	50.6	19.0	53.7	34.8	22.2	15.9	15.8
.9	03.18	12.7	28.6	50.9	19.5	54.5	35.8	23.5	17.5	17.8
16.0	0 03.20	0 12.8	0 28.8	0 51.2	1 20.0	1 55.2	2 36.8	3 24.8	4 19.1	5 19.8
.1	03.22	12.9	29.0	51.5	20.5	55.9	37.8	26.0	20.7	21.8
.2	03.24	13.0	29.2	51.8	21.0	56.6	38.7	27.3	22.3	23.8
.3	03.26	13.0	29.3	52.2	21.5	57.3	39.7	28.6	23.9	25.8
.4	03.28	13.1	29.5	52.5	22.0	58.1	40.7	29.9	25.6	27.8
16.5	0 03.30	0 13.2	0 29.7	0 52.8	1 22.5	1 58.8	2 41.7	3 31.1	4 27.2	5 29.8
.6	03.32	13.3	29.9	53.1	23.0	59.5	42.7	32.4	28.8	31.8
.7	03.34	13.4	30.1	53.4	23.5	2 00.2	43.6	33.7	30.4	33.8
.8	03.36	13.4	30.2	53.8	24.0	00.9	44.6	35.0	32.0	35.8
.9	03.38	13.5	30.4	54.1	24.5	01.7	45.6	36.3	33.6	37.8
17.0	0 03.40	0 13.6	0 30.6	0 54.4	1 25.0	2 02.4	2 46.6	3 37.5	4 35.3	5 39.8
.1	03.42	13.7	30.8	54.7	25.5	03.1	47.5	38.8	36.9	41.8
.2	03.44	13.8	31.0	55.0	26.0	03.8	48.5	40.1	38.5	43.7
.3	03.46	13.8	31.1	55.4	26.5	04.5	49.5	41.4	40.1	45.7
.4	03.48	13.9	31.3	55.7	27.0	05.3	50.5	42.7	41.7	47.7
17.5	0 03.50	0 14.0	0 31.5	0 56.0	1 27.5	2 06.0	2 51.5	3 43.9	4 43.4	5 49.7
.6	03.52	14.1	31.7	56.3	28.0	06.7	52.4	45.2	45.0	51.7
.7	03.54	14.2	31.9	56.6	28.5	07.4	53.4	46.5	46.6	53.7
.8	03.56	14.2	32.0	57.0	29.0	08.1	54.4	47.8	48.2	55.7
.9	03.58	14.3	32.2	57.3	29.5	08.9	55.4	49.0	49.8	5.77

TABLE XV.—DEFLECTION ANGLES FOR 10-CHORD SPIRAL

Δ	1	2	3	4	5	6	7	8	9	10
	° ′	° ′	° ′	° ′	° ′	° ′	° ′	° ′	° ′	° ′
18.0	0 03.60	0 14.4	0 32.4	0 57.6	1 30.0	2 09.6	2 56.4	3 50.3	4 51.5	5 59.7
.1	03.62	14.5	32.6	57.9	30.5	10.3	57.3	51.6	53.1	6 01.7
.2	03.64	14.6	32.8	58.2	31.0	11.0	58.3	52.9	54.7	03.7
.3	03.66	14.6	32.9	58.6	31.5	11.7	59.3	54.2	56.3	05.7
.4	03.68	14.7	33.1	58.9	32.0	12.5	3 00.3	55.4	57.9	07.7
18.5	0 03.70	0 14.8	0 33.3	0 59.2	1 32.5	2 13.2	3 01.3	3 56.7	4 59.5	6 09.7
.6	03.72	14.9	33.5	59.5	33.0	13.9	02.2	58.0	5 01.2	11.7
.7	03.74	15.0	33.7	59.8	33.5	14.6	03.2	59.3	02.8	13.7
.8	03.76	15.0	33.8	1 00.2	34.0	15.3	04.2	4 00.6	04.4	16.7
.9	03.78	15.1	34.0	00.5	34.5	16.1	05.2	01.8	06.0	17.7
19.0	0 03.80	0 15.2	0 34.2	1 00.8	1 35.0	2 16.8	3 06.2	4 03.1	5 07.6	6 19.7
.1	03.82	15.3	34.4	01.1	35.5	17.5	07.1	04.4	09.2	21.7
.2	03.84	15.4	34.6	01.4	36.0	18.2	08.1	05.7	10.9	23.7
.3	03.86	15.4	34.7	01.8	36.5	18.9	09.1	06.9	12.5	25.6
.4	03.88	15.5	34.9	02.1	37.0	19.7	10.1	08.2	14.1	27.6
19.5	0 03.90	0 15.6	0 35.1	1 02.4	1 37.5	2 20.4	3 11.1	4 09.5	5 15.7	6 29.6
.6	03.92	15.7	35.3	02.7	38.0	21.1	12.0	10.8	17.3	31.6
.7	03.94	15.8	35.5	03.0	38.5	21.8	13.0	12.1	18.9	33.6
.8	03.96	15.8	35.6	03.4	39.0	22.5	14.0	13.3	20.6	35.6
.9	03.98	15.9	35.8	03.7	39.5	23.3	15.0	14.6	22.2	37.6
20.0	0 04.00	0 16.0	0 36.0	1 04.0	1 40.0	2 24.0	3 16.0	4 15.9	5 23.8	6 39.6
.1	04.02	16.1	36.2	04.3	40.5	24.7	16.9	17.2	25.4	41.6
.2	04.04	16.2	36.4	04.6	41.0	25.4	17.9	18.5	27.0	43.6
.3	04.06	16.2	36.5	05.0	41.5	26.1	18.9	19.7	28.6	45.6
.4	04.08	16.3	36.7	05.3	42.0	26.9	19.9	21.0	30.3	47.6
20.5	0 04.10	0 16.4	0 36.9	1 05.6	1 42.5	2 27.6	3 20.9	4 22.3	5 31.9	6 49.6
.6	04.12	16.5	37.1	05.9	43.0	28.3	21.8	23.6	33.5	51.6
.7	04.14	16.6	37.3	06.2	43.5	29.0	22.8	24.8	35.1	53.6
.8	04.16	16.6	37.4	06.6	44.0	29.7	23.8	26.1	36.7	55.6
.9	04.18	16.7	37.6	06.9	44.5	30.5	24.8	27.4	38.3	57.5
21.0	0 04.20	0 16.8	0 37.8	1 07.2	1 45.0	2 31.2	3 25.8	4 28.7	5 40.0	6 59.5
.1	04.22	16.9	38.0	07.5	45.5	31.9	26.7	30.0	41.6	7 01.5
.2	04.24	17.0	38.2	07.8	46.0	32.6	27.7	31.2	43.2	03.5
.3	04.26	17.0	38.3	08.2	46.5	33.4	28.7	32.5	44.8	05.5
.4	04.28	17.1	38.5	08.5	47.0	34.1	29.7	33.8	46.4	07.5
21.5	0 04.30	0 17.2	0 38.7	1 08.8	1 47.5	2 34.8	3 30.7	4 35.1	5 48.0	7 09.5
.6	04.32	17.3	38.9	09.1	48.0	35.5	31.6	36.4	49.7	11.5
.7	04.34	17.4	39.1	09.4	48.5	36.2	32.6	37.6	51.3	13.5
.8	04.36	17.4	39.2	09.8	49.0	37.0	33.6	38.9	52.9	15.5
.9	04.38	17.5	39.4	10.1	49.5	37.7	34.6	40.2	54.5	17.5
22.0	0 04.40	0 17.6	0 39.6	1 10.4	1 50.0	2 38.4	3 35.5	4 41.5	5 56.1	7 19.5
.1	04.42	17.7	39.8	10.7	50.5	39.1	36.5	42.7	58.7	21.5
.2	04.44	17.8	40.0	11.0	51.0	39.8	37.5	44.0	59.3	23.5
.3	04.46	17.8	40.1	11.4	51.5	40.6	38.5	45.3	6 01.0	25.5
.4	04.48	17.9	40.3	11.7	52.0	41.3	39.5	46.6	02.6	27.5
22.5	0 04.50	0 18.0	0 40.5	1 12.0	1 52.5	2 42.0	3 40.5	4 47.9	6 04.2	7 29.4
.6	04.52	18.1	40.7	12.3	53.0	42.7	41.4	49.1	05.8	31.4
.7	04.54	18.2	40.9	12.6	53.5	43.4	42.4	50.4	07.4	33.4
.8	04.56	18.2	41.0	13.0	54.0	44.2	43.4	51.7	09.0	35.4
.9	04.58	18.3	41.2	13.3	54.5	44.9	44.4	53.0	10.7	37.4
23.0	0 04.60	0 18.4	0 41.4	1 13.6	1 55.0	2 45.6	3 45.3	4 54.2	6 12.3	7 39.4
.1	04.62	18.5	41.6	13.9	55.5	46.3	46.3	55.5	13.9	41.4
.2	04.64	18.6	41.8	14.2	56.0	47.0	47.3	56.8	15.5	43.4
.3	04.66	18.6	41.9	14.6	56.5	47.8	48.3	58.1	17.1	45.4
.4	04.68	18.7	42.1	14.9	57.0	48.5	49.2	59.4	18.7	47.4
23.5	0 04.70	0 18.8	0 42.3	1 15.2	1 57.5	2 49.2	3 50.2	5 00.6	6 20.4	7 49.4
.6	04.72	18.9	42.5	15.5	58.0	49.9	51.2	01.9	22.0	51.3
.7	04.74	19.0	42.7	15.8	58.5	50.6	52.2	03.2	23.6	53.3
.8	04.76	19.0	42.8	16.2	59.0	51.4	53.2	04.5	25.2	55.3
.9	04.78	19.1	43.0	16.5	59.5	52.1	54.2	05.7	26.8	57.3

TABLE XVI.—COEFFICIENTS OF a_1 FOR DEFLECTIONS TO ANY CHORD POINT ON SPIRAL*

Deflection to Chord Point No.	Transit at Chord Point Number																					Deflection to Chord Point No.
	0	1	2	3	4	5	6	7	8	9	10	11	12	13	14	15	16	17	18	19	20	
T.S. = 0	0	2	8	18	32	50	72	98	128	162	200	242	288	338	392	450	512	578	648	722	800	T.S. = 0
1	1	0	5	14	27	44	65	90	119	152	189	230	275	324	377	434	495	560	629	702	779	1
2	4	4	0	8	20	36	56	80	108	140	176	216	260	308	360	416	476	540	608	680	756	2
3	9	10	7	0	11	26	45	68	95	126	161	200	243	290	341	396	455	518	585	656	731	3
4	16	18	16	10	0	14	32	54	80	110	144	182	224	270	320	374	432	494	560	630	704	4
5	25	28	27	22	13	0	17	38	63	92	125	162	203	248	297	350	407	468	533	602	675	5
6	36	40	40	36	28	16	0	20	44	72	104	140	180	224	272	324	380	440	504	572	644	6
7	49	54	55	52	45	34	19	0	23	50	81	116	155	198	245	296	351	410	473	540	611	7
8	64	70	72	70	64	54	40	22	0	26	56	90	128	170	216	266	320	378	440	506	576	8
9	81	88	91	90	85	76	63	46	25	0	29	62	98	140	185	234	287	344	405	470	539	9
10	100	108	112	112	108	100	88	72	52	28	0	32	68	108	152	200	252	308	368	432	500	10
11	121	130	135	136	133	126	115	100	81	58	31	0	35	74	117	164	215	270	329	392	459	11
12	144	154	160	162	160	154	144	130	112	90	64	34	0	38	80	126	176	230	288	350	416	12
13	169	180	187	189	189	184	175	162	145	124	99	70	37	0	41	86	135	188	245	306	371	13
14	196	208	216	220	216	216	208	196	180	160	136	108	76	40	0	44	92	144	200	260	324	14
15	225	238	247	253	253	250	243	232	217	198	175	148	117	82	43	0	47	98	153	212	275	15
16	256	270	280	286	288	286	280	270	256	238	216	190	160	126	88	46	0	50	104	162	224	16
17	289	304	315	322	325	324	319	310	297	280	259	234	205	172	135	94	49	0	53	110	171	17
18	324	340	352	360	364	364	360	352	340	324	304	280	252	220	184	144	100	52	0	56	116	18
19	361	378	391	400	405	406	403	396	385	370	351	328	301	270	235	196	153	106	55	0	59	19
20	400	418	432	442	448	450	448	442	432	418	400	378	352	322	288	250	208	162	112	58	0	20

*See examples on next page and theory in Art. 5-3.

70

TABLE XVI-C.—CORRECTIONS TO TABLE XVI FOR LARGE DEFLECTIONS (MINUTES)

Δ	Ratio of l_s to L_s					
	0.5	0.6	0.7	0.8	0.9	1.0
15°	--	0.01	0.02	0.04	0.09	0.17
20	0.01	0.02	0.05	0.11	0.22	0.41
25	0.01	0.04	0.10	0.21	0.43	0.81
30	0.02	0.07	0.16	0.37	0.74	1.40
32	0.03	0.08	0.20	0.45	0.90	1.70
34	0.03	0.10	0.24	0.54	1.09	2.05
36	0.04	0.11	0.29	0.64	1.29	2.43
38	0.04	0.13	0.34	0.75	1.52	2.86
40	0.05	0.16	0.39	0.88	1.78	3.34
41	0.06	0.17	0.42	0.94	1.91	3.60
42	0.06	0.18	0.46	1.01	2.06	3.87
43	0.06	0.19	0.49	1.09	2.21	4.16
44	0.07	0.21	0.53	1.17	2.37	4.46
45	0.07	0.22	0.56	1.25	2.54	4.77

Table XVI provides a rapid method of obtaining deflections to locate any chord point of a spiral from a transit set up at any other point. It is valid for any number of equally-spaced chord points up to twenty, *provided that a_1 is always defined as the deflection from the tangent at T.S. to the first chord point.* Calculate a_1 from the relation a_1 (in degrees) = $\dfrac{20\Delta \text{ (in degrees)}}{n^2}$, where n = the number of equal chords in the spiral.

For large deflections and long sights the results obtained by using Table XVI should be altered by applying small corrections found by interpolation from Table XVI-C. *For sights toward the S.C., these corrections are subtracted; for sights toward the T.S., they are added.* The source of these corrections is explained in Appendix A.

EXAMPLE 1. Given: A spiral with L_s = 150 ft and Δ = 6°, to be staked as a 3-chord spiral.

$$a_1 = \frac{20 \times 6}{9} = 13.33'$$

Deflections from the tangent at the T.S. are found by multiplying 13.33' by the coefficients 1, 4, 9. Local tangent at S.C. is found by turning off deflection of $13.33 \times 18 = 4°00'$ from backsight to T.S. No corrections are required.

EXAMPLE 2. Given: A spiral with L_s = 800 ft and Δ = 32°, to be staked as a 20-chord spiral.

$$a_1 = \frac{20 \times 32}{400} = 1.6'$$

Deflections from the tangent at the T.S. are found by multiplying 1.6' by coefficients 0 to 400, found in the column headed "Transit at 0." Corrections vary from −0.5' for chord point 16 to −1.7', for the sight to the S.C. If chord points 13 to S.C. are located from a set-up at point 12, deflections from local tangent are found by multiplying 1.6' by coefficients 37 to 352. The corrections are negligible, the maximum value being +0.08' for the backsight to the T.S.

TABLE XVII.—LEVEL SECTIONS $\frac{1}{4}$:1

Height	CU YD PER 100-FT STATION							
	Base 14	Base 16	Base 18	Base 20	Base 24	Base 30	Base 40	Per Ft of Added Base
0.5	26	30	34	37	45	56	74	1.85
1.0	53	60	68	75	90	112	149	3.70
1.5	80	91	102	113	135	169	224	5.56
2.0	107	122	137	152	181	226	300	7.41
2.5	135	154	172	191	228	284	376	9.26
3.0	163	186	208	231	275	342	453	11.11
3.5	193	219	245	271	322	400	530	12.96
4.0	222	252	281	311	370	459	607	14.81
4.5	252	285	319	352	419	519	685	16.67
5.0	282	319	356	394	468	579	764	18.52
5.5	313	354	395	435	517	639	843	20.37
6.0	344	389	433	478	567	700	922	22.22
6.5	376	424	472	521	617	761	1002	24.07
7.0	408	460	512	564	668	823	1083	25.93
7.5	441	497	552	608	719	885	1163	27.78
8.0	474	533	593	652	770	948	1245	29.63
8.5	508	571	634	696	822	1011	1326	31.48
9.0	542	608	675	742	875	1075	1408	33.33
9.5	576	647	717	787	928	1139	1491	35.18
10.0	611	685	759	833	981	1204	1574	37.04
10.5	647	724	802	880	1035	1269	1658	38.89
11.0	682	764	845	927	1090	1334	1742	40.74
11.5	719	804	889	974	1144	1400	1826	42.59
12.0	756	844	933	1022	1200	1467	1911	44.44
12.5	793	885	978	1071	1256	1534	1996	46.30
13.0	831	926	1023	1119	1312	1601	2082	48.15
13.5	869	969	1069	1169	1369	1669	2169	50.00
14.0	907	1010	1115	1219	1426	1737	2256	51.85
14.5	947	1054	1161	1269	1484	1806	2343	53.70
15.0	986	1096	1208	1319	1542	1875	2431	55.56
15.5	1026	1141	1256	1371	1600	1945	2519	57.41
16.0	1067	1184	1304	1422	1659	2015	2607	59.26
16.5	1108	1230	1352	1474	1719	2085	2696	61.11
17.0	1149	1274	1401	1527	1779	2157	2786	62.96
17.5	1191	1321	1450	1580	1839	2228	2876	64.82
18.0	1233	1366	1500	1633	1900	2300	2967	66.67
18.5	1276	1413	1550	1687	1961	2373	3058	68.52
19.0	1319	1460	1601	1742	2023	2445	3149	70.37
19.5	1363	1508	1652	1797	2085	2519	3241	72.22
20	1407	1556	1704	1852	2148	2593	3333	74.07
21	1497	1653	1808	1964	2275	2742	3520	77.78
22	1589	1752	1915	2078	2404	2893	3707	81.48
23	1682	1853	2023	2194	2534	3045	3897	85.19
24	1778	1956	2133	2311	2667	3200	4089	88.89
25	1875	2060	2245	2431	2801	3357	4282	92.59
26	1974	2166	2359	2552	2937	3514	4478	96.30
27	2075	2274	2475	2675	3075	3675	4675	100.00
28	2178	2384	2593	2800	3215	3837	4874	103.70
29	2282	2496	2712	2927	3356	4001	5075	107.41
30	2389	2611	2833	3056	3500	4167	5278	111.11
31	2497	2726	2956	3186	3645	4334	5482	114.81
32	2607	2844	3081	3319	3793	4504	5689	118.52
33	2719	2964	3208	3453	3942	4675	5897	122.22
34	2833	3085	3337	3589	4093	4848	6108	125.93
35	2949	3208	3468	3727	4245	5023	6320	129.63
36	3067	3333	3600	3867	4400	5200	6533	133.33
37	3186	3460	3734	4008	4556	5379	6749	137.04
38	3307	3589	3870	4152	4715	5559	6967	140.74
39	3431	3719	4008	4297	4875	5742	7186	144.44
40	3556	3852	4148	4444	5037	5926	7407	148.15

TABLE XVII.—LEVEL SECTIONS $\frac{1}{2}:1$

Height	CU YD PER 100-FT STATION							
	Base 14	Base 16	Base 18	Base 20	Base 24	Base 30	Base 40	Per Ft of Added Base
0.5	26	30	34	38	45	56	75	1.85
1.0	54	61	69	76	91	113	150	3.70
1.5	82	93	104	115	138	171	226	5.56
2.0	111	126	141	156	185	230	304	7.41
2.5	141	160	178	197	234	289	382	9.26
3.0	172	194	217	239	283	350	461	11.11
3.5	204	230	256	282	334	412	541	12.96
4.0	237	267	296	326	385	474	622	14.81
4.5	271	304	338	371	438	538	704	16.67
5.0	306	343	380	417	491	602	787	18.52
5.5	341	382	423	463	545	667	871	20.37
6.0	378	422	467	511	600	733	956	22.22
6.5	415	463	512	560	656	800	1041	24.07
7.0	454	506	557	609	713	869	1128	25.93
7.5	493	549	604	660	771	938	1215	27.78
8.0	533	593	652	711	830	1007	1304	29.63
8.5	575	638	700	763	889	1078	1393	31.48
9.0	617	683	750	817	950	1150	1483	33.33
9.5	660	730	800	871	1012	1223	1575	35.18
10.0	704	778	852	926	1074	1296	1667	37.04
10.5	749	826	904	982	1138	1371	1760	38.89
11.0	794	876	957	1039	1202	1446	1854	40.74
11.5	841	926	1012	1097	1267	1523	1949	42.59
12.0	889	978	1067	1156	1333	1600	2044	44.44
12.5	937	1030	1123	1215	1400	1678	2141	46.30
13.0	987	1083	1180	1276	1469	1757	2239	48.15
13.5	1037	1138	1238	1338	1538	1838	2338	50.00
14.0	1089	1193	1296	1400	1607	1919	2437	51.85
14.5	1141	1248	1356	1463	1678	2000	2538	53.70
15.0	1194	1306	1417	1528	1750	2083	2639	55.56
15.5	1249	1363	1478	1593	1823	2167	2741	57.41
16.0	1304	1422	1541	1659	1896	2252	2844	59.26
16.5	1360	1482	1604	1726	1971	2338	2949	61.11
17.0	1417	1543	1669	1794	2046	2424	3054	62.96
17.5	1475	1604	1734	1863	2123	2512	3160	64.82
18.0	1533	1667	1800	1933	2200	2600	3267	66.67
18.5	1593	1730	1867	2004	2278	2689	3375	68.52
19.0	1654	1794	1935	2076	2357	2780	3483	70.37
19.5	1715	1860	2004	2149	2438	2871	3593	72.22
20	1778	1926	2074	2222	2519	2963	3704	74.07
21	1906	2061	2217	2372	2683	3115	3928	77.78
22	2037	2200	2363	2526	2852	3341	4156	81.48
23	2172	2343	2513	2683	3024	3535	4387	85.19
24	2311	2489	2667	2844	3200	3733	4622	88.89
25	2454	2639	2824	3009	3380	3935	4861	92.59
26	2600	2793	2985	3178	3563	4141	5104	96.30
27	2750	2950	3150	3350	3750	4350	5350	100.00
28	2904	3111	3319	3526	3941	4563	5600	103.70
29	3061	3276	3491	3706	4135	4780	5854	107.41
30	3222	3444	3667	3889	4333	5000	6111	111.11
31	3387	3617	3846	4076	4535	5224	6372	114.81
32	3556	3793	4030	4267	4741	5452	6637	118.52
33	3728	3972	4217	4461	4950	5683	6906	122.22
34	3904	4156	4407	4659	5163	5919	7178	125.93
35	4083	4343	4602	4861	5380	6157	7454	129.63
36	4267	4533	4800	5067	5600	6400	7733	133.33
37	4454	4728	5002	5276	5824	6646	8017	137.04
38	4644	4926	5207	5489	6052	6896	8304	140.74
39	4839	5128	5417	5706	6283	7150	8594	144.44
40	5037	5333	5630	5926	6519	7407	8889	148.15

TABLE XVII.—LEVEL SECTIONS 1:1

Height	CU YD PER 100-FT STATION							
	Base 14	Base 16	Base 18	Base 20	Base 24	Base 30	Base 40	Per Ft of Added Base
0.5	27	31	34	38	45	56	75	1.85
1.0	56	63	70	78	93	115	152	3.70
1.5	81	97	108	119	142	175	231	5.56
2.0	119	133	148	163	193	237	311	7.41
2.5	153	171	190	208	245	301	394	9.26
3.0	189	211	233	256	300	367	478	11.11
3.5	227	253	279	305	356	434	564	12.96
4.0	267	296	326	356	415	504	652	14.81
4.5	308	342	375	408	475	575	742	16.67
5.0	352	389	426	463	537	648	833	18.52
5.5	397	438	479	519	601	723	927	20.37
6.0	444	489	533	578	667	800	1022	22.22
6.5	494	542	590	638	734	879	1119	24.07
7.0	544	596	648	700	804	959	1219	25.93
7.5	597	653	708	764	875	1042	1319	27.78
8.0	652	711	770	830	948	1126	1422	29.63
8.5	708	771	834	897	1023	1212	1527	31.48
9.0	767	833	900	967	1100	1300	1633	33.33
9.5	827	897	968	1038	1179	1390	1742	35.18
10.0	889	963	1037	1111	1259	1481	1852	37.04
10.5	953	1031	1108	1186	1342	1575	1964	38.89
11.0	1019	1100	1181	1263	1426	1670	2078	40.74
11.5	1086	1171	1256	1342	1512	1768	2194	42.59
12.0	1156	1244	1333	1422	1600	1867	2311	44.44
12.5	1227	1319	1412	1505	1690	1968	2431	46.30
13.0	1300	1396	1493	1589	1781	2070	2552	48.15
13.5	1375	1475	1575	1675	1875	2175	2675	50.00
14.0	1452	1556	1659	1763	1970	2281	2800	51.85
14.5	1531	1638	1745	1853	2068	2390	2927	53.70
15.0	1611	1722	1833	1944	2167	2500	3056	55.56
15.5	1694	1808	1923	2038	2268	2612	3186	57.41
16.0	1778	1896	2015	2133	2370	2726	3319	59.26
16.5	1864	1986	2108	2231	2475	2842	3453	61.11
17.0	1952	2078	2204	2330	2581	2959	3589	62.96
17.5	2042	2171	2301	2431	2690	3079	3727	64.82
18.0	2133	2267	2400	2533	2800	3200	3867	66.67
18.5	2227	2364	2501	2638	2912	3323	4008	68.52
19.0	2322	2463	2604	2744	3026	3448	4152	70.37
19.5	2419	2564	2708	2853	3142	3575	4297	72.22
20	2519	2667	2815	2963	3259	3704	4444	74.07
21	2722	2878	3033	3189	3500	3967	4744	77.78
22	2933	3096	3259	3422	3748	4237	5052	81.48
23	3152	3322	3493	3663	4004	4515	5367	85.19
24	3378	3556	3733	3911	4267	4800	5689	88.89
25	3611	3796	3981	4167	4537	5093	6019	92.59
26	3852	4044	4237	4430	4815	5393	6356	96.30
27	4100	4300	4500	4700	5100	5700	6700	100.00
28	4356	4563	4770	4978	5393	6015	7052	103.70
29	4619	4833	5048	5263	5693	6337	7411	107.41
30	4889	5111	5333	5556	6000	6667	7778	111.11
31	5167	5396	5626	5856	6315	7004	8152	114.81
32	5452	5689	5926	6163	6637	7348	8533	118.52
33	5744	5989	6233	6478	6967	7700	8922	122.22
34	6044	6296	6548	6800	7304	8059	9319	125.93
35	6352	6611	6870	7130	7648	8426	9722	129.63
36	6667	6933	7200	7467	8000	8800	10133	133.33
37	6989	7263	7537	7811	8359	9181	10552	137.04
38	7319	7600	7881	8163	8726	9570	10978	140.74
39	7656	7944	8233	8522	9100	9967	11411	144.44
40	8000	8296	8593	8889	9481	10370	11852	148.15

TABLE XVII.—LEVEL SECTIONS 1½:1

Height	CU YD PER 100-FT STATION							Per Ft of Added Base
	Base 14	Base 16	Base 18	Base 20	Base 24	Base 30	Base 40	
0.5	27	31	35	38	46	57	75	1.85
1.0	57	65	72	80	94	117	154	3.70
1.5	90	101	113	124	146	179	235	5.56
2.0	126	141	156	170	200	244	319	7.41
2.5	164	183	201	220	257	313	405	9.26
3.0	206	228	250	272	317	383	494	11.11
3.5	250	275	301	327	379	457	587	12.96
4.0	296	326	356	385	444	533	681	14.81
4.5	346	379	413	446	513	613	779	16.67
5.0	398	435	472	509	583	694	880	18.52
5.5	453	494	535	575	657	779	983	20.37
6.0	511	556	600	644	733	867	1089	22.22
6.5	572	620	668	716	813	957	1198	24.07
7.0	635	687	739	791	894	1050	1309	25.93
7.5	701	757	813	868	.979	1146	1424	27.78
8.0	770	830	889	948	1067	1244	1541	29.63
8.5	841	905	968	1031	1157	1346	1661	31.48
9.0	917	983	1050	1117	1250	1450	1783	33.33
9.5	994	1064	1135	1205	1346	1557	1909	35.18
10.0	1074	1148	1222	1296	1444	1667	2037	37.04
10.5	1157	1235	1313	1390	1546	1779	2168	38.89
11.0	1243	1324	1406	1487	1650	1894	2302	40.74
11.5	1331	1416	1501	1587	1757	2013	2438	42.59
12.0	1422	1511	1600	1689	1867	2133	2578	44.44
12.5	1516	1609	1701	1794	1979	2257	2720	46.30
13.0	1613	1709	1806	1902	2094	2383	2865	48.15
13.5	1713	1813	1913	2013	2213	2513	3013	50.00
14.0	1815	1919	2022	2126	2333	2644	3163	51.85
14.5	1920	2027	2135	2242	2457	2779	3316	53.70
15.0	2028	2139	2250	2361	2583	2917	3472	55.56
15.5	2138	2253	2368	2483	2713	3057	3631	57.41
16.0	2252	2370	2489	2607	2844	3200	3793	59.26
16.5	2368	2490	2613	2735	2979	3346	3957	61.11
17.0	2487	2613	2739	2865	3117	3494	4124	62.96
17.5	2609	2738	2868	2998	3257	3646	4294	64.82
18.0	2733	2867	3000	3133	3400	3800	4467	66.67
18.5	2861	2998	3135	3272	3546	3957	4642	68.52
19.0	2991	3131	3272	3413	3694	4117	4820	70.37
19.5	3124	3268	3413	3557	3846	4279	5001	72.22
20	3259	3407	3556	3704	4000	4444	5185	74.07
21	3539	3694	3850	4006	4317	4783	5561	77.78
22	3830	3993	4156	4319	4644	5133	5948	81.48
23	4131	4302	4472	4643	4983	5494	6346	85.19
24	4444	4622	4800	4978	5333	5867	6756	88.89
25	4769	4954	5139	5324	5694	6250	7176	92.59
26	5104	5296	5489	5681	6067	6644	7607	96.30
27	5450	5650	5850	6050	6450	7050	8050	100.00
28	5807	6015	6222	6430	6844	7467	8514	103.70
29	6176	6391	6606	6820	7250	7894	8969	107.41
30	6556	6778	7000	7222	7667	8333	9444	111.11
31	6946	7176	7406	7635	8094	8783	9931	114.81
32	7348	7585	7822	8059	8533	9244	10430	118.52
33	7761	8006	8250	8494	8983	9717	10939	122.22
34	8185	8437	8689	8941	9444	10200	11459	125.93
35	8620	8880	9139	9398	9917	10694	11991	129.63
36	9067	9333	9600	9867	10400	11200	12533	133.33
37	9524	9798	10072	10346	10894	11717	13087	137.04
38	9993	10274	10556	10837	11400	12244	13652	140.74
39	10472	10761	11050	11339	11917	12783	14228	144.44
40	10963	11259	11556	11852	12444	13333	14815	148.15

TABLE XVII.—LEVEL SECTIONS 2:1

Height	CU YD PER 100-FT STATION							
	Base 14	Base 16	Base 18	Base 20	Base 24	Base 30	Base 40	Per Ft of Added Base
0.5	28	31	35	39	46	57	76	1.85
1.0	59	67	74	81	96	119	156	3.70
1.5	94	106	117	128	150	183	239	5.56
2.0	133	148	163	178	207	252	326	7.41
2.5	176	194	213	231	269	324	417	9.26
3.0	222	244	267	289	333	400	511	11.11
3.5	272	298	324	350	402	480	609	12.96
4.0	326	356	385	415	474	563	711	14.81
4.5	383	417	450	483	550	650	817	16.67
5.0	444	481	519	556	630	741	926	18.52
5.5	509	550	591	631	714	835	1039	20.37
6.0	578	622	667	711	800	933	1156	22.22
6.5	650	698	746	794	891	1035	1276	24.07
7.0	726	778	830	881	985	1141	1400	25.93
7.5	806	861	917	972	1083	1250	1528	27.78
8.0	889	948	1007	1067	1185	1363	1659	29.63
8.5	976	1039	1102	1165	1291	1480	1794	31.48
9.0	1067	1133	1200	1267	1400	1600	1933	33.33
9.5	1161	1231	1302	1372	1513	1724	2076	35.18
10.0	1259	1333	1407	1481	1630	1852	2222	37.04
10.5	1361	1439	1517	1594	1750	1983	2372	38.89
11.0	1467	1548	1630	1711	1874	2119	2526	40.74
11.5	1576	1661	1746	1831	2002	2257	2683	42.59
12.0	1689	1778	1867	1956	2133	2400	2844	44.44
12.5	1806	1898	1991	2083	2269	2546	3009	46.30
13.0	1926	2022	2119	2215	2407	2696	3178	48.15
13.5	2050	2150	2250	2350	2550	2850	3350	50.00
14.0	2178	2281	2385	2489	2696	3007	3526	51.85
14.5	2309	2417	2524	2631	2846	3169	3706	53.70
15.0	2444	2556	2667	2778	3000	3333	3889	55.56
15.5	2583	2698	2813	2928	3157	3502	4076	57.41
16.0	2726	2844	2963	3081	3319	3674	4267	59.26
16.5	2872	2994	3117	3239	3483	3850	4461	61.11
17.0	3022	3148	3274	3400	3652	4030	4659	62.96
17.5	3176	3306	3435	3565	3824	4213	4861	64.82
18.0	3333	3467	3600	3733	4000	4400	5067	66.67
18.5	3494	3631	3769	3906	4180	4591	5276	68.52
19.0	3659	3800	3941	4081	4363	4785	5489	70.37
19.5	3828	3972	4117	4261	4550	4983	5706	72.22
20	4000	4148	4296	4444	4741	5185	5926	74.07
21	4356	4511	4667	4822	5133	5600	6378	77.78
22	4730	4889	5052	5215	5541	6030	6844	81.48
23	5111	5281	5452	5622	5963	6474	7326	85.19
24	5511	5689	5867	6044	6400	6933	7822	88.89
25	5926	6111	6296	6481	6852	7407	8333	92.59
26	6356	6548	6741	6933	7319	7896	8859	96.30
27	6800	7000	7200	7400	7800	8400	9400	100.00
28	7259	7467	7674	7881	8296	8919	9956	103.70
29	7733	7948	8163	8378	8807	9452	10526	107.41
30	8222	8444	8667	8889	9333	10000	11111	111.11
31	8726	8956	9185	9415	9874	10563	11711	114.81
32	9244	9481	9719	9956	10430	11141	12326	118.52
33	9778	10022	10267	10511	11000	11733	12956	122.22
34	10326	10578	10830	11081	11585	12341	13600	125.93
35	10889	11148	11407	11667	12185	12963	14259	129.63
36	11467	11733	12000	12267	12800	13600	14933	133.33
37	12059	12333	12607	12881	13430	14252	15622	137.04
38	12667	12948	13230	13511	14074	14919	16326	140.74
39	13289	13578	13867	14156	14733	15600	17044	144.44
40	13926	14222	14519	14815	15407	16296	17778	148.15

TABLE XVII.—LEVEL SECTIONS **3:1**

Height	CU YD PER 100-FT STATION							
	Base 14	Base 16	Base 18	Base 20	Base 24	Base 30	Base 40	Per Ft of Added Base
0.5	29	32	36	40	47	58	77	1.85
1.0	63	70	78	85	100	122	159	3.70
1.5	103	114	125	136	158	192	247	5.56
2.0	148	163	178	193	222	267	341	7.41
2.5	199	218	236	255	292	347	440	9.26
3.0	256	278	300	322	367	433	544	11.11
3.5	318	344	369	395	447	525	655	12.96
4.0	385	415	444	474	533	622	770	14.81
4.5	458	492	525	558	625	725	892	16.67
5.0	537	574	611	648	722	833	1019	18.52
5.5	621	662	703	744	825	947	1151	20.37
6.0	711	756	800	844	933	1067	1289	22.22
6.5	806	855	903	951	1047	1192	1432	24.07
7.0	907	959	1011	1063	1167	1322	1581	25.93
7.5	1014	1069	1125	1181	1292	1458	1736	27.78
8.0	1126	1185	1244	1304	1422	1600	1896	29.63
8.5	1244	1306	1369	1432	1558	1747	2062	31.48
9.0	1367	1433	1500	1567	1700	1900	2233	33.33
9.5	1495	1566	1636	1706	1847	2058	2410	35.18
10.0	1630	1704	1778	1852	2000	2222	2593	37.04
10.5	1769	1847	1925	2003	2158	2392	2781	38.89
11.0	1915	1996	2078	2159	2322	2567	2974	40.74
11.5	2066	2150	2236	2321	2492	2747	3173	42.59
12.0	2222	2311	2400	2489	2667	2933	3378	44.44
12.5	2384	2477	2569	2662	2847	3125	3588	46.30
13.0	2552	2648	2744	2841	3033	3322	3804	48.15
13.5	2725	2825	2925	3025	3225	3525	4025	50.00
14.0	2904	3007	3111	3215	3422	3733	4252	51.85
14.5	3088	3195	3303	3410	3625	3947	4484	53.70
15.0	3278	3389	3500	3611	3833	4167	4722	55.56
15.5	3473	3588	3703	3818	4047	4392	4966	57.41
16.0	3674	3793	3911	4030	4267	4622	5215	59.26
16.5	3881	4003	4125	4247	4492	4858	5469	61.11
17.0	4093	4219	4344	4470	4722	5100	5730	62.96
17.5	4310	4440	4569	4699	4958	5347	5995	64.82
18.0	4533	4667	4800	4933	5200	5600	6267	66.67
18.5	4762	4899	5036	5173	5447	5858	6544	68.52
19.0	4996	5137	5278	5419	5700	6122	6826	70.37
19.5	5236	5381	5525	5669	5958	6392	7114	72.22
20	5481	5630	5778	5926	6222	6667	7407	74.07
21	5989	6144	6300	6456	6767	7233	8011	77.78
22	6519	6681	6844	7007	7333	7822	8637	81.48
23	7070	7241	7411	7581	7922	8433	9285	85.19
24	7644	7822	8000	8178	8533	9067	9956	88.89
25	8241	8426	8611	8796	9167	9722	10648	92.59
26	8859	9052	9244	9437	9822	10400	11363	96.30
27	9500	9700	9900	10100	10500	11100	12100	100.00
28	10163	10370	10578	10785	11200	11822	12859	103.70
29	10848	11063	11278	11493	11922	12567	13641	107.41
30	11556	11778	12000	12222	12667	13333	14444	111.11
31	12285	12515	12744	12974	13433	14122	15270	114.81
32	13037	13274	13511	13748	14222	14933	16119	118.52
33	13811	14056	14300	14544	15033	15767	16989	122.22
34	14607	14859	15111	15363	15867	16622	17881	125.93
35	15426	15685	15944	16204	16722	17500	18796	129.63
36	16267	16533	16800	17067	17600	18400	19733	133.33
37	17130	17404	17678	17952	18500	19322	20693	137.04
38	18015	18296	18578	18859	19422	20267	21674	140.74
39	18922	19211	19500	19789	20367	21233	22678	144.44
40	19852	20148	20444	20741	21333	22222	23704	148.15

The coefficients in the tables on the opposite page provide a rapid method of correcting the level-section quantities of Table XVII for transverse ground slopes.

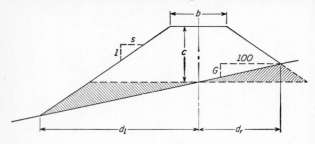

From the figure,

$$d_l = \frac{b}{2} + sc + \frac{sd_lG}{100}$$

or

$$d_l = \frac{\frac{b}{2} + sc}{1 - \frac{sG}{100}} \tag{1}$$

Similarly,

$$d_r = \frac{\frac{b}{2} + sc}{1 + \frac{sG}{100}} \tag{2}$$

From equation 6–3, the area of the level section is $A_L = c(b+cs)$. On a transverse slope, the level-section area is increased by one triangular area and decreased by another, as shown by the cross-hatched areas in the figure. The resulting net area A is

$$A = A_L + \frac{1}{2}\left(\frac{b}{2} + sc\right)\left(\frac{d_lG}{100}\right) - \frac{1}{2}\left(\frac{b}{2} + sc\right)\left(\frac{d_rG}{100}\right)$$

which reduces to

$$A = A_L + \frac{G}{200}\left(\frac{b}{2} + sc\right)\left(d_l - d_r\right) \tag{3}$$

When equations 1 and 2 are substituted in equation 3, the net area A reduces to

$$A = A_L + \left(c + \frac{b}{2s}\right)^2 \left[\frac{s^3}{\left(\frac{100}{G}\right)^2 - s^2}\right] \tag{4}$$

Therefore,

$$\text{Cr Cu yd per 100 ft} = \text{level-section yardage} + C\left(c + \frac{b}{2s}\right)^2$$

78

TABLE XVII.—A. VALUES OF b/2S

Base	Side Slope Ratio, s					
b	$\frac{1}{4}$:1	$\frac{1}{2}$:1	1:1	1$\frac{1}{2}$:1	2:1	3:1
14	28	14	7	4.67	3.50	2.33
16	32	16	8	5.33	4	2.67
18	36	18	9	6	4.50	3
20	40	20	10	6.67	5	3.33
24	48	24	12	8	6	4
30	60	30	15	10	7.5	5
40	80	40	20	13.3	10	6.67
50	100	50	25	16.7	12.5	8.33
60	120	60	30	20	15	10

TABLE XVII.—B. VALUES OF C

Ground Slope	Side Slope Ratio, s					
G	$\frac{1}{4}$:1	$\frac{1}{2}$:1	1:1	1$\frac{1}{2}$:1	2:1	3:1
5%	0.0001	0.0012	0.0093	0.0313	0.0748	0.2558
10%	0.0006	0.0046	0.0374	0.1278	0.3086	1.099
15%	0.0013	0.0105	0.0852	0.2962	0.7325	3.821
20%	0.0023	0.0187	0.1543	0.5494	1.411	6.250
25%	0.0036	0.0294	0.2469	0.9090	2.469	14.29
30%	0.0052	0.0426	0.3663	1.411	4.167	47.37
35%	0.0071	0.0585	0.5170	2.113	7.117	
40%	0.0093	0.0771	0.7054	3.125	13.17	
45%	0.0119	0.0988	0.9405	4.650	31.59	
50%	0.0147	0.1234	1.235	7.143		
60%	0.0213	0.1831	2.083	23.68		
70%	0.0292	0.2585	3.557			
80%	0.0386	0.3526	6.584			
90%	0.0494	0.4702	15.79			
100%	0.0617	0.6172				

where
$$C=\left(\frac{100}{27}\right)\left[\frac{s^3}{\left(\frac{100}{G}\right)^2-s^2}\right]$$

Example. Given: a cross section on a uniform transverse ground slope G of 20%. Other data are: base $b=30$ ft; center cut or fill $c=15$ ft; side slope ratio $s=1\frac{1}{2}$:1.

From Table XVII,
    Level-section quantity = 2917 cu yd per sta.
From Tables XVII.-A and XVII.-B,
    Correction for slope =
    $(15+10)^2(0.5494)$ = 343 cu yd per sta.
Yardage corrected for slope = 3260 cu yd per sta.

TABLE XVIII.—TRIANGULAR PRISMS. CUBIC YARDS
PER 50 FEET

Height or Width	Width or Height								
	1	2	3	4	5	6	7	8	9
0.1	0.09	0.19	0.28	0.37	0.46	0.56	0.65	0.74	0.83
.2	0.19	0.37	0.56	0.74	0.93	1.11	1.30	1.48	1.67
.3	0.28	0.56	0.83	1.11	1.39	1.67	1.94	2.22	2.50
.4	0.37	0.74	1.11	1.48	1.85	2.22	2.59	2.96	3.33
0.5	0.46	0.93	1.39	1.85	2.31	2.78	3.24	3.70	4.17
.6	0.56	1.11	1.67	2.22	2.78	3.33	3.89	4.44	5.00
.7	0.65	1.30	1.94	2.59	3.24	3.89	4.54	5.19	5.83
.8	0.74	1.48	2.22	2.96	3.70	4.44	5.19	5.93	6.67
.9	0.83	1.67	2.50	3.33	4.17	5.00	5.83	6.67	7.50
1.0	0.93	1.85	2.78	3.70	4.63	5.56	6.48	7.41	8.33
.1	1.02	2.04	3.06	4.07	5.09	6.11	7.13	8.15	9.17
.2	1.11	2.22	3.33	4.44	5.56	6.67	7.78	8.89	10.00
.3	1.20	2.41	3.61	4.81	6.02	7.22	8.43	9.63	10.83
.4	1.30	2.59	3.89	5.19	6.48	7.78	9.07	10.37	11.67
1.5	1.39	2.78	4.17	5.56	6.94	8.33	9.72	11.11	12.50
.6	1.48	2.96	4.44	5.93	7.41	8.89	10.37	11.85	13.33
.7	1.57	3.15	4.72	6.30	7.87	9.44	11.02	12.59	14.17
.8	1.67	3.33	5.00	6.67	8.33	10.00	11.67	13.33	15.00
.9	1.76	3.52	5.28	7.04	8.80	10.56	12.31	14.07	15.83
2.0	1.85	3.70	5.56	7.41	9.26	11.11	12.96	14.81	16.67
.1	1.94	3.89	5.83	7.78	9.72	11.67	13.61	15.56	17.50
.2	2.04	4.07	6.11	8.15	10.19	12.22	14.26	16.30	18.33
.3	2.13	4.26	6.39	8.52	10.65	12.78	14.91	17.04	19.17
.4	2.22	4.44	6.67	8.89	11.11	13.33	15.56	17.78	20.00
2.5	2.31	4.63	6.94	9.26	11.57	13.89	16.20	18.52	20.83
.6	2.41	4.81	7.22	9.63	12.04	14.44	16.85	19.26	21.67
.7	2.50	5.00	7.50	10.00	12.50	15.00	17.50	20.00	22.50
.8	2.59	5.19	7.78	10.37	12.96	15.56	18.15	20.74	23.33
.9	2.69	5.37	8.06	10.74	13.43	16.11	18.80	21.48	24.17
3.0	2.78	5.56	8.33	11.11	13.89	16.67	19.44	22.22	25.00
.1	2.87	5.74	8.61	11.48	14.35	17.22	20.09	22.96	25.83
.2	2.96	5.93	8.89	11.85	14.81	17.78	20.74	23.70	26.67
.3	3.06	6.11	9.17	12.22	15.28	18.33	21.39	24.44	27.50
.4	3.15	6.30	9.44	12.59	15.74	18.89	22.04	25.19	28.33
3.5	3.24	6.48	9.72	12.96	16.20	19.44	22.69	25.93	29.17
.6	3.33	6.67	10.00	13.33	16.67	20.00	23.33	26.67	30.00
.7	3.43	6.85	10.28	13.70	17.13	20.56	23.98	27.41	30.83
.8	3.52	7.04	10.56	14.07	17.59	21.11	24.63	28.15	31.67
.9	3.61	7.22	10.83	14.44	18.06	21.67	25.28	28.89	32.50
4.0	3.70	7.41	11.11	14.81	18.52	22.22	25.93	29.63	33.33
.1	3.80	7.59	11.39	15.19	18.98	22.78	26.57	30.37	34.17
.2	3.89	7.78	11.67	15.56	19.44	23.33	27.22	31.11	35.00
.3	3.98	7.96	11.94	15.93	19.91	23.89	27.87	31.85	35.83
.4	4.07	8.15	12.22	16.30	20.37	24.44	28.52	32.59	36.67
4.5	4.17	8.33	12.50	16.67	20.83	25.00	29.17	33.33	37.50
.6	4.26	8.52	12.78	17.04	21.30	25.56	29.81	34.07	38.33
.7	4.35	8.70	13.06	17.41	21.76	26.11	30.46	34.81	39.17
.8	4.44	8.89	13.33	17.78	22.22	26.67	31.11	35.56	40.00
.9	4.54	9.07	13.61	18.15	22.69	27.22	31.76	36.30	40.83
5.0	4.63	9.26	13.89	18.52	23.15	27.78	32.41	37.04	41.67
.1	4.72	9.44	14.17	18.89	23.61	28.33	33.06	37.78	42.50
.2	4.81	9.63	14.44	19.26	24.07	28.89	33.70	38.52	43.33
.3	4.91	9.81	14.72	19.63	24.54	29.44	34.35	39.26	44.17
.4	5.00	10.00	15.00	20.00	25.00	30.00	35.00	40.00	45.00
5.5	5.09	10.19	15.28	20.37	25.46	30.56	35.65	40.74	45.83
.6	5.19	10.37	15.56	20.74	25.93	31.11	36.30	41.48	46.67
.7	5.28	10.56	15.83	21.11	26.39	31.67	36.94	42.22	47.50
.8	5.37	10.74	16.11	21.48	26.85	32.22	37.59	42.96	48.33
.9	5.46	10.93	16.39	21.85	27.31	32.78	38.24	43.70	49.17

TABLE XVIII.—TRIANGULAR PRISMS. CUBIC YARDS PER 50 FEET

Height or Width	Width or Height								
	1	2	3	4	5	6	7	8	9
6.0	5.56	11 11	16.67	22.22	27.78	33.33	38.89	44.44	50.00
.1	5.65	11.30	16.94	22.59	28.24	33.89	39.54	45.19	50.83
.2	5.74	11.48	17.22	22.96	28.70	34.44	40.19	45.93	51.67
.3	5.83	11.67	17.50	23.33	29.17	35.00	40.83	46.67	52.50
.4	5.93	11.85	17.78	23.70	29.63	35.56	41.48	47.41	53.33
6.5	6.02	12.04	18.06	24.07	30.09	36.11	42.13	48.15	54.17
.6	6.11	12.22	18.33	24.44	30.56	36.67	42.78	48.89	55.00
.7	6.20	12.41	18.61	24.81	31.02	37.22	43.43	49.63	55.83
.8	6.30	12.59	18.89	25.19	31.48	37.78	44.07	50.37	56.67
.9	6.39	12.78	19.17	25.56	31.94	38.33	44.72	51.11	57.50
7.0	6.48	12.96	19.44	25.93	32.41	38.89	45.37	51.85	58.33
.1	6.57	13.15	19.72	26.30	32.87	39.44	46.02	52.59	59.17
.2	6.67	13.33	20.00	26.67	33.33	40.00	46.67	53.33	60.00
.3	6.76	13.52	20.28	27.04	33.80	40.56	47.31	54.07	60.83
.4	6.85	13.70	20.56	27.41	34.26	41.11	47.96	54.81	61.67
7.5	6.94	13.89	20.83	27.78	34.72	41.67	48.61	55.56	62.50
.6	7.04	14.07	21.11	28.15	35.19	42.22	49.26	56.30	63.33
.7	7.13	14.26	21.39	28.52	35.65	42.78	49.91	57.04	64.17
.8	7.22	14.44	21.67	28.89	36.11	43.33	50.56	57.78	65.00
.9	7.31	14.63	21.94	29.26	36.57	43.89	51.20	58.52	65.83
8.0	7.41	14.81	22.22	29.63	37.04	44.44	51.85	59.26	66.67
.1	7.50	15.00	22.50	30.00	37.50	45.00	52.50	60.00	67.50
.2	7.59	15.19	22.78	30.37	37.96	45.56	53.15	60.74	68.33
.3	7.69	15.37	23.06	30.74	38.43	46.11	53.80	61.48	69.17
.4	7.78	15.56	23.33	31.11	38.89	46.67	54.44	62.22	70.00
8.5	7.87	15.74	23.61	31.48	39.35	47.22	55.09	62.96	70.83
.6	7.96	15.93	23.89	31.85	39.81	47.78	55.74	63.70	71.67
.7	8.06	16.11	24.17	32.22	40.28	48.33	56.39	64.44	72.50
.8	8.15	16.30	24.44	32.59	40.74	48.89	57.04	65.19	73.33
.9	8.24	16.48	24.72	32.96	41.20	49.44	57.69	65.93	74.17
9.0	8.33	16.67	25.00	33.33	41.67	50.00	58.33	66.67	75.00
.1	8.43	16.85	25.28	33.70	42.13	50.56	58.98	67.41	75.83
.2	8.52	17.04	25.56	34.07	42.59	51.11	59.63	68.15	76.67
.3	8.61	17.22	25.83	34.44	43.06	51.67	60.28	68.89	77.50
.4	8.70	17.41	26.11	34.81	43.52	52.22	60.93	69.63	78.33
9.5	8.80	17.59	26.39	35.19	43.98	52.78	61.57	70.37	79.17
.6	8.89	17.78	26.67	35.56	44.44	53.33	62.22	71.11	80.00
.7	8.98	17.96	26.94	35.93	44.91	53.89	62.87	71.85	80.83
.8	9.07	18.15	27.22	36.30	45.37	54.44	63.52	72.59	81.67
.9	9.17	18.33	27.50	36.67	45.83	55.00	64.17	73.33	82.50
10.0	9.26	18.52	27.78	37.04	46.30	55.56	64.81	74.07	83.33
.1	9.35	18.70	28.06	37.41	46.76	56.11	65.46	74.81	84.17
.2	9.44	18.89	28.33	37.78	47.22	56.67	66.11	75.56	85.00
.3	9.54	19.07	28.61	38.15	47.69	57.22	66.76	76.30	85.83
.4	9.63	19.26	28.89	38.52	48.15	57.78	67.41	77.04	86.67
10.5	9.72	19.44	29.17	38.89	48.61	58.33	68.06	77.78	87.50
.6	9.81	19.63	29.44	39.26	49.07	58.89	68.70	78.52	88.33
.7	9.91	19.81	29.72	39.63	49.54	59.44	69.35	79.26	89.17
.8	10.00	20.00	30.00	40.00	50.00	60.00	70.00	80.00	90.00
.9	10.09	20.19	30.28	40.37	50.46	60.56	70.65	80.74	90.83
11.0	10.19	20.37	30.56	40.74	50.93	61.11	71.30	81.48	91.67
.1	10.28	20.56	30.83	41.11	51.39	61.67	71.94	82.22	92.50
.2	10.37	20.74	31.11	41.48	51.85	62.22	72.59	82.96	93.33
.3	10.46	20.93	31.39	41.85	52.31	62.78	73.24	83.70	94.17
.4	10.56	21.11	31.67	42.22	52.78	63.33	73.89	84.44	95.00
11.5	10.65	21.30	31.94	42.59	53.24	63.89	74.54	85.19	95.83
.6	10.74	21.48	32.22	42.96	53.70	64.44	75.19	85.93	96.67
.7	10.83	21.67	32.50	43.33	54.17	65.00	75.83	86.67	97.50
.8	10.93	21.85	32.78	43.70	54.63	65.56	76.48	87.41	98.33
.9	11.02	22.04	33.06	44.07	55.09	66.11	77.13	88.15	99.17

TABLE XVIII.—TRIANGULAR PRISMS. CUBIC YARDS
PER 50 FEET

Height or Width	Width or Height								
	1	2	3	4	5	6	7	8	9
12.0	11.11	22.22	33.33	44.44	55.56	66.67	77.78	88.89	100.00
.1	11.20	22.41	33.61	44.81	56.02	67.22	78.43	89.63	100.83
.2	11.30	22.59	33.89	45.19	56.48	67.78	79.07	90.37	101.67
.3	11.39	22.78	34.17	45.56	56.94	68.33	79.72	91.11	102.50
.4	11.48	22.96	34.44	45.93	57.41	68.89	80.37	91.85	103.33
12.5	11.57	23.15	34.72	46.30	57.87	69.44	81.02	92.59	104.17
.6	11.67	23.33	35.00	46.67	58.33	70.00	81.67	93.33	105.00
.7	11.76	23.52	35.28	47.04	58.80	70.56	82.31	94.07	105.83
.8	11.85	23.70	35.56	47.41	59.26	71.11	82.96	94.81	106.67
.9	11.94	23.89	35.83	47.78	59.72	71.67	83.61	95.56	107.50
13.0	12.04	24.07	36.11	48.15	60.19	72.22	84.26	96.30	108.33
.1	12.13	24.26	36.39	48.52	60.65	72.78	84.91	97.04	109.17
.2	12.22	24.44	36.67	48.89	61.11	73.33	85.56	97.78	110.00
.3	12.31	24.63	36.94	49.26	61.57	73.89	86.20	98.52	110.83
.4	12.41	24.81	37.22	49.63	62.04	74.44	86.85	99.26	111.67
13.5	12.50	25.00	37.50	50.00	62.50	75.00	87.50	100.00	112.50
.6	12.59	25.19	37.78	50.37	62.96	75.56	88.15	100.74	113.33
.7	12.69	25.37	38.06	50.74	63.43	76.11	88.80	101.48	114.17
.8	12.78	25.56	38.33	51.11	63.89	76.67	89.44	102.22	115.00
.9	12.87	25.74	38.61	51.48	64.35	77.22	90.09	102.96	115.83
14.0	12.96	25.93	38.89	51.85	64.81	77.78	90.74	103.70	116.67
.1	13.06	26.11	39.17	52.22	65.28	78.33	91.39	104.44	117.50
.2	13.15	26.30	39.44	52.59	65.74	78.89	92.04	105.19	118.33
.3	13.24	26.48	39.72	52.96	66.20	79.44	92.69	105.93	119.17
.4	13.33	26.67	40.00	53.33	66.67	80.00	93.33	106.67	120.00
14.5	13.43	26.85	40.28	53.70	67.13	80.56	93.98	107.41	120.83
.6	13.52	27.04	40.56	54.07	67.59	81.11	94.63	108.15	121.67
.7	13.61	27.22	40.83	54.44	68.06	81.67	95.28	108.89	122.50
.8	13.70	27.41	41.11	54.81	68.52	82.22	95.93	109.63	123.33
.9	13.80	27.59	41.39	55.19	68.98	82.78	96.57	110.37	124.17
15.0	13.89	27.78	41.67	55.56	69.44	83.33	97.22	111.11	125.00
.1	13.98	27.96	41.94	55.93	69.91	83.89	97.87	111.85	125.83
.2	14.07	28.15	42.22	56.30	70.37	84.44	98.52	112.59	126.67
.3	14.17	28.33	42.50	56.67	70.83	85.00	99.17	113.33	127.50
.4	14.26	28.52	42.78	57.04	71.30	85.56	99.81	114.07	128.33
15.5	14.35	28.70	43.06	57.41	71.76	86.11	100.46	114.81	129.17
.6	14.44	28.89	43.33	57.78	72.22	86.67	101.11	115.56	130.00
.7	14.54	29.07	43.61	58.15	72.69	87.22	101.76	116.30	130.83
.8	14.63	29.26	43.89	58.52	73.15	87.78	102.41	117.04	131.67
.9	14.72	29.44	44.17	58.89	73.61	88.33	103.06	117.78	132.50
16.0	14.81	29.63	44.44	59.26	74.07	88.89	103.70	118.52	133.33
.1	14.91	29.81	44.72	59.63	74.54	89.44	104.35	119.26	134.17
.2	15.00	30.00	45.00	60.00	75.00	90.00	105.00	120.00	135.00
.3	15.09	30.19	45.28	60.37	75.46	90.56	105.65	120.74	135.83
.4	15.19	30.37	45.56	60.74	75.93	91.11	106.30	121.48	136.67
16.5	15.28	30.56	45.83	61.11	76.39	91.67	106.94	122.22	137.50
.6	15.37	30.74	46.11	61.48	76.85	92.22	107.59	122.96	138.33
.7	15.46	30.93	46.39	61.85	77.31	92.78	108.24	123.70	139.17
.8	15.56	31.11	46.67	62.22	77.78	93.33	108.89	124.44	140.00
.9	15.65	31.30	46.94	62.59	78.24	93.89	109.54	125.19	140.83
17.0	15.74	31.48	47.22	62.96	78.70	94.44	110.19	125.93	141.67
.1	15.83	31.67	47.50	63.33	79.17	95.00	110.83	126.67	142.50
.2	15.93	31.85	47.78	63.70	79.63	95.56	111.48	127.41	143.33
.3	16.02	32.04	48.06	64.07	80.09	96.11	112.13	128.15	144.17
.4	16.11	32.22	48.33	64.44	80.56	96.67	112.78	128.89	145.00
17.5	16.20	32.41	48.61	64.81	81.02	97.22	113.43	129.63	145.83
.6	16.30	32.59	48.89	65.19	81.48	97.78	114.07	130.37	146.67
.7	16.39	32.78	49.17	65.56	81.94	98.33	114.72	131.11	147.50
.8	16.48	32.96	49.44	65.93	82.41	98.89	115.37	131.85	148.33
.9	16.57	33.15	49.72	66.30	82.87	99.44	116.02	132.59	149.17

TABLE XVIII.—TRIANGULAR PRISMS. CUBIC YARDS PER 50 FEET

Height or Width	Width or Height								
	1	2	3	4	5	6	7	8	9
18.0	16.67	33.33	50.00	66.67	83.33	100.00	116.67	133.33	150.00
.1	16.76	33.52	50.28	67.04	83.80	100.56	117.31	134.07	150.83
.2	16.85	33.70	50.56	67.41	84.26	101.11	117.96	134.81	151.67
.3	16.94	33.89	50.83	67.78	84.72	101.67	118.61	135.56	152.50
.4	17.04	34.07	51.11	68.15	85.19	102.22	119.26	136.30	153.33
18.5	17.13	34.26	51.39	68.52	85.65	102.78	119.91	137.04	154.17
.6	17.22	34.44	51.67	68.89	86.11	103.33	120.56	137.78	155.00
.7	17.31	34.63	51.94	69.26	86.57	103.89	121.20	138.52	155.83
.8	17.41	34.81	52.22	69.63	87.04	104.44	121.85	139.26	156.67
.9	17.50	35.00	52.50	70.00	87.50	105.00	122.50	140.00	157.50
19.0	17.59	35.19	52.78	70.37	87.96	105.56	123.15	140.74	158.33
.1	17.69	35.37	53.06	70.74	88.43	106.11	123.80	141.48	159.17
.2	17.78	35.56	53.33	71.11	88.89	106.67	124.44	142.22	160.00
.3	17.87	35.74	53.61	71.48	89.35	107.22	125.09	142.96	160.83
.4	17.96	35.93	53.89	71.85	89.81	107.78	125.74	143.70	161.67
19.5	18.06	36.11	54.17	72.22	90.28	108.33	126.39	144.44	162.50
.6	18.15	36.30	54.44	72.59	90.74	108.89	127.04	145.19	163.33
.7	18.24	36.48	54.72	72.96	91.20	109.44	127.69	145.93	164.17
.8	18.33	36.67	55.00	73.33	91.67	110.00	128.33	146.67	165.00
.9	18.43	36.85	55.28	73.70	92.13	110.56	128.98	147.41	165.83
20.0	18.52	37.04	55.56	74.07	92.59	111.11	129.63	148.15	166.67
.1	18.61	37.22	55.83	74.44	93.06	111.67	130.28	148.89	167.50
.2	18.70	37.41	56.11	74.81	93.52	112.22	130.93	149.63	168.33
.3	18.80	37.59	56.39	75.19	93.98	112.78	131.57	150.37	169.17
.4	18.89	37.78	56.67	75.56	94.44	113.33	132.22	151.11	170.00
20.5	18.98	37.96	56.94	75.93	94.91	113.89	132.87	151.85	170.83
.6	19.07	38.15	57.22	76.30	95.37	114.44	133.52	152.59	171.67
.7	19.17	38.33	57.50	76.67	95.83	115.00	134.17	153.33	172.50
.8	19.26	38.52	57.78	77.04	96.30	115.56	134.81	154.07	173.33
.9	19.35	38.70	58.06	77.41	96.76	116.11	135.46	154.81	174.17
21.0	19.44	38.89	58.33	77.78	97.22	116.67	136.11	155.56	175.00
.1	19.54	39.07	58.61	78.15	97.69	117.22	136.76	156.30	175.83
.2	19.63	39.26	58.89	78.52	98.15	117.78	137.41	157.04	176.67
.3	19.72	39.44	59.17	78.89	98.61	118.33	138.06	157.78	177.50
.4	19.81	39.63	59.44	79.26	99.07	118.89	138.70	158.52	178.33
21.5	19.91	39.81	59.72	79.63	99.54	119.44	139.35	159.26	179.17
.6	20.00	40.00	60.00	80.00	100.00	120.00	140.00	160.00	180.00
.7	20.09	40.19	60.28	80.37	100.46	120.56	140.65	160.74	180.83
.8	20.19	40.37	60.56	80.74	100.93	121.11	141.30	161.48	181.67
.9	20.28	40.56	60.83	81.11	101.39	121.67	141.94	162.22	182.50
22.0	20.37	40.74	61.11	81.48	101.85	122.22	142.59	162.96	183.33
.1	20.46	40.93	61.39	81.85	102.31	122.78	143.24	163.70	184.17
.2	20.56	41.11	61.67	82.22	102.78	123.33	143.89	164.44	185.00
.3	20.65	41.30	61.94	82.59	103.24	123.89	144.54	165.19	185.83
.4	20.74	41.48	62.22	82.96	103.70	124.44	145.19	165.93	186.67
22.5	20.83	41.67	62.50	83.33	104.17	125.00	145.83	166.67	187.50
.6	20.93	41.85	62.78	83.70	104.63	125.56	146.48	167.41	188.33
.7	21.02	42.04	63.06	84.07	105.09	126.11	147.13	168.15	189.17
.8	21.11	42.22	63.33	84.44	105.56	126.67	147.78	168.89	190.00
.9	21.20	42.41	63.61	84.81	106.02	127.22	148.43	169.63	190.83
23.0	21.30	42.59	63.89	85.19	106.48	127.78	149.07	170.37	191.67
.1	21.39	42.78	64.17	85.56	106.94	128.33	149.72	171.11	192.50
.2	21.48	42.96	64.44	85.93	107.41	128.89	150.37	171.85	193.33
.3	21.57	43.15	64.72	86.30	107.87	129.44	151.02	172.59	194.17
.4	21.67	43.33	65.00	86.67	108.33	130.00	151.67	173.33	195.00
23.5	21.76	43.52	65.28	87.04	108.80	130.56	152.31	174.07	195.83
.6	21.85	43.70	65.56	87.41	109.26	131.11	152.96	174.81	196.67
.7	21.94	43.89	65.83	87.78	109.72	131.67	153.61	175.56	197.50
.8	22.04	44.07	66.11	88.15	110.19	132.22	154.26	176.30	198.33
.9	22.13	44.26	66.39	88.52	110.65	132.78	154.91	177.04	199.17

TABLE XVIII.—TRIANGULAR PRISMS. CUBIC YARDS
PER 50 FEET

Height or Width	Width or Height								
	1	2	3	4	5	6	7	8	9
24.0	22.22	44.44	66.67	88.89	111.11	133.33	155.56	177.78	200.00
.1	22.31	44.63	66.94	89.26	111.57	133.89	156.20	178.52	200.83
.2	22.41	44.81	67.22	89.63	112.04	134.44	156.85	179.26	201.67
.3	22.50	45.00	67.50	90.00	112.50	135.00	157.50	180.00	202.50
.4	22.59	45.19	67.78	90.37	112.96	135.56	158.15	180.74	203.33
24.5	22.69	45.37	68.06	90.74	113.43	136.11	158.80	181.48	204.17
.6	22.78	45.56	68.33	91.11	113.89	136.67	159.44	182.22	205.00
.7	22.87	45.74	68.61	91.48	114.35	137.22	160.09	182.96	205.83
.8	22.96	45.93	68.89	91.85	114.81	137.78	160.74	183.70	206.67
.9	23.06	46.11	69.17	92.22	115.28	138.33	161.39	184.44	207.50
25.0	23.15	46.30	69.44	92.59	115.74	138.89	162.04	185.19	208.33
.1	23.24	46.48	69.72	92.96	116.20	139.44	162.69	185.93	209.17
.2	23.33	46.67	70.00	93.33	116.67	140.00	163.33	186.67	210.00
.3	23.43	46.85	70.28	93.70	117.13	140.56	163.98	187.41	210.83
.4	23.52	47.04	70.56	94.07	117.59	141.11	164.63	188.15	211.67
25.5	23.61	47.22	70.83	94.44	118.06	141.67	165.28	188.89	212.50
.6	23.70	47.41	71.11	94.81	118.52	142.22	165.93	189.63	213.33
.7	23.80	47.59	71.39	95.19	118.98	142.78	166.57	190.37	214.17
.8	23.89	47.78	71.67	95.56	119.44	143.33	167.22	191.11	215.00
.9	23.98	47.96	71.94	95.93	119.91	143.89	167.87	191.85	215.83
26.0	24.07	48.15	72.22	96.30	120.37	144.44	168.52	192.59	216.67
.1	24.17	48.33	72.50	96.67	120.83	145.00	169.17	193.33	217.50
.2	24.26	48.52	72.78	97.04	121.30	145.56	169.81	194.07	218.33
.3	24.35	48.70	73.06	97.41	121.76	146.11	170.46	194.81	219.17
.4	24.44	48.89	73.33	97.78	122.22	146.67	171.11	195.56	220.00
26.5	24.54	49.07	73.61	98.15	122.69	147.22	171.76	196.30	220.83
.6	24.63	49.26	73.89	98.52	123.15	147.78	172.41	197.04	221.67
.7	24.72	49.44	74.17	98.89	123.61	148.33	173.06	197.78	222.50
.8	24.81	49.63	74.44	99.26	124.07	148.89	173.70	198.52	223.33
.9	24.91	49.81	74.72	99.63	124.54	149.44	174.35	199.26	224.17
27.0	25.00	50.00	75.00	100.00	125.00	150.00	175.00	200.00	225.00
.1	25.09	50.19	75.28	100.37	125.46	150.56	175.65	200.74	225.83
.2	25.19	50.37	75.56	100.74	125.93	151.11	176.30	201.48	226.67
.3	25.28	50.56	75.83	101.11	126.39	151.67	176.94	202.22	227.50
.4	25.37	50.74	76.11	101.48	126.85	152.22	177.59	202.96	228.33
27.5	25.46	50.93	76.39	101.85	127.31	152.78	178.24	203.70	229.17
.6	25.56	51.11	76.67	102.22	127.78	153.33	178.89	204.44	230.00
.7	25.65	51.30	76.94	102.59	128.24	153.89	179.54	205.19	230.83
.8	25.74	51.48	77.22	102.96	128.70	154.44	180.19	205.93	231.67
.9	25.83	51.67	77.50	103.33	129.17	155.00	180.83	206.67	232.50
28.0	25.93	51.85	77.78	103.70	129.63	155.56	181.48	207.41	233.33
.1	26.02	52.04	78.06	104.07	130.09	156.11	182.13	208.15	234.17
.2	26.11	52.22	78.33	104.44	130.56	156.67	182.78	208.89	235.00
.3	26.20	52.41	78.61	104.81	131.02	157.22	183.43	209.63	235.83
.4	26.30	52.59	78.89	105.19	131.48	157.78	184.07	210.37	236.67
28.5	26.39	52.78	79.17	105.56	131.94	158.33	184.72	211.11	237.50
.6	26.48	52.96	79.44	105.93	132.41	158.89	185.37	211.85	238.33
.7	26.57	53.15	79.72	106.30	132.87	159.44	186.02	212.59	239.17
.8	26.67	53.33	80.00	106.67	133.33	160.00	186.67	213.33	240.00
.9	26.76	53.52	80.28	107.04	133.80	160.56	187.31	214.07	240.83
29.0	26.85	53.70	80.56	107.41	134.26	161.11	187.96	214.81	241.67
.1	26.94	53.89	80.83	107.78	134.72	161.67	188.61	215.56	242.50
.2	27.04	54.07	81.11	108.15	135.19	162.22	189.26	216.30	243.33
.3	27.13	54.26	81.39	108.52	135.65	162.78	189.91	217.04	244.17
.4	27.22	54.44	81.67	108.89	136.11	163.33	190.56	217.78	245.00
29.5	27.31	54.63	81.94	109.26	136.57	163.89	191.20	218.52	245.83
.6	27.41	54.81	82.22	109.63	137.04	164.44	191.85	219.26	246.67
.7	27.50	55.00	82.50	110.00	137.50	165.00	192.50	220.00	247.50
.8	27.59	55.19	82.78	110.37	137.96	165.56	193.15	220.74	248.33
.9	27.69	55.37	83.06	110.74	138.43	166.11	193.80	221.48	249.17

TABLE XVIII.—TRIANGULAR PRISMS. CUBIC YARDS
PER 50 FEET

Height or Width	Width or Height								
	1	2	3	4	5	6	7	8	9
30.0	27.78	55.56	83.33	111.11	138.89	166.67	194.44	222.22	250.00
.1	27.87	55.74	83.61	111.48	139.35	167.22	195.09	222.96	250.83
.2	27.96	55.93	83.89	111.85	139.81	167.78	195.74	223.70	251.67
.3	28.06	56.11	84.17	112.22	140.28	168.33	196.39	224.44	252.50
.4	28.15	56.30	84.44	122.59	140.74	168.89	197.04	225.19	253.33
30.5	28.24	56.48	84.72	112.96	141.20	169.44	197.69	225.93	254.17
.6	28.33	56.67	85.00	113.33	141.67	170.00	198.33	226.67	255.00
.7	28.43	56.85	85.28	113.70	142.13	170.56	198.98	227.41	255.83
.8	28.52	57.04	85.56	114.07	142.59	171.11	199.63	228.15	256.67
.9	28.61	57.22	85.83	114.44	143.06	171.67	200.28	228.89	257.50
31.0	28.70	57.41	86.11	114.81	143.52	172.22	200.93	229.63	258.33
.1	28.80	57.59	86.39	115.19	143.98	172.78	201.57	230.37	259.17
.2	28.89	57.78	86.67	115.56	144.44	173.33	202.22	231.11	260.00
.3	28.98	57.96	86.94	115.93	144.91	173.89	202.87	231.85	260.83
.4	29.07	58.15	87.22	116.30	145.37	174.44	203.52	232.59	261.67
31.5	29.17	58.33	87.50	116.67	145.83	175.00	204.17	233.33	262.50
.6	29.26	58.52	87.78	117.04	146.30	175.56	204.81	234.07	263.33
.7	29.35	58.70	88.06	117.41	146.76	176.11	205.46	234.81	264.17
.8	29.44	58.89	88.33	117.78	147.22	176.67	206.11	235.56	265.00
.9	29.54	59.07	88.61	118.15	147.69	177.22	206.76	236.30	265.83
32.0	29.63	59.26	88.89	118.52	148.15	177.78	207.41	237.04	266.67
.1	29.72	59.44	89.17	118.89	148.61	178.33	208.06	237.78	267.50
.2	29.81	59.63	89.44	119.26	149.07	178.89	208.70	238.52	268.33
.3	29.91	59.81	89.72	119.63	149.54	179.44	209.35	239.26	269.17
.4	30.00	60.00	90.00	120.00	150.00	180.00	210.00	240.00	270.00
32.5	30.09	60.19	90.28	120.37	150.46	180.56	210.65	240.74	280.83
.6	30.19	60.37	90.56	120.74	150.93	181.11	211.30	241.48	271.67
.7	30.28	60.56	90.83	121.11	151.39	181.67	211.94	242.22	272.50
.8	30.37	60.74	91.11	121.48	151.85	182.22	212.59	242.96	273.33
.9	30.46	60.93	91.39	121.85	152.31	182.78	213.24	243.70	274.17
33.0	30.56	61.11	91.67	122.22	152.78	183.33	213.89	244.44	275.00
.1	30.65	61.30	91.94	122.59	153.24	183.89	214.54	245.19	275.83
.2	30.74	61.48	92.22	122.96	153.70	184.44	215.19	245.93	276.67
.3	30.83	61.67	92.50	123.33	154.17	185.00	215.83	246.67	277.50
.4	30.93	61.85	92.78	123.70	154.63	185.56	216.48	247.41	278.33
33.5	31.02	62.04	93.06	124.07	155.09	186.11	217.13	248.15	279.17
.6	31.11	62.22	93.33	124.44	155.56	186.67	217.78	248.89	280.00
.7	31.20	62.41	93.61	124.81	156.02	187.22	218.43	249.63	280.83
.8	31.30	62.59	93.89	125.19	156.48	187.78	219.07	250.37	281.67
.9	31.39	62.78	94.17	125.56	156.94	188.33	219.72	251.11	282.50
34.0	31.48	62.96	94.44	125.93	157.41	188.89	220.37	251.85	283.33
.1	31.57	63.15	94.72	126.30	157.87	189.44	221.02	252.59	284.17
.2	31.67	63.33	95.00	126.67	158.33	190.00	221.67	253.33	285.00
.3	31.76	63.52	95.28	127.04	158.80	190.56	222.31	254.07	285.83
.4	31.85	63.70	95.56	127.41	159.26	191.11	222.96	254.81	286.67
34.5	31.94	63.89	95.83	127.78	159.72	191.67	223.61	255.56	287.50
.6	32.04	64.07	96.11	128.15	160.19	192.22	224.26	256.30	288.33
.7	32.13	64.26	96.39	128.52	160.65	192.78	224.91	257.04	289.17
.8	32.22	64.44	96.67	128.89	161.11	193.33	225.56	257.78	290.00
.9	32.31	64.63	96.94	129.26	161.57	193.89	226.20	258.52	290.83
35.0	32.41	64.81	97.22	129.63	162.04	194.44	226.85	259.26	291.67
.1	32.50	65.00	97.50	130.00	162.50	195.00	227.50	260.00	292.50
.2	32.59	65.19	97.78	130.37	162.96	195.56	228.15	260.74	293.33
.3	32.69	65.37	98.06	130.74	163.43	196.11	228.80	261.48	294.17
.4	32.78	65.56	98.33	131.11	163.89	196.67	229.44	262.22	295.00
35.5	32.87	65.74	98.61	131.48	164.35	197.22	230.09	262.96	295.83
.6	32.96	65.93	98.89	131.85	164.81	197.78	230.74	263.70	296.67
.7	33.06	66.11	99.17	132.22	165.28	198.33	231.39	264.44	297.50
.8	33.15	66.30	99.44	132.59	165.74	198.89	232.04	265.19	298.33
.9	33.24	66.48	99.72	132.96	166.20	199.44	232.69	265.93	299.17

TABLE XVIII.—TRIANGULAR PRISMS. CUBIC YARDS
PER 50 FEET

Height or Width	Width or Height								
	1	2	3	4	5	6	7	8	9
36.0	33.33	66.67	100.00	133.33	166.67	200.00	233.33	266.67	300.00
.1	33.43	66.85	100.28	133.70	167.13	200.56	233.98	267.41	300.83
.2	33.52	67.04	100.56	134.07	167.59	201.11	234.63	268.15	301.67
.3	33.61	67.22	100.83	134.44	168.06	201.67	235.28	268.89	302.50
.4	33.70	67.41	101.11	134.81	168.52	202.22	235.93	269.63	303.33
36.5	33.80	67.59	101.39	135.19	168.98	202.78	236.57	270.37	304.17
.6	33.89	67.78	101.67	135.56	169.44	203.33	237.22	271.11	305.00
.7	33.98	67.96	101.94	135.93	169.91	203.89	237.87	271.85	305.83
.8	34.07	68.15	102.22	136.30	170.37	204.44	238.52	272.59	306.67
.9	34.17	68.33	102.50	136.67	170.83	205.00	239.17	273.33	307.50
37.0	34.26	68.52	102.78	137.04	171.30	205.56	239.81	274.07	308.33
.1	34.35	68.70	103.06	137.41	171.76	206.11	240.46	274.81	309.17
.2	34.44	68.89	103.33	137.78	172.22	206.67	241.11	275.56	310.00
.3	34.54	69.07	103.61	138.15	172.69	207.22	241.76	276.30	310.83
.4	34.63	69.26	103.89	138.52	173.15	207.78	242.41	277.04	311.67
37.5	34.72	69.44	104.17	138.89	173.61	208.33	243.06	277.78	312.50
.6	34.81	69.63	104.44	139.26	174.07	208.89	243.70	278.52	313.33
.7	34.91	69.81	104.72	139.63	174.54	209.44	244.35	279.26	314.17
.8	35.00	70.00	105.00	140.00	175.00	210.00	245.00	280.00	315.00
.9	35.09	70.19	105.28	140.37	175.46	210.56	245.65	280.74	315.83
38.0	35.19	70.37	105.56	140.74	175.93	211.11	246.30	281.48	316.67
.1	35.28	70.56	105.83	141.11	176.39	211.67	246.94	282.22	317.50
.2	35.37	70.74	106.11	141.48	176.85	212.22	247.59	282.96	318.33
.3	35.46	70.93	106.39	141.85	177.31	212.78	248.24	283.70	319.17
.4	35.56	71.11	106.67	142.22	177.78	213.33	248.89	284.44	320.00
38.5	35.65	71.30	106.94	142.59	178.24	213.89	249.54	285.19	320.83
.6	35.74	71.48	107.22	142.96	178.70	214.44	250.19	285.93	321.67
.7	35.83	71.67	107.50	143.33	179.17	215.00	250.83	286.67	322.50
.8	35.93	71.85	107.78	143.70	179.63	215.56	251.48	287.41	323.33
.9	36.02	72.04	108.06	144.07	180.09	216.11	252.13	288.15	324.17
39.0	36.11	72.22	108.33	144.44	180.56	216.67	252.78	288.89	325.00
.1	36.20	72.41	108.61	144.81	181.02	217.22	253.43	289.63	325.83
.2	36.30	72.59	108.89	145.19	181.48	217.78	254.07	290.37	326.67
.3	36.39	72.78	109.17	145.56	181.94	218.33	254.72	291.11	327.50
.4	36.48	72.96	109.44	145.93	182.41	218.89	255.37	291.85	328.33
39.5	36.57	73.15	109.72	146.30	182.87	219.44	256.02	292.59	329.17
.6	36.67	73.33	110.00	146.67	183.33	220.00	256.67	293.33	330.00
.7	36.76	73.52	110.28	147.04	183.80	220.56	257.31	294.07	330.83
.8	36.85	73.70	110.56	147.41	184.26	221.11	257.96	294.81	331.67
.9	36.94	73.89	110.83	147.78	184.72	221.67	258.61	295.56	332.50
40.0	37.04	74.07	111.11	148.15	185.19	222.22	259.26	296.30	333.33
.1	37.13	74.26	111.39	148.52	185.65	222.78	259.91	297.04	334.17
.2	37.22	74.44	111.67	148.89	186.11	223.33	260.56	297.78	335.00
.3	37.31	74.63	111.94	149.26	186.57	223.89	261.20	298.52	335.83
.4	37.41	74.81	112.22	149.63	187.04	224.44	261.85	299.26	336.67
40.5	37.50	75.00	112.50	150.00	187.50	225.00	262.50	300.00	337.50
.6	37.59	75.19	112.78	150.37	187.96	225.56	263.15	300.74	338.33
.7	37.69	75.37	113.06	150.74	188.43	226.11	263.80	301.48	339.17
.8	37.78	75.56	113.33	151.11	188.89	226.67	264.44	302.22	340.00
.9	37.87	75.74	113.61	151.48	189.35	227.22	265.09	302.96	340.83
41.0	37.96	75.93	113.89	151.85	189.81	227.78	265.74	303.70	341.67
.1	38.06	76.11	114.17	152.22	190.28	228.33	266.39	304.44	342.50
.2	38.15	76.30	114.44	152.59	190.74	228.89	267.04	305.19	343.33
.3	38.24	76.48	114.72	152.96	191.20	229.44	267.69	305.93	344.17
.4	38.33	76.67	115.00	153.33	191.67	230.00	268.33	306.67	345.00
41.5	38.43	76.85	115.28	153.70	192.13	230.56	268.98	307.41	345.83
.6	38.52	77.04	115.56	154.07	192.59	231.11	269.63	308.15	346.67
.7	38.61	77.22	115.83	154.44	193.06	231.67	270.28	308.89	347.50
.8	38.70	77.41	116.11	154.81	193.52	232.22	270.93	309.63	348.33
.9	38.80	77.59	116.39	155.19	193.98	232.78	271.57	310.37	349.17

TABLE XVIII.—TRIANGULAR PRISMS. CUBIC YARDS
PER 50 FEET

Height or Width	Width or Height								
	1	2	3	4	5	6	7	8	9
42.0	38.89	77.78	116.67	155.56	194.44	233.33	272.22	311.11	350.00
.1	38.98	77.96	116.94	155.93	194.91	233.89	272.87	311.85	350.83
.2	39.07	78.15	117.22	156.30	195.37	234.44	273.52	312.59	351.67
.3	39.17	78.33	117.50	156.67	195.83	235.00	274.17	313.33	352.50
.4	39.26	78.52	117.78	157.04	196.30	235.56	274.81	314.07	353.33
42.5	39.35	78.70	118.06	157.41	196.76	236.11	275.46	314.81	354.17
.6	39.44	78.89	118.33	157.78	197.22	236.67	276.11	315.56	355.00
.7	39.54	79.07	118.61	158.15	197.69	237.22	276.76	316.30	355.83
.8	39.63	79.26	118.89	158.52	198.15	237.78	277.41	317.04	356.67
.9	39.72	79.44	119.17	158.89	198.61	238.33	278.06	317.78	357.50
43.0	39.81	79.63	119.44	159.26	199.07	238.89	278.70	318.52	358.33
.1	39.91	79.81	119.72	159.63	199.54	239.44	279.35	319.26	359.17
.2	40.00	80.00	120.00	160.00	200.00	240.00	280.00	320.00	360.00
.3	40.09	80.19	120.28	160.37	200.46	240.56	280.65	320.74	360.83
.4	40.19	80.37	120.56	160.74	200.93	241.11	281.30	321.48	361.67
43.5	40.28	80.56	120.83	161.11	201.39	241.67	281.94	322.22	362.50
.6	40.37	80.74	121.11	161.48	201.85	242.22	282.59	322.96	363.33
.7	40.46	80.93	121.39	161.85	202.31	242.78	283.24	323.70	364.17
.8	40.56	81.11	121.67	162.22	202.78	243.33	283.89	324.44	365.00
.9	40.65	81.30	121.94	162.59	203.24	243.89	284.54	325.19	365.83
44.0	40.74	81.48	122.22	162.96	203.70	244.44	285.19	325.93	366.67
.1	40.83	81.67	122.50	163.33	204.17	245.00	285.83	326.67	367.50
.2	40.93	81.85	122.78	163.70	204.63	245.56	286.48	327.41	368.33
.3	41 02	82.04	123.06	164.07	205.09	246.11	287.13	328.15	369.17
.4	41.11	82.22	123.33	164.44	205.56	246.67	287.78	328.89	370.00
44.5	41.20	82.41	123.61	164.81	206.02	247.22	288.43	329.63	370.83
.6	41.30	82.59	123.89	165.19	206.48	247.78	289.07	330.37	371.67
.7	41.39	82.78	124.17	165.56	206.94	248.33	289.72	331.11	372.50
.8	41.48	82.96	124.44	165.93	207.41	248.89	290.37	331.85	373.33
.9	41.57	83.15	124.72	166.30	207.87	249.44	291.02	332.59	374.17
45.0	41.67	83.33	125.00	166.67	208.33	250.00	291.67	333.33	375.00
.1	41.76	83.52	125.28	167.04	208.80	250.56	292.31	334.07	375.83
.2	41.85	83.70	125.56	167.41	209.26	251.11	292.96	334.81	376.67
.3	41.94	83.89	125.83	167.78	209.72	251.67	293.61	335.56	377.50
.4	42.04	84.07	126.11	168.15	210.19	252.22	294.26	336.30	378.33
45.5	42.13	84.26	126.39	168.52	210.65	252.78	294.91	337.04	379.17
.6	42.22	84.44	126.67	168.89	211.11	253.33	295.56	337.78	380.00
.7	42.31	84.63	126.94	169.26	211.57	253.89	296.20	338.52	380.83
.8	42.41	84.81	127.22	169.63	212.04	254.44	296.85	339.26	381.67
.9	42.50	85.00	127.50	170.00	212.50	255.00	297.50	340.00	382.50
46.0	42.59	85.19	127.78	170.37	212.96	255.56	298.15	340.74	383.33
.1	42.69	85.37	128.06	170.74	213.43	256.11	298.80	341.48	384.17
.2	42.78	85.56	128.33	171.11	213.89	256.67	299.44	342.22	385.00
.3	42.87	85.74	128.61	171.48	214.35	257.22	300.09	342.96	385.83
.4	42.96	85.93	128.89	171.85	214.81	257.78	300.74	343.70	386.67
46.5	43.06	86.11	129.17	172.22	215.28	258.33	301.39	344.44	387.50
.6	43.15	86.30	129.44	172.59	215.74	258.89	302.04	345.19	388.33
.7	43.24	86.48	129.72	172.96	216.20	259.44	302.69	345.93	389.17
.8	43.33	86.67	130.00	173.33	216.67	260.00	303.33	346.67	390.00
.9	43.43	86.85	130.28	173.70	217.13	260.56	303.98	347.41	390.83
47.0	43.52	87.04	130.56	174.07	217.59	261.11	304.63	348.15	391.67
.1	43.61	87.22	130.83	174.44	218.06	261.67	305.28	348.89	392.50
.2	43.70	87.41	131.11	174.81	218.52	262.22	305.93	349.63	393.33
.3	43.80	87.59	131.39	175.19	218.98	262.78	306.57	350.37	394.17
.4	43.89	87.78	131.67	175.56	219.44	263.33	307.22	351.11	395.00
47.5	43.98	87.96	131.94	175.93	219.91	263.89	307.87	351.85	395.83
.6	44.07	88.15	132.22	176.30	220.37	264.44	308.52	352.59	396.67
.7	44.17	88.33	132.50	176.67	220.83	265.00	309.17	353.33	397.50
.8	44.26	88.52	132.78	177.04	221.30	265.56	309.81	354.07	398.33
.9	44.35	88.70	133.06	177.41	221.76	266.11	310.46	354.81	399.17

TABLE XVIII.—TRIANGULAR PRISMS. CUBIC YARDS PER 50 FEET

Height or Width	Width or Height								
	1	2	3	4	5	6	7	8	9
48.0	44.44	88.89	133.33	177.78	222.22	266.67	311.11	355.56	400.00
.1	44.54	89.07	133.61	178.15	222.69	267.22	311.76	356.30	400.83
.2	44.63	89.26	133.89	178.52	223.15	267.78	312.41	357.04	401.67
.3	44.72	89.44	134.17	178.89	223.61	268.33	313.06	357.78	402.50
.4	44.81	89.63	134.44	179.26	224.07	268.89	313.70	358.52	403.33
48.5	44.91	89.81	134.72	179.63	224.54	269.44	314.35	359.26	404.17
.6	45.00	90.00	135.00	180.00	225.00	270.00	315.00	360.00	405.00
.7	45.09	90.19	135.28	180.37	225.46	270.56	315.65	360.74	405.83
.8	45.19	90.37	135.56	180.74	225.93	271.11	316.30	361.48	406.67
.9	45.28	90.56	135.83	181.11	226.39	271.67	316.94	352.22	407.50
49.0	45.37	90.74	136.11	181.48	226.85	272.22	317.59	362.96	408.33
.1	45.46	90.93	136.39	181.85	227.31	272.78	318.24	363.70	409.17
.2	45.56	91.11	136.67	182.22	227.78	273.33	318.89	364.44	410.00
.3	45.65	91.30	136.94	182.59	228.24	273.89	319.54	365.19	410.83
.4	45.74	91.48	137.22	182.96	228.70	274.44	320.19	365.93	411.67
49.5	45.83	91.67	137.50	183.33	229.17	275.00	320.83	366.67	412.50
.6	45.93	91.85	137.78	183.70	229.63	275.56	321.48	367.41	413.33
.7	46.02	92.04	138.06	184.07	230.09	276.11	322.13	368.15	414.17
.8	46.11	92.22	138.33	184.44	230.56	276.67	322.78	368.89	415.00
.9	46.20	92.41	138.61	184.81	231.02	277.22	323.43	369.63	415.83
50.0	46.30	92.59	138.89	185.19	231.48	277.78	324.07	370.37	416.67
.1	46.39	92.78	139.17	185.56	231.94	278.33	324.72	371.11	417.50
.2	46.48	92.96	139.44	185.93	232.41	278.89	325.37	371.85	418.33
.3	46.57	93.15	139.72	186.30	232.87	279.44	326.02	372.59	419.17
.4	46.67	93.33	140.00	186.67	233.33	280.00	326.67	373.33	420.00
50.5	46.76	93.52	140.28	187.04	233.80	280.56	327.31	374.07	420.83
.6	46.85	93.70	140.56	187.41	234.26	281.11	327.96	374.81	421.67
.7	46.94	93.89	140.83	187.78	234.72	281.67	328.61	375.56	422.50
.8	47.04	94.07	141.11	188.15	235.19	282.22	329.26	376.30	423.33
.9	47.13	94.26	141.39	188.52	235.65	282.78	329.91	377.04	424.17
51.0	47.22	94.44	141.67	188.89	236.11	283.33	330.56	377.78	425.00
.1	47.31	94.63	141.94	189.26	236.57	283.89	331.20	378.52	425.83
.2	47.41	94.81	142.22	189.63	237.04	284.44	331.85	379.26	426.67
.3	47.50	95.00	142.50	190.00	237.50	285.00	332.50	380.00	427.50
.4	47.59	95.19	142.78	190.37	237.96	285.56	333.15	380.74	428.33
51.5	47.69	95.37	143.06	190.74	238.43	286.11	333.80	381.48	429.17
.6	47.78	95.56	143.33	191.11	238.89	286.67	334.44	382.22	430.00
.7	47.87	95.74	143.61	191.48	239.35	287.22	335.09	382.96	430.83
.8	47.96	95.93	143.89	191.85	239.81	287.78	335.74	383.70	431.67
.9	48.06	96.11	144.17	192.22	240.28	288.33	336.39	384.44	432.50
52.0	48.15	96.30	144.44	192.59	240.74	288.89	337.04	385.19	433.33
.1	48.24	96.48	144.72	192.96	241.20	289.44	337.69	385.93	434.17
.2	48.33	96.67	145.00	193.33	241.67	290.00	338.33	386.67	435.00
.3	48.43	96.85	145.28	193.70	242.13	290.56	338.98	387.41	435.83
.4	48.52	97.04	145.56	194.07	242.59	291.11	339.63	388.15	436.67
52.5	48.61	97.22	145.83	194.44	243.06	291.67	340.28	388.89	437.50
.6	48.70	97.41	146.11	194.81	243.52	292.22	340.93	389.63	438.33
.7	48.80	97.59	146.39	195.19	243.98	292.78	341.57	390.37	439.17
.8	48.89	97.78	146.67	195.56	244.44	293.33	342.22	391.11	440.00
.9	48.98	97.96	146.94	195.93	244.91	293.89	342.87	391.85	440.83
53.0	49.07	98.15	147.22	196.30	245.37	294.44	343.52	392.59	441.67
.1	49.17	98.33	147.50	196.67	245.83	295.00	344.17	393.33	442.50
.2	49.26	98.52	147.78	197.04	246.30	295.56	344.81	394.07	443.33
.3	49.35	98.70	148.06	197.41	246.76	296.11	345.46	394.81	444.17
.4	49.44	98.89	148.33	197.78	247.22	296.67	346.11	395.56	445.00
53.5	49.54	99.07	148.61	198.15	247.69	297.22	346.76	396.30	445.83
.6	49.63	99.26	148.89	198.52	248.15	297.78	347.41	397.04	446.67
.7	49.72	99.44	149.17	198.89	248.61	298.33	348.06	397.78	447.50
.8	49.81	99.63	•149.44	199.26	249.07	298.89	348.70	398.52	448.33
.9	49.91	99.81	149.72	199.63	249.54	299.44	349.35	399.26	449.17

TABLE XVIII.—TRIANGULAR PRISMS. CUBIC YARDS
PER 50 FEET

Height or Width	Width or Height								
	1	2	3	4	5	6	7	8	9
54.0	50.00	100.00	150.00	200.00	250.00	300.00	350.00	400.00	450.00
.1	50.09	100.19	150.28	200.37	250.46	300.56	350.65	400.74	450.83
.2	50.19	100.37	150.56	200.74	250.93	301.11	.351.30	401.48	451.67
.3	50.28	100.56	150.83	201.11	251.39	301.67	351.94	402.22	452.50
.4	50.37	100.74	151.11	201.48	251.85	302.22	352.59	402.96	453.33
54.5	50.46	100.93	151.39	201.85	252.31	302.78	353.24	403.70	454.17
.6	50.56	101.11	151.67	202.22	252.78	303.33	353.89	404.44	455.00
.7	50.65	101.30	151.94	202.59	253.24	303.89	354.54	405.19	455.83
.8	50.74	101.48	152.22	202.96	253.70	304.44	355.19	405.93	456.67
.9	50.83	101.67	152.50	203.33	254.17	305.00	355.83	406.67	457.50
55.0	50.93	101.85	152.78	203.70	254.63	305.56	356.48	407.41	458.33
.1	51.02	102.04	153.06	204.07	255.09	306.11	357.13	408.15	459.17
.2	51.11	102.22	153.33	204.44	255.56	306.67	357.78	408.89	460.00
.3	51.20	102.41	153.61	204.81	256.02	307.22	358.43	409.63	460.83
.4	51.30	102.59	153.89	205.19	256.48	307.78	359.07	410.37	461.67
55.5	51.39	102.78	154.17	205.56	256.94	308.33	359.72	411.11	462.50
.6	51.48	102.96	154.44	205.93	257.41	308.89	360.37	411.85	463.33
.7	51.57	103.15	154.72	206.30	257.87	309.44	361.02	412.59	464.17
.8	51.67	103.33	155.00	206.67	258.33	310.00	361.67	413.33	465.00
.9	51.76	103.52	155.28	207.04	258.80	310.56	362.31	414.07	465.83
56.0	51.85	103.70	155.56	207.41	259.26	311.11	362.96	414.81	466.67
.1	51.94	103.89	155.83	207.78	259.72	311.67	363.61	415.56	467.50
.2	52.04	104.07	156.11	208.15	260.19	312.22	364.26	416.30	468.33
.3	52.13	104.26	156.39	208.52	260.65	312.78	364.91	417.04	469.17
.4	52.22	104.44	156.67	208.89	261.11	313.33	365.56	417.78	470.00
56.5	52.31	104.63	156.94	209.26	261.57	313.89	366.20	418.52	470.83
.6	52.41	104.81	157.22	209.63	252.04	314.44	366.85	419.26	471.67
.7	52.50	105.00	157.50	210.00	262.50	315.00	367.50	420.00	472.50
.8	52.59	105.19	157.78	210.37	262.96	315.56	368.15	420.74	473.33
.9	52.69	105.37	158.06	210.74	263.43	316.11	368.80	421.48	474.17
57.0	52.78	105.56	158.33	211.11	263.89	316.67	369.44	422.22	475.00
.1	52.87	105.74	158.61	211.48	264.35	317.22	370.09	422.96	475.83
.2	52.96	105.93	158.89	211.85	264.81	317.78	370.74	423.70	476.67
.3	53.06	106.11	159.17	212.22	265.28	318.33	371.39	424.44	477.50
.4	53.15	106.30	159.44	212.59	265.74	318.89	372.04	425.19	478.33
57.5	53.24	106.48	159.72	212.96	266.20	319.44	372.69	425.93	479.17
.6	53.33	106.67	160.00	213.33	266.67	320.00	373.33	426.67	480.00
.7	53.43	106.85	160.28	213.70	267.13	320.56	373.98	427.41	480.83
.8	53.52	107.04	160.56	214.07	267.59	321.11	374.63	428.15	481.67
.9	53.61	107.22	160.83	214.44	268.06	321.67	375.28	428.89	482.50
58.0	53.70	107.41	161.11	214.81	268.52	322.22	375.93	429.63	483.33
.1	53.80	107.59	161.39	215.19	268.98	322.78	376.57	430.37	484.17
.2	53.89	107.78	161.67	215.56	269.44	323.33	377.22	431.11	485.00
.3	53.98	107.96	161.94	215.93	269.91	323.89	377.87	431.85	485.83
.4	54.07	108.15	162.22	216.30	270.37	324.44	378.52	432.59	486.67
58.5	54.17	108.33	162.50	216.67	270.83	325.00	379.17	433.33	487.50
.6	54.26	108.52	162.78	217.04	271.30	325.56	379.81	434.07	488.33
.7	54.35	108.70	163.06	217.41	271.76	326.11	380.46	434.81	489.17
.8	54.44	108.89	163.33	217.78	272.22	326.67	381.11	435.56	490.00
.9	54.54	109.07	163.61	218.15	272.69	327.22	381.76	436.30	490.83
59.0	54.63	109.26	163.89	218.52	273.15	327.78	382.41	437.04	491.67
.1	54.72	109.44	164.17	218.89	273.61	328.33	383.06	437.78	492.50
.2	54.81	109.63	164.44	219.26	274.07	328.89	383.70	438.52	493.33
.3	54.91	109.81	164.72	219.63	274.54	329.44	384.35	439.26	494.17
.4	55.00	110.00	165.00	220.00	275.00	330.00	385.00	440.00	495.00
59.5	55.09	110.19	165.28	220.37	275.46	330.56	385.65	440.74	495.83
.6	55.19	110.37	165.56	220.74	275.93	331.11	386.30	441.48	496.67
.7	55.28	110.56	165.83	221.11	276.39	331.67	386.94	442.22	497.50
.8	55.37	110.74	166.11	221.48	276.85	332.22	387.59	442.96	498.33
.9	55.46	110.93	166.39	221.85	277.31	332.78	388.24	443.70	499.17

TABLE XIX.—CUBIC YARDS PER 100-FOOT STATION

CU YD ↓	0	100	200	300	400	500	600	700	800	900	1000	1100
			SUM OF END AREAS IN SQ. FT									
0.0	0	54	108	162	216	270	324	378	432	486	540	594
1.9	1	55	109	163	217	271	325	379	433	487	541	595
3.7	2	56	110	164	218	272	326	380	434	488	542	596
5.6	3	57	111	165	219	273	327	381	435	489	543	597
7.4	4	58	112	166	220	274	328	382	436	490	544	598
9.3	5	59	113	167	221	275	329	383	437	491	545	599
11.1	6	60	114	168	222	276	330	384	438	492	546	600
13.0	7	61	115	169	223	277	331	385	439	493	547	601
14.8	8	62	116	170	224	278	332	386	440	494	548	602
16.7	9	63	117	171	225	279	333	387	441	495	549	603
18.5	10	64	118	172	226	280	334	388	442	496	550	604
20.4	11	65	119	173	227	281	335	389	443	497	551	605
22.2	12	66	120	174	228	282	336	390	444	498	552	606
24.1	13	67	121	175	229	283	337	391	445	499	553	607
25.9	14	68	122	176	230	284	338	392	446	500	554	608
27.8	15	69	123	177	231	285	339	393	447	501	555	609
29.6	16	70	124	178	232	286	340	394	448	502	556	610
31.5	17	71	125	179	233	287	341	395	449	503	557	611
33.3	18	72	126	180	234	288	342	396	450	504	558	612
35.2	19	73	127	181	235	289	343	397	451	505	559	613
37.0	20	74	128	182	236	290	344	398	452	506	560	614
38.9	21	75	129	183	237	291	345	399	453	507	561	615
40.7	22	76	130	184	238	292	346	400	454	508	562	616
42.6	23	77	131	185	239	293	347	401	455	509	563	617
44.4	24	78	132	186	240	294	348	402	456	510	564	618
46.3	25	79	133	187	241	295	349	403	457	511	565	619
48.1	26	80	134	188	242	296	350	404	458	512	566	620
50.0	27	81	135	189	243	297	351	405	459	513	567	621
51.9	28	82	136	190	244	298	352	406	460	514	568	622
53.7	29	83	137	191	245	299	353	407	461	515	569	623
55.6	30	84	138	192	246	300	354	408	462	516	570	624
57.4	31	85	139	193	247	301	355	409	463	517	571	625
59.3	32	86	140	194	248	302	356	410	464	518	572	626
61.1	33	87	141	195	249	303	357	411	465	519	573	627
63.0	34	88	142	196	250	304	358	412	466	520	574	628
64.8	35	89	143	197	251	305	359	413	467	521	575	629
66.7	36	90	144	198	252	306	360	414	468	522	576	630
68.5	37	91	145	199	253	307	361	415	469	523	577	631
70.4	38	92	146	200	254	308	362	416	470	524	578	632
72.2	39	93	147	201	255	309	363	417	471	525	579	633
74.1	40	94	148	202	256	310	364	418	472	526	580	634
75.9	41	95	149	203	257	311	365	419	473	527	581	635
77.8	42	96	150	204	258	312	366	420	474	528	582	636
79.6	43	97	151	205	259	313	367	421	475	529	583	637
81.5	44	98	152	206	260	314	368	422	476	530	584	638
83.3	45	99	153	207	261	315	369	423	477	531	585	639
85.2	46	100	154	208	262	316	370	424	478	532	586	640
87.0	47	101	155	209	263	317	371	425	479	533	587	641
88.9	48	102	156	210	264	318	372	426	480	534	588	642
90.7	49	103	157	211	265	319	373	427	481	535	589	643
92.6	50	104	158	212	266	320	374	428	482	536	590	644
94.4	51	105	159	213	267	321	375	429	483	537	591	645
96.3	52	106	160	214	268	322	376	430	484	538	592	646
98.1	53	107	161	215	269	323	377	431	485	539	593	647
	0	100	200	300	400	500	600	700	800	900	1000	1100

1200	1300	1400	1500	1600	1700	1800	1900	2000	2100	← CU YD ↓
		SUM	OF	END	AREAS	IN	SQ	FT		
648	702	756	810	864	918	972	1026	1080	1134	0.0
649	703	757	811	865	919	973	1027	1081	1135	1.9
650	704	758	812	866	920	974	1028	1082	1136	3.7
651	705	759	813	867	921	975	1029	1083	1137	5.6
652	706	760	814	868	922	976	1030	1084	1138	7.4
653	707	761	815	869	923	977	1031	1085	1139	9.3
654	708	762	816	870	924	978	1032	1086	1140	11.1
655	709	763	817	871	925	979	1033	1087	1141	13.0
656	710	764	818	872	926	980	1034	1088	1142	14.8
657	711	765	819	873	927	981	1035	1089	1143	16.7
658	712	766	820	874	928	982	1036	1090	1144	18.5
659	713	767	821	875	929	983	1037	1091	1145	20.4
660	714	768	822	876	930	984	1038	1092	1146	22.2
661	715	769	823	877	931	985	1039	1093	1147	24.1
662	716	770	824	878	932	986	1040	1094	1148	25.9
663	717	771	825	879	933	987	1041	1095	1149	27.8
664	718	772	826	880	934	988	1042	1096	1150	29.6
665	719	773	827	881	935	989	1043	1097	1151	31.5
666	720	774	828	882	936	990	1044	1098	1152	33.3
667	721	775	829	883	937	991	1045	1099	1153	35.2
668	722	776	830	884	938	992	1046	1100	1154	37.0
669	723	777	831	885	939	993	1047	1101	1155	38.9
670	724	778	832	886	940	994	1048	1102	1156	40.7
671	725	779	833	887	941	995	1049	1103	1157	42.6
672	726	780	834	888	942	996	1050	1104	1158	44.4
673	727	781	835	889	943	997	1051	1105	1159	46.3
674	728	782	836	890	944	998	1052	1106	1160	48.1
675	729	783	837	891	945	999	1053	1107	1161	50.0
676	730	784	838	892	946	1000	1054	1108	1162	51.9
677	731	785	839	893	947	1001	1055	1109	1163	53.7
678	732	786	840	894	948	1002	1056	1110	1164	55.6
679	733	787	841	895	949	1003	1057	1111	1165	57.4
680	734	788	842	896	950	1004	1058	1112	1166	59.3
681	735	789	843	897	951	1005	1059	1113	1167	61.1
682	736	790	844	898	952	1006	1060	1114	1168	63.0
683	737	791	845	899	953	1007	1061	1115	1169	64.8
684	738	792	846	900	954	1008	1062	1116	1170	66.7
685	739	793	847	901	955	1009	1063	1117	1171	68.5
686	740	794	848	902	956	1010	1064	1118	1172	70.4
687	741	795	849	903	957	1011	1065	1119	1173	72.2
688	742	796	850	904	958	1012	1066	1120	1174	74.1
689	743	797	851	905	959	1013	1067	1121	1175	75.9
690	744	798	852	906	960	1014	1068	1122	1176	77.8
691	745	799	853	907	961	1015	1069	1123	1177	79.6
692	746	800	854	908	962	1016	1070	1124	1178	81.5
693	747	801	855	909	963	1017	1071	1125	1179	83.3
694	748	802	856	910	964	1018	1072	1126	1180	85.2
695	749	803	857	911	965	1019	1073	1127	1181	87.0
696	750	804	858	912	966	1020	1074	1128	1182	88.9
697	751	805	859	913	967	1021	1075	1129	1183	90.7
698	752	806	860	914	968	1022	1076	1130	1184	92.6
699	753	807	861	915	969	1023	1077	1131	1185	94.4
700	754	808	862	916	970	1024	1078	1132	1186	96.3
701	755	809	863	917	971	1025	1079	1133	1187	98.1
1200	1300	1400	1500	1600	1700	1800	1900	2000	2100	

TABLE XX.—NATURAL SINES, COSINES,

Explanation

This table is adapted to the rapid solution of route-surveying problems by computing machine. Its special advantages are: (1) six significant figures; (2) most-frequently used functions in one table; (3) "streamline" interpolation for multiples of 10″ and 15″; (4) chances for mistakes reduced by elimination of column headings at bottom of page and by use of only one degree per page.

Precise angle and distance measurements in route surveying justify one more figure than in the usual 5-place table, but hardly justify 7-place tables.

In a large number of curve formulas the sine and versine of the same angle appear. Other combinations are sin-tan-cos and sin-cos-tan-vers. The appearance of these functions in the same table should save time. The omission of cotangents is of little consequence since they are rarely used in route surveying; if needed, they are equivalent to the tangent of the complement.

The most serious defect of most tables of natural functions is the absence of a convenient aid in interpolating for seconds. This defect is remedied in Table XX, largely through the use of sets of corrections for multiples of 10″ and 15″. These multiples are the ones most frequently needed when single or double angles are turned with a 20″, 30″, or 1′ instrument.

Example. Find the tangent of 28° 18′ 45″. Answer: 0.538444+281 = 0.538725.

The foregoing is the quickest method and is sufficiently precise for most purposes. However, because the sets of corrections are exact at the middle of the indicated range, slightly greater precision would be obtained in this example by adding a correction of 282, since the 45″ correction at 28° 30′ is 283. This method gives 0.538726. Many computers would prefer to subtract the 15″ correction of 94 from the tangent of 28° 19′ (an excellent method), giving also 0.538726. Use of these more precise methods is recommended for finding exsecants of angles between 45° and 60°, and for tangents and exsecants of angles above 70°.

Obviously, corrections for any number of seconds could be obtained speedily, if the field work justifies, by combining the tabulated corrections and shifting the decimal point.

'	Sine	Corr. for Sec.	Cosine	Corr. for Sec.	Versine	Exsec	Corr. for Sec.	Corr. for Sec.	Tangent	'
		+		− +			+	+		
0	Zero		One		Zero	Zero			Zero	0
1	.000291		One		Zero	Zero			.000291	1
2	0582		One		Zero	Zero			0582	2
3	0873		One		Zero	Zero			0873	3
4	1164		.999999		.000001	.000001			1164	4
5	.001454		.999999		.000001	.000001			.001454	5
6	1745		9998		0002	0001			1745	6
7	2036		9998		0002	0002			2036	7
8	2327		9997	By	0003	0003	By		2327	8
9	2618		9997	Inspec-	0003	0003	Inspec-		2618	9
10	.002909		.999996	tion	.000004	.000004	tion		.002909	10
11	3200	" Corr.	9995		0005	0005		" Corr.	3200	11
12	3491	10 48	9994		0006	0006		10 48	3491	12
13	3782	15 73	9993		0007	0007		15 73	3782	13
14	4072	20 97	9992		0008	0008		20 97	4072	14
15	.004363	30 145	.999990		.000010	.000010		30 145	.004363	15
16	4654	40 194	9989		0011	0011		40 194	4654	16
17	4945	45 218	9988		0012	0012		45 218	4945	17
18	5236	50 242	9986		0014	0014		50 242	5236	18
19	5527		9985		0015	0015			5527	19
20	.005818		.999983		.000017	.000017			.905818	20
21	6109		9981		0019	0019			6109	21
22	6400		9980		0020	0020			6400	22
23	6690		9978		0022	0022			6690	23
24	6981		9976		0024	0024			6981	24
25	.007272		.999974		.000026	.000026			.007272	25
26	7563		9971		0029	0029			7563	26
27	7854		9969		0031	0031			7854	27
28	8145		9967		0033	0033			8145	28
29	8436		9964		0036	0036			8436	29
30	.008726		.999962		.000038	.000038			.008727	30
31	9017		9959		0041	0041			9018	31
32	9308		9957		0043	0043			9309	32
33	9599		9954		0046	0046			9600	33
34	9890		9951		0049	0049			9890	34
35	.010181		.999948		.000052	.000052			.010181	35
36	0472		9945		0055	0055			0472	36
37	0763		9942		0058	0058			0763	37
38	1054		9939		0061	0061			1054	38
39	1344		9936		0064	0064			1345	39
40	.011635		.999932		.000068	.000068			.011636	40
41	1926	" Corr.	9929		0071	0071		" Corr.	1927	41
42	2217	10 48	9925		0075	0075		10 48	2218	42
43	2508	15 73	9922		0078	0078		15 73	2509	43
44	2799	20 97	9918		0082	0082		20 97	2800	44
45	.013090	30 145	.999914		.000086	.000086		30 145	.013091	45
46	3380	40 194	9910		0090	0090		40 194	3382	46
47	3671	45 218	9906		0094	0094		45 218	3673	47
48	3962	50 242	9902		0098	0098		50 242	3964	48
49	4253		9898		0102	0102			4254	49
50	.014544		.999894		.000106	.000106			.014545	50
51	4835		9890		0110	0110			4836	51
52	5126		9886		0114	0114			5127	52
53	5416		9881		0119	0119			5418	53
54	5707		9877		0123	0123			5709	54
55	.015998		.999872		.000128	.000128			.016000	55
56	6289		9867		0133	0133			6291	56
57	6580		9862		0138	0138			6582	57
58	6871		9858		0142	0142			6873	58
59	7162		9853		0147	0147			7164	59
60	.017452		.999848		.000152	.000152			.017455	60

TABLE XX.—NATURAL SINES, COSINES,
1°

'	Sine	Corr. for Sec.	Cosine	Corr. for Sec.	Versine	Exsec	Corr. for Sec.	Corr. for Sec.	Tangent	'
		+		− +			+	+		
0	.017452		.999848		.000152	.000152			.017455	0
1	7743		9843		0157	0157			7746	1
2	8034		9837		0163	0163			8037	2
3	8325		9832		0168	0168			8328	3
4	8616		9827		0173	0173			8619	4
5	.018907		.999821		.000179	.000179			.018910	5
6	9197		9816		0184	0184			9201	6
7	9488		9810		0190	0190			9492	7
8	9779		9804		0196	0196			9783	8
9	.020070		9799		0201	0201			.020074	9
10	.020361		.999793		.000207	.000207			.020365	10
11	0652	" Corr.	9787	" Corr.	0213	0213	" Corr.	" Corr.	0656	11
12	0942	10 48	9781	10 1	0219	0219	10 1	10 49	0947	12
13	1233	15 73	9774	15 2	0226	0226	15 2	15 73	1238	13
14	1524	20 97	9768	20 2	0232	0232	20 2	20 97	1529	14
15	.021815	30 145	.999762	30 3	.000238	.000238	30 3	30 146	.021820	15
16	2106	40 194	9756	40 4	0244	0244	40 4	40 194	2111	16
17	2396	45 218	9749	45 5	0251	0251	45 5	45 218	2402	17
18	2687	50 242	9743	50 5	0257	0257	50 5	50 243	2693	18
19	2978		9736		0264	0264			2984	19
20	.023269		.999729		.000271	.000271			.023275	20
21	3560		9722		0278	0278			3566	21
22	3851		9716		0284	0284			3857	22
23	4141		9709		0291	0291			4148	23
24	4432		9702		0298	0299			4439	24
25	.024723		.999694		.000306	.000306			.024730	25
26	5014		9687		0313	0313			5022	26
27	5305		9680		0320	0320			5313	27
28	5595		9672		0328	0328			5604	28
29	5886		9665		0335	0335			5895	29
30	.026177		.999657		.000343	.000343			.026186	30
31	6468		9650		0350	0350			6477	31
32	6758		9642		0358	0358			6768	32
33	7049		9634		0366	0366			7059	33
34	7340		9626		0374	0374			7350	34
35	.027631		.999618		.000382	.000382			.027641	35
36	7922		9610		0390	0390			7932	36
37	8212		9602		0398	0398			8224	37
38	8503		9594		0406	0406			8515	38
39	8794		9585		0415	0415			8806	39
40	.029085		.999577		.000423	.000423			.029097	40
41	9376	" Corr.	9568	" Corr.	0432	0432	" Corr.	" Corr.	9388	41
42	9666	10 48	9560	10 1	0440	0440	10 1	10 49	9679	42
43	9957	15 73	9551	15 2	0449	0449	15 2	15 73	9970	43
44	.030248	20 97	9542	20 3	0458	0458	20 3	20 97	.030262	44
45	.030538	30 145	.999534	30 4	.000466	.000467	30 4	30 146	.030553	45
46	0829	40 194	9525	40 6	0475	0476	40 6	40 194	0844	46
47	1120	45 218	9516	45 7	0484	0485	45 7	45 218	1135	47
48	1411	50 242	9507	50 7	0493	0494	50 7	50 243	1426	48
49	1701		9497		0503	0503			1717	49
50	.031992		.999488		.000512	.000512			.032009	50
51	2283		9479		0521	0521			2300	51
52	2574		9469		0531	0531			2591	52
53	2864		9460		0540	0540			2882	53
54	3155		9450		0550	0550			3173	54
55	.033446		.999440		.000559	.000560			.033465	55
56	3737		9431		0569	0570			3756	56
57	4027		9421		0579	0579			4047	57
58	4318		9411		0589	0589			4338	58
59	4609		9401		0599	0599			4629	59
60	.034899		.999391		.000609	.000609			.034921	60

'	Sine	Corr. for Sec. +	Cosine	Corr. for Sec. - +	Versine	Exsec	Corr. for Sec. +	Corr. for Sec. +	Tangent	'
0	.034900		.999391		.000609	.000610			.034921	0
1	5190		9381		0619	0620			5212	1
2	5481		9370		0630	0630			5503	2
3	5772		9360		0640	0640			5794	3
4	6062		9350		0650	0651			6086	4
5	.036353		.999339		.000661	.000661			.036377	5
6	6644		9328		0672	0672			6668	6
7	6934		9318		0682	0683			6960	7
8	7225		9307		0693	0694			7251	8
9	7516		9296		0704	0704			7542	9
10	.037806		.999285		.000715	.000715			.037834	10
11	8097	" Corr.	9274	" Corr.	0726	0726	" Corr.	" Corr.	8125	11
12	8388	10 48	9263	10 2	0737	0738	10 2	10 49	8416	12
13	8678	15 73	9252	15 3	0748	0749	15 3	15 73	8707	13
14	8969	20 97	9240	20 4	0760	0760	20 4	20 97	8999	14
15	.039260	30 145	.999229	30 6	.000771	.000772	30 6	30 146	.039290	15
16	9550	40 194	9218	40 8	0782	0783	40 8	40 194	9581	16
17	9841	45 218	9206	45 9	0794	0795	45 9	45 219	9873	17
18	.040132	50 242	9194	50 10	0806	0806	50 10	50 243	.040164	18
19	0422		9183		0817	0818			0456	19
20	.040713		.999171		.000829	.000830			.040747	20
21	1004		9159		0841	0842			1038	21
22	1294		9147		0853	0854			1330	22
23	1585		9135		0865	0866			1621	23
24	1876		9123		0877	0878			1912	24
25	.042166		.999111		.000889	.000890			.042204	25
26	2457		9098		0902	0902			2495	26
27	2748		9086		0914	0915			2787	27
28	3038		9073		0927	0927			3078	28
29	3329		9061		0939	0940			3370	29
30	.043619		.999048		.000952	.000953			.043661	30
31	3910		9036		0964	0965			3952	31
32	4201		9023		0977	0978			4244	32
33	4491		9010		0990	0991			4535	33
34	4782		8997		1003	1004			4827	34
35	.045072		.998984		.001016	.001017			.045118	35
36	5363		8971		1029	1030			5410	36
37	5654		8957		1043	1044			5701	37
38	5944		8944		1056	1057			5993	38
39	6235		8931		1069	1070			6284	39
40	.046525		.998917		.001083	.001084			.046576	40
41	6816	" Corr.	8904	" Corr.	1096	1098	" Corr.	" Corr.	6867	41
42	7106	10 48	8890	10 2	1110	1111	10 2	10 49	7159	42
43	7397	15 73	8876	15 3	1124	1125	15 3	15 73	7450	43
44	7688	20 97	8862	20 5	1138	1139	20 5	20 97	7742	44
45	.047978	30 145	.998848	30 7	.001152	.001153	30 7	30 146	.048033	45
46	8269	40 194	8834	40 9	1166	1167	40 9	40 194	8325	46
47	8559	45 218	8820	45 10	1180	1181	45 10	45 219	8617	47
48	8850	50 242	8806	50 12	1194	1195	50 12	50 243	8908	48
49	9140		8792		1208	1210			9200	49
50	.049431		.998778		.001222	.001224			.049491	50
51	9721		8763		1237	1238			9783	51
52	.050012		8749		1251	1253			.050075	52
53	0302		8734		1266	1268			0366	53
54	0593		8719		1281	1282			0658	54
55	.050884		.998705		.001295	.001297			.050950	55
56	1174		8690		1310	1312			1241	56
57	1464		8675		1325	1327			1533	57
58	1755		8660		1340	1342			1824	58
59	2046		8645		1355	1357			2116	59
60	.052336		.998630		.001370	.001372			.052408	60

TABLE XX.—NATURAL SINES, COSINES,
3°

'	Sine	Corr. for Sec. +	Cosine	Corr. for Sec. − +	Versine	Exsec	Corr. for Sec. +	Corr. for Sec. +	Tangent	'
0	.052336		.998630		.001370	.001372			.052408	0
1	2626		8614		1386	1388			2700	1
2	2917		8599		1401	1403			2991	2
3	3207		8584		1416	1418			3283	3
4	3498		8568		1432	1434			3575	4
5	.053788		.998552		.001448	.001450			.053866	5
6	4079		8537		1463	1466			4158	6
7	4369		8521		1479	1481			4450	7
8	4660		8505		1495	1497			4742	8
9	4950		8489		1511	1513			5033	9
10	.055241		.998473		.001527	.001529			.055325	10
11	5531	" Corr.	8457	" Corr.	1543	1545	" Corr.	" Corr.	5617	11
12	5822	10 48	8441	10 3	1559	1562	10 3	10 49	5909	12
13	6112	15 73	8424	15 4	1576	1578	15 4	15 73	6200	13
14	6402	20 97	8408	20 5	1592	1594	20 5	20 97	6492	14
15	.056693	30 145	.998392	30 8	.001608	.001611	30 8	30 146	.056784	15
16	6983	40 194	8375	40 11	1625	1628	40 11	40 195	7076	16
17	7274	45 218	8358	45 12	1642	1644	45 12	45 219	7368	17
18	7564	50 242	8342	50 14	1658	1661	50 14	50 243	7660	18
19	7854		8325		1675	1678			7952	19
20	.058145		.998308		.001692	.001695			.058243	20
21	8435		8291		1709	1712			8535	21
22	8726		8274		1726	1729			8827	22
23	9016		8257		1743	1746			9119	23
24	9306		8240		1760	1763			9411	24
25	.059597		.998222		.001778	.001781			.059703	25
26	9887		8205		1795	1798			9995	26
27	.060178		8188		1812	1816			.060287	27
28	0468		8170		1830	1833			0579	28
29	0758		8152		1848	1851			0871	29
30	.061048		.998135		.001865	.001869			.061163	30
31	1339		8117		1883	1887			1455	31
32	1629		8099		1901	1904			1747	32
33	1920		8081		1919	1922			2039	33
34	2210		8063		1937	1941			2331	34
35	.062500		.998045		.001955	.001959			.062623	35
36	2790		8027		1973	1977			2915	36
37	3081		8008		1992	1996			3207	37
38	3371		7990		2010	2014			3499	38
39	3661		7972		2028	2033			3791	39
40	.063952		.997953		.002047	.002051			.064083	40
41	4242	" Corr.	7934	" Corr.	2066	2070	" Corr.	" Corr.	4375	41
42	4532	10 48	7916	10 3	2084	2089	10 3	10 49	4667	42
43	4823	15 73	7897	15 5	2103	2108	15 5	15 73	4959	43
44	5113	20 97	7878	20 6	2122	2127	20 6	20 97	5251	44
45	.065403	30 145	.997859	30 9	.002141	.002146	30 9	30 146	.065544	45
46	5693	40 194	7840	40 13	2160	2165	40 13	40 195	5836	46
47	5984	45 218	7821	45 14	2179	2184	45 14	45 219	6128	47
48	6274	50 242	7802	50 16	2198	2203	50 16	50 243	6420	48
49	6564		7782		2218	2223			6712	49
50	.066854		.997763		.002237	.002242			.067004	50
51	7145		7743		2257	2262			7297	51
52	7435		7724		2276	2282			7589	52
53	7725		7704		2296	2301			7881	53
54	8015		7684		2316	2321			8173	54
55	.068306		.997664		.002336	.002341			.068465	55
56	8596		7644		2356	2361			8758	56
57	8886		7624		2376	2381			9050	57
58	9176		7604		2396	2401			9342	58
59	9466		7584		2416	2422			9634	59
60	.069756		.997564		.002436	.002442			.069927	60

'	Sine	Corr. for Sec.	Cosine	Corr. for Sec.	Versine	Exsec	Corr. for Sec.	Corr. for Sec.	Tangent	'
0	.069756	+	.997564	− +	.002436	.002442	+	+	.069927	0
1	.070047		7544		2456	2462			.070219	1
2	0337		7523		2477	2483			0512	2
3	0627		7503		2497	2504			0804	3
4	0917		7482		2518	2524			1096	4
5	.071207		.997462		.002538	.002545			.071388	5
6	1497		7441		2559	2566			1681	6
7	1788		7420		2580	2587			1973	7
8	2078		7399		2601	2608			2266	8
9	2368		7378		2622	2629			2558	9
10	.072658		.997357		.002643	.002650			.072850	10
11	2948	" Corr.	7336	" Corr.	2664	2671	" Corr.	" Corr.	3143	11
12	3238	10 48	7314	10 4	2686	2693	10 4	10 49	3435	12
13	3528	15 73	7293	15 5	2707	2714	15 5	15 73	3728	13
14	3818	20 97	7272	20 7	2728	2736	20 7	20 97	4020	14
15	.074148	30 145	:997250	30 11	.002750	.002757	30 11	30 146	.074313	15
16	4399	40 193	7229	40 14	2771	2779	40 14	40 195	4605	16
17	4689	45 218	7207	45 16	2793	2801	45 16	45 219	4898	17
18	4979	50 242	7185	50 18	2815	2823	50 18	50 244	5190	18
19	5269		7163		2837	2845			5483	19
20	.075559		.997141		.002859	.002867			.075776	20
21	5849		7119		2881	2889			6068	21
22	6139		7097		2903	2911			6361	22
23	6429		7075		2925	2934			6653	23
24	6719		7053		2947	2956			6946	24
25	.077009		.997030		.002970	.002979			.077238	25
26	7299		7008		2992	3001			7531	26
27	7589		6985		3015	3024			7824	27
28	7879		6963		3037	3046			8116	28
29	8169		6940		3060	3069			8409	29
30	.078459		.996917		.003083	.003092			.078702	30
31	8749		6894		3106	3115			8994	31
32	9039		6872		3128	3138			9287	32
33	9329		6848		3152	3162			9580	33
34	9619		6825		3175	3185			9873	34
35	.079909		.996802		.003198	.003208			.080165	35
36	.080199		· 6779		3221	3232			0458	36
37	0489		6756		3244	3255			0751	37
38	0779		6732		3268	3279			1044	38
39	1069		6708		3292	3302			1336	39
40	.081359		.996685		.003315	.003326			.081629	40
41	1649	" Corr.	6661	" Corr.	3339	3350	" Corr.	" Corr.	1922	41
42	1939	10 48	6637	10 4	3363	3374	10 4	10 49	2215	42
43	2228	15 72	6614	15 6	3386	3398	15 6	15 73	2508	43
44	2518	20 97	6590	20 8	3410	3422	20 8	20 98	2801	44
45	.082808	30 145	.996566	30 12	.003434	.003446	30 12	30 146	.083094	45
46	3098	40 193	6541	40 16	3459	3471	40 16	40 195	3387	46
47	3368	45 217	6517	45 18	3483	3495	45 18	45 220	3679	47
48	3678	50 242	6493	50 20	3507	3520	50 20	50 244	3972	48
49	3968		6468		3532	3544			4265	49
50	.084258		.996444		.003556	.003569			.084558	50
51	4547		6420		3580	3593			4851	51
52	4837		6395		3605	3618			5144	52
53	5127		6370		3630	3643			5437	53
54	5417		6345		3655	3668			5730	54
55	.085707		.996320		.003680	.003693			.086023	55
56	5997		6295		3705	3718			6316	56
57	6286		6270		3730	3744			6609	57
58	6576		6245		3755	3769			6902	58
59	6866		6220		3780	3794			7196	59
60	.087156		.996195		.003805	.003820			.087489	60

TABLE XX.—NATURAL SINES, COSINES,
5°

'	Sine	Corr. for Sec. +	Cosine	Corr. for Sec. − +	Versine	Exsec	Corr. for Sec. +	Corr. for Sec. +	Tangent	'
0	.087156		.996195		.003805	.003820			.087489	0
1	7446		6169		3831	3845			7782	1
2	7735		6144		3856	3871			8075	2
3	8025		6118		3882	3897			8368	3
4	8315		6093		3907	3923			8661	4
5	.088605		.996067		.003933	.003949			.088954	5
6	8894		6041		3959	3975			9246	6
7	9184		6015		3985	4001			9541	7
8	9474		5989		4011	4027			9834	8
9	9764		5963		4037	4053			.090127	9
10	.090053		5937		4063	4080			0421	10
11	0343	" Corr.	5911	" Corr.	4089	4106	" Corr.	" Corr.	0714	11
12	0633	10 48	5884	10 4	4116	4133	10 4	10 49	1007	12
13	0922	15 72	5858	15 7	4142	4159	15 7	15 73	1300	13
14	1212	20 97	5832	20 9	4168	4186	20 9	20 98	1594	14
15	.091502	30 145	.995805	30 13	.004195	.004213	30 13	30 147	.091887	15
16	1791	40 193	5778	40 18	4222	4240	40 18	40 196	2180	16
17	2081	45 217	5752	45 20	4248	4267	45 20	45 220	2474	17
18	2371	50 241	5725	50 22	4275	4294	50 22	50 244	2767	18
19	2660		5698		4302	4321			3061	19
20	.092950		.995671		.004329	.004348			.093354	20
21	3240		5644		4356	4375			3647	21
22	3529		5616		4384	4403			3941	22
23	3819		5589		4411	4430			4234	23
24	4108		5562		4438	4458			4528	24
25	.094398		.995534		.004466	.004486			.094821	25
26	4688		5507		4493	4513			5115	26
27	4977		5480		4520	4541			5408	27
28	5267		5452		4548	4569			5702	28
29	5556		5424		4576	4597			5996	29
30	.095846		.995396		.004604	.004625			.096289	30
31	6135		5368		4632	4653			6583	31
32	6425		5340		4660	4682			6876	32
33	6714		5312		4688	4710			7170	33
34	7004		5284		4716	4738			7464	34
35	.097293		.995256		.004744	.004767			.097757	35
36	7583		5227		4773	4796			8051	36
37	7872		5199		4801	4824			8345	37
38	8162		5170		4830	4853			8638	38
39	8451		5142		4858	4882			8932	39
40	.098741		.995113		.004887	.004911			.099226	40
41	9030	" Corr.	5084	" Corr.	4916	4940	" Corr.	" Corr.	9520	41
42	9320	10 48	5056	10 5	4944	4969	10 5	10 49	9813	42
43	9609	15 72	5027	15 7	4973	4998	15 7	15 73	.100107	43
44	9899	20 96	4998	20 10	5002	5028	20 10	20 98	0401	44
45	.100188	30 145	.994968	30 15	.005032	.005057	30 15	30 147	.100695	45
46	0478	40 193	4939	40 20	5061	5086	40 20	40 196	0989	46
47	0767	45 217	4910	45 22	5090	5116	45 22	45 220	1282	47
48	1056	50 241	4881	50 24	5119	5146	50 24	50 245	1576	48
49	1346		4851		5149	5175			1870	49
50	.101635		.994822		.005178	.005205			.102164	50
51	1924		4792		5208	5235			2458	51
52	2214		4762		5238	5265			2752	52
53	2503		4733		5267	5295			3046	53
54	2792		4703		5297	5325			3340	54
55	.103082		.994673		.005327	.005356			.103634	55
56	3371		4643		5357	5386			3928	56
57	3660		4613		5387	5416			4222	57
58	3950		4582		5418	5447			4516	58
59	4239		4552		5448	5478			4810	59
60	.104528		.994522		.005478	.005508			.105104	60

'	Sine	Corr. for Sec. +	Cosine	Corr. for Sec. − +	Versine	Exsec	Corr. for Sec. +	Corr. for Sec. +	Tangent	'
0	.104528		.994522		.005478	.005508			.105104	0
1	4818		4491		5509	5539			5398	1
2	5107		4461		5539	5570			5692	2
3	5396		4430		5570	5601			5987	3
4	5686		4400		5600	5632			6281	4
5	.105975		.994369		.005631	.005663			.106575	5
6	6264		4338		5662	5694			6869	6
7	6553		4307		5693	5726			7163	7
8	6842		4276		5724	5757			7458	8
9	7132		4245		5755	5788			7752	9
10	.107421		.994214		.005786	.005820			.108046	10
11	7710	" Corr.	4182	" Corr.	5818	5852	" Corr.	" Corr.	8340	11
12	7999	10 48	4151	10 5	5849	5883	10 5	10 49	8635	12
13	8288	15 72	4120	15 8	5880	5915	15 8	15 74	8929	13
14	8578	20 96	4088	20 11	5912	5947	20 11	20 98	9223	14
15	.108867	30 145	.994056	30 16	.005944	.005979	30 16	30 147	.109518	15
16	9156	40 193	4025	40 21	5975	6011	40 21	40 196	9812	16
17	9445	45 217	3993	45 24	6007	6044	45 24	45 221	.110107	17
18	9734	50 241	3961	50 26	6039	6076	50 27	50 245	0401	18
19	.110023		3929		6071	6108			0696	19
20	.110313		.993897		.006103	.006140			.110990	20
21	0602		3865		6135	6173			1284	21
22	0891		3833		6167	6206			1579	22
23	1180		3800		6200	6238			1873	23
24	1469		3768		6232	6271			2168	24
25	.111758		.993736		.006264	.006304			.112462	25
26	2047		3703		6297	6337			2757	26
27	2336		3670		6330	6370			3052	27
28	2625		3638		6362	6403			3346	28
29	2914		3605		6395	6436			3641	29
30	.113203		.993572		.006428	.006470			.113936	30
31	3492		3539		6461	6503			4230	31
32	3781		3506		6494	6537			4525	32
33	4070		3473		6527	6570			4820	33
34	4359		3440		6560	6604			5114	34
35	.114648		.993406		.006594	.006638			.115409	35
36	4937		3373		6627	6671			5704	36
37	5226		3339		6661	6705			5999	37
38	5515		3306		6694	6739			6294	38
39	5804		3272		6728	6774			6588	39
40	.116093		.993238		.006762	.006808			.116883	40
41	6382	" Corr.	3204	" Corr.	6796	6842	" Corr.	" Corr.	7178	41
42	6671	10 48	3171	10 6	6829	6876	10 6	10 49	7473	42
43	6960	15 72	3137	15 9	6863	6911	15 9	15 74	7768	43
44	7248	20 96	3103	20 11	6897	6945	20 12	20 98	8063	44
45	.117537	30 144	.993069	30 17	.006931	.006980	30 17	30 147	.118358	45
46	7826	40 193	3034	40 23	6966	7015	40 23	40 197	8653	46
47	8115	45 217	3000	45 26	7000	7049	45 26	45 221	8948	47
48	8404	50 241	2966	50 29	7034	7084	50 29	50 246	9243	48
49	8693		2931		7069	7119			9538	49
50	.118982		.992896		.007104	.007154			.119833	50
51	9270		2862		7138	7190			.120128	51
52	9559		2827		7173	7225			0423	52
53	9848		2792		7208	7260			0718	53
54	.120137		2757		7243	7296			1013	54
55	.120426		.992722		.007278	.007331			.121308	55
56	0714		2687		7313	7367			1604	56
57	1003		2652		7348	7402			1899	57
58	1292		2617		7383	7438			2194	58
59	1581		2582		7418	7474			2489	59
60	.121869		.992546		.007454	.007510			.122785	60

TABLE XX.—NATURAL SINES, COSINES,

7°

'	Sine	Corr. for Sec. +	Cosine	Corr. for Sec. − +	Versine	Exsec	Corr. for Sec. +	Corr. for Sec. +	Tangent	'
0	.121869		.992546		.007454	.007510			.122785	0
1	2158		2511		7489	7546			3080	1
2	2447		2475		7525	7582			3375	2
3	2736		2439		7561	7618			3670	3
4	3024		2404		7596	7654			3966	4
5	.123313		.992368		.007632	.007691			.124261	5
6	3602		2332		7668	7727			4557	6
7	3890		2296		7704	7764			4852	7
8	4179		2260		7740	7800			5147	8
9	4467		2224		7776	7837			5443	9
10	.124756		.992187		.007813	.007874			.125738	10
11	5045	" Corr.	2151	" Corr.	7849	7911	" Corr.	" Corr.	6034	11
12	5333	10 48	2115	10 6	7885	7948	10 6	10 49	6329	12
13	5622	15 72	2078	15 9	7922	7985	15 9	15 74	6625	13
14	5910	20 96	2042	20 12	7958	8022	20 12	20 99	6920	14
15	.126199	30 144	.992005	30 18	.007995	.008060	30 19	30 148	.127216	15
16	6488	40 192	1968	40 25	8032	8097	40 25	40 197	7512	16
17	6776	45 216	1931	45 28	8069	8134	45 28	45 222	7807	17
18	7065	50 241	1894	50 31	8106	8172	50 31	50 246	8103	18
19	7353		1857		8143	8209			8399	19
20	.127642		.991820		.008180	.008247			.128694	20
21	7930		1783		8217	8285			8990	21
22	8219		1746		8254	8323			9286	22
23	8507		1709		8291	8361			9582	23
24	8796		1671		8329	8399			9877	24
25	.129084		.991634		.008366	.008437			.130173	25
26	9372		1596		8404	8475			0469	26
27	9661		1558		8442	8514			0765	27
28	9949		1521		8479	8552			1061	28
29	10238		1483		8517	8590			1357	29
30	.130526		.991445		.008555	.008629			.131652	30
31	0815		1407		8593	8668			1948	31
32	1103		1369		8631	8706			2244	32
33	1391		1331		8669	8745			2540	33
34	1680		1292		8708	8784			2836	34
35	.131968		.991254		.008746	.008823			.133132	35
36	2256		1216		8784	8862			3428	36
37	2545		1177		8823	8902			3725	37
38	2833		1138		8862	8941			4021	38
39	3121		1100		8900	8980			4317	39
40	.133410		.991061		.008939	.009020			.134613	40
41	3698	" Corr.	1022	" Corr.	8976	9059	" Corr.	" Corr.	4909	41
42	3986	10 48	0983	10 7	9017	9099	10 7	10 49	5205	42
43	4274	15 72	0944	15 10	9056	9139	15 10	15 74	5502	43
44	4563	20 96	0905	20 13	9095	9178	20 13	20 99	5798	44
45	.134851	30 144	.990866	30 20	.009134	.009218	30 20	30 148	.136094	45
46	5139	40 192	0827	40 26	9173	9258	40 27	40 198	6390	46
47	5427	45 216	0787	45 29	9213	9296	45 30	45 222	6687	47
48	5716	50 240	0748	50 33	9252	9339	50 33	50 247	6983	48
49	6004		0708		9292	9379			7279	49
50	.136292		.990669		.009331	.009419			.137576	50
51	6580		0629		9371	9460			7872	51
52	6868		0589		9411	9500			8168	52
53	7156		0549		9451	9541			8465	53
54	7444		0510		9490	9582			8762	54
55	.137733		.990469		.009531	.009622			.139058	55
56	8021		0429		9571	9663			9354	56
57	8309		0389		9611	9704			9651	57
58	8597		0349		9651	9745			9948	58
59	8885		0308		9692	9786			.140244	59
60	.139173		.990268		.009732	.009828			.140541	60

'	Sine	Corr. for Sec.	Cosine	Corr. for Sec.	Versine	Exsec	Corr. for Sec.	Corr. for Sec.	Tangent	'
0	.139173	+	.990268	− +	.009732	.009828	+	+	.140541	0
1	9461		0228		9772	9869			0838	1
2	9749		0187		9813	9910			1134	2
3	.140037		0146		9854	9952			1431	3
4	0325		0106		9894	9993			1728	4
5	.140613		.990065		.009935	.010035			.142024	5
6	0901		0024		9976	0077			2321	6
7	1189		.989983		.010017	. 0119			2618	7
8	1477		9942		0058	0161			2915	8
9	1765		9900		0100	0203			3212	9
10	.142053		.989859		.010141	.010245			.143508	10
11	2341	" Corr. 10 48	9818	" Corr. 10 7	0182	0287	" Corr. 10 7	" Corr. 10 50	3805	11
12	2629	15 72	9776	15 10	0224	0329	15 11	15 74	4102	12
13	2917	20 96	9735	20 14	0265	0372	20 14	20 99	4399	13
14	3205		9693		0307	0414			4696	14
15	.143493	30 144	.989651	30 21	.010349	.010457	30 21	30 149	.144993	15
16	3780	40 192	9610	40 28	0390	0500	40 28	40 198	5290	16
17	4068	45 216	9568	45 31	0432	0542	45 32	45 223	5587	17
18	4356	50 240	9526	50 35	0474	0585	50 36	50 248	5884	18
19	4644		9484		0516	0628			6181	19
20	.144932		.989442		.010558	.010671			.146478	20
21	5220		9399		0601	0714			6776	21
22	5508		9357		0643	0757			7073	22
23	5795		9315		0685	0801			7370	23
24	6083		9272		0728	0844			7667	24
25	.146371		.989230		.010770	.010888			.147964	25
26	6658		9187		0813	0931			8262	26
27	6946		9144		0856	0975			8559	27
28	7234		9102		0898	1018			8856	28
29	7522		9059		0941	1062			9154	29
30	.147809		.989016		.010984	.011106			.149451	30
31	8097		8973		1027	1150			9748	31
32	8385		8930		1070	1194			.150046	32
33	8672		8886		1114	1238			0343	33
34	8960		8843		1157	1283			0641	34
35	.149248		.988800		.011200	.011327			.150938	35
36	9535		8756		1244	1372			1236	36
37	9823		8713		1287	1416			1533	37
38	.150111		8669		1331	1461			1831	38
39	0398		8626		1374	1505			2128	39
40	.150686		.988582		.011418	.011550			.152426	40
41	0973	" Corr. 10 48	8538	" Corr. 10 7	1462	1595	" Corr. 10 8	" Corr. 10 50	2724	41
42	1261	15 72	8494	15 11	1506	1640	15 11	15 74	3022	42
43	1548	20 96	8450	20 15	1550	1685	20 15	20 99	3319	43
44	1836		8406		1594	1730			3617	44
45	.152123	30 144	.988362	30 22	.011638	.011776	30 23	30 149	.153915	45
46	2411	40 192	8317	40 29	1683	1821	40 30	40 199	4212	46
47	2698	45 216	8273	45 33	1727	1866	45 34	45 223	4510	47
48	2986	50 240	8228	50 37	1772	1912	50 38	50 248	4808	48
49	3273		8184		1816	1958			5106	49
50	.153561		.988139		.011861	.012003			.155404	50
51	3848		8094		1906	2049			5702	51
52	4136		8050		1950	2095			6000	52
53	4423		8005		1995	2141			6298	53
54	4710		7960		2040	2187			6596	54
55	.154998		.987915		.012085	.012233			.156894	55
56	5285		7870		2130	2279			7192	56
57	5572		7824		2176	2326			7490	57
58	5860		7779		2221	2372			7788	58
59	6147		7734		2266	2418			8086	59
60	.156434		.987688		.012312	.012465			.158384	60

TABLE XX.—NATURAL SINES, COSINES,

9°

'	Sine	Corr. for Sec. (+)	Cosine	Corr. for Sec. (− +)	Versine	Exsec	Corr. for Sec. (+)	Corr. for Sec. (+)	Tangent	'
0	.156434		.987688		.012312	.012465			.158384	0
1	6722		7643		2357	2512			8683	1
2	7009		7597		2403	2559			8981	2
3	7296		7551		2449	2606			9279	3
4	7584		7506		2494	2652			9577	4
5	.157871		.987460		.012540	.012700			.159876	5
6	8158		7414		2586	2747			.160174	6
7	8445		7368		2632	2794			0472	7
8	8732		7322		2678	2841			0771	8
9	9020		7275		2725	2889			1069	9
10	.159307		.987229		.012771	.012936			.161368	10
11	9594	" Corr.	7183	" Corr.	2817	2984	" Corr.	" Corr.	1666	11
12	9881	10 48	7136	10 8	2864	3031			1965	12
13	.160168	15 72	7090	15 12	2910	3079			2263	13
14	0456	20 96	7043	20 16	2957	3127			2562	14
15	.160743	30 144	.986996	30 23	.013004	.013175	30 24	30 150	.162860	15
16	1030	40 191	6950	40 31	3050	3223	40 32	40 199	3159	16
17	1317	45 215	6903	45 35	3097	3271	45 36	45 224	3458	17
18	1604	50 239	6856	50 39	3144	3319	50 40	50 249	3756	18
19	1891		6809		3191	3368			4055	19
20	.162178		.986762		.013238	.013416			.164354	20
21	2465		6714		3286	3465			4652	21
22	2752		6667		3333	3513			4951	22
23	3039		6620		3380	3562			5250	23
24	3326		6572		3428	3611			5549	24
25	.163613		.986525		.013475	.013660			.165848	25
26	3900		6477		3523	3708			6147	26
27	4187		6429		3571	3757			6446	27
28	4474		6382		3618	3807			6745	28
29	4761		6334		3666	3856			7044	29
30	.165048		.986286		.013714	.013905			.167343	30
31	5334		6238		3762	3954			7642	31
32	5621		6189		3811	4004			7941	32
33	5908		6141		3859	4054			8240	33
34	6195		6093		3907	4103			8539	34
35	.166482		.986044		.013956	.014153			.168838	35
36	6769		5996		4004	4203			9137	36
37	7056		5948		4052	4253			9437	37
38	7342		5899		4101	4303			9736	38
39	7629		5850		4150	4353			.170035	39
40	.167916		.985801		.014199	.014403			.170334	40
41	8203	" Corr.	5752	" Corr.	4248	4454	" Corr.	" Corr.	0634	41
42	8489	10 48	5704	10 8	4296	4504	10 8	10 50	0933	42
43	8776	15 72	5654	15 12	4346	4554	15 13	15 75	1232	43
44	9063	20 96	5605	20 16	4395	4605	20 17	20 100	1532	44
45	.169350	30 143	.985556	30 25	.014444	.014656	30 25	30 150	.171831	45
46	9636	40 191	5507	40 33	4493	4706	40 34	40 200	2131	46
47	9923	45 215	5457	45 37	4543	4757	45 38	45 225	2430	47
48	.170210	50 239	5408	50 41	4592	4808	50 42	50 250	2730	48
49	0496		5358		4642	4859			3030	49
50	.170783		.985309		.014691	.014910			.173329	50
51	1069		5259		4741	4962			3629	51
52	1356		5209		4791	5013			3928	52
53	1642		5159		4841	5064			4228	53
54	1929		5109		4891	5116			4528	54
55	.172216		.985059		.014941	.015167			.174828	55
56	2502		5009		4991	5219			5128	56
57	2789		4959		5041	5271			5427	57
58	3075		4909		5091	5323			5727	58
59	3362		4858		5142	5375			6027	59
60	.173648		.984808		.015192	.015427			.176327	60

'	Sine	Corr. for Sec. +	Cosine	Corr. for Sec. − +	Versine	Exsec	Corr. for Sec. +	Corr. for Sec. +	Tangent	'
0	.173648		.984808		.015192	.015427			.176327	0
1	3935		4757		5243	5479			6630	1
2	4221		4707		5293	5531			6927	2
3	4508		4656		5344	5583			7227	3
4	4794		4605		5395	5636			7527	4
5	.175080		.984554		.015446	.015688			.177827	5
6	5367		4503		5497	5741			8127	6
7	5653		4452		5548	5793			8427	7
8	5940		4401		5599	5846			8727	8
9	6226		4350		5650	5899			9028	9
10	.176512		.984298		.015702	.015952			.179328	10
11	6798	" Corr.	4247	" Corr.	5753	6005	" Corr.	" Corr.	9628	11
12	7085	10 48	4196	10 9	5804	6058	10 9	10 50	9928	12
13	7371	15 72	4144	15 13	5856	6111	15 13	15 75	.180229	13
14	7657	20 95	4092	20 17	5908	6165	20 18	20 100	0529	14
15	.177944	30 143	.984041	30 26	.015959	.016218	30 27	30 150	.180830	15
16	8230	40 191	3989	40 35	6011	6272	40 36	40 200	1130	16
17	8516	45 215	3937	45 39	6063	6325	45 40	45 225	1430	17
18	8802	50 239	3885	50 43	6115	6379	50 45	50 250	1731	18
19	9088		3833		6167	6433			2031	19
20	.179375		.983781		.016219	.016486			.182332	20
21	9661		3729		6271	6540			2632	21
22	9947		3676		6324	6595			2933	22
23	.180233		3624		6376	6649			3234	23
24	0519		3572		6428	6703			3534	24
25	.180805		.983519		.016481	.016757			.183835	25
26	1091		3466		6534	6812			4136	26
27	1377		3414		6586	6866			4436	27
28	1664		3361		6639	6921			4737	28
29	1950		3308		6692	6976			5038	29
30	.182236		.983255		.016745	.017030			.185339	30
31	2522		3202		6798	7085			5640	31
32	2808		3149		6851	7140			5941	32
33	3094		3096		6904	7195			6242	33
34	3380		3042		6958	7250			6543	34
35	.183665		.982989		.017011	.017306			.186844	35
36	3951		2935		7065	7361			7145	36
37	4237		2882		7118	7416			7446	37
38	4523		2828		7172	7472			7747	38
39	4809		2774		7226	7528			8048	39
40	.185095		.982721		.017279	.017583			.188350	40
41	5381	" Corr.	2667	" Corr.	7333	7639	" Corr.	" Corr.	8651	41
42	5667	10 48	2613	10 9	7387	7695	10 9	10 50	8952	42
43	5952	15 71	2559	15 14	7441	7751	15 14	15 75	9253	43
44	6238	20 95	2505	20 18	7495	7807	20 19	20 100	9555	44
45	.186524	30 143	.982450	30 27	.017550	.017863	30 28	30 151	.189856	45
46	6810	40 190	2396	40 36	7604	7919	40 37	40 201	.190157	46
47	7096	45 214	2342	45 41	7658	7976	45-42	45 226	0459	47
48	7381	50 238	2287	50 45	7713	8032	50 47	50 251	0760	48
49	7667		2233		7767	8089			1062	49
50	.187953		.982178		.017822	.018145			.191363	50
51	8238		2123		7877	8202			1665	51
52	8524		2069		7931	8259			1966	52
53	8810		2014		7986	8316			2268	53
54	9095		1959		8041	8373			2570	54
55	.189381		.981904		.018096	.018430			.192871	55
56	9667		1848		8152	8487			3173	56
57	9952		1793		8207	8544			3475	57
58	.190238		1738		8262	8602			3777	58
59	0523		1683		8317	8659			4078	59
60	.190809		.981627		.018373	.018717			.194380	60

TABLE XX.—NATURAL SINES, COSINES,

11°

'	Sine	Corr. for Sec. (+ −)	Cosine	Corr. for Sec. (− +)	Versine	Exsec	Corr. for Sec. (+)	Corr. for Sec. (+)	Tangent	'
0	.190809		.981627		.018373	.018717			.194380	0
1	1094		1572		8428	8774			4682	1
2	1380		1516		8484	8832			4984	2
3	1666		1460		8540	8890			5286	3
4	1951		1404		8596	8948			5588	4
5	.192236		.981349		.018651	.019006			.195890	5
6	2522		1293		8707	9064			6192	6
7	2807		1237		8763	9122			6494	7
8	3093		1180		8820	9180			6796	8
9	3378		1124		8876	9239			7099	9
10	.193664		.981068		.018932	.019297			.197401	10
11	3949	10 48	1012	10 9	8988	9356	10 10	10 50	7703	11
12	4234	15 71	0955	15 14	9045	9415	15 15	15 76	8005	12
13	4520	20 95	0899	20 19	9101	9473	20 20	20 101	8308	13
14	4805		0842		9158	9532			8610	14
15	.195090	30 143	.980785	30 23	.019215	.019591	30 29	30 151	.198912	15
16	5376	40 190	0728	40 38	9272	9650	40 39	40 202	9215	16
17	5661	45 214	0672	45 43	9328	9709	45 44	45 227	9517	17
18	5946	50 238	0615	50 47	9385	9769	50 49	50 252	9820	18
19	6231		0558		9442	9828			.200122	19
20	.196517		.980500		.019500	.019887			.200435	20
21	6802		0443		9557	9947			0727	21
22	7087		0386		9614	.020006			1030	22
23	7372		0329		9671	0066			1333	23
24	7657		0271		9729	0126			1635	24
25	.197942		.980214		.019786	.020186			.201938	25
26	8228		0156		9844	0246			2241	26
27	8513		0098		9902	0306			2544	27
28	8798		0040		9960	0366			2846	28
29	9083		.979983		.020017	0426			3149	29
30	.199368		.979925		.020075	.020487			.203452	30
31	9653		9867		0133	0547			3755	31
32	9938		9809		0191	0608			4058	32
33	.200223		9750		0250	0668			4361	33
34	0508		9692		0308	0729			4664	34
35	.200793		.979634		.020366	.020790			.204967	35
36	1078		9575		0425	0851			5270	36
37	1363		9517		0483	0912			5574	37
38	1648		9458		0542	0973			5877	38
39	1933		9399		0601	1034			6180	39
40	.202218		.979341		.020659	.021095			.206483	40
41	2502	10 47	9282	10 10	0718	1157	10 10	10 51	6787	41
42	2787	15 71	9223	15 15	0777	1218	15 15	15 76	7090	42
43	3072	20 95	9164	20 20	0836	1280	20 21	20 101	7393	43
44	3357		9105		0895	1341			7697	44
45	.203642	30 142	.979046	30 30	.020954	.021403	30 31	30 152	.208000	45
46	3926	40 190	8986	40 40	1014	1465	40 41	40 202	8304	46
47	4211	45 214	8927	45 44	1073	1527	45 46	45 228	8607	47
48	4496	50 237	8867	50 49	1133	1589	50 51	50 253	8911	48
49	4781		8808		1192	1651			9214	49
50	.205066		.978748		.021252	.021713			.209518	50
51	5350		8689		1311	1776			9822	51
52	5635		8629		1371	1838			.210126	52
53	5920		8569		1431	1900			0429	53
54	6204		8509		1491	1963			0733	54
55	.206489		.978449		.021551	.022026			.211037	55
56	6773		8389		1611	2088			1341	56
57	7058		8329		1671	2151			1645	57
58	7343		8268		1732	2214			1949	58
59	7627		8208		1792	2277			2252	59
60	.207912		.978148		.021852	.022341			.212557	60

'	Sine	Corr. for Sec. +	Cosine	Corr. for Sec. −	Versine +	Exsec	Corr. for Sec. +	Corr. for Sec. +	Tangent	'
0	.207912		.978148		.021852	.022341			.212557	0
1	8196		8087		1913	2404			2861	1
2	8481		8026		1974	2467			3165	2
3	8765		7966		2034	2531			3469	3
4	9050		7905		2095	2594			3773	4
5	.209334		.977844		.022156	.022658			.214077	5
6	9619		7783		2217	2722			4381	6
7	9903		7722		2278	2785			4686	7
8	.210187		7661		2339	2849			4990	8
9	0472		7600		2400	2913			5294	9
10	.210756	" Corr.	.977539	" Corr.	.022461	.022977	" Corr.	" Corr.	.215599	10
11	1040	10 47	7477	10 10	2523	3042	10 11	10 51	5903	11
12	1325	15 71	7416	15 15	2584	3106	15 16	15 76	6208	12
13	1609	20 95	7354	20 21	2646	3170	20 21	20 102	6512	13
14	1893		7293		2707	3235			6817	14
15	.212178	30 142	.977231	30 31	.022769	.023299	30 32	30 152	.217121	15
16	2462	40 189	7169	40 41	2831	3364	40 43	40 203	7426	16
17	2746	45 213	7108	45 46	2892	3429	45 49	45 228	7731	17
18	3030	50 237	7046	50 51	2954	3494	50 54	50 254	8035	18
19	3315		6984		3016	3559			8340	19
20	.213599		.976922		.023078	.023624			.218645	20
21	3883		6859		3141	3689			8950	21
22	4167		6797		3203	3754			9254	22
23	4451		6735		3265	3820			9559	23
24	4735		6672		3328	3885			9864	24
25	.215019		.976610		.023390	.023950			.220169	25
26	5304		6547		3453	4016			0474	26
27	5588		6484		3516	4082			0779	27
28	5872		6422		3578	4148			1084	28
29	6156		6359		3641	4214			1390	29
30	.216440		.976296		.023704	.024280			.221695	30
31	6724		6233		3767	4346			2000	31
32	7008		6170		3830	4412			2305	32
33	7292		6107		3893	4478			2610	33
34	7575		6044		3956	4544			2916	34
35	.217859		.975980		.024020	.024611			.223221	35
36	8143		5917		4083	4678			3526	36
37	8427		5853		4147	4744			3832	37
38	−8711		5790		4210	4811			4137	38
39	8995		5726		4274	4878			4443	39
40	.219279		.975662		.024338	.024945			.224748	40
41	9562	" Corr.	5598	" Corr.	4402	5012	" Corr.	" Corr.	5054	41
42	9846	10 47	5534	10 11	4466	5079	10 11	10 51	5360	42
43	.220130	15 71	5471	15 16	4529	5146	15 17	15 76	5665	43
44	0414	20 95	5406	20 21	4594	5214	20 23	20 102	5971	44
45	.220697	30 142	.975342	30 32	.024658	.025281	30 34	30 153	.226277	45
46	0981	40 189	5278	40 43	4722	5349	40 45	40 204	6583	46
47	1265	45 213	5214	45 48	4786	5416	45 51	45 229	6888	47
48	1548	50 236	5149	50 53	4851	5484	50 56	50 255	7194	48
49	1832		5085		4915	5552			7500	49
50	.222116		.975020		.024980	.025620			.227806	50
51	2399		4956		5044	5688			8112	51
52	2683		4891		5109	5756			8416	52
53	2967		4826		5174	5824			8724	53
54	3250		4761		5239	5892			9031	54
55	.223534		.974696		.025304	.025961			.229337	55
56	3817		4631		5369	6029			9643	56
57	4101		4566		5434	6098			9949	57
58	4384		4501		5499	6166			.230256	58
59	4668		4436		5564	6235			0562	59
60	.224951		.974370		.025630	.026304			.230868	60

TABLE XX.—NATURAL SINES, COSINES,
13°

'	Sine	Corr. for Sec. (+)	Cosine	Corr. for Sec. (− +)	Versine	Exsec	Corr. for Sec. (+)	Corr. for Sec. (+)	Tangent	'
0	.224951		.974370		.025630	.026304			.230868	0
1	5234		4305		5695	6373			1175	1
2	5518		4239		5761	6442			1481	2
3	5801		4173		5827	6511			1788	3
4	6085		4108		5892	6581			2094	4
5	.226368		.974042		.025958	.026650			.232401	5
6	6651		3976		6024	6719			2707	6
7	6935		3910		6090	6789			3014	7
8	7218		3844		6156	6859			3321	8
9	7501		3778		6222	6928			3627	9
10	.227784	" Corr.	.973712	" Corr.	.026288	.026998	" Corr.	" Corr.	.233934	10
11	8068	10 47	3645	10 11	6355	7068	10 12	10 51	4241	11
12	8351	15 71	3579	15 17	6421	7138	15 18	15 77	4548	12
13	8634	20 94	3512	20 22	6488	7208	20 23	20 102	4855	13
14	8917		3446		6554	7278			5162	14
15	.229200	30 142	.973379	30 33	.026621	.027349	30 35	30 153	.235469	15
16	9484	40 189	3312	40 44	6688	7419	40 47	40 205	5776	16
17	9767	45 212	3246	45 56	6754	7490	45 53	45 230	6083	17
18	.230050	50 236	3179	50 56	6821	7560	50 59	50 256	6390	18
19	0333		3112		6888	7631			6697	19
20	.230616		.973045		.026955	.027702			.237004	20
21	0899		2978		7022	7773			7312	21
22	1182		2910		7090	7844			7619	22
23	1465		2843		7157	7915			7926	23
24	1748		2776		7224	7986			8234	24
25	.232031		.972708		.027292	.028057			.238541	25
26	2314		2641		7359	8129			8848	26
27	2597		2573		7427	8200			9156	27
28	2880		2506		7494	8272			9464	28
29	3162		2438		7562	8343			9771	29
30	.233445		.972370		.027630	.028415			.240079	30
31	3728		2302		7698	8487			0386	31
32	4011		2234		7766	8559			0694	32
33	4294		2166		7834	8631			1002	33
34	4577		2098		7902	8703			1310	34
35	.234859		.972029		.027971	.028776			.241618	35
36	5142		1961		8039	8848			1926	36
37	5425		1893		8107	8920			2233	37
38	5708		1824		8176	8993			2541	38
39	5990		1755		8245	9066			2849	39
40	.236273	" Corr.	.971687	" Corr.	.028313	.029138	" Corr.	" Corr.	.243158	40
41	6556		1618	10 12	8382	9211	10 12	10 51	3466	41
42	6838		1549	15 17	8451	9284	15 18	15 77	3774	42
43	7121	15 71	1480	20 23	8520	9357	20 24	20 103	4082	43
44	7403	20 94	1411		8589	9430			4390	44
45	.237686	30 141	.971342	30 35	.028658	.029503	30 37	30 154	.244698	45
46	7968	40 188	1273	40 46	8727	9577	40 49	40 206	5007	46
47	8251	45 212	1204	45 52	8796	9650	45 55	45 231	5315	47
48	8534	50 235	1134	50 58	8866	9724	50 61	50 257	5624	48
49	8816		1065		8935	9797			5932	49
50	.239098		.970995		.029005	.029871			.246240	50
51	9381		0926		9074	9945			6549	51
52	9663		0856		9144	.030019			6858	52
53	9946		0786		9214	0093			7166	53
54	.240228		0716		9284	0167			7475	54
55	.240510		.970647		.029353	.030241			.247784	55
56	0793		0577		9423	0315			8092	56
57	1075		0506		9494	0390			8401	57
58	1357		0436		9564	0464			8710	58
59	1640		0366		9634	0539			9019	59
60	.241922		.970296		.029704	.030614			.249328	60

′	Sine	Corr. for Sec. +	Cosine	Corr. for Sec. − +	Versine	Exsec	Corr. for Sec. +	Corr. for Sec. +	Tangent	′
0	.241922	+	.970296		.029704	.030614			.249328	0
1	2204		0225		9775	0688			9637	1
2	2486		0155		9845	0763			9946	2
3	2768		0084		9916	0838			.250255	3
4	3051		0014		9986	0913			0564	4
5	.243333		.969943		.030057	.030989			.250873	5
6	3615		9872		0128	1064			1183	6
7	3897		9801		0199	1139			1492	7
8	4179		9730		0270	1215			1801	8
9	4461		9659		0341	1290			2111	9
10	.244743		.969588		.030412	.031366			.252420	10
11	5025	″ Corr.	9517	″ Corr.	0483	1442	″ Corr.	″ Corr.	2729	11
12	5307	10 47	9445	10 12	0555	1518	10 .13	10 52	3039	12
13	5589	15 70	9374	15 18	0626	1594	15 19	15 77	3348	13
14	5871	20 94	9302	20 24	0698	1670	20 25	20 103	3658	14
15	.246153	30 141	.969231	30 36	.030769	.031746	30 38	30 155	.253968	15
16	6435	40 188	9159	40 48	0841	1822	40 51	40 206	4277	16
17	6717	45 211	9088	45 54	0912	1898	45 57	45 233	4587	17
18	6999	50 235	9016	50 60	0984	1975	50 64	50 258	4897	18
19	7281		8944		1056	2052			5207	19
20	.247563		.968872		.031128	.032128			.255516	20
21	7844		8800		1200	2205			5826	21
22	8126		8728		1272	2282			6136	22
23	8408		8656		1344	2359			6446	23
24	8690		8583		1417	2436			6756	24
25	.248972		.968511		.031489	.032513			.257066	25
26	9253		8438		1562	2590			7377	26
27	9535		8366		1634	2668			7687	27
28	9817		8293		1707	2745			7997	28
29	.250098		8220		1780	2823			8307	29
30	.250380		.968148		.031852	.032900			.258618	30
31	0662		8075		1925	2978			8928	31
32	0943		8002		1998	3056			9238	32
33	1225		7929		2071	3134			9549	33
34	1506		7856		2144	3212			9859	34
35	.251788		.967782		.032218	.033290			.260170	35
36	2069		7709		2291	3368			0480	36
37	2351		7636		2364	3447			0791	37
38	2632		7562		2438	3525			1102	38
39	2914		7489		2511	3604			1413	39
40	.253195		.967415		.032585	.033682			.261723	40
41	3477	″ Corr.	7342	″ Corr.	2658	3761	″ Corr.	″ Corr.	2034	41
42	3758	10 47	7268	10 12	2732	3840	10 13	10 52	2345	42
43	4039	15 70	7194	15 19	2806	3919	15 20	15 78	2656	43
44	4321	20 94	7120	20 25	2880	3998	20 26	20 104	2967	44
45	.254602	30 141	.967046	30 37	.032954	.034077	30 40	30 156	.263278	45
46	4883	40 183	6972	40 49	3028	4156	40 53	40 207	3589	46
47	5164	45 211	6898	45 56	3102	4236	45 59	45 233	3900	47
48	5445	50 234	6823	50 62	3177	4315	50 66	50 259	4211	48
49	5727		6749		3251	4395			4523	49
50	.256008		.966675		.033325	.034474			.264834	50
51	6289		6600		3400	4554			5145	51
52	6570		6526		3474	4634			5457	52
53	6852		6451		3549	4714			5768	53
54	7133		6376		3624	4794			6079	54
55	.257414		.966301		.033699	.034874			.266391	55
56	7695		6226		3774	4954			6702	56
57	7976		6151		3849	5035			7014	57
58	8257		6076		3924	5115			7326	58
59	8538		ˣ 6001		3999	5196			7637	59
60	.258819		.965926		.034074	.035276			.267949	60

TABLE XX.—NATURAL SINES, COSINES,
15°

'	Sine	Corr. for Sec.	Cosine	Corr. for Sec.	Versine	Exsec	Corr. for Sec.	Corr. for Sec.	Tangent	'
		+		− +			+	+		
0	.258819		.965926		.034074	.035276			.267949	0
1	9100		5850		4150	5357			8261	1
2	9381		5775		4225	5438			8573	2
3	9662		5700		4300	5519			8885	3
4	9943		5624		4376	5600			9197	4
5	.260224		.965548		.034452	.035681			.269509	5
6	0504		5473		4527	5762			9821	6
7	0785		5397		4603	5844			.270133	7
8	1066		5321		4679	5925			0445	8
9	1347		5245		4755	6006			0757	9
10	.261628		.965169		.034831	.036088			.271069	10
11	1908	" Corr.	5093	" Corr.	4907	6170	" Corr.	" Corr.	1382	11
12	2189	10 47	5016	10 13	4984	6252	10 14	10 52	1694	12
13	2470	15 70	4940	15 19	5060	6334	15 21	15 78	2006	13
14	2751	20 94	4864	20 25	5136	6416	20 27	20 104	2319	14
15	.263031	30 140	.964787	30 38	.035213	.036498	30 41	30 156	.272631	15
16	3312	40 187	4711	40 51	5289	6580	40 55	40 208	2944	16
17	3592	45 210	4634	45 57	5366	6662	45 62	45 234	3256	17
18	3873	50 234	4557	50 64	5443	6745	50 68	50 260	3569	18
19	4154		4481		5519	6828			3882	19
20	.264434		.964404		.035596	.036910			.274194	20
21	4715		4327		5673	6993			4507	21
22	4995		4250		5750	7076			4820	22
23	5276		4173		5827	7159			5133	23
24	5556		4095		5905	7242			5446	24
25	.265837		.964018		.035982	.037325			.275759	25
26	6117		3941		6059	7408			6072	26
27	6397		3863		6137	7492			6385	27
28	6678		3786		6214	7575			6698	28
29	6958		3708		6292	7658			7011	29
30	.267238		.963630		.036370	.037742			.277324	30
31	7519		3553		6447	7826			7638	31
32	7799		3475		6525	7910			7951	32
33	8079		3397		6603	7994			8265	33
34	8359		3319		6681	8078			8578	34
35	2268640		.963241		.036759	.038162			.278892	35
36	8920		3163		6837	8246			9205	36
37	9200		3084		6916	8331			9519	37
38	9480		3006		6994	8415			9832	38
39	9760		2928		7072	8500			.280146	39
40	.270040		.962849		.037151	.038584			.280460	40
41	0320	" Corr.	2770	" Corr.	7230	8669	" Corr.	" Corr.	0774	41
42	0600	10 47	2692	10 13	7308	8754	10 14	10 52	1087	42
43	0880	15 70	2613	15 20	7387	8839	15 21	15 78	1401	43
44	1160	20 93	2534	20 26	7466	8924	20 28	20 105	1715	44
45	.271440	30 140	.962455	30 40	.037545	.039009	30 43	30 156	.282029	45
46	1720	40 187	2376	40 53	7624	9095	40 57	40 209	2343	46
47	2000	45 210	2297	45 59	7703	9180	45 64	45 235	2657	47
48	2280	50 233	2218	50 66	7782	9266	50 71	50 262	2972	48
49	2560		2139		7861	9351			3286	49
50	.272840		.962059		.037941	.039437			.283600	50
51	3120		1980		8020	9523			3914	51
52	3400		1900		8100	9608			4229	52
53	3679		1821		8179	9694			4543	53
54	3959		1741		8259	9781			4858	54
55	.274239		.961662		.038338	.039867			.285172	55
56	4519		1582		8418	9953			5487	56
57	4798		1502		8498	.040040			5801	57
58	5078		1422		8578	0126			6116	58
59	5358		1342		8658	0213			6431	59
60	.275637		.961262		.038738	.040299			.286745	60

16°

'	Sine	Corr. for Sec.	Cosine	Corr. for Sec.	Versine	Exsec	Corr. for Sec.	Corr. for Sec.	Tangent	'
0	.275637	+	.961262	− +	.038738	.040299	+	+	.286745	0
1	5917		1182		8818	0386			7060	1
2	6197		1101		8899	0473			7375	2
3	6476		1021		8979	0560			7690	3
4	6756		0940		9060	0647			8005	4
5	.277035		.960860		.039140	.040735			.288320	5
6	7315		0779		9221	0822			8635	6
7	7594		0698		9302	0909			8950	7
8	7874		0618		9382	0997			9266	8
9	8153		0537		9463	1084			9581	9
10	.278432		.960456		.039544	.041172			.289896	10
11	8712	" Corr. · 10 47	0375	" Corr. · 10 14	9625	1260	" Corr. · 10 15	" Corr. · 10 53	.290211	11
12	8991	15 70	0294	15 20	9706	1348	15 22	15 79	0527	12
13	9270	20 93	0212	20 27	9788	1436	20 29	20 105	0842	13
14	9550		0131		9869	1524			1158	14
15	.279829	30 140	.960050	30 41	.039950	.041613	30 44	30 158	.291473	15
16	.280108	40 186	.959968	40 54	.040032	1701	40 59	40 210	1789	16
17	0388	45 209	9887	45 61	0113	1789	45 66	45 237	2105	17
18	0667	50 233	9805	50 68	0195	1878	50 74	50 263	2420	18
19	0946		9724		0276	1967			2736	19
20	.281225		.959642		.040358	.042055			.293052	20
21	1504		9560		0440	2144			3368	21
22	1783		9478		0522	2233			3684	22
23	2062		9396		0604	2322			4000	23
24	2342		9314		0686	2412			4316	24
25	.282620		.959232		.040768	.042501			.294632	25
26	2900		9150		0850	2590			4948	26
27	3178		9067		0933	2680			5264	27
28	3458		8985		1015	2769			5581	28
29	3736		8902		1098	2859			5897	29
30	.284015		.958820		.041180	.042949			.296214	30
31	4294		8737		1263	3039			6530	31
32	4573		8654		1346	3129			6846	32
33	4852		8572		1428	3219			7163	33
34	5131		8489		1511	3309			7480	34
35	.285410		.958406		.041594	.043400			.297796	35
36	5688		8323		1677	3490			8113	36
37	5967		8239		1761	3580			8430	37
38	6246		8156		1844	3671			8746	38
39	6525		8073		1927	3762			9063	39
40	.286803		.957990		.042010	.043853			.299380	40
41	7082	" Corr. · 10 46	7906	" Corr. · 10 14	2094	3944	" Corr. · 10 16	" Corr. · 10 53	9697	41
42	7360	15 70	7822	15 21	2178	4035	15 23	15 79	.300014	42
43	7639	20 93	7739	20 28	2261	4126	20 30	20 106	0332	43
44	7918		7655		2345	4217			0649	44
45	.288196	30 139	.957571	30 42	.042429	.044309	30 46	30 159	.300966	45
46	8475	40 186	7488	40 56	2512	4400	40 61	40 212	1283	46
47	8753	45 209	7404	45 63	2596	4492	45 69	45 238	1600	47
48	9032	50 232	7320	50 70	2680	4583	50 76	50 264	1918	48
49	9310		7235		2765	4675			2235	49
50	.289589		.957151		.042849	.044767			.302553	50
51	9867		7067		2933	4859			2870	51
52	.290146		6982		3018	4951			3188	52
53	0424		6898		3102	5043			3506	53
54	0702		6814		3186	5136			3823	54
55	.290980		.956729		.043271	.045228			.304141	55
56	1259		6644		3356	5321			4459	56
57	1537		6560		3440	5413			4777	57
58	1815		6475		3525	5506			5095	58
59	2094		6390		3610	5599			5413	59
60	.292372		.956305		.043695	.045692			.305731	60

TABLE XX.—NATURAL SINES, COSINES,

17°

'	Sine	Corr. for Sec.	Cosine	Corr. for Sec.	Versine	Exsec	Corr. for Sec.	Corr. for Sec.	Tangent	'
				− +		+		+		
0	.292372		.956305		.043695	.045692			.305731	0
1	2650		6220		3780	5785			6049	1
2	2928		6134		3866	5878			6367	2
3	3206		6049		3951	5971			6685	3
4	3484		5964		4036	6065			7003	4
5	.293762		.955878		.044122	.046158			.307322	5
6	4040		5793		4207	6252			7640	6
7	4318		5707		4293	6345			7959	7
8	4596		5622		4378	6439			8277	8
9	4874		5536		4464	6533			8596	9
10	.295152		.955450		.044550	.046627			.308914	10
11	5430	" Corr.	5364	" Corr.	4636	6721	" Corr.	" Corr	9233	11
12	5708	10 46	5278	10 14	4722	6815	10 16	10 53	9552	12
13	5986	15 69	5192	15 22	4808	6910	15 24	15 80	9870	13
14	6264	20 93	5106	20 29	4894	7004	20 32	20 106	.310189	14
15	.296542	30 139	.955020	30 43	.044980	.047099	30 47	30 159	.310508	15
16	6819	40 185	4934	40 58	5066	7193	40 63	40 213	0827	16
17	7097	45 208	4847	45 65	5153	7288	45 71	45 239	1146	17
18	7375	50 231	4761	50 72	5239	7383	50 79	50 266	1465	18
19	7653		4674		5326	7478			1784	19
20	.297930		.954588		.045412	.047573			.312104	20
21	8208		4501		5499	7668			2423	21
22	8486		4414		5586	7763			2742	22
23	8763		4327		5673	7859			3062	23
24	9041		4240		5760	7954			3381	24
25	.299318		.954153		.045847	.048050			.313700	25
26	9596		4066		5934	8145			4020	26
27	9873		3979		6021	8241			4340	27
28	.300151		3892		6108	8337			4659	28
29	0428		3804		6196	8433			4979	29
30	.300706		.953717		.046283	.048529			.315299	30
31	0983		3629		6371	8625			5619	31
32	1261		3542		6458	8722			5938	32
33	1538		3454		6546	8818			6258	33
34	1815		3366		6634	8915			6578	34
35	.302093		.953279		.046721	.049011			.316899	35
36	2370		3191		6809	9108			7219	36
37	2647		3103		6897	9205			7539	37
38	2924		3015		6985	9302			7859	38
39	3202		2926		7074	9399			8179	39
40	.303479		.952838		.047162	.049496			.318500	40
41	3756	" Corr.	2750	" Corr.	7250	9593	" Corr.	" Corr.	8820	41
42	4033	10 46	2662	10 15	7338	9691	10 16	10 53	9141	42
43	4310	15 69	2573	15 22	7427	9788	15 24	15 80	9461	43
44	4587	20 92	2484	20 30	7516	9886	20 33	20 107	9782	44
45	.304864	30 138	.952396	30 44	.047604	.049984	30 49	30 160	.320102	45
46	5141	40 185	2307	40 59	7693	.050082	40 65	40 214	0423	46
47	5418	45 208	2218	45 67	7782	0179	45 73	45 241	0744	47
48	5695	50 231	2129	50 74	7871	0277	50 82	50 267	1065	48
49	5972		2040		7960	0376			1386	49
50	.306249		.951951		.048049	.050474			.321707	50
51	6526		1862		8138	0572			2028	51
52	6803		1773		8227	0671			2349	52
53	7080		1684		8316	0769			2670	53
54	7357		1594		8406	0868			2991	54
55	.307633		.951505		.048495	.050967			.323312	55
56	7910		1415		8585	1066			3634	56
57	8187		1326		8674	1165			3955	57
58	8464		1236		8764	1264			4277	58
59	8740		1146		8854	1363			4598	59
60	.309017		.951056		.048944	.051462			.324920	60

'	Sine	Corr. for Sec. +	Cosine	Corr. for Sec. - +	Versine	Exsec	Corr. for Sec. +	Corr. for Sec. +	Tangent	'
0	.309017		.951056		.048944	.051462			.324920	0
1	9294		0967		9033	1562			5241	1
2	9570		0877		9123	1661			5563	2
3	9847		0786		9214	1761			5885	3
4	.310123		0696		9304	1861			6207	4
5	.310400		.950606		.049394	.051960			.326528	5
6	0676		0516		9484	2060			6850	6
7	0953		0425		9575	2160			7172	7
8	1229		0335		9665	2261			7494	8
9	1506		0244		9756	2361			7816	9
10	.311782		.950154		.049846	.052461			.328139	10
11	2059	" Corr	0063	" Corr	9937	2562	" Corr	" Corr	8461	11
12	2335	10 46	.949972	10 15	.050028	2662	10 17	10 54	8783	12
13	2611	15 69	9881	15 23	0119	2763	15 25	15 81	9106	13
14	2888	20 92	9790	20 30	0210	2864	20 34	20 107	9428	14
15	.313164	30 138	.949699	30 46	.050301	.052965	30 51	30 161	.329750	15
16	3440	40 184	9608	40 61	0392	3066	40 67	40 215	.330073	16
17	3716	45 207	9517	45 68	0483	3167	45 76	45 242	0396	17
18	3992	50 230	9426	50 76	0574	3269	50 84	50 269	0718	18
19	4269		9334		0666	3370			1041	19
20	.314545		.949243		.050757	.053471			.331364	20
21	4821		9151		0849	3573			1687	21
22	5097		9060		0940	3675			2010	22
23	5373		8968		1032	3776			2333	23
24	5649		8876		1124	3878			332656	24
25	.315925		.948784		.051216	.053980			.332979	25
26	6201		8692		1308	4083			3302	26
27	6477		8600		1400	4185			3625	27
28	6753		8508		1492	4287			3948	28
29	7029		8416		1584	4390			4272	29
30	.317305		.948324		.051676	.054492			.334595	30
31	7580		8231		1769	4595			4919	31
32	7856		8139		1861	4698			5242	32
33	8132		8046		1954	4801			5566	33
34	8408		7954		2046	4904			5890	34
35	.318684		.947861		.052139	.055007			.336213	35
36	8959		7768		2232	5110			6537	36
37	9235		7676		2324	5213			6861	37
38	9511		7583		2417	5317			7185	38
39	9786		7490		2510	5420			7509	39
40	.320062		.947397		.052603	.055524			.337833	40
41	0337	" Corr	7304	" Corr	2696	5628	" Corr	" Corr	8157	41
42	0613	10 46	7210	10 16	2790	5732	10 17	10 54	8481	42
43	0888	15 69	7117	15 23	2883	5836	15 26	15 81	8806	43
44	1164	20 92	7024	20 31	2976	5940	20 35	20 108	9130	44
45	.321440	30 138	.946930	30 47	.053070	.056044	30 52	30 162	.339454	45
46	1715	40 184	6837	40 62	3163	6148	40 70	40 216	9779	46
47	1990	45 207	6743	45 70	3257	6253	45 78	45 243	.340103	47
48	2266	50 229	6649	50 78	3351	6358	50 87	50 270	0428	48
49	2541		6556		3444	6462			0752	49
50	.322816		.946462		.053538	.056567			.341077	50
51	3092		6368		3632	6672			1402	51
52	3367		6274		3726	6777			1727	52
53	3642		6180		3820	6882			2052	53
54	3917		6085		3915	6987			2376	54
55	.324193		.945991		.054009	.057092			.342702	55
56	4468		5897		4103	7198			3027	56
57	4743		5802		4198	7303			3352	57
58	5018		5708		4292	7409			3677	58
59	5293		5613		4387	7515			4002	59
60	.325568		.945519		.054481	.057621			.344328	60

TABLE XX.—NATURAL SINES, COSINES,
19°

'	Sine	Corr. for Sec. +	Cosine	Corr. for Sec. − +	Versine	Exsec	Corr. for Sec. +	Corr. for Sec. +	Tangent	'
0	.325568		.945519		.054481	.057621			.344328	0
1	5843		5424		4576	7727			4653	1
2	6118		5329		4671	7833			4978	2
3	6393		5234		4766	7939			5304	3
4	6668		5139		4861	8045			5630	4
5	.326943		.945044		.054956	.058152			.345955	5
6	7218		4949		5051	8258			6281	6
7	7493		4854		5146	8365			6607	7
8	7768		4758		5242	8472			6933	8
9	8042		4663		5337	8579			7259	9
10	.328317		.944568		.055432	.058686			.347585	10
11	8592	" Corr. 10 46	4472	" Corr. 10 16	5528	8793	" Corr. 10 18	" Corr. 10 54	7911	11
12	8867	15 69	4376	15 24	5624	8900	15 27	15 82	8237	12
13	9141	20 92	4281	20 32	5719	9007	20 36	20 109	8563	13
14	9416		4185		5815	9115			8889	14
15	.329691	30 137	.944089	30 48	.055911	.059222	30 54	30 163	.349216	15
16	9965	40 183	3993	40 64	6007	9330	40 72	40 218	9542	16
17	.330240	45 206	3897	45 72	6103	9438	45 81	45 245	9868	17
18	0514	50 229	3801	50 80	6199	9545	50 90	50 272	.350195	18
19	0789		3705		6295	9653			0522	19
20	.331063		.943608		.056392	.059762			.350848	20
21	1338		3512		6488	9870			1175	21
22	1612		3416		6584	9978			1502	22
23	1887		3319		6681	.060086			1829	23
24	2161		3223		6777	0195			2156	24
25	.332436		.943126		.056874	.060304			.352483	25
26	2710		3029		6971	0412			2810	26
27	2984		2932		7068	0521			3137	27
28	3258		2836		7164	0630			3464	28
29	3533		2739		7261	0740			3791	29
30	.333807		.942642		.057358	.060849			.354119	30
31	4081		2544		7456	0958			4446	31
32	4355		2447		7553	1068			4773	32
33	4629		2350		7650	1177			5101	33
34	4903		2252		7748	1287			5429	34
35	.335178		.942155		.057845	.061397			.355756	35
36	5452		2058		7942	1506			6084	36
37	5726		1960		8040	1616			6412	37
38	6000		1862		8138	1726			6740	38
39	6274		1764		8236	1837			7068	39
40	.336548		.941666		.058334	.061947			.357396	40
41	6821	" Corr. 10 46	1569	" Corr. 10 16	8431	2058	" Corr. 10 19	" Corr 10 55	7724	41
42	7095	15 68	1470	15 25	8530	2168	15 28	15 82	8052	42
43	7369	20 91	1372	20 33	8628	2279	20 37	20 109	8380	43
44	7643		1274		8726	2390			8708	44
45	.337917	30 137	.941176	30 49	.058824	.062500	30 56	30 164	.359037	45
46	8190	40 183	1078	40 66	8922	2612	40 74	40 219	9365	46
47	8464	45 205	0979	45 74	9021	2723	45 83	45 246	9694	47
48	8738	50 228	0881	50 82	9119	2834	50 93	50 274	.360022	48
49	9012		0782		9218	2945			0351	49
50	.339285		.940684		.059316	.063067			.360680	50
51	9559		0585		9415	3168			1008	51
52	9832		0486		9514	3280			1337	52
53	.340106		0387		9613	3392			1666	53
54	0380		0268		9712	3504			1995	54
55	.340653		.940189		.059811	.063616			.362324	55
56	0926		0090		9910	3728			2653	56
57	1200		.939991		.060009	3840			2982	57
58	1473		9891		0109	3953			3312	58
59	1747		9792		0208	4065			3641	59
60	.342020		.939693		.060307	.064178			.363970	60

'	Sine	Corr. for Sec. +	Cosine	Corr. for Sec. − +	Versine	Exsec	Corr. for Sec. +	Corr. for Sec. +	Tangent	'
0	.342020		.939693		.060307	.064178			.363970	0
1	2294		9593		0407	4290			4300	1
2	2567		9494		0506	4403			4629	2
3	2840		9394		0606	4516			4959	3
4	3113		9294		0706	4629			5288	4
5	.343386		.939194		.060806	.064742			.365618	5
6	3660		9094		0906	4856			5948	6
7	3933		8994		1006	4969			6278	7
8	4206		8894		1106	5083			6608	8
9	4479		8794		1206	5196			6938	9
10	.344752		.938694		.061306	.065310			.367268	10
11	5025	" Corr.	8593	" Corr.	1407	5424	" Corr.	" Corr.	7598	11
12	5298	10 45	8493	10 17	1507	5538	10 19	10 55	7928	12
13	5571	15 68	8392	15 25	1608	5652	15 29	15 83	8259	13
14	5844	20 91	8292	20 34	1708	5766	20 38	20 110	8589	14
15	.346117	30 136	.938191	30 50	.061809	.065881	30 57	30 165	.368920	15
16	6390	40 182	8091	40 67	1909	5995	40 76	40 220	9250	16
17	6663	45 205	7990	50 84	2010	6110	45 86	45 248	9581	17
18	6936	50 227	7889		2111	6224	50 95	50 275	9911	18
19	7208		7788		2212	6339			.370242	19
20	.347481		.937687		.062313	.066454			.370573	20
21	7754		7586		2414	6569			0904	21
22	8027		7485		2515	6684			1235	22
23	8299		7383		2617	6799			1566	23
24	8572		7282		2718	6915			1897	24
25	.348845		.937181		.062819	.067030			.372228	25
26	9117		7079		2921	7146			2559	26
27	9390		6977		3023	7262			2890	27
28	9662		6876		3124	7377			3222	28
29	9935		6774		3226	7493			3553	29
30	.350207		.936672		.063328	.067609			.373885	30
31	0480		6570		3430	7726			4216	31
32	0752		6468		3532	7842			4548	32
33	1025		6366		3634	7958			4880	33
34	1297		6264		3736	8075			5212	34
35	.351569		.936162		.063838	.068191			.375543	35
36	1842		6060		3940	8308			5875	36
37	2114		5957		4043	8425			6207	37
38	2386		5855		4145	8542			6539	38
39	2658		5752		4248	8659			6872	39
40	.352931		.935650		.064350	.068776			.377204	40
41	3203	" Corr.	5547	" Corr.	4453	8894	" Corr.	" Corr.	7536	41
42	3475	10 45	5444	10 17	4556	9011	10 20	10 55	7868	42
43	3747	15 68	5341	15 26	4659	9129	15 29	15 83	8201	43
44	4019	20 91	5238	20 34	4762	9246	20 39	20 111	8534	44
45	.354291	30 136	.935135	30 52	.064865	.069364	30 59	30 166	.378866	45
46	4563	40 181	5032	40 69	4968	9482	40 79	40 222	9199	46
47	4835	45 204	4929	50 77	5071	9600	50 98	45 250	9532	47
48	5107	50 227	4826	50 86	5174	9718		50 277	9864	48
49	5379		4722		5278	9836			.380197	49
50	.355651		.934619		.065381	.069955			.380530	50
51	5923		4515		5485	.070073			0863	51
52	6194		4412		5588	0192			1196	52
53	6466		4308		5692	0311			1530	53
54	6738		4204		5796	0430			1863	54
55	.357010		.934101		.065899	.070548			.382196	55
56	7281		3997		6003	0668			2530	56
57	7553		3893		6107	0787			2863	57
58	7825		3789		6211	0906			3197	58
59	8096		3685		6315	1025			3530	59
60	.358368		.933580		.066420	.071145			.383864	60

113

TABLE XX.—NATURAL SINES, COSINES,
21°

'	Sine	Corr. for Sec. +	Cosine	Corr. for Sec. − +	Versine	Exsec	Corr. for Sec. +	Corr. for Sec. +	Tangent	'
0	.358368		.933580		.066420	.071145			.383864	0
1	8640		3476		6524	1265			4198	1
2	8911		3372		6628	1384			4532	2
3	9182		3267		6733	1504			4866	3
4	9454		3163		6837	1624			5200	4
5	.359725		.933058		.066942	.071744			.385534	5
6	9997		2954		7046	1865			5868	6
7	.360268		2849		7151	1985	" Corr. 10 20	" Corr. 10 56	6202	7
8	0540		2744		7256	2106	15 30	15 84	6536	8
9	0811		2639		7361	2226	20 40	20 112	6871	9
10	.361082		.932534		.067466	.072347	30 60	30 167	.387205	10
11	1353	" Corr. 10 45	2429	" Corr. 10 18	7571	2468	40 81	40 223	7540	11
12	1625	15 68	2324	15 26	7676	2589	45 91	45 251	7874	12
13	1896	20 90	2219	20 35	7781	2710	50 101	50 279	8209	13
14	2167		2113		7887	2831			8544	14
15	.362438	30 136	.932008	30 53	.067992	.072952			.388879	15
16	2709	40 181	1902	40 70	8098	3074			9214	16
17	2980	45 203	1797	45 79	8203	3195			9549	17
18	3251	50 226	1691	50 88	8309	3317			9884	18
19	3522		1586		8414	3439			.390219	19
20	.363793		.931480		.068520	.073561			.390554	20
21	4064		1374		8626	3683			0889	21
22	4335		1268		8732	3805			1225	22
23	4606		1162		8838	3927			1560	23
24	4877		1056		8944	4050			1896	24
25	.365148		.930950		.069050	.074172			.392231	25
26	5418		0843		9157	4295	" Corr. 10 21	" Corr. 10 56	2567	26
27	5689		0737		9263	4417	15 31	15 84	2903	27
28	5960		0631		9369	4540	20 41	20 112	3239	28
29	6231		0524		9476	4663			3574	29
30	.366501		.930418		.069582	.074786	30 62	30 168	.393910	30
31	6772		0311		9689	4910	40 82	40 224	4246	31
32	7042		0204		9796	5033	45 92	45 252	4583	32
33	7313		0097		9903	5156	50 103	50 280	4919	33
34	7584		.929990		.070010	5280			5255	34
35	.367854		.929884		.070116	.075404			.395592	35
36	8125		9776		0224	5527			5928	36
37	8395		9669		0331	5651			6264	37
38	8665		9562		0438	5775			6601	38
39	8936		9455		0545	5900			6938	39
40	.369206		.929348		.070652	.076024			.397275	40
41	9476	" Corr.	9240	" Corr.	0760	6148			7611	41
42	9747	10 45	9133	10 16	0867	6273			7948	42
43	.370017	15 68	9025	15 27	0975	6397			8285	43
44	0287	20 90	8917	20 36	1083	6522			8622	44
45	.370557	30 135	.928810	30 54	.071190	.076647			.398960	45
46	0828	40 180	8702	40 72	1298	6772	" Corr. 10 21	" Corr. 10 56	9297	46
47	1098	45 203	8594	45 81	1406	6897	15 31	15 84	9634	47
48	1368	50 225	8486	50 90	1514	7022	20 42	20 113	9972	48
49	1638		8378		1622	7148			.400309	49
50	.371908		.928270		.071730	.077273	30 63	30 169	.400646	50
51	2178		8161		1839	7399	40 84	40 225	0984	51
52	2448		8053		1947	7525	45 94	45 253	1322	52
53	2718		7945		2055	7650	50 105	50 281	1660	53
54	2988		7836		2164	7776			1997	54
55	.373268		.927728		.072272	.077902			.402335	55
56	3528		7619		2381	8029			2673	56
57	3797		7510		2490	8155			3012	57
58	4067		7402		2598	8282			3350	58
59	4337		7293		2707	8408			3688	59
60	.374607		.927184		.072816	.078535			.404026	60

114

'	Sine	Corr. for Sec. +	Cosine	Corr. for Sec. − +	Versine	Exsec	Corr. for Sec. +	Corr. for Sec. +	Tangent	'
0	.374607		.927184		.072816	.078535			.404026	0
1	4876		7075		2925	8662			4365	1
2	5146		6966		3034	8788			4703	2
3	5416		6857		3143	8916			5042	3
4	5685		6747		3253	9043			5380	4
5	.375955		.926638		.073362	.079170			.405719	5
6	6224		6529		3471	9298	" Corr.	" Corr.	6058	6
7	6494		6419		3581	9425	10 21	10 57	6397	7
8	6763		6310		3690	9553	15 32	15 85	6736	8
9	7033		6200		3800	9680	20 43	20 113	7075	9
10	.377302		.926090		.073910	.079808	30 64	30 170	.407414	10
11	7571	" Corr.	5980	" Corr.	4020	9936	40 85	40 226	7753	11
12	7841	10 45	5871	10 18	4129	.080065	45 96	45 254	8092	12
13	8110	15 67	5761	15 28	4239	0193	50 107	50 283	8432	13
14	8379	20 90	5651	20 37	4349	0321			8771	14
15	.378649	30 135	.925540	30 55	.074460	.080450			.409111	15
16	8918	40 180	5430	40 73	4570	0578			9450	16
17	9187	45 202	5320	45 83	4680	0707			9790	17
18	9456	50 224	5210	50 92	4790	0836			.410130	18
19	9725		5099		4901	0965			0470	19
20	.379994		.924989		.075011	.081094			.410810	20
21	.380263		4878		5122	1223			1150	21
22	0532		4768		5232	1353			1490	22
23	0801		4657		5343	1482			1830	23
24	1070		4546		5454	1612			2170	24
25	.381339		.924435		.075565	.081742			.412511	25
26	1608		4324		5676	1872	" Corr.	" Corr.	2851	26
27	1877		4213		5787	2002	10 22	10 57	3192	27
28	2146		4102		5898	2132	15 33	15 85	3532	28
29	2415		3991		6009	2262	20 43	20 114	3873	29
30	.382683		.923880		.076120	.082392	30 65	30 170	.414214	30
31	2952		3768		6232	2523	40 87	40 227	4554	31
32	3221		3657		6343	2653	45 98	45 256	4895	32
33	3490		3545		6455	2784	50 109	50 284	5236	33
34	3758		3434		6566	2915			5577	34
35	.384027		.923322		.076678	.083046			.415919	35
36	4295		3210		6790	3177			6260	36
37	4564		3098		6902	3308			6601	37
38	4832		2986		7014	3440			6943	38
39	5101		2874		7126	3571			7284	39
40	.385369		.922762		.077238	.083702			.417626	40
41	5638	" Corr.	2650	" Corr.	7350	3834			7967	41
42	5906	10 45	2538	10 19	7462	3966			8309	42
43	6174	15 67	2426	15 28	7574	4098			8651	43
44	6443	20 89	2313	20 37	7687	4230			8993	44
45	.386711	30 134	.922201	30 56	.077799	.084362			.419335	45
46	6979	40 179	2088	40 75	7912	4495	" Corr.	" Corr.	9677	46
47	7247	45 201	1976	45 84	8024	4627	10 22	10 57	.420019	47
48	7516	50 224	1863	50 94	8137	4760	15 33	15 86	0361	48
49	7784		1750		8250	4892	20 44	20 114	0704	49
50	.388052		.921638		.078362	.085025	30 66	30 171	.421046	50
51	8320		1525		8475	5158	40 89	40 228	1388	51
52	8588		1412		8588	5291	45 100	45 257	1731	52
53	8856		1299		8701	5424	50 111	50 285	2074	53
54	9124		1185		8815	5558			2416	54
55	.389392		.921072		.078928	.085691			.422759	55
56	9660		0959		9041	5825			3102	56
57	9928		0846		9154	5958			3445	57
58	.390196		0732		9268	6092			3788	58
59	0463		0618		9382	6226			4132	59
60	.390731		.920505		.079495	.086360			.424475	60

TABLE XX.—NATURAL SINES, COSINES,
23°

'	Sine	Corr. for Sec. +	Cosine	Corr. for Sec. − +	Versine	Exsec	Corr. for Sec. +	Corr. for Sec. +	Tangent	'
0	.390731		.920505		.079495	.086360			.424475	0
1	0999		0391		9609	6495			4818	1
2	1267		0277		9723	6629			5162	2
3	1534		0164		9836	6763			5505	3
4	1802		0050		9950	6898			5849	4
5	.392070		.919936		.080064	.087033			.426192	5
6	2337		9822		0178	7168	" Corr.	" Corr.	6536	6
7	2605		9707		0293	7302	10 23	10 57	6880	7
8	2872		9593		0407	7438	15 34	15 86	7224	8
9	3140		9479		0521	7573	20 45	20 115	7568	9
10	.393407	" Corr.	.919364	" Corr.	.080636	.087708	30 68	30 172	.427912	10
11	3674	10 45	9250	10 19	0750	7844	40 90	40 230	8256	11
12	3942	15 67	9135	15 29	0865	7979	45 102	45 258	8600	12
13	4209	20 89	9021	20 38	0979	8115	50 113	50 287	8945	13
14	4477		8906		1094	8251			9289	14
15	.394744	30 134	.918791	30 57	.081209	.088387			.429634	15
16	5011	40 178	8676	40 77	1324	8523			9978	16
17	5278	45 200	8561	45 86	1439	8659			.430323	17
18	5546	50 223	8446	50 96	1554	8795			0668	18
19	5813		8331		1669	8932			1013	19
20	.396080		.918216		.081784	.089068			.431358	20
21	6347		8101		1899	9205			1703	21
22	6614		7986		2014	9342			2048	22
23	6881		7870		2130	9479			2393	23
24	7148		7755		2245	9616			2739	24
25	.397415		.917639		.082361	.089753			.433084	25
26	7682		7523		2477	9890	" Corr.	" Corr.	3430	26
27	7949		7408		2592	.090028	10 23	10 58	3775	27
28	8216		7292		2708	0166	15 34	15 86	4121	28
29	8482		7176		2824	0303	20 46	20 115	4466	29
30	.398749		.917060		.082940	.090441	30 69	30 173	.434812	30
31	9016		6944		3056	0579	40 92	40 231	5158	31
32	9282		6828		3172	0717	50 115	45 259	5504	32
33	9549		6712		3288	0855		50 288	5850	33
34	9816		6596		3404	0994			6197	34
35	.400082		.916479		.083521	.091132			.436543	35
36	0349		6363		3637	1271			6889	36
37	0616		6246		3754	1410			7236	37
38	0882		6130		3870	1548			7582	38
39	1149		6013		3987	1688			7929	39
40	.401415		.915896		.084104	.091827			.438276	40
41	1681	" Corr.	5780	" Corr.	4220	1966			8622	41
42	1948	10 44	5663	10 20	4337	2105			8969	42
43	2214	15 67	5546	15 29	4454	2245			9316	43
44	2480	20 89	5429	20 39	4571	2384			9663	44
45	.402747	30 133	.915312	30 59	.084688	.092524			.440010	45
46	3013	40 178	5194	40 78	4806	2664	" Corr.	" Corr.	0358	46
47	3279	45 200	5077	45 88	4923	2804	10 23	10 58	0705	47
48	3545	50 222	4960	50 98	5040	2944	15 35	15 87	1053	48
49	3811		4842		5158	3085	20 47	20 116	1400	49
50	.404078		.914725		.085275	.093225	30 70	30 174	.441748	50
51	4344		4607		5393	3366	40 94	40 232	2095	51
52	4610		4490		5510	3506	45 105	45 261	2443	52
53	4876		4372		5628	3647	50 117	50 290	2791	53
53	5142		4254		5746	3788			3139	54
55	.405408		.914136		.085864	.093929			.443487	55
56	5673		4018		5982	4070			3835	56
57	5939		3900		6100	4212			4183	57
58	6205		3782		6218	4353			4532	58
59	6471		3664		6336	4495			4880	59
60	.406737		.913546		.086454	.094636			.445229	60

'	Sine	Corr. for Sec. (+)	Cosine	Corr. for Sec. (− +)	Versine	Exsec	Corr. for Sec. (+)	Corr. for Sec. (+)	Tangent	'
0	.406737		.913546		.086454	.094636			.445229	0
1	7002		3427		6573	4778			5577	1
2	7268		3309		6691	4920			5926	2
3	7534		3190		6810	5062			6275	3
4	7799		3072		6928	5204			6624	4
5	.408065		.912953		.087047	.095347	″ Corr	″ Corr	.446973	5
6	8330		2834		7166	5489	10″ 24	10″ 58	7322	6
7	8596		2715		7285	5632	15″ 36	15″ 87	7671	7
8	8862		2596		7404	5775	20″ 48	20″ 116	8020	8
9	9127		2478		7522	5917			8369	9
10	.409392	″ Corr	.912358	″ Corr	.087642	.096060	30″ 72	30″ 175	.448719	10
11	9658	10″ 44	2239	10″ 20	7761	6204	40″ 95	40″ 233	9068	11
12	9923	15″ 66	2120	15″ 30	7880	6347	45″ 107	45″ 262	9418	12
13	.410188	20″ 88	2001	20″ 40	7999	6490	50″ 119	50″ 291	9768	13
14	0454		1882		8118	6634			.450117	14
15	.410719	30″ 133	.911762	30″ 60	.088238	.096777			.450467	15
16	0984	40″ 177	1642	40″ 80	8358	6921			0817	16
17	1249	45″ 199	1523	45″ 90	8477	7065			1167	17
18	1514	50″ 221	1403	50″ 100	8597	7209			1517	18
19	1780		1284		8716	7353			1868	19
20	.412044		.911164		.088836	.097498			.452218	20
21	2310		1044		8956	7642			2568	21
22	2574		0924		9076	7787			2919	22
23	2840		0804		9196	7931			3269	23
24	3104		0684		9316	8076			3620	24
25	.413369		.910564		.089436	.098221	″ Corr	″ Corr	.453971	25
26	3634		0443		9557	8366	10″ 24	10″ 59	4322	26
27	3899		0323		9677	8511	15″ 36	15″ 88	4673	27
28	4164		0202		9798	8657	20″ 49	20″ 117	5024	28
29	4428		0082		9918	8802			5375	29
30	.414693		.909961		.090039	.098948	30″ 73	30″ 176	.455726	30
31	4958		9841		0159	9094	40″ 97	40″ 234	6078	31
32	5223		9720		0280	9240	45″ 109	45″ 263	6429	32
33	5487		9599		0401	9386	50″ 121	50″ 293	6781	33
34	5752		9478		0522	9532			7132	34
35	.416016		.909357		.090643	.099678			.457484	35
36	6281		9236		0764	9824			7836	36
37	6545		9115		0885	9971			8188	37
38	6810		8994		1006	.100118			8540	38
39	7074		8872		1128	0264			8892	39
40	.417338	″ Corr	.908751	″ Corr	.091249	.100411			.459244	40
41	7603	10″ 44	8630	10″ 20	1370	0558			9596	41
42	7867	15″ 66	8508	15″ 30	1492	0706			9949	42
43	8131	20″ 88	8387	20″ 41	1613	0853			.460301	43
44	8396		8265		1735	1000			0654	44
45	.418660	30″ 132	.908143	30″ 61	.091857	.101148	″ Corr	″ Corr	.461006	45
46	8924	40″ 176	8021	40″ 81	1979	1296	10″ 25	10″ 59	1359	46
47	9188	45″ 198	7900	45″ 91	2100	1444	15″ 37	15″ 88	1712	47
48	9452	50″ 220	7778	50″ 101	2222	1592	20″ 49	20″ 118	2065	48
49	9716		7655		2345	1740			2418	49
50	.419980		.907533		.092467	.101888	30″ 74	30″ 177	.462771	50
51	.420244		7411		2589	2036	40″ 99	40″ 235	3124	51
52	0508		7289		2711	2185	45″ 111	45″ 265	3478	52
53	0772		7166		2834	2334	50″ 123	50″ 294	3831	53
54	1036		7044		2956	2482			4184	54
55	.421300		.906922		.093078	.102631			.464538	55
56	1563		6799		3201	2780			4892	56
57	1827		6676		3324	2930			5246	57
58	2091		6554		3446	3079			5600	58
59	2355		6431		3569	3228			5954	59
60	.422618		.906308		.093692	.103378			.466308	60

TABLE XX.—NATURAL SINES, COSINES,
25°

′	Sine	Cosine	Versine	Exsec	Tangent	′
0	.422618	.906308	.093692	.103378	.466308	0
1	2882	6185	3815	3528	6662	1
2	3146	6062	3938	3678	7016	2
3	3409	5939	4061	3828	7370	3
4	3672	5815	4185	3978	7725	4
5	.423936	.905692	.094308	.104128	.468080	5
6	4199	5569	4431	4278	8434	6
7	4463	5445	4555	4429	8789	7
8	4726	5322	4678	4580	9144	8
9	4990	5198	4802	4730	9499	9
10	.425253	.905075	.094925	.104881	.469854	10
11	5516	4951	5049	5032	.470209	11
12	5779	4827	5173	5184	0564	12
13	6042	4703	5297	5335	0920	13
14	6306	4579	5421	5486	1275	14
15	.426569	.904455	.095545	.105638	.471631	15
16	6832	4331	5669	5790	1986	16
17	7095	4207	5793	5942	2342	17
18	7358	4082	5918	6094	2698	18
19	7621	3958	6042	6246	3054	19
20	.427884	.903834	.096166	.106398	.473410	20
21	8147	3709	6291	6551	3766	21
22	8410	3585	6415	6703	4122	22
23	8672	3460	6540	6856	4478	23
24	8935	3335	6665	7009	4835	24
25	.429198	.903210	.096790	.107162	.475191	25
26	9461	3086	6914	7315	5548	26
27	9723	2961	7039	7468	5905	27
28	9986	2836	7164	7621	6262	28
29	.430248	2710	7290	7775	6618	29
30	.430511	.902585	.097415	.107928	.476976	30
31	0774	2460	7540	8082	7333	31
32	1036	2335	7665	8236	7690	32
33	1299	2209	7791	8390	8047	33
34	1561	2084	7916	8544	8405	34
35	.431823	.901958	.098042	.108699	.478762	35
36	2086	1832	8168	8853	9120	36
37	2348	1707	8293	9008	9477	37
38	2610	1581	8419	9163	9835	38
39	2873	1455	8545	9318	.480193	39
40	.433135	.901329	.098671	.109473	.480551	40
41	3397	1203	8797	9628	0909	41
42	3659	1077	8923	9783	1268	42
43	3921	0951	9049	9938	1626	43
44	4183	0825	9175	.110094	1984	44
45	.434445	.900698	.099302	.110250	.482343	45
46	4707	0572	9428	0406	2701	46
47	4969	0445	9555	0562	3060	47
48	5231	0319	9681	0718	3419	48
49	5493	0192	9808	0874	3778	49
50	.435755	.900065	.099935	.111030	.484137	50
51	6017	.899939	.100061	1187	4496	51
52	6278	9812	0188	1344	4855	52
53	6540	9685	0315	1500	5214	53
54	6802	9558	0442	1657	5574	54
55	.437063	.899431	.100569	.111814	.485933	55
56	7325	9304	0696	1972	6293	56
57	7587	9176	0824	2129	6653	57
58	7848	9049	0951	2286	7013	58
59	8110	8922	1078	2444	7373	59
60	.438371	.898794	.101206	.112602	.487733	60

Corr. for Sec. (Sine, +):

″	Corr.	″	Corr.
10	44	30	132
15	66	40	175
20	88	45	197
		50	219

″	Corr.	″	Corr.
10	44	30	131
15	65	40	175
20	87	45	196
		50	218

Corr. for Sec. (Cosine, −):

″	Corr.	″	Corr.
10	21	30	62
15	31	40	83
20	41	45	93
		50	103

″	Corr.	″	Corr.
10	21	30	63
15	32	40	84
20	42	45	95
		50	105

Corr. for Sec. (Exsec, +):

″	Corr.	″	Corr.
10	25	10	59
15	38	15	89
20	50	20	118
30	76	30	178
40	101	40	236
45	113	45	266
50	126	50	296

″	Corr.	″	Corr.
10	26	10	60
15	38	15	89
20	51	20	119
30	77	30	179
40	103	40	238
45	115	45	268
50	128	50	298

″	Corr.	″	Corr.
10	26	10	60
15	39	15	90
20	52	20	120
30	78	30	180
40	104	40	239
45	117	45	269
50	130	50	299

'	Sine	Corr. for Sec. +	Cosine	Corr. for Sec. − +	Versine	Exsec	Corr. for Sec. +	Corr. for Sec. +	Tangent	'
0	.438371		.898794		.101206	.112602			.487733	0
1	8633		8666		1334	2760			8093	1
2	8894		8539		1461	2918			8453	2
3	9155		8411		1589	3076			8813	3
4	9417		8283		1717	3234			9174	4
5	.439678		.898156		.101844	.113393	" Corr.	" Corr.	.489534	5
6	9939		8028		1972	3552	10 27	10 60	9895	6
7	.440200		7900		2100	3710	15 40	15 90	.490256	7
8	0462		7772		2228	3869	20 53	20 120	0617	8
9	0723		7643		2357	4028			0978	9
10	.440984		.897515		.102485	.114187	30 80	30 181	.491339	10
11	1245	" Corr.	7387	" Corr.	2613	4347	40 106	40 241	1700	11
12	1506	10 43	7258	10 21	2742	4506	45 119	45 271	2061	12
13	1767	15 65	7130	15 32	2870	4666	50 133	50 301	2422	13
14	2028	20 87	7001	20 43	2999	4826			2784	14
15	.442289	30 130	.896873	30 64	.103127	.114945			.493145	15
16	2550	40 174	6744	40 86	3256	5145			3507	16
17	2810	45 196	6615	45 97	3385	5306			3869	17
18	3071	50 217	6486	50 107	3514	5466			4231	18
19	3332		6358		3642	5626			4593	19
20	.443593		.896228		.103772	.115787			.494955	20
21	3853		6099		3901	5948			5317	21
22	4114		5970		4030	6108			5679	22
23	4375		5841		4159	6269			6042	23
24	4635		5712		4288	6431			6404	24
25	.444896		.895582		.104418	.116592			.496767	25
26	5156		5453		4547	6753	" Corr.	" Corr.	7130	26
27	5417		5323		4677	6915	10 27	10 61	7492	27
28	5677		5194		4806	7077	15 41	15 91	7855	28
29	5938		5064		4936	7238	20 54	20 121	8218	29
30	.446198		.894934		.105066	.117400	30 81	30 182	.498582	30
31	6458		4804		5196	7562	40 108	40 242	8945	31
32	6718		4675		5325	7725	45 122	45 272	9308	32
33	6979		4545		5455	7887	50 135	50 303	9672	33
34	7239		4415		5585	8050			.500035	34
35	.447499		.894284		.105716	.118212			.500399	35
36	7759		4154		5846	8375			0763	36
37	8019		4024		5976	8538			1127	37
38	8279		3894		6106	8701			1491	38
39	8539		3763		6237	8865			1855	39
40	.448799		.893633		.106367	.119028			.502219	40
41	9059	" Corr.	3502	" Corr.	6498	9192			2583	41
42	9319	10 43	3371	10 22	6629	9355			2948	42
43	9579	15 65	3241	15 33	6759	9519			3312	43
44	9839	20 87	3110	20 44	6890	9683			3677	44
45	.450098	30 130	.892979	30 65	.107021	.119847			.504042	45
46	0358	40 173	2848	40 87	7152	.120012	" Corr.	" Corr.	4406	46
47	0618	50 216	2717	45 98	7283	0176	10 27	10 61	4771	47
48	0878		2586	50 109	7414	0340	15 41	15 91	5136	48
49	1137		2455		7545	0505	20 55	20 122	5502	49
50	.451397		.892323		.107677	.120670	30 82	30 183	.505867	50
51	1656		2192		7808	0835	40 110	40 244	6232	51
52	1916		2061		7939	1000	45 124	45 274	6598	52
53	2175		1929		8071	1165	50 137	50 304	6963	53
54	2435		1798		8202	1331			7329	54
55	.452694		.891666		.108334	.121496			.507695	55
56	2954		1534		8466	1662			8061	56
57	3213		1402		8598	1828			8427	57
58	3472		1270		8730	1994			8793	58
59	3731		1138		8862	2160			9159	59
60	.453990		.891006		.108994	.122326			.509525	60

TABLE XX.—NATURAL SINES, COSINES,
27°

′	Sine	Corr. for Sec. +	Cosine	Corr. for Sec. − +	Versine	Exsec	Corr. for Sec. +	Corr. for Sec. +	Tangent	′
0	.453990		.891006		.108994	.122326			.509525	0
1	4250		0874		9126	2493			9892	1
2	4509		0742		9258	2659			.510258	2
3	4768		0610		9390	2826			0625	3
4	5027		0478		9522	2993			0992	4
5	.455286		.890345		.109655	.123160			.511359	5
6	5545		0213		9787	3327	" Corr.	" Corr.	1726	6
7	5804		0080		9920	3494	10 28	10 61	2093	7
8	6063		.889948		.110052	3662	15 42	15 92	2460	8
9	6322		9815		0185	3829	20 56	20 122	2828	9
10	.456580		.889682		.110318	.123997			.513195	10
11	6839	" Corr.	9549	" Corr.	0451	4165	30 84	30 184	3562	11
12	7098	10 43	9416	10 22	0584	4333	40 112	40 245	3930	12
13	7357	15 65	9283	15 33	0717	4501	45 126	45 276	4298	13
14	7615	20 86	9150	20 44	0850	4669	50 140	50 306	4666	14
15	.457874	30 129	.889017	30 67	.110983	.124838			.515034	15
16	8132	40 172	8884	40 89	1116	5006			5402	16
17	8391	45 194	8751	45 100	1249	5175			5770	17
18	8650	50 215	8617	50 111	1383	5344			6138	18
19	8908		8484		1516	5513			6507	19
20	.459166		.888350		.111650	.125682			.516876	20
21	9425		8217		1783	5851			7244	21
22	9683		8083		1917	6021			7613	22
23	9942		7949		2051	6190			7982	23
24	.460200		7815		2185	6360			8351	24
25	.460458		.887682		.112318	.126530			.518720	25
26	0716		7548		2452	6700	" Corr.	" Corr.	9089	26
27	0974		7413		2587	6870	10 28	10 62	9458	27
28	1232		7279		2721	7041	15 43	15 92	9828	28
29	1491		7145		2855	7211	20 57	20 123	.520197	29
30	.461749		.887011		.112989	.127382			.520567	30
31	2007		6876		3124	7553	30 85	30 185	0937	31
32	2265		6742		3258	7724	40 114	40 246	1307	32
33	2522		6608		3392	7895	45 128	45 277	1677	33
34	2780		6473		3527	8066	50 142	50 308	2047	34
35	.463038		.886338		.113662	.128237			.522417	35
36	3296		6204		3796	8409			2787	36
37	3554		6069		3931	8581			3158	37
38	3812		5934		4066	8752			3528	38
39	4069		5799		4201	8924			3899	39
40	.464327		.885664		.114336	.129096			.524270	40
41	4584	" Corr.	5529	" Corr.	4471	9269			4641	41
42	4842	10 43	5394	10 23	4606	9441			5012	42
43	5100	15 64	5258	15 34	4742	9614			5383	43
44	5357	20 86	5123	20 45	4877	9786			5754	44
45	.465614	30 129	.884988	30 68	.115012	.129959			.526126	45
46	5872	40 172	4852	40 90	5148	.130132			6497	46
47	6129	45 193	4717	45 102	5283	0306	" Corr.	" Corr.	6868	47
48	6387	50 214	4581	50 113	5419	0479	10 29	10 62	7240	48
49	6644		4445		5555	0652	15 43	15 93	7612	49
50	.466901		.884310		.115690	.130826			.527984	50
51	7158		4174		5826	1000	30 87	30 186	8356	51
52	7416		4038		5962	1174	40 116	40 248	8728	52
53	7673		3902		6098	1348	45 130	45 279	9100	53
54	7930		3766		6234	1522	50 145	50 310	9473	54
55	.468187		.883630		.116370	.131696			.529845	55
56	8444		3493		6507	1871			.530218	56
57	8701		3357		6643	2045			0591	57
58	8958		3221		6779	2220			0963	58
59	9215		3084		6916	2395			1336	59
60	.469472		.882948		.117052	.132570			.531709	60

'	Sine	Corr. for Sec. +	Cosine	Corr. for Sec. − +	Versine	Exsec	Corr. for Sec. +	Corr. for Sec.. +	Tangent	'
0	.469472		.882948		.117052	.132570			.531709	0
1	9728		2811		7189	2745			2083	1
2	9985		2674		7326	2921			2456	2
3	.470242		2538		7462	3096			2829	3
4	0499		2401		7599	3272			3203	4
5	.470755		.882264		.117736	.133448			.533576	5
6	1012		2127		7873	3624	10 29	10 62	3950	6
7	1268		1990		8010	3800	15 44	15 94	4324	7
8	1525		1853		8147	3976	20 59	20 125	4698	8
9	1782		1716		8284	4153			5072	9
10	.472038		.881578		.118422	.134329	30 88	30 187	.535446	10
11	2294	10 43	1441	10 23	8559	4506	40 118	40 249	5821	11
12	2551	15 64	1304	15 34	8696	4683	45 133	45 281	6195	12
13	2807	20 85	1166	20 46	8834	4860	50 147	50 312	6570	13
14	3063		1028		8972	5037			6945	14
15	.473320	30 128	.880891	30 69	.119109	.135215			.537319	15
16	3576	40 171	0753	40 92	9247	5392			7694	16
17	3832	45 192	0615	45 103	9385	5570			8069	17
18	4088	50 213	0477	50 115	9523	5748			8444	18
19	4344		0339		9661	5926			8820	19
20	.474600		.880201		.119799	.136104			.539195	20
21	4856		0063		9937	6282			9571	21
22	5112		.879925		.120075	6460			9946	22
23	5368		9787		0213	6639			.540322	23
24	5624		9649		0351	6818			0698	24
25	.475880		.879510		.120490	.136996			.541074	25
26	6136		9372		0628	7176	10 30	10 63	1450	26
27	6392		9233		0767	7355	15 45	15 94	1826	27
28	6647		9095		0905	7534	20 60	20 126	2203	28
29	6903		8956		1044	7714			2579	29
30	.477159		.878817		.121183	.137893	30 90	30 188	.542956	30
31	7414		8678		1322	8073	40 120	40 251	3332	31
32	7670		8539		1461	8253	45 135	45 283	3709	32
33	7926		8400		1600	8433	50 150	50 314	4086	33
34	8181		8261		1739	8613			4463	34
35	.478436		.878122		.121878	.138794			.544840	35
36	8692		7983		2017	8974			5218	36
37	8947		7844		2156	9155			5595	37
38	9203		7704		2296	9336			5973	38
39	9458		7565		2435	9517			6350	39
40	.479713		.877425		.122575	.139698			.546728	40
41	9968	10 42	7286	10 23	2714	9879			7106	41
42	.480224	15 64	7146	15 35	2854	.140061			7484	42
43	0479	20 85	7006	20 47	2994	0242			7862	43
44	0734		6867		3133	0424			8240	44
45	.480989	30 127	.876727	30 70	.123273	.140606			.548619	45
46	1244	40 171	6587	40 93	3413	0788	10 30	10 63	8997	46
47	1499	45 191	6447	45 105	3553	0971	15 46	15 95	9376	47
48	1754	50 212	6307	50 117	3693	1153	20 61	20 126	9755	48
49	2009		6166		3834	1336			.550134	49
50	.482263		.876026		.123974	.141518	30 91	30 190	.550512	50
51	2518		5886		4114	1701	40 122	40 253	0892	51
52	2773		5746		4254	1884	45 137	45 284	1271	52
53	3028		5605		4395	2067	50 152	50 316	1650	53
54	3282		5464		4536	2251			2030	54
55	.483537		.875324		.124676	.142434			.552409	55
56	3792		5183		4817	2618			2789	56
57	4046		5042		4958	2802			3169	57
58	4301		4902		5098	2986			3549	58
59	4555		4761		5239	3170			3929	59
60	.484810		.874620		.125380	.143354			.554309	60

TABLE XX.—NATURAL SINES, COSINES,
29°

'	Sine	Corr. for Sec. +	Cosine	Corr. for Sec. − +	Versine	Exsec	Corr. for Sec. +	Corr. for Sec. +	Tangent	'
0	.484810		.874620		.125380	.143354			.554309	0
1	5064		4479		5521	3538			4689	1
2	5318		4338		5662	3723			5070	2
3	5573		4196		5804	3908			5450	3
4	5827		4055		5945	4093			5831	4
5	.486081		.873914		.126086	.144278	Corr.	Corr.	.556212	5
6	6335		3772		6228	4463	10 31	10 64	6593	6
7	6590		3631		6369	4648	15 46	15 95	6974	7
8	6844		3489		6511	4834	20 62	20 127	7355	8
9	7098		3348		6652	5020			7736	9
10	.487352		.873206		.126794	.145206	30 93	30 191	.558118	10
11	7606	Corr.	3064	Corr.	6936	5392	40 124	40 254	8499	11
12	7860	10 42	2922	10 24	7078	5578	45 140	45 286	8881	12
13	8114	15 63	2780	15 36	7220	5764	50 155	50 318	9263	13
14	8367	20 85	2638	20 47	7362	5950			9645	14
15	.488621	30 127	.872496	30 71	.127504	.146137			.560027	15
16	8875	40 169	2354	40 95	7646	6324			0409	16
17	9129	45 190	2212	45 107	7788	6511			0791	17
18	9382	50 211	2069	50 118	7931	6698			1174	18
19	9636		1927		8073	6885			1556	19
20	.489890		.871784		.128216	.147073			.561939	20
21	.490143		1642		8358	7260			2322	21
22	0397		1499		8501	7448			2705	22
23	0650		1357		8643	7636			3088	23
24	0904		1214		8786	7824			3471	24
25	.491157		.871071		.128929	.148012	Corr.	Corr.	.563854	25
26	1410		0928		9072	8200	10 32	10 64	4238	26
27	1664		0785		9215	8389	15 47	15 96	4621	27
28	1917		0642		9358	8578	20 63	20 128	5005	28
29	2170		0499		9501	8766			5389	29
30	.492424		.870356		.129644	.148956	30 95	30 192	.565773	30
31	2677		0212		9788	9145	40 126	40 256	6157	31
32	2930		0069		9931	9334	45 143	45 288	6541	32
33	3183		.869926		.130074	9524	50 158	50 320	6925	33
34	3436		9782		0218	9713			7310	34
35	.493689		.869639		.130361	.149903			.567694	35
36	3942		9495		0505	.150093			8079	36
37	4195		9351		0649	0283			8464	37
38	4448		9207		0793	0473			8849	38
39	4700		9064		0936	0664			9234	39
40	.494953		.868920		.131080	.150854			.569619	40
41	5206	Corr.	8776	Corr.	1224	1045			.570004	41
42	5459	10 42	8632	10 24	1368	1236			039C	42
43	5711	15 63	8487	15 36	1513	1427			0776	43
44	5964	20 84	8343	20 48	1657	1618			1161	44
45	.496216	30 126	.868199	30 72	.131801	.151810			.571547	45
46	6469	40 168	8054	40 96	1946	2002	Corr.	Corr.	1933	46
47	6722	45 189	7910	45 108	2090	2193	10 32	10 64	2319	47
48	6974	50 210	7766	50 120	2234	2385	15 48	15 97	2705	48
49	7226		7621		2379	2577	20 64	20 129	3092	49
50	.497479		.867476		.132524	.152769	30 96	30 193	.573478	50
51	7731		7331		2669	2962	40 128	40 258	3865	51
52	7983		7187		2813	3154	45 144	45 290	4252	52
53	8236		7042		2958	3347	50 160	50 322	4638	53
54	8488		6897		3103	3540			5026	54
55	.498740		.866752		.133248	.153733			.575413	55
56	8992		6607		3393	3926			5800	56
57	9244		6461		3539	4120			6187	57
58	9496		6316		3684	4313			6575	58
59	9748		6171		3829	4507			6962	59
60	.500000		.866025		.133975	.154700			.577350	60

VERSINES, EXSECANTS, AND TANGENTS
30°

'	Sine	Corr. for Sec. +	Cosine	Corr. for Sec. − +	Versine	Exsec	Corr. for Sec. +	Corr. for Sec. +	Tangent	'
0	.500000		.866025		.133975	.154700			.577350	0
1	0252		5880		4120	4894			7738	1
2	0504		5734		4266	5089			8126	2
3	0756		5589		4411	5283			8514	3
4	1007		5443		4557	5478			8903	4
5	.501259		.865297		.134703	.155672			.579291	5
6	1511		5151		4849	5867	" Corr. 10 33	" Corr. 10 65	9680	6
7	1762		5006		4994	6062	15 49	15 97	.580068	7
8	2014		4860		5140	6257	20 65	20 130	0457	8
9	2266		4713		5287	6452			0846	9
10	.502517		.864567		.135433	.156648	30 98	30 195	.581235	10
11	2768	" Corr. 10 42	4421	" Corr. 10 24	5579	6844	40 130	40 259	1624	11
12	3020	15 63	4275	15 37	5725	7039	45 147	45 292	2014	12
13	3271	20 84	4128	20 49	5872	7235	50 163	50 324	2403	13
14	3523		3982		6018	7432			2793	14
15	.503774	30 126	.863836	30 73	.136164	.157628			.583183	15
16	4025	40 167	3689	40 98	6311	7824			3573	16
17	4276	45 187	3542	45 110	6458	8021			3963	17
18	4528	50 209	3396	50 122	6604	8218			4353	18
19	4779		3249		6751	8415			4743	19
20	.505030		.863102		.136898	.158012			.585134	20
21	5281		2955		7045	8609			5524	21
22	5532		2808		7192	9006			5915	22
23	5783		2661		7339	9204			6306	23
24	6034		2514		7486	9402			6696	24
25	.506285		.862366		.137634	.159600			.587088	25
26	6536		2219		7781	9798	" Corr. 10 33	" Corr. 10 65	7479	26
27	6786		2072		7928	9996	15 50	15 99	7870	27
28	7037		1924		8076	.160195	20 66	20 131	8262	28
29	7288		1777		8223	0393			8653	29
30	.507538		.861629		.138371	.160592	30 100	30 196	.589045	30
31	7789		1482		8518	0791	40 133	40 261	9437	31
32	8040		1334		8666	0990	45 149	45 294	9829	32
33	8290		1186		8814	1189	50 166	50 327	.590221	33
34	8541		1038		8962	1389			0613	34
35	.508791		.860890		.139110	.161588			.591006	35
36	9041		0742		9258	1788			1398	36
37	9292		0594		9406	1988			1791	37
38	9542		0446		9554	2188			2184	38
39	9792		0298		9702	2389			2577	39
40	.510043		.860149		.139851	.162589			.592970	40
41	0293	" Corr. 10 42	0001	" Corr. 10 25	9999	2790			3363	41
42	0543	15 62	859852	15 37	.140148	2990			3756	42
43	0793	20 83	9704	20 50	0296	3191			4150	43
44	1043		9555		0445	3392			4544	44
45	.511293	30 125	.859406	30 74	.140594	163594			.594938	45
46	1543	40 167	9258	40 99	0742	3795	" Corr. 10 34	" Corr. 10 66	5331	46
47	1793	45 187	9109	45 112	0891	3997	15 51	15 99	5726	47
48	2043	50 208	8960	50 124	1040	4199	20 67	20 132	6120	48
49	2293		8811		1189	4401			6514	49
50	.512542		.858662		.141338	.164602	30 101	30 197	.596908	50
51	2792		8513		1487	4805	40 135	40 263	7303	51
52	3042		8364		1636	5008	45 152	45 296	7698	52
53	3292		8214		1786	5210	50 169	50 329	8093	53
54	3541		8065		1935	5413			8488	54
55	.513791		.857916		.142084	.165616			.598883	55
56	4040		7766		2234	5819			9278	56
57	4290		7616		2384	6022			9674	57
58	4539		7467		2533	6226			.600069	58
59	4789		7317		2683	6430			0465	59
60	.515038		.857167		.142833	.166633			.600861	60

TABLE XX.—NATURAL SINES, COSINES,
31°

'	Sine	Corr. for Sec. +	Cosine	Corr. for Sec. - +	Versine	Exsec	Corr. for Sec. +	Corr. for Sec. +	Tangent	'
0	.515038		.857167		.142833	.166633			.600861	0
1	5287		7017		2983	6837			1257	1
2	5537		6868		3132	7042			1653	2
3	5786		6718		3282	7246			2049	3
4	6035		6567		3433	7450			2445	4
5	.516284		.856417		.143583	.167655			.602842	5
6	6533		6267		3733	7860	" Corr.	" Corr.	3239	6
7	6782		6117		3883	8065	10 34	10 66	3635	7
8	7031		5966		4034	8270	15 51	15 99	4032	8
9	7280		5816		4184	8476	20 69	20 132	4429	9
10	.517529		.855666		.144334	.168681	30 103	30 199	.604827	10
11	7778	" Corr.	5515	" Corr.	4485	8887	40 137	40 265	5224	11
12	8027	10 41	5364	10 25	4636	9093	45 154	45 298	5622	12
13	8276	15 62	5214	15 38	4786	9299	50 171	50 331	6019	13
14	8525	20 83	5063	20 50	4937	9505			6417	14
15	.518773	30 124	.854912	30 76	.145088	.169711			.606815	15
16	9022	40 166	4761	40 101	5239	9918			7213	16
17	9270	45 186	4610	45 113	5390	.170124			7611	17
18	9519	50 207	4459	50 126	5541	0331			8010	18
19	9768		4308		5692	0538			8408	19
20	.520016		.854156		.145844	.170746			.608807	20
21	0265		4005		5995	0953			9205	21
22	0513		3854		6146	1161			9604	22
23	0761		3702		6298	1368			.610003	23
24	1010		3551		6449	1576			0403	24
25	.521258		.853399		.146601	.171784			.610802	25
26	1506		3248		6752	1993	" Corr.	" Corr.	1201	26
27	1754		3096		6904	2201	10 35	10 67	1601	27
28	2002		2944		7056	2410	15 52	15 100	2001	28
29	2250		2792		7208	2619	20 70	20 133	2401	29
30	.522499		.852640		.147360	.172828	30 105	30 200	.612801	30
31	2747		2488		7512	3037	40 139	40 267	3201	31
32	2994		2336		7664	3246	45 157	45 300	3601	32
33	3242		2184		7816	3456	50 174	50 333	4002	33
34	3490		2032		7968	3665			4402	34
35	.523738		.851879		.148121	.173875			.614803	35
36	3986		1727		8273	4085			5204	36
37	4234		1574		8426	4295			5605	37
38	4481		1422		8578	4506			6006	38
39	4729		1269		8731	4716			6408	39
40	.524977		.851117		.148883	.174927			.616809	40
41	5224	" Corr.	0964	" Corr.	9036	5138			7211	41
42	5472	10 41	0811	10 26	9189	5349			7613	42
43	5719	15 62	0658	15 38	9342	5560			8014	43
44	5966	20 82	0505	20 51	9495	5772			8417	44
45	.526214	30 124	.850352	30 77	.149648	.175983			.618819	45
46	6461	40 165	0199	40 102	9801	6195	" Corr.	" Corr.	9221	46
47	6708	45 186	0046	45 115	9954	6407	10 35	10 67	9624	47
48	6956	50 206	.849893	50 128	.150107	6619	15 53	15 101	.620026	48
49	. 7203		9739		0261	6831	20 71	20 134	0429	49
50	.527450		.849586		.150414	.177044	30 106	30 202	.620832	50
51	7697		9432		0568	7257	40 142	40 269	1235	51
52	7944		9279		0721	7469	45 160	45 302	1638	52
53	8191		9125		0875	7682	50 177	50 336	2042	53
54	8438		8972		1028	7896			2445	54
55	.528685		.848818		.151182	.178109			.622849	55
56	8932		8664		1336	8322			3253	56
57	9179		8510		1490	8536			3657	57
58	9426		8356		1644	8750			4061	58
59	9673		8202		1798	8964			4465	59
60	.529919		.848048		.151952	.179178			.624869	60

'	Sine	Corr. for Sec. +	Cosine	Corr. for Sec. − +	Versine	Exsec	Corr. for Sec. +	Corr. for Sec. +	Tangent	'
0	.529919		.848048		.151952	.179178			.624869	0
1	.530166		7894		2106	9393	" Corr	" Corr	5274	1
2	0412		7740		2260	9607	10 36	10 68	5679	2
3	0659		7585		2415	9822	15 54	15 101	6083	3
4	0906		7431		2569	.180037	20 72	20 135	6488	4
5	.531152		.847276		.152724	.180252	30 108	30 203	.626894	5
6	1399		7122		2878	0468	40 144	40 270	7299	6
7	1645		6967		3033	0683	45 162	45 304	7704	7
8	1891		6813		3187	0899	50 180	50 338	8110	8
9	2138		6658		3342	1115			8516	9
10	.532384		.846503		.153497	.181331			.628922	10
11	2630	" Corr	6348	" Corr	3652	1547			9327	11
12	2876	10 41	6193	10 26	3807	1763			9734	12
13	3122	15 61	6038	15 39	3962	1980			.630140	13
14	3368	20 82	5883	20 52	4117	2197			0546	14
15	.533614	30 123	.845728	30 78	.154272	.182414	" Corr	" Corr	.630953	15
16	3860	40 164	5573	40 103	4427	2631	10 36	10 68	1360	16
17	4106	45 185	5417	45 116	4583	2848	15 55	15 103	1767	17
18	4352	50 205	5262	50 129	4738	3065	20 73	20 136	2174	18
19	4598		5106		4894	3283			2581	19
20	.534844		.844951		.155049	.183501	30 109	30 204	.632988	20
21	5090		4795		5205	3719	40 146	40 272	3396	21
22	5336		4640		5360	3937	45 164	45 306	3804	22
23	5581		4484		5516	4155	50 182	50 340	4211	23
24	5827		4328		5672	4374			4619	24
25	.536072		.844172		.155828	.184593			.635027	25
26	6318		4016		5984	4812			5436	26
27	6563		3860		6140	5031			5844	27
28	6809		3704		6296	5250			6253	28
29	7054		3548		6452	5469			6661	29
30	.537300		.843391		.156609	.185689	" Corr	" Corr	.637070	30
31	7545		3235		6765	5909	10 37	10 68	7479	31
32	7790		3079		6921	6129	15 55	15 103	7888	32
33	8035		2922		7078	6349	20 74	20 137	8298	33
34	8281		2766		7234	6569			8707	34
35	.538526		.842609		.157391	.186790	30 111	30 205	.639117	35
36	8771		2452		7548	7011	40 147	40 273	9527	36
37	9016		2296		7704	7232	45 166	45 308	9937	37
38	9261		2139		7861	7453	50 184	50 342	.640347	38
39	9506		1982		8018	7674			0757	39
40	.539751		.841825		.158175	.187895			.641167	40
41	9996	" Corr	1668	" Corr	8332	8117			1578	41
42	.540240	10 41	1511	10 26	8489	8339			1989	42
43	0485	15 61	1354	15 39	8646	8561			2399	43
44	0730	20 82	1196	20 52	8804	8783			2810	44
45	.540974	30 122	.841039	30 79	.158961	.189006	" Corr	" Corr	.643222	45
46	1219	40 163	0882	40 105	9118	9228	10 37	10 69	3633	46
47	1464	45 183	0724	45 118	9276	9451	15 56	15 103	4044	47
48	1708	50 204	0567	50 131	9433	9674	20 75	20 137	4456	48
49	1953		0409		9591	9897			4868	49
50	.542197		.840251		.159749	.190120	30 112	30 206	.645280	50
51	2442		0094		9906	0344	40 149	40 275	5692	51
52	2686		.839936		.160064	0567	45 168	45 309	6104	52
53	2930		9778		0222	0791	50 186	50 344	6516	53
54	3174		9620		0380	1015			6929	54
55	.543419		.839462		.160538	.191239			.647342	55
56	3663		9304		0696	1464			7755	56
57	3907		9146		0854	1688			8168	57
58	4151		8987		1013	1913			8581	58
59	4395		8829		1171	2138			8994	59
60	.544639		.838671		.161329	.192363			.649408	60

TABLE XX.—NATURAL SINES, COSINES,
33°

'	Sine	Corr. for Sec. +	Cosine	Corr. for Sec. −	Versine +	Exsec	Corr. for Sec. +	Corr. for Sec. +	Tangent	'
0	.544639		.838671		.161329	.192363			.649408	0
1	4883		8512		1488	2589	" Corr. 10 38	" Corr. 10 69	9821	1
2	5127		8354		1646	2814	15 57	15 104	.650235	2
3	5371		8195		1805	3040	20 76	20 138	0649	3
4	5614		8036		1964	3266			1063	4
5	.545858		.837878		.162122	.193492	30 113	30 207	.651477	5
6	6102		7719		2281	3718	40 151	40 276	1892	6
7	6346		7560		2440	3945	45 170	45 311	2306	7
8	6589		7401		2599	4171	50 189	50 346	2721	8
9	6833		7242		2758	4398			3136	9
10	.547076		.837083		.162917	.194625			.653551	10
11	7320	" Corr. 10 41	6924	" Corr. 10 20	3076	4852			3966	11
12	7563	15 61	6764	15 40	3236	5080			4382	12
13	7807	20 81	6605	20 53	3395	5307			4797	13
14	8050		6446		3554	5535			5213	14
15	.548293	30 122	.836286	30 80	.163714	.195763			.655629	15
16	8536	40 162	6127	40 106	3873	5991	" Corr. 10 38	" Corr. 10 69	6045	16
17	8780	45 182	5967	45 120	4033	6219	15 57	15 104	6461	17
18	9023	50 203	5807	50 133	4193	6448	20 77	20 139	6877	18
19	9266		5648		4352	6677			7294	19
20	.549509		.835488		.164512	.196906	30 115	30 209	.657710	20
21	9752		5328		4672	7135	40 153	40 278	8127	21
22	9995		5168		4832	7364	45 172	45 313	8544	22
23	.550238		5008		4992	7593	50 191	50 348	8961	23
24	0481		4848		5152	7823			9378	24
25	.550724		.834688		.165312	.198053			.659796	25
26	0966		4528		5472	8283			.660214	26
27	1209		4367		5633	8513			0631	27
28	1452		4207		5793	8744			1049	28
29	1694		4046		5954	8974			1467	29
30	.551937		.833886		.166114	.199205			.661886	30
31	2180		3725		6275	9436	" Corr. 10 39	" Corr. 10 70	2304	31
32	2422		3565		6435	9667	15 58	15 105	2722	32
33	2664		3404		6596	9898	20 77	20 140	3141	33
34	2907		3243		6757	.200130			3560	34
35	.553149		.833082		.166918	.200362	30 116	30 210	.663979	35
36	3392		2921		7079	0594	40 155	40 280	4398	36
37	3634		2760		7240	0826	45 174	45 315	4818	37
38	3876		2599		7401	1058	50 194	50 350	5237	38
39	4118		2438		7562	1291			5657	39
40	.554360		.832277		.167723	.201523			.666077	40
41	4602	" Corr. 10 40	2116	" Corr. 10 27	7884	1756			6497	41
42	4844	15 60	1954	15 40	8046	1989			6917	42
43	5086	20 81	1793	20 54	8207	2223			7337	43
44	5328		1631		8369	2456			7758	44
45	.555570	30 121	.831470	30 81	.168530	.202690			.668179	45
46	5812	40 161	1308	40 108	8692	2924	" Corr. 10 39	" Corr. 10 70	8600	46
47	6054	45 181	1146	45 121	8854	3158	15 59	15 106	9020	47
48	6296	50 202	0984	50 135	9016	3392	20 78	20 141	9442	48
49	6537		0823		9177	3626			9863	49
50	.556779		.830661		.169339	.203861	30 118	30 211	.670284	50
51	7021		0499		9501	4096	40 157	40 281	0706	51
52	7262		0337		9663	4331	45 176	45 316	1128	52
53	7504		0174		9826	4566	50 196	50 352	1550	53
54	7745		0012		9988	4801			1972	54
55	.557986		.829850		.170150	.205037			.672394	55
56	8228		9688		0312	5273			2817	56
57	8469		9525		0475	5509			3240	57
58	8710		9363		0637	5745			3662	58
59	8952		9200		0800	5981			4085	59
60	.559193		.829038		.170962	.206218			.674508	60

'	Sine	Corr. for Sec. +	Cosine	Corr. for Sec. - +	Versine	Exsec	Corr. for Sec. +	Corr. for Sec. +	Tangent	'
0	.559193		.829038		.170962	.206218			.674508	0
1	9434		8875		1125	6455	" Corr.	" Corr	4932	1
2	9675		8712		1288	6692	10 40	10 71	5355	2
3	9916		8549		1451	6929	15 60	15 106	5779	3
4	.560157		8386		1614	7166	20 79	20 141	6203	4
5	.560398		.828223		.171777	.207404	30 119	30 212	.676627	5
6	0639		8060		1940	7642	40 159	40 283	7051	6
7	0880		7897		2103	7879	45 179	45 318	7475	7
8	1121		7734		2266	8118	50 198	50 354	7900	8
9	1361		7571		2429	8356			8324	9
10	.561602		.827407		.172593	.208594			.678749	10
11	1843	" Corr.	7244	" Corr.	2756	8833			9174	11
12	2083	10 40	7081	10 27	2919	9072			9599	12
13	2324	15 60	6917	15 41	3083	9311			.680025	13
14	2564	20 80	6753	20 55	3247	9550			0450	14
15	.562805	30 120	.826590	30 82	.173410	.209790	" Corr.	" Corr.	.680876	15
16	3045	40 159	6426	40 109	3574	.210030	10 40	10 71	1302	16
17	3286	45 180	6262	45 123	3738	0270	15 60	15 107	1728	17
18	3526	50 200	6098	50 136	3902	0510	20 80	20 142	2154	18
19	3766		5934		4066	0750			2580	19
20	.564007		.825770		.174230	.210990	30 121	30 213	.683007	20
21	4247		5606		4394	1231	40 161	40 285	3433	21
22	4487		5442		4558	1472	45 181	45 320	3860	22
23	4727		5278		4722	1713	50 201	50 356	4287	23
24	4967		5114		4886	1954			4714	24
25	.565207		.824949		.175051	.212196			.685142	25
26	5447		4785		5215	2438			5569	26
27	5687		4620		5380	2680			5997	27
28	5927		4456		5544	2922			6425	28
29	6166		4291		5709	3164			6853	29
30	.566406		.824126		.175874	.213406			.687281	30
31	6646		3961		6039	3649	" Corr.	" Corr.	7709	31
32	6886		3796		6204	3892	10 41	10 72	8138	32
33	7125		3632		6366	4135	15 61	15 107	8567	33
34	7365		3467		6533	4378	20 81	20 143	8996	34
35	.567604		.823302		.176698	.214622	30 122	30 215	.689425	35
36	7844		3136		6864	4866	40 163	40 286	9854	36
37	8083		2971		7029	5109	45 183	45 322	.690283	37
38	8322		2806		7194	5354	50 203	50 358	0713	38
39	8562		2640		7360	5598			1142	39
40	.568801		.822475		.177525	.215842			.691572	40
41	9040	" Corr.	2310	" Corr.	7690	6087			2003	41
42	9280	10 39	2144	10 28	7856	6332			2433	42
43	9519	15 60	1978	15 41	8022	6577			2863	43
44	9758	20 80	1813	20 55	8187	6822			3294	44
45	.569997	30 119	.821647	30 83	.178353	.217068			.693725	45
46	.570236	40 159	1481	40 110	8519	7314	" Corr.	" Corr.	4156	46
47	0475	45 179	1315	45 124	8685	7559	10 41	10 72	4587	47
48	0714	50 199	1149	50 138	8851	7806	15 62	15 108	5018	48
49	0952		0983		9017	8052	20 81	20 144	5450	49
50	.571191		.820817		.179183	.218298	30 124	30 216	.695681	50
51	1430		0651		9349	8545	40 165	40 288	6313	51
52	1669		0485		9515	8792	45 185	45 324	6745	52
53	1907		0318		9682	9039	50 206	50 360	7177	53
54	2146		0152		9848	9286			7610	54
55	.572384		.819985		.180015	.219534			.698042	55
56	2623		9819		0181	9782			8475	56
57	2861		9652		0346	.220030			8908	57
58	3100		9486		0514	0278			9341	58
59	3338		9319		0681	0526			9774	59
60	.573576		.819152		.180848	.220775			.700208	60

TABLE XX.—NATURAL SINES, COSINES,
35°

′	Sine	Cosine	Versine	Exsec	Tangent	′
0	.573576	.819152	.180848	.220775	.700208	0
1	3815	8985	1015	1023	0641	1
2	4053	8818	1182	1272	1075	2
3	4291	8651	1349	1522	1509	3
4	4529	8484	1516	1771	1943	4
5	.574767	.818317	.181683	.222020	.702377	5
6	5005	8150	1850	2270	2812	6
7	5243	7982	2018	2520	3246	7
8	5481	7815	2185	2770	3681	8
9	5719	7648	2352	3021	4116	9
10	.575957	.817480	.182520	.223271	.704552	10
11	6195	7312	2688	3522	4987	11
12	6432	7145	2855	3773	5422	12
13	6670	6977	3023	4024	5858	13
14	6908	6809	3191	4276	6294	14
15	.577145	.816642	.183358	.224527	.706730	15
16	7383	6474	3526	4779	7166	16
17	7620	6306	3694	5031	7603	17
18	7858	6138	3862	5284	8040	18
19	8095	5970	4030	5536	8476	19
20	.578332	.815801	.184199	.225789	.708913	20
21	8570	5633	4367	6042	9350	21
22	8807	5465	4535	6295	9788	22
23	9044	5296	4704	6548	.710225	23
24	9281	5128	4872	6802	0663	24
25	.579518	.814959	.185041	.227055	.711101	25
26	9755	4791	5209	7309	1539	26
27	9992	4622	5378	7563	1977	27
28	.580229	4453	5547	7818	2416	28
29	0466	4284	5716	8072	2854	29
30	.580703	.814116	.185884	.228327	.713293	30
31	0940	3947	6053	8582	3732	31
32	1176	3778	6222	8837	4171	32
33	1413	3608	6392	9092	4611	33
34	1650	3439	6561	9348	5050	34
35	.581886	.813270	.186730	.229604	.715490	35
36	2123	3101	6899	9860	5930	36
37	2360	2931	7069	.230116	6370	37
38	2596	2762	7238	0372	6810	38
39	2832	2592	7408	0629	7250	39
40	.583069	.812423	.187577	.230886	.717691	40
41	3305	2253	7747	1143	8132	41
42	3541	2084	7916	1400	8573	42
43	3777	1914	8086	1658	9014	43
44	4014	1744	8256	1916	9455	44
45	.584250	.811574	.188426	.232174	.719897	45
46	4486	1404	8596	2432	.720339	46
47	4722	1234	8766	2690	0781	47
48	4958	1064	8936	2949	1223	48
49	5194	0894	9106	3207	1665	49
50	.585429	.810723	.189277	.233466	.722108	50
51	5665	0553	9447	3726	2550	51
52	5901	0383	9617	3985	2993	52
53	6137	0212	9788	4245	3436	53
54	6372	0042	9958	4504	3879	54
55	.586608	.809871	.190129	.234764	.724323	55
56	6844	9700	0300	5025	4766	56
57	7079	9530	0470	5285	5210	57
58	7314	9359	0641	5546	5654	58
59	7550	9188		5807	6098	59
60	.587785	.809017	.190983	.236068	.726542	60

Corr. for Sec. — Sine (+)

10 40	15 59	20 79	30 119	40 158	45 178	50 198
10 39	15 59	20 79	30 118	40 157	45 177	50 197

Corr. for Sec. — Cosine (− +)

10 28	15 42	20 56	30 84	40 112	45 126	50 140
10 28	15 42	20 57	30 85	40 113	45 127	50 142

Corr. for Sec. — Exsec / Tangent (two columns)

First Corr.							Second Corr.						
10 42	15 63	20 83	30 125	40 167	45 188	50 208	10 72	15 109	20 145	30 217	40 290	45 326	50 362
10 42	15 63	20 84	30 127	40 169	45 190	50 211	10 73	15 109	20 146	30 219	40 292	45 328	50 365
10 43	15 64	20 85	30 128	40 171	45 192	50 214	10 73	15 110	20 147	30 220	40 293	45 330	50 367
10 43	15 65	20 87	30 130	40 173	45 195	50 216	10 74	15 111	20 148	30 222	40 295	45 332	50 369

'	Sine	Corr. for Sec.	Cosine	Corr. for Sec.	Versine	Exsec	Corr. for Sec.	Corr. for Sec.	Tangent	'
0	.587785	+	.809017	− +	.190983	.236068	+	+	.726542	0
1	8021		8846		1154	6329	⁕ Corr.	⁕ Corr.	6987	1
2	8256		8675		1325	6591	10 44	10 74	7432	2
3	8491		8504		1496	6853	15 66	15 111	7877	3
4	8726		8332		1668	7115	20 88	20 149	8322	4
5	.588961		.808161		.191839	.237377	30 131	30 223	.728767	5
6	9196		7990		2010	7639	40 175	40 297	9212	6
7	9431		7818		2182	7902	45 197	45 334	9658	7
8	9666		7647		2353	8165	50 219	50 372	.730104	8
9	9901		7475		2525	8428			0550	9
10	.590136		.807304		.192696	.238691			.730996	10
11	0371	⁕ Corr.	7132	⁕ Corr.	2868	8955			1443	11
12	0606	10 39	6960	10 29	3040	9218			1889	12
13	0840	15 59	6788	15 43	3212	9482			2336	13
14	1075	20 78	6617	20 57	3383	9746			2783	14
15	.591310	30 117	.806445	30 86	.193555	.240011			.733230	15
16	1544	40 156	6273	40 115	3727	0275	⁕ Corr.	⁕ Corr.	3678	16
17	1779	45 176	6100	45 129	3900	0540	10 44	10 75	4125	17
18	2013	50 195	5928	50 143	4072	0805	15 67	15 112	4573	18
19	2248		5756		4244	1070	20 89	20 150	5021	19
20	.592482		.805584		.194416	.241336	30 133	30 224	.735469	20
21	2716		5411		4589	1602	40 177	40 299	5917	21
22	2950		5239		4761	1868	45 200	45 337	6366	22
23	3185		5066		4934	2134	50 222	50 374	6815	23
24	3419		4894		5106	2400			7264	24
25	.593653		.804721		.195279	.242666			.737713	25
26	3887		4548		5452	2933			8162	26
27	4121		4376		5624	3200			8612	27
28	4355		4203		5797	3468			9061	28
29	4589		4030		5970	3735			9511	29
30	.594823		.803857		.196143	.244003			.739961	30
31	5057		3684		6316	4270	⁕ Corr.	⁕ Corr.	.740411	31
32	5290		3511		6489	4538	10 45	10 75	0862	32
33	5524		3338		6662	4807	15 67	15 113	1312	33
34	5758		3164		6836	5075	20 90	20 151	1763	34
35	.595991		.802991		.197009	.245344	30 135	30 226	.742214	35
36	6225		2818		7182	5613	40 180	40 301	2666	36
37	6458		2644		7356	5882	45 202	45 339	3117	37
38	6692		2470		7530	6152	50 225	50 376	3569	38
39	6925		2297		7703	6421			4020	39
40	.597159		.802123		.197877	.246691			.744472	40
41	7392	⁕ Corr.	1950	⁕ Corr.	8050	6961			4925	41
42	7625	10 39	1776	10 29	8224	7232			5377	42
43	7858	15 58	1602	15 44	8398	7502			5830	43
44	8092	20 78	1428	20 58	8572	7773			6282	44
45	.598325	30 117	.801254	30 87	.198746	.248044			.746735	45
46	8558	40 155	1080	40 116	8920	8315	⁕ Corr.	⁕ Corr.	7189	46
47	8791	45 175	0906	45 131	9094	8587	10 45	10 76	7642	47
48	9024	50 194	0731	50 145	9269	8858	15 68	15 114	8096	48
49	9256		0557		9443	9130	20 91	20 152	8549	49
50	.599489		.800383		.199617	.249402	30 136	30 227	.749003	50
51	9722		0208		9792	9675	40 182	40 303	9458	51
52	9955		0034		9966	9947	45 205	45 341	9912	52
53	.600188		.799859		.200141	.250220	50 227	50 379	.750366	53
54	0420		9685		0315	0493			0821	54
55	.600653		.799510		.200490	.250766			.751276	55
56	0885		9335		0665	1040			1731	56
57	1118		9160		0840	1313			2187	57
58	1350		8986		1014	1587			2642	58
59	1583		8810		1190	1861			3098	59
60	.601815		.798636		.201364	.252136			.753554	60

TABLE XX.—NATURAL SINES, COSINES,
37°

'	Sine	Corr. for Sec. +	Cosine	Corr. for Sec. − +	Versine	Exsec	Corr. for Sec. +	Corr. for Sec. +	Tangent	'
0	.601815		.798636		.201364	.252136			.753554	0
1	2047		8460		1540	2410	# Corr.	# Corr.	4010	1
2	2280		8285		1715	2685	10 46	10 76	4467	2
3	2512		8110		1890	2960	15 69	15 114	4923	3
4	2744		7935		2065	3235	20 92	20 153	5380	4
5	.602976		.797759		.202241	.253511	30 138	30 229	.755837	5
6	3208		7584		2416	3786	40 184	40 305	6294	6
7	3440		7408		2592	4062	45 207	45 343	6751	7
8	3672		7233		2767	4339	50 230	50 381	7209	8
9	3904		7057		2943	4615			7667	9
10	.604136		.796882		.203118	.254892			.758125	10
11	4367	# Corr.	6706	# Corr.	3294	5168			8583	11
12	4599	10 39	6530	10 29	3470	5446			9041	12
13	4831	15 58	6354	15 44	3646	5723			9500	13
14	5062	20 77	6178	20 59	3822	6000			9959	14
15	.605294	30 116	.796002	30 88	.203998	.256278			.760418	15
16	5526	40 154	5826	40 117	4174	6556	# Corr.	# Corr.	0877	16
17	5757	45 174	5650	45 132	4350	6835	10 47	10 114	1336	17
18	5988	50 193	5474	50 147	4526	7113	15 70	15 115	1796	18
19	6220		5297		4703	7392	20 93	20 154	2256	19
20	.606451		.795121		.204879	.257670	30 140	30 230	.762716	20
21	6682		4944		5056	7950	40 186	40 307	3176	21
22	6914		4768		5232	8229	45 210	45 345	3636	22
23	7145		4591		5409	8509	50 233	50 384	4097	23
24	7376		4415		5585	8788			4558	24
25	.607607		.794238		.205762	.259069			.765019	25
26	7838		4061		5939	9349			5480	26
27	8069		3884		6116	9629			5941	27
28	8300		3707		6293	9910			6403	28
29	8531		3530		6470	.260191			6865	29
30	.608761		.793353		.206647	.260472			.767327	30
31	8992		3176		6824	0754	# Corr.	# Corr.	7789	31
32	9223		2999		7001	1036	10 47	10 77	8252	32
33	9454		2822		7178	1318	15 71	15 116	8714	33
34	9684		2644		7356	1600	20 94	20 155	9177	34
35	.609915		.792467		.207533	.261882	30 142	30 232	.769640	35
36	.610145		2290		7710	2165	40 189	40 309	.770104	36
37	0376		2112		7888	2448	45 212	45 348	0567	37
38	0606		1934		8066	2731	50 236	50 386	1031	38
39	0836		1757		8243	3014			1495	39
40	.611067		.791579		.208421	.263298			.771959	40
41	1297	# Corr.	1401	# Corr.	8599	3581			2423	41
42	1527	10 38	1224	10 30	8776	3865			2888	42
43	1757	15 57	1046	15 45	8954	4150			3353	43
44	1987	20 77	0868	20 59	9132	4434			3818	44
45	.612217	30 115	.790690	30 89	.209310	.264719			.774283	45
46	2447	40 153	0512	40 119	9488	5004	# Corr.	# Corr.	4748	46
47	2677	45 173	0333	45 134	9667	5289	10 48	10 78	5214	47
48	2907	50 192	0155	50 148	9845	5574	15 72	15 117	5680	48
49	3137		.789977		.210023	5860	20 95	20 156	6146	49
50	.613367		.789798		.210202	.266146	30 143	30 233	.776612	50
51	3596		9620		0380	6432	40 191	40 311	7078	51
52	3826		9441		0559	6719	45 215	45 350	7545	52
53	4056		9263		0737	7005	50 239	50 389	8012	53
54	4285		9084		0916	7292			8479	54
55	.614515		.788905		.211095	.267579			.778946	55
56	4744		8727		1273	7866			9414	56
57	4974		8548		1452	8154			9881	57
58	5203		8369		1631	8442			.780349	58
59	5432		8190		1810	8730			0617	59
60	.615662		.788011		.211989	.269018			.781286	60

'	Sine	Corr. for Sec. +	Cosine	Corr. for Sec. -	Versine +	Exsec +	Corr. for Sec. +	Corr. for Sec. +	Tangent	'
0	.615662		.788011		.211989	.269018			.781286	0
1	5891	* Corr.	7832		2168	9307	* Corr.	* Corr.	1754	1
2	6120	10 48	7652		2348	9596	10 48	10 78	2223	2
3	6349	15 73	7473		2527	9884	15 73	15 117	2692	3
4	6570	20 97	7294		2706	.270174	20 97	20 157	3161	4
5	.616807	30 145	.767114		.212886	.270463	30 145	30 235	.783630	5
6	7036	40 193	6935		3065	0753	40 193	40 313	4100	6
7	7265	45 218	6756		3244	1043	45 218	45 352	4570	7
8	7494	50 242	6576		3424	1333	50 242	50 392	5040	8
9	7722		6396		3604	1624			5510	9
10	.617951		.786216		.213784	.271914			.785981	10
11	8180	* Corr.	6037	* Corr.	3963	2205			6452	11
12	8408	10 38	5857	10 30	4143	2496			6922	12
13	8637	15 57	5677	15 45	4323	2788			7394	13
14	8866	20 76	5497	20 60	4503	3079			7865	14
15	.619094	30 114	.785317	30 90	.214683	.273371			.788336	15
16	9322	40 152	5137	40 120	4863	3663	* Corr.	* Corr.	8808	16
17	9551	45 171	4957	45 135	5043	3956	10 49	10 79	9280	17
18	9779	50 190	4776	50 150	5224	4248	15 73	15 118	9752	18
19	.620007		4596		5404	4541	20 98	20 158	.790225	19
20	.620236		.784416		.215584	.274834	30 147	30 237	.790698	20
21	0464		4235		5765	5128	40 196	40 316	1170	21
22	0692		4055		5945	5421	45 220	45 355	1643	22
23	0920		3874		6126	5715	50 245	50 394	2117	23
24	1148		3694		6306	6009			2590	24
25	.621376		.783513		.216487	.276303			.793064	25
26	1604		3332		6668	6598			3538	26
27	1831		3151		6849	6893			4012	27
28	2059		2970		7030	7188			4486	28
29	2287		2789		7211	7483			4961	29
30	.622515		.782608		.217392	.277779			.795436	30
31	2742		2427		7573	8074	* Corr.	* Corr.	5911	31
32	2970		2246		7754	8370	10 50	10 79	6386	32
33	3197		2065		7935	8667	15 74	15 119	6862	33
34	3425		1883		8117	8963	20 99	20 159	7337	34
35	.623652		.781702		.218298	.279260	30 149	30 238	.797813	35
36	3880		1520		8480	9557	40 198	40 318	8290	36
37	4107		1339		8661	9854	45 223	45 357	8766	37
38	4334		1157		8843	.280152	50 248	50 397	9242	38
39	4561		0976		9024	0450			9719	39
40	.624788		.780794		.219206	.280748			.800196	40
41	5016	* Corr.	0612	* Corr.	9388	1046			0674	41
42	5243	10 38	0430	10 30	9570	1344			1151	42
43	5470	15 57	0248	15 46	9752	1643			1629	43
44	5697	20 76	0066	20 61	9934	1942			2107	44
45	.625924	30 113	.779884	30 91	.220116	.282241			.802585	45
46	6150	40 151	9702	40 121	0298	2541	* Corr.	* Corr.	3063	46
47	6377	45 170	9520	45 137	0480	2840	10 50	10 80	3542	47
48	6604	50 189	9338	50 152	0662	3140	15 75	15 120	4021	48
49	6830		9156		0844	3441	20 100	20 160	4500	49
50	.627057		.778973		.221027	.283741	30 151	30 240	.804979	50
51	7284		8791		1209	4042	40 201	40 320	5458	51
52	7510		8608		1392	4343	45 226	45 360	5938	52
53	7737		8426		1574	4644	50 251	50 400	6418	53
54	7963		8243		1757	4944			6898	54
55	.628189		.778060		.221940	.285247			.807379	55
56	8416		7878		2122	5549			7859	56
57	8642		7695		2305	5851			8340	57
58	8868		7512		2488	6154			8821	58
59	9094		7329		2671	6457			9302	59
60	.629320		.777146		.222854	.286760			.809784	60

TABLE XX.—NATURAL SINES, COSINES,
39°

'	Sine	Corr. for Sec.	Cosine	Corr. for Sec.	Versine	Exsec	Corr. for Sec.	Corr. for Sec.	Tangent	'
0	.629320	+	.777146	− +	.222854	.286760	+	+	.809784	0
1	9546		6963		3037	7063	* Corr.	* Corr.	.810266	1
2	9772		6780		3220	7366	10 51	10 80	0748	2
3	9998		6596		3404	7670	15 76	15 121	1230	3
4	.630224		6413		3587	7974	20 102	20 161	1712	4
5	.630450		.776230		.223770	.288278	30 152	30 242	.812195	5
6	0676		6046		3954	8583	40 203	40 322	2678	6
7	0902		5863		4137	8888	45 229	45 362	3161	7
8	1127		5679		4321	9192	50 254	50 403	3644	8
9	1353		5496		4504	9498			4128	9
10	.631578		.775312		.224688	.289803			.814612	10
11	1804	* Corr.	5128	* Corr.	4872	.290109			5096	11
12	2029	10 38	4944	10 31	5056	0415			5580	12
13	2255	15 56	4761	15 46	5239	0721			6065	13
14	2480	20 75	4577	20 61	5423	1028			6549	14
15	.632705	30 113	.774393	30 92	.225607	.291335	* Corr.	* Corr.	.817034	15
16	2931	40 150	4209	40 123	5791	1642	10 51	10 81	7520	16
17	3156	50 188	4024	45 138	5976	1949	15 77	15 121	8005	17
18	3381		3840	50 153	6160	2256	20 103	20 162	8490	18
19	3606		3656		6344	2564			8976	19
20	.633831		.773472		.226528	.292872	30 154	30 243	.819462	20
21	4056		3287		6713	3181	40 205	40 324	9949	21
22	4281		3103		6897	3489	45 231	45 364	.820435	22
23	4506		2918		7082	3798	50 256	50 405	0922	23
24	4730		2734		7266	4107			1409	24
25	.634955		.772549		.227451	.294416	* Corr.	* Corr.	.821896	25
26	5180		2364		7636	4726	10 52	10 81	2384	26
27	5405		2179		7821	5036	15 78	15 122	2872	27
28	5629		1994		8006	5346	20 104	20 163	3360	28
29	5854		1810		8190	5656			3848	29
30	.636078		.771625		.228375	.295967	30 155	30 244	.824336	30
31	6303		1440		8560	6278	40 207	40 326	4825	31
32	6527		1254		8746	6589	45 233	45 367	5314	32
33	6751		1069		8931	6900	50 259	50 407	5803	33
34	6976		0884		9116	7212			6292	34
35	.637200		.770699		.229301	.297524			.826782	35
36	7424		0513		9487	7836			7272	36
37	7648		0328		9672	8149			7762	37
38	7872		0142		9858	8461			8252	38
39	8096		.769957		.230043	8774			8743	39
40	.638320		.769771		.230229	.299088	* Corr.	* Corr.	.829234	40
41	8544	* Corr.	9585	* Corr.	0415	9401	10 52	10 82	9725	41
42	8768	10 37	9400	10 31	0600	9715	15 78	15 123	.830216	42
43	8992	15 56	9214	15 46	0786	.300029	20 105	20 164	0708	43
44	9215	20 75	9028	20 62	0972	0343			1199	44
45	.639439	30 112	.768842	30 93	.231158	.300658	30 157	30 246	.831691	45
46	9663	40 149	8656	40 124	1344	0972	40 209	40 328	2183	46
47	9886	45 168	8470	45 139	1530	1288	45 235	45 369	2676	47
48	.640110	50 186	8284	50 155	1716	1603	50 262	50 410	3169	48
49	0333		8097		1903	1918			3662	49
50	.640557		.767911		.232089	.302234	* Corr.	* Corr.	.834155	50
51	0780		7725		2275	2550	10 53	10 82	4648	51
52	1003		7538		2462	2867	15 79	15 124	5142	52
53	1226		7352		2648	3183	20 106	20 165	5636	53
54	1450		7165		2835	3500			6130	54
55	.641673		.766978		.233022	.303818	30 159	30 247	.836624	55
56	1896		6792		3208	4135	40 211	40 330	7119	56
57	2119		6605		3395	4453	45 238	45 371	7614	57
58	2342		6418		3582	4771	50 264	50 412	8109	58
59	2565		6231		3769	5089			8604	59
60	.642788		.766044		.233956	.305407			.839100	60

'	Sine	Corr. for Sec. +	Cosine	Corr. for Sec. +	Versine	Exsec	Corr. for Sec. +	Corr for Sec. +	Tangent	'
0	.642788		.766044		.233956	305407			.839100	0
1	3010		5857		4143	5726	" Corr.	" Corr	9596	1
2	3233		5670		4330	6045	10 53	10 83	.840092	2
3	3456		5483		4517	6364	15 80	15 124	0588	3
4	3678		5296		4704	6684	20 107	20 166	1084	4
5	.643901		.765109		.234891	.307004	30 160	30 249	.841581	5
6	4124		4921		5079	7324	40 214	40 333	2078	6
7	4346		4734		5266	7644	45 240	40 373	2576	7
8	4568		4546		5454	7965	50 267	50 414	3073	8
9	4791		4359		5641	8286			3571	9
10	.645013		.764171		.235829	.308607			.844069	10
11	5236	" Corr.	3984	" Corr.	6016	8928			4567	11
12	5458	10 37	3796	10 31	6204	9250			5066	12
13	5680	15 55	3608	15 47	6392	9572			5564	13
14	5902	20 74	3420	20 63	6580	9894			6063	14
15	.646124	30 110	.763232	30 94	.236768	.310217			.846562	15
16	6346	40 148	3044	40 125	6956	0540	" Corr.	" Corr.	7062	16
17	6568	45 166	2856	45 141	7144	0863	10 54	10 83	7562	17
18	6790	50 185	2668	50 157	7332	1186	15 81	15 125	8062	18
19	7012		2480		7520	1510	20 108	20 167	8562	19
20	.647233		.762292		.237708	311833	30 162	30 250	.849062	20
21	7455		2104		7896	2158	40 216	40 333	9563	21
22	7677		1915		8085	2482	45 243	45 375	.850064	22
23	7898		1727		8273	2807	50 270	50 417	0565	23
24	8120		1538		8462	3132			1067	24
25	.648341		.761350		.238650	.313457			.851568	25
26	8563		1161		8839	3782	" Corr.	" Corr.	2070	26
27	8784		0972		9028	4108	10 54	10 84	2573	27
28	9006		0784		9216	4434	15 82	15 126	3075	28
29	9227		0595		9405	4760	20 109	20 168	3578	29
30	.649448		.760406		.239594	.315087	30 163	30 262	.854081	30
31	9669		0217		9783	5414	40 218	40 335	4584	31
32	9890		0028		9972	5741	45 245	45 377	5087	32
33	.650111		.759839		.240161	6068	50 272	50 419	5591	33
34	0332		9650		0350	6396			6095	34
35	.650553		.759461		.240539	.316724			.856599	35
36	0774		9271		0729	7052			7104	36
37	0995		9082		0918	7381			7608	37
38	1216		8893		1107	7710			8113	38
39	1437		8703		1297	8039			8618	39
40	.651657		.758514		.241486	.318368			.859124	40
41	1878	" Corr.	8324	" Corr.	1676	8698	" Corr.	" Corr.	9630	41
42	2098	10 37	8134	10 32	1866	9027	10 55	10 85	.860136	42
43	2319	15 55	7945	15 47	2055	9358	15 83	15 127	0642	43
44	2539	20 73	7755	20 63	2245	9688	20 110	20 169	1148	44
45	.652760	30 110	.757565	30 95	.242435	.320019	30 165	30 253	.861655	45
46	2980	40 147	7375	40 127	2625	0350	40 220	40 337	2162	46
47	3200	45 165	7185	45 142	2815	0681	45 248	45 380	2669	47
48	3421	50 184	6995	50 158	3005	1013	50 275	50 422	3177	48
49	3641		6805		3195	1344			3685	49
50	.653861		.756615		.243385	.321676			.864193	50
51	4081		6425		3575	2009	" Corr.	" Corr.	4701	51
52	4301		6234		3766	2342	10 56	10 85	5209	52
53	4521		6044		3956	2674	15 83	15 127	5718	53
54	4741		5854		4146	3008	20 111	20 170	6227	54
55	.654961		.755663		.244337	.323341	30 167	30 255	.866736	55
56	5180		5472		4528	3675	40 222	40 339	7246	56
57	5400		5282		4718	4009	45 250	45 382	7756	57
58	5620		5091		4909	4344	50 278	50 424	8266	58
59	5840		4900		5100	4678			8776	59
60	.656059		.754710		.245290	.325013			.869287	60

TABLE XX.—NATURAL SINES, COSINES,
41°

	Sine	Corr. for Sec. +	Cosine	Corr. for Sec. − +	Versine	Exsec	Corr. for Sec. +	Corr. for Sec. +	Tangent	
0	.656059		.754710		.245290	.325013			.869287	0
1	6278		4519		5481	5348	" Corr.	" Corr.	9798	1
2	6498		4328		5672	5684	10 56	10 85	.870309	2
3	6717		4137		5863	6019	15 84	15 128	0820	3
4	6937		3946		6054	6355	20 112	20 171	1332	4
5	.657156		.753755		.246245	.326692	30 168	30 256	.871844	5
6	7375		3563		6437	7028	40 225	40 342	2356	6
7	7594		3372		6628	7365	45 253	45 384	2868	7
8	7814		3181		6819	7702	50 281	50 427	3381	8
9	8033		2989		7011	8040			3894	9
10	.658252		.752798		.247202	.328378			.874407	10
11	8471	" Corr.	2606	" Corr.	7394	8716			4920	11
12	8690	10 36	2415	10 32	7585	9054			5434	12
13	8908	15 55	2223	15 48	7777	9392			5948	13
14	9127	20 73	2032	20 64	7968	9731			6462	14
15	.659346	30 108	.751840	30 96	.248160	.330071			.876976	15
16	9564	40 146	1648	40 128	8352	0410	" Corr.	" Corr.	7491	16
17	9783	45 164	1456	45 144	8544	0750	10 57	10 86	8006	17
18	.660002	50 182	1264	50 160	8736	1090	15 85	15 129	8522	18
19	0220		1072		8928	1430	20 113	20 172	9037	19
20	.660439		.750880		.249120	.331771	30 170	30 258	.879553	20
21	0657		0688		9312	2112	40 227	40 343	.880069	21
22	0875		0496		9504	2453	45 255	45 387	0585	22
23	1094		0303		9697	2794	50 284	50 429	1102	23
24	1312		0111		9889	3136			1619	24
25	.661530		.749919		.250081	.333478			.882136	25
26	1748		9726		0274	3820	" Corr.	" Corr.	2653	26
27	1966		9534		0466	4163	10 57	10 86	3171	27
28	2184		9341		0659	4506	15 86	15 130	3689	28
29	2402		9148		0852	4849	20 115	20 173	4207	29
30	.662620		.748956		.251044	.335192	30 172	30 259	.884725	30
31	2838		8763		1237	5536	40 229	40 346	5244	31
32	3056		8570		1430	5880	45 258	45 389	5763	32
33	3273		8377		1623	6225	50 286	50 432	6282	33
34	3491		8184		1816	6569			6802	34
35	.663709		.747991		.252009	.336914			.887322	35
36	3926		7798		2202	7259			7842	36
37	4144		7605		2395	7605			8362	37
38	4361		7412		2588	7951			8882	38
39	4578		7218		2782	8297			9403	39
40	.664796		.747025		.252975	.338643			.889924	40
41	5013	" Corr.	6832	" Corr.	3168	8990	" Corr.	" Corr.	.890446	41
42	5230	10 36	6638	10 32	3362	9337	10 58	10 87	0968	42
43	5448	15 54	6445	15 48	3555	9684	15 87	15 130	1489	43
44	5665	20 72	6251	20 65	3749	.340032	20 116	20 174	2012	44
45	.665882	40 145	.746057	40 129	.253943	.340380	30 174	30 261	.892534	45
46	6099	45 163	5864	45 145	4136	0728	40 232	40 348	3057	46
47	6316	50 181	5670	50 161	4330	1076	45 260	45 391	3580	47
48	6532		5476		4524	1425	50 289	50 435	4103	48
49	6749		5282		4718	1774			4627	49
50	.666966		.745088		.254912	.342123			.895151	50
51	7183		4894		5106	2473	" Corr.	" Corr.	5675	51
52	7399		4700		5300	2823	10 58	10 87	6199	52
53	7616		4506		5494	3173	15 88	15 131	6724	53
54	7833		4312		5688	3523	20 117	20 175	7249	54
55	.668049		.744117		.255883	.343874	30 175	30 263	.897774	55
56	8266		3923		6077	4225	40 234	40 350	8299	56
57	8482		3728		6272	4577	45 263	45 394	8825	57
58	8698		3534		6466	4928	50 292	50 438	9351	58
59	8914		3339		6661	5280			9878	59
60	.669131		.743145		.256855	.345633			.900404	60

'	Sine	Corr. for Sec. +	Cosine	Corr. for Sec. - +	Versine	Exsec	Corr. for Sec. +	Corr. for Sec. +	Tangent	'
0	.669131		.743145		.256855	.345633			.900404	0
1	9347		2950		7050	5985	" Corr.	" Corr.	0931	1
2	9563		2755		7245	6338	10 59	10 88	1458	2
3	9779		2561		7439	6691	15 89	15 132	1985	3
4	9995		2366		7634	7045	20 118	20 176	2513	4
5	.670211		.742171		.257829	.347399	30 177	30 264	.903041	5
6	0427		1976		8024	7753	40 236	40 352	3569	6
7	0642		1781		8219	8107	45 266	45 396	4098	7
8	0858		1586		8414	8462	50 295	50 440	4627	8
9	1074		1390		8610	8817			5156	9
10	.671290		.741195		.258805	.349172			.905685	10
11	1505	" Corr.	1000	" Corr.	9000	9528	" Corr. 10 59	" Corr. 10 88	6215	11
12	1721	10 36	0805	10 33	9195	9884	15 89	15 133	6745	12
13	1936	15 54	0609	15 49	9391	.350240	20 119	20 177	7275	13
14	2152	20 72	0414	20 65	9586	0596			7805	14
15	.672367	30 108	.740218	30 98	.259782	.350953	30 179	30 266	.908336	15
16	2582	40 144	0022	40 130	9978	1310	40 238	40 354	8867	16
17	2797	45 161	.739827	45 147	.260173	1668	45 268	45 398	9398	17
18	3012	50 179	9631	50 163	0369	2025	50 298	50 443	9930	18
19	3228		9435		0565	2383			.910462	19
20	.673443		.739239		.260761	.352742			.910994	20
21	3658		9044		0956	3100	" Corr. 10 60	" Corr. 10 89	1526	21
22	3873		8848		1152	3459	15 90	15 133	2059	22
23	4088		8652		1348	3818	20 120	20 178	2592	23
24	4302		8455		1545	4178			3126	24
25	.674517		.738259		.261741	.354538	30 180	30 267	.913659	25
26	4732		8063		1937	4898	40 240	40 356	4193	26
27	4947		7867		2133	5258	45 270	45 400	4727	27
28	5161		7670		2330	5619	50 300	50 445	5262	28
29	5376		7474		2526	5980			5796	29
30	.675590		.737277		.262723	.356342			.916331	30
31	5805		7081		2919	6703	" Corr. 10 61	" Corr. 10 89	6866	31
32	6019		6884		3116	7065	15 91	15 134	7402	32
33	6233		6688		3312	7428	20 121	20 179	7938	33
34	6448		6491		3509	7790			8474	34
35	.676662		.736294		.263706	.358153	30 182	30 268	.919010	35
36	6876		6097		3903	8516	40 242	40 358	9547	36
37	7090		5900		4100	8880	45 272	45 403	.920084	37
38	7304		5703		4297	9244	50 303	50 447	0621	38
39	7518		5506		4494	9608			1159	39
40	.677732		.735309		.264691	.359972			.921697	40
41	7946	" Corr.	5112	" Corr.	4888	.360337	" Corr. 10 61	" Corr. 10 90	2235	41
42	8160	10 36	4915	10 33	5085	0702	15 92	15 135	2773	42
43	8373	15 53	4717	15 49	5283	1068	20 122	20 180	3312	43
44	8587	20 71	4520	20 66	5480	1433			3851	44
45	.678801	30 107	.734322	30 99	.265678	.361800	30 183	30 270	.924390	45
46	9014	40 142	4125	40 132	5875	2166	40 244	40 360	4930	46
47	9228	45 160	3928	45 148	6072	2532	45 275	45 405	5470	47
48	9441	50 178	3730	50 165	6270	2899	50 305	50 450	6010	48
49	9655		3532		6468	3267			6551	49
50	.679868		.733334		.266666	.363634			.927091	50
51	.680081		3137		6863	4002	" Corr. 10 62	" Corr. 10 90	7632	51
52	0295		2939		7061	4370	15 92	15 136	8174	52
53	0508		2741		7259	4739	20 123	20 181	8715	53
54	0721		2543		7457	5108			9257	54
55	.680934		.732345		.267655	.365477	30 185	30 271	.929800	55
56	1147		2147		7853	5846	40 246	40 362	.930342	56
57	1360		1949		8051	6216	45 277	45 407	0885	57
58	1573		1750		8250	6586	50 308	50 452	1428	58
59	1786		1552		8448	6957			1971	59
60	.681998		.731354		.268646	.367328			.932515	60

TABLE XX.—NATURAL SINES, COSINES,
43°

'	Sine	Corr. for Sec. (+)	Cosine	Corr. for Sec.	Versine	Exsec (+)	Corr. for Sec. (+)	Corr. for Sec. (+)	Tangent	'
0	.681998		.731354		.268646	.367328	Corr.	Corr.	.932515	0
1	2211		1155		8845	7698	10 62	10 91	3059	1
2	2424		0957		9043	8070	15 93	15 136	3603	2
3	2636		0758		9242	8442	20 124	20 182	4148	3
4	2849		0560		9440	8814			4693	4
5	.683061		.730361		.269639	369186	30 186	30 273	.935238	5
6	3274		0162		9838	9559	40 248	40 364	5783	6
7	3486		.729964		.270036	9932	45 280	45 409	6329	7
8	3698		9765		0235	370305	50 311	50 454	6875	8
9	3911		9566		0434	0678			7422	9
10	.684123	Corr.	.729367	Corr.	.270633	.371052	Corr.	Corr.	.937968	10
11	4335	10 35	9168	10 33	0832	1427	10 63	10 91	8515	11
12	4547	15 53	8969	15 50	1031	1801	15 94	15 137	9062	12
13	4759	20 71	8770	20 66	1230	2176	20 125	20 183	9610	13
14	4971		8570		1430	2551			.940158	14
15	.685183	30 106	.728371	30 100	.271629	372927	30 188	30 274	.940706	15
16	5395	40 140	8172	40 133	1828	3303	40 250	40 366	1254	16
17	5607	45 159	7972	45 150	2028	3679	45 282	45 409	1803	17
18	5818	50 176	7773	50 166	2227	4055	50 313	50 457	2352	18
19	6030		7573		2427	4432			2902	19
20	.686242		.727374		272626	374809			.943451	20
21	6453		7174		2826	5187	10 63	10 92	4001	21
22	6665		6974		3026	5564	15 95	15 138	4552	22
23	6876		6774		3226	5943	20 126	20 184	5102	23
24	7088		6575		3425	6321			5653	24
25	.687299		.726375		.273625	376700	30 190	30 274	.946204	25
26	7510		6175		3825	7079	40 253	40 368	6756	26
27	7721		5975		4025	7458	45 282	45 414	7307	27
28	7932		5775		4225	7838	50 316	50 459	7860	28
29	8144		5575		4425	8218			8412	29
30	688355		.725374		.274626	.378598			.948965	30
31	8566		5174		4826	8979	10 64	10 92	9518	31
32	8776		4974		5026	9360	15 96	15 139	.950071	32
33	8987		4773		5227	9742	20 127	20 185	0624	33
34	9198		4573		5427	.380123			1178	34
35	.689409		.724372		.275628	.380505	30 191	30 277	.951733	35
36	9620		4172		5828	0888	40 255	40 370	2287	36
37	9830		3971		6029	1270	45 287	45 416	2842	37
38	.690041		3770		6230	1653	50 319	50 462	3397	38
39	0251		3570		6430	2037			3953	39
40	.690462	Corr.	.723369	Corr.	.276631	.382420	Corr.	Corr.	.954508	40
41	0672	10 35	3168	10 34	6832	2804	10 64	10 93	5064	41
42	0882	15 53	2967	15 50	7033	3189	15 96	15 139	5621	42
43	1093	20 70	2766	20 67	7234	3573	20 129	20 186	6177	43
44	1303		2565		7435	3958			6734	44
45	.691513	30 105	.722364	30 101	.277636	.384344	30 193	30 279	.957292	45
46	1723	40 140	2163	40 134	7837	4729	40 257	40 372	7849	46
47	1933	45 158	1962	45 151	8038	5115	45 289	45 418	8407	47
48	2143	50 175	1760	50 168	8240	5502	50 321	50 465	8966	48
49	2353		1559		8441	5888			9524	49
50	.692563		.721357		.278643	.386275			.960083	50
51	2773		1156		8844	6663	10 65	10 93	0642	51
52	2982		0954		9046	7050	15 97	15 140	1202	52
53	3192		0753		9247	7438	20 130	20 187	1761	53
54	3402		0551		9449	7827			2322	54
55	.693611		.720349		.279651	.388215	30 194	30 280	.962882	55
56	3821		0148		9852	8604	40 259	40 374	3443	56
57	4030		.719946		.280054	8994	45 292	45 421	4004	57
58	4240		9744		0256	9383	50 324	50 467	4565	58
59	4449		9542		0458	9773			5127	59
60	.694658		.719340		.280660	.390164			.965689	60

'	Sine	Corr. for Sec.	Cosine	Corr. for Sec.	Versine	Exsec	Corr. for Sec.	Corr. for Sec.	Tangent	'
0	.694658		.719340		.280660	.390164			.965689	0
1	4868		9138		0862	0554	10 65	10 94	6251	1
2	5077		8936		1064	0945	15 98	15 141	6814	2
3	5286		8733		1267	1337	20 131	20 188	7377	3
4	5495		8531		1469	1728			7940	4
5	.695704		.718329		.281671	.392120	30 196	30 282	.968504	5
6	5913		8126		1874	2513	40 262	40 376	9067	6
7	6122		7924		2076	2905	45 294	45 423	9632	7
8	6330		7721		2279	3298	50 327	50 470	.970196	8
9	6539		7519		2481	3692			0761	9
10	.696748		.717316		.282684	.394086			.971326	10
11	6956	10 35	7113	10 34	2887	4480	10 66	10 94	1892	11
12	7165	15 52	6911	15 51	3089	4874	15 99	15 142	2458	12
13	7374	20 69	6708	20 68	3292	5269	20 132	20 189	3024	13
14	7582		6505		3495	5664			3590	14
15	.697790	30 104	.716302	30 101	.283698	.396059	30 198	30 284	.974157	15
16	7999	40 139	6099	40 135	3901	6455	40 264	40 378	4724	16
17	8207	45 156	5896	45 152	4104	6851	45 297	45 428	5291	17
18	8415	50 174	5693	50 169	4307	7248	50 329	50 473	5859	18
19	8623		5490		4510	7644			6427	19
20	.698832		.715286		.284714	.398042			.976996	20
21	9040		5083		4917	8439	10 67	10 95	7564	21
22	9248		4880		5120	8837	15 100	15 143	8133	22
23	9456		4676		5324	9235	20 133	20 190	8703	23
24	9663		4473		5527	9634			9272	24
25	.699871		714269		.285731	400032	30 200	30 284	.979842	25
26	700079		4066		5934	0432	40 266	40 380	.980413	26
27	0287		3862		6138	0831	45 299	45 428	0983	27
28	0494		3658		6342	1231	50 333	50 475	1554	28
29	0702		3454		6546	1632			2126	29
30	.700909		.713250		.286750	.402032			.982697	30
31	1117		3046		6954	2433	10 67	10 96	3269	31
32	1324		2843		7157	2834	15 101	15 143	3842	32
33	1531		2638		7362	3236	20 134	20 191	4414	33
34	1739		2434		7566	3638			4987	34
35	.701946		.712230		.287770	404040	30 201	30 287	.985560	35
36	2153		2026		7974	4443	40 268	40 382	6134	36
37	2360		1822		8178	4846	45 302	45 430	6708	37
38	2567		1617		8383	5249	50 336	50 478	7282	38
39	2774		1413		8587	5653			7857	39
40	702981		.711209		.288791	.406057			.988432	40
41	3188		1004		8996	6462	10 68	10 96	9007	41
42	3395	10 34	0800	10 34	9200	6866	15 102	15 144	9582	42
43	3601	15 52	0595	15 51	9405	7272	20 135	20 192	.990158	43
44	3808	20 69	0390	20 68	9610	7677			0735	44
45	.704015	30 103	.710185	30 102	.289815	.408083	30 203	30 288	.991311	45
46	4221	40 138	709981	40 137	290019	8489	40 271	40 385	1888	46
47	4428	45 155	9776	45 154	0224	8896	45 305	45 433	2465	47
48	4634	50 172	9571	50 171	0429	9303	50 338	50 481	3043	48
49	4841		9366		0634	9710			3621	49
50	705047		.709161		.290839	410118			.994199	50
51	5253		8956		1044	0526	10 68	10 97	4778	51
52	5459		8750		1250	0934	15 102	15 145	5357	52
53	5666		8545		1455	1343	20 137	20 193	5936	53
54	5872		8340		1660	1752			6515	54
55	.706078		.708134		.291866	.412161	30 205	30 290	.997095	55
56	6284		7929		2071	2571	40 273	40 387	7676	56
57	6489		7724		2276	2981	45 307	45 435	8256	57
58	6695		7518		2482	3392	50 341	50 484	8837	58
59	6901		7312		2688	3802			9418	59
60	.707107		.707107		.292893	.414214			1.00000	60

TABLE XX.—NATURAL SINES, COSINES,
45°

'	Sine	Corr. for Sec. +	Cosine	Corr. for Sec. − +	Versine	Exsec	Corr. for Sec. +	Corr. for Sec. +	Tangent	'
0	.707107		.707107		.292893	.414214			1.00000	0
1	7312		6901		3099	4625	" Corr.		.00058	1
2	7518		6695		3305	5037	10 69		.00116	2
3	7724		6489		3511	5449	15 103		.00175	3
4	7929		6284		3716	5862	20 138		.00233	4
5	.708134		.706078		.293922	.416275	30 207		1.00291	5
6	8340		5872		4128	6688	40 276		.00350	6
7	8545		5666		4334	7102	45 310		.00408	7
8	8750		5459		4541	7516	50 344		.00467	8
9	8956		5253		4747	7931			.00525	9
10	.709161		.705047		.294953	.418345			1.00583	10
11	9366	" Corr.	4841	" Corr.	5159	8760	" Corr.	" Corr	.00642	11
12	9571	10 34	4634	10 34	5366	9176	10 69	10 10	.00701	12
13	9776	15 51	4428	15 52	5572	9592	15 104	15 15	.00759	13
14	9981	20 68	.4221	20 69	5779	.420008	20 139	20 20	.00818	14
15	.710185	30 102	.704015	30 103	.295985	.420425	30 208	30 29	1.00876	15
16	0390	40 137	3808	40 138	6192	0842	40 278	40 39	.00935	16
17	0595	45 154	3601	45 155	6399	1259	45 313	45 44	.00994	17
18	0800	50 171	3395	50 172	6605	1677	50 347	50 49	.01053	18
19	1004		3188		6812	2095			.01112	19
20	.711209		.702981		.297019	.422513			1.01170	20
21	1413		2774		7226	2932	" Corr.		.01229	21
22	1617		2567		7433	3351	10 70		.01288	22
23	1822		2360		7640	3771	15 105		.01347	23
24	2026		2153		7847	4191	20 140		.01406	24
25	.712230		.701946		.298054	.424611	30 210		1.01465	25
26	2434		1739		8261	5032	40 280		.01524	26
27	2638		1531		8469	5453	45 316		.01583	27
28	2843		1324		8676	5874	50 351		.01642	28
29	3046		1117		8883	6296			.01702	29
30	.713250		.700909		.299091	.426718			1.01761	30
31	3454		0702		9298	7141	" Corr.		.01820	31
32	3658		0494		9506	7564	10 71		.01879	32
33	3862		0287		9713	7987	15 106		.01939	33
34	4066		0079		9921	8410	20 141		.01998	34
35	.714269		.699871		.300129	.428834	30 212		1.02057	35
36	4473		9663		0337	9259	40 283		.02117	36
37	4676		9456		0544	9684	45 318		.02176	37
38	4880		9248		0752	.430109	50 354		.02236	38
39	5083		9040		0960	0534			.02295	39
40	.715286		.698832		.301168	.430960			1.02355	40
41	5490	" Corr.	8623	" Corr.	1377	1386	" Corr.	" Corr	.02414	41
42	5693	10 34	8415	10 35	1585	1813	10 69	10 10	.02474	42
43	5896	15 51	8207	15 52	1793	2240	15 107	15 15	.02533	43
44	6099	20 68	7999	20 69	2001	2667	20 143	20 20	.02593	44
45	.716302	30 101	.697790	30 104	.302210	.433095	30 214	30 30	1.02653	45
46	6505	40 135	7582	40 139	2418	3523	40 285	40 40	.02713	46
47	6708	45 152	7374	45 156	2626	3952	45 321	45 45	.02772	47
48	6911	50 169	7165	50 174	2835	4380	50 357	50 50	.02832	48
49	7113		6956		3044	4810			.02892	49
50	.717316		.696748		.303262	.435239			1.02952	50
51	7519		6539		3461	5669	" Corr.		.03012	51
52	7721		6330		3670	6100	10 72		.03072	52
53	7924		6122		3878	6530	15 108		.03132	53
54	8126		5913		4087	6962	20 144		.03192	54
55	.718329		.695704		.304296	.437393	30 216		1.03252	55
56	8531		5495		4505	7825	40 288		.03312	56
57	8733		5286		4714	8257	45 324		.03372	57
58	8936		5077		4923	8690	50 360		.03433	58
59	9138		4868		5132	9123			.03493	59
60	.719340		.694658		.305342	.439556			1.03553	60

′	Sine	Corr. for Sec. +	Cosine	Corr. for Sec. −	Versine	Exsec	Corr. for Sec. +	Corr. for Sec. +	Tangent	′
0	.719340		.694658		.305342	.439556			1.03553	0
1	9542		4449		5551	9990	" Corr.		.03613	1
2	9744		4240		5760	.440425	10 73		.03674	2
3	9946		4030		5970	0859	15 109		.03734	3
4	.720148		3821		6179	1294	20 145		.03794	4
5	.720349		.693611		.306389	.441730	30 218		1.03855	5
6	0551		3402		6598	2165	40 290		.03915	6
7	0753		3192		6808	2601	45 327		.03976	7
8	0954		2982		7018	3038	50 363		.04036	8
9	1156		2773		7227	3475			.04097	9
10	.721357	" Corr.	.692563	" Corr.	.307437	.443912	" Corr		1.04158	10
11	1559	10 34	2353	10 35	7647	4350	10 73		.04218	11
12	1760	15 50	2143	15 53	7857	4788	15 110		.04279	12
13	1962	20 67	1933	20 70	8067	5226	20 147		.04340	13
14	2163		1723		8277	5665			.04401	14
15	.722564	30 101	.691513	30 105	.308487	.446104	30 220		1.04461	15
16	2565	40 134	1303	40 140	8697	6544	40 293		.04522	16
17	2766	45 151	1093	45 158	8907	6984	45 330		.04583	17
18	2967	50 168	0882	50 175	9118	7424	50 366		.04644	18
19	3168		0672		9328	7865			.04705	19
20	.723369		.690462		.309538	.448306	" Corr.		1.04766	20
21	3570		0251		9749	8748	10 74		.04827	21
22	3770		0041		9959	9190	15 111		.04888	22
23	3971		.689830		.310170	9632	20 148		.04949	23
24	4172		9620		0380	.450075			.05010	24
25	.724372		.689409		.310591	.450518	30 222		1.05072	25
26	4573		9198		0802	0962	40 296		.05133	26
27	4773		8987		1013	1406	45 333		.05194	27
28	4974		8776		1224	1850	50 370		.05255	28
29	5174		8566		1434	2295			.05317	29
30	.725374		.688355		.311645	.452740	" Corr.		1.05378	30
31	5575		8144		1856	3185	10 75		.05439	31
32	5775		7932		2068	3631	15 112		.05501	32
33	5975		7721		2279	4077	20 149		.05562	33
34	6175		7510		2490	4524			.05624	34
35	.726375		.687299		.312701	.454971	30 224		1.05685	35
36	6575		7088		2912	5419	40 298		.05747	36
37	6774		6876		3124	5867	45 336		.05809	37
38	6974		6665		3335	6315	50 373		.05870	38
39	7174		6453		3547	6764			.05932	39
40	.727374	" Corr.	.686242	" Corr.	.313758	.457213	" Corr.	" Corr.	1.05994	40
41	7573	10 33	6030	10 35	3970	7662	10 75	10 10	.06056	41
42	7773	15 50	5818	15 53	4182	8112	15 113	15 15	.06117	42
43	7972	20 66	5607	20 71	4393	8562	20 150	20 21	.06179	43
44	8172		5395		4605	9013			.06241	44
45	.728371	30 100	.685183	30 106	.314817	.459464	30 226	30 31	1.06303	45
46	8570	40 133	4971	40 141	5029	9916	40 301	40 41	.06365	46
47	8770	45 150	4759	45 159	5241	.460368	45 339	45 46	.06427	47
48	8969	50 166	4547	50 176	5453	0820	50 376	50 52	.06489	48
49	9168		4335		5665	1273			.06551	49
50	.729367		.684123		.315877	.461726			1.06613	50
51	9566		3911		6089	2179	" Corr.		.06676	51
52	9765		3698		6302	2633	10 76		.06738	52
53	9964		3486		6514	3088	15 114		.06800	53
54	.730162		3274		6726	3542	20 152		.06862	54
55	.730361		.683061		.316939	.463997	30 228		1.06925	55
56	0560		2849		7151	4453	40 304		.06987	56
57	0758		2636		7364	4909	45 342		.07049	57
58	0957		2424		7576	5365	50 380		.07112	58
59	1155		2211		7789	5822			.07174	59
60	.731354		.681998		.318002	.466279			1.07237	60

TABLE XX.—NATURAL SINES, COSINES,

47°

'	Sine	Corr. for Sec. +	Cosine	Corr. for Sec. - +	Versine	Exsec	Corr. for Sec. +	Corr. for Sec. +	Tangent	'
0	.731354		.681998		.318002	.466279			1.07237	0
1	1552		1786		8214	6737	" Corr.		.07299	1
2	1750		1573		8427	7195	10 77		.07362	2
3	1949		1360		8640	7653	15 115		.07425	3
4	2147		1147		8853	8112	20 153		.07487	4
5	.732345		.680934		.319066	.468571	30 230		1.07550	5
6	2543		0721		9279	9031	40 306		.07613	6
7	2741		0508		9492	9491	45 345		.07676	7
8	2939		0295		9705	9951	50 383		.07738	8
9	3137		0081		9919	.470412			.07801	9
10	.733334	" Corr.	.679868	" Corr.	.320132	.470874	" Corr.	" Corr.	1.07864	10
11	3532	10 33	9655	10 36	0345	1335	10 77	10 11	.07927	11
12	3730	15 49	9441	15 53	0559	1798	15 115	15 16	.07990	12
13	3928	20 66	9228	20 71	0772	2260	20 155	20 21	.08053	13
14	4125		9014		0986	2723			.08116	14
15	.734322	30 99	.678801	30 107	.321199	.473186	30 232	30 32	1.08179	15
16	4520	40 132	8587	40 142	1413	3650	40 309	40 42	.08243	16
17	4717	45 148	8373	45 160	1627	4114	45 348	45 47	.08306	17
18	4915	50 165	8160	50 178	1840	4579	50 386	50 53	.08369	18
19	5112		7946		2054	5044			.08432	19
20	.735309		.677732		.322268	.475510	" Corr.		1.08496	20
21	5506		7518		2482	5975	10 78		.08559	21
22	5703		7304		2696	6442	15 117		.08622	22
23	5900		7090		2910	6908	20 156		.08686	23
24	6097		6876		3124	7376			.08749	24
25	.736294		.676662		.323338	.477843	30 234		1.08813	25
26	6491		6448		3552	8311	40 312		.08876	26
27	6688		6233		3767	8780	45 351		.08940	27
28	6884		6019		3981	9248	50 390		.09003	28
29	7081		5805		4195	9718			.09067	29
30	.737277		.675590		.324410	.480187	" Corr.		1.09131	30
31	7474		5376		4624	0657	10 79		.09195	31
32	7670		5161		4839	1128	15 118		.09258	32
33	7867		4947		5053	1599	20 157		.09322	33
34	8063		4732		5268	2070			.09386	34
35	.738259		.674517		.325483	.482542	30 236		1.09450	35
36	8455		4302		5698	3014	40 315		.09514	36
37	8652		4088		5912	3487	45 354		.09578	37
38	8848		3873		6127	3960	50 393		.09642	38
39	9044		3658		6342	4433			.09706	39
40	.739239	" Corr.	.673443	" Corr.	.326557	.484907	" Corr.	" Corr.	1.09770	40
41	9435	10 33	3228	10 36	6772	5382	10 79	10 11	.09834	41
42	9631	15 49	3012	15 54	6988	5856	15 119	15 16	.09899	42
43	9827	20 65	2797	20 72	7203	6332	20 159	20 21	.09963	43
44	.740022		2582		7418	6807			.10027	44
45	.740218	30 98	.672367	30 108	.327633	.487283	30 238	30 32	1.10091	45
46	0414	40 130	2152	40 144	7848	7760	40 318	40 43	.10156	46
47	0609	45 147	1936	45 161	8064	8237	45 357	45 48	.10220	47
48	0805	50 163	1721	50 179	8279	8714	50 397	50 54	.10285	48
49	1000		1505		8495	9192			.10349	49
50	.741195		.671290		.328710	.489670	" Corr.		1.10414	50
51	1390		1074		8926	.490149	10 80		.10478	51
52	1586		0858		9142	0628	15 120		.10543	52
53	1781		0642		9358	1108	20 160		.10608	53
54	1976		0427		9573	1588			.10672	54
55	.742171		.670211		.329789	.492068	30 240		1.10737	55
56	2366		.669995		.330005	2549	40 320		.10802	56
57	2561		9779		0221	3030	45 361		.10867	57
58	2755		9563		0437	3512	50 401		.10931	58
59	2950		9347		0653	3994			.10996	59
60	.743145		.669131		.330869	.494476			1.11061	60

'	Sine	Corr. for Sec.	Cosine	Corr. for Sec.	Versine	Exsec	Corr. for Sec.	Corr. for Sec.	Tangent	'
0	.743145	+	.669131	- +	.330869	.494476	+	+	1.11061	0
1	3339		8914		1086	4960	" Corr.	" Corr.	.11126	1
2	3534		8698		1302	5443	10 81		.11191	2
3	3728		8482		1518	5927	15 121		.11256	3
4	3923		8266		1734	6411	20 162		.11321	4
5	.744117		.668049		.331951	.496896	30 243		1.11387	5
6	4312		7833		2167	7381	40 323		.11452	6
7	4506		7616		2384	7867	45 364		.11517	7
8	4700		7399		2601	8353	50 404		.11582	8
9	4894		7183		2817	8840			.11648	9
10	.745088		.666966		.333034	.499327			1.11713	10
11	5282	" Corr.	6749	" Corr.	3251	9814	" Corr.	" Corr.	.11778	11
12	5476	10 32	6532	10 36	3468	.500302	10 82	10 11	.11844	12
13	5670	15 48	6316	15 54	3684	0790	15 122	15 16	.11909	13
14	5864	20 65	6099	20 72	3901	1279	20 163	20 22	.11975	14
15	.746057	30 97	.665882	30 108	.334118	.501768	30 245	30 33	1.12041	15
16	6251	40 129	5665	40 145	4335	2258	40 326	40 44	.12106	16
17	6445	45 145	5448	45 163	4552	2748	45 367	45 49	.12172	17
18	6638	50 161	5230	50 181	4770	3239	50 408	50 55	.12238	18
19	6832		5013		4987	3730			.12303	19
20	.747025		.664796		.335204	.504221			1.12369	20
21	7218		4578		5422	4713	" Corr.		.12435	21
22	7412		4361		5639	5205	10 82		.12501	22
23	7605		4144		5856	5698	15 124		.12567	23
24	7798		3926		6074	6192	20 165		.12633	24
25	.747991		.663709		.336291	.506685	30 247		1.12699	25
26	8184		3491		6509	7179	40 329		.12765	26
27	8377		3273		6727	7674	45 371		.12831	27
28	8570		3056		6944	8169	50 412		.12897	28
29	8763		2838		7162	8664			.12963	29
30	.748956		.662620		.337380	.509160			1.13029	30
31	9148		2402		7598	9657	" Corr.		.13096	31
32	9341		2184		7816	.510154	10 83		.13162	32
33	9534		1966		8034	0651	15 125		.13228	33
34	9726		1748		8252	1149	20 166		.13295	34
35	.749919		.661530		.338470	.511647	30 249		1.13361	35
36	.750111		1312		8688	2146	40 332		.13428	36
37	0303		1094		8906	2645	45 374		.13494	37
38	0496		0875		9125	3145	50 416		.13561	38
39	0688		0657		9343	3645			.13627	39
40	.750880		.660439		.339561	.514145			1.13694	40
41	1072	" Corr.	0220	" Corr.	9780	4646	" Corr.	" Corr.	.13761	41
42	1264	10 32	0002	10 36	9998	5148	10 84	10 11	.13828	42
43	1456	15 48	.659783	15 55	.340217	5650	15 126	15 17	.13894	43
44	1648	20 64	9564	20 73	0436	6152	20 168	20 22	.13961	44
45	.751840	30 96	.659346	30 109	.340654	.516655	30 252	30 33	1.14028	45
46	2032	40 128	9127	40 146	0873	7158	40 336	40 45	.14095	46
47	2223	45 144	8908	45 164	1092	7662	45 378	45 50	.14162	47
48	2415	50 160	8690	50 182	1310	8166	50 419	50 56	.14229	48
49	2606		8471		1529	8671			.14296	49
50	.752798		.658252		.341748	.519176			1.14363	50
51	2989		8033		1967	9682	" Corr.		.14430	51
52	3181		7814		2186	.520188	10 85		.14498	52
53	3372		7594		2406	0694	15 127		.14565	53
54	3563		7375		2625	1201	20 169		.14632	54
55	.753755		.657156		.342844	.521709	30 254		1.14699	55
56	3946		6937		3063	2217	40 339		.14767	56
57	4137		6717		3283	2725	45 381		.14834	57
58	4328		6498		3502	3234	50 423		.14902	58
59	4519		6278		3722	3743			.14969	59
60	.754710		.656059		.343941	.524253			1.15037	60

141

TABLE XX.—NATURAL SINES, COSINES,
49°

'	Sine	Corr. for Sec.	Cosine	Corr. for Sec.	Versine	Exsec	Corr. for Sec.	Corr. for Sec.	Tangent	'
0	.754710	+	.656059	− +	.343941	.524253	+	+	1.15037	0
1	4900		5840		4160	4763			.15104	1
2	5091		5620		4380	5274	10 85	10 11	.15172	2
3	5282		5400		4600	5785	15 128	15 17	.15240	3
4	5472		5180		4820	6297	20 171	20 23	.15308	4
5	.755663		.654961		.345039	.526809	30 256		1.15375	5
6	5854		4741		5259	7322	40 342		.15443	6
7	6044		4521		5479	7835	45 384		.15511	7
8	6234		4301		5699	8349	50 427		.15579	8
9	6425		4081		5919	8863			.15647	9
10	.756615		.653861		.346139	.529377			1.15715	10
11	6805	Corr	3641	Corr	6359	9892	Corr		.15783	11
12	6995	10 32	3421	10 37	6579	.530408	10 86		.15851	12
13	7185	15 47	3200	15 55	6800	0924	15 129		.15919	13
14	7375	20 63	2980	20 73	7020	1440	20 172		.15987	14
15	.757565	30 95	.652760	30 110	.347240	.531957	30 259	30 34	1.16056	15
16	7755	40 127	2539	40 147	7461	2475	40 345	40 46	.16124	16
17	7945	45 142	2319	45 165	7681	2992	45 388	45 51	.16192	17
18	8134	50 158	2098	50 184	7902	3511	50 431	50 57	.16261	18
19	8324		1878		8122	4030			.16329	19
20	.758514		.651657		.348343	.534549	Corr		1.16398	20
21	8703		1437		8563	5069	10 87		.16466	21
22	8893		1216		8784	5589	15 131		.16535	22
23	9082		0995		9005	6110	20 174		.16603	23
24	9271		0774		9226	6631			.16672	24
25	.759461		.650553		.349447	.537153	30 261		1 16741	25
26	9650		0332		9668	7675	40 348		.16809	26
27	9839		0111		9889	8198	45 392		.16878	27
28	.760028		.649890		.350110	8721	50 435		.16947	28
29	0217		9669		0331	9245			.17016	29
30	.760406		.649448		.350552	.539769	Corr		1.17085	30
31	0595		9227		0773	.540294	10 88		.17154	31
32	0784		9006		0994	0819	15 132		17223	32
33	0972		8784		1216	1344	20 176		.17292	33
34	1161		8563		1437	1871			.17361	34
35	.761350		.648341		.351659	.542397	30 264		1.17430	35
36	1538		8120		1880	2924	40 351		.17500	36
37	1727		7898		2102	3452	45 395		.17569	37
38	1915		7677		2323	3980	50 439		.17638	38
39	2104		7455		2545	4509			.17708	39
40	.762292		.647233		.352767	.545038	Corr		1.17777	40
41	2480	Corr	7012	Corr	2988	5567	10 89	Corr	.17846	41
42	2668	10 31	6790	10 37	3210	6097	15 133	10 12	.17916	42
43	2856	15 47	6568	15 55	3432	6628	20 177	15 17	.17986	43
44	3044	20 63	6346	20 74	3654	7159		20 23	.18055	44
45	.763232	30 94	.646124	30 111	.353876	.547691	30 266	30 35	1.18125	45
46	3420	40 125	5902	40 148	4098	8223	40 355	40 46	.18194	46
47	3608	45 141	5680	45 166	4320	8755	45 399	45 52	.18264	47
48	3796	50 157	5458	50 185	4542	9288	50 443	50 58	.18334	48
49	3984		5236		4764	9822			.18404	49
50	.764171		.645013		.354987	.550356	Corr		1.18474	50
51	4359		4791		5209	0890	10 89		.18544	51
52	4546		4568		5432	1425	15 134		.18614	52
53	4734		4346		5654	1961	20 179		.18684	53
54	4921		4124		5876	2497			.18754	54
55	.765109		.643901		.356099	.553034	30 269		1.18824	55
56	5296		3678		6322	3571	40 358		.18894	56
57	5483		3456		6544	4108	45 403		.18964	57
58	5670		3233		6767	4646	50 448		.19035	58
59	5857		3010		6990	5185			.19105	59
60	.766044		.642788		.357212	.555724			1.19175	60

'	Sine	Corr. for Sec.	Cosine	Corr. for Sec.	Versine	Exsec	Corr. for Sec.	Corr. for Sec.	Tangent	'
0	.766044	+	.642788	− +	.357212	.555724	+	+	1.19175	0
1	6231		2565		7435	6263	" Corr.		.19246	1
2	6418		2342		7658	6804	10 90		.19316	2
3	6605		2119		7881	7344	15 136		.19387	3
4	6792		1896		8104	7885	20 181		.19457	4
5	.766978		.641673		.358327	.558427	30 271		1.19528	5
6	7165		1450		8550	8969	40 361		.19599	6
7	7352		1226		8774	9512	45 407		.19669	7
8	7538		1003		8997	.560055	50 452		.19740	8
9	7725		0780		9220	0598			.19811	9
10	.767911		.640557		.359443	.561142			1.19882	10
11	8097	" Corr.	0333	" Corr.	9667	1687	" Corr.	" Corr.	.19953	11
12	8284	10 31	0110	10 37	9890	2232	10 91	10 12	.20024	12
13	8470	15 46	.639886	15 56	.360114	2778	15 137	15 18	.20095	13
14	8656	20 62	9663	20 75	0337	3324	20 182	20 24	.20166	14
15	.768842	30 93	.639439	30 112	.360561	.563871	30 274	30 36	1.20237	15
16	9028	40 124	9215	40 149	0785	4418	40 365	40 47	.20308	16
17	9214	50 155	8992	45 168	1008	4966	45 410	45 53	.20379	17
18	9400		8768	50 186	1232	5514	50 456	50 59	.20451	18
19	9585		8544		1456	6063			.20522	19
20	.769771		.638320		.361680	.566612			1.20593	20
21	9957		8096		1904	7162	" Corr.		.20665	21
22	.770142		7872		2128	7712	10 92		.20736	22
23	0328		7648		2352	8263	15 138		.20808	23
24	0513		7424		2576	8814	20 184		.20879	24
25	.770699		.637200		.362800	.569366	30 276		1.20951	25
26	0884		6976		3024	9919	40 368		.21023	26
27	1069		6751		3249	.570472	45 414		.21094	27
28	1254		6527		3473	1025	50 460		.21166	28
29	1440		6303		3697	1579			.21238	29
30	.771625		.636078		.363922	.572134			1.21310	30
31	1810		5854		4146	2689	" Corr.		.21382	31
32	1994		5629		4371	3244	10 93		.21454	32
33	2179		5405		4595	3800	15 139		.21526	33
34	2364		5180		4820	4357	20 186		.21598	34
35	.772549		.634955		.365045	.574914	30 279		1.21670	35
36	2734		4730		5270	5472	40 372		.21742	36
37	2918		4506		5494	6030	45 418		.21814	37
38	3103		4281		5719	6589	50 465		.21886	38
39	3287		4056		5944	7148			.21959	39
40	.773472		.633831		.366169	.577708			1.22031	40
41	3656	" Corr.	3606	" Corr.	6394	8268	" Corr.	" Corr.	.22104	41
42	3840	10 31	3381	10 38	6619	8829	10 94	10 12	.22176	42
43	4024	15 46	3156	15 56	6844	9390	15 141	15 18	.22249	43
44	4209	20 61	2931	20 75	7069	9952	20 188	20 24	.22321	44
45	.774393	30 92	.632705	30 113	.367295	.580515	30 281	30 36	1.22394	45
46	4577	40 123	2480	40 150	7520	1078	40 375	40 48	.22467	46
47	4761	45 138	2255	45 169	7745	1641	45 422	45 55	.22539	47
48	4944	50 153	2029	50 188	7971	2205	50 469	50 61	.22612	48
49	5128		1804		8196	2770			.22685	49
50	.775312		.631578		.368422	.583335			1.22758	50
51	5496		1353		8647	3900	" Corr.		.22831	51
52	5679		1127		8873	4467	10 95		.22904	52
53	5863		0902		9098	5033	15 142		.22977	53
54	6046		0676		9324	5601	20 189		.23050	54
55	.776230		.630450		.369550	.586168	30 284		1.23123	55
56	6413		0224		9776	6737	40 379		.23196	56
57	6596		.629998		.370002	7306	45 426		.23270	57
58	6780		9772		0228	7875	50 474		.23343	58
59	6963		9546		0454	8445			.23416	59
60	.777146		.629320		.370680	.589016			1.23490	60

143

TABLE XX.—NATURAL SINES, COSINES,
51°

'	Sine	Corr. for Sec.	Cosine	Corr. for Sec.	Versine	Exsec	Corr. for Sec.	Corr. for Sec.	Tangent	'
0	.777146	+	.629320	− +	.370680	.589016	+	+	1.23490	0
1	7329		9094		0906	9587	Corr.		.23563	1
2	7512		8868		1132	.590158	10 96		.23637	2
3	7695		8642		1358	0731	15 143		.23710	3
4	7878		8416		1584	1303	20 191		.23784	4
5	.778060		.628189		.371811	.591877	30 287		1.23858	5
6	8243		7963		2037	2450	40 382		.23931	6
7	8426		7737		2263	3025	45 430		.24005	7
8	8608		7510		2490	3600	50 478		.24079	8
9	8791		7284		2716	4175			.24153	9
10	.778973		.627057		.372943	.594751			1.24227	10
11	9156	Corr.	6830	Corr.	3170	5328	Corr.	Corr.	.24301	11
12	9338	10 30	6604	10 38	3396	5905	10 97	10 12	.24375	12
13	9520	15 46	6377	15 57	3623	6482	15 145	15 19	.24449	13
14	9702	20 61	6150	20 76	3850	7061	20 193	20 25	.24523	14
15	.779884	30 91	.625924	30 113	.374076	.597639	30 290	30 37	1.24597	15
16	.780066	40 121	5697	40 151	4303	8219	40 386	40 50	.24672	16
17	0248	45 137	5470	45 170	4530	8799	45 434	45 56	.24746	17
18	0430	50 152	5243	50 189	4757	9379	50 483	50 62	.24820	18
19	0612		5016		4984	9960			.24895	19
20	.780794		.624788		.375212	.600542			1.24969	20
21	0976		4561		5439	1124	Corr.		.25044	21
22	1157		4334		5666	1706	10 97		.25118	22
23	1339		4107		5893	2290	15 146		.25193	23
24	1520		3880		6120	2873	20 195		.25268	24
25	.781702		.623652		.376348	.603458	30 292		1.25343	25
26	1883		3425		6575	4043	40 390		.25417	26
27	2065		3197		6803	4628	45 439		.25492	27
28	2246		2970		7030	5214	50 487		.25567	28
29	2427		2742		7258	5801			.25642	29
30	.782608		.622515		.377485	.606388			1.25717	30
31	2789		2287		7713	6976	Corr.		.25792	31
32	2970		2059		7941	7564	10 98		.25867	32
33	3151		1831		8169	8153	15 148		.25943	33
34	3332		1604		8396	8742	20 197		.26018	34
35	.783513		.621376		.378624	.609332	30 295		1.26093	35
36	3694		1148		8852	9923	40 394		.26169	36
37	3874		0920		9080	.610514	45 443		.26244	37
38	4055		0692		9308	1106	50 492		.26320	38
39	4235		0464		9536	1698			.26395	39
40	.784416		.620236		.379764	.612291			1.26471	40
41	4596	Corr.	0007	Corr.	9993	2884	Corr.	Corr.	.26546	41
42	4776	10 30	.619779	10 38	.380221	3478	10 99	10 13	.26622	42
43	4957	15 45	9551	15 57	0449	4073	15 149	15 19	.26698	43
44	5137	20 60	9322	20 76	0678	4668	20 199	20 25	.26774	44
45	.785317	30 90	.619094	30 114	.380906	.615264	30 298	30 38	1.26849	45
46	5497	40 120	8866	40 152	1134	5860	40 397	40 51	.26925	46
47	5677	45 135	8637	45 171	1363	6457	45 447	45 57	.27001	47
48	5857	50 150	8408	50 190	1592	7054	50 497	50 63	.27077	48
49	6037		8180		1820	7652			.27153	49
50	.786216		.617951		.382049	.618251			1.27230	50
51	6396		7722		2278	8850	Corr.		.27306	51
52	6576		7494		2506	9450	10 100		.27382	52
53	6756		7265		2735	.620050	15 151		.27458	53
54	6935		7036		2964	0651	20 201		.27535	54
55	.787114		.616807		.383193	.621253	30 301		1.27611	55
56	7294		6578		3422	1855	40 401		.27688	56
57	7473		6349		3651	2458	45 452		.27764	57
58	7652		6120		3880	3061	50 502		.27841	58
59	7832		5891		4109	3665			.27917	59
60	.788011		.615662		.384338	.624269	.		1.27994	60

'	Sine	Corr. for Sec. +	Cosine	Corr. for Sec. − +	Versine	Exsec	Corr. for Sec. +	Corr. for Sec. +	Tangent	'
0	.788011		.615662		.384338	.624269			1.27994	0
1	8190		5432		4568	4874			.28071	1
2	8369		5203		4797	5480	10 101		.28148	2
3	8548		4974		5026	6086	15 152		.28225	3
4	8727		4744		5256	6693	20 203		.28302	4
5	.788905		.614515		.385485	.627300	30 304		1.28379	5
6	9084		4285		5715	7908	40 405		.28456	6
7	9263		4056		5944	8517	45 456		.28533	7
8	9441		3826		6174	9126	50 507		.28610	8
9	9620		3596		6404	9736			.28687	9
10	.789798		.613367		.386633	.630346			1.28764	10
11	9977	" Corr.	3137	" Corr.	6863	0957	" Corr.	" Corr.	.28842	11
12	.790155	10 30	2907	10 38	7093	1569	10 102	10 13	.28919	12
13	0333	15 45	2677	15 57	7323	2181	15 153	15 19	.28997	13
14	0512	20 59	2447	20 "7	7553	2794	20 205	20 26	.29074	14
15	.790690	30 89	.612217	30 115	.387783	.633407	30 307	30 39	1.29152	15
16	0868	40 119	1987	40 153	8013	4021	40 409	40 52	.29229	16
17	1046	45 134	1757	45 173	8243	4636	45 460	45 58	.29307	17
18	1224	50 148	1527	50 192	8473	5251	50 512	50 65	.29385	18
19	1401		1297		8703	5866			.29463	19
20	.791579		.611067		.388933	.636483			1.29541	20
21	1757		0836		9164	7100	" Corr.		.29618	21
22	1934		0606		9394	7717	10 103		.29696	22
23	2112		0376		9624	8336	15 155		.29775	23
24	2290		0145		9855	8954	20 207		.29853	24
25	.792467		.609915		.390085	.639574	30 310		1.29931	25
26	2644		9684		0316	.640194	40 413		.30009	26
27	2822		9454		0546	0814	45 465		.30087	27
28	2999		9223		0777	1435	50 517		.30166	28
29	3176		8992		1008	2057			.30244	29
30	.793353		.608761		.391239	.642680			1.30323	30
31	3530		8531		1469	3303	" Corr.		.30401	31
32	3707		8300		1700	3926	10 104		.30480	32
33	3884		8069		1931	4551	15 157		.30558	33
34	4061		7838		2162	5175	20 209		.30637	34
35	.794238		.607607		.392393	.645801	30 313		1.30716	35
36	4415		7376		2624	6427	40 417		.30795	36
37	4591		7145		2855	7054	45 470		.30873	37
38	4768		6914		3086	7681	50 522		.30952	38
39	4944		6682		3318	8309			.31031	39
40	.795121		.606451		.393549	.648938			1.31110	40
41	5297	" Corr.	6220	" Corr.	3780	9567	" Corr.	" Corr.	.31190	41
42	5474	10 29	5988	10 39	4012	.650197	10 105	10 13	.31269	42
43	5650	15 44	5757	15 58	4243	0827	15 158	15 20	.31348	43
44	5826	20 59	5526	20 77	4474	1458	20 211	20 26	.31427	44
45	.796002	30 88	.605294	30 116	.394706	.652090	30 316	30 40	1.31507	45
46	6178	40 117	5062	40 154	4938	2722	40 421	40 53	.31586	46
47	6354	45 132	4831	45 174	5169	3355	45 474	45 60	.31666	47
48	6530	50 147	4599	50 193	5401	3988	50 527	50 66	.31745	48
49	6706		4367		5633	4623			.31825	49
50	.796882		.604136		.395864	.655258			1.31904	50
51	7057		3904		6096	5893	" Corr.		.31984	51
52	7233		3672		6328	6529	10 106		.32064	52
53	7408		3440		6560	7166	15 160		.32144	53
54	7584		3208		6792	7803	20 213		.32224	54
55	.797759		.602976		.397024	.658441	30 319		1.32304	55
56	7935		2744		7256	9080	40 426		.32384	56
57	8110		2512		7488	9719	45 479		.32464	57
58	8285		2280		7720	.660359	50 532		.32544	58
59	8460		2047		7953	0999			.32624	59
60	.798636		.601815		.398185	.661640			1.32704	60

TABLE XX.—NATURAL SINES, COSINES,

53°

'	Sine	Corr. for Sec. +	Cosine	Corr. for Sec. −	Versine +	Exsec	Corr. for Sec. +	Corr. for Sec. +	Tangent	'
0	.798636		.601815		.398185	.661640			1.32704	0
1	8810		1583		8417	2282			.32785	1
2	8986		1350		8650	2924	10 107		.32865	2
3	9160		1118		8882	3567	15 161		.32946	3
4	9335		0885		9115	4211	20 215		.33026	4
5	.799510		.600653		.399347	.664855	30 322		1.33107	5
6	9685		0420		9580	5500	40 430		.33188	6
7	9859		0188		9812	6146	50 537		.33268	7
8	.800034		.599955		.400045	6792			.33349	8
9	0208		9722		0278	7439			.33430	9
10	.800383		.599489		.400511	.668086			1.33511	10
11	0557	" Corr.	9256	" Corr.	0744	8734	" Corr.	" Corr.	.33592	11
12	0731	10 29	9024	10 39	0976	9383	10 108	10 14	.33673	12
13	0906	15 44	8791	15 58	1209	.670033	15 163	15 20	.33754	13
14	1080	20 58	8558	20 78	1442	0683	20 217	20 27	.33835	14
15	.801254	30 87	.598325	30 117	.401675	.671334	30 326	30 41	1.33916	15
16	1428	40 116	8092	40 155	1908	1985	40 434	40 54	.33998	16
17	1602	45 131	7858	45 175	2142	2637	45 489	45 61	.34079	17
18	1776	50 145	7625	50 194	2375	3290	50 543	50 68	.34160	18
19	1950		7392		2608	3943			.34242	19
20	.802123		.597159		.402841	.674597			1.34323	20
21	2297		6925		3075	5252	" Corr.		.34405	21
22	2470		6692		3308	5907	10 110		.34487	22
23	2644		6458		3542	6563	15 164		.34568	23
24	2818		6225		3775	7220	20 219		.34650	24
25	.802991		.595991		.404009	.677877	30 329		1.34732	25
26	3164		5758		4242	8535	40 438		.34814	26
27	3338		5524		4476	9193	45 493		.34896	27
28	3511		5290		4710	9852	50 548		.34978	28
29	3684		5057		4943	.680512			.35060	29
30	.803857		.594823		.405177	.681173			1.35142	30
31	4030		4589		5411	1834	" Corr.		.35224	31
32	4203		4355		5645	2496	10 111		.35307	32
33	4376		4121		5879	3159	15 166		.35389	33
34	4548		3887		6113	3822	20 222		.35472	34
35	.804721		.593653		.406347	.684486	30 332		1.35554	35
36	4894		3419		6581	5150	40 443		.35637	36
37	5066		3185		6815	5816	45 498		.35719	37
38	5239		2950		7050	6481	50 554		.35802	38
39	5411		2716		7284	7148			.35885	39
40	.805584		.592482		.407518	.687815			1.35968	40
41	5756	" Corr.	2248	" Corr.	7752	8483	" Corr.	" Corr.	.36051	41
42	5928	10 29	2013	10 39	7987	9152	10 112	10 14	.36134	42
43	6100	15 43	1779	15 59	8221	9821	15 168	15 21	.36217	43
44	6273	20 57	1544	20 78	8456	.690491	20 224	20 28	.36300	44
45	.806445	30 86	.591310	30 117	.408690	.691161	30 336	30 42	1.36383	45
46	6617	40 115	1075	40 156	8925	1833	40 447	40 55	.36466	46
47	6788	45 129	0840	45 176	9160	2504	45 503	45 62	.36549	47
48	6960	50 143	0606	50 195	9394	3177	50 559	50 69	.36633	48
49	7132		0371		9629	3850			.36716	49
50	.807304		.590136		.409864	.694524			1.36800	50
51	7475		.589901		.410099	5199	" Corr.		.36883	51
52	7647		9666		0334	5874	10 113		.36967	52
53	7818		9431		0569	6550	15 170		.37050	53
54	7990		9196		0804	7227	20 226		.37134	54
55	.808161		.588961		.411039	.697904	30 339		1.37218	55
56	8332		8726		1274	8582	40 452		.37302	56
57	8504		8491		1509	9261	45 509		.37386	57
58	8675		8256		1744	9941	50 565		.37470	58
59	8846		8021		1979	.700621			.37554	59
60	.809017		.587785		.412215	.701302			1.37638	60

'	Sine	Corr. for Sec.	Cosine	Corr. for Sec.	Versine	Exsec	Corr. for Sec.	Corr. for Sec.	Tangent	'
0	.809017	+	.587785	− +	.412215	.701302	+	+	1.37638	0
1	9188		7550		2450	1983	" Corr.		.37722	1
2	9359		7314		2686	2665	10 114		.37807	2
3	9530		7079		2921	3348	15 171		.37891	3
4	9700		6844		3156	4032	20 228		.37976	4
5	.809871		.586608		.413392	.704716	30 342		1.38060	5
6	.810042		6372		3628	5401	40 457		.38145	6
7	0212		6137		3863	6087	45 514		.38229	7
8	0383		5901		4099	6773	50 571		.38314	8
9	0553		5665		4335	7460			.38399	9
10	.810723		.585429		.414571	.708148			1.38484	10
11	0894	" Corr.	5194	" Corr.	4806	8836	" Corr.	" Corr.	.38568	11
12	1064	10 28	4958	10 39	5042	9525	10 115	10 14	.38653	12
13	1234	15 42	4722	15 59	5278	.710215	15 173	15 21	.38738	13
14	1404	20 57	4486	20 79	5514	0906	20 231	20 28	.38824	14
15	.811574	30 85	.584250	30 118	.415750	.711597	30 346	30 43	1.38909	15
16	1744	40 113	4014	40 157	5986	2289	40 461	40 57	.38994	16
17	1914	45 127	3777	45 177	6223	2982	45 519	45 64	.39079	17
18	2084	50 142	3541	50 197	6459	3675	50 577	50 71	.39165	18
19	2253		3305		6695	4369			.39250	19
20	.812423		.583069		.416931	.715064			1.39336	20
21	2592		2832		7168	5759	" Corr.		.39421	21
22	2762		2596		7404	6456	10 116		.39507	22
23	2931		2360		7640	7152	15 175		.39593	23
24	3101		2123		7877	7850	20 233		.39679	24
25	.813270		.581886		.418114	.718548	30 350		1.39764	25
26	3439		1650		8350	9248	40 466		.39850	26
27	3608		1413		8587	9947	45 524		.39936	27
28	3778		1176		8824	.720648	50 583		.40022	28
29	3947		0940		9060	1349			.40109	29
30	.814116		.580703		.419297	.722051			1.40195	30
31	4284		0466		9534	2753	" Corr.		.40281	31
32	4453		0229		9771	3457	10 118		.40367	32
33	4622		.579992		.420008	4161	15 177		.40454	33
34	4791		9755		0245	4866	20 235		.40540	34
35	.814959		.579518		.420482	.725571	30 353		1.40627	35
36	5128		9281		0719	6277	40 471		.40714	36
37	5296		9044		0956	6984	45 530		.40800	37
38	5465		8807		1193	7692	50 588		.40887	38
39	5633		8570		1430	8400			.40974	39
40	.815801		.578332		.421668	.729110			1.41061	40
41	5970	" Corr.	8095	" Corr.	1905	9820	" Corr.	" Corr.	.41148	41
42	6138	10 28	7858	10 40	2142	.730530	10 119	10 15	.41235	42
43	6306	15 42	7620	15 59	2380	1241	15 178	15 22	.41322	43
44	6474	20 56	7383	20 79	2617	1954	20 238	20 29	.41409	44
45	.816642	30 84	.577145	30 119	.422855	.732666	30 357	30 44	1.41497	45
46	6809	40 112	6908	40 158	3092	3380	40 476	40 58	.41584	46
47	6977	45 126	6670	45 178	3330	4094	45 535	45 66	.41672	47
48	7145	50 140	6432	50 198	3568	4809	50 595	50 73	.41759	48
49	7312		6195		3805	5525			.41847	49
50	.817480		.575957		.424043	.736241			1.41934	50
51	7648		5719		4281	6958	" Corr.		.42022	51
52	7815		5481		4519	7676	10 120		.42110	52
53	7982		5243		4757	8395	15 180		.42198	53
54	8150		5005		4995	9114	20 240		.42286	54
55	.818317		.574767		.425233	.739835	30 360		1.42374	55
56	8484		4529		5471	.740556	40 480		.42462	56
57	8651		4291		5709	1277	45 541		.42550	57
58	8818		4053		5947	2000	50 601		.42638	58
59	8985		3815		6185	2723			.42726	59
60	.819152		.573576		.426424	.743447			1.42815	60

TABLE XX.—NATURAL SINES, COSINES,
55°

'	Sine	Corr. for Sec.	Cosine	Corr. for Sec.	Versine	Exsec	Corr. for Sec.	Corr. for Sec.	Tangent	'
0	.819152	+	.573576	− +	.426424	.743447	+	+	1.42815	0
1	9319		3338		6662	4172	" Corr.		.42903	1
2	9486		3100		6900	4897	10 121		.42992	2
3	9652		2861		7139	5623	15 182		.43080	3
4	9819		2623		7377	6350	20 243		.43169	4
5	.819985		.572384		.427616	.747078	30 364		1.43258	5
6	.820152		2146		7854	7806	40 486		.43347	6
7	0318		1907		8093	8535	45 546		.43436	7
8	0485		1669		8331	9265	50 607		.43525	8
9	0651		1430		8570	9996			.43614	9
10	.820817		.571191		.428809	.750727			1.43703	10
11	0983	" Corr.	0952	" Corr.	9048	1460	" Corr.	" Corr.	.43792	11
12	1149	10 28	0714	10 39	9286	2192	10 123	10 15	.43881	12
13	1315	15 41	0475	15 60	9525	2926	15 184	15 22	.43970	13
14	1481	20 55	0236	20 80	9764	3661	20 245	20 30	.44060	14
15	.821647	30 83	.569997	30 119	.430003	.754396	30 368	30 45	1.44149	15
16	1813	40 110	9758	40 159	0242	5132	40 491	40 60	.44239	16
17	1978	45 124	9519	45 179	0481	5869	45 552	45 67	.44329	17
18	2144	50 138	9280	50 199	0720	6606	50 613	50 75	.44418	18
19	2310		9040		0960	7345			.44508	19
20	.822475		.568801		.431199	.758084			1.44598	20
21	2640		8562		1438	8824	" Corr.		.44688	21
22	2806		8322		1678	9564	10 124		.44778	22
23	2971		8083		1917	.760306	15 186		.44868	23
24	3136		7844		2156	1048	20 248		.44958	24
25	.823302		.567604		.432396	.761791	30 372		1.45048	25
26	3467		7365		2635	2534	40 496		.45139	26
27	3632		7125		2875	3279	45 558		.45229	27
28	3796		6886		3114	4024	50 62U		45320	28
29	3961		6646		3354	4770			.45410	29
30	.824126		.566406		.433594	.765517			1.45501	30
31	4291		6166		3834	6265	" Corr.		.45592	31
32	4456		5927		4073	7013	10 125		.45682	32
33	4620		5687		4313	7762	15 188		.45773	33
34	4785		5447		4553	8512	20 251		.45864	34
35	.824949		.565207		.434793	.769263	30 376		1.45955	35
36	5114		4967		5033	.770015	40 501		.46046	36
37	5278		4727		5273	0767	45 564		.46137	37
38	5442		4487		5513	1520	50 626		.46229	38
39	5606		4247		5753	2274			.46320	39
40	.825770		.564007		.435993	.773029			1.46411	40
41	5934	" Corr.	3766	" Corr.	6234	3784	" Corr.	" Corr.	.46503	41
42	6098	10 27	3526	10 40	6474	4541	10 127	10 15	.46595	42
43	6262	15 41	3286	15 60	6714	5298	15 190	15 23	.46686	43
44	6426	20 55	3045	20 80	6955	6056	20 253	20 31	.46778	44
45	.826590	30 82	.562805	30 120	.437195	.776815	30 380	30 46	1.46870	45
46	6753	40 109	2564	40 159	7436	7574	40 506	40 61	.46962	46
47	6917	45 123	2324	45 180	7676	8334	45 570	45 69	.47054	47
48	7081	50 136	2083	50 200	7917	9096	50 633	50 77	.47146	48
49	7244		1843		8157	9857			.47238	49
50	.827407		.561602		.438398	.780620			1.47330	50
51	7571		1361		8639	1384	" Corr.		.47422	51
52	7734		1121		8879	2148	10 128		.47514	52
53	7897		0880		9120	2913	15 192		.47607	53
54	8060		0639		9361	3679	20 256		.47699	54
55	.828223		.560398		.439602	.784446	30 384		1.47792	55
56	8386		0157		9843	5213	40 512		.47885	56
57	8549		.559916		.440084	5982	45 576		.47977	57
58	8712		9675		0325	6751	50 640		.48070	58
59	8875		9434		0566	7521			.48163	59
60	.829038		.559193		.440807	.788292			1.48256	60

'	Sine	Corr. for Sec. +	Cosine	Corr. for Sec. − +	Versine	Exsec	Corr. for Sec. +	Corr. for Sec. +	Tangent	'
0	.829038		.559193		.440807	.788292			1.48256	0
1	9200		8952		1048	9063	" Corr.		.48349	1
2	9363		8710		1290	9836	10 129		.48442	2
3	9525		8469		1531	.790609	15 194		.48536	3
4	9688		8228		1772	1383	20 259		.48629	4
5	.829850		.557986		.442014	.792158	30 388		1.48722	5
6	.830012		7745		2255	2934	40 517		.48816	6
7	0174		7504		2496	3710	45 582		.48909	7
8	0337		7262		2738	4488	50 646		.49003	8
9	0499		7021		2979	5266			.49097	9
10	.830661		.556779		.443221	.796045			1.49190	10
11	0823	" Corr.	6537	" Corr.	3463	6825	" Corr.	" Corr.	.49284	11
12	0984	10 27	6296	10 40	3704	7605	10 131	10 16	.49378	12
13	1146	15 40	6054	15 60	3946	8387	15 196	15 24	.49472	13
14	1308	20 54	5812	20 81	4188	9169	20 261	20 31	.49566	14
15	.831470	30 81	.555570	30 121	.444430	.799952	30 392	30 47	1.49661	15
16	1631	40 108	5328	40 161	4672	.800736	40 523	40 63	.49755	16
17	1793	45 120	5086	45 181	4914	1521	45 588	45 71	.49849	17
18	1954	50 135	4844	50 202	5156	2307	50 653	50 79	.49944	18
19	2116		4602		5398	3094			.50038	19
20	.832277		.554360		.445640	.803881			1.50133	20
21	2438		4118		5882	4669	" Corr.		.50228	21
22	2599		3876		6124	5458	10 132		.50322	22
23	2760		3634		6366	6248	15 198		.50417	23
24	2921		3392		6608	7039	20 264		.50512	24
25	.833082		.553149		.446851	.807830	30 396		1.50607	25
26	3243		2907		7093	8623	40 528		.50702	26
27	3404		2664		7336	9416	45 594		.50797	27
28	3565		2422		7578	.810210	50 660		.50893	28
29	3725		2180		7820	1005			.50988	29
30	.833886		.551937		.448063	.811801			1.51084	30
31	4046		1694		8306	2598	" Corr.		.51179	31
32	4207		1452		8548	3395	10 133		.51275	32
33	4367		1209		8791	4194	15 200		.51370	33
34	4528		0966		9034	4993	20 267		.51466	34
35	.834688		.550724		.449276	.815793	30 400		1.51562	35
36	4848		0481		9519	6594	40 534		.51658	36
37	5008		0238		9762	7396	45 601		.51754	37
38	5168		.549995		.450005	8198	50 667		.51850	38
39	5328		9752		0248	9002			.51946	39
40	.835488		.549509		.450491	.819806			1.52043	40
41	5648	" Corr.	9266	" Corr.	0734	.820612	" Corr.	" Corr.	.52139	41
42	5807	10 27	9023	10 41	0977	1418	10 135	10 16	.52235	42
43	5967	15 40	8780	15 61	1220	2225	15 202	15 24	.52332	43
44	6127	20 53	8536	20 81	1464	3033	20 270	20 32	.52429	44
45	.836286	30 80	.548293	30 122	.451707	.823842	30 405	30 48	1.52525	45
46	6446	40 106	8050	40 162	1950	4651	40 540	40 66	.52622	46
47	6605	45 120	7807	45 182	2193	5462	45 607	45 73	.52719	47
48	6764	50 133	7563	50 203	2437	6273	50 675	50 81	.52816	48
49	6924		7320		2680	7085			.52913	49
50	.837083		.547076		.452924	.827898			1.53010	50
51	7242		6833		3167	8712	" Corr.		.53107	51
52	7401		6589		3411	9527	10 136		.53205	52
53	7560		6346		3654	.830343	15 205		.53302	53
54	7719		6102		3898	1160	20 273		.53400	54
55	.837878		.545858		.454142	.831977	30 409		1.53497	55
56	8036		5614		4386	2796	40 546		.53595	56
57	8195		5371		4629	3615	45 614		.53693	57
58	8354		5127		4873	4435	50 682		.53791	58
59	8512		4883		5117	5256			.53888	59
60	.838671		.544639		.455361	.836078			1.53986	60

TABLE XX.—NATURAL SINES, COSINES,
57°

'	Sine	Corr. for Sec. +	Cosine	Corr. for Sec. - +	Versine	Exsec	Corr. for Sec. +	Corr. for Sec. +	Tangent	'
0	.838671		.544639		.455361	.836078			1.53986	0
1	8829		4395		5605	6901			.54085	1
2	8987		4151		5849	7725			.54183	2
3	9146		3907		6093	8550			.54281	3
4	9304		3663		6337	9375			.54379	4
5	.839462		.543419		.456581	.840202	30 414		1.54478	5
6	9620		3174		6826	1029	40 552		.54576	6
7	9778		2930		7070	1857	45 621		.54675	7
8	9936		2686		7314	2687	50 689		.54774	8
9	.840094		2442		7558	3517			.54873	9
10	.840251		.542197		.457803	.844348			1.54972	10
11	0409	" Corr.	1953	" Corr.	8047	5180	" Corr.	" Corr.	.55071	11
12	0567	10 26	1708	10 41	8292	6012	10 139	10 17	.55170	12
13	0724	15 39	1464	15 61	8536	6846	15 209	15 26	.55269	13
14	0882	20 52	1219	20 82	8781	7681	20 279	20 33	.55368	14
15	.841039	30 79	.540974	30 122	.459026	.848516	30 418	30 50	1.55467	15
16	1196	40 105	0730	40 163	9270	9352	40 558	40 66	.55567	16
17	1354	45 118	0485	45 183	9515	.850190	45 627	45 75	.55666	17
18	1511	50 131	0240	50 204	9760	1028	50 697	50 83	.55766	18
19	1668		.539996		.460004	1867			.55866	19
20	.841825		.539751		.460249	.852707			1.55966	20
21	1982		9506		0494	3548	" Corr.		.56065	21
22	2139		9261		0739	4390	10 141		.56165	22
23	2296		9016		0984	5233	15 211		.56265	23
24	2452		8771		1229	6077	20 282		.56366	24
25	.842609		.538526		.461474	.856922	30 423		1.56466	25
26	2766		8281		1719	7767	40 564		.56566	26
27	2922		8035		1965	8614	45 634		.56667	27
28	3079		7790		2210	9461	50 705		.56767	28
29	3235		7545		2455	.860310			.56868	29
30	.843391		.537300		.462700	.861159			1.56969	30
31	3548		7054		2946	2009	" Corr.		.57069	31
32	3704		6809		3191	2860	10 142		.57170	32
33	3860		6563		3437	3713	15 214		.57271	33
34	4016		6318		3682	4566	20 285		.57372	34
35	.844172		.536072		.463928	.865420	30 427		1.57474	35
36	4328		5827		4173	6275	40 570		.57575	36
37	4484		5581		4419	7131	45 641		.57676	37
38	4640		5336		4664	7988	50 712		.57778	38
39	4795		5090		4910	8845			.57879	39
40	.844951		.534844		.465156	.869704			1.57981	40
41	5106	" Corr.	4598	" Corr.	5402	.870564	" Corr.	" Corr.	.58083	41
42	5262	10 26	4352	10 41	5648	1424	10 144	10 17	.58184	42
43	5417	15 39	4106	15 61	5894	2286	15 216	15 26	.58286	43
44	5573	20 52	3860	20 82	6140	3148	20 288	20 34	.58388	44
45	.845728	30 78	.533614	30 123	.466386	.874012	30 432	30 51	1.58490	45
46	5883	40 103	3368	40 164	6632	4876	40 576	40 68	.58593	46
47	6038	45 116	3122	45 185	6878	5742	45 648	45 77	.58695	47
48	6193	50 129	2876	50 205	7124	6608	50 720	50 85	.58797	48
49	6348		2630		7370	7476			.58900	49
50	.846503		.532384		.467616	.878344			1.59002	50
51	6658		2138		7862	9213	" Corr.		.59105	51
52	6813		1891		8109	.880083	10 145		.59208	52
53	6967		1645		8355	0954	15 218		.59311	53
54	7122		1399		8601	1827	20 291		.59414	54
55	.847276		.531152		.468848	.882700	30 437		1.59517	55
56	7431		0906		9094	3574	40 583		.59620	56
57	7585		0659		9341	4449	45 655		.59723	57
58	7740		0412		9588	5325	50 728		.59826	58
59	7894		0166		9834	6202			.59930	59
60	.848048		.529919		.470081	.887080			1.60033	60

'	Sine	Corr. for Sec.	Cosine	Corr. for Sec.	Versine	Exsec	Corr. for Sec.	Corr. for Sec.	Tangent	'
0	.848048	+	.529919	- +	.470081	.887080	+	+	1.60033	0
1	8202		9673		0327	7959	" Corr.		.60137	1
2	8356		9426		0574	8839	10 147		.60241	2
3	8510		9179		0821	9720	15 221		.60345	3
4	8664		8932		1068	.890602	20 295		.60449	4
5	.848818		.528685		.471315	.891484	30 442		1.60553	5
6	8972		8438		1562	2368	40 589		.60657	6
7	9125		8191		1809	3253	45 663		.60761	7
8	9279		7944		2056	4139	50 737		.60865	8
9	9432		7697		2303	5026			.60970	9
10	.849586		.527450		.472550	.895914			1.61074	10
11	9739	" Corr.	7203	" Corr.	2797	6803	" Corr.	" Corr.	.61179	11
12	9893	10 26	6956	10 41	3044	7692	10 149	10 18	.61283	12
13	.850046	15 38	6708	15 62	3292	8583	15 223	15 26	.61388	13
14	0199	20 51	6461	20 82	3539	9475	20 298	20 35	.61493	14
15	.850352	30 77	.526214	30 124	.473786	.900368	30 447	30 53	1.61598	15
16	0505	40 102	5966	40 165	4034	1262	40 596	40 70	.61703	16
17	0658	45 115	5719	45 186	4281	2156	45 670	45 79	.61808	17
18	0811	50 128	5472	50 206	4528	3052	50 745	50 88	.61914	18
19	0964		5224		4776	3949			.62019	19
20	.851117		.524977		.475023	.904847			1.62125	20
21	1269		4729		5271	5746	" Corr.		.62230	21
22	1422		4481		5519	6646	10 151		.62336	22
23	1574		4234		5766	7546	15 226		.62442	23
24	1727		3986		6014	8448	20 301		.62548	24
25	.851879		.523738		.476262	.909351	30 452		1.62654	25
26	2032		3490		6510	.910255	40 603		.62760	26
27	2184		3242		6758	1160	45 678		.62866	27
28	2336		2994		7006	2066	50 753		.62972	28
29	2488		2747		7253	2973			.63079	29
30	.852640		.522499		.477501	.913881			1.63185	30
31	2792		2250		7750	4790	" Corr.		.63292	31
32	2944		2002		7998	5700	10 152		.63398	32
33	3096		1754		8246	6611	15 229		.63505	33
34	3248		1506		8494	7523	20 305		.63612	34
35	.853399		.521258		.478742	.918436	30 457		1.63719	35
36	3551		1010		8990	9350	40 609		.63826	36
37	3702		0761		9239	.920266	45 686		.63934	37
38	3854		0513		9487	1182	50 762		.64041	38
39	4005		0265		9735	2099			.64148	39
40	.854156		.520016		.479984	.923017			1.64256	40
41	4308	" Corr.	.519768	" Corr.	.480232	3937	" Corr.	" Corr.	.64363	41
42	4459	10 25	9519	10 41	0481	4857	10 154	10 18	.64471	42
43	4610	15 38	9270	15 62	0730	5778	15 231	15 27	.64579	43
44	4761	20 50	9022	20 83	0978	6701	20 308	20 36	.64687	44
45	.854912	30 76	.518773	30 124	.481227	.927624	30 462	30 54	1.64795	45
46	5063	40 101	8525	40 166	1475	8549	40 616	40 72	.64903	46
47	5214	45 113	8276	45 186	1724	9475	45 693	45 81	.65011	47
48	5364	50 126	8027	50 207	1973	.930401	50 770	50 90	.65120	48
49	5515		7778		2222	1329			.65228	49
50	.855666		.517529		.482471	.932258			1.65337	50
51	5816		7280		2720	3188	" Corr.		.65445	51
52	5966		7031		2969	4118	10 156		.65554	52
53	6117		6782		3218	5050	15 234		.65663	53
54	6267		6533		3467	5984	20 312		.65772	54
55	.856417		.516284		.483716	.936918	30 468		1.65881	55
56	6567		6035		3965	7853	40 623		.65990	56
57	6718		5786		4214	8789	45 701		.66099	57
58	6868		5537		4463	9726	50 779		.66209	58
59	7017		5287		4713	.940665			.66318	59
60	.857167		.515038		.484962	.941604			1.66428	60

TABLE XX.—NATURAL SINES, COSINES,
59°

′	Sine	Corr. for Sec. +	Cosine	Corr. for Sec. − +	Versine	Exsec	Corr. for Sec. +	Corr. for Sec. +	Tangent	′
0	.857167		.515038		.484962	.941604			1.66428	0
1	7317		4789		5211	2544	Corr.		.66538	1
2	7467		4539		5461	3486	10 158		.66647	2
3	7616		4290		5710	4429	15 236		.66757	3
4	7766		4040		5960	5372	20 315		.66867	4
5	.857916		.513791		.486209	.946317	30 473		1.66978	5
6	8065		3541		6459	7263	40 630		.67088	6
7	8214		3292		6708	8210	45 709		.67198	7
8	8364		3042		6958	9158	50 788		.67309	8
9	8513		2792		7208	.950108			.67419	9
10	.858662	Corr.	.512542	Corr.	.487458	.951058	Corr.	Corr.	1.67530	10
11	8811	10 25	2293	10 42	7707	2009	10 159	10 19	.67641	11
12	8960	15 37	2043	15 62	7957	2962	15 239	15 28	.67752	12
13	9109	20 50	1793	20 83	8207	3915	20 319	20 37	.67863	13
14	9258		1543		8457	4870			.67974	14
15	.859406	30 74	.511293	30 125	.488707	.955825	30 478	30 56	1.68085	15
16	9555	40 99	1043	40 167	8957	6782	40 638	40 74	.68196	16
17	9704	45 112	0793	45 187	9207	7740	45 718	45 83	.68308	17
18	9852	50 124	0543	50 208	9457	8699	50 797	50 93	.68419	18
19	.860001		0293		9707	9659			.68531	19
20	.860149		.510043		.489957	.960621			1.68643	20
21	0298		.509792		.490208	1583	Corr.		.68754	21
22	0446		9542		0458	2546	10 161		.68866	22
23	0594		9292		0708	3511	15 242		.68979	23
24	0742		9041		0959	4477	20 323		.69091	24
25	.860890		.508791		.491209	.965444	30 484		1.69203	25
26	1038		8541		1459	6411	40 645		.69316	26
27	1186		8290		1710	7380	45 726		.69428	27
28	1334		8040		1960	8351	50 807		.69541	28
29	1482		7789		2211	9322			.69653	29
30	.861629		.507538		.492462	.970294			1.69766	30
31	1777		7288		2712	1268	Corr.		.69879	31
32	1924		7037		2963	2243	10 163		.69992	32
33	2072		6786		3214	3218	15 245		.70106	33
34	2219		6536		3464	4195	20 326		.70219	34
35	.862366		.506285		.493715	.975174	30 490		1.70332	35
36	2514		6034		3966	6153	40 653		.70446	36
37	2661		5783		4217	7133	45 734		.70560	37
38	2808		5532		4468	8115	50 816		.70673	38
39	2955		5281		4719	9097			.70787	39
40	.863102	Corr.	.505030	Corr.	.494970	.980081	Corr.	Corr.	1.70901	40
41	3249	10 24	4779	10 42	5221	1066	10 165	10 19	.71015	41
42	3396	15 37	4528	15 63	5472	2052	15 248	15 29	.71129	42
43	3542	20 49	4276	20 84	5724	3039	20 330	20 38	.71244	43
44	3689		4025		5975	4028			.71358	44
45	.863836	30 73	.503774	30 126	.496226	.985017	30 495	30 57	1.71473	45
46	3982	40 98	3523	40 167	6477	6008	40 660	40 76	.71588	46
47	4128	45 110	3271	45 188	6729	7000	45 743	45 86	.71702	47
48	4275	50 122	3020	50 209	6980	7993	50 826	50 96	.71817	48
49	4421		2768		7232	8987			.71932	49
50	.864567		.502517		.497483	.989982			1.72047	50
51	4713		2266		7734	.990979	Corr.		.72163	51
52	4860		2014		7986	1976	10 167		.72278	52
53	5006		1762		8238	2975	15 251		.72393	53
54	5151		1511		8489	3975	20 334		.72509	54
55	.865297		.501259		.498741	.994976	30 501		1.72625	55
56	5443		1007		8993	5979	40 668		.72741	56
57	5589		0756		9244	6982	45 752		.72857	57
58	5734		0504		9496	7987	50 835		.72973	58
59	5880		0252		9748	8993			.73089	59
60	.866025		.500000		.500000	1.00000			1.73205	60

'	Sine	Corr. for Sec. +	Cosine	Corr. for Sec. − +	Versine	Exsec	Corr. for Sec. +	Corr. for Sec. +	Tangent	'
0	.866025		.500000		.500000	1.00000			1.73205	0
1	6171		9748		0252	.00101			.73321	1
2	6316		9496		0504	.00202			.73438	2
3	6461		9244		0756	.00303			.73555	3
4	6607		8992		1008	.00404			.73671	4
5	.866752		.498740		.501260	1.00505	" Corr.	" Corr.	1.73788	5
6	6897		8488		1512	.00607	10 17	10 20	.73905	6
7	7042		8236		1764	.00708	15 25	15 29	.74022	7
8	7187		7983		2017	.00810	20 34	20 39	.74140	8
9	7331		7731		2269	.00912			.74257	9
10	.867476	" Corr.	.497479	" Corr.	.502521	1.01014	30 51	30 59	1.74375	10
11	7621	10 24	7226	10 42	2774	.01116	40 68	40 78	.74492	11
12	7766	15 36	6974	15 63	3026	.01218	45 76	45 88	.74610	12
13	7910	20 48	6722	20 84	3278	.01320	50 85	50 98	.74728	13
14	8054		6469		3531	.01422			.74846	14
15	.868199	30 72	.496216	30 126	.503784	1.01525			1.74964	15
16	8343	40 96	5964	40 168	4036	.01628			.75082	16
17	8487	45 108	5711	45 189	4289	.01730			.75200	17
18	8632	50 120	5459	50 210	4541	.01833			.75319	18
19	8776		5206		4794	.01936			.75437	19
20	.868920		.494953		.505047	1.02039			1.75556	20
21	9064		4700		5300	.02143			.75675	21
22	9207		4448		5552	.02246			.75794	22
23	9351		4195		5805	.02349			.75913	23
24	9495		3942		6058	.02453			.76032	24
25	.869639		.493689		.506311	1.02557			1.76151	25
26	9782		3436		6564	.02661	" Corr.	" Corr.	.76271	26
27	9926		3183		6817	.02765	10 17	10 20	.76390	27
28	.870069		2930		7070	.02869	15 26	15 30	.76510	28
29	0212		2677		7323	.02973	20 35	20 40	.76630	29
30	.870356		.492424		.507576	1.03077	30 52	30 60	1.76749	30
31	0499		2170		7830	.03182	40 70	40 80	.76869	31
32	0642		1917		8083	.03286	45 78	45 90	.76990	32
33	0785		1664		8336	.03391	50 87	50 100	.77110	33
34	0928		1410		8590	.03496			.77230	34
35	.871071		.491157		.508843	1.03601			1.77351	35
36	1214		0904		9096	.03706			.77471	36
37	1357		0650		9350	.03811			.77592	37
38	1499		0397		9603	.03916			.77713	38
39	1642		0143		9857	.04022			.77834	39
40	.871784	" Corr.	.489890	" Corr.	.510110	1.04128			1.77955	40
41	1927	10 24	9636	10 42	0364	.04233			.78077	41
42	2069	15 36	9382	15 63	0618	.04339			.78198	42
43	2212	20 47	9129	20 85	0871	.04445			.78319	43
44	2354		8875		1125	.04551			.78441	44
45	.872496	30 71	.488621	30 127	.511379	1.04658			1.78563	45
46	2638	40 95	8367	40 169	1633	.04764	" Corr.	" Corr.	.78685	46
47	2780	45 107	8114	45 190	1886	.04870	10 18	10 20	.78807	47
48	2922	50 118	7860	50 211	2140	.04977	15 27	15 31	.78929	48
49	3064		7606		2394	.05084	20 36	20 41	.79051	49
50	.873206		.487352		.512648	1.05191	30 53	30 61	1.79174	50
51	3348		7098		2902	.05298	40 71	40 82	.79296	51
52	3489		6844		3156	.05405	45 80	45 92	.79419	52
53	3631		6590		3410	.05512	50 89	50 102	.79542	53
54	3772		6335		3665	.05619			.79665	54
55	.873914		.486081		.513919	1.05727			1.79788	55
56	4055		5827		4173	.05835			.79911	56
57	4196		5573		4427	.05942			.80034	57
58	4338		5318		4682	.06050			.80158	58
59	4479		5064		4936	.06158			.80281	59
60	.874620		.484810		.515190	1.06267			1.80405	60

TABLE XX.—NATURAL SINES, COSINES,
61°

'	Sine	Corr. for Sec. +	Cosine	Corr. for Sec. − +	Versine	Exsec	Corr. for Sec. +	Corr. for Sec. +	Tangent	'
0	.874620		.484810		.515190	1.06267			1.80405	0
1	4761		4555		5445	.06375			.80529	1
2	4902		4301		5699	.06483			.80653	2
3	5042		4046		5954	.06592			.80777	3
4	5183		3792		6208	.06701			.80901	4
5	.875324		.483537		.516463	1.06809			1.81025	5
6	5464		3282		6718	.06918			.81150	6
7	5605		3028		6972	.07027	" Corr. 10 18	" Corr. 10 21	.71274	7
8	5746		2773		7227	.07137	15 27	15 31	.81399	8
9	5886		2518		7482	.07246	20 37	20 42	.81524	9
10	.876026		.482263		.517737	1.07356	30 55	30 63	1.81649	10
11	6166	" Corr. 10 23	2009	" Corr. 10 42	7991	.07465	40 73	40 83	.81774	11
12	6307	15 35	1754	15 64	8246	.07575	45 82	45 94	.81899	12
13	6447	20 47	1499	20 85	8501	.07685	50 91	50 104	.82025	13
14	6587		1244		8756	.07795			.82150	14
15	.876727	30 70	.480989	30 127	.519011	1.07905			1.82276	15
16	6867	40 93	0734	40 170	9266	.08015			.82402	16
17	7006	45 105	0479	45 191	9521	.08126			.82528	17
18	7146	50 117	0224	50 212	9776	.08236			.82654	18
19	7286		.479968		.520032	.08347			.82780	19
20	.877425		.479713		.520287	1.08458			1.82906	20
21	7565		9458		0542	.08569			.83033	21
22	7704		9203		0797	.08680			.83159	22
23	7844		8947		1053	.08791			.83286	23
24	7983		8692		1308	.08903			.83413	24
25	.878122		.478436		.521564	1.09014			1.83540	25
26	8261		8181		1819	.09126	" Corr. 10 19	" Corr. 10 21	.83667	26
27	8400		7926		2074	.09238	15 28	15 32	.83794	27
28	8539		7670		2330	.09350	20 37	20 43	.83922	28
29	8678		7414		2586	.09462			.84049	29
30	.878817		.477159		.522841	1.09574	30 56	30 64	1.84177	30
31	8956		6903		3097	.09686	40 75	40 85	.84305	31
32	9095		6647		3353	.09799	45 84	45 96	.84433	32
33	9233		6392		3608	.09911	50 94	50 106	.84561	33
34	9372		6136		3864	.10024			.84689	34
35	.879510		.475880		.524120	1.10137			1.84818	35
36	9649		5624		4376	.10250			.84946	36
37	9787		5368		4632	.10363			.85075	37
38	9925		5112		4888	.10477			.85204	38
39	.880063		4856		5144	.10590			.85333	39
40	.880201		.474600		.525400	1.10704			1.85462	40
41	0339	" Corr. 10 23	4344	" Corr. 10 43	5656	.10817			.85591	41
42	0477	15 34	4088	15 64	5912	.10931			.85720	42
43	0615	20 46	3832	20 85	6168	.11045			.85850	43
44	0753		3576		6424	.11159			.85979	44
45	.880891	30 69	.473320	30 128	.526680	1.11274			1.86109	45
46	1028	40 92	3063	40 171	6937	.11388	" Corr. 10 19	" Corr. 10 22	.86239	46
47	1166	45 115	2807	45 192	7193	.11503	15 29	15 33	.86369	47
48	1304	50 115	2551	50 213	7449	.11617	20 38	20 44	.86499	48
49	1441		2294		7706	.11732			.86630	49
50	.881578		.472038		.527962	1.11847	30 58	30 65	1.86760	50
51	1716		1782		8218	.11963	40 77	40 87	.86891	51
52	1853		1525		8475	.12078	45 87	45 98	.87021	52
53	1990		1268		8732	.12193	50 96	50 109	.87152	53
54	2127		1012		8988	.12309			.87283	54
55	.882264		.470755		.529245	1.12425			1.87415	55
56	2401		0499		9501	.12540			.87546	56
57	2538		0242		9758	.12657			.87677	57
58	2674		.469985		.530015	.12773			.87809	58
59	2811		9728		0272	.12889			.87941	59
60	.882948		.469472		.530528	1.13005			1.88073	60

154

'	Sine	Corr. for Sec.	Cosine	Corr. for Sec.	Versine	Exsec	Corr. for Sec.	Corr. for Sec.	Tangent	'
0	.882948	+	.469472	- +	.530528	1.13005	+	+	1.88073	0
1	3084		9215		0785	.13122			.88205	1
2	3221		8958		1042	.13239			.88337	2
3	3357		8701		1299	.13356			.88469	3
4	3493		8444		1556	.13473			.88602	4
5	.883630		.468187		.531813	1.13590			1.88734	5
6	3766		7930		2070	.13707	" Corr.	" Corr.	.88867	6
7	3902		7673		2327	.13825	10 20	10 22	.89000	7
8	4038		7416		2584	.13942	15 30	15 33	.89133	8
9	4174		7158		2842	.14060	20 39	20 44	.89266	9
10	.884310		.466901		.533099	1.14178	30 59	30 67	1.89400	10
11	4445	" Corr.	6644	" Corr.	3356	.14296	40 79	40 89	.89533	11
12	4581	10 23	6387	10 43	3613	.14414	45 89	45 100	.89667	12
13	4717	15 34	6129	15 64	3871	.14533	50 98	50 111	.89801	13
14	4852	20 45	5872	20 86	4131	.14651			.89935	14
15	.884988	30 68	.465614	30 129	.534386	1.14770			1.90069	15
16	5123	40 90	5357	40 172	4643	.14889			.90203	16
17	5258	45 102	5100	45 193	4900	.15008			.90337	17
18	5394	50 113	4842	50 214	5158	.15127			.90472	18
19	5529		4584		5416	.15246			.90607	19
20	.885664		.464327		.535673	1.15366			1.90741	20
21	5799		4069		5931	.15485			.90876	21
22	5934		3812		6188	.15605			.91012	22
23	6069		3554		6446	.15725			.91147	23
24	6204		3296		6704	.15845			.91282	24
25	.886338		.463038		.536962	1.15965			1.91418	25
26	6473		2780		7220	.16085	" Corr.	" Corr.	.91554	26
27	6608		2522		7478	.16206	10 20	10 23	.91690	27
28	6742		2265		7735	.16326	15 30	15 34	.91826	28
29	6876		2007		7993	.16447	20 40	20 45	.91962	29
30	.887011		.461749		.538251	1.16568	30 61	30 68	1.92098	30
31	7145		1491		8509	.16689	40 81	40 91	.92235	31
32	7279		1232		8768	.16810	45 91	45 102	.92371	32
33	7413		0974		9026	.16932	50 101	50 114	.92508	33
34	7548		0716		9284	.17053			.92645	34
35	.887682		.460458		.539542	1.17175			1.92782	35
36	7815		0200		9800	.17297			.92920	36
37	7949		.459942		.540058	.17419			.93057	37
38	8083		9683		0317	.17541			.93195	38
39	8217		9425		0575	.17663			.93332	39
40	.888350		.459166		.540834	1.17786			1.93470	40
41	8484	" Corr.	8908	" Corr.	1092	.17909			.93608	41
42	8617	10 22	8650	10 43	1350	.18031			.93746	42
43	8751	15 33	8391	15 65	1609	.18154			.93885	43
44	8884	20 44	8132	20 86	1868	.18277			.94023	44
45	.889017	30 67	.457874	30 129	.542126	1.18401			1.94162	45
46	9150	40 89	7615	40 172	2385	.18524	" Corr.	" Corr.	.94301	46
47	9283	45 100	7357	45 194	2643	.18648	10 21	10 23	.94440	47
48	9416	50 111	7098	50 215	2902	.18772	15 31	15 35	.94579	48
49	9549		6839		3161	.18895	20 41	20 47	.94718	49
50	.889682		.456580		.543420	1.19019	30 62	30 70	1.94858	50
51	9815		6322		3678	.19144	40 83	40 93	.94997	51
52	9948		6063		3937	.19268	45 93	45 105	.95137	52
53	.890080		5804		4196	.19393	50 104	50 116	.95277	53
54	0213		5545		4455	.19517			.95417	54
55	.890345		.455286		.544714	1.19642			1.95557	55
56	0478		5027		4973	.19767			.95698	56
57	0610		4768		5232	.19892			.95838	57
58	0742		4509		5491	.20018			.95979	58
59	0874		4250		5750	.20143			.96120	59
60	.891006		.453990		.546010	1.20269			1.96261	60

TABLE XX.—NATURAL SINES, COSINES,
63°

'	Sine	Cosine	Versine	Exsec	Tangent	'
0	.891006	.453990	.546010	1.20269	1.96261	0
1	1138	3731	6269	.20395	.96402	1
2	1270	3472	6528	.20521	.96544	2
3	1402	3213	6787	.20647	.96685	3
4	1534	2954	7046	.20773	.96827	4
5	.891666	.452694	.547306	1.20900	1.96969	5
6	1798	2435	7565	.21026	.97111	6
7	1929	2175	7825	.21153	.97253	7
8	2061	1916	8084	.21280	.97395	8
9	2192	1656	8344	.21407	.97538	9
10	.892323	.451397	.548603	1.21535	1.97680	10
11	2455	1137	8863	.21662	.97823	11
12	2586	0878	9122	.21790	.97966	12
13	2717	0618	9382	.21918	.98110	13
14	2848	0358	9642	.22045	.98253	14
15	.892979	.450098	.549902	1.22174	1.98396	15
16	3110	.449839	.550161	.22302	.98540	16
17	3241	9579	0421	.22430	.98684	17
18	3371	9319	0681	.22559	.98828	18
19	3502	9059	0941	.22688	.98972	19
20	.893633	.448799	.551201	1.22817	1.99116	20
21	3763	8539	1461	.22946	.99261	21
22	3894	8279	1721	.23075	.99406	22
23	4024	8019	1981	.23205	.99550	23
24	4154	7759	2241	.23334	.99695	24
25	.894284	.447499	.552501	1.23464	1.99841	25
26	4415	7239	2761	.23594	1.99986	26
27	4545	6979	3021	.23724	2.00131	27
28	4675	6718	3282	.23855	.00277	28
29	4804	6458	3542	.23985	.00423	29
30	.894934	.446198	.553802	1.24116	2.00569	30
31	5064	5938	4062	.24247	.00715	31
32	5194	5677	4323	.24378	.00862	32
33	5323	5417	4583	.24509	.01008	33
34	5453	5156	4844	.24640	.01155	34
35	.895582	.444896	.555104	1.24772	2.01302	35
36	5712	4635	5365	.24903	.01449	36
37	5841	4375	5625	.25035	.01596	37
38	5970	4114	5886	.25167	.01743	38
39	6099	3853	6147	.25300	.01891	39
40	.896228	.443593	.556407	1.25432	2.02039	40
41	6358	3332	6668	.25565	.02187	41
42	6486	3071	6929	.25697	.02335	42
43	6615	2810	7190	.25830	.02483	43
44	6744	2550	7450	.25963	.02631	44
45	.896873	.442289	.557711	1.26097	2.02780	45
46	7001	2028	7972	.26230	.02929	46
47	7130	1767	8233	.26364	.03078	47
48	7258	1506	8494	.26498	.03227	48
49	7387	1245	8755	.26632	.03376	49
50	.897515	.440984	.559016	1.26766	2.03526	50
51	7643	0723	9277	.26900	.03675	51
52	7772	0462	9538	.27035	.03825	52
53	7900	0200	9800	.27169	.03975	53
54	8028	.439939	.560061	.27304	.04125	54
55	.898156	.439678	.560322	1.27439	2.04276	55
56	8283	9417	0583	.27574	.04426	56
57	8411	9155	0845	.27710	.04577	57
58	8539	8894	1106	.27845	.04728	58
59	8666	8633	1367	.27981	.04879	59
60	.898794	.438371	.561629	1.28117	2.05030	60

Column headers: Sine — Corr. for Sec. (+); Cosine — Corr. for Sec. (− +); Versine; Exsec — Corr. for Sec. (+); Corr. for Sec. (+); Tangent.

Corr. for Sec. (interpolation blocks):

Sine — 10 22, 15 33, 20 44, 30 65, 45 98, 50 109; 10 21, 15 32, 20 43, 30 64, 40 86, 45 97, 50 107

Cosine — 10 43, 15 65, 20 87, 30 130, 40 173, 50 216; 10 43, 15 65, 20 87, 30 130, 40 173, 45 196, 50 217

Exsec — 10 21, 15 32, 20 42; 30 64, 40 85, 45 96, 50 106; 10 22, 15 33, 20 44, 30 65, 40 87, 50 109; 10 22, 15 34, 20 45, 30 67, 40 90, 45 101, 50 112

Tangent — 10 24, 15 36, 20 48; 30 71, 40 95, 45 107, 50 119; 10 24, 15 37, 20 49, 30 73, 45 110, 50 122; 10 25, 15 37, 20 50, 30 75, 40 100, 45 112, 50 125

'	Sine	Corr. for Sec.	Cosine	Corr. for Sec.	Versine	Exsec	Corr. for Sec.	Corr. for Sec.	Tangent	'
		+		− +		+				
0	.898794		.438371		.561629	1.28117			2.05030	0
1	8922		8110		1890	.28253	" Corr.	" Corr.	.05182	1
2	9049		7848		2152	.28390	10 23	10 25	.05333	2
3	9176		7587		2413	.28526	15 34	15 38	.05485	3
4	9304		7325		2675	.28663	20 46	20 51	.05637	4
5	.899431		.437063		.562937	1.28800	30 69	30 76	2.05790	5
6	9558		6802		3198	.28937	40 92	40 102	.05942	6
7	9685		6540		3460	.29074	45 103	45 114	.06094	7
8	9812		6278		3722	.29211	50 114	50 127	.06247	8
9	9939		6017		3983	.29349			.06400	9
10	.900065		.435755		.564245	1.29487			2.06553	10
11	0192	" Corr.	5493	" Corr.	4507	.29625			.06706	11
12	0319	10 21	5231	10 44	4769	.29763			.06860	12
13	0445	15 32	4969	15 65	5031	.29901			.07014	13
14	0572	20 42	4707	20 87	5293	.30040			.07167	14
15	.900698	30 63	.434445	30 131	.565555	1.30179			2.07321	15
16	0825	40 84	4183	40 175	5817	.30318	" Corr.	" Corr.	.07476	16
17	0951	45 95	3921	45 196	6079	.30457	10 23	10 26	.07630	17
18	1077	50 105	3659	50 218	6341	.30596	15 35	15 39	.07785	18
19	1203		3397		6603	.30735	20 47	20 52	.07939	19
20	.901329		.433135		.566865	1.30875	30 70	30 78	2.08094	20
21	1455		2873		7127	.31015	40 93	40 104	.08250	21
22	1581		2610		7390	.31155	45 105	45 117	.08405	22
23	1707		2348		7652	.31295	50 117	50 130	.08560	23
24	1832		2086		7914	.31436			.08716	24
25	.901958		.431823		.568177	1.31576			2.08872	25
26	2084		1561		8439	.31717			.09028	26
27	2209		1299		8701	.31858			.09184	27
28	2335		1036		8964	.31999			.09341	28
29	2460		0774		9226	.32140			.09498	29
30	.902585		.430511		.569489	1.32282			2.09654	30
31	2710		0248		9752	.32424	" Corr.	" Corr.	.09811	31
32	2836		.429986		.570014	.32566	10 24	10 25	.09969	32
33	2961		9723		0277	.32708	15 36	15 40	.10126	33
34	3086		9461		0539	.32850	20 48	20 53	.10284	34
35	.903210		.429198		.570802	1.32993	30 72	30 79	2.10442	35
36	3335		8935		1065	.33135	40 95	40 106	.10600	36
37	3460		8672		1328	.33278	45 107	45 119	.10758	37
38	3585		8410		1590	.33422	50 119	50 132	.10916	38
39	3709		8147		1853	.33565			.11075	39
40	.903834		.427884		.572116	1.33708			2.11233	40
41	3958	" Corr.	7621	" Corr.	2379	.33852			.11392	41
42	4082	10 21	7358	10 44	2642	.33996			.11552	42
43	4207	15 31	7095	15 66	2905	.34140			.11711	43
44	4331	20 41	6832	20 88	3168	.34284			.11871	44
45	.904455	30 62	.426569	30 132	.573431	1.34429			2.12030	45
46	4579	40 83	6306	40 175	3694	.34573	" Corr.	" Corr.	.12190	46
47	4703	45 93	6042	45 197	3958	.34718	10 24	10 27	.12350	47
48	4827	50 103	5779	50 219	4221	.34863	15 37	15 40	.12511	48
49	4951		5516		4484	.35009	20 49	20 54	.12671	49
50	.905075		.425253		.574747	1.35154	30 73	30 81	2.12832	50
51	5198		4990		5010	.35300	40 97	40 108	.12993	51
52	5322		4726		5274	.35446	45 110	45 121	.13154	52
53	5445		4463		5537	.35592	50 122	50 134	.13316	53
54	5569		4199		5801	.35738			.13477	54
55	.905692		.423936		.576064	1.35885			2.13639	55
56	5815		3672		6328	.36031			.13801	56
57	5939		3409		6591	.36178			.13963	57
58	6062		3146		6854	.36325			.14125	58
59	6185		2882		7118	.36473			.14288	59
60	.906308		.422618		.577382	1.36620			2.14451	60

TABLE XX.—NATURAL SINES, COSINES,
65°

'	Sine	Corr. for Sec.	Cosine	Corr. for Sec.	Versine	Exsec	Corr. for Sec.	Corr. for Sec.	Tangent	'
0	.906308	+	.422618	− +	.577382	1.36620	+	+	2.14451	0
1	6431		2355		7645	.36768	"Corr.	"Corr.	.14614	1
2	6554		2091		7909	.36916	10 25	10 27	.14777	2
3	6676		1827		8173	.37064	15 37	15 41	.14940	3
4	6799		1563		8437	.37212	20 50	20 55	.15104	4
5	.906922		.421300		.578700	1.37361	30 75	30 82	2.15268	5
6	7044		1036		8964	.37509	40 99	40 110	.15432	6
7	7166		0772		9228	.37658	45 112	45 123	.15596	7
8	7289		0508		9492	.37808	50 124	50 137	.15760	8
9	7411		0244		9756	.37957			.15925	9
10	.907533		.419980		.580020	1.38106			2.16090	10
11	7655	"Corr.	9716	"Corr.	0284	.38256			.16255	11
12	7778	10 20	9452	10 44	0548	.38406			.16420	12
13	7900	15 30	9188	15 66	0812	.38556			.16585	13
14	8021	20 41	8924	20 88	1076	.38707			.16751	14
15	.908143	30 61	.418660	30 132	.581340	1.38857			2.16917	15
16	8265	40 81	8396	40 176	1604	.39008	"Corr.	"Corr.	.17083	16
17	8387	45 91	8131	45 198	1869	.39159	10 25	10 28	.17249	17
18	8508	50 101	7867	50 220	2133	.39311	15 38	15 43	.17416	18
19	8630		7603		2397	.39462	20 51	20 56	.17582	19
20	.908751		.417338		.582662	1.39614	30 76	30 84	2.17749	20
21	8872		7074		2926	.39766	40 102	40 112	.17916	21
22	8994		6810		3190	.39918	45 114	45 126	.18084	22
23	9115		6545		3455	.40070	50 127	50 140	.18251	23
24	9236		6281		3719	.40222			.18419	24
25	.909357		.416016		.583984	1.40375			2.18587	25
26	9478		5752		4248	.40528			.18755	26
27	9599		5487		4513	.40681			.18923	27
28	9720		5223		4777	.40835			.19092	28
29	9841		4958		5042	.40988			.19261	29
30	.909961		.414693		.585307	1.41142			2.19430	30
31	.910082		4428		5572	.41296	"Corr.	"Corr.	.19599	31
32	0202		4164		5836	.41450	10 26	10 28	.19769	32
33	0323		3899		6101	.41605	15 38	15 43	.19938	33
34	0443		3634		6366	.41760	20 52	20 57	.20108	34
35	.910563		.413369		.586631	1.41914	30 78	30 85	2.20278	35
36	0684		3104		6896	.42070	40 104	40 114	.20449	36
37	0804		2840		7160	.42225	45 117	45 128	.20619	37
38	0924		2574		7426	.42380	50 130	50 142	.20790	38
39	1044		2310		7690	.42536			.20961	39
40	.911164		.412044		.587956	1.42692			2.21132	40
41	1284	"Corr.	1780	"Corr.	8220	.42848			.21304	41
42	1403	10 20	1514	10 44	8486	.43005			.21475	42
43	1523	15 30	1249	15 66	8751	.43162			.21647	43
44	1642	20 40	0984	20 88	9016	.43318			.21819	44
45	.911762	30 60	.410719	30 133	.589281	1.43476			2.21992	45
46	1882	40 80	0454	40 177	9546	.43633	"Corr.	"Corr.	.22164	46
47	2001	45 90	0188	45 199	9812	.43790	10 26	10 29	.22337	47
48	2120	50 100	.409923	50 221	.590077	.43948	15 40	15 44	.22510	48
49	2239		9658		0342	.44106	20 53	20 58	.22683	49
50	.912358		.409392		.590608	1.44264	30 79	30 87	2.22857	50
51	2478		9127		0873	.44423	40 106	40 116	.23030	51
52	2596		8862		1138	.44582	45 119	45 131	.23204	52
53	2715		8596		1404	.44741	50 132	50 145	.23378	53
54	2834		8330		1670	.44900			.23553	54
55	.912953		.408065		.591935	1.45059			2.23727	55
56	3072		7799		2201	.45219			.23902	56
57	3190		7534		2466	.45378			.24077	57
58	3309		7268		2732	.45539			.24252	58
59	3427		7002		2998	.45699			.24428	59
60	.913546		.406737		.593263	1.45859			2.24604	60

'	Sine	Corr. for Sec.	Cosine	Corr. for Sec.	Versine	Exsec	Corr. for Sec.	Corr. for Sec.	Tangent	'
0	.913546	+	.406737	− +	.593263	1.45859	+		2.24604	0
1	3664		6471		3529	.46020	" Corr.	" Corr.	.24780	1
2	3782		6205		3795	.46181	10 27	10 30	.24956	2
3	3900		5939		4061	.46342	15 41	15 44	.25132	3
4	4018		5673		4327	.46504	20 54	20 59	.25309	4
5	.914136		.405408		.594592	1.46665	30 81	30 89	2.25486	5
6	4254		5142		4858	.46827	40 108	40 118	.25663	6
7	4372		4876		5124	.46989	45 122	45 133	.25840	7
8	4490		4610		5390	.47152	50 135	50 148	.26018	8
9	4607		4344		5656	.47314			.26196	9
10	.914725		.404078		.595922	1.47477			2.26374	10
11	4842	" Corr.	3811	" Corr.	6189	.47640			.26552	11
12	4960	10 20	3545	10 44	6455	.47804			.26730	12
13	5077	15 29	3279	15 67	6721	.47967			.26909	13
14	5194	20 39	3013	20 89	6987	.48131			.27088	14
15	.915312	30 59	.402747	30 133	.597253	1.48295			2.27267	15
16	5429	40 78	2480	40 178	7520	.48459	" Corr.	" Corr.	.27447	16
17	5546	45 88	2214	45 200	7786	.48624	10 27	10 30	.27626	17
18	5663	50 98	1948	50 222	8052	.48789	15 41	15 45	.27806	18
19	5780		1681		8319	.48954	20 55	20 69	.27987	19
20	.915896		.401415		.598585	1.49119	30 82	30 90	2.28167	20
21	6013		1149		8851	.49284	40 110	40 120	.28348	21
22	6130		0882		9118	.49450	45 124	45 135	.28528	22
23	6246		0616		9384	.49616	50 137	50 150	.28710	23
24	6363		0349		9651	.49782			.28891	24
25	.916479		.400082		.599918	1.49948			2.29073	25
26	6596		.399816		.600184	.50115	" Corr.	" Corr.	.29254	26
27	6712		9549		0451	.50282	10 28	10 31	.29437	27
28	6828		9282		0718	.50449	15 42	15 46	.29619	28
29	6944		9016		0984	.50617	20 56	20 61	.29801	29
30	.917060		.398749		.601251	1.50784	30 84	30 92	2.29984	30
31	7176		8482		1518	.50952	40 112	40 122	.30167	31
32	7292		8216		1784	.51120	45 126	45 137	.30351	32
33	7408		7949		2051	.51289	50 140	50 153	.30534	33
34	7523		7682		2318	.51457			.30718	34
35	.917639		.397415		.602585	1.51626			2.30902	35
36	7755		7148		2852	.51795			.31086	36
37	7870		6881		3119	.51965			.31271	37
38	7986		6614		3386	.52134			.31456	38
39	8101		6347		3653	.52304			.31641	39
40	.918216		.396080		.603920	1.52474			2.31826	40
41	8331	" Corr.	5813	" Corr.	4187	.52645	" Corr.	" Corr.	.32012	41
42	8446	10 19	5546	10 45	4454	.52815	10 28	10 31	.32197	42
43	8561	15 29	5278	15 67	4722	.52986	15 43	15 46	.32383	43
44	8676	20 38	5011	20 89	4989	.53157	20 57	20 62	.32570	44
45	.918791	30 57	.394744	30 134	.605256	1.53329	30 85	30 93	2.32756	45
46	8906	40 77	4477	40 178	5523	.53500	40 114	40 124	.32943	46
47	9021	45 86	4209	45 200	5791	.53672	45 128	45 139	.33130	47
48	9135	50 96	3942	50 223	6058	.53845	50 142	50 155	.33317	48
49	9250		3674		6326	.54017			.33505	49
50	.919364		.393407		.606593	1.54190			2.33693	50
51	9479		3140		6860	.54363	" Corr.	" Corr.	.33881	51
52	9593		2872		7128	.54536	10 29	10 32	.34069	52
53	9707		2605		7395	.54709	15 43	15 47	.34258	53
54	9822		2337		7663	.54883	20 58	20 63	.34447	54
55	.919936		.392070		.607930	1.55057	30 87	30 95	2.34636	55
56	.920050		1802		8198	.55231	40 116	40 126	.34825	56
57	0164		1534		8466	.55405	45 130	45 142	.35015	57
58	0277		1267		8733	.55580	50 145	50 158	.35205	58
59	0391		0999		9001	.55755			.35395	59
60	.920505		.390731		.609269	1.55930			2.35585	60

TABLE XX.—NATURAL SINES, COSINES,
67°

'	Sine	Corr. for Sec.	Cosine	Corr. for Sec.	Versine	Exsec	Corr. for Sec.	Corr. for Sec.	Tangent	'
0	.920505	+	.390731	− +	.609269	1.55930	+	+	2.35585	0
1	0618		0463		9537	.56106	" Corr.	" Corr.	.35776	1
2	0732		0196		9804	.56282	10 30	10 32	.35967	2
3	0846		.389928		.610072	.56455	15 44	15 48	.36158	3
4	0959		9660		0340	.56634	20 59	20 64	.36349	4
5	.921072		.389392		.610608	1.56811	30 89	30 96	2.36541	5
6	1185		9124		0876	.56988	40 118	40 129	.36733	6
7	1299		8856		1144	.57165	45 133	45 145	.36925	7
8	1412		8588		1412	.57342	50 148	50 161	.37118	8
9	1525		8320		1680	.57520			.37311	9
10	.921638		.388052		.611948	1.57698			2.37504	10
11	1750	" Corr.	7784	" Corr.	2216	.57876			.37697	11
12	1863	10 19	7516	10 45	2484	.58054			.37891	12
13	1976	15 28	7247	15 67	2753	.58233			.38084	13
14	2088	20 37	6979	20 89	3021	.58412			.38279	14
15	.922201	30 56	.386711	30 134	.613289	1.58591			2.38473	15
16	2313	40 75	6443	40 179	3557	.58771	" Corr.	" Corr.	.38668	16
17	2426	45 84	6174	45 201	3826	.58950	10 30	10 33	.38862	17
18	2538	50 94	5906	50 224	4094	.59130	15 45	15 49	.39058	18
19	2650		5638		4362	.59311	20 60	20 65	.39253	19
20	.922762		.385369		.614631	1.59491	30 90	30 98	2.39449	20
21	2874		5101		4899	.59672	40 120	40 130	.39645	21
22	2986		4832		5168	.59853	45 135	45 147	.39841	22
23	3098		4564		5436	.60035	50 150	50 163	.40038	23
24	3210		4295		5705	.60217			.40235	24
25	.923322		.384027		.615973	1.60399			2.40432	25
26	3434		3758		6242	.60581	" Corr.	" Corr.	.40629	26
27	3545		3490		6510	.60763	10 31	10 33	.40827	27
28	3657		3221		6779	.60946	15 46	15 50	.41025	28
29	3768		2952		7048	.61129	20 61	20 66	.41223	29
30	.923880		.382683		.617317	1.61313	30 92	30 99	2.41421	30
31	3991		2415		7585	.61496	40 122	40 133	.41620	31
32	4102		2146		7854	.61680	45 138	45 149	.41819	32
33	4213		1877		8123	.61864	50 153	50 166	.42019	33
34	4324		1608		8392	.62049			.42218	34
35	.924435		.381339		.618661	1.62234			2.42418	35
36	4546		1070		8930	.62419			.42618	36
37	4657		0801		9199	.62604			.42819	37
38	4768		0532		9468	.62790			.43019	38
39	4878		0263		9737	.62976			.43220	39
40	.924989		.379994		.620006	1.63162	+	+	2.43422	40
41	5099	" Corr.	9725	" Corr.	0275	.63348	" Corr.	" Corr.	.43623	41
42	5210	10 19	9456	10 45	0544	.63535	10 31	10 34	.43825	42
43	5320	15 28	9187	15 67	0813	.63722	15 47	15 51	.44027	43
44	5430	20 37	8918	20 90	1082	.63909	20 62	20 67	.44230	44
45	.925540	30 55	.378649	30 135	.621351	1.64097	30 94	30 101	2.44433	45
46	5651	40 73	8379	40 180	1621	.64285	40 125	40 135	.44636	46
47	5761	45 83	8110	45 202	1890	.64473	45 140	45 152	.44839	47
48	5871	50 92	7841	50 224	2159	.64662	50 156	50 168	.45043	48
49	5980		7571		2429	.64851			.45246	49
50	.926090		.377302		.622698	1.65040	+	+	2.45451	50
51	6200		7033		2967	.65229	" Corr.	" Corr.	.45655	51
52	6310		6763		3237	.65419	10 32	10 34	.45860	52
53	6419		6494		3506	.65609	15 48	15 51	.46065	53
54	6529		6224		3776	.65799	20 64	20 69	.46270	54
55	.926638		.375955		.624045	1.65989	30 95	30 103	2.46476	55
56	6747		5685		4315	.66180	40 127	40 137	.46682	56
57	6857		5416		4584	.66371	45 143	45 154	.46888	57
58	6966		5146		4854	.66563	50 159	50 171	.47095	58
59	7075		4876		5124	.66755			.47302	59
60	.927184		.374607		.625393	1.66947			2.47509	60

'	Sine	Corr. for Sec.	Cosine	Corr. for Sec.	Versine	Exsec	Corr. for Sec.	Corr. for Sec.	Tangent	'
0	.927184	+	.374607	- +	.625393	1.66947			2.47509	0
1	7293		4337		5663	.67139	" Corr.	" Corr.	.47716	1
2	7402		4067		5933	.67332	10 32	10 35	.47924	2
3	7510		3797		6203	.67525	15 48	15 52	.48132	3
4	7619		3528		6472	.67718	20 65	20 70	.48340	4
5	.927728		.373258		.626742	1.67911	30 97	30 104	2.48549	5
6	7836		2988		7012	.68105	40 130	40 139	.48758	6
7	7945		2718		7282	.68299	45 145	45 157	.48967	7
8	8053		2448		7552	.68494	50 162	50 174	.49177	8
9	8161		2178		7822	.68689			.49386	9
10	.928270		.371908		.628092	1.68884			2.49597	10
11	8378	" Corr.	1638	" Corr.	8362	.69079	" Corr.	" Corr.	.49807	11
12	8486	10 18	1368	10 45	8632	.69275	10 33	10 35	.50018	12
13	8594	15 27	1098	15 68	8902	.69471	15 49	15 53	.50229	13
14	8702	20 36	0828	20 90	9172	.69667	20 66	20 71	.50440	14
15	.928810	30 54	.370557	30 135	.629443	1.69864	30 98	30 106	2.50652	15
16	8917	40 72	0287	40 180	9713	.70061	40 131	40 141	.50864	16
17	9025	45 81	0017	45 203	9983	.70258	45 148	45 159	.51076	17
18	9133	50 90	.369747	50 225	.630253	.70455	50 164	50 177	.51289	18
19	9240		9476		0524	.70653			.51502	19
20	.929348		.369206		.630794	1.70851			2.51715	20
21	9455		8936		1064	.71050	" Corr.	" Corr.	.51929	21
22	9562		8665		1335	.71249	10 33	10 36	.52142	22
23	9669		8395		1605	.71448	15 50	15 54	.52357	23
24	9776		8125		1875	.71647	20 67	20 72	.52571	24
25	.929884		.367854		.632146	1.71847	30 100	30 108	2.52786	25
26	9990		7584		2416	.72047	40 133	40 143	.53001	26
27	.930097		7313		2687	.72247	45 150	45 161	.53217	27
28	0204		7042		2958	.72448	50 167	50 179	.53432	28
29	0311		6772		3228	.72649			.53648	29
30	.930418		.366501		.633499	1.72850			2.53865	30
31	0524		6231		3769	.73052	" Corr.	" Corr.	.54082	31
32	0631		5960		4040	.73254	10 34	10 36	.54299	32
33	0737		5689		4311	.73456	15 51	15 54	.54516	33
34	0843		5418		4582	.73659	20 68	20 73	.54734	34
35	.930950		.365148		.634852	1.73862	30 102	30 109	2.54952	35
36	1056		4877		5123	.74065	40 136	40 146	.55170	36
37	1162		4606		5394	.74269	45 152	45 164	.55389	37
38	1268		4335		5665	.74473	50 169	50 182	.55608	38
39	1374		4064		5936	.74677			.55827	39
40	.931480		.363793		.636207	1.74881			2.56046	40
41	1586	" Corr.	3522	" Corr.	6478	.75086	" Corr.	" Corr.	.56266	41
42	1691	10 18	3251	10 45	6749	.75292	10 34	10 37	.56487	42
43	1797	15 26	2980	15 68	7020	.75497	15 52	15 55	.56707	43
44	1902	20 35	2709	20 90	7291	.75703	20 69	20 74	.56928	44
45	.932008	30 53	.362438	30 136	.637562	1.75909	30 103	30 111	2.57150	45
46	2113	40 70	2167	40 181	7833	.76116	40 138	40 148	.57371	46
47	2219	45 79	1896	45 203	8104	.76323	45 155	45 166	.57593	47
48	2324	50 88	1625	50 226	8375	.76530	50 172	50 185	.57815	48
49	2429		1353		8647	.76737			.58038	49
50	.932534		.361082		.638918	1.76945			2.58261	50
51	2639		0811		9189	.77154	" Corr.	" Corr.	.58484	51
52	2744		0540		9460	.77362	10 35	10 37	.58708	52
53	2849		0268		9732	.77571	15 52	15 56	.58932	53
54	2954		.359997		.640003	.77780	20 70	20 75	.59156	54
55	.933058		.359725		.640275	1.77990	30 105	30 112	2.59381	55
56	3163		9454		0546	.78200	40 140	40 150	.59606	56
57	3267		9182		0818	.78410	45 157	45 168	.59831	57
58	3372		8911		1089	.78621	50 175	50 187	.60057	58
59	3476		8640		1360	.78832			.60283	59
60	.933580		.358368		.641632	1.79043			2.60509	60

TABLE XX.—NATURAL SINES, COSINES,
69°

'	Sine	Corr. for Sec.	Cosine	Corr. for Sec.	Versine	Exsec	Corr. for Sec.	Corr. for Sec.	Tangent	'
0	.933580	+	.358368	- +	.641632	1.79043	+	+	2.60509	0
1	3685		8096		1904	.79254			.60736	1
2	3789		7825		2175	.79466	10 36	10 38	.60963	2
3	3893		7553		2447	.79679	15 53	15 57	.61190	3
4	3997		7281		2719	.79891	20 71	20 76	.61418	4
5	.934101		.357010		.642990	1.80104	30 107	30 114	2.61646	5
6	4204		6738		3262	.80318	40 142	40 152	.61874	6
7	4308		6466		3534	.80531	45 160	45 171	.62103	7
8	4412		6194		3806	.80746	50 178	50 190	.62332	8
9	4515		5923		4077	.80960			.62561	9
10	.934619		.355651		.644349	1.81175			2.62791	10
11	4722	" Corr.	5379	" Corr.	4621	.81390	" Corr.	" Corr.	.63021	11
12	4826	10 17	5107	10 45	4893	.81605	10 36	10 39	.63252	12
13	4929	15 26	4835	15 68	5165	.81821	15 54	15 58	.63483	13
14	5032	20 34	4563	20 91	5437	.82037	20 72	20 77	.63714	14
15	.935135	30 52	.354291	30 136	.645709	1.82254	30 108	30 116	2.63945	15
16	5238	40 69	4019	40 181	5981	.82471	40 145	40 156	.64177	16
17	5341	45 77	3747	45 204	6253	.82688	45 163	45 174	.64410	17
18	5444	50 86	3475	50 227	6525	.82906	50 181	50 193	.64642	18
19	5547		3203		6797	.83124			.64875	19
20	.935650		.352931		.647069	1.83342			2.65109	20
21	5752		2658		7342	.83561	" Corr.	" Corr.	.65342	21
22	5855		2386		7614	.83780	10 37	10 39	.65576	22
23	5957		2114		7886	.83999	15 55	15 59	.65811	23
24	6060		1842		8158	.84219	20 73	20 78	.66046	24
25	.936162		.351569		.648431	1.84439	30 110	30 118	2.66281	25
26	6264		1297		8703	.84659	40 147	40 157	.66516	26
27	6366		1025		8975	.84880	45 165	45 177	.66752	27
28	6468		0752		9248	.85102	50 184	50 196	.66989	28
29	6570		0480		9520	.85323			.67225	29
30	.936672		.350207		.649793	1.85545			2.67462	30
31	6774		.349935		.650065	.85767	" Corr.	" Corr.	.67700	31
32	6876		9662		0338	.85990	10 37	10 40	.67937	32
33	6977		9390		0610	.86213	15 56	15 60	.68175	33
34	7079		9117		0883	.86437	20 75	20 80	.68414	34
35	.937181		.348845		.651155	1.86661	30 112	30 120	2.68653	35
36	7282		8572		1428	.86885	40 149	40 160	.68892	36
37	7383		8299		1701	.87109	45 168	45 179	.69131	37
38	7485		8027		1973	.87334	50 187	50 199	.69371	38
39	7586		7754		2246	.87560			.69612	39
40	.937687		.347481		.652519	1.87785			2.69853	40
41	7788	" Corr.	7208	" Corr.	2792	.88011	" Corr.	" Corr.	.70094	41
42	7889	10 17	6936	10 45	3064	.88238	10 38	10 40	.70335	42
43	7990	15 25	6663	15 68	3337	.88465	15 57	15 61	.70577	43
44	8091	20 34	6390	20 91	3610	.88692	20 76	20 81	.70819	44
45	.938191	30 50	.346117	30 136	.653883	1.88920	30 114	30 121	2.71062	45
46	8292	40 67	5844	40 182	4156	.89148	40 152	40 162	.71305	46
47	8392	45 76	5571	45 205	4429	.89376	45 171	45 182	.71548	47
48	8493	50 84	5298	50 227	4702	.89605	50 190	50 202	.71792	48
49	8593		5025		4975	.89834			.72036	49
50	.938694		.344752		.655248	1.90063			2.72281	50
51	8794		4479		5521	.90293	" Corr.	" Corr.	.72526	51
52	8894		4206		5794	.90524	10 39	10 41	.72771	52
53	8994		3933		6067	.90754	15 58	15 62	.73017	53
54	9094		3660		6340	.90986	20 77	20 82	.73263	54
55	.939194		.343386		.656614	1.91217	30 116	30 123	2.73509	55
56	9294		3113		6887	.91449	40 156	40 165	.73756	56
57	9394		2840		7160	.91681	45 174	45 185	.74004	57
58	9494		2567		7433	.91914	50 193	50 206	.74251	58
59	9593		2294		7706	.92147			.74499	59
60	.939693		.342020		.657980	1.92380			2.74748	60

'	Sine	Corr. for Sec.	Cosine	Corr. for Sec.	Versine	Exsec	Corr. for Sec.	Corr. for Sec.	Tangent	'
0	.939693	+	.342020	- +	.657980	1.92380	+	+	2.74748	0
1	9792		1747		8253	.92614	" Corr.	" Corr.	.74997	1
2	9891		1473		8527	.92849	10 39	10 42	.75246	2
3	9991		1200		8800	.93083	15 59	15 63	.75496	3
4	.940090		0926		9074	.93318	20 78	20 84	.75746	4
5	.940189		.340653		.659347	1.93554	30 118	30 125	2.75996	5
6	0288		0380		9620	.93790	40 157	40 167	.76247	6
7	0387		0106		9894	.94026	45 177	45 188	.76498	7
8	0486		.339832		.660168	.94263	50 196	50 209	.76750	8
9	0585		9559		0441	.94500			.77002	9
10	.940684		.339285		.660715	1.94737			2.77254	10
11	0782	" Corr.	9012	" Corr.	0988	.94975	" Corr.	" Corr.	.77507	11
12	0881	10 16	8738	10 46	1262	.95213	10 40	10 42	.77761	12
13	0979	15 25	8464	15 68	1536	.95452	15 60	15 64	.78014	13
14	1078	20 33	8190	20 91	1810	.95691	20 80	20 85	.78269	14
15	.941176	30 49	.337917	30 137	.662083	1.95931	30 120	30 127	2.78523	15
16	1274	40 66	7643	40 183	2357	.96171	40 160	40 170	.78778	16
17	1372	45 74	7369	45 205	2631	.96411	45 180	45 191	.79033	17
18	1470	50 82	7095	50 228	2905	.96652	50 200	50 212	.79289	18
19	1569		6821		3179	.96893			.79545	19
20	.941666		.336548		.663452	1.97135			2.79802	20
21	1764		6274		3726	.97377	" Corr.	" Corr.	.80059	21
22	1862		6000		4000	.97619	10 41	10 43	.80316	22
23	1960		5726		4274	.97862	15 61	15 65	.80574	23
24	2058		5452		4548	.98106	20 81	20 86	.80833	24
25	.942155		.335178		.664822	1.98349	30 122	30 130	2.81091	25
26	2252		4903		5097	.98594	40 163	40 173	.81350	26
27	2350		4629		5371	.98838	45 183	45 194	.81610	27
28	2447		4355		5645	.99083	50 203	50 216	.81870	28
29	2544		4081		5919	.99329			.82130	29
30	.942642		.333807		.666193	1.99574			2.82391	30
31	2739		3533		6467	.99821	" Corr.	" Corr.	.82653	31
32	2836		3258		6742	2.00067	10 41	10 44	.82914	32
33	2932		2984		7016	.00315	15 62	15 66	.83176	33
34	3029		2710		7290	.00562	20 83	20 88	.83439	34
35	.943126		.332436		.667564	2.00810	30 124	30 132	2.83702	35
36	3223		2161		7839	.01059	40 166	40 176	.83965	36
37	3319		1887		8113	.01308	45 186	45 198	.84229	37
38	3416		1612		8388	.01557	50 207	50 220	.84494	38
39	3512		1338		8662	.01807			.84758	39
40	.943608		.331063		.668937	2.02057			2.85023	40
41	3705	" Corr.	0789	" Corr.	9211	.02308	" Corr.	" Corr.	.85289	41
42	3801	10 16	0514	10 46	9486	.02559	10 42	10 45	.85555	42
43	3897	15 24	0240	15 69	9760	.02810	15 63	15 67	.85822	43
44	3993	20 32	.329965	20 92	.670035	.03062	20 84	20 89	.86089	44
45	.944089	30 48	.329691	30 137	.670309	2.03315	30 126	30 134	2.86356	45
46	4185	40 64	9416	40 183	0584	.03568	40 169	40 179	.86624	46
47	4281	45 72	9141	45 206	0859	.03821	45 190	45 201	.86892	47
48	4376	50 80	8867	50 229	1133	.04075	50 211	50 223	.87161	48
49	4472		8592		1408	.04329			.87430	49
50	.944568		.328317		.671683	2.04584			2.87700	50
51	4663		8042		1958	.04839	" Corr.	" Corr.	.87970	51
52	4758		7768		2232	.05094	10 43	10 45	.88240	52
53	4854		7493		2507	.05350	15 64	15 68	.88511	53
54	4949		7218		2782	.05607	20 86	20 91	.88783	54
55	.945044		.326943		.673057	2.05864	30 129	30 136	2.89055	55
56	5139		6668		3332	.06121	40 172	40 182	.89327	56
57	5234		6393		3607	.06379	45 193	45 204	.89600	57
58	5329		6118		3882	.06637	50 214	50 227	.89873	58
59	5424		5843		4157	.06896			.90147	59
60	.945519		.325568		.674432	2.07155			2.90421	60

TABLE XX.—NATURAL SINES, COSINES,
71°

'	Sine	Corr. for Sec.	Cosine	Corr. for Sec.	Versine	Exsec	Corr. for Sec.	Corr. for Sec.	Tangent	'
0	.945519	+	.325568	– +	.674432	2.07155	+	+	2.90421	0
1	5613		5293		4707	.07415	" Corr.	" Corr.	.90696	1
2	5708		5018	" Corr.	4982	.07675	10 44	10 46	.90971	2
3	5802		4743	10 44	5257	.07936	15 66	15 69	.91246	3
4	5897		4468	15 66	5532	.08197	20 87	20 92	.91523	4
5	.945991		.324193	20 87	.675807	2.08459	30 131	30 139	2.91799	5
6	6085		3917	30 131	6083	.08721	40 175	40 185	.92076	6
7	6180		3642	40 175	6358	.08983	45 197	45 208	.92354	7
8	6274		3367	45 197	6633	.09246	50 218	50 231	.92632	8
9	6368		3092	50 218	6908	.09510			.92910	9
10	.946462		.322816		.677184	2.09774			2.93189	10
11	6556	" Corr.	2541	" Corr.	7459	.10038	" Corr.	" Corr.	.93468	11
12	6649	10 16	2266	10 46	7734	.10303	10 44	10 47	.93748	12
13	6743	15 23	1990	15 69	8010	.10568	15 67	15 70	.94028	13
14	6837	20 31	1715	20 92	8285	.10834	20 89	20 94	.94309	14
15	.946930	30 47	.321440	30 138	.678560	2.11101	30 133	30 141	2.94590	15
16	7024	40 62	1164	40 184	8836	.11367	40 178	40 188	.94872	16
17	7117	45 70	0888	45 207	9112	.11635	45 200	45 211	.95155	17
18	7210	50 78	0613	50 229	9387	.11903	50 222	50 235	.95437	18
19	7304		0337		9663	.12171			.95720	19
20	.947397		.320062		.679938	2.12440			2.96004	20
21	7490		.319786		.680214	.12709	" Corr.	" Corr.	.96288	21
22	7583		9511		0489	.12979	10 45	10 48	.96573	22
23	7676		9235		0765	.13249	15 68	15 72	.96858	23
24	7768		8959		1041	.13520	20 91	20 96	.97144	24
25	.947861		.318684		.681316	2.13791	30 136	30 143	2.97430	25
26	7954		8408		1592	.14063	40 181	40 191	.97717	26
27	8046		8132		1868	.14335	45 204	45 215	.98004	27
28	8139		7856		2144	.14608	50 226	50 239	.98292	28
29	8231		7580		2420	.14881			.98580	29
30	.948324		.317305		.682695	2.15155			2.98868	30
31	8416		7029		2971	.15429	" Corr.	" Corr.	.99158	31
32	8508		6753		3247	.15704	10 46	10 49	.99447	32
33	8600		6477		3523	.15979	15 69	15 73	.99738	33
34	8692		6201		3799	.16255	20 92	20 97	3.00028	34
35	.948784		.315925		.684075	2.16531	30 138	30 146	3.00319	35
36	8876		5649		4351	.16808	40 185	40 194	.00611	36
37	8968		5373		4627	.17085	45 208	45 219	.00903	37
38	9060		5097		4903	.17363	50 231	50 243	.01196	38
39	9151		4821		5179	.17641			.01489	39
40	.949243		.314545		.685455	2.17920			3.01783	40
41	9334	" Corr.	4269	" Corr.	5731	.18199	" Corr.	" Corr.	.02077	41
42	9426	10 15	3992	10 46	6008	.18479	10 47	10 49	.02372	42
43	9517	15 23	3716	15 69	6284	.18759	15 70	15 74	.02667	43
44	9608	20 30	3440	20 92	6560	.19040	20 94	20 99	.02963	44
45	.949699	30 46	.313164	30 138	.686836	2.19322	30 141	30 148	3.03260	45
46	9790	40 61	2888	40 184	7112	.19604	40 188	40 198	.03556	46
47	.9881	45 68	2611	45 207	7389	.19886	45 211	45 223	.03854	47
48	9972	50 76	2335	50 230	7665	.20169	50 235	50 247	.04152	48
49	.950063		2059		7941	.20453			.04450	49
50	.950154		.311782		.688218	2.20737			3.04749	50
51	0244		1506		8494	.21021	" Corr.	" Corr.	.05049	51
52	0335		1229		8771	.21306	10 48	10 50	.05349	52
53	0425		0953		9047	.21592	15 72	15 76	.05649	53
54	0516		0676		9324	.21878	20 96	20 101	.05950	54
55	.950606		.310400		.689600	2.22165	30 144	30 151	3.06252	55
56	0696		0123		9877	.22452	40 192	40 201	.06554	56
57	0786		.309847		.690153	.22740	45 215	45 227	.06857	57
58	0877		9570		0430	.23028	50 239	50 252	.07160	58
59	0967		9294		0706	.23317			.07464	59
60	.951056		.309017		.690983	2.23607			3.07768	60

'	Sine	Corr. for Sec.	Cosine	Corr. for Sec.	Versine	Exsec	Corr. for Sec.	Corr. for Sec.	Tangent	'
0	.951056	+	.309017	− +	.690983	2.23607	+	+	3.07768	0
1	1146		8740		1260	.23897	" Corr.	" Corr.	.08073	1
2	1236	10 15	8464		1536	.24187	10 49	10 51	.08379	2
3	1326	15 22	8187		1813	.24478	15 73	15 77	.08685	3
4	1415	20 30	7910		2090	.24770	20 98	20 103	.08991	4
5	.951505		.307633		.692367	2.25062	30 146	30 154	3.09298	5
6	1594	30 44	7357		2643	.25355	40 195	40 205	.09606	6
7	1684	40 59	7080		2920	.25648	45 220	45 231	.09914	7
8	1773	45 67	6803		3197	.25942	50 244	50 256	.10223	8
9	1862	50 74	6526		3474	.26237			.10532	9
10	.951951		.306249		.693751	2.26531			3.10842	10
11	2040	" Corr.	5972	" Corr.	4028	.26827	" Corr.	" Corr.	.11153	11
12	2129	10 15	5695	10 46	4305	.27123	10 50	10 52	.11464	12
13	2218	15 22	5418	15 69	4582	.27420	15 75	15 78	.11775	13
14	2307	20 30	5141	20 92	4859	.27717	20 99	20 104	.12087	14
15	.952396	30 44	.304864	30 138	.695136	2.28015	30 149	30 157	3.12400	15
16	2484	40 59	4587	40 185	5413	.28313	40 199	40 209	.12713	16
17	2573	45 67	4310	45 208	5690	.28612	45 224	45 235	.13027	17
18	2662	50 74	4033	50 231	5967	.28912	50 249	50 261	.13341	18
19	2750		3756		6244	.29212			.13656	19
20	.952838		.303479		.696521	2.29512			3.13972	20
21	2926		3202		6798	.29814	" Corr.	" Corr.	.14288	21
22	3015		2924		7076	.30115	10 51	10 53	.14605	22
23	3103		2647		7353	.30418	15 76	15 80	.14922	23
24	3191		2370		7630	.30721	20 101	20 106	.15240	24
25	.953279		.302093		.697907	2.31024	30 152	30 159	3.15558	25
26	3366		1815		8185	.31328	40 203	40 213	.15877	26
27	3454		1538		8462	.31633	45 228	45 239	.16197	27
28	3542		1261		8739	.31939	50 253	50 266	.16517	28
29	3629		0983		9017	.32244			.16838	29
30	.953717		.300706		.699294	2.32551			3.17159	30
31	3804		0428		9572	.32858	" Corr.	" Corr.	.17481	31
32	3892		0151		9849	.33166	10 52	10 54	.17804	32
33	3979		.299873		.700127	.33474	15 78	15 81	.18127	33
34	4066		9596		0404	.33783	20 103	20 108	.18451	34
35	.954153		.299318		.700682	2.34092	30 155	30 162	3.18775	35
36	4240		9041		0959	.34403	40 207	40 217	.19100	36
37	4327		8763		1237	.34713	45 233	45 244	.19426	37
38	4414		8486		1514	.35025	50 258	50 271	.19752	38
39	4501		8208		1792	.35336			.20079	39
40	.954588		.297930		.702070	2.35649			3.20406	40
41	4674	" Corr.	7653	" Corr.	2347	.35962	" Corr.	" Corr.	.20734	41
42	4761	10 14	7375	10 46	2625	.36276	10 53	10 55	.21063	42
43	4847	15 22	7097	15 69	2903	.36590	15 79	15 83	.21392	43
44	4934	20 29	6819	20 93	3181	.36905	20 105	20 110	.21722	44
45	.955020	30 43	.296542	30 139	.703458	2.37221	30 158	30 166	3.22053	45
46	5106	40 58	6264	40 185	3736	.37537	40 211	40 221	.22384	46
47	5192	45 65	5986	45 208	4014	.37854	45 237	45 248	.22715	47
48	5278	50 72	5708	50 231	4292	.38171	50 263	50 276	.23048	48
49	5364		5430		4570	.38489			.23381	49
50	.955450		.295152		.704848	2.38808			3.23714	50
51	5536		4874		5126	.39128	" Corr.	" Corr.	.24049	51
52	5622		4596		5404	.39448	10 54	10 56	.24383	52
53	5707		4318		5682	.39768	15 81	15 84	.24719	53
54	5793		4040		5960	.40089	20 107	20 112	.25055	54
55	.955878		.293762		.706238	2.40411	30 161	30 169	3.25392	55
56	5964		3484		6516	.40734	40 215	40 225	.25729	56
57	6049		3206		6794	.41057	45 242	45 253	.26067	57
58	6134		2928		7072	.41381	50 269	50 281	.26406	58
59	6220		2650		7350	.41705			.26745	59
60	.956305		.292372		.707628	2.42030			3.27085	60

TABLE XX.—NATURAL SINES, COSINES,

73°

'	Sine	Corr. for Sec.	Cosine	Corr. for Sec.	Versine	Exsec	Corr. for Sec.	Corr. for Sec.	Tangent	'
0	.956305	+	.292372	− +	.707628	2.42030	+	+	3.27085	0
1	6390		2094		7906	.42356			.27426	1
2	6475		1815		8185	.42683	10 55	10 57	.27767	2
3	6560		1537		8463	.43010	15 82	15 86	.28109	3
4	6644		1259		8741	.43337	20 110	20 115	.28452	4
5	.956729		.290980		.709020	2.43666	30 164	30 172	3.28795	5
6	6814		0702		9298	.43995	40 219	40 229	.29139	6
7	6898		0424		9576	.44324	45 247	45 258	.29483	7
8	6982		0146		9854	.44655	50 274	50 287	.29829	8
9	7067		.289867		.710133	.44986			.30174	9
10	.957151		.289589		.710411	2.45317			3.30521	10
11	7235	" Corr.	9310	" Corr.	0690	.45650	" Corr.	" Corr.	.30868	11
12	7320	10 14	9032	10 46	0968	.45983	10 56	10 58	.31216	12
13	7404	15 21	8753	15 70	1247	.46316	15 84	15 88	.31565	13
14	7488	20 28	8475	20 93	1525	.46651	20 112	20 117	.31914	14
15	.957571	30 42	.288196	30 139	.711804	2.46986	30 168	30 175	3.32264	15
16	7655	40 56	7918	40 186	2082	.47321	40 224	40 234	.32614	16
17	7739	45 63	7639	45 209	2361	.47658	45 252	45 263	.32965	17
18	7822	50 70	7360	50 232	2640	.47995	50 280	50 292	.33317	18
19	7906		7082		2918	.48333			.33670	19
20	.957990		.286803		.713197	2.48671			3.34023	20
21	8073		6525		3475	.49010	" Corr.	" Corr.	.34377	21
22	8156		6246		3754	.49350	10 57	10 59	.34732	22
23	8239		5967		4033	.49691	15 86	15 89	.35087	23
24	8323		5688		4312	.50032	20 114	20 119	.35443	24
25	.958406		.285410		.714590	2.50374	30 171	30 179	3.35800	25
26	8489		5131		4869	.50716	40 228	40 236	.36158	26
27	8572		4852		5148	.51060	45 257	45 268	.36516	27
28	8654		4573		5427	.51404	50 285	50 298	.36875	28
29	8737		4294		5708	.51748			.37234	29
30	.958820		.284015		.715985	2.52094			3.37594	30
31	8902		3736		6264	.52440	" Corr.	" Corr.	.37955	31
32	8985		3458		6542	.52787	10 58	10 61	.38317	32
33	9067		3178		6822	.53134	15 87	15 91	.38679	33
34	9150		2900		7100	.53482	20 117	20 122	.39042	34
35	.959232		.282620		.717380	2.53831	30 171	30 175	3.39406	35
36	9314		2342		7658	.54181	40 233	40 243	.39771	36
37	9396		2062		7938	.54531	45 262	45 273	.40136	37
38	9478		1783		8217	.54883	50 291	50 304	.40502	38
39	9560		1504		8496	.55234			.40869	39
40	.959642		.281225		.718775	2.55587			3.41236	40
41	9724	" Corr.	0946	" Corr.	9054	.55940	" Corr.	" Corr.	.41604	41
42	9805	10 14	0667	10 47	9333	.56294	10 59	10 62	.41973	42
43	9887	15 20	0388	15 70	9612	.56649	15 89	15 93	.42343	43
44	9968	20 27	0108	20 93	9892	.57005	20 119	20 124	.42713	44
45	.960050	30 41	.279829	30 140	.720171	2.57361	30 178	30 186	3.43084	45
46	0131	40 54	9550	40 186	0450	.57718	40 238	40 248	.43456	46
47	0212	45 61	9270	45 209	0730	.58076	45 268	45 279	.43829	47
48	0294	50 68	8991	50 233	1009	.58434	50 297	50 310	.44202	48
49	0375		8712		1288	.58794			.44576	49
50	.960456		.278432		.721568	2.59154			3.44951	50
51	0537		8153		1847	.59514	" Corr.	" Corr.	.45327	51
52	0618		7874		2126	.59876	10 61	10 63	.45703	52
53	0698		7594		2406	.60238	15 91	15 95	.46080	53
54	0779		7315		2685	.60601	20 122	20 126	.46458	54
55	.960860		.277035		.722965	2.60965	30 182	30 190	3.46837	55
56	0940		6756		3244	.61330	40 243	40 253	.47216	56
57	1021		6476		3524	.61695	45 273	45 285	.47596	57
58	1101		6196		3804	.62061	50 304	50 316	.47977	58
59	1182		5917		4083	.62428			.48359	59
60	.961262		.275637		.724363	2.62796			3.48741	60

'	Sine	Corr. for Sec.	Cosine	Corr. for Sec.	Versine	Exsec	Corr. for Sec.	Corr. for Sec.	Tangent	'
0	.961262	+	.275637	− +	.724363	2.62796	+	+	3.48741	0
1	1342		5358		4642	.63164			.49125	1
2	1422		5078		4922	.63533	" Corr. 10 62	" Corr. 10 65	.49509	2
3	1502		4798		5202	.63903	15 93	15 97	.49894	3
4	1582		4519		5481	.64274	20 124	20 129	.50279	4
5	.961662		.274239		.725761	2.64645	30 186	30 194	3.50666	5
6	1741		3959		6041	.65018	40 248	40 258	.51053	6
7	1821		3679		6321	.65391	45 279	45 290	.51441	7
8	1900		3400		6600	.65765	50 310	50 323	.51829	8
9	1980		3120		6880	.66140			.52219	9
10	.962059		.272840		.727160	2.66515			3.52609	10
11	2139	" Corr.	· 2560	" Corr.	7440	.66892	" Corr. 10 63	" Corr. 10 66	.53001	11
12	2218	10 13	2280	10 47	7720	.67269	15 95	15 99	.53393	12
13	2297	15 20	2000	15 70	8000	.67647	20 127	20 132	.53785	13
14	2376	20 26	1720	20 93	8280	.68025			.54179	14
15	.962455	30 40	.271440	30 140	.728562	2.68405	30 190	30 198	3.54573	15
16	2534	40 53	1160	40 187	8840	.68785	40 254	40 263	.54968	16
17	2613	45 59	0880	45 210	9120	.69167	45 285	45 296	.55364	17
18	2692	50 66	0600	50 233	9400	.69549	50 317	50 329	.55761	18
19	2770		0320		9680	.69931			.56159	19
20	.962849		.270040		.729960	2.70315			3.56569	20
21	2928		.269760		.730240	.70700	" Corr. 10 65	" Corr. 10 67	.56957	21
22	3006		9480		0520	.71085	15 97	15 101	.57357	22
23	3084		9200		0800	.71471	20 130	20 134	.57758	23
24	3163		8920		1080	.71858			.58160	24
25	.963241		.268640		.731360	2.72246	30 194	30 202	3.58562	25
26	3319		8359		1641	.72635	40 259	40 269	.58966	26
27	3397		8079		1921	.73024	45 292	45 303	.59370	27
28	3475		7799		2201	.73414	50 324	50 336	.59775	28
29	3553		7519		2481	.73806			.60181	29
30	.963630		.267238		.732762	2.74198			3.60588	30
31	3708		6958		3042	.74591	" Corr. 10 66	" Corr. 10 69	.60996	31
32	3786		6678		3322	.74984	15 99	15 103	.61405	32
33	3863		6397		3603	.75379	20 132	20 137	.61814	33
34	3941		6117		3883	.75775			.62224	34
35	.964018		.265837		.734163	2.76171	30 199	30 206	3.62636	35
36	4095		5556		4444	.76568	40 265	40 275	.63048	36
37	4173		5276		4724	.76966	45 298	45 309	.63461	37
38	4250		4995		5005	.77365	50 331	50 343	.63874	38
39	4327		4715		5285	.77765			.64289	39
40	.964404		.264434		.735566	2.78166			3.64705	40
41	4481	" Corr.	4154	" Corr.	5846	.78568	" Corr. 10 68	" Corr. 10 70	.65121	41
42	4557	10 13	3873	10 47	6127	.78970	15 102	15 105	.65538	42
43	4634	15 19	3592	15 70	6408	.79374	20 135	20 140	.65957	43
44	4711	20 25	3312	20 94	6688	.79778			.66376	44
45	.964787	30 38	.263031	30 140	.736969	2.80183	30 203	30 210	3.66796	45
46	4864	40 51	2751	40 187	7249	.80589	40 271	40 281	.67217	46
47	4940	45 57	2470	45 210	7530	.80996	45 305	45 316	.67638	47
48	5016	50 64	2189	50 234	7811	.81404	50 338	50 351	.68061	48
49	5093		1908		8092	.81813			.68485	49
50	.965169		.261628		.738372	2.82223			3.68909	50
51	5245		1347		8653	.82633	" Corr. 10 69	" Corr. 10 71	.69335	51
52	5321		1066		8934	.83045	15 104	15 107	.69761	52
53	5397		0785		9215	.83457	20 138	20 143	.70188	53
54	5473		0504		9496	.83871			.70616	54
55	.965548		.260224		.739776	2.84285	30 208	30 215	3.71046	55
56	5624		.259943		.740057	.84700	40 277	40 287	.71476	56
57	5700		9662		0338	.85116	45 311	45 322	.71907	57
58	5775		9381		0619	.85533	50 346	50 358	.72338	58
59	5850		9100		0900	.85951			.72771	59
60	.965926		.258819		.741181	2.86370			3.73205	60

TABLE XX.—NATURAL SINES, COSINES,
75°

'	Sine	Corr. for Sec.	Cosine	Corr. for Sec.	Versine	Exsec	Corr. for Sec.	Corr. for Sec.	Tangent	'
0	.965926	+	.258819	- +	.741181	2.86370	+	+	3.73205	0
1	6001		8538		1462	.86790	" Corr.	" Corr.	.73640	1
2	6076		8257		1743	.87211	10 71	10 73	.74075	2
3	6151		7976		2024	.87633	15 106	15 110	.74512	3
4	6226		7695		2305	.88056	20 142	20 146	.74950	4
5	.966301		.257414		.742586	2.88479	30 212	30 220	3.75388	5
6	6376		7133		2867	.88904	40 283	40 293	.75828	6
7	6451		6852		3148	.89330	45 319	45 330	.76268	7
8	6526		6570		3430	.89756	50 354	50 366	.76709	8
9	6600		6289		3711	.90184			.77152	9
10	.966675		.256008		.743992	2.90612			3.77595	10
11	6749	" Corr.	5727	" Corr.	4273	.91042	" Corr.	" Corr.	.78040	11
12	6823	10 12	5446	10 47	4554	.91473	10 72	10 75	.78485	12
13	6898	15 19	5164	15 70	4836	.91904	15 109	15 112	.78931	13
14	6972	20 25	4883	20 94	5117	.92337	20 145	20 150	.79378	14
15	.967046	30 37	.254602	30 141	.745398	2.92770	30 217	30 225	3.79827	15
16	7120	40 49	4321	40 188	5679	.93204	40 290	40 299	.80276	16
17	7194	45 56	4039	45 211	5961	.93640	45 326	45 337	.80726	17
18	7268	50 62	3758	50 234	6242	.94076	50 362	50 374	.81177	18
19	7342		3477		6523	.94514			.81630	19
20	.967415		.253195		.746805	2.94952			3.82083	20
21	7489		2914		7086	.95392	" Corr.	" Corr.	.82537	21
22	7562		2632		7368	.95832	10 74	10 77	.82992	22
23	7636		2351		7649	.96274	15 111	15 115	.83449	23
24	7709		2069		7931	.96716	20 148	20 153	.83906	24
25	.967782		.251788		.748212	2.97160	30 222	30 230	3.84364	25
26	7856		1506		8494	.97604	40 296	40 306	.84824	26
27	7929		1225		8775	.98050	45 333	45 344	.85284	27
28	8002		0943		9057	.98497	50 370	50 383	.85745	28
29	8075		0662		9338	.98944			.86208	29
30	.968148		.250380		.749620	2.99393			3.86671	30
31	8220		0098		9902	.99843	" Corr.	" Corr.	.87136	31
32	8293		.249817		.750183	3.00293	10 76	10 78	.87601	32
33	8366		9535		0465	.00745	15 114	15 117	.88068	33
34	8438		9253		0747	.01198	20 152	20 157	.88536	34
35	.968511		.248972		.751028	3.01652	30 230	30 235	3.89004	35
36	8583		8690		1310	.02107	40 303	40 313	.89474	36
37	8656		8408		1592	.02563	45 341	45 352	.89945	37
38	8728		8126		1874	.03020	50 379	50 391	.90417	38
39	8800		7844		2156	.03479			.90890	39
40	.968872		.247563		.752437	3.03938			3.91364	40
41	8944	" Corr.	7281	" Corr.	2719	.04398	" Corr.	" Corr.	.91839	41
42	9016	10 12	6999	10 47	3001	.04860	10 78	10 80	.92316	42
43	9088	15 18	6717	15 70	3283	.05322	15 116	15 120	.92793	43
44	9159	20 24	6435	20 94	3565	.05786	20 155	20 160	.93271	44
45	.969231	30 36	.246153	30 141	.753847	3.06251	30 233	30 240	3.93751	45
46	9302	40 48	5871	40 188	4129	.06717	40 310	40 320	.94232	46
47	9374	45 54	5589	45 211	4411	.07184	45 349	45 360	.94713	47
48	9445	50 60	5307	50 235	4693	.07652	50 388	50 400	.95196	48
49	9517		5025		4975	.08121			.95680	49
50	.969588		.244743		.755257	3.08591			3.96165	50
51	9659		4461		5539	.09063	" Corr.	" Corr.	.96651	51
52	9730		4179		5821	.09535	10 79	10 82	.97139	52
53	9801		3897		6103	.10009	15 119	15 123	.97627	53
54	9872		3615		6385	.10484	20 159	20 164	.98117	54
55	.969943		.243333		.756667	3.10960	30 239	30 246	3.98607	55
56	.970014		3051		6949	.11437	40 318	40 328	.99099	56
57	0084		2768		7232	.11915	45 358	45 369	.99592	57
58	0155		2486		7514	.12394	50 398	50 410	4.00086	58
59	0225		2204		7796	.12875			.00582	59
60	.970296		.241922		.758078	3.13357			4.01078	60

VERSINES, EXSECANTS, AND TANGENTS
76°

'	Sine	Corr. for Sec.	Cosine	Corr. for Sec.	Versine	Exsec	Corr. for Sec.	Corr. for Sec.	Tangent	'
		+		− +			+	+		
0	.970296		.241922		.758078	3.13357			4.01078	0
1	0366		1640		8360	.13839	" Corr.	" Corr.	.01576	1
2	0436		1357		8643	.14323	10 81	10 84	.02074	2
3	0506		1075		8925	.14809	15 122	15 126	.02574	3
4	0577		0793		9207	.15295	20 163	20 168	.03076	4
5	.970647		.240510		.759490	3.15782	30 244	30 252	4.03578	5
6	0716		0228		9772	.16271	40 326	40 336	.04081	6
7	0786		.239946		.760054	.16761	45 367	45 378	.04586	7
8	0856		9663		0337	.17252	50 407	50 420	.05092	8
9	0926		9381		0619	.17744			.05599	9
10	.970995		.239098		.760902	3.18238			4.06107	10
11	1065	" Corr.	8816	" Corr.	1184	.18733	" Corr.	" Corr.	.06616	11
12	1134	10 12	8534	10 47	1466	.19228	10 83	10 86	.07127	12
13	1204	15 17	8251	15 71	1749	.19725	15 125	15 129	.07639	13
14	1273	20 23	7968	20 94	2032	.20224	20 167	20 172	.08152	14
15	.971342	30 35	.237686	30 141	.762314	3.20723	30 250	30 258	4.08666	15
16	1411	40 46	7403	40 188	2597	.21224	40 334	40 344	.09182	16
17	1480	45 52	7121	45 212	2879	.21726	45 376	45 387	.09699	17
18	1549	50 58	6838	50 235	3162	.22229	50 417	50 430	.10216	18
19	1618		6556		3444	.22734			.10736	19
20	.971687		.236273		.763727	3.23239			4.11256	20
21	1755		5990		4010	.23746	" Corr.	" Corr.	.11778	21
22	1824		5708		4292	.24255	10 85	10 88	.12301	22
23	1893		5425		4575	.24764	15 128	15 132	.12825	23
24	1961		5142		4858	.25275	20 171	20 176	.13350	24
25	.972029		.234859		.765141	3.25787	30 257	30 264	4.13877	25
26	2098		4577		5423	.26300	40 342	40 352	.14405	26
27	2166		4294		5706	.26814	45 385	45 396	.14934	27
28	2234		4011		5989	.27330	50 428	50 440	.15465	28
29	2302		3728		6272	.27847			.15997	29
30	.972370		.233445		.766555	3.28366			4.16530	30
31	2438		3162		6838	.28885	" Corr.	" Corr.	.17064	31
32	2506		2880		7120	.29406	10 88	10 90	.17600	32
33	2573		2597		7403	.29929	15 132	15 135	.18137	33
34	2641		2314		7686	.30452	20 175	20 180	.18675	34
35	.972708		.232031		.767969	3.30977	30 263	30 270	4.19215	35
36	2776		1748		8252	.31503	40 351	40 361	.19756	36
37	2843		1465		8535	.32031	45 395	45 406	.20298	37
38	2910		1182		8818	.32560	50 438	50 451	.20842	38
39	2978		0899		9101	.33090			.21387	39
40	.973045		.230616		.769384	3.33622			4.21933	40
41	3112	" Corr.	0333	" Corr.	9667	.34154	" Corr.	" Corr.	.22481	41
42	3179	10 11	0050	10 47	9950	.34689	10 90	10 92	.23030	42
43	3246	15 17	.229767	15 71	.770233	.35224	15 135	15 139	.23580	43
44	3312	20 22	9484	20 94	0516	.35761	20 180	20 185	.24132	44
45	.973379	30 33	.229200	30 142	.770800	3.36299	30 270	30 277	4.24685	45
46	3446	40 44	8917	40 189	1083	.36839	40 360	40 370	.25239	46
47	3512	45 50	8634	45 212	1366	.37380	45 405	45 416	.25795	47
48	3579	50 56	8351	50 236	1649	.37923	50 450	50 462	.26352	48
49	3645		8068		1932	.38466			.26911	49
50	.973712		.227784		.772216	3.39012			4.27471	50
51	3778		7501		2499	.39558	" Corr.	" Corr.	.28032	51
52	3844		7218		2782	.40106	10 92	10 95	.28595	52
53	3910		6935		3065	.40656	15 138	15 142	.29159	53
54	3976		6651		3349	.41206	20 185	20 189	.29724	54
55	.974042		.226368		.773632	3.41759	30 277	30 284	4.30291	55
56	4108		6085		3915	.42312	40 369	40 379	.30860	56
57	4173		5801		4199	.42867	45 415	45 426	.31430	57
58	4239		5518		4482	.43424	50 461	50 474	.32001	58
59	4305		5234		4766	.43982			.32573	59
60	.974370		.224951		.775049	3.44541			4.33148	60

169

TABLE XX.—NATURAL SINES, COSINES,
77°

'	Sine	Corr. for Sec. +	Cosine	Corr. for Sec. - +	Versine	Exsec	Diff. 10″		Tangent	'
0	.974370		.224951		.775049	3.44541	93.5	95.8	4.33148	0
1	4436		4668		5332	.45102	93.7	96.2	.33723	1
2	4501		4384		5616	.45664	94.0	96.5	.34300	2
3	4566		4101		5899	.46228	94.2	96.7	.34879	3
4	4631		3817		6183	.46793	94.5	96.8	.35459	4
5	.974696		.223534		.776466	3.47360	94.7	97.2	4.36040	5
6	4761		3250		6750	.47928	95.0	97.3	.36623	6
7	4826		2967		7033	.48498	95.2	97.7	.37207	7
8	4891		2683		7317	.49069	95.5	98.0	.37793	8
9	4956		2399		7601	.49642	95.7	98.0	.38381	9
10	.975020		.222116		.777884	3.50216	95.8	98.5	4.38969	10
11	5085	″ Corr.	1832	″ Corr.	8168	.50791	96.2	98.7	.39560	11
12	5149	10 11	1548	10 47	8452	.51368	96.5	98.8	.40152	12
13	5214	15 16	1265	15 71	8735	.51947	96.8	99.2	.40745	13
14	5278	20 21	0981	20 95	9019	.52527	97.0	99.3	.41340	14
15	.975342	30 32	.220697	30 142	.779303	3.53109	97.2	99.7	4.41936	15
16	5406	40 43	0414	40 189	9586	.53692	97.5	100.0	.42534	16
17	5471	45 48	0130	45 213	9870	.54277	97.7	100.2	.43134	17
18	5534	50 53	.219846	50 236	.780154	.54863	98.0	100.5	.43735	18
19	5598		9562		0438	.55451	98.3	100.7	.44338	19
20	.975662		.219279		.780721	3.56041	98.5	101.0	4.44942	20
21	5726		8995		1005	.56632	98.7	101.2	.45548	21
22	5790		8711		1289	.57224	99.0	101.5	.46155	22
23	5853		8427		1573	.57819	99.2	101.7	.46764	23
24	5917		8143		1857	.58414	99.7	102.0	.47374	24
25	.975980		.217859		.782141	3.59012	99.8	102.3	4.47986	25
26	6044		7575		2425	.59611	100.0	102.5	.48600	26
27	6107		7292		2708	.60211	100.3	102.8	.49215	27
28	6170		7008		2992	.60813	100.7	103.2	.49832	28
29	6233		6724		3276	.61417	101.0	103.3	.50451	29
30	.976296		.216440		.783560	3.62023	101.2	103.7	4.51071	30
31	6359		6156		3844	.62630	101.3	103.8	.51693	31
32	6422		5872		4128	.63238	101.8	104.2	.52316	32
33	6484		5588		4412	.63849	102.0	104.5	.52941	33
34	6547		5304		4696	.64461	102.2	104.7	.53568	34
35	.976610		.215019		.784981	3.65074	102.7	105.0	4.54196	35
36	6672		4735		5265	.65690	102.8	105.3	.54826	36
37	6735		4451		5549	.66307	103.0	105.5	.55458	37
38	6797		4167		5833	.66925	103.3	105.8	.56091	38
39	6859		3883		6117	.67545	103.7	106.2	.56726	39
40	.976922		.213599		.786401	3.68167	104.0	106.3	4.57363	40
41	6984	″ Corr.	3315	″ Corr.	6685	.68791	104.3	106.7	.58001	41
42	7046	10 10	3030	10 47	6970	.69417	104.5	107.0	.58641	42
43	7108	15 15	2746	15 71	7254	.70044	104.8	107.3	.59283	43
44	7169	20 21	2462	20 95	7538	.70673	105.0	107.5	.59927	44
45	.977231	30 31	.212178	30 142	.787822	3.71303	105.3	107.8	4.60572	45
46	7293	40 41	1893	40 189	8107	.71935	105.7	108.2	.61219	46
47	7354	45 46	1609	45 213	8391	.72569	106.0	108.3	.61868	47
48	7416	50 51	1325	50 237	8675	.73205	106.3	108.8	.62518	48
49	7477		1040		8960	.73843	106.5	109.0	.63171	49
50	.977538		.210756		.789244	3.74482	106.8	109.2	4.63825	50
51	7600		0472		9528	.75123	107.2	109.7	.64480	51
52	7661		0187		9813	.75766	107.5	109.8	.65138	52
53	7722		.209903		.790097	.76411	107.7	110.2	.65797	53
54	7783		9619		0381	.77057	108.0	110.5	.66458	54
55	.977844		.209334		.790666	3.77705	108.3	110.8	4.67121	55
56	7905		9050		0950	.78355	108.7	111.0	.67786	56
57	7966		8765		1235	.79007	109.0	111.5	.68452	57
58	8026		8481		1519	.79661	109.2	111.7	.69121	58
59	8087		8196		1804	.80316	109.3	112.0	.69791	59
60	.978148		.207912		.792088	3.80973			4.70463	60

'	Sine	Corr. for Sec. +	Cosine	Corr. for Sec. − +	Versine	Exsec	Diff. 10″		Tangent	'
0	.978148		.207912		.792088	3.80973			4.70463	0
1	8208		7627		2373	.81633	110.0	112.3	.71137	1
2	8268		7343		2657	.82294	110.2	112.7	.71813	2
3	8329		7058		2942	.82956	110.3	112.8	.72490	3
4	8389		6773		3227	.83621	110.8	113.3	.73170	4
							111.2	113.5		
5	.978449		.206489		.793511	3.84288			4.73851	5
6	8509		6204		3796	.84956	111.3	113.8	.74534	6
7	8569		5920		4080	.85627	111.8	114.2	.75219	7
8	8629		5635		4365	.86299	112.0	114.5	.75906	8
9	8689		5350		4650	.86973	112.3	114.8	.76595	9
							112.7	115.2		
10	.978748		.205066		.794934	3.87649			4.77286	10
11	8808	″ Corr. / 10 10	4781	″ Corr. / 10 47	5219	.88327	113.0	115.3	.77978	11
12	8867	15 15	4496	15 71	5504	.89007	113.3	115.8	.78673	12
13	8927	20 20	4211	20 95	5789	.89689	113.7	116.2	.79370	13
14	8986		3926		6074	.90373	114.0	116.8	.80068	14
							114.2	116.8		
15	.979046	30 30	.203642	30 142	.796358	3.91058			4.80769	15
16	9105	40 40	3357	40 190	6643	.91746	114.7	117.0	.81471	16
17	9164	45 44	3072	45 214	6928	.92436	115.0	117.3	.82175	17
18	9223	50 49	2787	50 237	7213	.93128	115.3	117.8	.82882	18
19	9282		2502		7498	.93821	115.5	118.0	.83590	19
							116.0	118.3		
20	.979341		.202218		.797782	3.94517			4.84300	20
21	9399		1933		8067	.95215	116.3	118.8	.85013	21
22	9458		1648		8352	.95914	116.5	119.0	.85727	22
23	9517		1363		8637	.96616	117.0	119.5	.86444	23
24	9575		1078		8922	.97320	117.3	119.7	.87162	24
							117.5	120.0		
25	.979634		.200793		.799207	3.98025			4.87882	25
26	9692		0508		9492	.98733	118.0	120.5	.88605	26
27	9750		0223		9777	.99443	118.3	120.8	.89330	27
28	9809		.199938		.800062	4.00155	118.7	121.0	.90056	28
29	9867		9653		0347	.00869	119.0	121.5	.90785	29
							119.3	121.8		
30	.979925		.199368		.800632	4.01585			4.91516	30
31	9983		9083		0917	.02303	119.7	122.2	.92249	31
32	.980040		8798		1202	.03024	120.2	122.5	.92984	32
33	0098		8513		1487	.03746	120.3	122.8	.93721	33
34	0156		8228		1772	.04471	120.8	123.2	.94460	34
							121.0	123.5		
35	.980214		.197942		.802058	4.05197			4.95201	35
36	0271		7657		2343	.05926	121.5	124.0	.95945	36
37	0329		7372		2628	.06657	121.8	124.2	.96690	37
38	0386		7087		2913	.07390	122.2	124.7	.97438	38
39	0443		6802		3198	.08125	122.5	125.0	.98188	39
							123.0	125.3		
40	.980500		.196517		.803483	4.08863			4.98940	40
41	0558	″ Corr. / 10 9	6231	″ Corr. / 10 48	3769	.09602	123.2	125.8	.99695	41
42	0615	15 14	5946	15 71	4054	.10344	123.7	126.0	5.00451	42
43	0672	20 19	5661	20 95	4339	.11088	124.0	126.5	.01210	43
44	0728		5376		4624	.11835	124.5	127.0	.01971	44
							124.7	127.2		
45	.980785	30 28	.195090	30 143	.804910	4.12583			5.02734	45
46	0842	40 38	4805	40 190	5195	.13334	125.2	127.5	.03499	46
47	0899	45 43	4520	45 214	5480	.14087	125.5	128.0	.04267	47
48	0955	50 47	4234	50 238	5766	.14842	125.8	128.3	.05037	48
49	1012		3949		6051	.15599	126.2	128.7	.05809	49
							126.7	129.0		
50	.981068		.193664		.806336	4.16359			5.06584	50
51	1124		3378		6622	.17121	127.0	129.3	.07360	51
52	1180		3093		6907	.17886	127.5	129.8	.08139	52
53	1237		2807		7193	.18652	127.7	130.3	.08921	53
54	1293		2522		7478	.19421	128.2	130.5	.09704	54
							128.7	131.0		
55	.981349		.192236		.807764	4.20193			5.10490	55
56	1404		1951		8049	.20966	128.8	131.5	.11279	56
57	1460		1666		8334	.21742	129.3	131.7	.12069	57
58	1516		1380		8620	.22520	129.7	132.2	.12862	58
59	1572		1094		8906	.23301	130.2	132.7	.13658	59
60	.981627		.190809		.809191	4.24084		130.5	132.8	5.14455	60

TABLE XX.—NATURAL SINES, COSINES,
79°

'	Sine	Corr. for Sec.	Cosine	Corr. for Sec.	Versine	Exsec	Diff. 10"		Tangent	'
0	.981627	+	.190809	− +	.809191	4.24084	131.0	133.5	5.14455	0
1	1683		0523		9477	.24870	131.3	133.7	.15256	1
2	1738		0238		9762	.25658	131.7	134.2	.16058	2
3	1793		.189952		.810048	.26448	132.2	134.7	.16863	3
4	1848		9667		0333	.27241	132.5	134.8	.17671	4
5	.981904		.189381		.810619	4.28036	132.8	135.5	5.18480	5
6	1959		9095		0905	.28833	133.5	135.7	.19293	6
7	2014		8810		1190	.29634	133.7	136.3	.20107	7
8	2069		8524		1476	.30436	134.2	136.5	.20925	8
9	2123		8238		1762	.31241	134.7	137.0	.21744	9
10	.982178		.187953		.812047	4.32049	135.0	137.5	5.22566	10
11	2233	Corr. 10 9	7667	Corr.	2333	.32859	135.3	137.8	.23391	11
12	2287	15 14	7381	10 48	2619	.33671	135.8	138.3	.24218	12
13	2342	20 18	7096	15 71	2904	.34486	136.3	138.7	.25048	13
14	2396		6810	20 95	3190	.35304	136.7	139.2	.25880	14
15	.982450	30 27	.186524	30 143	.813476	4.36124	137.2	139.7	5.26715	15
16	2505	40 36	6238	40 190	3762	.36947	137.5	140.0	.27553	16
17	2559	45 41	5952	45 214	4048	.37772	138.0	140.3	.28393	17
18	2613	50 45	5667	50 238	4333	.38600	138.3	140.8	.29235	18
19	2667		5381		4619	.39430	138.8		.30080	19
20	.982721		.185095		.814905	4.40263	139.3	141.7	5.30928	20
21	2774		4809		5191	.41099	139.7	142.2	.31778	21
22	2828		4523		5477	.41937	140.2	142.7	.32631	22
23	2882		4237		5763	.42778	140.7	143.0	.33487	23
24	2935		3951		6049	.43622	141.0	143.5	.34345	24
25	.982989		.183665		.816335	4.44468	141.5	144.0	5.35206	25
26	3042		3380		6620	.45317	142.0	144.3	.36070	26
27	3096		3094		6906	.46169	142.3	144.8	.36936	27
28	3149		2808		7192	.47023	142.8	145.3	.37805	28
29	3202		2522		7478	.47881	143.2	145.8	.38677	29
30	.983255		.182236		.817764	4.48740	143.8	146.2	5.39552	30
31	3308		1950		8050	.49603	144.2	146.7	.40429	31
32	3361		1664		8336	.50468	144.8	147.2	.41309	32
33	3414		1377		8623	.51337	145.2	147.7	.42192	33
34	3466		1091		8909	.52208	145.5	148.0	.43078	34
35	.983519		.180805		.819195	4.53081	146.2	148.5	5.43966	35
36	3572		0519		9481	.53958	146.5	149.0	.44857	36
37	3624		0233		9767	.54837	147.0	149.5	.45751	37
38	3676		.179947		.820053	.55720	147.2	150.0	.46648	38
39	3729		9661		0339	.56605	147.5	150.5	.47548	39
40	.983781		.179375		.820625	4.57493	148.3	150.8	5.48451	40
41	3833	Corr. 10 9	9088	Corr.	0912	.58383	149.0	151.3	.49356	41
42	3885	15 13	8802	10 48	1198	.59277	149.5	152.0	.50264	42
43	3937	20 17	8516	15 72	1484	.60174	149.8	152.3	.51176	43
44	3989		8230	20 95	1770	.61073	150.5	152.8	.52090	44
45	.984041	30 26	.177944	30 143	.822056	4.61976	150.8	153.3	5.53007	45
46	4092	40 35	7657	40 191	2343	.62881	151.5	154.0	.53927	46
47	4144	45 39	7371	45 215	2629	.63790	151.8	154.3	.54851	47
48	4196	50 43	7085	50 239	2915	.64701	152.5	154.8	.55777	48
49	4247		6798		3202	.65616	152.8	155.3	.56706	49
50	.984298		.176512		.823488	4.66533	153.5	155.8	5.57638	50
51	4350		6226		3774	.67454	153.8	156.3	.58573	51
52	4401		5940		4060	.68377	154.5	156.8	.59511	52
53	4452		5653		4347	.69304	154.8	157.5	.60452	53
54	4503		5367		4633	.70234	155.3	157.8	.61397	54
55	.984554		.175080		.824920	4.71166	156.0	158.5	5.62344	55
56	4605		4794		5206	.72102	156.5	158.8	.63295	56
57	4656		4508		5492	.73041	157.0	159.5	.64248	57
58	4707		4221		5779	.73983	157.7	160.0	.65205	58
59	4757		3935		6065	.74929	158.0	160.5	.66165	59
60	.984808		.173648		.826352	4.75877			5.67128	60

'	Sine	Corr. for Sec. +	Cosine	Corr. for Sec. − +	Versine	Exsec	Diff. 10"		Tangent	'
0	.984808		.173648		.826352	4.75877	158.7	161.0	5.67128	0
1	4858		3362		6638	.76829	159.2	161.7	.68094	1
2	4909		3075		6925	.77784	159.7	162.2	.69064	2
3	4959		2789		7211	.78742	160.2	162.7	.70037	3
4	5009		2502		7498	.79703	160.7	163.2	.71013	4
5	.985059		.172216		.827784	4.80667	161.3	163.7	5.71992	5
6	5109		1929		8071	.81635	161.8	164.3	.72974	6
7	5159		1642		8358	.82606	162.5	164.8	.73960	7
8	5209		1356		8644	.83581	162.8	165.3	.74949	8
9	5259		1069		8931	.84558	163.5	166.0	.75941	9
10	.985309		.170783		.829217	4.85539	164.2	166.5	5.76937	10
11	5358	* Corr.	0496	* Corr.	9504	.86524	164.5	167.0	.77936	11
12	5408	10 8	0210	10 48	9790	.87511	165.2	167.7	.78938	12
13	5457	15 12	.169923	15 72	.830077	.88502	165.8	168.2	.79944	13
14	5507	20 16	9636	20 96	0364	.89497	166.3	168.8	.80953	14
15	.985556	30 25	.169350	30 143	.830650	4.90495	166.8	169.3	5.81966	15
16	5605	40 33	9063	40 191	0937	.91496	167.5	169.8	.82982	16
17	5654	45 37	8776	45 215	1224	.92501	168.0	170.5	.84001	17
18	5704	50 41	8489	50 239	1511	.93509	168.7	171.2	.85024	18
19	5752		8203		1797	.94521	169.3	171.5	.86051	19
20	.985801		.167916		.832084	4.95536	169.8	172.3	5.87080	20
21	5850		7629		2371	.96555	170.3	172.8	.88114	21
22	5899		7342		2658	.97577	171.0	173.3	.89151	22
23	5948		7056		2944	.98603	171.7	174.2	.90191	23
24	5996		6769		3231	.99633	172.2	174.5	.91236	24
25	.986044		.166482		.833518	5.00666	172.7	175.3	5.92283	25
26	6093		6195		3805	.01702	173.5	175.8	.93335	26
27	6141		5908		4092	.02743	174.0	176.3	.94390	27
28	6189		5621		4379	.03787	174.5	177.0	.95448	28
29	6238		5334		4666	.04834	175.3	177.7	.96510	29
30	.986286		.165048		.834952	5.05886	175.8	178.3	5.97576	30
31	6334		4761		5239	.06941	176.5	179.0	.98646	31
32	6382		4474		5526	.08000	177.0	179.5	.99720	32
33	6429		4187		5813	.09062	177.7	180.2	6.00797	33
34	6477		3900		6100	.10128	178.5	180.7	.01878	34
35	.986525		.163613		.836387	5.11199	179.0	181.5	6.02962	35
36	6572		3326		6674	.12273	179.5	182.0	.04051	36
37	6620		3039		6961	.13350	180.3	182.8	.05143	37
38	6667		2752		7248	.14432	180.8	183.3	.06240	38
39	6714		2465		7535	.15517	181.7	184.0	.07340	39
40	.986762		.162178		.837822	5.16607	182.2	184.7	6.08444	40
41	6809	* Corr.	1891	* Corr.	8109	.17700	182.8	185.3	.09552	41
42	6856	10 8	1604	10 48	8396	.18797	183.7	185.8	.10664	42
43	6903	15 12	1317	15 72	8683	.19898	184.3	186.7	.11779	43
44	6950	20 16	1030	20 96	8970	.21004	184.8	187.3	.12899	44
45	.986996	30 23	.160743	30 144	.839257	5.22113	185.5	188.0	6.14023	45
46	7043	40 31	0456	40 191	9544	.23226	186.2	188.7	.15151	46
47	7090	45 35	0168	45 215	9832	.24343	186.8	189.3	.16283	47
48	7136	50 39	.159881	50 239	.840119	.25464	187.7	190.0	.17419	48
49	7183		9594		0406	.26590	188.2	190.7	.18559	49
50	.987229		.159307		.840693	5.27719	189.0	191.3	6.19703	50
51	7275		9020		0980	.28853	189.7	192.0	.20851	51
52	7322		8732		1268	.29991	190.3	192.8	.22003	52
53	7368		8445		1555	.31133	191.0	193.5	.23160	53
54	7414		8158		1842	.32279	191.7	194.2	.24321	54
55	.987460		.157871		.842129	5.33429	192.5	194.8	6.25486	55
56	7506		7584		2416	.34584	193.2	195.7	.26655	56
57	7551		7296		2704	.35743	193.8	196.3	.27829	57
58	7597		7009		2991	.36906	194.5	197.0	.29007	58
59	7643		6722		3278	.38073	195.3	197.7	.30189	59
60	.987688		.156434		.843566	5.39245			6.31375	60

TABLE XX.—NATURAL SINES, COSINES,
81°

'	Sine	Corr. for Sec.	Cosine	Corr. for Sec.	Versine	Exsec	Diff. 10"		Tangent	'
0	.987688	+	.156434	− +	.843566	5.39245			6.31375	0
1	7734		6147		3853	.40422	196.2	198.5	.32566	1
2	7779		5860		4140	.41602	196.7	199.2	.33761	2
3	7824		5572		4428	.42787	197.5	200.0	.34961	3
4	7870		5285		4715	.43977	198.3	200.7	.36165	4
							199.0	201.5		
5	.987915		.154998		.845002	5.45171			6.37374	5
6	7960		4710		5290	.46369	199.7	202.2	.38587	6
7	8005		4423		5577	.47572	200.5	202.8	.39804	7
8	8050		4136		5864	.48779	201.2	203.7	.41026	8
9	8094		3848		6152	.49991	202.0	204.5	.42253	9
							202.8	205.2		
10	.988139		.153561		.846439	5.51208			6.43484	10
11	8184	" Corr.	3273	" Corr.	6727	.52429	203.5	206.0	.44720	11
12	8228	10 7	2986	10 48	7014	.53655	204.3	206.8	.45961	12
13	8273	15 11	2698	15 72	7302	.54886	205.2	207.5	.47206	13
14	8317	20 15	2411	20 96	7589	.56121	205.8	208.4	.48456	14
							206.7	209.0		
15	.988362	30 22	.152123	30 144	.847877	5.57361			6.49710	15
16	8406	40 29	1836	40 192	8164	.58606	207.5	210.0	.50970	16
17	8450	45 33	1548	45 216	8452	.59855	208.2	210.7	.52234	17
18	8494	50 37	1261	50 240	8739	.61110	209.2	211.5	.53503	18
19	8538		0973		9027	.62369	209.8	212.3	.54777	19
							210.7	213.0		
20	.988582		.150686		.849314	5.63633			6.56055	20
21	8626		0398		9602	.64902	211.5	214.0	.57339	21
22	8669		0111		9889	.66176	212.3	214.7	.58627	22
23	8713		.149823		.850177	.67454	213.0	215.7	.59921	23
24	8756		9535		0465	.68738	214.0	216.3	.61219	24
							214.8	217.3		
25	.988800		.149248		.850752	5.70027			6.62523	25
26	8843		8960		1040	.71321	215.7	218.0	.63831	26
27	8886		8672		1328	.72620	216.9	218.8	.65144	27
28	8930		8385		1615	.73924	217.3	219.8	.66463	28
29	8973		8097		1903	.75233	218.2	220.7	.67787	29
							219.0	221.5		
30	.989016		.147809		.852191	5.76547			6.69116	30
31	9059		7522		2478	.77866	219.8	222.3	.70450	31
32	9102		7234		2766	.79191	220.8	223.2	.71789	32
33	9144		6946		3054	.80521	221.7	224.0	.73133	33
34	9187		6658		3342	.81856	222.5	225.0	.74483	34
							223.3	225.8		
35	.989230		.146371		.853629	5.83196			6.75838	35
36	9272		6083		3917	.84542	224.3	226.8	.77199	36
37	9315		5795		4205	.85893	225.2	227.5	.78564	37
38	9357		5508		4492	.87250	226.2	228.7	.79936	38
39	9399		5220		4780	.88612	227.0	229.3	.81312	39
							227.8	230.3		
40	.989442		.144932		.855068	5.89979			6.82694	40
41	9484	" Corr.	4644	" Corr.	5356	.91352	228.8	231.3	.84082	41
42	9526	10 7	4356	10 48	5644	.92731	229.8	232.2	.85475	42
43	9568	15 10	4068	15 72	5932	.94115	230.7	233.2	.86874	43
44	9610	20 14	3780	20 96	6220	.95505	231.7	234.0	.88278	44
							232.5	235.0		
45	.989651	30 21	.143493	30 144	.856507	5.96900			6.89688	45
46	9693	40 28	3205	40 192	6795	.98301	233.5	236.0	.91104	46
47	9735	45 31	2917	45 216	7083	.99708	234.5	236.8	.92525	47
48	9776	50 35	2629	50 240	7371	6.01120	235.3	237.8	.93952	48
49	9818		2341		7659	.02538	236.3	238.8	.95385	49
							237.3	239.7		
50	.989859		.142053		.857947	6.03962			6.96823	50
51	9900		1765		8235	.05392	238.3	240.8	.98268	51
52	9942		1477		8523	.06828	239.3	241.7	.99718	52
53	9983		1189		8811	.08269	240.2	242.7	7.01174	53
54	.990024		0901		9099	.09717	241.3	243.8	.02637	54
							242.3	244.7		
55	.990065		.140613		.859387	6.11171			7.04105	55
56	0106		0325		9675	.12630	243.2	245.7	.05579	56
57	0146		0037		9963	.14096	244.3	246.7	.07059	57
58	0187		.139749		.860251	.15568	245.3	247.8	.08546	58
59	0228		9461		0539	.17046	246.3	248.7	.10038	59
							247.3	249.8		
60	.990268		.139173		.860827	6.18530			7.11537	60

'	Sine	Corr. for Sec. +	Cosine	Corr. for Sec. − +	Versine	Exsec	Diff. 10"		Tangent	'
0	.990268		.139173		.860827	6.18530	248.3	250.8	7.11537	0
1	0308		8885		1115	.20020	249.5	251.8	.13042	1
2	0349		8597		1403	.21517	250.3	253.0	.14553	2
3	0389		8309		1691	.23019	251.7	253.8	.16071	3
4	0429		8021		1979	.24529	252.5	255.2	.17594	4
5	.990469		.137733		.862267	6.26044	253.7	256.0	7.19125	5
6	0510		7444		2556	.27566	254.8	257.2	.20661	6
7	0549		7156		2844	.29095	255.8	258.3	.22204	7
8	0589		6868		3132	.30630	256.8	259.3	.23754	8
9	0629		6580		3420	.32171	258.0	260.5	.25310	9
10	.990669		.136292		.863708	6.33719	259.2	261.5	7.26873	10
11	0708		6004		3996	.35274	260.2	262.7	.28442	11
12	0748		5716		4284	.36835	261.3	263.7	.30018	12
13	0787		5427		4573	.38403	262.5	265.0	.31600	13
14	0827		5139		4861	.39978	263.7	266.0	.33190	14
15	.990866		.134851		.865149	6.41560	264.7	267.2	7.34786	15
16	0905		4563		5437	.43148	265.8	268.3	.36389	16
17	0944		4274		5726	.44743	267.2	269.5	.37999	17
18	0983		3986		6014	.46346	268.2	270.7	.39616	18
19	1022		3698		6302	.47955	269.3	271.8	.41240	19
20	.991061		.133410		.866590	6.49571	270.5	273.0	7.42871	20
21	1100		3121		6879	.51194	271.8	274.2	.44509	21
22	1138		2833		7167	.52825	272.8	275.3	.46154	22
23	1177		2545		7455	.54462	274.2	276.5	.47806	23
24	1216		2256		7744	.56107	275.3	277.8	.49465	24
25	.991254		.131968		.868032	6.57759	276.5	279.0	7.51132	25
26	1292		1680		8320	.59418	277.8	280.2	.52806	26
27	1331		1391		8609	.61085	279.0	281.5	.54487	27
28	1369		1103		8897	.62759	280.3	282.8	.56176	28
29	1407		0815		9185	.64441	281.5	283.8	.57872	29
30	.991445		.130526		.869474	6.66130	282.7	285.3	7.59575	30
31	1483		0238		9762	.67826	284.0	286.3	.61287	31
32	1521		.129949		.870051	.69530	285.3	287.8	.63005	32
33	1558		9661		0339	.71242	286.7	289.0	.64732	33
34	1596		9372		0628	.72962	287.8	290.3	.66466	34
35	.991634		.129084		.870916	6.74689	289.2	291.2	7.68208	35
36	1671		8796		1204	.76424	290.5	293.0	.69957	36
37	1709		8507		1493	.78167	291.8	294.2	.71715	37
38	1746		8219		1781	.79918	293.2	295.7	.73480	38
39	1783		7930		2070	.81677	294.3	296.8	.75254	39
40	.991820		.127642		.872358	6.83443	295.8	298.3	7.77035	40
41	1857		7353		2647	.85216	297.2	299.5	.78825	41
42	1894		7065		2935	.87001	298.5	301.0	.80622	42
43	1931		6776		3224	.88792	300.0	302.3	.82428	43
44	1968		6488		3512	.90592	301.3	303.7	.84242	44
45	.992005		.126199		.873801	6.92400	302.7	305.2	7.86064	45
46	2042		5910		4090	.94216	304.0	306.5	.87895	46
47	2078		5622		4378	.96040	305.5	308.0	.89734	47
48	2115		5333		4667	.97873	306.8	309.3	.91582	48
49	2151		5045		4955	.99714	308.3	310.7	.93438	49
50	.992187		.124756		.875244	7.01564	309.8	312.3	7.95302	50
51	2224		4467		5533	.03423	311.3	313.7	.97171	51
52	2260		4179		5821	.05291	312.7	315.0	.99058	52
53	2296		3890		6110	.07167	314.2	316.7	8.00948	53
54	2332		3602		6398	.09052	315.7	318.0	.02848	54
55	.992368		.123313		.876687	7.10946	317.2	319.7	8.04756	55
56	2404		3024		6976	.12849	318.5	321.0	.06674	56
57	2439		2736		7264	.14760	320.2	322.7	.08600	57
58	2475		2447		7553	.16681	321.8	324.2	.10536	58
59	2511		2158		7842	.18612	323.2	325.7	.12481	59
60	.992546		.121869		.878131	7.20551			8.14435	60

Correction for Seconds (Sine), rows 10–14:

"	Corr.
10	7
15	10
20	13
30	20
45	29
50	33

Correction for Seconds (Cosine), rows 11–14:

"	Corr.
10	48
15	72
20	96
30	144
45	216
50	240

Correction for Seconds (Sine), rows 41–45:

"	Corr.
10	6
15	9
20	12
30	18
45	28
50	31

Correction for Seconds (Cosine), rows 41–45:

"	Corr.
10	48
15	72
20	96
30	144
45	216
50	241

TABLE XX.—NATURAL SINES, COSINES,
83°

'	Sine	Corr. for Sec. +	Cosine	Corr. for Sec. - +	Versine	Exsec	Diff. 10"		Tangent	'
0	.992546		.121869		.878131	7.20551			8.14435	0
1	2582		1581		8419	.22500	324.8	327.2	.16398	1
2	2617		1292		8708	.24457	326.2	328.7	.18370	2
3	2652		1003		8997	.26425	328.0	330.3	.20352	3
4	2687		0714		9286	.28402	329.5	332.0	.22344	4
							331.0	333.5		
5	.992722		.120426		.879574	7.30388			8.24345	5
6	2757		0137		9863	.32384	332.7	335.0	.26355	6
7	2792		.119848		.880152	.34390	334.3	336.8	.28376	7
8	2827		9559		0441	.36405	335.8	338.3	.30406	8
9	2862		9270		0730	.38431	337.7	340.0	.32446	9
							339.2	341.7		
10	.992896		.118982		.881018	7.40466			8.34496	10
11	2931	" Corr.	8693	" Corr.	1307	.42511	340.8	343.2	.36555	11
12	2966	10 6	8404	10 48	1596	.44566	342.5	345.0	.38625	12
13	3000	15 9	8115	15 72	1885	.46632	344.3	346.7	.40705	13
14	3034	20 11	7826	20 96	2174	.48707	345.8	348.3	.42795	14
		30 17		30 144			347.7	350.2		
15	.993068	40 23	.117537	40 193	.882463	7.50793			8.44896	15
16	3103	45 26	7248	45 217	2752	.52889	349.3	351.8	.47007	16
17	3137	50 29	6960	50 241	3040	.54996	351.1	353.5	.49128	17
18	3171		6671		3329	.57113	352.8	355.2	.51259	18
19	3204		6382		3618	.59241	354.7	357.2	.53402	19
							356.5	358.8		
20	.993238		.116093		.883907	7.61379			8.55555	20
21	3272		5804		4196	.63528	358.2	360.5	.57718	21
22	3306		5515		4485	.65688	360.0	362.5	.59893	22
23	3339		5226		4774	.67859	361.8	364.2	.62078	23
24	3373		4937		5063	.70041	363.7	366.2	.64275	24
							365.5	367.8		
25	.993406		.114648		.885352	7.72234			8.66482	25
26	3440		4359		5641	.74438	367.3	369.8	.68701	26
27	3473		4070		5930	.76653	369.2	371.7	.70931	27
28	3506		3781		6219	.78880	371.2	373.5	.73172	28
29	3539		3492		6508	.81118	373.0	375.5	.75425	29
							374.8	377.3		
30	.993572		.113203		.886797	7.83367			8.77689	30
31	3605		2914		7086	.85628	376.3	379.2	.79964	31
32	3638		2625		7375	.87901	378.0	381.3	.82252	32
33	3670		2336		7664	.90186	380.0	383.2	.84551	33
34	3703		2047		7953	.92482	382.7	385.2	.86862	34
							384.8	387.2		
35	.993736		.111758		.888242	7.94791			8.89185	35
36	3768		1469		8531	.97111	386.7	389.2	.91520	36
37	3800		1180		8820	.99444	388.8	391.2	.93867	37
38	3833		0891		9109	8.01788	390.7	393.3	.96227	38
39	3865		0602		9398	.04146	393.0	395.2	.98598	39
							394.8	397.5		
40	.993897		.110313		.889687	8.06515			9.00983	40
41	3929	" Corr.	0023	" Corr.	9977	.08897	397.0	399.3	.03379	41
42	3961	10 5	.109734	10 48	.890266	.11292	399.2	401.7	.05789	42
43	3993	15 8	9445	15 72	0555	.13699	401.2	403.7	.08211	43
44	4025	20 11	9156	20 96	0844	.16120	403.5	405.8	.10646	44
		30 16		30 145			405.5	407.8		
45	.994056	40 21	.108867	40 193	.891133	8.18553			9.13093	45
46	4088	45 24	8578	45 217	1422	.20999	407.7	410.2	.15554	46
47	4120	50 26	8288	50 241	1712	.23459	410.0	412.3	.18028	47
48	4151		7999		2001	.25931	412.0	414.7	.20516	48
49	4182		7710		2290	.28417	414.3	417.0	.23016	49
							416.7	419.0		
50	.994214		.107421		.892579	8.30917			9.25530	50
51	4245		7132		2868	.33430	418.8	421.3	.28058	51
52	4276		6842		3158	.35957	421.2	423.5	.30599	52
53	4307		6553		3447	.38497	423.3	425.8	.33154	53
54	4338		6264		3736	.41052	425.8	428.3	.35724	54
							428.3	430.5		
55	.994369		.105975		.894025	8.43620			9.38307	55
56	4400		5686		4314	.46203	430.5	432.8	.40904	56
57	4430		5396		4604	.48800	432.8	435.2	.43515	57
58	4461		5107		4893	.51411	435.2	437.7	.46141	58
59	4491		4818		5182	.54037	437.7	440.0	.48781	59
							440.0	442.5		
60	.994522		.104528		.895472	8.56677			9.51436	60

′	Sine	Corr. for Sec. +	Cosine	Corr. for Sec. − +	Versine	Exsec	Diff. 10″		Tangent	′
0	.994522		.104528		.895472	8.56677	442.5	445.0	9.51436	0
1	4552		4239		5761	.59332	445.0	447.5	.54106	1
2	4582		3950		6050	.62002	447.5	449.8	.56791	2
3	4613		3660		6340	.64687	450.0	452.5	.59490	3
4	4643		3371		6629	.67387	452.7	455.0	.62205	4
5	.994673		.103082		.896918	8.70103	455.0	457.5	9.64935	5
6	4703		2792		7208	.72833	457.7	460.2	.67680	6
7	4733		2503		7497	.75579	460.3	462.7	.70441	7
8	4762		2214		7786	.78341	463.1	465.3	.73217	8
9	4792		1924		8076	.81119	465.5	468.0	.76009	9
10	.994822		.101635		.898365	8.83912	468.3	470.7	9.78817	10
11	4851		1346		8654	.86722	470.8	473.5	.81641	11
12	4881		1056		8944	.89547	473.7	476.0	.84482	12
13	4910		0767		9233	.92389	476.5	478.8	.87338	13
14	4939		0478		9522	.95248	479.2	481.7	.90211	14
15	.994968		.100188		.899812	8.98123	482.0	484.3	9.93101	15
16	4998		099899		.900101	9.01015	484.7	487.2	.96007	16
17	5027		9609		0391	.03923	- - -	- - -	.98930	17
18	5056		9320		0680	.06849	490.5	49.3	10.0187	18
19	5084		9030		0970	.09792	493.3	49.5	.0483	19
20	.995113		.098741		.901259	9.12752	496.3	50.0	10.0780	20
21	5142		8451		1549	.15730	499.2	50.2	.1080	21
22	5170		8162		1838	.18725	502.3	50.3	.1381	22
23	5199		7872		2128	.21739	505.2	50.8	.1683	23
24	5227		7583		2417	.24770	508.2	51.0	.1988	24
25	.995256		.097293		.902707	9.27819	511.3	51.3	10.2294	25
26	5284		7004		2996	.30887	514.2	51.8	.2602	26
27	5312		6714		3286	.33973	517.3	51.8	.2913	27
28	5340		6425		3575	.37077	520.7	52.3	.3224	28
29	5368		6135		3865	.40201	523.7	52.7	.3538	29
30	.995396		.095846		.904154	9.43343	527.0	53.0	10.3854	30
31	5424		5556		4444	.46505	530.0	53.2	.4172	31
32	5452		5267		4733	.49685	533.5	53.7	.4491	32
33	5480		4977		5023	.52886	536.7	53.8	.4813	33
34	5507		4688		5312	.56106	540.0	54.3	.5136	34
35	.995534		.094398		.905602	9.59346	543.2	54.5	10.5462	35
36	5562		4108		5892	.62605	546.5	54.8	.5789	36
37	5589		3819		6181	.65885	550.2	55.3	.6118	37
38	5616		3529		6471	.69186	553.5	55.5	.6450	38
39	5644		3240		6760	.72507	557.0	56.0	.6783	39
40	.995671		.092950		.907050	9.75849	560.5	56.3	10.7119	40
41	5698		2660		7340	.79212	564.0	56.7	.7457	41
42	5725		2371		7629	.82596	567.5	57.0	.7797	42
43	5752		2081		7919	.86001	571.2	57.3	.8139	43
44	5778		1791		8209	.89428	574.8	57.7	.8483	44
45	.995805		.091502		.908498	9.92877	578.5	58.2	10.8829	45
46	5832		1212		8788	.96348	582.2	58.3	.9178	46
47	5858		0922		9078	.99841	- -	59.0	.9528	47
48	5884		0633		9367	10.0336	58.8	59.2	.9882	48
49	5911		0343		9657	.0689	59.3	59.5	11.0237	49
50	.995937		.090053		.909947	10.1045	59.8	60.0	11.0594	50
51	5963		089764		.910236	.1404	60.2	60.3	.0954	51
52	5989		9474		0526	.1765	60.5	60.8	.1316	52
53	6015		9184		0816	.2128	60.8	61.2	.1681	53
54	6041		8894		1106	.2493	61.3	61.5	.2048	54
55	.996067		.088605		.911395	10.2861	61.7	62.0	11.2417	55
56	6093		8315		1685	.3231	62.2	62.3	.2789	56
57	6118		8025		1975	.3604	62.5	62.8	.3163	57
58	6144		7735		2265	.3979	63.0	63.2	.3540	58
59	6169		7446		2554	.4357	63.3	63.7	.3919	59
60	.996195		.087156		.912844	10.4737			11.4301	60

Corr. (Sine, rows 11–18):

″	Corr.
10	5
15	7
20	10
30	15
40	18
45	22
50	24

Corr. (Cosine, rows 11–18):

″	Corr.
10	48
15	72
20	96
30	145
40	193
45	217
50	241

Corr. (Sine, rows 41–47):

″	Corr.
10	4
15	7
20	9
30	13
40	18
45	20
50	22

Corr. (Cosine, rows 41–47):

″	Corr.
10	48
15	72
20	97
30	145
40	193
45	217
50	241

TABLE XX.—NATURAL SINES, COSINES,
85°

'	Sine	Corr. for Sec.	Cosine	Corr. for Sec.	Versine	Exsec	Diff. 10"	Tangent	'
0	.996195	+	.087156	- +	.912844	10.4737		11.4301	0
1	6220		6866		3134	.5120	63.9	.4685	1
2	6245		6576		3424	.5505	64.3	.5072	2
3	6270		6286		3714	.5893	64.8	.5461	3
4	6295		5997		4003	.6284	65.3 · 65.7	.5853	4
5	.996320		.085707		.914293	10.6677	66.1	11.6248	5
6	6345		5417		4583	.7073	66.5	.6645	6
7	6370		5127		4873	.7471	67.0	.7045	7
8	6395		4837		5163	.7873	67.4	.7448	8
9	6420		4547		5453	.8277	67.9	.7853	9
10	.996444		.084258		.915742	10.8684	68.3	11.8262	10
11	6468	" Corr. 10 4	3968	" Corr. 10 48	6032	.9093	68.8	.8673	11
12	6493	15 6	3678	15 72	6322	.9506	69.3	.9087	12
13	6517	20 8	3388	20 97	6612	.9921	69.8	.9504	13
14	6541		3098		6902	11.0340	70.3	.9923	14
15	.996566	30 12	.082808	30 145	.917192	11.0761	70.8	12.0346	15
16	6590	40 16	2518	40 193	7482	.1185	71.3	.0772	16
17	6614	45 18	2228	45 217	7772	.1612	71.8	.1201	17
18	6637	50 20	1938	50 242	8062	.2043	72.3	.1632	18
19	6661		1649		8351	.2476	72.8	.2067	19
20	.996685		.081359		.918641	11.2913	73.3	12.2505	20
21	6708		1069		8931	.3352	73.9	.2946	21
22	6732		0779		9221	.3795	74.5	.3390	22
23	6756		0489		9511	.4241	75.0	.3838	23
24	6779		0199		9801	.4690	75.5	.4288	24
25	.996802		.079909		.920091	11.5142	76.1	12.4742	25
26	6825		9619		0381	.5598	76.6	.5199	26
27	6848		9329		0671	.6057	77.2	.5660	27
28	6872		9039		0961	.6520	77.8	.6124	28
29	6894		8749		1251	.6986	78.3	.6591	29
30	.996917		.078459		.921541	11.7455	78.9	12.7062	30
31	6940		8169		1831	.7928	79.5	.7536	31
32	6963		7879		2121	.8404	80.2	.8014	32
33	6985		7589		2411	.8884	80.8	.8496	33
34	7008		7299		2701	.9368	81.4	.8981	34
35	.997030		.077009		.922991	11.9855	82.0	12.9469	35
36	7053		6719		3281	12.0346	82.6	.9962	36
37	7075		6429		3571	.0840	83.3	13.0458	37
38	7097		6139		3861	.1339	83.9	.0958	38
39	7119		5849		4151	.1841	84.5	.1461	39
40	.997141		.075559		.924441	12.2347	85.1	13.1969	40
41	7163	" Corr. 10 4	5269	" Corr. 10 48	4731	.2857	85.8	.2480	41
42	7185	15 5	4979	15 73	5021	.3371	86.4	.2996	42
43	7207	20 .7	4689	20 97	5311	(.3889	87.1	.3515	43
44	7229		4399		5601	.4411	87.8	.4039	44
45	.997250	30 11	.074108	30 145	.925892	12.4937	88.5	13.4566	45
46	7272	40 14	3818	40 193	6182	.5468	89.2	.5098	46
47	7293	45 16	3528	45 218	6472	.6002	89.9	.5634	47
48	7314	50 18	3238	50 242	6762	.6541	90.6	.6174	48
49	7336		2948		7052	.7084	91.3	.6719	49
50	.997357		.072658		.927342	12.7631	92.1	13.7267	50
51	7378		2368		7632	.8183	92.8	.7821	51
52	7399		2078		7922	.8739	93.6	.8378	52
53	7420		1788		8212	.9300	94.4	.8940	53
54	7441		1497		8503	.9865	95.2	.9507	54
55	.997462		.071207		.928793	13.0435	95.9	14.0079	55
56	7482		0917		9083	.1010	96.6	.0655	56
57	7503		0627		9373	.1589	97.5	.1235	57
58	7523		0337		9663	.2173	98.3	.1821	58
59	7544		0047		9953	.2762	99.2	.2411	59
60	.997564		.069756		.930244	13.3356		14.3007	60

178

'	Sine	Corr. for Sec. +	Cosine	Corr. for Sec. − +	Versine	Exsec	Diff. 10″	Tangent	'
0	.997564		.069756		.930244	13.3356		14.3007	0
1	7584		9466		0534	.3955	99.9	.3607	1
2	7604		9176		0824	.4559	100.8	.4212	2
3	7624		8886		1114	.5168	101.7	.4823	3
4	7644		8596		1404	.5782	102.5	.5438	4
5	.997664		.068306		.931694	13.6401	103.4	14.6059	5
6	7684		8015		1985	.7026	104.3	.6685	6
7	7704		7725		2275	.7656	105.2	.7317	7
8	7724		7435		2565	.8291	106.0	.7954	8
9	7743		7145		2855	.8932	106.9	.8596	9
10	.997763		.066854		.933146	13.9579	107.9	14.9244	10
11	7782	" Corr.	6564	" Corr.	3436	14.0231	108.9	.9898	11
12	7802	10 3	6274	10 48	3726	.0889	109.8	15.0557	12
13	7821	15 5	5984	15 73	4016	.1553	110.8	.1222	13
14	7840	20 6	5693	20 .97	4307	.2222	111.8	.1893	14
15	.997859	30 9	.065403	30 145	.934597	14.2898	112.8	15.2571	15
16	7878	40 13	5113	40 194	4887	.3579	113.8	.3254	16
17	7897	45 14	4823	45 218	5177	.4267	114.8	.3943	17
18	7916	50 16	4532	50 242	5468	.4961	115.8	.4638	18
19	7934		4242		5758	.5661	116.9	.5340	19
20	.997953		.063952		.936048	14.6368	117.9	15.6048	20
21	7972		3661		6339	.7081	118.9	.6762	21
22	7990		3371		6629	.7801	120.1	.7483	22
23	8008		3081		6919	.8527	121.2	.8211	23
24	8027		2790		7210	.9260	122.3	.8945	24
25	.998045		.062500		.937500	14.9999	123.4	15.9687	25
26	8063		2210		7790	15.0746	124.6	16.0435	26
27	8081		1920		8080	.1500	125.8	.1190	27
28	8099		1629		8371	.2261	126.9	.1952	28
29	8117		1339		8661	.3029	128.2	.2722	29
30	.998135		.061048		.938952	15.3804	129.4	16.3499	30
31	8152		0758		9242	.4587	130.6	.4283	31
32	8170		0468		9532	.5377	131.9	.5075	32
33	8188		0178		9822	.6175	133.1	.5874	33
34	8205		.059887		.940113	.6981	134.4	.6681	34
35	.998222		.059597		.940403	15.7794	135.7	16.7496	35
36	8240		9306		0694	.8616	137.1	.8319	36
37	8257		9016		0984	.9446	138.4	.9150	37
38	8274		8726		1274	16.0283	139.8	.9990	38
39	8291		8435		1565	.1130	141.2	17.0837	39
40	.998308	" Corr.	.058145	" Corr.	.941855	16.1984	142.6	17.1693	40
41	8325	10 3	7854	10 48	2146	.2848	144.1	.2558	41
42	8342	15 4	7564	15 73	2436	.3720	145.5	.3432	42
43	8358	20 5	7274	20 97	2726	.4600	146.9	.4314	43
44	8375		6983		3017	.5490	148.4	.5205	44
45	.998392	30 8	.056693	30 145	.943307	16.6389	150.0	17.6106	45
46	8408	40 11	6402	40 194	3598	.7298	151.5	.7015	46
47	8424	45 12	6112	45 218	3888	.8215	153.0	.7934	47
48	8441	50 14	5822	50 242	4178	.9142	154.7	.8863	48
49	8457		5531		4469	17.0079	156.4	.9802	49
50	.998473		.055241		.944759	17.1026	158.0	18.0750	50
51	8489		4950		5050	.1983	159.6	.1708	51
52	8505		4660		5340	.2950	161.3	.2677	52
53	8521		4369		5631	.3927	163.0	.3655	53
54	8537		4079		5921	.4915	164.8	.4645	54
55	.998552		.053788		.946212	17.5914	166.6	18.5645	55
56	8568		3498		6502	.6923	168.4	.6656	56
57	8584		3207		6793	.7944	170.2	.7678	57
58	8599		2917		7083	.8975	172.0	.8711	58
59	8614		2626		7374	18.0019	174.0	.9755	59
60	.998630		.052336		.947664	18.1073	175.9	19.0811	60

TABLE XX.—NATURAL SINES, COSINES,
87°

'	Sine	Corr. for Sec.	Cosine	Corr. for Sec.	Versine	Exsec	Diff. 10"	Tangent	'
0	.998630	+	.052336	− +	.947664	18.1073		19.0811	0
1	8645		2046		7954	.2140	177.9	.1879	1
2	8660		1755		8245	.3218	179.9	.2959	2
3	8675		1464		8536	.4309	181.9	.4051	3
4	8690		1174		8826	.5412	184.0	.5156	4
							186.1		
5	.998705		.050884		.949116	18.6528		19.6273	5
6	8719		0593		9407	.7656	188.2	.7403	6
7	8734		0302		9698	.8798	190.4	.8546	7
8	8749		0012		9988	.9952	192.6	.9702	8
9	8763		.049721		.950279	19.1121	194.9	20.0872	9
							197.2		
10	.998778		.049431		.950569	19.2303		20.2056	10
11	8792	" Corr.	9140	" Corr.	0860	.3499	199.4	.3253	11
12	8806	10 2	8850	10 48	1150	.4709	201.8	.4465	12
13	8820	15 3	8559	15 73	1441	.5934	204.3	.5691	13
14	8834	20 5	8269	20 97	1731	.7174	206.8	.6932	14
		30 7		30 145			209.4		
15	.998848	40 9	.047978	40 194	.952022	19.8428		20.8188	15
16	8862	45 10	7688	45 218	2312	.9698	211.9	.9460	16
17	8876	50 12	7397	50 242	2603	20.0984	214.4	21.0747	17
18	8890		7106		2894	.2285	216.9	.2049	18
19	8904		6816		3184	.3603	219.7	.3369	19
							222.4		
20	.998917		.046525		.953475	20.4937		21.4704	20
21	8931		6235		3765	.6288	225.3	.6056	21
22	8944		5944		4056	.7656	228.2	.7426	22
23	8957		5654		4346	.9041	231.0	.8813	23
24	8971		5363		4637	21.0444	233.9	22.0217	24
							237.0		
25	.998984		.045072		.954928	21.1865		22.1640	25
26	8997		4782		5218	.3305	240.1	.3081	26
27	9010		4491		5509	.4764	243.2	.4541	27
28	9023		4201		5799	.6241	246.3	.6020	28
29	9036		3910		6090	.7739	249.7	.7519	29
							253.0		
30	.999048		.043619		.956381	21.9256		22.9038	30
31	9061		3329		6671	22.0794	256.4	23.0577	31
32	9073		3038		6962	.2352	259.8	.2137	32
33	9086		2748		7252	.3932	263.4	.3718	33
34	9098		2457		7543	.5533	267.0	.5375	34
							270.6		
35	.999111		.042166		.957834	22.7156		23.6945	35
36	9123		1876		8124	.8802	274.5	.8593	36
37	9135		1585		8415	23.0471	278.3	24.0263	37
38	9147		1294		8706	.2164	282.3	.1957	38
39	9159		1004		8996	.3880	286.2	.3675	39
							290.3		
40	.999171		.040713		.959287	23.5621		24.5418	40
41	9183	" Corr.	0422	" Corr.	9578	.7387	294.3	.7185	41
42	9194	10 2	0132	10 48	9868	.9179	298.7	.8978	42
43	9206	15 3	.039841	15 73	.960160	24.0997	303.2	25.0798	43
44	9218	20 4	9550	20 97	0450	.2841	307.5	.2674	44
		30 6		30 145			312.1		
45	.999229	40 8	.039260	40 194	.960740	24.4713		25.4517	45
46	9240	45 9	8969	45 218	1031	.6613	316.8	.6418	46
47	9252	50 10	8678	50 242	1322	.8542	321.6	.8348	47
48	9263		8388		1612	25.0499	326.3	26.0307	48
49	9274		8097		1903	.2487	331.4	.2296	49
							336.5		
50	.999285		.037806		.962194	25.4505		26.4316	50
51	9296		7516		2484	.6555	341.7	.6367	51
52	9307		7225		2775	.8636	347.0	.8450	52
53	9318		6934		3066	26.0750	352.5	27.0566	53
54	9328		6644		3356	.2898	358.1	.2715	54
							363.8		
55	.999339		.036353		.963647	26.5080		27.4899	55
56	9350		6062		3938	.7298	369.7	.7117	56
57	9360		5772		4228	.9551	375.7	.9372	57
58	9370		5481		4519	27.1842	381.9	28.1664	58
59	9381		5190		4810	.4170	388.2	.3994	59
							394.7		
60	.999391		.034900		.965100	27.6537		28.6363	60

VERSINES, EXSECANTS, AND TANGENTS
88°

′	Sine	Corr. for Sec. +	Cosine −	Corr. for Sec. +	Versine	Exsec	Diff. 10″	Tangent	′
0	.999391		.034900		.965100	27.6537	401	28.6363	0
1	9401		4609		5391	27.8944	408	28.8771	1
2	9411		4318		5682	28.1392	415	29.1220	2
3	9421		4027		5973	28.3881	422	29.3711	3
4	9431		3737		6263	28.6414	429	29.6245	4
5	.999440		.033446		.966554	28.8990	437	29.8823	5
6	9450		3155		6845	29.1612	445	30.1446	6
7	9460		2864		7136	29.4280	453	30.4116	7
8	9469		2574		7426	29.6996	461	30.6833	8
9	9479		2283		7717	29.9761	469	30.9599	9
10	.999488		.031992		.968008	30.2576	478	31.2416	10
11	9497		1702		8298	30.5442	487	31.5284	11
12	9507		1411		8589	30.8362	496	31.8205	12
13	9516		1120		8880	31.1337	505	32.1181	13
14	9525		0829		9171	31.4367	515	32.4213	14
15	.999534		.030538		.969462	31.7455	525	32.7303	15
16	9542		0248		9752	32.0603	535	33.0452	16
17	9551		.029957		.970043	32.3812	545	33.3662	17
18	9560		9666		0334	32.7083	556	33.6935	18
19	9568		9376		0624	33.0420	567	34.0273	19
20	.999577		.029085		.970915	33.3823	579	34.3678	20
21	9585		8794		1206	33.7295	591	34.7151	21
22	9594		8503		1497	34.0838	603	35.0695	22
23	9602		8212		1788	34.4454	615	35.4313	23
24	9610		7922		2078	34.8145	628	35.8006	24
25	.999618		.027631		.972369	35.1914	641	36.1776	25
26	9626		7340		2660	35.5763	655	36.5627	26
27	9634		7049		2951	35.9695	670	36.9560	27
28	9642		6758		3242	36.3713	685	37.3579	28
29	9650		6468		3532	36.7818	700	37.7686	29
30	.999657		.026177		.973823	37.2016	715	38.1885	30
31	9665		5886		4114	37.6307	731	38.6177	31
32	9672		5595		4405	38.0696	748	39.0568	32
33	9680		5305		4695	38.5185	766	39.5059	33
34	9687		5014		4986	38.9780	784	39.9655	34
35	.999694		.024723		.975277	39.4482	803	40.4358	35
36	9702		4432		5568	39.9296	822	40.9174	36
37	9709		4141		5859	40.4227	842	41.4106	37
38	9716		3851		6149	40.9277	863	41.9158	38
39	9722		3560		6440	41.4452	884	42.4335	39
40	.999729		.023269		.976731	41.9757	907	42.9641	40
41	9736		2978		7022	42.5196	930	43.5081	41
42	9743		2687		7313	43.0775	954	44.0661	42
43	9749		2396		7604	43.6498	979	44.6386	43
44	...9756		2106		7894	44.2372	1005	45.2261	44
45	.999762		.021815		.978185	44.8403	1032	45.8294	45
46	9768		1524		8476	45.4596	1061	46.4489	46
47	9774		1233		8767	46.0960	1090	47.0853	47
48	9781		0942		9058	46.7500	1121	47.7395	48
49	9787		0652		9348	47.4224	1153	48.4121	49
50	.999793		.020361		.979639	48.1141	1186	49.1039	50
51	9799		0070		9930	48.8258	1221	49.8157	51
52	9804		.019779		.980221	49.5584	1258	50.5485	52
53	9810		9488		0512	50.3129	1296	51.3032	53
54	9816		9197		0803	51.0903	1336	52.0807	54
55	.999821		.018907		.981093	51.8916	1378	52.8821	55
56	9827		8616		1384	52.7179	1421	53.7086	56
57	9832		8325		1675	53.5705	1467	54.5613	57
58	9837		8034		1966	54.4505	1515	55.4415	58
59	9843		7743		2257	55.3595	1566	56.3506	59
60	.999848		.017452		.982548	56.2987		57.2900	60

Corr. for Sec. (Sine):

″ Corr.	
10	1
15	2
20	3
30	4
40	6
45	7
50	7

Corr. for Sec. (Cosine):

″ Corr.	
10	48
15	73
20	97
30	145
40	194
45	218
50	242

TABLE XX.—NATURAL TRIGONOMETRIC FUNCTIONS
89°

'	Sine	Corr. for Sec. +	Cosine	Corr. for Sec. - +	Versine	Exsec	Diff. 10"	Tangent	'
0	.999848		.017452		.982548	56.2987	1619	57.2900	0
1	9853		7162		2838	57.2698	1674	58.2612	1
2	9858		6871		3129	58.2743	1733	59.2659	2
3	9862		6580		3420	59.3141	1795	60.3058	3
4	9867		6289		3711	60.3910	1860	61.3829	4
5	.999872		.015998		.984002	61.5072	1929	62.4992	5
6	9877		5707		4293	62.6646	2002	63.6567	6
7	9881		5416		4584	63.8657	2079	64.8580	7
8	9886		5126		4874	65.1130	2161	66.1055	8
9	9890		4835		5165	66.4093	2247	67.4019	9
10	.999894		.014544		.985456	67.7574	2339	68.7501	10
11	9898	By	4253	" Corr.	5747	69.1605	2436	70.1533	11
12	9902	Inspec-	3962	10 48	6038	70.6221	2540	71.6151	12
13	9906	tion	3671	15 73	6329	72.1458	2650	73.1390	13
14	9910		3380	20 97	6620	73.7359	2768	74.7292	14
15	.999914		.013090	30 145	.986910	75.3966	2894	76.8900	15
16	9918		2799	40 194	7201	77.1327	3028	78.1263	16
17	9922		2508	45 218	7492	78.9497	3173	79.9434	17
18	9925		2217	50 242	7783	80.8532	3327	81.8470	18
19	9929		1926		8074	82.8495	3494	83.8435	19
20	.999932		.011635		.988365	84.9456	3673	85.9398	20
21	9936		1344		8656	87.1492	3866	88.1436	21
22	9939		1054		8946	89.4689	4075	90.4633	22
23	9942		0763		9237	91.9139	4302	92.9085	23
24	9945		0472		9528	94.4947	4547	95.4895	24
25	.999948		.010181		.989819	97.2230	482	98.2179	25
26	9951		.009890		.990110	100.112	511	101.107	26
27	9954		9599		0401	103.176	543	104.171	27
28	9957		9308		0692	106.431	578	107.426	28
29	9959		9017		0983	109.897	616	110.892	29
30	.999962		.008726		.991274	113.593	659	114.589	30
31	9964		8436		1564	117.544	706	118.540	31
32	9967		8145		1855	121.778	758	122.774	32
33	9969		7854		2146	126.325	816	127.321	33
34	9971		7563		2437	131.222	881	132.219	34
35	.999974		.007272		.992728	136.511	955	137.507	35
36	9976		6981		3019	142.241	1.038	143.237	36
37	9978		6690		3310	148.468	1.132	149.465	37
38	9980		6400		3600	155.262	1.240	156.259	38
39	9981		6109		3891	162.703	1.364	163.700	39
40	.999983		.005818		.994182	170.888	1.508	171.885	40
41	9985		5527	" Corr.	4473	179.935	1.675	180.932	41
42	9986		5236	10 48	4764	189.987	1.872	190.984	42
43	9988		4945	15 73	5055	201.221	2.107	202.219	43
44	9989		4654	20 97	5346	213.860	2.387	214.858	44
45	.999990		.004363	30 145	.995637	228.184	2.728	229.182	45
46	9992		4072	40 194	5928	244.554	3.148	245.552	46
47	9993		3782	45 218	6218	263.443	3.673	264.441	47
48	9994		3491	50 242	6509	285.479	4.341	286.478	48
49	9995		3200		6800	311.523	5.209	312.521	49
50	.999996		.002909		.997091	342.775	6.366	343.774	50
51	9997		2618		7382	380.972	7.958	381.971	51
52	9997		2327		7673	428.719	10.231	429.718	52
53	9998		2036		7964	490.107	13.642	491.106	53
54	9998		1745		8255	571.958	19.099	572.957	54
55	.999999		.001454		.998546	686.550	26.648	687.549	55
56	9999		1164		8836	858.437	47.75	859.436	56
57	One		0873		9127	1144.92	95.49	1145.92	57
58	One		0582		9418	1717.87	286.48	1718.87	58
59	One		0291		9709	3436.75		3437.75	59
60	One		Zero		One	Infin.		Infin.	60

182

TABLE XXI.—LOGARITHMS OF NUMBERS

No. 100 Log 000   No. 109 Log 040

N.	0	1	2	3	4	5	6	7	8	9	Diff.
100	000000	0434	0868	1301	1734	2166	2598	3029	3461	3891	432
101	4321	4751	5181	5609	6038	6466	6894	7321	7748	8174	428
102	8600	9026	9451	9876	*0300	*0724	*1147	*1570	*1993	*2415	424
103	012837	3259	3680	4100	4521	4940	5360	5779	6197	6616	420
104	7033	7451	7868	8284	8700	9116	9532	9947	*0361	*0775	416
105	021189	1603	2016	2428	2841	3252	3664	4075	4486	4896	412
106	5306	5715	6125	6533	6942	7350	7757	8164	8571	8978	408
107	9384	9789	*0195	*0600	*1004	*1408	*1812	*2216	*2619	*3021	404
108	033424	3826	4227	4628	5029	5430	5830	6230	6629	7028	400
109	7426	7825	8223	8620	9017	9414	9811	*0207	*0602	*0998	397

PROPORTIONAL PARTS

Diff.	1	2	3	4	5	6	7	8	9	Diff.
434	43	87	130	174	217	260	304	347	391	434
433	43	87	130	173	217	260	303	346	390	433
432	43	86	130	173	216	259	302	346	389	432
431	43	86	129	172	216	259	302	345	388	431
430	43	86	129	172	215	258	301	344	387	430
429	43	86	129	172	215	257	300	343	386	429
428	43	86	128	171	214	257	300	342	385	428
427	43	85	128	171	214	256	299	342	384	427
426	43	85	128	170	213	256	298	341	383	426
425	43	85	128	170	213	255	298	340	383	425
424	42	85	127	170	212	254	297	339	382	424
423	42	85	127	169	212	254	296	338	381	423
422	42	84	127	169	211	253	295	338	380	422
421	42	84	126	168	211	253	295	337	379	421
420	42	84	126	168	210	252	294	336	378	420
419	42	84	126	168	210	251	293	335	377	419
418	42	84	125	167	209	251	293	334	376	418
417	42	83	125	167	209	250	292	334	375	417
416	42	83	125	166	208	250	291	333	374	416
415	42	83	125	166	208	249	291	332	374	415
414	41	83	124	166	207	248	290	331	373	414
413	41	83	124	165	207	248	289	330	372	413
412	41	82	124	165	206	247	288	330	371	412
411	41	82	123	164	206	247	288	329	370	411
410	41	82	123	164	205	246	287	328	369	410
409	41	82	123	164	205	245	286	327	368	409
408	41	82	122	163	204	245	286	326	367	408
407	41	81	122	163	204	244	285	326	366	407
406	41	81	122	162	203	244	284	325	365	406
405	41	81	122	162	203	243	284	324	365	405
404	40	81	121	162	202	242	283	323	364	404
403	40	81	121	161	202	242	282	322	363	403
402	40	80	121	161	201	241	281	322	362	402
401	40	80	120	160	201	241	281	321	361	401
400	40	80	120	160	200	240	280	320	360	400
399	40	80	120	160	200	239	279	319	359	399
398	40	80	119	159	199	239	279	318	358	398
397	40	79	119	159	199	238	278	318	357	397
396	40	79	119	158	198	238	277	317	356	396
395	40	79	119	158	198	237	277	316	356	395
394	39	79	118	158	197	236	276	315	355	394
393	39	79	118	157	197	236	275	314	354	393
392	39	78	118	157	196	235	274	314	353	392
391	39	78	117	156	196	235	274	313	352	391
390	39	78	117	156	195	234	273	312	351	390
389	39	78	117	156	195	233	272	311	350	389
388	39	78	116	155	194	233	272	310	349	388

TABLE XXI.—LOGARITHMS OF NUMBERS

No. 110 Log 041   No. 124 Log 096

N.	0	1	2	3	4	5	6	7	8	9	Diff.
110	041393	1787	2182	2576	2969	3362	3755	4148	4540	4932	393
111	5323	5714	6105	6495	6885	7275	7664	8053	8442	8830	390
112	9218	9606	9993	*0380	*0766	*1153	*1538	*1924	*2309	*2694	386
113	053078	3463	3846	4230	4613	4996	5378	5760	6142	6524	383
114	6905	7286	7666	8046	8426	8805	9185	9563	9942	*0320	379
115	060698	1075	1452	1829	2206	2582	2958	3333	3709	4083	376
116	4458	4832	5206	5580	5953	6326	6699	7071	7443	7815	373
117	8186	8557	8928	9298	9668	*0038	*0407	*0776	*1145	*1514	370
118	071882	2250	2617	2985	3352	3718	4085	4451	4816	5182	366
119	5547	5912	6276	6640	7004	7368	7731	8094	8457	8819	363
120	079181	9543	9904	*0266	*0626	*0987	*1347	*1707	*2067	*2426	360
121	082785	3144	3503	3861	4219	4576	4934	5291	5647	6004	357
122	6360	6716	7071	7426	7781	8136	8490	8845	9198	9552	355
123	9905	*0258	*0611	*0963	*1315	*1667	*2018	*2370	*2721	*3071	352
124	093422	3772	4122	4471	4820	5169	5518	5866	6215	6562	349

PROPORTIONAL PARTS

Diff.	1	2	3	4	5	6	7	8	9	Diff.
387	39	77	116	155	194	232	271	310	348	387
386	39	77	116	154	193	232	270	309	347	386
385	39	77	116	154	193	231	270	308	347	385
384	38	77	115	154	192	230	269	307	346	384
383	38	77	115	153	192	230	268	306	345	383
382	38	76	115	153	191	229	267	306	344	382
381	38	76	114	152	191	229	267	305	343	381
380	38	76	114	152	190	228	266	304	342	380
379	38	76	114	152	190	227	265	303	341	379
378	38	76	113	151	189	227	265	302	340	378
377	38	75	113	151	189	226	264	302	339	377
376	38	75	113	150	188	226	263	301	338	376
375	38	75	113	150	188	225	263	300	338	375
374	37	75	112	150	187	224	262	299	337	374
373	37	75	112	149	187	224	261	298	336	373
372	37	74	112	149	186	223	260	298	335	372
371	37	74	111	148	186	223	260	297	334	371
370	37	74	111	148	185	222	259	296	333	370
369	37	74	111	148	185	221	258	295	332	369
368	37	74	110	147	184	221	258	294	331	368
367	37	73	110	147	184	220	257	294	330	367
366	37	73	110	146	183	220	256	293	329	366
365	37	73	110	146	183	219	256	292	329	365
364	36	73	109	146	182	218	255	291	328	364
363	36	73	109	145	182	218	254	290	327	363
362	36	72	109	145	181	217	253	290	326	362
361	36	72	108	144	181	217	253	289	325	361
360	36	72	108	144	180	216	252	288	324	360
359	36	72	108	144	180	215	251	287	323	359
358	36	72	107	143	179	215	251	286	322	358
357	36	71	107	143	179	214	250	286	321	357
356	36	71	107	142	178	214	249	285	320	356
355	36	71	107	142	178	213	249	284	320	355
354	35	71	106	142	177	212	248	283	319	354
353	35	71	106	141	177	212	247	282	318	353
352	35	70	106	141	176	211	246	282	317	352
351	35	70	105	140	176	211	246	281	316	351
350	35	70	105	140	175	210	245	280	315	350
349	35	70	105	140	175	209	244	279	314	349
348	35	70	104	139	174	209	244	278	313	348
347	35	69	104	139	174	208	243	278	312	347

TABLE XXI.—LOGARITHMS OF NUMBERS

No. 125 Log 097   No. 139 Log 145

N.	0	1	2	3	4	5	6	7	8	9	Diff.
125	096910	7257	7604	7951	8298	8644	8990	9335	9681	*0026	346
126	100371	0715	1059	1403	1747	2091	2434	2777	3119	3462	343
127	3804	4146	4487	4828	5169	5510	5851	6191	6531	6871	341
128	7210	7549	7888	8227	8565	8903	9241	9579	9916	*0253	338
129	110590	0925	1263	1599	1934	2270	2605	2940	3275	3609	335
130	113943	4277	4611	4944	5278	5611	5943	6276	6608	6940	333
131	7271	7603	7934	8265	8595	8926	9256	9586	9915	*0245	330
132	120574	0903	1231	1560	1888	2216	2544	2871	3198	3525	328
133	3852	4178	4504	4830	5156	5481	5806	6131	6456	6781	325
134	7105	7429	7753	8076	8399	8722	9045	9368	9690	*0012	323
135	130334	0655	0977	1298	1619	1939	2260	2580	2900	3219	321
136	3539	3858	4177	4496	4814	5133	5451	5769	6086	6403	318
137	6721	7037	7354	7671	7987	8303	8618	8934	9249	9564	316
138	9879	*0194	*0508	*0822	*1136	*1450	*1763	*2076	*2389	*2702	314
139	143015	3327	3639	3951	4263	4574	4885	5196	5507	5818	311

PROPORTIONAL PARTS

Diff.	1	2	3	4	5	6	7	8	9	Diff.
347	35	69	104	139	174	208	243	278	312	347
346	35	69	104	138	173	208	242	277	311	346
345	35	69	104	138	173	207	242	276	311	345
344	34	69	103	138	172	206	241	275	310	344
343	34	69	103	137	172	206	240	274	309	343
342	34	68	103	137	171	205	239	274	308	342
341	34	68	102	136	171	205	239	273	307	341
340	34	68	102	136	170	204	238	272	306	340
339	34	68	102	136	170	203	237	271	305	339
338	34	68	101	135	169	203	237	270	304	338
337	34	67	101	135	169	202	236	270	303	337
336	34	67	101	134	168	202	235	269	302	336
335	34	67	101	134	168	201	235	268	302	335
334	33	67	100	134	167	200	234	267	301	334
333	33	67	100	133	167	200	233	266	300	333
332	33	66	100	133	166	199	232	266	299	332
331	33	66	99	132	166	199	232	265	298	331
330	33	66	99	132	165	198	231	264	297	330
329	33	66	99	132	165	197	230	263	296	329
328	33	66	98	131	164	197	230	262	295	328
327	33	65	98	131	164	196	229	262	294	327
326	33	65	98	130	163	196	228	261	293	326
325	33	65	98	130	163	195	228	260	293	325
324	32	65	97	130	162	194	227	259	292	324
323	32	65	97	129	162	194	226	258	291	323
322	32	64	97	129	161	193	225	258	290	322
321	32	64	96	128	161	193	225	257	289	321
320	32	64	96	128	160	192	224	256	288	320
319	32	64	96	128	160	191	223	255	287	319
318	32	64	95	127	159	191	223	254	286	318
317	32	63	95	127	159	190	222	254	285	317
316	32	63	95	126	158	190	221	253	284	316
315	32	63	95	126	158	189	221	252	284	315
314	31	63	94	126	157	188	220	251	283	314
313	31	63	94	125	157	188	219	250	282	313
312	31	62	94	125	156	187	218	250	281	312
311	31	62	93	124	156	187	218	249	280	311
310	31	62	93	124	155	186	217	248	279	310
309	31	62	93	124	155	185	216	247	278	309
308	31	62	92	123	154	185	216	246	277	308
307	31	61	92	123	154	184	215	246	276	307

N.	0	1	2	3	4	5	6	7	8	9	Diff.
140	146128	6438	6748	7058	7367	7676	7985	8294	8603	8911	309
141	9219	9527	9835	*0142	*0449	*0756	*1063	*1370	*1676	*1982	307
142	152288	2594	2900	3205	3510	3815	4120	4424	4728	5032	305
143	5336	5640	5943	6246	6549	6852	7154	7457	7759	8061	303
144	8362	8664	8965	9266	9567	9868	*0168	*0469	*0769	*1068	301
145	161368	1667	1967	2266	2564	2863	3161	3460	3758	4055	299
146	4353	4650	4947	5244	5541	5838	6134	6430	6726	7022	297
147	7317	7613	7908	8203	8497	8792	9086	9380	9674	9968	295
148	170262	0555	0848	1141	1434	1726	2019	2311	2603	2895	293
149	3186	3478	3769	4060	4351	4641	4932	5222	5512	5802	291
150	176091	6381	6670	6959	7248	7536	7825	8113	8401	8689	289
151	8977	9264	9552	9839	*0126	*0413	*0699	*0986	*1272	*1558	287
152	181844	2129	2415	2700	2985	3270	3555	3839	4123	4407	285
153	4691	4975	5259	5542	5825	6108	6391	6674	6956	7239	283
154	7521	7803	8084	8366	8647	8928	9209	9490	9771	*0051	281
155	190332	0612	0892	1171	1451	1730	2010	2289	2567	2846	279
156	3125	3403	3681	3959	4237	4514	4792	5069	5346	5623	278
157	5900	6176	6453	6729	7005	7281	7556	7832	8107	8382	276
158	8657	8932	9206	9481	9755	*0029	*0303	*0577	*0850	*1124	274
159	201397	1670	1943	2216	2488	2761	3033	3305	3577	3848	272

PROPORTIONAL PARTS

Diff.	1	2	3	4	5	6	7	8	9	Diff.
306	31	61	92	122	153	184	214	245	275	306
305	31	61	92	122	153	183	214	244	275	305
304	30	61	91	122	152	182	213	243	274	304
303	30	61	91	121	152	182	212	242	273	303
302	30	60	91	121	151	181	211	242	272	302
301	30	60	90	120	151	181	211	241	271	301
300	30	60	90	120	150	180	210	240	270	300
299	30	60	90	120	150	179	209	239	269	299
298	30	60	89	119	149	179	209	238	268	298
297	30	59	89	119	149	178	208	238	267	297
296	30	59	89	118	148	178	207	237	266	296
295	30	59	89	118	148	177	207	236	266	295
294	29	59	88	118	147	176	206	235	265	294
293	29	59	88	117	147	176	205	234	264	293
292	29	58	88	117	146	175	204	234	263	292
291	29	58	87	116	146	175	204	233	262	291
290	29	58	87	116	145	174	203	232	261	290
289	29	58	87	116	145	173	202	231	260	289
288	29	58	86	115	144	173	202	230	259	288
287	29	57	86	115	144	172	201	230	258	287
286	29	57	86	114	143	172	200	229	257	286
285	29	57	86	114	143	171	200	228	257	285
284	28	57	85	114	142	170	199	227	256	284
283	28	57	85	113	142	170	198	226	255	283
282	28	56	85	113	141	169	197	226	254	282
281	28	56	84	112	141	169	197	225	253	281
280	28	56	84	112	140	168	196	224	252	280
279	28	56	84	112	140	167	195	223	251	279
278	28	56	83	111	139	167	195	222	250	278
277	28	55	83	111	139	166	194	222	249	277
276	28	55	83	110	138	166	193	221	248	276
275	28	55	83	110	138	165	193	220	248	275
274	27	55	82	110	137	164	192	219	247	274
273	27	55	82	109	137	164	191	218	246	273
272	27	54	82	109	136	163	190	218	245	272
271	27	54	81	108	136	163	190	217	244	271

TABLE XXI.—LOGARITHMS OF NUMBERS

No. 160 Log 204

No. 179 Log 255

N.	0	1	2	3	4	5	6	7	8	9	Diff.
160	204120	4391	4663	4934	5204	5475	5746	6016	6286	6556	271
161	6826	7096	7365	7634	7904	8173	8441	8710	8979	9247	269
162	9515	9783	*0051	*0319	*0586	*0853	*1121	*1388	*1654	*1921	267
163	212188	2454	2720	2986	3252	3518	3783	4049	4314	4579	266
164	4844	5109	5373	5638	5902	6166	6430	6694	6957	7221	264
165	217484	7747	8010	8273	8536	8798	9060	9323	9585	9846	262
166	220108	0370	0631	0892	1153	1414	1675	1936	2196	2456	261
167	2716	2976	3236	3496	3755	4015	4274	4533	4792	5051	259
168	5309	5568	5826	6084	6342	6600	6858	7115	7372	7630	258
169	7887	8144	8400	8657	8913	9170	9426	9682	9938	*0193	256
170	230449	0704	0960	1215	1470	1724	1979	2234	2488	2742	255
171	2996	3250	3504	3757	4011	4264	4517	4770	5023	5276	253
172	5528	5781	6033	6285	6537	6789	7041	7292	7544	7795	252
173	8046	8297	8548	8799	9049	9299	9550	9800	*0050	*0300	250
174	240549	0799	1048	1297	1546	1795	2044	2293	2541	2790	249
175	243038	3286	3534	3782	4030	4277	4525	4772	5019	5266	248
176	5513	5759	6006	6252	6499	6745	6991	7237	7482	7728	246
177	7973	8219	8464	8709	8954	9198	9443	9687	9932	*0176	245
178	250420	0664	0908	1151	1395	1638	1881	2125	2368	2610	243
179	2853	3096	3338	3580	3822	4064	4306	4548	4790	5031	242

PROPORTIONAL PARTS

Diff.	1	2	3	4	5	6	7	8	9	Diff.
272	27	54	82	109	136	163	190	218	245	272
271	27	54	81	108	136	163	190	217	244	271
270	27	54	81	108	135	162	189	216	243	270
269	27	54	81	108	135	161	188	215	242	269
268	27	54	80	107	134	161	188	214	241	268
267	27	53	80	107	134	160	187	214	240	267
266	27	53	80	106	133	160	186	213	239	266
265	27	53	80	106	133	159	186	212	239	265
264	26	53	79	106	132	158	185	211	238	264
263	26	53	79	105	132	158	184	210	237	263
262	26	52	79	105	131	157	183	210	236	262
261	26	52	78	104	131	157	183	209	235	261
260	26	52	78	104	130	156	182	208	234	260
259	26	52	78	104	130	155	181	207	233	259
258	26	52	77	103	129	155	181	206	232	258
257	26	51	77	103	129	154	180	206	231	257
256	26	51	77	102	128	154	179	205	230	256
255	26	51	77	102	128	153	179	204	230	255
254	25	51	76	102	127	152	178	203	229	254
253	25	51	76	101	127	152	177	202	228	253
252	25	50	76	101	126	151	176	202	227	252
251	25	50	75	100	126	151	176	201	226	251
250	25	50	75	100	125	150	175	200	225	250
249	25	50	75	100	125	149	174	199	224	249
248	25	50	74	99	124	149	174	198	223	248
247	25	49	74	99	124	148	173	198	222	247
246	25	49	74	98	123	148	172	197	221	246
245	25	49	74	98	123	147	172	196	221	245
244	24	49	73	98	122	146	171	195	220	244
243	24	49	73	97	122	146	170	194	219	243
242	24	48	73	97	121	145	169	194	218	242
241	24	48	72	96	121	145	169	193	217	241
240	24	48	72	96	120	144	168	192	216	240

N.	0	1	2	3	4	5	6	7	8	9	Diff.
180	255273	5514	5755	5996	6237	6477	6718	6958	7198	7439	241
181	7679	7918	8158	8398	8637	8877	9116	9355	9594	9833	239
182	260071	0310	0548	0787	1025	1263	1501	1739	1976	2214	238
183	2451	2688	2925	3162	3399	3636	3873	4109	4346	4582	237
184	4818	5054	5290	5525	5761	5996	6232	6467	6702	6937	235
185	267172	7406	7641	7875	8110	8344	8578	8812	9046	9279	234
186	9513	9746	9980	*0213	*0446	*0679	*0912	*1144	*1377	*1609	233
187	271842	2074	2306	2538	2770	3001	3233	3464	3696	3927	232
188	4158	4389	4620	4850	5081	5311	5542	5772	6002	6232	230
189	6462	6692	6921	7151	7380	7609	7838	8067	8296	8525	229
190	278754	8982	9211	9439	9667	9895	*0123	*0351	*0578	*0806	228
191	281033	1261	1488	1715	1942	2169	2396	2622	2849	3075	227
192	3301	3527	3753	3979	4205	4431	4656	4882	5107	5332	226
193	5557	5782	6007	6232	6456	6681	6905	7130	7354	7578	225
194	7802	8026	8249	8473	8696	8920	9143	9366	9589	9812	223
195	290035	0257	0480	0702	0925	1147	1369	1591	1813	2034	222
196	2256	2478	2699	2920	3141	3363	3584	3804	4025	4246	221
197	4466	4687	4907	5127	5347	5567	5787	6007	6226	6446	220
198	6665	6884	7104	7323	7542	7761	7979	8198	8416	8635	219
199	8853	9071	9289	9507	9725	9943	*0161	*0378	*0595	*0813	218
200	301030	1247	1464	1681	1898	2114	2331	2547	2764	2980	217
201	3196	3412	3628	3844	4059	4275	4491	4706	4921	5136	216
202	5351	5566	5781	5996	6211	6425	6639	6854	7068	7282	215
203	7496	7710	7924	8137	8351	8564	8778	8991	9204	9417	213
204	9630	9843	*0056	*0268	*0481	*0693	*0906	*1118	*1330	*1542	212

PROPORTIONAL PARTS

Diff.	1	2	3	4	5	6	7	8	9	Diff.
239	24	48	72	96	120	143	167	191	215	239
238	24	48	71	95	119	143	167	190	214	238
237	24	47	71	95	119	142	166	190	213	237
236	24	47	71	94	118	142	165	189	212	236
235	24	47	71	94	118	141	165	188	212	235
234	23	47	70	94	117	140	164	187	211	234
233	23	47	70	93	117	140	163	186	210	233
232	23	46	70	93	116	139	162	186	209	232
231	23	46	69	92	116	139	162	185	208	231
230	23	46	69	92	115	138	161	184	207	230
229	23	46	69	92	115	137	160	183	206	229
228	23	46	68	91	114	137	160	182	205	228
227	23	45	68	91	114	136	159	182	204	227
226	23	45	68	90	113	136	158	181	203	226
225	23	45	68	90	113	135	158	180	203	225
224	22	45	67	90	112	134	157	179	202	224
223	22	45	67	89	112	134	156	178	201	223
222	22	44	67	89	111	133	155	178	200	222
221	22	44	66	88	111	133	155	177	199	221
220	22	44	66	88	110	132	154	176	198	220
219	22	44	66	88	110	131	153	175	197	219
218	22	44	65	87	109	131	153	174	196	218
217	22	43	65	87	109	130	152	174	195	217
216	22	43	65	86	108	130	151	173	194	216
215	22	43	65	86	108	129	151	172	194	215
214	21	43	64	86	107	128	150	171	193	214
213	21	43	64	85	107	128	149	170	192	213
212	21	42	64	85	106	127	148	170	191	212

TABLE XXI.—LOGARITHMS OF NUMBERS

No. 205 Log 311　　　　　　　　　　　　No. 234 Log 370

N.	0	1	2	3	4	5	6	7	8	9	Diff.
205	311754	1966	2177	2389	2600	2812	3023	3234	3445	3656	211
206	3867	4078	4289	4499	4710	4920	5130	5340	5551	5760	210
207	5970	6180	6390	6599	6809	7018	7227	7436	7646	7854	209
208	8063	8272	8481	8689	8898	9106	9314	9522	9730	9938	208
209	320146	0354	0562	0769	0977	1184	1391	1598	1805	2012	207
210	322219	2426	2633	2839	3046	3252	3458	3665	3871	4077	206
211	4282	4488	4694	4899	5105	5310	5516	5721	5926	6131	205
212	6336	6541	6745	6950	7155	7359	7563	7767	7972	8176	204
213	8380	8583	8787	8991	9194	9398	9601	9805	*0008	*0211	203
214	330414	0617	0819	1022	1225	1427	1630	1832	2034	2236	202
215	332438	2640	2842	3044	3246	3447	3649	3850	4051	4253	202
216	4454	4655	4856	5057	5257	5458	5658	5859	6059	6260	201
217	6460	6660	6860	7060	7260	7459	7659	7858	8058	8257	200
218	8456	8656	8855	9054	9253	9451	9650	9849	*0047	*0246	199
219	340444	0642	0841	1039	1237	1435	1632	1830	2028	2225	198
220	342423	2620	2817	3014	3212	3409	3606	3802	3999	4196	197
221	4392	4589	4785	4981	5178	5374	5570	5766	5962	6157	196
222	6353	6549	6744	6939	7135	7330	7525	7720	7915	8110	195
223	8305	8500	8694	8889	9083	9278	9472	9666	9860	*0054	194
224	350248	0442	0636	0829	1023	1216	1410	1603	1796	1989	193
225	352183	2375	2568	2761	2954	3147	3339	3532	3724	3916	193
226	4108	4301	4493	4685	4876	5068	5260	5452	5643	5834	192
227	6026	6217	6408	6599	6790	6981	7172	7363	7554	7744	191
228	7935	8125	8316	8506	8696	8886	9076	9266	9456	9646	190
229	9835	*0025	*0215	*0404	*0593	*0783	*0972	*1161	*1350	*1539	189
230	361728	1917	2105	2294	2482	2671	2859	3048	3236	3424	188
231	3612	3800	3988	4176	4363	4551	4739	4926	5113	5301	188
232	5488	5675	5862	6049	6236	6423	6610	6796	6983	7169	187
233	7356	7542	7729	7915	8101	8287	8473	8659	8845	9030	186
234	9216	9401	9587	9772	9958	*0143	*0328	*0513	*0698	*0883	185

PROPORTIONAL PARTS

Diff.	1	2	3	4	5	6	7	8	9	Diff.
212	21	42	64	85	106	127	148	170	191	212
211	21	42	63	84	106	127	148	169	190	211
210	21	42	63	84	105	126	147	168	189	210
209	21	42	63	84	105	125	146	167	188	209
208	21	42	62	83	104	125	146	166	187	208
207	21	41	62	83	104	124	145	166	186	207
206	21	41	62	82	103	124	144	165	185	206
205	21	41	62	82	103	123	144	164	185	205
204	20	41	61	82	102	122	143	163	184	204
203	20	41	61	81	102	122	142	162	183	203
202	20	40	61	81	101	121	141	162	182	202
201	20	40	60	80	101	121	141	161	181	201
200	20	40	60	80	100	120	140	160	180	200
199	20	40	60	80	100	119	139	159	179	199
198	20	40	59	79	99	119	139	158	178	198
197	20	39	59	79	99	118	138	158	177	197
196	20	39	59	78	98	118	137	157	176	196
195	20	39	59	78	98	117	137	156	176	195
194	19	39	58	78	97	116	136	155	175	194
193	19	39	58	77	97	116	135	154	174	193
192	19	38	58	77	96	115	134	154	173	192
191	19	38	57	76	96	115	134	153	172	191
190	19	38	57	76	95	114	133	152	171	190
189	19	38	57	76	95	113	132	151	170	189
188	19	38	56	75	94	113	132	150	169	188

TABLE XXI.—LOGARITHMS OF NUMBERS

No. 235 Log 371

No. 264 Log 423

N.	0	1	2	3	4	5	6	7	8	9	Diff.
235	371068	1253	1437	1622	1806	1991	2175	2360	2544	2728	184
236	2912	3096	3280	3464	3647	3831	4015	4198	4382	4565	184
237	4748	4932	5115	5298	5481	5664	5846	6029	6212	6394	183
238	6577	6759	6942	7124	7306	7488	7670	7852	8034	8216	182
239	8398	8580	8761	8943	9124	9306	9487	9668	9849	*0030	181
240	380211	0392	0573	0754	0934	1115	1296	1476	1656	1837	181
241	2017	2197	2377	2557	2737	2917	3097	3277	3456	3636	180
242	3815	3995	4174	4353	4533	4712	4891	5070	5249	5428	179
243	5606	5785	5964	6142	6321	6499	6677	6856	7034	7212	178
244	7390	7568	7746	7923	8101	8279	8456	8634	8811	8989	178
245	389166	9343	9520	9698	9875	*0051	*0228	*0405	*0582	*0759	177
246	390935	1112	1288	1464	1641	1817	1993	2169	2345	2521	176
247	2697	2873	3048	3224	3400	3575	3751	3926	4101	4277	176
248	4452	4627	4802	4977	5152	5326	5501	5676	5850	6025	175
249	6199	6374	6548	6722	6896	7071	7245	7419	7592	7766	174
250	397940	8114	8287	8461	8634	8808	8981	9154	9328	9501	173
251	9674	9847	*0020	*0192	*0365	*0538	*0711	*0883	*1056	*1228	173
252	401401	1573	1745	1917	2089	2261	2433	2605	2777	2949	172
253	3121	3292	3464	3635	3807	3978	4149	4320	4492	4663	171
254	4834	5005	5176	5346	5517	5688	5858	6029	6199	6370	171
255	406540	6710	6881	7051	7221	7391	7561	7731	7901	8070	170
256	8240	8410	8579	8749	8918	9087	9257	9426	9595	9764	169
257	9933	*0102	*0271	*0440	*0609	*0777	*0946	*1114	*1283	*1451	169
258	411620	1788	1956	2124	2293	2461	2629	2796	2964	3132	168
259	3300	3467	3635	3803	3970	4137	4305	4472	4639	4806	167
260	414973	5140	5307	5474	5641	5808	5974	6141	6308	6474	167
261	6641	6807	6973	7139	7306	7472	7638	7804	7970	8135	166
262	8301	8467	8633	8798	8964	9129	9295	9460	9625	9791	165
263	9956	*0121	*0286	*0451	*0616	*0781	*0945	*1110	*1275	*1439	165
264	421604	1768	1933	2097	2261	2426	2590	2754	2918	3082	164

PROPORTIONAL PARTS

Diff.	1	2	3	4	5	6	7	8	9	Diff.
187	19	37	56	75	94	112	131	150	168	187
186	19	37	56	74	93	112	130	149	167	186
185	19	37	56	74	93	111	130	148	167	185
184	18	37	55	74	92	110	129	147	166	184
183	18	37	55	73	92	110	128	146	165	183
182	18	36	55	73	91	109	127	146	164	182
181	18	36	54	72	91	109	127	145	163	181
180	18	36	54	72	90	108	126	144	162	180
179	18	36	54	72	90	107	125	143	161	179
178	18	36	53	71	89	107	125	142	160	178
177	18	35	53	71	89	106	124	142	159	177
176	18	35	53	70	88	106	123	141	158	176
175	18	35	53	70	88	105	123	140	158	175
174	17	35	52	70	87	104	122	139	157	174
173	17	35	52	69	87	104	121	138	156	173
172	17	34	52	69	86	103	120	138	155	172
171	17	34	51	68	86	103	120	137	154	171
170	17	34	51	68	85	102	119	136	153	170
169	17	34	51	68	85	101	118	135	152	169
168	17	34	50	67	84	101	118	134	151	168
167	17	33	50	67	84	100	117	134	150	167
166	17	33	50	66	83	100	116	133	149	166
165	17	33	50	66	83	99	116	132	149	165
164	16	33	49	66	82	98	115	131	148	164

TABLE XXI.—LOGARITHMS OF NUMBERS

N.	0	1	2	3	4	5	6	7	8	9	Diff.
265	423246	3410	3574	3737	3901	4065	4228	4392	4555	4718	164
266	4882	5045	5208	5371	5534	5697	5860	6023	6186	6349	163
267	6511	6674	6836	6999	7161	7324	7486	7648	7811	7973	162
268	8135	8297	8459	8621	8783	8944	9106	9268	9429	9591	162
269	9752	9914	*0075	*0236	*0398	*0559	*0720	*0881	*1042	*1203	161
270	431364	1525	1685	1846	2007	2167	2328	2488	2649	2809	161
271	2969	3130	3290	3450	3610	3770	3930	4090	4249	4409	160
272	4569	4729	4888	5048	5207	5367	5526	5685	5844	6004	159
273	6163	6322	6481	6640	6799	6957	7116	7275	7433	7592	159
274	7751	7909	8067	8226	8384	8542	8701	8859	9017	9175	158
275	439333	9491	9648	9806	9964	*0122	*0279	*0437	*0594	*0752	158
276	440909	1066	1224	1381	1538	1695	1852	2009	2166	2323	157
277	2480	2637	2793	2950	3106	3263	3419	3576	3732	3889	157
278	4045	4201	4357	4513	4669	4825	4981	5137	5293	5449	156
279	5604	5760	5915	6071	6226	6382	6537	6692	6848	7003	155
280	447158	7313	7468	7623	7778	7933	8088	8242	8397	8552	155
281	8706	8861	9015	9170	9324	9478	9633	9787	9941	*0095	154
282	450249	0403	0557	0711	0865	1018	1172	1326	1479	1633	154
283	1786	1940	2093	2247	2400	2553	2706	2859	3012	3165	153
284	3318	3471	3624	3777	3930	4082	4235	4387	4540	4692	153
285	454845	4997	5150	5302	5454	5606	5758	5910	6062	6214	152
286	6366	6518	6670	6821	6973	7125	7276	7428	7579	7731	152
287	7882	8033	8184	8336	8487	8638	8789	8940	9091	9242	151
288	9392	9543	9694	9845	9995	*0146	*0296	*0447	*0597	*0748	151
289	460898	1048	1198	1348	1499	1649	1799	1948	2098	2248	150
290	462398	2548	2697	2847	2997	3146	3296	3445	3594	3744	150
291	3893	4042	4191	4340	4490	4639	4788	4936	5085	5234	149
292	5383	5532	5680	5829	5977	6126	6274	6423	6571	6719	149
293	6868	7016	7164	7312	7460	7608	7756	7904	8052	8200	148
294	8347	8495	8643	8790	8938	9085	9233	9380	9527	9675	148
295	469822	9969	*0116	*0263	*0410	*0557	*0704	*0851	*0998	*1145	147
296	471292	1438	1585	1732	1878	2025	2171	2318	2464	2610	146
297	2756	2903	3049	3195	3341	3487	3633	3779	3925	4071	146
298	4216	4362	4508	4653	4799	4944	5090	5235	5381	5526	146
299	5671	5816	5962	6107	6252	6397	6542	6687	6832	6976	145

PROPORTIONAL PARTS

Diff.	1	2	3	4	5	6	7	8	9	Diff.
164	16	33	49	66	82	98	115	131	148	164
163	16	33	49	65	82	98	114	130	147	163
162	16	32	49	65	81	97	113	130	146	162
161	16	32	48	64	81	97	113	129	145	161
160	16	32	48	64	80	96	112	128	144	160
159	16	32	48	64	80	95	111	127	143	159
158	16	32	47	63	79	95	111	126	142	158
157	16	31	47	63	79	94	110	126	141	157
156	16	31	47	62	78	94	109	125	140	156
155	16	31	47	62	78	93	109	124	140	155
154	15	31	46	62	77	92	108	123	139	154
153	15	31	46	61	77	92	107	122	138	153
152	15	30	46	61	76	91	106	122	137	152
151	15	30	45	60	76	91	106	121	136	151
150	15	30	45	60	75	90	105	120	135	150
149	15	30	45	60	75	89	104	119	134	149
148	15	30	44	59	74	89	104	118	133	148
147	15	29	44	59	74	88	103	118	132	147
146	15	29	44	58	73	88	102	117	131	146
145	15	29	44	58	73	87	102	116	131	145
144	14	29	43	58	72	86	101	115	130	144
143	14	29	43	57	72	86	100	114	129	143

N.	0	1	2	3	4	5	6	7	8	9	Diff.
300	477121	7266	7411	7555	7700	7844	7989	8133	8278	8422	145
301	8566	8711	8855	8999	9143	9287	9431	9575	9719	9863	144
302	480007	0151	0294	0438	0582	0725	0869	1012	1156	1299	144
303	1443	1586	1729	1872	2016	2159	2302	2445	2588	2731	143
304	2874	3016	3159	3302	3445	3587	3730	3872	4015	4157	143
305	484300	4442	4585	4727	4869	5011	5153	5295	5437	5579	142
306	5721	5863	6005	6147	6289	6430	6572	6714	6855	6997	142
307	7138	7280	7421	7563	7704	7845	7986	8127	8269	8410	141
308	8551	8692	8833	8974	9114	9255	9396	9537	9677	9818	141
309	9958	*0099	*0239	*0380	*0520	*0661	*0801	*0941	*1081	*1222	140
310	491362	1502	1642	1782	1922	2062	2201	2341	2481	2621	140
311	2760	2900	3040	3179	3319	3458	3597	3737	3876	4015	139
312	4155	4294	4433	4572	4711	4850	4989	5128	5267	5406	139
313	5544	5683	5822	5960	6099	6238	6376	6515	6653	6791	139
314	6930	7068	7206	7344	7483	7621	7759	7897	8035	8173	138
315	498311	8448	8586	8724	8862	8999	9137	9275	9412	9550	138
316	9687	9824	9962	*0099	*0236	*0374	*0511	*0648	*0785	*0922	137
317	501059	1196	1333	1470	1607	1744	1880	2017	2154	2291	137
318	2427	2564	2700	2837	2973	3109	3246	3382	3518	3655	136
319	3791	3927	4063	4199	4335	4471	4607	4743	4878	5014	136
320	505150	5286	5421	5557	5693	5828	5964	6099	6234	6370	136
321	6505	6640	6776	6911	7046	7181	7316	7451	7586	7721	135
322	7856	7991	8126	8260	8395	8530	8664	8799	8934	9068	135
323	9203	9337	9471	9606	9740	9874	*0009	*0143	*0277	*0411	134
324	510545	0679	0813	0947	1081	1215	1349	1482	1616	1750	134
325	511883	2017	2151	2284	2418	2551	2684	2818	2951	3084	133
326	3218	3351	3484	3617	3750	3883	4016	4149	4282	4415	133
327	4548	4681	4813	4946	5079	5211	5344	5476	5609	5741	133
328	5874	6006	6139	6271	6403	6535	6668	6800	6932	7064	132
329	7196	7328	7460	7592	7724	7855	7987	8119	8251	8382	132
330	518514	8646	8777	8909	9040	9171	9303	9434	9566	9697	131
331	9828	9959	*0090	*0221	*0353	*0484	*0615	*0745	*0876	*1007	131
332	521138	1269	1400	1530	1661	1792	1922	2053	2183	2314	131
333	2444	2575	2705	2835	2966	3096	3226	3356	3486	3616	130
334	3746	3876	4006	4136	4266	4396	4526	4656	4785	4915	130
335	525045	5174	5304	5434	5563	5693	5822	5951	6081	6210	129
336	6339	6469	6598	6727	6856	6985	7114	7243	7372	7501	129
337	7630	7759	7888	8016	8145	8274	8402	8531	8660	8788	129
338	8917	9045	9174	9302	9430	9559	9687	9815	9943	*0072	128
339	530200	0328	0456	0584	0712	0840	0968	1096	1223	1351	128

PROPORTIONAL PARTS

Diff.	1	2	3	4	5	6	7	8	9	Diff.
142	14	28	43	57	71	85	99	114	128	142
141	14	28	42	56	71	85	99	113	127	141
140	14	28	42	56	70	84	98	112	126	140
139	14	28	42	56	70	83	97	111	125	139
138	14	28	41	55	69	83	97	110	124	138
137	14	27	41	55	69	82	96	110	123	137
136	14	27	41	54	68	82	95	109	122	136
135	14	27	41	54	68	81	95	108	122	135
134	13	27	40	54	67	80	94	107	121	134
133	13	27	40	53	67	80	93	106	120	133
132	13	26	40	53	66	79	92	106	119	132
131	13	26	39	52	66	79	92	105	118	131
130	13	26	39	52	65	78	91	104	117	130
129	13	26	39	52	65	77	90	103	116	129
128	13	26	38	51	64	77	90	102	115	128
127	13	25	38	51	64	76	89	102	114	127

TABLE XXI.—LOGARITHMS OF NUMBERS
No. 340 Log 531   No. 379 Log 579

N.	0	1	2	3	4	5	6	7	8	9	Diff.
340	531479	1607	1734	1862	1990	2117	2245	2372	2500	2627	128
341	2754	2882	3009	3136	3264	3391	3518	3645	3772	3899	127
342	4026	4153	4280	4407	4534	4661	4787	4914	5041	5167	127
343	5294	5421	5547	5674	5800	5927	6053	6180	6306	6432	126
344	6558	6685	6811	6937	7063	7189	7315	7441	7567	7693	126
345	537819	7945	8071	8197	8322	8448	8574	8699	8825	8951	126
346	9076	9202	9327	9452	9578	9703	9829	9954	*0079	*0204	125
347	540329	0455	0580	0705	0830	0955	1080	1205	1330	1454	125
348	1579	1704	1829	1953	2078	2203	2327	2452	2576	2701	125
349	2825	2950	3074	3199	3323	3447	3571	3696	3820	3944	124
350	544068	4192	4316	4440	4564	4688	4812	4936	5060	5183	124
351	5307	5431	5555	5678	5802	5925	6049	6172	6296	6419	124
352	6543	6666	6789	6913	7036	7159	7282	7405	7529	7652	123
353	7775	7898	8021	8144	8267	8389	8512	8635	8758	8881	123
354	9003	9126	9249	9371	9494	9616	9739	9861	9984	*0106	123
355	550228	0351	0473	0595	0717	0840	0962	1084	1206	1328	122
356	1450	1572	1694	1816	1938	2060	2181	2303	2425	2547	122
357	2668	2790	2911	3033	3155	3276	3398	3519	3640	3762	121
358	3883	4004	4126	4247	4368	4489	4610	4731	4852	4973	121
359	5094	5215	5336	5457	5578	5699	5820	5940	6061	6182	121
360	556303	6423	6544	6664	6785	6905	7026	7146	7267	7387	120
361	7507	7627	7748	7868	7988	8108	8228	8349	8469	8589	120
362	8709	8829	8948	9068	9188	9308	9428	9548	9667	9787	120
363	9907	*0026	*0146	*0265	*0385	*0504	*0624	*0743	*0863	*0982	119
364	561101	1221	1340	1459	1578	1698	1817	1936	2055	2174	119
365	562293	2412	2531	2650	2769	2887	3006	3125	3244	3362	119
366	3481	3600	3718	3837	3955	4074	4192	4311	4429	4548	119
367	4666	4784	4903	5021	5139	5257	5376	5494	5612	5730	118
368	5848	5966	6084	6202	6320	6437	6555	6673	6791	6909	118
369	7026	7144	7262	7379	7497	7614	7732	7849	7967	8084	118
370	568202	8319	8436	8554	8671	8788	8905	9023	9140	9257	117
371	9374	9491	9608	9725	9842	9959	*0076	*0193	*0309	*0426	117
372	570543	0660	0776	0893	1010	1126	1243	1359	1476	1592	117
373	1709	1825	1942	2058	2174	2291	2407	2523	2639	2755	116
374	2872	2988	3104	3220	3336	3452	3568	3684	3800	3915	116
375	574031	4147	4263	4379	4494	4610	4726	4841	4957	5072	116
376	5188	5303	5419	5534	5650	5765	5880	5996	6111	6226	115
377	6341	6457	6572	6687	6802	6917	7032	7147	7262	7377	115
378	7492	7607	7722	7836	7951	8066	8181	8295	8410	8525	115
379	8639	8754	8868	8983	9097	9212	9326	9441	9555	9669	114

PROPORTIONAL PARTS

Diff.	1	2	3	4	5	6	7	8	9	Diff.
128	13	26	38	51	64	77	90	102	115	128
127	13	25	38	51	64	76	89	102	114	127
126	13	25	38	50	63	76	88	101	113	126
125	13	25	38	50	63	75	88	100	113	125
124	12	25	37	50	62	74	87	99	112	124
123	12	25	37	49	62	74	86	98	111	123
122	12	24	37	49	61	73	85	98	110	122
121	12	24	36	48	61	73	85	97	109	121
120	12	24	36	48	60	72	84	96	108	120
119	12	24	36	48	60	71	83	95	107	119
118	12	24	35	47	59	71	83	94	106	118
117	12	23	35	47	59	70	82	94	105	117
116	12	23	35	46	58	70	81	93	104	116

TABLE XXI.—LOGARITHMS OF NUMBERS
No. 380 Log 579   No. 419 Log 623

N.	0	1	2	3	4	5	6	7	8	9	Diff.
380	579784	9898	*0012	*0126	*0241	*0355	*0469	*0583	*0697	*0811	114
381	580925	1039	1153	1267	1381	1495	1608	1722	1836	1950	114
382	2063	2177	2291	2404	2518	2631	2745	2858	2972	3085	114
383	3199	3312	3426	3539	3652	3765	3879	3992	4105	4218	113
384	4331	4444	4557	4670	4783	4896	5009	5122	5235	5348	113
385	585461	5574	5686	5799	5912	6024	6137	6250	6362	6475	113
386	6587	6700	6812	6925	7037	7149	7262	7374	7486	7599	112
387	7711	7823	7935	8047	8160	8272	8384	8496	8608	8720	112
388	8832	8944	9056	9167	9279	9391	9503	9615	9726	9838	112
389	9950	*0061	*0173	*0284	*0396	*0507	*0619	*0730	*0842	*0953	112
390	591065	1176	1287	1399	1510	1621	1732	1843	1955	2066	111
391	2177	2288	2399	2510	2621	2732	2843	2954	3064	3175	111
392	3286	3397	3508	3618	3729	3840	3950	4061	4171	4282	111
393	4393	4503	4614	4724	4834	4945	5055	5165	5276	5386	110
394	5496	5606	5717	5827	5937	6047	6157	6267	6377	6487	110
395	596597	6707	6817	6927	7037	7146	7256	7366	7476	7586	110
396	7695	7805	7914	8024	8134	8243	8353	8462	8572	8681	110
397	8791	8900	9009	9119	9228	9337	9446	9556	9665	9774	109
398	9883	9992	*0101	*0210	*0319	*0428	*0537	*0646	*0755	*0864	109
399	600973	1082	1191	1299	1408	1517	1625	1734	1843	1951	109
400	602060	2169	2277	2386	2494	2603	2711	2819	2928	3036	108
401	3144	3253	3361	3469	3577	3686	3794	3902	4010	4118	108
402	4226	4334	4442	4550	4658	4766	4874	4982	5089	5197	108
403	5305	5413	5521	5628	5736	5844	5951	6059	6166	6274	108
404	6381	6489	6596	6704	6811	6919	7026	7133	7241	7348	107
405	607455	7562	7669	7777	7884	7991	8098	8205	8312	8419	107
406	8526	8633	8740	8847	8954	9061	9167	9274	9381	9488	107
407	9594	9701	9808	9914	*0021	*0128	*0234	*0341	*0447	*0554	107
408	610660	0767	0873	0979	1086	1192	1298	1405	1511	1617	106
409	1723	1829	1936	2042	2148	2254	2360	2466	2572	2678	106
410	612784	2890	2996	3102	3207	3313	3419	3525	3630	3736	106
411	3842	3947	4053	4159	4264	4370	4475	4581	4686	4792	106
412	4897	5003	5108	5213	5319	5424	5529	5634	5740	5845	105
413	5950	6055	6160	6265	6370	6476	6581	6686	6790	6895	105
414	7000	7105	7210	7315	7420	7525	7629	7734	7839	7943	105
415	618048	8153	8257	8362	8466	8571	8676	8780	8884	8989	105
416	9093	9198	9302	9406	9511	9615	9719	9824	9928	*0032	104
417	620136	0240	0344	0448	0552	0656	0760	0864	0968	1072	104
418	1176	1280	1384	1488	1592	1695	1799	1903	2007	2110	104
419	2214	2318	2421	2525	2628	2732	2835	2939	3042	3146	104

PROPORTIONAL PARTS

Diff.	1	2	3	4	5	6	7	8	9	Diff.
115	12	23	35	46	58	69	81	92	104	115
114	11	23	34	46	57	68	80	91	103	114
113	11	23	34	45	57	68	79	90	102	113
112	11	22	34	45	56	67	78	90	101	112
111	11	22	33	44	56	67	78	89	100	111
110	11	22	33	44	55	66	77	88	99	110
109	11	22	33	44	55	65	76	87	98	109
108	11	22	32	43	54	65	76	86	97	108
107	11	21	32	43	54	64	75	86	96	107
106	11	21	32	42	53	64	74	85	95	106
105	11	21	32	42	53	63	74	84	95	105
104	10	21	31	42	52	62	73	83	94	104
103	10	21	31	41	52	62	72	82	93	103

TABLE XXI.—LOGARITHMS OF NUMBERS

No. 420 Log 623   No. 464 Log 667

N.	0	1	2	3	4	5	6	7	8	9	Diff.
420	623249	3353	3456	3559	3663	3766	3869	3973	4076	4179	103
421	4282	4385	4488	4591	4695	4798	4901	5004	5107	5210	103
422	5312	5415	5518	5621	5724	5827	5929	6032	6135	6238	103
423	6340	6443	6546	6648	6751	6853	6956	7058	7161	7263	103
424	7366	7468	7571	7673	7775	7878	7980	8082	8185	8287	102
425	628389	8491	8593	8695	8797	8900	9002	9104	9206	9308	102
426	9410	9512	9613	9715	9817	9919	*0021	*0123	*0224	*0326	102
427	630428	0530	0631	0733	0835	0936	1038	1139	1241	1342	102
428	1444	1545	1647	1748	1849	1951	2052	2153	2255	2356	101
429	2457	2559	2660	2761	2862	2963	3064	3165	3266	3367	101
430	633468	3569	3670	3771	3872	3973	4074	4175	4276	4376	101
431	4477	4578	4679	4779	4880	4981	5081	5182	5283	5383	101
432	5484	5584	5685	5785	5886	5986	6087	6187	6287	6388	100
433	6488	6588	6688	6789	6889	6989	7089	7189	7290	7390	100
434	7490	7590	7690	7790	7890	7990	8090	8190	8290	8389	100
435	638489	8589	8689	8789	8888	8988	9088	9188	9287	9387	100
436	9486	9586	9686	9785	9885	9984	*0084	*0183	*0283	*0382	99
437	640481	0581	0680	0779	0879	0978	1077	1177	1276	1375	99
438	1474	1573	1672	1771	1871	1970	2069	2168	2267	2366	99
439	2465	2563	2662	2761	2860	2959	3058	3156	3255	3354	99
440	643453	3551	3650	3749	3847	3946	4044	4143	4242	4340	98
441	4439	4537	4636	4734	4832	4931	5029	5127	5226	5324	98
442	5422	5521	5619	5717	5815	5913	6011	6110	6208	6306	98
443	6404	6502	6600	6698	6796	6894	6992	7089	7187	7285	98
444	7383	7481	7579	7676	7774	7872	7969	8067	8165	8262	98
445	648360	8458	8555	8653	8750	8848	8945	9043	9140	9237	97
446	9335	9432	9530	9627	9724	9821	9919	*0016	*0113	*0210	97
447	650308	0405	0502	0599	0696	0793	0890	0987	1084	1181	97
448	1278	1375	1472	1569	1666	1762	1859	1956	2053	2150	97
449	2246	2343	2440	2536	2633	2730	2826	2923	3019	3116	97
450	653213	3309	3405	3502	3598	3695	3791	3888	3984	4080	96
451	4177	4273	4369	4465	4562	4658	4754	4850	4946	5042	96
452	5138	5235	5331	5427	5523	5619	5715	5810	5906	6002	96
453	6098	6194	6290	6386	6482	6577	6673	6769	6864	6960	96
454	7056	7152	7247	7343	7438	7534	7629	7725	7820	7916	96
455	658011	8107	8202	8298	8393	8488	8584	8679	8774	8870	95
456	8965	9060	9155	9250	9346	9441	9536	9631	9726	9821	95
457	9916	*0011	*0106	*0201	*0296	*0391	*0486	*0581	*0676	*0771	95
458	660865	0960	1055	1150	1245	1339	1434	1529	1623	1718	95
459	1813	1907	2002	2096	2191	2286	2380	2475	2569	2663	95
460	662758	2852	2947	3041	3135	3230	3324	3418	3512	3607	94
461	3701	3795	3889	3983	4078	4172	4266	4360	4454	4548	94
462	4642	4736	4830	4924	5018	5112	5206	5299	5393	5487	94
463	5581	5675	5769	5862	5956	6050	6143	6237	6331	6424	94
464	6518	6612	6705	6799	6892	6986	7079	7173	7266	7360	94

PROPORTIONAL PARTS

Diff.	1	2	3	4	5	6	7	8	9	Diff.
104	10	21	31	42	52	62	73	83	94	.104
103	10	21	31	41	52	62	72	82	93	103
102	10	20	31	41	51	61	71	82	92	102
101	10	20	30	40	51	61	71	81	91	101
100	10	20	30	40	50	60	70	80	90	100
99	10	20	30	40	50	59	69	79	89	99
98	10	20	29	39	49	59	69	78	88	98
97	10	19	29	39	49	58	68	78	87	97
96	10	19	29	38	48	58	67	77	86	96
95	10	19	29	38	48	57	67	76	86	95

N.	0	1	2	3	4	5	6	7	8	9	Diff.
465	667453	7546	7640	7733	7826	7920	8013	8106	8199	8293	93
466	8386	8479	8572	8665	8759	8852	8945	9038	9131	9224	93
467	9317	9410	9503	9596	9689	9782	9875	9967	*0060	*0153	93
468	670246	0339	0431	0524	0617	0710	0802	0895	0988	1080	93
469	1173	1265	1358	1451	1543	1636	1728	1821	1913	2005	93
470	672098	2190	2283	2375	2467	2560	2652	2744	2836	2929	92
471	3021	3113	3205	3297	3390	3482	3574	3666	3758	3850	92
472	3942	4034	4126	4218	4310	4402	4494	4586	4677	4769	92
473	4861	4953	5045	5137	5228	5320	5412	5503	5595	5687	92
474	5778	5870	5962	6053	6145	6236	6328	6419	6511	6602	92
475	676694	6785	6876	6968	7059	7151	7242	7333	7424	7516	91
476	7607	7698	7789	7881	7972	8063	8154	8245	8336	8427	91
477	8518	8609	8700	8791	8882	8973	9064	9155	9246	9337	91
478	9428	9519	9610	9700	9791	9882	9973	*0063	*0154	*0245	91
479	680336	0426	0517	0607	0698	0789	0879	0970	1060	1151	91
480	681241	1332	1422	1513	1603	1693	1784	1874	1964	2055	90
481	2145	2235	2326	2416	2506	2596	2686	2777	2867	2957	90
482	3047	3137	3227	3317	3407	3497	3587	3677	3767	3857	90
483	3947	4037	4127	4217	4307	4396	4486	4576	4666	4756	90
484	4845	4935	5025	5114	5204	5294	5383	5473	5563	5652	90
485	685742	5831	5921	6010	6100	6189	6279	6368	6458	6547	89
486	6636	6726	6815	6904	6994	7083	7172	7261	7351	7440	89
487	7529	7618	7707	7796	7886	7975	8064	8153	8242	8331	89
488	8420	8509	8598	8687	8776	8865	8953	9042	9131	9220	89
489	9309	9398	9486	9575	9664	9753	9841	9930	*0019	*0107	89
490	690196	0285	0373	0462	0550	0639	0728	0816	0905	0993	89
491	1081	1170	1258	1347	1435	1524	1612	1700	1789	1877	88
492	1965	2053	2142	2230	2318	2406	2494	2583	2671	2759	88
493	2847	2935	3023	3111	3199	3287	3375	3463	3551	3639	88
494	3727	3815	3903	3991	4078	4166	4254	4342	4430	4517	88
495	694605	4693	4781	4868	4956	5044	5131	5219	5307	5394	88
496	5482	5569	5657	5744	5832	5919	6007	6094	6182	6269	87
497	6356	6444	6531	6618	6706	6793	6880	6968	7055	7142	87
498	7229	7317	7404	7491	7578	7665	7752	7839	7926	8014	87
499	8101	8188	8275	8362	8449	8535	8622	8709	8796	8883	87
500	698970	9057	*0011	*0098	9317	*0184	9491	9578	9664	9751	87
501	9838	9924	*0011	*0098	*0184	*0271	*0358	*0444	*0531	*0617	87
502	700704	0790	0877	0963	1050	1136	1222	1309	1395	1482	86
503	1568	1654	1741	1827	1913	1999	2086	2172	2258	2344	86
504	2431	2517	2603	2689	2775	2861	2947	3033	3119	3205	86
505	703291	3377	3463	3549	3635	3721	3807	3893	3979	4065	86
506	4151	4236	4322	4408	4494	4579	4665	4751	4837	4922	86
507	5008	5094	5179	5265	5350	5436	5522	5607	5693	5778	86
508	5864	5949	6035	6120	6206	6291	6376	6462	6547	6632	85
509	6718	6803	6888	6974	7059	7144	7229	7315	7400	7485	85

PROPORTIONAL PARTS

Diff.	1	2	3	4	5	6	7	8	9	Diff.
94	9	19	28	38	47	56	66	75	85	94
93	9	19	28	37	47	56	65	74	84	93
92	9	18	28	37	46	55	64	74	83	92
91	9	18	27	36	46	55	64	73	82	91
90	9	18	27	36	45	54	63	72	81	90
89	9	18	27	36	45	53	62	71	80	89
88	9	18	26	35	44	53	62	70	79	88
87	9	17	26	35	44	52	61	70	78	87
86	9	17	26	34	43	52	60	69	77	86
85	9	17	26	34	43	51	60	68	77	85

TABLE XXI.—LOGARITHMS OF NUMBERS
No. 510 Log 707   No. 554 Log 744

N.	0	1	2	3	4	5	6	7	8	9	Diff.
510	707570	7655	7740	7826	7911	7996	8081	8166	8251	8336	85
511	8421	8506	8591	8676	8761	8846	8931	9015	9100	9185	85
512	9270	9355	9440	9524	9609	9694	9779	9863	9948	*0033	85
513	710117	0202	0287	0371	0456	0540	0625	0710	0794	0879	85
514	0963	1048	1132	1217	1301	1385	1470	1554	1639	1723	84
515	711807	1892	1976	2060	2144	2229	2313	2397	2481	2566	84
516	2650	2734	2818	2902	2986	3070	3154	3238	3323	3407	84
517	3491	3575	3659	3742	3826	3910	3994	4078	4162	4246	84
518	4330	4414	4497	4581	4665	4749	4833	4916	5000	5084	84
519	5167	5251	5335	5418	5502	5586	5669	5753	5836	5920	84
520	716003	6087	6170	6254	6337	6421	6504	6588	6671	6754	83
521	6838	6921	7004	7088	7171	7254	7338	7421	7504	7587	83
522	7671	7754	7837	7920	8003	8086	8169	8253	8336	8419	83
523	8502	8585	8668	8751	8834	8917	9000	9083	9165	9248	83
524	9331	9414	9497	9580	9663	9745	9828	9911	9994	*0077	83
525	720159	0242	0325	0407	0490	0573	0655	0738	0821	0903	83
526	0986	1068	1151	1233	1316	1398	1481	1563	1646	1728	82
527	1811	1893	1975	2058	2140	2222	2305	2387	2469	2552	82
528	2634	2716	2798	2881	2963	3045	3127	3209	3291	3374	82
529	3456	3538	3620	3702	3784	3866	3948	4030	4112	4194	82
530	724276	4358	4440	4522	4604	4685	4767	4849	4931	5013	82
531	5095	5176	5258	5340	5422	5503	5585	5667	5748	5830	82
532	5912	5993	6075	6156	6238	6320	6401	6483	6564	6646	82
533	6727	6809	6890	6972	7053	7134	7216	7297	7379	7460	81
534	7541	7623	7704	7785	7866	7948	8029	8110	8191	8273	81
535	728354	8435	8516	8597	8678	8759	8841	8922	9003	9084	81
536	9165	9246	9327	9408	9489	9570	9651	9732	9813	9893	81
537	9974	*0055	*0136	*0217	*0298	*0378	*0459	*0540	*0621	*0702	81
538	730782	0863	0944	1024	1105	1186	1266	1347	1428	1508	81
539	1589	1669	1750	1830	1911	1991	2072	2152	2233	2313	81
540	732394	2474	2555	2635	2715	2796	2876	2956	3037	3117	80
541	3197	3278	3358	3438	3518	3598	3679	3759	3839	3919	80
542	3999	4079	4160	4240	4320	4400	4480	4560	4640	4720	80
543	4800	4880	4960	5040	5120	5200	5279	5359	5439	5519	80
544	5599	5679	5759	5838	5918	5998	6078	6157	6237	6317	80
545	736397	6476	6556	6635	6715	6795	6874	6954	7034	7113	80
546	7193	7272	7352	7431	7511	7590	7670	7749	7829	7908	79
547	7987	8067	8146	8225	8305	8384	8463	8543	8622	8701	79
548	8781	8860	8939	9018	9097	9177	9256	9335	9414	9493	79
549	9572	9651	9731	9810	9889	9968	*0047	*0126	*0205	*0284	79
550	740363	0442	0521	0600	0678	0757	0836	0915	0994	1073	79
551	1152	1230	1309	1388	1467	1546	1624	1703	1782	1860	79
552	1939	2018	2096	2175	2254	2332	2411	2489	2568	2647	79
553	2725	2804	2882	2961	3039	3118	3196	3275	3353	3431	78
554	3510	3588	3667	3745	3823	3902	3980	4058	4136	4215	78

PROPORTIONAL PARTS

Diff.	1	2	3	4	5	6	7	8	9	Diff.
86	9	17	26	34	43	52	60	69	77	86
85	9	17	26	34	43	51	60	68	77	85
84	8	17	25	34	42	50	59	67	76	84
83	8	17	25	33	42	50	58	66	75	83
82	8	16	25	33	41	49	57	66	74	82
81	8	16	24	32	41	49	57	65	73	81
80	8	16	24	32	40	48	56	64	72	80
79	8	16	24	32	40	47	55	63	71	79

TABLE XXI.—LOGARITHMS OF NUMBERS
No. 555 Log 744   No. 599 Log 778

N.	0	1	2	3	4	5	6	7	8	9	Diff.
555	744293	4371	4449	4528	4606	4684	4762	4840	4919	4997	78
556	5075	5153	5231	5309	5387	5465	5543	5621	5699	5777	78
557	5855	5933	6011	6089	6167	6245	6323	6401	6479	6556	78
558	6634	6712	6790	6868	6945	7023	7101	7179	7256	7334	78
559	7412	7489	7567	7645	7722	7800	7878	7955	8033	8110	78
560	748188	8266	8343	8421	8498	8576	8653	8731	8808	8885	77
561	8963	9040	9118	9195	9272	9350	9427	9504	9582	9659	77
562	9736	9814	9891	9968	*0045	*0123	*0200	*0277	*0354	*0431	77
563	750508	0586	0663	0740	0817	0894	0971	1048	1125	1202	77
564	1279	1356	1433	1510	1587	1664	1741	1818	1895	1972	77
565	752048	2125	2202	2279	2356	2433	2509	2586	2663	2740	77
566	2816	2893	2970	3047	3123	3200	3277	3353	3430	3506	77
567	3583	3660	3736	3813	3889	3966	4042	4119	4195	4272	77
568	4348	4425	4501	4578	4654	4730	4807	4883	4960	5036	76
569	5112	5189	5265	5341	5417	5494	5570	5646	5722	5799	76
570	755875	5951	6027	6103	6180	6256	6332	6408	6484	6560	76
571	6636	6712	6788	6864	6940	7016	7092	7168	7244	7320	76
572	7396	7472	7548	7624	7700	7775	7851	7927	8003	8079	76
573	8155	8230	8306	8382	8458	8533	8609	8685	8761	8836	76
574	8912	8988	9063	9139	9214	9290	9366	9441	9517	9592	76
575	759668	9743	9819	9894	9970	*0045	*0121	*0196	*0272	*0347	75
576	760422	0498	0573	0649	0724	0799	0875	0950	1025	1101	75
577	1176	1251	1326	1402	1477	1552	1627	1702	1778	1853	75
578	1928	2003	2078	2153	2228	2303	2378	2453	2529	2604	75
579	2679	2754	2829	2904	2978	3053	3128	3203	3278	3353	75
580	763428	3503	3578	3653	3727	3802	3877	3952	4027	4101	75
581	4176	4251	4326	4400	4475	4550	4624	4699	4774	4848	75
582	4923	4998	5072	5147	5221	5296	5370	5445	5520	5594	75
583	5669	5743	5818	5892	5966	6041	6115	6190	6264	6338	74
584	6413	6487	6562	6636	6710	6785	6859	6933	7007	7082	74
585	767156	7230	7304	7379	7453	7527	7601	7675	7749	7823	74
586	7898	7972	8046	8120	8194	8268	8342	8416	8490	8564	74
587	8638	8712	8786	8860	8934	9008	9082	9156	9230	9303	74
588	9377	9451	9525	9599	9673	9746	9820	9894	9968	*0042	74
589	770115	0189	0263	0336	0410	0484	0557	0631	0705	0778	74
590	770852	0926	0999	1073	1146	1220	1293	1367	1440	1514	74
591	1587	1661	1734	1808	1881	1955	2028	2102	2175	2248	73
592	2322	2395	2468	2542	2615	2688	2762	2835	2908	2981	73
593	3055	3128	3201	3274	3348	3421	3494	3567	3640	3713	73
594	3786	3860	3933	4006	4079	4152	4225	4298	4371	4444	73
595	774517	4590	4663	4736	4809	4882	4955	5028	5100	5173	73
596	5246	5319	5392	5465	5538	5610	5683	5756	5829	5902	73
597	5974	6047	6120	6193	6265	6338	6411	6483	6556	6629	73
598	6701	6774	6846	6919	6992	7064	7137	7209	7282	7354	73
599	7427	7499	7572	7644	7717	7789	7862	7934	8006	8079	72

PROPORTIONAL PARTS

Diff.	1	2	3	4	5	6	7	8	9	Diff.
78	8	16	23	31	39	47	55	62	70	78
77	8	15	23	31	39	46	54	62	69	77
76	8	15	23	30	38	46	53	61	68	76
75	8	15	23	30	38	45	53	60	68	75
74	7	15	22	30	37	44	52	59	67	74
73	7	15	22	29	37	44	51	58	66	73
72	7	14	22	29	36	43	50	58	65	72

TABLE XXI.—LOGARITHMS OF NUMBERS
No. 600 Log 778   No. 649 Log 812

N.	0	1	2	3	4	5	6	7	8	9	Diff.
600	778151	8224	8296	8368	8441	8513	8585	8658	8730	8802	72
601	8874	8947	9019	9091	9163	9236	9308	9380	9452	9524	72
602	9596	9669	9741	9813	9885	9957	*0029	*0101	*0173	*0245	72
603	780317	0389	0461	0533	0605	0677	0749	0821	0893	0965	72
604	1037	1109	1181	1253	1324	1396	1468	1540	1612	1684	72
605	781755	1827	1899	1971	2042	2114	2186	2258	2329	2401	72
606	2473	2544	2616	2688	2759	2831	2902	2974	3046	3117	72
607	3189	3260	3332	3403	3475	3546	3618	3689	3761	3832	71
608	3904	3975	4046	4118	4189	4261	4332	4403	4475	4546	71
609	4617	4689	4760	4831	4902	4974	5045	5116	5187	5259	71
610	785330	5401	5472	5543	5615	5686	5757	5828	5899	5970	71
611	6041	6112	6183	6254	6325	6396	6467	6538	6609	6680	71
612	6751	6822	6893	6964	7035	7106	7177	7248	7319	7390	71
613	7460	7531	7602	7673	7744	7815	7885	7956	8027	8098	71
614	8168	8239	8310	8381	8451	8522	8593	8663	8734	8804	71
615	788875	8946	9016	9087	9157	9228	9299	9369	9440	9510	71
616	9581	9651	9722	9792	9863	9933	*0004	*0074	*0144	*0215	70
617	790285	0356	0426	0496	0567	0637	0707	0778	0848	0918	70
618	0988	1059	1129	1199	1269	1340	1410	1480	1550	1620	70
619	1691	1761	1831	1901	1971	2041	2111	2181	2252	2322	70
620	792392	2462	2532	2602	2672	2742	2812	2882	2952	3022	70
621	3092	3162	3231	3301	3371	3441	3511	3581	3651	3721	70
622	3790	3860	3930	4000	4070	4139	4209	4279	4349	4418	70
623	4488	4558	4627	4697	4767	4836	4906	4976	5045	5115	70
624	5185	5254	5324	5393	5463	5532	5602	5672	5741	5811	70
625	795880	5949	6019	6088	6158	6227	6297	6366	6436	6505	69
626	6574	6644	6713	6782	6852	6921	6990	7060	7129	7198	69
627	7268	7337	7406	7475	7545	7614	7683	7752	7821	7890	69
628	7960	8029	8098	8167	8236	8305	8374	8443	8513	8582	69
629	8651	8720	8789	8858	8927	8996	9065	9134	9203	9272	69
630	799341	9409	9478	9547	9616	9685	9754	9823	9892	9961	69
631	800029	0098	0167	0236	0305	0373	0442	0511	0580	0648	69
632	0717	0786	0854	0923	0992	1061	1129	1198	1266	1335	69
633	1404	1472	1541	1609	1678	1747	1815	1884	1952	2021	69
634	2089	2158	2226	2295	2363	2432	2500	2568	2637	2705	68
635	802774	2842	2910	2979	3047	3116	3184	3252	3321	3389	68
636	3457	3525	3594	3662	3730	3798	3867	3935	4003	4071	68
637	4139	4208	4276	4344	4412	4480	4548	4616	4685	4753	68
638	4821	4889	4957	5025	5093	5161	5229	5297	5365	5433	68
639	5501	5569	5637	5705	5773	5841	5908	5976	6044	6112	68
640	806180	6248	6316	6384	6451	6519	6587	6655	6723	6790	68
641	6858	6926	6994	7061	7129	7197	7264	7332	7400	7467	68
642	7535	7603	7670	7738	7806	7873	7941	8008	8076	8143	68
643	8211	8279	8346	8414	8481	8549	8616	8684	8751	8818	67
644	8886	8953	9021	9088	9156	9223	9290	9358	9425	9492	67
645	809560	9627	9694	9762	9829	9896	9964	*0031	*0098	*0165	67
646	810233	0300	0367	0434	0501	0569	0636	0703	0770	0837	67
647	0904	0971	1039	1106	1173	1240	1307	1374	1441	1508	67
648	1575	1642	1709	1776	1843	1910	1977	2044	2111	2178	67
649	2245	2312	2379	2445	2512	2579	2646	2713	2780	2847	67

PROPORTIONAL PARTS

Diff.	1	2	3	4	5	6	7	8	9	Diff.
73	7	15	22	29	37	44	51	58	66	73
72	7	14	22	29	36	43	50	58	65	72
71	7	14	21	28	36	43	50	57	64	71
70	7	14	21	28	35	42	49	56	63	70
69	7	14	21	28	35	41	48	55	62	69
68	7	14	20	27	34	41	48	54	61	68

TABLE XXI.—LOGARITHMS OF NUMBERS

No. 650 Log 812   No. 699 Log 845

N.	0	1	2	3	4	5	6	7	8	9.	Diff.
650	812913	2980	3047	3114	3181	3247	3314	3381	3448	3514	67
651	3581	3648	3714	3781	3848	3914	3981	4048	4114	4181	67
652	4248	4314	4381	4447	4514	4581	4647	4714	4780	4847	67
653	4913	4980	5046	5113	5179	5246	5312	5378	5445	5511	66
654	5578	5644	5711	5777	5843	5910	5976	6042	6109	6175	66
655	816241	6308	6374	6440	6506	6573	6639	6705	6771	6838	66
656	6904	6970	7036	7102	7169	7235	7301	7367	7433	7499	66
657	7565	7631	7698	7764	7830	7896	7962	8028	8094	8160	66
658	8226	8292	8358	8424	8490	8556	8622	8688	8754	8820	66
659	8885	8951	9017	9083	9149	9215	9281	9346	9412	9478	66
660	819544	9610	9676	9741	9807	9873	9939	*0004	*0070	*0136	66
661	820201	0267	0333	·0399	0464	0530	0595	0661	0727	0792	66
662	0858	0924	0989	1055	1120	1186	1251	1317	1382	1448	66
663	1514	1579	1645	1710	1775	1841	1906	1972	2037	2103	65
664	2168	2233	2299	2364	2430	2495	2560	2626	2691	2756	65
665	822822	2887	2952	3018	3083	3148	3213	3279	3344	3409	65
666	3474	3539	3605	3670	3735	3800	3865	3930	3996	4061	65
667	4126	4191	4256	4321	4386	4451	4516	4581	4646	4711	65
668	4776	4841	4906	4971	5036	5101	5166	5231	5296	5361	65
669	5426	5491	5556	5621	5686	5751	5815	5880	5945	6010	65
670	826075	6140	6204	6269	6334	6399	6464	6528	6593	6658	65
671	6723	6787	6852	6917	6981	7046	7111	7175	7240	7305	65
672	7369	7434	7499	7563	7628	7692	7757	7821	7886	7951	65
673	8015	8080	8144	8209	8273	8338	8402	8467	8531	8595	64
674	8660	8724	8789	8853	8918	8982	9046	9111	9175	9239	64
675	829304	9368	9432	9497	9561	9625	9690	9754	9818	9882	64
676	9947	*0011	*0075	*0139	*0204	*0268	*0332	*0396	*0460	*0525	64
677	830589	0653	0717	0781	0845	0909	0973	1037	1102	1166	64
678	1230	1294	1358	1422	1486	1550	1614	1678	1742	1806	64
679	1870	1934	1998	2062	2126	2189	2253	2317	2381	2445	64
680	832509	2573	2637	2700	2764	2828	2892	2956	3020	3083	64
681	3147	3211	3275	3338	3402	3466	3530	3593	3657	3721	64
682	3784	3848	3912	3975	4039	4103	4166	4230	4294	4357	64
683	4421	4484	4548	4611	4675	4739	4802	4866	4929	4993	64
684	5056	5120	5183	5247	5310	5373	5437	5500	5564	5627	63
685	835691	5754	5817	5881	5944	6007	6071	6134	6197	6261	63
686	6324	6387	6451	6514	6577	6641	6704	6767	6830	6894	63
687	6957	7020	7083	7146	7210	7273	7336	7399	7462	7525	63
688	7588	7652	7715	7778	7841	7904	7967	8030	8093	8156	63
689	8219	8282	8345	8408	8471	8534	8597	8660	8723	8786	63
690	838849	8912	8975	9038	9101	9164	9227	9289	9352	9415	63
691	9478	9541	9604	9667	9729	9792	9855	9918	9981	*0043	63
692	840106	0169	0232	0294	0357	0420	0482	0545	0608	0671	63
693	0733	0796	0859	0921	0984	1046	1109	1172	1234	1297	63
694	1359	1422	1485	1547	1610	1672	1735	1797	1860	1922	63
695	841985	2047	2110	2172	2235	2297	2360	2422	2484	2547	62
696	2609	2672	2734	2796	2859	2921	2983	3046	3108	3170	62
697	3233	3295	3357	3420	3482	3544	3606	3669	3731	3793	62
698	3855	3918	3980	4042	4104	4166	4229	4291	4353	4415	62
699	4477	4539	4601	4664	4726	4788	4850	4912	4974	5036	62

PROPORTIONAL PARTS

Diff.	1	2	3	4	5	6	7	8	9	Diff.
67	7	13	20	27	34	40	47	54	60	67
66	7	13	20	26	33	40	46	53	59	66
65	7	13	20	26	33	39	46	52	59	65
64	6	13	19	26	32	38	45	51	58	64
63	6	13	19	25	32	38	44	51	57	63
62	6	12	19	25	31	37	43	50	56	62

TABLE XXI.—LOGARITHMS OF NUMBERS

No. 700 Log 845   No. 749 Log 875

N.	0	1	2	3	4	5	6	7	8	9	Diff.
700	845098	5160	5222	5284	5346	5408	5470	5532	5594	5656	62
701	5718	5780	5842	5904	5966	6028	6090	6151	6213	6275	62
702	6337	6399	6461	6523	6585	6646	6708	6770	6832	6894	62
703	6955	7017	7079	7141	7202	7264	7326	7388	7449	7511	62
704	7573	7634	7696	7758	7819	7881	7943	8004	8066	8128	62
705	848189	8251	8312	8374	8435	8497	8559	8620	8682	8743	62
706	8805	8866	8928	8989	9051	9112	9174	9235	9297	9358	61
707	9419	9481	9542	9604	9665	9726	9788	9849	9911	9972	61
708	850033	0095	0156	0217	0279	0340	0401	0462	0524	0585	61
709	0646	0707	0769	0830	0891	0952	1014	1075	1136	1197	61
710	851258	1320	1381	1442	1503	1564	1625	1686	1747	1809	61
711	1870	1931	1992	2053	2114	2175	2236	2297	2358	2419	61
712	2480	2541	2602	2663	2724	2785	2846	2907	2968	3029	61
713	3090	3150	3211	3272	3333	3394	3455	3516	3577	3637	61
714	3698	3759	3820	3881	3941	4002	4063	4124	4185	4245	61
715	854306	4367	4428	4488	4549	4610	4670	4731	4792	4852	61
716	4913	4974	5034	5095	5156	5216	5277	5337	5398	5459	61
717	5519	5580	5640	5701	5761	5822	5882	5943	6003	6064	61
718	6124	6185	6245	6306	6366	6427	6487	6548	6608	6668	60
719	6729	6789	6850	6910	6970	7031	7091	7152	7212	7272	60
720	857332	7393	7453	7513	7574	7634	7694	7755	7815	7875	60
721	7935	7995	8056	8116	8176	8236	8297	8357	8417	8477	60
722	8537	8597	8657	8718	8778	8838	8898	8958	9018	9078	60
723	9138	9198	9258	9318	9379	9439	9499	9559	9619	9679	60
724	9739	9799	9859	9918	9978	*0038	*0098	*0158	*0218	*0278	60
725	860338	0398	0458	0518	0578	0637	0697	0757	0817	0877	60
726	0937	0996	1056	1116	1176	1236	1295	1355	1415	1475	60
727	1534	1594	1654	1714	1773	1833	1893	1952	2012	2072	60
728	2131	2191	2251	2310	2370	2430	2489	2549	2608	2668	60
729	2728	2787	2847	2906	2966	3025	3085	3144	3204	3263	60
730	863323	3382	3442	3501	3561	3620	3680	3739	3799	3858	59
731	3917	3977	4036	4096	4155	4214	4274	4333	4392	4452	59
732	4511	4570	4630	4689	4748	4808	4867	4926	4985	5045	59
733	5104	5163	5222	5282	5341	5400	5459	5519	5578	5637	59
734	5696	5755	5814	5874	5933	5992	6051	6110	6169	6228	59
735	866287	6346	6405	6465	6524	6583	6642	6701	6760	6819	59
736	6878	6937	6996	7055	7114	7173	7232	7291	7350	7409	59
737	7467	7526	7585	7644	7703	7762	7821	7880	7939	7998	59
738	8056	8115	8174	8233	8292	8350	8409	8468	8527	8586	59
739	8644	8703	8762	8821	8879	8938	8997	9056	9114	9173	59
740	869232	9290	9349	9408	9466	9525	9584	9642	9701	9760	59
741	9818	9877	9935	9994	*0053	*0111	*0170	*0228	*0287	*0345	59
742	870404	0462	0521	0579	0638	0696	0755	0813	0872	0930	58
743	0989	1047	1106	1164	1223	1281	1339	1398	1456	1515	58
744	1573	1631	1690	1748	1806	1865	1923	1981	2040	2098	58
745	872156	2215	2273	2331	2389	2448	2506	2564	2622	2681	58
746	2739	2797	2855	2913	2972	3030	3088	3146	3204	3262	58
747	3321	3379	3437	3495	3553	3611	3669	3727	3785	3844	58
748	3902	3960	4018	4076	4134	4192	4250	4308	4366	4424	58
749	4482	4540	4598	4656	4714	4772	4830	4888	4945	5003	58

PROPORTIONAL PARTS

Diff.	1	2	3	4	5	6	7	8	9	Diff.
62	6	12	19	25	31	37	43	50	56	62
61	6	12	18	24	31	37	43	49	55	61
60	6	12	18	24	30	36	42	48	54	60
59	6	12	18	24	30	35	41	47	53	59
58	6	12	17	23	29	35	41	46	52	58

TABLE XXI.—LOGARITHMS OF NUMBERS
No. 750   Log 875

No. 799   Log 903

N.	0	1	2	3	4	5	6	7	8	9	Diff.
750	875061	5119	5177	5235	5293	5351	5409	5466	5524	5582	58
751	5540	5698	5756	5813	5871	5929	5987	6045	6102	6160	58
752	6218	6276	6333	6391	6449	6507	6564	6622	6680	6737	58
753	6795	6853	6910	6968	7026	7083	7141	7199	7256	7314	58
754	7371	7429	7487	7544	7602	7659	7717	7774	7832	7889	58
755	877947	8004	8062	8119	8177	8234	8292	8349	8407	8464	57
756	8522	8579	8637	8694	8752	8809	8866	8924	8981	9039	57
757	9096	9153	9211	9268	9325	9383	9440	9497	9555	9612	57
758	9669	9726	9784	9841	9898	9956	*0013	*0070	*0127	*0185	57
759	880242	0299	0356	0413	0471	0528	0585	0642	0699	0756	57
760	880814	0871	0928	0985	1042	1099	1156	1213	1271	1328	57
761	1385	1442	1499	1556	1613	1670	1727	1784	1841	1898	57
762	1955	2012	2069	2126	2183	2240	2297	2354	2411	2468	57
763	2525	2581	2638	2695	2752	2809	2866	2923	2980	3037	57
764	3093	3150	3207	3264	3321	3377	3434	3491	3548	3605	57
765	883661	3718	3775	3832	3888	3945	4002	4059	4115	4172	57
766	4229	4285	4342	4399	4455	4512	4569	4625	4682	4739	57
767	4795	4852	4909	4965	5022	5078	5135	5192	5248	5305	57
768	5361	5418	5474	5531	5587	5644	5700	5757	5813	5870	57
769	5926	5983	6039	6096	6152	6209	6265	6321	6378	6434	56
770	886491	6547	6604	6660	6716	6773	6829	6885	6942	6998	56
771	7054	7111	7167	7223	7280	7336	7392	7449	7505	7561	56
772	7617	7674	7730	7786	7842	7898	7955	8011	8067	8123	56
773	8179	8236	8292	8348	8404	8460	8516	8573	8629	8685	56
774	8741	8797	8853	8909	8965	9021	9077	9134	9190	9246	56
775	889302	9358	9414	9470	9526	9582	9638	9694	9750	9806	56
776	9862	9918	9974	*0030	*0086	*0141	*0197	*0253	*0309	*0365	56
777	890421	0477	0533	0589	0645	0700	0756	0812	0868	0924	56
778	0980	1035	1091	1147	1203	1259	1314	1370	1426	1482	56
779	1537	1593	1649	1705	1760	1816	1872	1928	1983	2039	56
780	892095	2150	2206	2262	2317	2373	2429	2484	2540	2595	56
781	2651	2707	2762	2818	2873	2929	2985	3040	3096	3151	56
782	3207	3262	3318	3373	3429	3484	3540	3595	3651	3706	56
783	3762	3817	3873	3928	3984	4039	4094	4150	4205	4261	55
784	4316	4371	4427	4482	4538	4593	4648	4704	4759	4814	55
785	894870	4925	4980	5036	5091	5146	5201	5257	5312	5367	55
786	5423	5478	5533	5588	5644	5699	5754	5809	5864	5920	55
787	5975	6030	6085	6140	6195	6251	6306	6361	6416	6471	55
788	6526	6581	6636	6692	6747	6802	6857	6912	6967	7022	55
789	7077	7132	7187	7242	7297	7352	7407	7462	7517	7572	55
790	897627	7682	7737	7792	7847	7902	7957	8012	8067	8122	55
791	8176	8231	8286	8341	8396	8451	8506	8561	8615	8670	55
792	8725	8780	8835	8890	8944	8999	9054	9109	9164	9218	55
793	9273	9328	9383	9437	9492	9547	9602	9656	9711	9766	55
794	9821	9875	9930	9985	*0039	*0094	*0149	*0203	*0258	*0312	55
795	900367	0422	0476	0531	0586	0640	0695	0749	0804	0859	55
796	0913	0968	1022	1077	1131	1186	1240	1295	1349	1404	55
797	1458	1513	1567	1622	1676	1731	1785	1840	1894	1948	54
798	2003	2057	2112	2166	2221	2275	2329	2384	2438	2492	54
799	2547	2601	2655	2710	2764	2818	2873	2927	2981	3036	54

PROPORTIONAL PARTS

Diff.	1	2	3	4	5	6	7	8	9	Diff.
57	6	11	17	23	29	34	40	46	51	57
56	6	11	17	22	28	34	39	45	50	56
55	6	11	17	22	28	33	39	44	50	55
54	5	11	16	22	27	32	38	43	49	54

N.	0	1	2	3	4	5	6	7	8	9	Diff.
800	903090	3144	3199	3253	3307	3361	3416	3470	3524	3578	54
801	3633	3687	3741	3795	3849	3904	3958	4012	4066	4120	54
802	4174	4229	4283	4337	4391	4445	4499	4553	4607	4661	54
803	4716	4770	4824	4878	4932	4986	5040	5094	5148	5202	54
804	5256	5310	5364	5418	5472	5526	5580	5634	5688	5742	54
805	905796	5850	5904	5958	6012	6066	6119	6173	6227	6281	54
806	6335	6389	6443	6497	6551	6604	6658	6712	6766	6820	54
807	6874	6927	6981	7035	7089	7143	7196	7250	7304	7358	54
808	7411	7465	7519	7573	7626	7680	7734	7787	7841	7895	54
809	7949	8002	8056	8110	8163	8217	8270	8324	8378	8431	54
810	908485	8539	8592	8646	8699	8753	8807	8860	8914	8967	54
811	9021	9074	9128	9181	9235	9289	9342	9396	9449	9503	54
812	9556	9610	9663	9716	9770	9823	9877	9930	9984	*0037	53
813	910091	0144	0197	0251	0304	0358	0411	0464	0518	0571	53
814	0624	0678	0731	0784	0838	0891	0944	0998	1051	1104	53
815	911158	1211	1264	1317	1371	1424	1477	1530	1584	1637	53
816	1690	1743	1797	1850	1903	1956	2009	2063	2116	2169	53
817	2222	2275	2328	2381	2435	2488	2541	2594	2647	2700	53
818	2753	2806	2859	2913	2966	3019	3072	3125	3178	3231	53
819	3284	3337	3390	3443	3496	3549	3602	3655	3708	3761	53
820	913814	3867	3920	3973	4026	4079	4132	4184	4237	4290	53
821	4343	4396	4449	4502	4555	4608	4660	4713	4766	4819	53
822	4872	4925	4977	5030	5083	5136	5189	5241	5294	5347	53
823	5400	5453	5505	5558	5611	5664	5716	5769	5822	5875	53
824	5927	5980	6033	6085	6138	6191	6243	6296	6349	6401	53
825	916454	6507	6559	6612	6664	6717	6770	6822	6875	6927	53
826	6980	7033	7085	7138	7190	7243	7295	7348	7400	7453	53
827	7506	7558	7611	7663	7716	7768	7820	7873	7925	7978	52
828	8030	8083	8135	8188	8240	8293	8345	8397	8450	8502	52
829	8555	8607	8659	8712	8764	8816	8869	8921	8973	9026	52
830	919078	9130	9183	9235	9287	9340	9392	9444	9496	9549	52
831	9601	9653	9706	9758	9810	9862	9914	9967	*0019	*0071	52
832	920123	0176	0228	0280	0332	0384	0436	0489	0541	0593	52
833	0645	0697	0749	0801	0853	0906	0958	1010	1062	1114	52
834	1166	1218	1270	1322	1374	1426	1478	1530	1582	1634	52
835	921686	1738	1790	1842	1894	1946	1998	2050	2102	2154	52
836	2206	2258	2310	2362	2414	2466	2518	2570	2622	2674	52
837	2725	2777	2829	2881	2933	2985	3037	3089	3140	3192	52
838	3244	3296	3348	3399	3451	3503	3555	3607	3658	3710	52
839	3762	3814	3865	3917	3969	4021	4072	4124	4176	4228	52
840	924279	4331	4383	4434	4486	4538	4589	4641	4693	4744	52
841	4796	4848	4899	4951	5003	5054	5106	5157	5209	5261	52
842	5312	5364	5415	5467	5518	5570	5621	5673	5725	5776	52
843	5828	5879	5931	5982	6034	6085	6137	6188	6240	6291	51
844	6342	6394	6445	6497	6548	6600	6651	6702	6754	6805	51
845	926857	6908	6959	7011	7062	7114	7165	7216	7268	7319	51
846	7370	7422	7473	7524	7576	7627	7678	7730	7781	7832	51
847	7883	7935	7986	8037	8088	8140	8191	8242	8293	8345	51
848	8396	8447	8498	8549	8601	8652	8703	8754	8805	8857	51
849	8908	8959	9010	9061	9112	9163	9215	9266	9317	9368	51

PROPORTIONAL PARTS

Diff.	1	2	3	4	5	6	7	8	9	Diff.
55	6	11	17	22	28	33	39	44	50	55
54	5	11	16	22	27	32	38	43	49	54
53	5	11	16	21	27	32	37	42	48	53
52	5	10	16	21	26	31	36	42	47	52

TABLE XXI.—LOGARITHMS OF NUMBERS

N.	0	1	2	3	4	5	6	7	8	9	Diff.
850	929419	9470	9521	9572	9623	9674	9725	9776	9827	9879	51
851	9930	9981	*0032	*0083	*0134	*0185	*0236	*0287	*0338	*0389	51
852	930440	0491	0542	0592	0643	0694	0745	0796	0847	0898	51
853	0949	1000	1051	1102	1153	1204	1254	1305	1356	1407	51
854	1458	1509	1560	1610	1661	1712	1763	1814	1865	1915	51
855	931966	2017	2068	2118	2169	2220	2271	2322	2372	2423	51
856	2474	2524	2575	2626	2677	2727	2778	2829	2879	2930	51
857	2981	3031	3082	3133	3183	3234	3285	3335	3386	3437	51
858	3487	3538	3589	3639	3690	3740	3791	3841	3892	3943	51
859	3993	4044	4094	4145	4195	4246	4296	4347	4397	4448	51
860	934498	4549	4599	4650	4700	4751	4801	4852	4902	4953	50
861	5003	5054	5104	5154	5205	5255	5306	5356	5406	5457	50
862	5507	5558	5608	5658	5709	5759	5809	5860	5910	5960	50
863	6011	6061	6111	6162	6212	6262	6313	6363	6413	6463	50
864	6514	6564	6614	6665	6715	6765	6815	6865	6916	6966	50
865	937016	7066	7117	7167	7217	7267	7317	7367	7418	7468	50
866	7518	7568	7618	7668	7718	7769	7819	7869	7919	7969	50
867	8019	8069	8119	8169	8219	8269	8320	8370	8420	8470	50
868	8520	8570	8620	8670	8720	8770	8820	8870	8920	8970	50
869	9020	9070	9120	9170	9220	9270	9320	9369	9419	9469	50
870	939519	9569	9619	9669	9719	9769	9819	9869	9918	9968	50
871	940018	0068	0118	0168	0218	0267	0317	0367	0417	0467	50
872	0516	0566	0616	0666	0716	0765	0815	0865	0915	0964	50
873	1014	1064	1114	1163	1213	1263	1313	1362	1412	1462	50
874	1511	1561	1611	1660	1710	1760	1809	1859	1909	1958	50
875	942008	2058	2107	2157	2207	2256	2306	2355	2405	2455	50
876	2504	2554	2603	2653	2702	2752	2801	2851	2901	2950	50
877	3000	3049	3099	3148	3198	3247	3297	3346	3396	3445	49
878	3495	3544	3593	3643	3692	3742	3791	3841	3890	3939	49
879	3989	4038	4088	4137	4186	4236	4285	4335	4384	4433	49
880	944483	4532	4581	4631	4680	4729	4779	4828	4877	4927	49
881	4976	5025	5074	5124	5173	5222	5272	5321	5370	5419	49
882	5469	5518	5567	5616	5665	5715	5764	5813	5862	5912	49
883	5961	6010	6059	6108	6157	6207	6256	6305	6354	6403	49
884	6452	6501	6551	6600	6649	6698	6747	6796	6845	6894	49
885	946943	6992	7041	7090	7140	7189	7238	7287	7336	7385	49
886	7434	7483	7532	7581	7630	7679	7728	7777	7826	7875	49
887	7924	7973	8022	8070	8119	8168	8217	8266	8315	8364	49
888	8413	8462	8511	8560	8609	8657	8706	8755	8804	8853	49
889	8902	8951	8999	9048	9097	9146	9195	9244	9292	9341	49
890	949390	9439	9488	9536	9585	9634	9683	9731	9780	9829	49
891	9878	9926	9975	*0024	*0073	*0121	*0170	*0219	*0267	*0316	49
892	950365	0414	0462	0511	0560	0608	0657	0706	0754	0803	49
893	0851	0900	0949	0997	1046	1095	1143	1192	1240	1289	49
894	1338	1386	1435	1483	1532	1580	1629	1677	1726	1775	49
895	951823	1872	1920	1969	2017	2066	2114	2163	2211	2260	48
896	2308	2356	2405	2453	2502	2550	2599	2647	2696	2744	48
897	2792	2841	2889	2938	2986	3034	3083	3131	3180	3228	48
898	3276	3325	3373	3421	3470	3518	3566	3615	3663	3711	48
899	3760	3808	3856	3905	3953	4001	4049	4098	4146	4194	48

PROPORTIONAL PARTS

Diff.	1	2	3	4	5	6	7	8	9	Diff.
51	5	10	15	20	26	31	36	41	46	51
50	5	10	15	20	25	30	35	40	45	50
49	5	10	15	20	25	29	34	39	44	49
48	5	10	14	19	24	29	34	38	43	48

TABLE XXI.—LOGARITHMS OF NUMBERS
No. 900 Log 954

No. 949 Log 977

N.	0	1	2	3	4	5	6	7	8	9	Diff.
900	954243	4291	4339	4387	4435	4484	4532	4580	4628	4677	48
901	4725	4773	4821	4869	4918	4966	5014	5062	5110	5158	48
902	5207	5255	5303	5351	5399	5447	5495	5543	5592	5640	48
903	5688	5736	5784	5832	5880	5928	5976	6024	6072	6120	48
904	6168	6216	6265	6313	6361	6409	6457	6505	6553	6601	48
905	956649	6697	6745	6793	6840	6888	6936	6984	7032	7080	48
906	7128	7176	7224	7272	7320	7368	7416	7464	7512	7559	48
907	7607	7655	7703	7751	7799	7847	7894	7942	7990	8038	48
908	8086	8134	8181	8229	8277	8325	8373	8421	8468	8516	48
909	8564	8612	8659	8707	8755	8803	8850	8898	8946	8994	48
910	959041	9089	9137	9185	9232	9280	9328	9375	9423	9471	48
911	9518	9566	9614	9661	9709	9757	9804	9852	9900	9947	48
912	9995	*0042	*0090	*0138	*0185	*0233	*0280	*0328	*0376	*0423	48
913	960471	0518	0566	0613	0661	0709	0756	0804	0851	0899	48
914	0946	0994	1041	1089	1136	1184	1231	1279	1326	1374	48
915	961421	1469	1516	1563	1611	1658	1706	1753	1801	1848	47
916	1895	1943	1990	2038	2085	2132	2180	2227	2275	2322	47
917	2369	2417	2464	2511	2559	2606	2653	2701	2748	2795	47
918	2843	2890	2937	2985	3032	3079	3126	3174	3221	3268	47
919	3316	3363	3410	3457	3504	3552	3599	3646	3693	3741	47
920	963788	3835	3882	3929	3977	4024	4071	4118	4165	4212	47
921	4260	4307	4354	4401	4448	4495	4542	4590	4637	4684	47
922	4731	4778	4825	4872	4919	4966	5013	5061	5108	5155	47
923	5202	5249	5296	5343	5390	5437	5484	5531	5578	5625	47
924	5672	5719	5766	5813	5860	5907	5954	6001	6048	6095	47
925	966142	6189	6236	6283	6329	6376	6423	6470	6517	6564	47
926	6611	6658	6705	6752	6799	6845	6892	6939	6986	7033	47
927	7080	7127	7173	7220	7267	7314	7361	7408	7454	7501	47
928	7548	7595	7642	7688	7735	7782	7829	7875	7922	7969	47
929	8016	8062	8109	8156	8203	8249	8296	8343	8390	8436	47
930	968483	8530	8576	8623	8670	8716	8763	8810	8856	8903	47
931	8950	8996	9043	9090	9136	9183	9229	9276	9323	9369	47
932	9416	9463	9509	9556	9602	9649	9695	9742	9789	9835	47
933	9882	9928	9975	*0021	*0068	*0114	*0161	*0207	*0254	*0300	47
934	970347	0393	0440	0486	0533	0579	0626	0672	0719	0765	46
935	970812	0858	0904	0951	0997	1044	1090	1137	1183	1229	46
936	1276	1322	1369	1415	1461	1508	1554	1601	1647	1693	46
937	1740	1786	1832	1879	1925	1971	2018	2064	2110	2157	46
938	2203	2249	2295	2342	2388	2434	2481	2527	2573	2619	46
939	2666	2712	2758	2804	2851	2897	2943	2989	3035	3082	46
940	973128	3174	3220	3266	3313	3359	3405	3451	3497	3543	46
941	3590	3636	3682	3728	3774	3820	3866	3913	3959	4005	46
942	4051	4097	4143	4189	4235	4281	4327	4374	4420	4466	46
943	4512	4558	4604	4650	4696	4742	4788	4834	4880	4926	46
944	4972	5018	5064	5110	5156	5202	5248	5294	5340	5386	46
945	975432	5478	5524	5570	5616	5662	5707	5753	5799	5845	46
946	5891	5937	5983	6029	6075	6121	6167	6212	6258	6304	46
947	6350	6396	6442	6488	6533	6579	6625	6671	6717	6763	46
948	6808	6854	6900	6946	6992	7037	7083	7129	7175	7220	46
949	7266	7312	7358	7403	7449	7495	7541	7586	7632	7678	46

PROPORTIONAL PARTS

Diff.	1	2	3	4	5	6	7	8	9	Diff.
49	5	10	15	20	25	29	34	39	44	49
48	5	10	14	19	24	29	34	38	43	48
47	5	9	14	19	24	28	33	38	42	47
46	5	9	14	18	23	28	32	37	41	46

TABLE XXI.—LOGARITHMS OF NUMBERS
No. 950 Log 977
No. 999 Log 999

N.	0	1	2	3	4	5	6	7	8	9	Diff.
950	977724	7769	7815	7861	7906	7952	7998	8043	8089	8135	46
951	8181	8226	8272	8317	8363	8409	8454	8500	8546	8591	46
952	8637	8683	8728	8774	8819	8865	8911	8956	9002	9047	46
953	9093	9138	9184	9230	9275	9321	9366	9412	9457	9503	46
954	9548	9594	9639	9685	9730	9776	9821	9867	9912	9958	46
955	980003	0049	0094	0140	0185	0231	0276	0322	0367	0412	45
956	0458	0503	0549	0594	0640	0685	0730	0776	0821	0867	45
957	0912	0957	1003	1048	1093	1139	1184	1229	1275	1320	45
958	1366	1411	1456	1501	1547	1592	1637	1683	1728	1773	45
959	1819	1864	1909	1954	2000	2045	2090	2135	2181	2226	45
960	982271	2316	2362	2407	2452	2497	2543	2588	2633	2678	46
961	2723	2769	2814	2859	2904	2949	2994	3040	3085	3130	45
962	3175	3220	3265	3310	3356	3401	3446	3491	3536	3581	45
963	3626	3671	3716	3762	3807	3852	3897	3942	3987	4032	45
964	4077	4122	4167	4212	4257	4302	4347	4392	4437	4482	45
965	984527	4572	4617	4662	4707	4752	4797	4842	4887	4932	45
966	4977	5022	5067	5112	5157	5202	5247	5292	5337	5382	45
967	5426	5471	5516	5561	5606	5651	5696	5741	5786	5830	45
968	5875	5920	5965	6010	6055	6100	6144	6189	6234	6279	45
969	6324	6369	6413	6458	6503	6548	6593	6637	6682	6727	45
970	986772	6817	6861	6906	6951	6996	7040	7085	7130	7175	45
971	7219	7264	7309	7353	7398	7443	7488	7532	7577	7622	45
972	7666	7711	7756	7800	7845	7890	7934	7979	8024	8068	45
973	8113	8157	8202	8247	8291	8336	8381	8425	8470	8514	45
974	8559	8604	8648	8693	8737	8782	8826	8871	8916	8960	45
975	989005	9049	9094	9138	9183	9227	9272	9316	9361	9405	45
976	9450	9494	9539	9583	9628	9672	9717	9761	9806	9850	44
977	9895	9939	9983	*0028	*0072	*0117	*0161	*0206	*0250	*0294	44
978	990339	0383	0428	0472	0516	0561	0605	0650	0694	0738	44
979	0783	0827	0871	0916	0960	1004	1049	1093	1137	1182	44
980	991226	1270	1315	1359	1403	1448	1492	1536	1580	1625	44
981	1669	1713	1758	1802	1846	1890	1935	1979	2023	2067	44
982	2111	2156	2200	2244	2288	2333	2377	2421	2465	2509	44
983	2554	2598	2642	2686	2730	2774	2819	2863	2907	2951	44
984	2995	3039	3083	3127	3172	3216	3260	3304	3348	3392	44
985	993436	3480	3524	3568	3613	3657	3701	3745	3789	3833	44
986	3877	3921	3965	4009	4053	4097	4141	4185	4229	4273	44
987	4317	4361	4405	4449	4493	4537	4581	4625	4669	4713	44
988	4757	4801	4845	4889	4933	4977	5021	5065	5108	5152	44
989	5196	5240	5284	5328	5372	5416	5460	5504	5547	5591	44
990	995635	5679	5723	5767	5811	5854	5898	5942	5986	6030	44
991	6074	6117	6161	6205	6249	6293	6337	6380	6424	6468	44
992	6512	6555	6599	6643	6687	6731	6774	6818	6862	6906	44
993	6949	6993	7037	7080	7124	7168	7212	7255	7299	7343	44
994	7386	7430	7474	7517	7561	7605	7648	7692	7736	7779	44
995	997823	7867	7910	7954	7998	8041	8085	8129	8172	8216	44
996	8259	8303	8347	8390	8434	8477	8521	8564	8608	8652	44
997	8695	8739	8782	8826	8869	8913	8956	9000	9043	9087	44
998	9131	9174	9218	9261	9305	9348	9392	9435	9479	9522	44
999	9565	9609	9652	9696	9739	9783	9826	9870	9913	9957	43

PROPORTIONAL PARTS

Diff.	1	2	3	4	5	6	7	8	9	Diff.
46	5	9	14	18	23	28	32	37	41	46
45	5	9	14	18	23	27	32	36	41	45
44	4	9	13	18	22	26	31	35	40	44
43	4	9	13	17	22	26	30	34	39	43

TABLE XXI-A.—7-PLACE LOGARITHMS OF NUMBERS FROM 1 to 100

No.	Log.	No.	Log.	No.	Log.	No.	Log.
1	0.0000000	26	1.4149733	51	1.7075702	76	1.8808136
2	0.3010300	27	1.4313638	52	1.7160033	77	1.8864907
3	0.4771213	28	1.4471580	53	1.7242759	78	1.8920946
4	0.6020600	29	1.4623980	54	1.7323938	79	1.8976271
5	0.6989700	30	1.4771213	55	1.7403627	80	1.9030900
6	0.7781513	31	1.4913617	56	1.7481880	81	1.9084850
7	0.8450980	32	1.5051500	57	1.7558749	82	1.9138139
8	0.9030900	33	1.5185139	58	1.7634280	83	1.9190781
9	0.9542425	34	1.5314789	59	1.7708520	84	1.9242793
10	1.0000000	35	1.5440680	60	1.7781513	85	1.9294189
11	1.0413927	36	1.5563025	61	1.7853298	86	1.9344985
12	1.0791812	37	1.5682017	62	1.7923917	87	1.9395193
13	1.1139434	38	1.5797836	63	1.7993405	88	1.9444827
14	1.1461280	39	1.5910646	64	1.8061800	89	1.9493900
15	1.1760913	40	1.6020600	65	1.8129134	90	1.9542425
16	1.2041200	41	1.6127839	66	1.8195439	91	1.9590414
17	1.2304489	42	1.6232493	67	1.8260748	92	1.9637878
18	1.2552725	43	1.6334685	68	1.8325089	93	1.9684829
19	1.2787536	44	1.6434527	69	1.8388491	94	1.9731279
20	1.3010300	45	1.6532125	70	1.8450980	95	1.9777236
21	1.3222193	46	1.6627578	71	1.8512583	96	1.9822712
22	1.3424227	47	1.6720979	72	1.8573325	97	1.9867717
23	1.3617278	48	1.6812412	73	1.8633229	98	1.9912261
24	1.3802112	49	1.6901961	74	1.8692317	99	1.9956352
25	1.3979400	50	1.6989700	75	1.8750613	100	2.0000000

TABLE XXI-B.—7-PLACE LOGARITHMS OF USEFUL CONSTANTS

Constant	Symbol	Number	Log.
Ratio of circum. to diameter	π	3.1415927	0.4971499
Ratio of dia. to circumference	$\frac{1}{\pi}$	0.3183099	9.5028501
1 radian. Deg. in arc = radius	$\frac{180}{\pi}$	57.295780	1.7581226
Minutes in arc equal to radius	$\frac{10800}{\pi}$	3437.7468	3.5362739
Length of 1° arc, unit radius	$\frac{\pi}{180}$	0.01745329	8.2418774
Length of 1' arc, unit radius	$\frac{\pi}{10800}$	0.00029089	6.4637261
Base of hyperbolic logarithms	ε	2.7182818	0.4342945

Angles Less Than 3°.—Owing to the rapid variation in sine, tangent, and cotangent of small angles, the usual straight-line method of interpolation for seconds may not be sufficiently precise. A closer method is based upon the fact that natural sines and tangents of small angles are closely proportional to the angles themselves.

In this table, f refers to a trigonometric function, and s refers to the number of seconds in an angle. Although $\log f$ varies rapidly, $(\log f - \log s)$ varies so slowly that it may be determined from values at $1'$ intervals.

EXAMPLE.—Find log tan 0° 38′ 42″.

$$\frac{\tan 38'42''}{\tan 38'} = \frac{38'\ 42''}{38'} = \frac{2322''}{2280''}$$

or $\log \tan 38' 42'' = \log 2322 + (\log \tan 2280'' - \log 2280)$
or $\log f = \log s\ \ \ \ + (\log f - \log s)$

$$\log s = 3.365862$$
$$\underline{\log f - \log s = 4.685593\ (-10)}$$
$$\log \tan 38' 42'' = 8.051455\ (-10)$$

In the reverse process of finding an angle to seconds when its logarithmic sine, tangent, or cotangent is given, first determine by inspection the value of $(\log f - \log s)$ or of $(\log f + \log s)$. Then subtract the given $\log f$ in such a way as to leave $+\log s$, and find the required angle.

Angles Greater Than 3°.—In the bulk of the table the use of the Diff. per $1''$ is replaced by a quicker method in the form of sets of corrections for multiples of $10''$ and $15''$. The number of these sets varies so as to limit the maximum error for a $50''$ correction to one in the sixth place of the logarithm anywhere within the indicated range.

Thus, log sin 36° 18′ 50″ is found quickly to be 9.772331 $+144 = 9.772475$. Because the sets of corrections are exact at the middle of the indicated range, slightly greater precision would be obtained in this example by adding a correction of 143, since the $50''$ correction at 36° 30′ is 142. This gives log sin 36° 18′ 50″ = 9.772474. Many computers subtract the $10''$ correction of 29 from log sin 36° 19′.

Obviously, corrections for any number of seconds could be obtained speedily, if the field work justifies, by combining the corrections and shifting the decimal point.

'	"	sin	log f −log s			tan	cot	log f +log s	cos	
	s	log f	4.685	575	575	log f		5.314	ten	60
0	0	−Inf.		575	575	−Inf.	+Inf.	425	ten	60
1	60	6.463726		575	575	6.463726	3.536274	425	ten	59
2	120	6.764756		575	575	6.764756	3.235244	425	ten	58
3	180	6.940847		575	575	6.940847	3.059153	425	ten	57
4	240	7.065786		575	575	7.065786	2.934214	425	ten	56
5	300	7.162696		575	575	7.162696	2.837304	425	ten	55
6	360	.241877		575	575	.241878	.758122	425	9.999999	54
7	420	.308824		575	575	.308825	.691175	425	.999999	53
8	480	.366816		574	576	.366817	.633183	424	.999999	52
9	540	.417968		574	576	.417970	.582030	424	.999999	51
10	600	7.463726		574	576	7.463727	2.536273	424	9.999998	50
11	660	.505118		574	576	.505120	.494880	424	.999998	49
12	720	.542906		574	577	.542909	.457091	423	.999997	48
13	780	.577668		574	577	.577672	.422328	423	.999997	47
14	840	.609853		574	577	.609857	.390143	423	.999996	46
15	900	7.639816		573	578	7.639820	2.360180	422	9.999996	45
16	960	.667845		573	578	.667849	.332151	422	.999995	44
17	1020	.694173		573	578	.694179	.305821	422	.999995	43
18	1080	.718997		573	579	.719003	.280997	421	.999994	42
19	1140	.742478		573	579	.742484	.257516	421	.999993	41
20	1200	7.764754		572	580	7.764761	2.235239	420	9.999992	40
21	1260	.785943		572	580	.785951	.214049	420	.999992	39
22	1320	.806146		572	581	.806155	.193845	419	.999991	38
23	1380	.825451		572	581	.825460	.174540	419	.999990	37
24	1440	.843934		571	582	.843944	.156056	418	.999989	36
25	1500	7.861662		571	583	7.861674	2.138326	417	9.999988	35
26	1560	.878695		571	583	.878708	.121292	417	.999988	34
27	1620	.895085		570	584	.895099	.104901	416	.999987	33
28	1680	.910879		570	584	.910894	.089106	416	.999986	32
29	1740	.926119		570	585	.926134	.073866	415	.999985	31
30	1800	7.940842		569	586	7.940858	2.059142	414	9.999983	30
31	1860	.955082		569	587	.955100	.044900	413	.999982	29
32	1920	.968870		569	587	.968889	.031111	413	.999981	28
33	1980	.982233		568	588	.982253	.017747	412	.999980	27
34	2040	.995198		568	589	.995219	2.004781	411	.999979	26
35	2100	8.007787		567	590	8.007809	1.992191	410	9.999977	25
36	2160	.020021		567	591	.020044	.979956	409	.999976	24
37	2220	.031919		566	592	.031945	.968055	408	.999975	23
38	2280	.043501		566	593	.043527	.956473	407	.999973	22
39	2340	.054781		566	593	.054809	.945191	407	.999972	21
40	2400	8.065776		565	594	8.065806	1.934194	406	9.999971	20
41	2460	.076500		565	595	.076531	.923469	405	.999969	19
42	2520	.086965		564	596	.086997	.913003	404	.999968	18
43	2580	.097183		564	598	.097217	.902783	402	.999966	17
44	2640	.107167		563	599	.107203	.892797	401	.999974	16
45	2700	8.116926		562	600	8.116963	1.883037	400	9.999963	15
46	2760	.126471		562	601	.126510	.873490	399	.999961	14
47	2820	.135810		561	602	.135851	.864149	398	.999959	13
48	2880	.144953		561	603	.144996	.855004	397	.999958	12
49	2940	.153907		560	604	.153952	.846048	396	.999956	11
50	3000	8.162681		560	605	8.162727	1.837273	395	9.999954	10
51	3060	.171280		559	607	.171328	.828672	393	.999952	9
52	3120	.179713		558	608	.179763	.820237	392	.999950	8
53	3180	.187985		558	609	.188036	.811964	391	.999948	7
54	3240	.196102		557	611	.196156	.803844	389	.999946	6
55	3300	8.204070		556	612	8.204126	1.795874	388	9.999944	5
56	3360	.211895		556	613	.211953	.788047	387	.999942	4
57	3420	.219581		555	615	.219641	.780359	385	.999940	3
58	3480	.227134		554	616	.227195	.772805	384	.999938	2
59	3540	.234557		554	618	.234621	.765379	382	.999936	1
60	3600	8.241855		553	619	8.241921	1.758079	381	9.999934	0
	s	log f	4.685			log f	log f	5.314		
	"	cos	log f −log s			cot	tan	log f +log s	sin	'

TABLE XXII.—LOGARITHMIC SINES,

1° 178°

'	"	sin	log f	–log s	tan	cot	log f / +log s	cos	'
	s	log f	4.685		log f	log f	5.314		
0	3600	8.241855	553	619	8.241921	1.758079	381	9.999934	60
1	3660	.249033	552	620	.249102	1.750898	380	9.999932	59
2	3720	.256094	551	622	.256165	1.743835	378	.999929	58
3	3780	.263042	551	623	.263115	1.736885	377	.999927	57
4	3840	.269881	550	625	.269956	1.730044	377	.999925	56
5	3900	8.276614	549	627	8.276691	1.723309	375	9.999922	55
6	3960	.283243	548	628	.283323	1.716677	373	.999920	54
7	4020	.289773	547	630	.289856	1.710144	372	.999918	53
8	4080	.296207	547	632	.296292	1.703708	370	.999915	52
9	4140	.302546	546	633	.302634	1.697366	368	.999913	51
10	4200	8.308794	545	635	8.308884	1.691116	365	9.999910	50
11	4260	.314954	544	637	.315046	1.684954	363	.999907	49
12	4320	.321027	543	638	.321122	1.678878	362	.999905	48
13	4380	.327016	542	640	.327114	1.672886	360	.999902	47
14	4440	.332924	541	642	.333025	1.666975	358	.999899	46
15	4500	8.338753	540	644	8.338856	1.661144	356	9.999897	45
16	4560	.344504	539	646	.344610	1.655390	354	.999894	44
17	4620	.350181	539	648	.350289	1.649711	352	.999891	43
18	4680	.355783	538	649	.355895	1.644105	351	.999888	42
19	4740	.361315	537	651	.361430	1.638570	349	.999885	41
20	4800	8.366777	536	653	8.366895	1.633105	347	9.999882	40
21	4860	.372171	535	655	.372292	1.627708	345	.999879	39
22	4920	.377499	534	657	.377622	1.622378	343	.999876	38
23	4980	.382762	533	659	.382889	1.617111	341	.999873	37
24	5040	.387962	532	661	.388092	1.611908	339	.999870	36
25	5100	8.393101	531	663	8.393234	1.606766	337	9.999867	35
26	5160	.398179	530	665	.398315	1.601685	334	.999864	34
27	5220	.403199	529	668	.403338	1.596662	332	.999861	33
28	5280	.408161	527	670	.408304	1.591696	330	.999858	32
29	5340	.413068	526	672	.413213	1.586787	328	.999854	31
30	5400	8.417919	525	674	8.418068	1.581932	326	9.999851	30
31	5460	.422717	524	676	.422869	1.577131	324	.999848	29
32	5520	.427462	523	679	.427618	1.572382	321	.999844	28
33	5580	.432156	522	681	.432315	1.567685	319	.999841	27
34	5640	.436800	521	683	.436962	1.563038	317	.999838	26
35	5700	8.441394	520	685	8.441560	1.558440	315	9.999834	25
36	5760	.445941	518	688	.446110	1.553890	312	.999831	24
37	5820	.450440	517	690	.450613	1.549387	310	.999827	23
38	5880	.454893	516	693	.455070	1.544930	307	.999824	22
39	5940	.459301	515	695	.459481	1.540519	305	.999820	21
40	6000	8.463665	514	697	8.463849	1.536151	303	9.999816	20
41	6060	.467985	512	700	.468172	1.531828	300	.999813	19
42	6120	.472263	511	702	.472454	1.527546	298	.999809	18
43	6180	.476498	510	705	.476693	1.523307	295	.999805	17
44	6240	.480693	509	707	.480892	1.519108	293	.999801	16
45	6300	8.484848	507	710	8.485050	1.514950	290	9.999797	15
46	6360	.488963	506	713	.489170	1.510830	287	.999794	14
47	6420	.493040	505	715	.493250	1.506750	285	.999790	13
48	6480	.497078	503	718	.497293	1.502707	282	.999786	12
49	6540	.501080	502	720	.501298	1.498702	280	.999782	11
50	6600	8.505045	501	723	8.505267	1.494733	277	9.999778	10
51	6660	.508974	499	726	.509200	1.490800	274	.999774	9
52	6720	.512867	498	729	.513098	1.486902	271	.999769	8
53	6780	.516726	497	731	.516961	1.483039	269	.999765	7
54	6840	.520551	495	734	.520790	1.479210	266	.999761	6
55	6900	8.524343	494	737	8.524586	1.475414	263	9.999757	5
56	6960	.528102	492	740	.528349	1.471651	260	.999753	4
57	7020	.531828	491	743	.532080	1.467920	257	.999748	3
58	7080	.535523	490	745	.535779	1.464221	255	.999744	2
59	7140	.539186	488	748	.539447	1.460553	252	.999740	1
60	7200	8.542819	487	751	8.543084	1.456916	249	9.999735	0
	s	log f	4.685		log f	log f	5.314		

"	cos	log f / –log s	cot	tan	log f / +log s	sin	'

'	"	sin	log f −log s		tan	cot	log f +log s	cos	
	s	log f	4.685		log f	log f	5.314		
0	7200	8.542819	487	751	8.543084	1.456916	249	9.999735	60
1	7260	.546422	485	754	.546691	.453309	246	.999731	59
2	7320	.549995	484	757	.550268	.449732	243	.999726	58
3	7380	.553539	482	760	.553817	.446183	240	.999722	57
4	7440	.557054	481	763	.557336	.442664	237	.999717	56
5	7500	8.560540	479	766	8.560828	1.439172	234	9.999713	55
6	7560	.563999	478	769	.564291	.435709	231	.999708	54
7	7620	.567431	476	773	.567727	.432273	227	.999704	53
8	7680	.570836	475	776	.571137	.428863	224	.999699	52
9	7740	.574214	473	779	.574520	.425480	221	.999694	51
10	7800	8.577566	471	782	8.577877	1.422123	218	9.999689	50
11	7860	.580892	470	785	.581208	.418792	215	.999685	49
12	7920	.584193	468	788	.584514	.415486	212	.999680	48
13	7980	.587469	467	792	.587795	.412205	208	.999675	47
14	8040	.590721	465	795	.591051	.408949	205	.999670	46
15	8100	8.593948	463	798	8.594283	1.405717	202	9.999665	45
16	8160	.597152	462	802	.597492	.402508	198	.999660	44
17	8220	.600332	460	805	.600677	.399323	195	.999655	43
18	8280	.603489	458	808	.603839	.396161	192	.999650	42
19	8340	.606623	457	812	.606978	.393022	188	.999645	41
20	8400	8.609734	455	815	8.610094	1.389906	185	9.999640	40
21	8460	.612823	453	818	.613189	.386811	182	.999635	39
22	8520	.615891	451	822	.616262	.383738	178	.999629	38
23	8580	.618937	450	825	.619313	.380687	175	.999624	37
24	8640	.621962	448	829	.622343	.377657	171	.999619	36
25	8700	8.624965	446	833	8.625352	1.374648	167	9.999614	35
26	8760	.627948	444	836	.628340	.371660	164	.999608	34
27	8820	.630911	443	840	.631308	.368692	160	.999603	33
28	8880	.633854	441	843	.634256	.365744	157	.999597	32
29	8940	.636776	439	847	.637184	.362816	153	.999592	31
30	9000	8.639680	437	851	8.640093	1.359907	149	9.999586	30
31	9060	.642563	435	854	.642982	.357018	146	.999581	29
32	9120	.645428	433	858	.645853	.354147	142	.999575	28
33	9180	.648274	431	862	.648704	.351296	138	.999570	27
34	9240	.651102	430	866	.651537	.348463	134	.999564	26
35	9300	8.653911	428	869	8.654352	1.345648	131	9.999558	25
36	9360	.656702	426	873	.657149	.342851	127	.999553	24
37	9420	.659475	424	877	.659928	.340072	123	.999547	23
38	9480	.662230	422	881	.662689	.337311	119	.999541	22
39	9540	.664968	420	885	.665433	.334567	115	.999535	21
40	9600	8.667689	418	889	8.668160	1.331840	111	9.999529	20
41	9660	.670393	416	893	.670870	.329130	107	.999524	19
42	9720	.673080	414	897	.673563	.326437	103	.999518	18
43	9780	.675751	412	900	.676239	.323761	100	.999512	17
44	9840	.678405	410	905	.678900	.321100	095	.999506	16
45	9900	8.681043	408	909	8.681544	1.318456	091	9.999500	15
46	9960	.683665	406	913	.684172	.315828	087	.999493	14
47	10020	.686272	404	917	.686784	.313216	083	.999487	13
48	10080	.688863	402	921	.689381	.310619	079	.999481	12
49	10140	.691438	400	925	.691963	.308037	075	.999475	11
50	10200	8.693998	398	929	8.694529	1.305471	071	9.999469	10
51	10260	.696543	396	933	.697081	.302919	067	.999463	9
52	10320	.699073	394	937	.699617	.300383	063	.999456	8
53	10380	.701589	392	942	.702139	.297861	058	.999450	7
54	10440	.704090	389	946	.704646	.295354	054	.999443	6
55	10500	8.706577	387	950	8.707140	1.292860	050	9.999437	5
56	10560	.709049	385	955	.709618	.290382	045	.999431	4
57	10620	.711507	383	959	.712083	.287917	041	.999424	3
58	10680	.713952	381	963	.714534	.285466	037	.999418	2
59	10740	.716383	379	968	.716972	.283028	032	.999411	1
60	10800	8.718800	376	972	8.719396	1.280604	028	9.999404	0
	s	log f		4.685	log f	log f	5.314		
	"	cos	log f −log s		cot	tan	log f +log s	sin	'

'	sin	D.1"	cos	Corr. for Sec.	tan	D.1"	cot	
0	8.718800	40.07	9.999404		8.719396	40.17	1.280604	60
1	.721204	39.85	.999398		.721806	39.97	.278194	59
2	.723595	39.62	.999391		.724204	39.73	.275796	58
3	.725972	39.42	.999384		.726588	39.52	.273412	57
4	.728337	39.18	.999378		.728959	39.30	.271041	56
5	8.730688	38.98	9.999371		8.731317	39.10	1.268683	55
6	.733027	38.78	.999364		.733663	38.88	.266337	54
7	.735354	38.55	.999357		.735996	38.68	.264004	53
8	.737667	38.37	.999350		.738317	38.48	.261683	52
9	.739969	38.17	.999343		.740626	38.27	.259374	51
10	8.742259	37.95	9.999336		8.742922	38.08	1.257078	50
11	.744536	37.77	.999329	" Corr.	.745207	37.87	.254793	49
12	.746802	37.55	.999322	10 1	.747479	37.68	.252521	48
13	.749055	37.37	.999315	15 2	.749740	37.48	.250260	47
14	.751297	37.18	.999308	20 2	.751989	37.30	.248011	46
15	8.753528	37.00	9.999301	30 4	8.754227	37.10	1.245773	45
16	.755747	36.80	.999294	40 5	.756453	36.92	.243547	44
17	.757955	36.60	.999287	45 5	.758668	36.73	.241332	43
18	.760151	36.43	.999279	50 6	.760872	36.55	.239128	42
19	.762337	36.23	.999272		.763065	36.35	.236935	41
20	8.764511	36.07	9.999265		8.765246	36.18	1.234754	40
21	.766675	35.88	.999257		.767417	36.02	.232583	39
22	.768828	35.70	.999250		.769578	35.82	.230422	38
23	.770970	35.52	.999242		.771727	35.65	.228273	37
24	.773101	35.37	.999235		.773866	35.48	.226134	36
25	8.775223	35.17	9.999227		8.775995	35.32	1.224005	35
26	.777333	35.02	.999220		.778114	35.13	.221886	34
27	.779434	34.83	.999212		.780222	34.97	.219778	33
28	.781524	34.68	.999205		.782320	34.80	.217680	32
29	.783605	34.50	.999197		.784408	34.63	.215592	31
30	8.785675	34.35	9.999189		8.786486	34.47	1.213514	30
31	.787736	34.18	.999181		.788554	34.32	.211446	29
32	.789787	34.02	.999174		.790613	34.15	.209387	28
33	.791828	33.85	.999166		.792662	33.98	.207338	27
34	.793859	33.70	.999158		.794701	33.83	.205299	26
35	8.795881	33.55	9.999150		8.796731	33.68	1.203269	25
36	.797894	33.38	.999142		.798752	33.52	.201248	24
37	.799897	33.25	.999134		.800763	33.37	.199237	23
38	.801892	33.07	.999126		.802765	33.22	.197235	22
39	.803876	32.93	.999118		.804758	33.07	.195242	21
40	8.805852	32.78	9.999110		8.806742	32.92	1.193258	20
41	.807819	32.63	.999102	" Corr.	.808717	32.77	.191283	19
42	.809777	32.48	.999094	10 1	.810683	32.63	.189317	18
43	.811726	32.35	.999086	15 2	.812641	32.47	.187359	17
44	.813667	32.20	.999077	20 3	.814589	32.33	.185411	16
45	8.815599	32.05	9.999069	30 4	8.816529	32.20	1.183471	15
46	.817522	31.90	.999061	40 5	.818461	32.05	.181539	14
47	.819436	31.78	.999053	45 6	.820384	31.90	.179616	13
48	.821343	31.62	.999044	50 7	.822298	31.78	.177702	12
49	.823240	31.50	.999036		.824205	31.63	.175795	11
50	8.825130	31.35	9.999027		8.826103	31.48	1.173897	10
51	.827011	31.22	.999019		.827992	31.37	.172008	9
52	.828884	31.08	.999010		.829874	31.23	.170126	8
53	.830749	30.97	.999002		.831748	31.08	.168252	7
54	.832607	30.82	.998993		.833613	30.97	.166387	6
55	8.834456	30.68	9.998984		8.835471	30.83	1.164529	5
56	.836297	30.55	.998976		.837321	30.70	.162679	4
57	.838130	30.43	.998967		.839163	30.58	.160837	3
58	.839956	30.30	.998958		.840998	30.45	.159002	2
59	.841774	30.18	.998950		.842825	30.32	.157175	1
60	8.843585		9.998941		8.844644		1.155356	0
	cos	D.1"	sin	Corr. for Sec.	cot	D.1"	tan	'

'	sin	D.1"	cos	Corr. for Sec.	tan	D.1"	cot	
0	8.843585	30.03	9.998941		8.844644	30.18	1.155356	60
1	.845387	29.93	.998932		.846455	30.08	.153545	59
2	.847183	29.80	.998923		.848260	29.95	.151740	58
3	.848971	29.67	.998914		.850057	29.82	.149943	57
4	.850751	29.57	.998905		.851846	29.70	.148154	56
5	8.852525	29.43	9.998896		8.853628	29.58	1.146372	55
6	.854291	29.30	.998887		.855403	29.47	.144597	54
7	.856049	29.20	.998878		.857171	29.35	.142829	53
8	.857801	29.08	.998869		.858932	29.23	.141068	52
9	.859546	28.95	.998860		.860686	29.12	.139314	51
10	8.861283	28.85	9.998851		8.862433	29.00	1.137567	50
11	.863014	28.73	.998841	" Corr.	.864173	28.88	.135827	49
12	.864738	28.62	.998832	10 2	.865906	28.77	.134094	48
13	.866455	28.50	.998823	15 2	.867632	28.65	.132368	47
14	.868165	28.38	.998813	20 3	.869351	28.55	.130649	46
15	8.869868	28.28	9.998804	30 5	8.871064	28.43	1.128936	45
16	.871565	28.17	.998795	40 6	.872770	28.32	.127230	44
17	.873255	28.05	.998785	45 7	.874469	28.22	.125531	43
18	.874938	27.95	.998776	50 8	.876162	28.12	.123838	42
19	.876615	27.83	.998766		.877849	28.00	.122151	41
20	8.878285	27.73	9.998757		8.879529	27.88	1.120471	40
21	.879949	27.63	.998747		.881202	27.78	.118798	39
22	.881607	27.52	.998738		.882869	27.68	.117131	38
23	.883258	27.42	.998728		.884530	27.58	.115470	37
24	.884903	27.32	.998718		.886185	27.47	.113815	36
25	8.886542	27.20	9.998708		8.887833	27.38	1.112167	35
26	.888174	27.12	.998699		.889476	27.27	.110524	34
27	.889801	27.00	.998689		.891112	27.17	.108888	33
28	.891421	26.90	.998679		.892742	27.07	.107258	32
29	.893035	26.80	.998669		.894366	26.97	.105634	31
30	8.894643	26.72	9.998659		8.895984	26.87	1.104016	30
31	.896246	26.60	.998649		.897596	26.78	.102404	29
32	.897842	26.50	.998639		.899203	26.67	.100797	28
33	.899432	26.42	.998629		.900803	26.58	.099197	27
34	.901017	26.32	.998619		.902398	26.48	.097602	26
35	8.902596	26.22	9.998609		8.903987	26.38	1.096013	25
36	.904169	26.12	.998599		.905570	26.28	.094430	24
37	.905736	26.02	.998589		.907147	26.20	.092853	23
38	.907297	25.93	.998578		.908719	26.10	.091281	22
39	.908853	25.85	.998568		.910285	26.02	.089715	21
40	8.910404	25.75	9.998558		8.911846	25.92	1.088154	20
41	.911949	25.65	.998548	" Corr.	.913401	25.83	.086599	19
42	.913488	25.57	.998537	10 2	.914951	25.73	.085049	18
43	.915022	25.47	.998527	15 3	.916495	25.65	.083505	17
44	.916550	25.38	.998516	20 3	.918034	25.57	.081966	16
45	8.918073	25.30	9.998506	30 5	8.919568	25.47	1.080432	15
46	.919591	25.20	.998495	40 7	.921096	25.38	.078904	14
47	.921103	25.12	.998485	45 8	.922619	25.28	.077381	13
48	.922610	25.03	.998474	50 9	.924136	25.22	.075864	12
49	.924112	24.95	.998464		.925649	25.12	.074351	11
50	8.925609	24.85	9.998453		8.927156	25.03	1.072844	10
51	.927100	24.78	.998442		.928658	24.95	.071342	9
52	.928587	24.68	.998431		.930155	24.87	.069845	8
53	.930068	24.60	.998421		.931647	24.78	.068353	7
54	.931544	24.52	.998410		.933134	24.70	.066866	6
55	8.933015	24.43	9.998399		8.934616	24.62	1.065384	5
56	.934481	24.35	.998388		.936093	24.53	.063907	4
57	.935942	24.27	.998377		.937565	24.45	.062435	3
58	.937398	24.20	.998366		.939032	24.37	.060968	2
59	.938850	24.10	.998355		.940494	24.30	.059506	1
60	8.940296		9.998344		8.941952		1.058048	0
	cos	D.1"	sin	Corr. for Sec.	cot	D.1"	tan	'

TABLE XXII.—LOGARITHMIC SINES,

'	sin	D.1"	cos	Corr for Sec.	tan	D.1"	cot	
0	8.940296	24.03	9.998344		8.941952	24.20	1.058048	60
1	.941738	23.93	.998333		.943404	24.13	.056596	59
2	.943174	23.87	.998322		.944852	24.05	.055148	58
3	.944606	23.80	.998311		.946295	23.98	.053705	57
4	.946034	23.70	.998300		.947734	23.90	.052266	56
5	8.947456	23.63	9.998289		8.949168	23.82	1.050832	55
6	.948874	23.55	.998277		.950597	23.73	.049403	54
7	.950287	23.48	.998266		.952021	23.67	.047979	53
8	.951696	23.40	.998255		.953441	23.58	.046559	52
9	.953100	23.32	.998243		.954856	23.52	.045144	51
10	8.954499	23.25	9.998232		8.956267	23.45	1.043733	50
11	.955894	23.17	.998220	" Corr.	.957674	23.35	.042326	49
12	.957284	23.10	.998209	10 2	.959075	23.30	.040925	48
13	.958670	23.03	.998197	15 3	.960473	23.22	.039527	47
14	.960052	22.95	.998186	20 4	.961866	23.15	.038134	46
15	8.961429	22.87	9.998174	30 6	8.963255	23.07	1.036745	45
16	.962801	22.82	.998163	40 8	.964639	23.00	.035361	44
17	.964170	22.73	.998151	45 9	.966019	22.92	.033981	43
18	.965534	22.65	.998139	50 10	.967394	22.87	.032606	42
19	.966893	22.60	.998128		.968766	22.78	.031234	41
20	8.968249	22.52	9.998116		8.970133	22.72	1.029867	40
21	.969600	22.45	.998104		.971496	22.65	.028504	39
22	.970947	22.37	.998092		.972855	22.55	.027145	38
23	.972289	22.32	.998080		.974209	22.52	.025791	37
24	.973628	22.23	.998068		.975560	22.43	.024440	36
25	8.974962	22.18	9.998056		8.976906	22.37	1.023094	35
26	.976293	22.10	.998044		.978248	22.30	.021752	34
27	.977619	22.03	.998032		.979586	22.25	.020414	33
28	.978941	21.97	.998020		.980921	22.17	.019079	32
29	.980259	21.90	.998008		.982251	22.10	.017749	31
30	8.981573	21.83	9.997996		8.983577	22.03	1.016423	30
31	.982883	21.77	.997984		.984899	21.97	.015101	29
32	.984189	21.70	.997972		.986217	21.92	.013783	28
33	.985491	21.63	.997959		.987532	21.83	.012468	27
34	.986789	21.57	.997947		.988842	21.78	.011158	26
35	8.988083	21.52	9.997935		8.990149	21.70	1.009851	25
36	.989374	21.43	.997922		.991451	21.65	.008549	24
37	.990660	21.38	.997910		.992750	21.58	.007250	23
38	.991943	21.32	.997897		.994045	21.53	.005955	22
39	.993222	21.25	.997885		.995337	21.45	.004663	21
40	8.994497	21.18	9.997872		8.996624	21.40	1.003376	20
41	.995768	21.13	.997860	" Corr.	.997908	21.33	.002092	19
42	.997036	21.05	.997847	10 2	8.999188	21.28	1.000812	18
43	.998299	21.02	.997835	15 3	9.000465	21.22	0.999535	17
44	8.999560	20.93	.997822	20 4	.001738	21.15	.998262	16
45	9.000816	20.88	9.997809	30 6	9.003007	21.08	0.996993	15
46	.002069	20.82	.997797	40 8	.004272	21.03	.995728	14
47	.003318	20.75	.997784	45 10	.005534	20.97	.994466	13
48	.004563	20.70	.997771	50 11	.006792	20.92	.993208	12
49	.005805	20.65	.997758		.008047	20.85	.991953	11
50	9.007044	20.57	9.997745		9.009298	20.80	0.990702	10
51	.008278	20.53	.997732		.010546	20.73	.989454	9
52	.009510	20.45	.997719		.011790	20.68	.988210	8
53	.010737	20.42	.997706		.013031	20.62	.986969	7
54	.011962	20.33	.997693		.014268	20.57	.985732	6
55	9.013182	20.30	9.997680		9.015502	20.50	0.984498	5
56	.014400	20.22	.997667		.016732	20.45	.983268	4
57	.015613	20.18	.997654		.017959	20.40	.982041	3
58	.016824	20.12	.997641		.019183	20.33	.980817	2
59	.018031	20.07	.997628		.020403	20.28	.979597	1
60	9.019235		9.997614		9.021620		0.978380	0
	cos	D.1"	sin	Corr for Sec.	cot	D.1"	tan	•

'	sin	D.1"	cos	Corr. for Sec.	tan	D.1"	cot	
0	9.019235	20.00	9.997614		9.021620	20.23	0.978380	60
1	.020435	19.95	.997601		.022834	20.17	.977166	59
2	.021632	19.88	.997588		.024044	20.12	.975956	58
3	.022825	19.85	.997574		.025251	20.07	.974749	57
4	.024016	19.78	.997561		.026455	20.00	.973545	56
5	9.025203	19.72	9.997547		9.027655	19.95	0.972345	55
6	.026386	19.68	.997534		.028852	19.90	.971148	54
7	.027567	19.62	.997520		.030046	19.85	.969954	53
8	.028744	19.57	.997507		.031237	19.80	.968763	52
9	.029918	19.52	.997493		.032425	19.73	.967575	51
10	9.031089	19.47	9.997480		9.033609	19.70	0.966391	50
11	.032257	19.40	.997466	" Corr.	.034791	19.63	.965209	49
12	.033421	19.35	.997452	10 2	.035969	19.58	.964031	48
13	.034582	19.32	.997439	15 3	.037144	19.53	.962856	47
14	.035741	19.25	.997425	20 5	.038316	19.48	.961684	46
15	9.036896	19.20	9.997411	30 7	9.039485	19.43	0.960515	45
16	.038048	19.15	.997397	40 9	.040651	19.37	.959349	44
17	.039197	19.08	.997383	45 10	.041813	19.33	.958187	43
18	.040342	19.05	.997369	50 12	.042973	19.28	.957027	42
19	.041485	19.00	.997355		.044130	19.23	.955870	41
20	9.042625	18.95	9.997341		9.045284	19.17	0.954716	40
21	.043762	18.88	.997327		.046434	19.13	.953566	39
22	.044895	18.85	.997313		.047582	19.08	.952418	38
23	.046026	18.80	.997299		.048727	19.03	.951273	37
24	.047154	18.75	.997285		.049869	18.98	.950131	36
25	9.048279	18.68	9.997271		9.051008	18.93	0.948992	35
26	.049400	18.65	.997257		.052144	18.88	.947856	34
27	.050519	18.60	.997242		.053277	18.83	.946723	33
28	.051635	18.57	.997228		.054407	18.80	.945593	32
29	.052749	18.50	.997214		.055535	18.73	.944465	31
30	9.053859	18.45	9.997199		9.056659	18.70	0.943341	30
31	.054966	18.42	.997185		.057781	18.65	.942219	29
32	.056071	18.35	.997170		.058900	18.60	.941100	28
33	.057172	18.32	.997156		.060016	18.57	.939984	27
34	.058271	18.27	.997141		.061130	18.50	.938870	26
35	9.059367	18.22	9.997127		9.062240	18.47	0.937760	25
36	.060460	18.18	.997112		.063348	18.42	.936652	24
37	.061551	18.13	.997098		.064453	18.38	.935547	23
38	.062639	18.08	.997083		.065556	18.32	.934444	22
39	.063724	18.03	.997068		.066655	18.28	.933345	21
40	9.064806	17.98	9.997053		9.067752	18.23	0.932248	20
41	.065885	17.95	.997039	" Corr.	.068846	18.20	.931154	19
42	.066962	17.90	.997024	10 2	.069938	18.15	.930062	18
43	.068036	17.85	.997009	15 4	.071027	18.10	.928973	17
44	.069107	17.82	.996994	20 5	.072113	18.07	.927887	16
45	9.070176	17.77	9.996979	30 7	9.073197	18.02	0.926803	15
46	.071242	17.73	.996964	40 10	.074278	17.97	.925722	14
47	.072306	17.67	.996949	45 11	.075356	17.93	.924644	13
48	.073366	17.63	.996934	50 12	.076432	17.88	.923568	12
49	.074424	17.60	.996919		.077505	17.85	.922495	11
50	9.075480	17.55	9.996904		9.078576	17.80	0.921424	10
51	.076533	17.50	.996889		.079644	17.77	.920356	9
52	.077583	17.47	.996874		.080710	17.72	.919290	8
53	.078631	17.42	.996858		.081773	17.67	.918227	7
54	.079676	17.38	.996843		.082833	17.63	.917167	6
55	9.080719	17.33	9.996828		9.083891	17.60	0.916109	5
56	.081759	17.30	.996812		.084947	17.55	.915053	4
57	.082797	17.25	.996797		.086000	17.50	.914000	3
58	.083832	17.20	.996782		.087050	17.47	.912950	2
59	.084864	17.17	.996766		.088098	17.43	.911902	1
60	9.085894		9.996751		9.089144		0.910856	0

| | cos | D.1" | sin | Corr. for Sec. | cot | D.1" | tan | ' |

TABLE XXII.—LOGARITHMIC SINES,

7°

1.72°

'	sin	D.1"	cos	Corr. for Sec.	tan	D.1"	cot	
0	9.085894	17.13	9.996751		9.089144	17.38	0.910856	60
1	.086922	17.08	.996735		.090187	17.35	.909813	59
2	.087947	17.05	.996720		.091228	17.30	.908772	58
3	.088970	17.00	.996704		.092266	17.27	.907734	57
4	.089990	16.97	.996688		.093302	17.23	.906698	56
5	9.091008	16.93	9.996673		9.094336	17.18	0.905664	55
6	.092024	16.88	.996657		.095367	17.13	.904633	54
7	.093037	16.83	.996641		.096395	17.12	.903605	53
8	.094047	16.82	.996625		.097422	17.07	.902578	52
9	.095056	16.77	.996610		.098446	17.03	.901554	51
10	9.096062	16.72	9.996594	" Corr.	9.099468	16.98	0.900532	50
11	.097065	16.68	.996578	10 3	.100487	16.95	.899513	49
12	.098066	16.65	.996562	15 4	.101504	16.92	.898496	48
13	.099065	16.62	.996546	20 5	.102519	16.88	.897481	47
14	.100062	16.57	.996530	30 8	.103532	16.83	.896468	46
15	9.101056	16.53	9.996514	40 11	9.104542	16.80	0.895458	45
16	.102048	16.48	.996498	45 12	.105550	16.77	.894450	44
17	.103037	16.47	.996482	50 13	.106556	16.72	.893444	43
18	.104025	16.42	.996465		.107559	16.68	.892441	42
19	.105010	16.37	.996449		.108560	16.65	.891440	41
20	9.105992	16.35	9.996433		9.109559	16.62	0.890441	40
21	.106973	16.30	.996417		.110556	16.58	.889444	39
22	.107951	16.27	.996400		.111551	16.53	.888449	38
23	.108927	16.23	.996384		.112543	16.50	.887457	37
24	.109901	16.23	.996368		.113533	16.47	.886467	36
25	9.110873	16.15	9.996351		9.114521	16.43	0.885479	35
26	.111842	16.12	.996335		.115507	16.40	.884493	34
27	.112809	16.08	.996318		.116491	16.35	.883509	33
28	.113774	16.05	.996302		.117472	16.33	.882528	32
29	.114737	16.02	.996285		.118452	16.28	.881548	31
30	9.115698	15.97	9.996269		9.119429	16.25	0.880571	30
31	.116656	15.95	.996252		.120404	16.22	.879596	29
32	.117613	15.90	.996235		.121377	16.18	.878623	28
33	.118567	15.87	.996219		.122348	16.15	.877652	27
34	.119519	15.83	.996202		.123317	16.12	.876683	26
35	9.120469	15.80	9.996185		9.124284	16.08	0.875716	25
36	.121417	15.75	.996168		.125249	16.03	.874751	24
37	.122362	15.73	.996151		.126211	16.02	.873789	23
38	.123306	15.70	.996134		.127172	15.97	.872828	22
39	.124248	15.65	.996117		.128130	15.95	.871870	21
40	9.125187	15.63	9.996100	" Corr.	9.129087	15.90	0.870913	20
41	.126125	15.58	.996083	10 3	.130041	15.88	.869959	19
42	.127060	15.55	.996066	15 4	.130994	15.83	.869006	18
43	.127993	15.53	.996049	20 5	.131944	15.82	.868056	17
44	.128925	15.48	.996032	30 9	.132893	15.77	.867107	16
45	9.129854	15.45	9.996015	40 11	9.133839	15.75	0.866161	15
46	.130781	15.45	.995998	45 13	.134784	15.70	.865216	14
47	.131706	15.40	.995980	50 14	.135726	15.68	.864274	13
48	.132630	15.35	.995963		.136667	15.63	.863333	12
49	.133551	15.32	.995946		.137605	15.62	.862395	11
50	9.134470	15.28	9.995928		9.138542	15.57	0.861458	10
51	.135387	15.27	.995911		.139476	15.55	.860524	9
52	.136303	15.22	.995894		.140409	15.52	.859591	8
53	.137216	15.20	.995876		.141340	15.48	.858660	7
54	.138128	15.15	.995859		.142269	15.45	.857731	6
55	9.139037	15.12	9.995841		9.143196	15.42	0.856804	5
56	.139944	15.10	.995823		.144121	15.38	.855879	4
57	.140850	15.07	.995806		.145044	15.37	.854956	3
58	.141754	15.02	.995788		.145966	15.32	.854034	2
59	.142655	15.00	.995771		.146885	15.30	.853115	1
60	9.143555		9.995753		9.147803		0.852197	0
	cos	D.1"	sin	Corr. for Sec.	cot	D.1"	tan	'

'	sin	D.1"	cos	Corr. for Sec.	tan	D.1"	cot	
0	9.143555	14.97	9.995753		9.147803	15.25	0.852197	60
1	.144453	14.93	.995735		.148718	15.23	.851282	59
2	.145349	14.90	.995717		.149632	15.20	.850368	58
3	.146243	14.88	.995699		.150544	15.17	.849456	57
4	.147136	14.83	.995681		.151454	15.15	.848546	56
5	9.148026	14.82	9.995664		9.152363	15.10	0.847637	55
6	.148915	14.78	.995646		.153269	15.08	.846731	54
7	.149802	14.73	.995628		.154174	15.05	.845826	53
8	.150686	14.72	.995610		.155077	15.02	.844923	52
9	.151569	14.70	.995591		.155978	14.98	.844022	51
10	9.152451	14.65	9.995573	" Corr.	9.156877	14.97	0.843123	50
11	.153330	14.63	.995555	10 3	.157775	14.93	.842225	49
12	.154208	14.58	.995537	15 5	.158671	14.90	.841329	48
13	.155083	14.57	.995519	20 6	.159565	14.87	.840435	47
14	.155957	14.55	.995501	30 9	.160457	14.83	.839543	46
15	9.156830	14.50	9.995482	40 12	9.161347	14.82	0.838653	45
16	.157700	14.48	.995464	45 14	.162236	14.78	.837764	44
17	.158569	14.43	.995446	50 15	.163123	14.75	.836877	43
18	.159435	14.43	.995427		.164008	14.73	.835992	42
19	.160301	14.38	.995409		.164892	14.70	.835108	41
20	9.161164	14.35	9.995390		9.165774	14.67	0.834226	40
21	.162025	14.33	.995372		.166654	14.63	.833346	39
22	.162885	14.30	.995353		.167532	14.62	.832468	38
23	.163743	14.28	.995335		.168409	14.58	.831591	37
24	.164600	14.23	.995316		.169284	14.55	.830716	36
25	9.165454	14.22	9.995297		9.170157	14.53	0.829843	35
26	.166307	14.20	.995278		.171029	14.50	.828971	34
27	.167159	14.15	.995260		.171899	14.47	.828101	33
28	.168008	14.13	.995241		.172767	14.45	.827233	32
29	.168856	14.10	.995222		.173634	14.42	.826366	31
30	9.169702	14.08	9.995203		9.174499	14.38	0.825501	30
31	.170547	14.03	.995184		.175362	14.37	.824638	29
32	.171389	14.02	.995165		.176224	14.33	.823776	28
33	.172230	14.00	.995146		.177084	14.30	.822916	27
34	.173070	13.97	.995127		.177942	14.28	.822058	26
35	9.173908	13.93	9.995108		9.178799	14.27	0.821201	25
36	.174744	13.90	.995089		.179655	14.22	.820345	24
37	.175578	13.88	.995070		.180508	14.20	.819492	23
38	.176411	13.85	.995051		.181360	14.18	.818640	22
39	.177242	13.83	.995032		.182211	14.13	.817789	21
40	9.178072	13.80	9.995013	" Corr.	9.183059	14.13	0.816941	20
41	.178900	13.77	.994993	10 3	.183907	14.08	.816093	19
42	.179726	13.75	.994974	15 5	.184752	14.08	.815248	18
43	.180551	13.72	.994955	20 6	.185597	14.03	.814403	17
44	.181374	13.70	.994935	30 10	.186439	14.02	.813561	16
45	9.182196	13.67	9.994916	40 13	9.187280	14.00	0.812720	15
46	.183016	13.63	.994896	45 15	.188120	13.97	.811880	14
47	.183834	13.62	.994877	50 16	.188958	13.93	.811042	13
48	.184651	13.58	.994857		.189794	13.92	.810206	12
49	.185466	13.57	.994838		.190629	13.88	.809371	11
50	9.186280	13.53	9.994818		9.191462	13.87	0.808538	10
51	.187092	13.52	.994798		.192294	13.83	.807706	9
52	.187903	13.48	.994778		.193124	13.82	.806876	8
53	.188712	13.45	.994759		.193953	13.78	.806047	7
54	.189519	13.43	.994739		.194780	13.77	.805220	6
55	9.190325	13.42	9.994720		9.195606	13.73	0.804394	5
56	.191130	13.38	.994700		.196430	13.72	.803570	4
57	.191933	13.35	.994680		.197253	13.68	.802747	3
58	.192734	13.33	.994660		.198074	13.67	.801926	2
59	.193534	13.30	.994640		.198894	13.65	.801106	1
60	9.194332		9.994620		9.199713		0.800287	0
	cos	D.1"	sin	Corr. for Sec.	cot	D.1"	tan	'

98°   81°

217

TABLE XXII.—LOGARITHMIC SINES,

'	sin	D.1"	cos	Corr. for Sec.	tan	D.1"	cot	
0	9.194332	13.28	9.994620		9.199713	13.60	0.800287	60
1	.195129	13.27	.994600		.200529	13.60	.799471	59
2	.195925	13.23	.994580		.201345	13.57	.798655	58
3	.196719	13.20	.994560		.202159	13.53	.797841	57
4	.197511	13.18	.994540		.202971	13.52	.797029	56
5	9.198302	13.15	9.994519		9.203782	13.50	0.796218	55
6	.199091	13.13	.994499		.204592	13.47	.795408	54
7	.199879	13.13	.994479		.205400	13.45	.794600	53
8	.200666	13.08	.994459		.206207	13.43	.793793	52
9	.201451	13.05	.994438		.207013	13.40	.792987	51
10	9.202234	13.05	9.994418		9.207817	13.37	0.792183	50
11	.203017	13.00	.994398	" Corr.	.208619	13.35	.791381	49
12	.203797	13.00	.994377	10 3	.209420	13.33	.790580	48
13	.204577	12.95	.994357	15 5	.210220	13.30	.789780	47
14	.205354	12.95	.994336	20 7	.211018	13.28	.788982	46
15	9.206131	12.92	9.994316	30 10	9.211815	13.27	0.788185	45
16	.206906	12.88	.994295	40 14	.212611	13.23	.787389	44
17	.207679	12.88	.994274	45 15	.213405	13.22	.786595	43
18	.208452	12.83	.994254	50 17	.214198	13.18	.785802	42
19	.209222	12.83	.994233		.214989	13.18	.785011	41
20	9.209992	12.80	9.994212		9.215780	13.13	0.784220	40
21	.210760	12.77	.994191		.216568	13.13	.783432	39
22	.211526	12.75	.994171		.217356	13.10	.782644	38
23	.212291	12.73	.994150		.218142	13.07	.781858	37
24	.213055	12.72	.994129		.218926	13.07	.781074	36
25	9.213818	12.68	9.994108		9.219710	13.03	0.780290	35
26	.214579	12.65	.994087		.220492	13.00	.779508	34
27	.215338	12.65	.994066		.221272	13.00	.778728	33
28	.216097	12.62	.994045		.222052	12.97	.777948	32
29	.216854	12.58	.994024		.222830	12.95	.777170	31
30	9.217609	12.57	9.994003		9.223607	12.92	0.776393	30
31	.218363	12.55	.993982		.224382	12.90	.775618	29
32	.219116	12.53	.993960		.225156	12.88	.774844	28
33	.219868	12.50	.993939		.225929	12.85	.774071	27
34	.220618	12.48	.993918		.226700	12.85	.773300	26
35	9.221367	12.47	9.993897		9.227471	12.80	0.772529	25
36	.222115	12.43	.993875		.228239	12.80	.771761	24
37	.222861	12.42	.993854		.229007	12.77	.770993	23
38	.223606	12.38	.993832		.229773	12.77	.770227	22
39	.224349	12.38	.993811		.230539	12.72	.769461	21
40	9.225092	12.35	9.993789		9.231302	12.72	0.768698	20
41	.225833	12.33	.993768	" Corr.	.232065	12.68	.767935	19
42	.226573	12.30	.993746	10 4	.232826	12.67	.767174	18
43	.227311	12.28	.993725	15 5	.233586	12.65	.766414	17
44	.228048	12.27	.993703	20 7	.234345	12.63	.765655	16
45	9.228784	12.23	9.993681	30 11	9.235103	12.60	0.764897	15
46	.229518	12.23	.993660	40 14	.235859	12.58	.764141	14
47	.230252	12.20	.993638	45 16	.236614	12.57	.763386	13
48	.230984	12.18	.993616	50 18	.237368	12.53	.762632	12
49	.231715	12.15	.993594		.238120	12.53	.761880	11
50	9.232444	12.13	9.993572		9.238872	12.50	0.761128	10
51	.233172	12.12	.993550		.239622	12.48	.760378	9
52	.233899	12.10	.993528		.240371	12.45	.759629	8
53	.234625	12.07	.993506		.241118	12.45	.758882	7
54	.235349	12.07	.993484		.241865	12.42	.758135	6
55	9.236073	12.03	9.993462		9.242610	12.40	0.757390	5
56	.236795	12.00	.993440		.243354	12.38	.756646	4
57	.237515	12.00	.993418		.244097	12.37	.755903	3
58	.238235	11.97	.993396		.244839	12.33	.755161	2
59	.238953	11.95	.993374		.245579	12.33	.754421	1
60	9.259670		9.993351		9.246319		0.753681	0
	cos	D.1"	sin	Corr. for Sec.	cot	D.1"	tan	'

'	sin	D.1"	cos	Corr. for Sec.	tan	D.1"	cot	
0	9.239670	11.93	9.993351		9.246319	12.30	0.753681	60
1	.240386	11.92	.993329		.247057	12.28	.752943	59
2	.241101	11.88	.993307		.247794	12.27	.752206	58
3	.241814	11.87	.993284		.248530	12.23	.751470	57
4	.242526	11.85	.993262		.249264	12.23	.750736	56
5	9.243237	11.83	9.993240		9.249998	12.20	0.750000	55
6	.243947	11.82	.993217		.250730	12.18	.749270	54
7	.244656	11.78	.993195		.251461	12.17	.748539	53
8	.245363	11.77	.993172		.252191	12.15	.747809	52
9	.246069	11.77	.993149		.252920	12.13	.747080	51
10	9.246775	11.72	9.993127		9.253648	12.10	0.746352	50
11	.247478	11.72	.993104	" Corr.	.254374	12.10	.745626	49
12	.248181	11.70	.993081	10 4	.255100	12.07	.744900	48
13	.248883	11.70	.993059	15 6	.255824	12.05	.744176	47
14	.249583	11.67	.993036	20 8	.256547	12.03	.743453	46
15	9.250282	11.65	9.993013	30 11	9.257269	12.02	0.742731	45
16	.250980	11.63	.992990	40 15	.257990	12.00	.742010	44
17	.251677	11.62	.992967	45 17	.258710	11.98	.741290	43
18	.252373	11.60	.992944	50 19	.259429	11.95	.740571	42
19	.253067	11.57	.992921		.260146	11.95	.739854	41
20	9.253761	11.57	9.992898		9.260863	11.92	0.739137	40
21	.254453	11.53	.992875		.261578	11.90	.738422	39
22	.255144	11.52	.992852		.262292	11.88	.737708	38
23	.255834	11.50	.992829		.263005	11.87	.736995	37
24	.256523	11.48	.992806		.263717	11.85	.736283	36
25	9.257211	11.47	9.992783		9.264428	11.83	0.735572	35
26	.257898	11.45	.992759		.265138	11.82	.734862	34
27	.258583	11.42	.992736		.265847	11.80	.734153	33
28	.259268	11.42	.992713		.266555	11.77	.733445	32
29	.259951	11.38	.992690		.267261	11.77	.732739	31
30	9.260633	11.37	9.992666		9.267967	11.73	0.732033	30
31	.261314	11.35	.992643		.268671	11.73	.731329	29
32	.261994	11.33	.992619		.269375	11.70	.730625	28
33	.262673	11.32	.992596		.270077	11.70	.729923	27
34	.263351	11.30	.992572		.270779	11.67	.729221	26
35	9.264027	11.27	9.992549		9.271479	11.65	0.728521	25
36	.264703	11.27	.992525		.272178	11.63	.727822	24
37	.265377	11.23	.992501		.272876	11.62	.727124	23
38	.266051	11.23	.992478		.273573	11.60	.726427	22
39	.266723	11.20	.992454		.274269	11.58	.725731	21
40	9.267395	11.20	9.992430		9.274964	11.57	0.725036	20
41	.268065	11.17	.992406	" Corr.	.275658	11.55	.724342	19
42	.268734	11.15	.992382	10 4	.276351	11.53	.723649	18
43	.269402	11.13	.992359	15 6	.277043	11.52	.722957	17
44	.270069	11.12	.992335	20 8	.277734	11.50	.722266	16
45	9.270735	11.10	9.992311	30 12	9.278424	11.48	0.721576	15
46	.271400	11.08	.992287	40 16	.279113	11.47	.720887	14
47	.272064	11.07	.992263	45 18	.279801	11.45	.720199	13
48	.272726	11.03	.992239	50 20	.280488	11.43	.719512	12
49	.273388	11.03	.992214		.281174	11.40	.718826	11
50	9.274049	11.03	9.992190		9.281858	11.40	0.718142	10
51	.274708	10.98	.992166		.282542	11.38	.717458	9
52	.275367	10.98	.992142		.283225	11.37	.716775	8
53	.276025	10.97	.992118		.283907	11.35	.716093	7
54	.276681	10.93	.992093		.284588	11.33	.715412	6
55	9.277337	10.93	9.992069		9.285268	11.32	0.714732	5
56	.277991	10.90	.992044		.285947	11.28	.714053	4
57	.278645	10.90	.992020		.286624	11.28	.713376	3
58	.279297	10.87	.991996		.287301	11.27	.712699	2
59	.279948	10.85	.991971		.287977	11.25	.712023	1
60	9.280599	10.85	9.991947		9.288652		0.711348	0
	cos	D.1"	sin	Corr. for Sec.	cot	D.1"	tan	'

100°   79°

TABLE XXII.—LOGARITHMIC SINES,

'	sin	D.1"	cos	Corr. for Sec.	tan	D.1"	cot	
0	9.280599	10.82	9.991947		9.288652	11.23	0.711348	60
1	.281248	10.82	.991922		.289326	11.22	.710674	59
2	.281897	10.78	.991897		.289999	11.20	.710001	58
3	.282544	10.77	.991873		.290671	11.18	.709329	57
4	.283190	10.77	.991848		.291342	11.18	.708658	56
5	9.283836	10.73	9.991823		9.292013	11.15	.707987	55
6	.284480	10.73	.991799		.292682	11.13	.707318	54
7	.285124	10.70	.991774		.293350	11.12	.706650	53
8	.285766	10.70	.991749		.294017	11.12	.705983	52
9	.286408	10.67	.991724		.294684	11.08	.705316	51
10	9.287048	10.67	9.991699		9.295349	11.07	0.704651	50
11	.287688	10.63	.991674	" Corr.	.296013	11.07	.703987	49
12	.288326	10.63	.991649	10 4	.296677	11.03	.703323	48
13	.288964	10.60	.991624	15 6	.297339	11.03	.702661	47
14	.289600	10.60	.991599	20 8	.298001	11.02	.701999	46
15	9.290236	10.57	9.991574	30 13	9.298662	11.00	0.701338	45
16	.290870	10.57	.991549	40 17	.299322	10.97	.700678	44
17	.291504	10.55	.991524	45 19	.299980	10.97	.700020	43
18	.292137	10.52	.991498	50 21	.300638	10.95	.699362	42
19	.292768	10.52	.991473		.301295	10.93	.698705	41
20	9.293399	10.50	9.991448		9.301951	10.93	0.698049	40
21	.294029	10.48	.991422		.302607	10.90	.697393	39
22	.294658	10.47	.991397		.303261	10.88	.696739	38
23	.295286	10.45	.991372		.303914	10.88	.696086	37
24	.295913	10.43	.991346		.304567	10.85	.695433	36
25	9.296539	10.42	9.991321		9.305218	10.85	0.694782	35
26	.297164	10.42	.991295		.305869	10.83	.694131	34
27	.297788	10.40	.991270		.306519	10.82	.693481	33
28	.298412	10.40	.991244		.307168	10.80	.692832	32
29	.299034	10.37	.991218		.307816	10.78	.692184	31
30	9.299655	10.35	9.991193		9.308463	10.77	0.691537	30
31	.300276	10.35	.991167		.309109	10.75	.690891	29
32	.300895	10.32	.991141		.309754	10.75	.690246	28
33	.301514	10.32	.991115		.310399	10.72	.689601	27
34	.302132	10.30	.991090		.311042	10.72	.688958	26
35	9.302748	10.27	9.991064		9.311685	10.70	0.688315	25
36	.303364	10.27	.991038		.312327	10.68	.687673	24
37	.303979	10.25	.991012		.312968	10.67	.687032	23
38	.304593	10.23	.990986		.313608	10.65	.686392	22
39	.305207	10.23	.990960		.314247	10.63	.685753	21
40	9.305819	10.20	9.990934		9.314885	10.63	0.685115	20
41	.306430	10.18	.990908	" Corr.	.315523	10.60	.684477	19
42	.307041	10.18	.990882	10 4	.316159	10.60	.683841	18
43	.307650	10.15	.990855	15 7	.316795	10.58	.683205	17
44	.308259	10.15	.990829	20 9	.317430	10.57	.682570	16
45	9.308867	10.13	9.990803	30 13	9.318064	10.55	0.681936	15
46	.309474	10.12	.990777	40 18	.318697	10.55	.681303	14
47	.310080	10.10	.990750	45 20	.319330	10.52	.680670	13
48	.310685	10.08	.990724	50 22	.319961	10.52	.680039	12
49	.311289	10.07	.990697		.320592	10.50	.679408	11
50	9.311893	10.07	9.990671		9.321222	10.48	0.678778	10
51	.312495	10.03	.990645		.321851	10.47	.678149	9
52	.313097	10.03	.990618		.322479	10.45	.677521	8
53	.313698	10.02	.990591		.323106	10.45	.676894	7
54	.314297	9.98	.990565		.323733	10.42	.676267	6
55	9.314897	10.00	9.990538		9.324358	10.42	0.675642	5
56	.315495	9.97	.990511		.324983	10.40	.675017	4
57	.316092	9.95	.990485		.325607	10.40	.674393	3
58	.316689	9.95	.990458		.326231	10.37	.673769	2
59	.317284	9.92	.990431		.326853	10.37	.673147	1
60	9.317879	9.92	9.990404		9.327475		0.672525	0
	cos	D.1"	sin	Corr. for Sec.	cot	D.1"	tan	'

'	sin	D.1"	cos	Corr. for Sec.	tan	D.1"	cot	
0	9.317879	9.90	9.990404		9.327475	10.33	0.672525	60
1	.318473	9.88	.990378		.328095	10.33	.671905	59
2	.319066	9.87	.990351		.328715	10.32	.671285	58
3	.319658	9.85	.990324		.329334	10.32	.670666	57
4	.320249	9.85	.990297		.329953	10.28	.670047	56
5	9.320840	9.83	9.990270		9.330570	10.28	0.669430	55
6	.321430	9.82	.990243		.331187	10.27	.668813	54
7	.322019	9.80	.990215		.331803	10.25	.668197	53
8	.322607	9.78	.990188		.332418	10.25	.667582	52
9	.323194	9.77	.990161		.333033	10.22	.666967	51
10	9.323780	9.77	9.990134		9.333646	10.22	0.666354	50
11	.324366	9.73	.990107	" Corr.	.334259	10.20	.665741	49
12	.324950	9.73	.990079	10 5	.334871	10.18	.665129	48
13	.325534	9.72	.990052	15 7	.335482	10.18	.664518	47
14	.326117	9.72	.990025	20 9	.336093	10.15	.663907	46
15	9.326700	9.68	9.989997	30 14	9.336702	10.15	0.663298	45
16	.327281	9.68	.989970	40 18	.337311	10.13	.662689	44
17	.327862	9.67	.989942	45 21	.337919	10.13	.662081	43
18	.328442	9.65	.989915	50 23	.338527	10.10	.661473	42
19	.329021	9.63	.989887		.339133	10.10	.660867	41
20	9.329599	9.62	9.989860		9.339739	10.08	0.660261	40
21	.330176	9.62	.989832		.340344	10.07	.659656	39
22	.330753	9.60	.989804		.340948	10.07	.659052	38
23	.331329	9.57	.989777		.341552	10.05	.658448	37
24	.331903	9.58	.989749		.342155	10.03	.657845	36
25	9.332478	9.55	9.989721		9.342757	10.02	0.657243	35
26	.333051	9.55	.989693		.343358	10.00	.656642	34
27	.333624	9.52	.989665		.343958	10.00	.656042	33
28	.334195	9.53	.989637		.344558	9.98	.655442	32
29	.334767	9.50	.989610		.345157	9.97	.654843	31
30	9.335337	9.48	9.989582		9.345755	9.97	0.654245	30
31	.335906	9.48	.989553		.346353	9.93	.653647	29
32	.336475	9.47	.989525		.346949	9.93	.653051	28
33	.337043	9.45	.989497		.347545	9.93	.652455	27
34	.337610	9.43	.989469		.348141	9.90	.651859	26
35	9.338176	9.43	9.989441		9.348735	9.90	0.651265	25
36	.338742	9.42	.989413		.349329	9.88	.650671	24
37	.339307	9.40	.989385		.349922	9.87	.650078	23
38	.339871	9.38	.989356		.350514	9.87	.649486	22
39	.340434	9.37	.989328		.351106	9.85	.648894	21
40	9.340996	9.37	9.989300		9.351697	9.83	0.648303	20
41	.341558	9.35	.989271	" Corr.	.352287	9.82	.647713	19
42	.342119	9.33	.989243	10 5	.352876	9.82	.647124	18
43	.342679	9.33	.989214	15 7	.353465	9.80	.646535	17
44	.343239	9.30	.989186	20 10	.354053	9.78	.645947	16
45	9.343797	9.30	9.989157	30 15	9.354640	9.78	0.645360	15
46	.344355	9.28	.989128	40 19	.355227	9.77	.644773	14
47	.344912	9.28	.989100	45 21	.355813	9.75	.644187	13
48	.345469	9.25	.989071	50 24	.356398	9.73	.643602	12
49	.346024	9.25	.989042		.356982	9.73	.643018	11
50	9.346579	9.25	9.989014		9.357566	9.72	0.642434	10
51	.347134	9.22	.988985		.358149	9.70	.641851	9
52	.347687	9.22	.988956		.358731	9.70	.641269	8
53	.348240	9.20	.988927		.359313	9.67	.640687	7
54	.348792	9.18	.988898		.359893	9.68	.640107	6
55	9.349343	9.17	9.988869		9.360474	9.65	0.639526	5
56	.349893	9.17	.988840		.361053	9.65	.638947	4
57	.350443	9.15	.988811		.361632	9.63	.638368	3
58	.350992	9.13	.988782		.362210	9.62	.637790	2
59	.351540	9.13	.988753		.362787	9.62	.637213	1
60	9.352088		9.988724		9.363364		0.636636	0
	cos	D.1"	sin	Corr. for Sec.	cot	D.1"	tan	'

TABLE XXII.—LOGARITHMIC SINES,

'	sin	D.1"	cos	Corr. for Sec.	tan	D.1"	cot	
0	9.352088		9.988724		9.363364		0.636636	60
1	.352635	9.12	.988695		.363940	9.60	.636060	59
2	.353181	9.10	.988666		.364515	9.58	.635485	58
3	.353726	9.08	.988636		.365090	9.58	.634910	57
4	.354271	9.08	.988607		.365664	9.57	.634336	56
5	9.354815	9.07	9.988578		9.366237	9.55	0.633763	55
6	.355358	9.05	.988548		.366810	9.55	.633190	54
7	.355901	9.05	.988519		.367382	9.53	.632618	53
8	.356443	9.03	.988489		.367953	9.52	.632047	52
9	.356984	9.02	.988460		.368524	9.52	.631476	51
		9.00				9.50		
10	9.357524		9.988430		9.369094		0.630906	50
11	.358064	9.00	.988401	" Corr.	.369663	9.48	.630337	49
12	.358603	8.98	.988371	10 5	.370232	9.48	.629768	48
13	.359141	8.97	.988342	15 7	.370799	9.45	.629201	47
14	.359678	8.95	.988312	20 10	.371367	9.47	.628633	46
15	9.360215	8.95	9.988282	30 15	9.371933	9.43	0.628067	45
16	.360752	8.95	.988252	40 20	.372499	9.43	.627501	44
17	.361287	8.92	.988223	45 22	.373064	9.42	.626936	43
18	.361822	8.92	.988193	50 25	.373629	9.42	.626371	42
19	.362356	8.90	.988163		.374193	9.40	.625807	41
		8.88				9.38		
20	9.362889		9.988133		9.374756		0.625244	40
21	.363422	8.88	.988103		.375319	9.38	.624681	39
22	.363954	8.87	.988073		.375881	9.37	.624119	38
23	.364485	8.85	.988043		.376442	9.35	.623558	37
24	.365016	8.85	.988013		.377003	9.35	.622997	36
25	9.365546	8.83	9.987983		9.377563	9.33	0.622437	35
26	.366075	8.82	.987953		.378122	9.32	.621878	34
27	.366604	8.82	.987922		.378681	9.32	.621319	33
28	.367131	8.78	.987892		.379239	9.30	.620761	32
29	.367659	8.80	.987862		.379797	9.30	.620203	31
		8.77				9.28		
30	9.368185		9.987832		9.380354		0.619646	30
31	.368711	8.77	.987801		.380910	9.27	.619090	29
32	.369236	8.75	.987771		.381466	9.27	.618534	28
33	.369761	8.75	.987740		.382020	9.23	.617980	27
34	.370285	8.73	.987710		.382575	9.25	.617425	26
35	9.370808	8.72	9.987679		9.383129	9.23	0.616871	25
36	.371330	8.70	.987649		.383682	9.22	.616318	24
37	.371852	8.70	.987618		.384234	9.20	.615766	23
38	.372373	8.68	.987588		.384786	9.20	.615214	22
39	.372894	8.68	.987557		.385337	9.18	.614663	21
		8.67				9.18		
40	9.373414		9.987526		9.385888		0.614112	20
41	.373933	8.65	.987496	" Corr.	.386438	9.17	.613562	19
42	.374452	8.65	.987465	10 5	.386987	9.15	.613013	18
43	.374970	8.63	.987434	15 8	.387536	9.15	.612464	17
44	.375487	8.62	.987403	20 10	.388084	9.13	.611916	16
45	9.376003	8.60	9.987372	30 15	9.388631	9.12	0.611369	15
46	.376519	8.60	.987341	40 21	.389178	9.12	.610822	14
47	.377035	8.60	.987310	45 23	.389724	9.10	.610276	13
48	.377549	8.57	.987279	50 26	.390270	9.10	.609730	12
49	.378063	8.57	.987248		.390815	9.08	.609185	11
		8.57				9.08		
50	9.378577		9.987217		9.391360		0.608640	10
51	.379089	8.53	.987186		.391903	9.05	.608097	9
52	.379601	8.53	.987155		.392447	9.07	.607553	8
53	.380113	8.53	.987124		.392989	9.03	.607011	7
54	.380624	8.52	.987092		.393531	9.03	.606469	6
55	9.381134	8.50	9.987061		9.394073	9.03	0.605927	5
56	.381643	8.48	.987030		.394614	9.02	.605386	4
57	.382152	8.48	.986998		.395154	9.00	.604846	3
58	.382661	8.48	.986967		.395694	9.00	.604306	2
59	.383168	8.45	.986936		.396233	8.98	.603767	1
60	9.383675	8.45	9.986904		9.396771	8.97	0.603229	0
	cos	D.1"	sin	Corr. for Sec.	cot	D.1"	tan	'

'	sin	D.1"	cos	Corr. for Sec.	tan	D.1"	cot	
0	9.383675	8.45	9.986904		9.396771	8.97	0.603229	60
1	.384182	8.42	.986873		.397309	8.95	.602691	59
2	.384687	8.42	.986841		.397846	8.95	.602154	58
3	.385192	8.42	.986809		.398383	8.93	.601617	57
4	.385697	8.40	.986778		.398919	8.93	.601081	56
5	9.386201	8.38	9.986746		9.399455	8.92	0.600545	55
6	.386704	8.38	.986714		.399990	8.90	.600010	54
7	.387207	8.37	.986682		.400524	8.90	.599476	53
8	.387709	8.35	.986651		.401058	8.88	.598942	52
9	.388210	8.35	.986619		.401591	8.88	.598409	51
10	9.388711	8.33	9.986587		9.402124	8.87	0.597876	50
11	.389211	8.33	.986555	" Corr.	.402656	8.85	.597344	49
12	.389711	8.32	.986523	10 5	.403187	8.85	.596813	48
13	.390210	8.30	.986491	15 8	.403718	8.85	.596282	47
14	.390708	8.30	.986459	20 11	.404249	8.82	.595751	46
15	9.391206	8.28	9.986427	30 16	9.404778	8.83	0.595222	45
16	.391703	8.27	.986395	45 24	.405308	8.80	.594692	44
17	.392199	8.27	.986363	50 27	.405836	8.80	.594164	43
18	.392695	8.27	.986331		.406364	8.80	.593636	42
19	.393191	8.23	.986299		.406892	8.68	.593108	41
20	9.393685	8.23	9.986266		9.407419	8.77	0.592581	40
21	.394179	8.23	.986234		.407945	8.77	.592055	39
22	.394673	8.22	.986202		.408471	8.75	.591529	38
23	.395166	8.20	.986169		.408996	8.75	.591004	37
24	.395658	8.20	.986137		.409521	8.73	.590479	36
25	9.396150	8.18	9.986104		9.410045	8.73	0.589955	35
26	.396641	8.18	.986072		.410569	8.72	.589431	34
27	.397132	8.15	.986039		.411092	8.72	.588908	33
28	.397621	8.17	.986007		.411615	8.70	.588385	32
29	.398111	8.15	.985974		.412137	8.68	.587863	31
30	9.398600	8.13	9.985942		9.412658	8.68	0.587342	30
31	.399088	8.12	.985909		.413179	8.67	.586821	29
32	.399575	8.12	.985876		.413699	8.67	.586301	28
33	.400062	8.12	.985843		.414219	8.65	.585781	27
34	.400549	8.10	.985811		.414738	8.65	.585262	26
35	9.401035	8.08	9.985778		9.415257	8.63	0.584743	25
36	.401520	8.08	.985745		.415775	8.63	.584225	24
37	.402005	8.07	.985712		.416293	8.62	.583707	23
38	.402489	8.05	.985679		.416810	8.60	.583190	22
39	.402972	8.05	.985646		.417326	8.60	.582674	21
40	9.403455	8.05	9.985613		9.417842	8.60	0.582158	20
41	.403938	8.03	.985580	" Corr.	.418358	8.58	.581642	19
42	.404420	8.02	.985547	10 6	.418873	8.57	.581127	18
43	.404901	8.02	.985514	15 8	.419387	8.57	.580613	17
44	.405382	8.00	.985480	20 11	.419901	8.57	.580099	16
45	9.405862	7.98	9.985447	30 17	9.420415	8.53	0.579585	15
46	.406341	7.98	.985414	40 22	.420927	8.55	.579073	14
47	.406820	7.98	.985381	45 25	.421440	8.53	.578560	13
48	.407299	7.97	.985347	50 28	.421952	8.52	.578048	12
49	.407777	7.95	.985314		.422463	8.52	.577537	11
50	9.408254	7.95	9.985280		9.422974	8.50	0.577026	10
51	.408731	7.93	.985247		.423484	8.48	.576516	9
52	.409207	7.92	.985213		.423993	8.50	.576007	8
53	.409682	7.92	.985180		.424503	8.47	.575497	7
54	.410157	7.92	.985146		.425011	8.47	.574989	6
55	9.410632	7.90	9.985113		9.425519	8.47	0.574481	5
56	.411106	7.88	.985079		.426027	8.45	.573973	4
57	.411579	7.88	.985045		.426534	8.45	.573466	3
58	.412052	7.87	.985011		.427041	8.43	.572959	2
59	.412524	7.87	.984978		.427547	8.42	.572453	1
60	9.412996		9.984944		9.428052		0.571948	0

	cos	D.1"	sin	Corr. for Sec.	cot	D.1"	tan	'

TABLE XXII.—LOGARITHMIC SINES,

'	sin	D.1"	cos	Corr. for Sec.	tan	D.1"	cot	
0	9.412996	7.85	9.984944		9.428052	8.43	0.571948	60
1	.413467	7.85	.984910		.428558	8.40	.571442	59
2	.413938	7.83	.984876		.429062	8.40	.570938	58
3	.414408	7.83	.984842		.429566	8.40	.570434	57
4	.414878	7.82	.984808		.430070	8.38	.569930	56
5	9.415347	7.80	9.984774		9.430573	8.37	0.569427	55
6	.415815	7.80	.984740		.431075	8.37	.568925	54
7	.416283	7.80	.984706		.431577	8.37	.568423	53
8	.416751	7.77	.984672		.432079	8.35	.567921	52
9	.417217	7.78	.984638		.432580	8.33	.567420	51
10	9.417684	7.77	9.984603		9.433080	8.33	0.566920	50
11	.418150	7.75	.984569	" Corr.	.433580	8.33	.566420	49
12	.418615	7.73	.984535	10 6	.434080	8.33	.565920	48
13	.419079	7.75	.984500	15 9	.434579	8.32	.565421	47
14	.419544	7.72	.984466	20 11	.435078	8.32	.564922	46
15	9.420007	7.72	9.984432	30 17	9.435576	8.30	0.564424	45
16	.420470	7.72	.984397	40 23	.436073	8.28	.563927	44
17	.420933	7.70	.984363	45 26	.436570	8.28	.563430	43
18	.421395	7.70	.984328	50 29	.437067	8.28	.562933	42
19	.421857	7.68	.984294		.437563	8.27	.562437	41
20	9.422318	7.67	9.984259		9.438059	8.27	0.561941	40
21	.422778	7.67	.984224		.438554	8.25	.561446	39
22	.423238	7.65	.984190		.439048	8.23	.560952	38
23	.423697	7.65	.984155		.439543	8.23	.560457	37
24	.424156	7.65	.984120		.440036	8.22	.559964	36
25	9.424615	7.63	9.984085		9.440529	8.22	0.559471	35
26	.425073	7.62	.984050		.441022	8.22	.558978	34
27	.425530	7.62	.984015		.441514	8.20	.558486	33
28	.425987	7.60	.983981		.442006	8.20	.557994	32
29	.426443	7.60	.983946		.442497	8.18	.557503	31
30	9.426899	7.58	9.983911		9.442988	8.18	0.557012	30
31	.427354	7.58	.983875		.443479	8.15	.556521	29
32	.427809	7.57	.983840		.443968	8.17	.556032	28
33	.428263	7.57	.983805		.444458	8.15	.555542	27
34	.428717	7.55	.983770		.444947	8.13	.555053	26
35	9.429170	7.55	9.983735		9.445435	8.13	0.554565	25
36	.429623	7.53	.983700		.445923	8.13	.554077	24
37	.430075	7.53	.983664		.446411	8.12	.553589	23
38	.430527	7.52	.983629		.446898	8.10	.553102	22
39	.430978	7.52	.983594		.447384	8.10	.552616	21
40	9.431429	7.50	9.983558		9.447870	8.10	0.552130	20
41	.431879	7.50	.983523	" Corr.	.448356	8.08	.551644	19
42	.432329	7.48	.983487	10 6	.448841	8.08	.551159	18
43	.432778	7.47	.983452	15 9	.449326	8.07	.550674	17
44	.433226	7.48	.983416	20 12	.449810	8.07	.550190	16
45	9.433675	7.45	9.983381	30 18	9.450294	8.05	0.549706	15
46	.434122	7.45	.983345	40 24	.450777	8.05	.549223	14
47	.434569	7.45	.983309	45 27	.451260	8.05	.548740	13
48	.435016	7.43	.983273	50 30	.451743	8.03	.548257	12
49	.435462	7.43	.983238		.452225	8.02	.547775	11
50	9.435908	7.42	9.983202		9.452706	8.02	0.547294	10
51	.436353	7.42	.983166		.453187	8.02	.546813	9
52	.436798	7.40	.983130		.453668	8.00	.546332	8
53	.437242	7.40	.983094		.454148	8.00	.545852	7
54	.437686	7.38	.983058		.454628	7.98	.545372	6
55	9.438129	7.38	9.983022		9.455107	7.98	0.544893	5
56	.438572	7.37	.982986		.455586	7.97	.544414	4
57	.439014	7.37	.982950		.456064	7.97	.543936	3
58	.439456	7.35	.982914		.456542	7.95	.543458	2
59	.439897	7.35	.982878		.457019	7.95	.542981	1
60	9.440338		9.982842		9.457496		0.542504	0
	cos	D.1"	sin	Corr. for Sec.	cot	D.1"	tan	'

'	sin	D.1"	cos	Corr. for Sec.	tan	D.1"	cot	
0	9.440338	7.33	9.982842		9.457496	7.95	0.542504	60
1	.440778	7.33	.982805		.457973	7.93	.542027	59
2	.441218	7.33	.982769		.458449	7.93	.541551	58
3	.441658	7.30	.982733		.458925	7.92	.541075	57
4	.442096	7.32	.982696		.459400	7.92	.540600	56
5	9.442535	7.30	9.982660		9.459875	7.92	0.540125	55
6	.442973	7.28	.982624		.460349	7.90	.539651	54
7	.443410	7.28	.982587		.460823	7.90	.539177	53
8	.443847	7.28	.982551		.461297	7.90	.538703	52
9	.444284	7.27	.982514		.461770	7.88	.538230	51
10	9.444720	7.25	9.982477		9.462242	7.87	0.537758	50
11	.445155	7.25	.982441	" Corr.	.462715	7.88	.537285	49
12	.445590	7.25	.982404	10 6	.463186	7.85	.536814	48
13	.446025	7.23	.982367	15 9	.463658	7.87	.536342	47
14	.446459	7.23	.982331	20 12	.464128	7.83	.535872	46
15	9.446893	7.22	9.982294	30 18	9.464599	7.85	0.535401	45
16	.447326	7.22	.982257	40 25	.465069	7.83	.534931	44
17	.447759	7.20	.982220	45 28	.465539	7.83	.534461	43
18	.448191	7.20	.982183	50 31	.466008	7.82	.533992	42
19	.448623	7.18	.982146		.466477	7.82	.533523	41
20	9.449054	7.18	9.982109		9.466945	7.80	0.533055	40
21	.449485	7.17	.982072		.467413	7.80	.532587	39
22	.449915	7.17	.982035		.467880	7.78	.532120	38
23	.450345	7.17	.981998		.468347	7.78	.531653	37
24	.450775	7.15	.981961		.468814	7.78	.531186	36
25	9.451204	7.13	9.981924		9.469280	7.77	0.530720	35
26	.451632	7.13	.981886		.469746	7.77	.530254	34
27	.452060	7.13	.981849		.470211	7.75	.529789	33
28	.452488	7.12	.981812		.470676	7.75	.529324	32
29	.452915	7.12	.981774		.471141	7.75	.528859	31
30	9.453342	7.10	9.981737		9.471605	7.73	0.528395	30
31	.453768	7.10	.981700		.472069	7.73	.527931	29
32	.454194	7.08	.981662		.472532	7.72	.527468	28
33	.454619	7.08	.981625		.472995	7.72	.527005	27
34	.455044	7.08	.981587		.473457	7.70	.526543	26
35	9.455469	7.07	9.981549		9.473919	7.70	0.526081	25
36	.455893	7.05	.981512		.474381	7.68	.525619	24
37	.456316	7.05	.981474		.474842	7.68	.525158	23
38	.456739	7.05	.981436		.475303	7.67	.524697	22
39	.457162	7.03	.981399		.475763	7.67	.524237	21
40	9.457584	7.03	9.981361		9.476223	7.67	0.523777	20
41	.458006	7.02	.981323	" Corr.	.476683	7.65	.523317	19
42	.458427	7.02	.981285	10 6	.477142	7.65	.522858	18
43	.458848	7.00	.981247	15 10	.477601	7.63	.522399	17
44	.459268	7.00	.981209	20 13	.478059	7.63	.521941	16
45	9.459688	7.00	9.981171	30 19	9.478517	7.63	0.521483	15
46	.460108	6.98	.981133	40 25	.478975	7.62	.521025	14
47	.460527	6.98	.981095	45 29	.479432	7.62	.520568	13
48	.460946	6.97	.981057	50 32	.479889	7.60	.520111	12
49	.461364	6.97	.981019		.480345	7.60	.519655	11
50	9.461782	6.95	9.980981		9.480801	7.60	0.519199	10
51	.462199	6.95	.980942		.481257	7.58	.518743	9
52	.462616	6.93	.980904		.481712	7.58	.518288	8
53	.463032	6.93	.980866		.482167	7.57	.517833	7
54	.463448	6.93	.980827		.482621	7.57	.517379	6
55	9.463864	6.92	9.980789		9.483075	7.57	0.516925	5
56	.464279	6.92	.980750		.483529	7.55	.516471	4
57	.464694	6.90	.980712		.483982	7.55	.516018	3
58	.465108	6.90	.980673		.484435	7.55	.515565	2
59	.465522	6.88	.980635		.484887	7.53	.515113	1
60	9.465935		9.980596		9.485339	7.53	0.514661	0

| | cos | D.1" | sin | Corr. for Sec. | cot | D.1" | tan | ' |

TABLE XXII.—LOGARITHMIC SINES,

'	sin	D.1"	cos	Corr. for Sec.	tan	D.1"	cot	
0	9.465935	6.88	9.980596		9.485339	7.53	0.514661	60
1	.466348	6.88	.980558		.485791	7.52	.514209	59
2	.466761	6.87	.980519		.486242	7.52	.513758	58
3	.467173	6.87	.980480		.486693	7.50	.513307	57
4	.467585	6.85	.980442		.487143	7.50	.512857	56
5	9.467996	6.85	9.980403		9.487593	7.50	0.512407	55
6	.468407	6.83	.980364		.488043	7.48	.511957	54
7	.468817	6.83	.980325		.488492	7.48	.511508	53
8	.469227	6.83	.980286		.488941	7.48	.511059	52
9	.469637	6.82	.980247		.489390	7.47	.510610	51
10	9.470046	6.82	9.980208		9.489838	7.47	0.510162	50
11	.470455	6.80	.980169	" Corr.	.490286	7.45	.509714	49
12	.470863	6.80	.980130	10 7	.490733	7.45	.509267	48
13	.471271	6.80	.980091	15 10	.491180	7.45	.508820	47
14	.471679	6.78	.980052	20 13	.491627	7.45	.508373	46
15	9.472086	6.77	9.980012	30 20	9.492073	7.43	0.507927	45
16	.472492	6.77	.979973	40 26	.492519	7.43	.507481	44
17	.472898	6.77	.979934	45 29	.492965	7.43	.507035	43
18	.473304	6.77	.979895	50 33	.493410	7.42	.506590	42
19	.473710	6.75	.979855		.493854	7.42	.506146	41
20	9.474115	6.73	9.979816		9.494299	7.40	0.505701	40
21	.474519	6.73	.979776		.494743	7.40	.505257	39
22	.474923	6.73	.979737		.495186	7.38	.504814	38
23	.475327	6.72	.979697		.495630	7.40	.504370	37
24	.475730	6.72	.979658		.496073	7.38	.503927	36
25	9.476133	6.72	9.979618		9.496515	7.37	0.503485	35
26	.476536	6.72	.979579		.496957	7.37	.503043	34
27	.476938	6.70	.979539		.497399	7.37	.502601	33
28	.477340	6.70	.979499		.497841	7.37	.502159	32
29	.477741	6.68	.979459		.498282	7.35	.501718	31
30	9.478142	6.68	9.979420		9.498722	7.33	0.501278	30
31	.478542	6.67	.979380		.499163	7.35	.500837	29
32	.478942	6.67	.979340		.499603	7.33	.500397	28
33	.479342	6.67	.979300		.500042	7.32	.499958	27
34	.479741	6.65	.979260		.500481	7.32	.499519	26
35	9.480140	6.65	9.979220		9.500920	7.32	0.499080	25
36	.480539	6.65	.979180		.501359	7.30	.498641	24
37	.480937	6.63	.979140		.501797	7.30	.498203	23
38	.481334	6.62	.979100		.502235	7.28	.497765	22
39	.481731	6.62	.979059		.502672	7.28	.497328	21
40	9.482128	6.62	9.979019		9.503109	7.28	0.496891	20
41	.482525	6.62	.978979	" Corr.	.503546	7.27	.496454	19
42	.482921	6.60	.978939	10 7	.503982	7.27	.496018	18
43	.483316	6.58	.978898	15 10	.504418	7.27	.495582	17
44	.483712	6.60	.978858	20 13	.504854	7.25	.495146	16
45	9.484107	6.58	9.978817	30 20	9.505289	7.25	0.494711	15
46	.484501	6.57	.978777	40 27	.505724	7.25	.494276	14
47	.484895	6.57	.978737	45 30	.506159	7.23	.493841	13
48	.485289	6.55	.978696	50 34	.506593	7.23	.493407	12
49	.485682	6.55	.978655		.507027	7.22	.492973	11
50	9.486075	6.53	9.978615		9.507460	7.22	0.492540	10
51	.486467	6.55	.978574		.507893	7.22	.492107	9
52	.486860	6.52	.978533		.508326	7.22	.491674	8
53	.487251	6.53	.978493		.508759	7.20	.491241	7
54	.487643	6.52	.978452		.509191	7.18	.490809	6
55	9.488034	6.50	9.978411		9.509622	7.20	0.490378	5
56	.488424	6.50	.978370		.510054	7.20	.489946	4
57	.488814	6.50	.978329		.510485	7.18	.489515	3
58	.489204	6.48	.978288		.510916	7.18	.489084	2
59	.489593	6.48	.978247		.511346	7.17	.488654	1
60	9.489982		9.978206		9.511776	7.17	0.488224	0
	cos	D.1"	sin	Corr. for Sec.	cot	D.1"	tan	'

'	sin	D.1"	cos	Corr. for Sec.	tan	D.1"	cot	
0	9.489982	6.48	9.978206		9.511776	7.17	0.488224	60
1	.490371	6.47	.978165		.512206	7.15	.487794	59
2	.490759	6.47	.978124		.512635	7.15	.487365	58
3	.491147	6.47	.978083		.513064	7.15	.486936	57
4	.491535	6.45	.978042		.513493	7.13	.486507	56
5	9.491922	6.45	9.978001		9.513921	7.13	0.486079	55
6	.492308	6.43	.977959		.514349	7.13	.485651	54
7	.492695	6.43	.977918		.514777	7.12	.485223	53
8	.493081	6.42	.977877		.515204	7.12	.484796	52
9	.493466	6.42	.977835		.515631	7.10	.484369	51
10	9.493851	6.42	9.977794		9.516057	7.12	0.483943	50
11	.494236	6.42	.977752	" Corr.	.516484	7.10	.483516	49
12	.494621	6.40	.977711	10 7	.516910	7.10	.483090	48
13	.495005	6.38	.977669	15 10	.517335	7.08	.482665	47
14	.495388	6.40	.977628	20 14	.517761	7.10	.482239	46
15	9.495772	6.37	9.977586	30 21	9.518186	7.08	0.481814	45
16	.496154	6.38	.977544	40 28	.518610	7.07	.481390	44
17	.496537	6.37	.977503	45 31	.519034	7.07	.480966	43
18	.496919	6.37	.977461	50 35	.519458	7.07	.480542	42
19	.497301	6.35	.977419		.519882	7.05	.480118	41
20	9.497682	6.37	9.977377		9.520305	7.05	0.479695	40
21	.498064	6.33	.977335		.520728	7.05	.479272	39
22	.498444	6.35	.977293		.521151	7.03	.478849	38
23	.498825	6.32	.977251		.521573	7.03	.478427	37
24	.499204	6.33	.977209		.521995	7.03	.478005	36
25	9.499584	6.32	9.977167		9.522417	7.02	0.477583	35
26	.499963	6.32	.977125		.522838	7.02	.477182	34
27	.500342	6.32	.977083		.523259	7.02	.476741	33
28	.500721	6.30	.977041		.523680	7.00	.476320	32
29	.501099	6.28	.976999		.524100	7.00	.475900	31
30	9.501476	6.30	9.976957		9.524520	7.00	0.475480	30
31	.501854	6.28	.976914		.524940	6.98	.475060	29
32	.502231	6.27	.976872		.525359	6.98	.474641	28
33	.502607	6.28	.976830		.525778	6.98	.474222	27
34	.502984	6.27	.976787		.526197	6.97	.473803	26
35	9.503360	6.25	9.976745		9.526615	6.97	0.473385	25
36	.503735	6.25	.976702		.527033	6.97	.472967	24
37	.504110	6.25	.976660		.527451	6.95	.472549	23
38	.504485	6.25	.976617		.527868	6.95	.472132	22
39	.504860	6.23	.976574		.528285	6.95	.471715	21
40	9.505234	6.23	9.976532		9.528702	6.95	0.471298	20
41	.505608	6.22	.976489	" Corr.	.529119	6.93	.470881	19
42	.505981	6.22	.976446	10 7	.529535	6.93	.470465	18
43	.506354	6.22	.976404	15 11	.529951	6.93	.470049	17
44	.506727	6.20	.976361	20 14	.530366	6.92	.469634	16
45	9.507099	6.20	9.976318	30 21	9.530781	6.92	0.469219	15
46	.507471	6.20	.976275	40 29	.531196	6.92	.468804	14
47	.507843	6.18	.976232	45 32	.531611	6.90	.468389	13
48	.508214	6.18	.976189	50 36	.532025	6.90	.467975	12
49	.508585	6.18	.976146		.532439	6.90	.467561	11
50	9.508956	6.17	9.976103		9.532853	6.88	0.467147	10
51	.509326	6.17	.976060		.533266	6.88	.466734	9
52	.509696	6.15	.976017		.533679	6.88	.466321	8
53	.510065	6.15	.975974		.534092	6.87	.465908	7
54	.510434	6.15	.975930		.534504	6.87	.465496	6
55	9.510803	6.15	9.975887		9.534916	6.87	0.465084	5
56	.511172	6.13	.975844		.535328	6.85	.464672	4
57	.511540	6.12	.975800		.535739	6.85	.464261	3
58	.511907	6.13	.975757		.536150	6.85	.463850	2
59	.512275	6.12	.975714		.536561	6.85	.463439	1
60	9.512642		9.975670		9.536972		0.463028	0

	cos	D.1"	sin	Corr. for Sec.	cot	D.1"	tan	'

108°   71°

227

TABLE XXII.—LOGARITHMIC SINES,

'	sin	D.1"	cos	Corr. for Sec.	tan	D.1"	cot	
0	9.512642	6.12	9.975670		9.536972	6.83	0.463028	60
1	.513009	6.10	.975627		.537382	6.83	.462618	59
2	.513375	6.10	.975583		.537792	6.83	.462208	58
3	.513741	6.10	.975539		.538202	6.82	.461798	57
4	.514107	6.08	.975496		.538611	6.82	.461389	56
5	9.514472	6.08	9.975452		9.539020	6.82	0.460980	55
6	.514837	6.08	.975408		.539429	6.80	.460571	54
7	.515202	6.07	.975365		.539837	6.80	.460163	53
8	.515566	6.07	.975321		.540245	6.80	.459755	52
9	.515930	6.07	.975277		.540653	6.80	.459347	51
10	9.516294	6.05	9.975233		9.541061	6.78	0.458939	50
11	.516657	6.05	.975189	" Corr.	.541468	6.78	.458532	49
12	.517020	6.03	.975145	10 7	.541875	6.77	.458125	48
13	.517382	6.05	.975101	15 11	.542281	6.77	.457719	47
14	.517745	6.03	.975057	20 15	.542688	6.77	.457312	46
15	9.518107	6.02	9.975013	30 22	9.543094	6.75	0.456906	45
16	.518468	6.02	.974969	40 29	.543499	6.77	.456501	44
17	.518829	6.02	.974925	45 33	.543905	6.75	.456095	43
18	.519190	6.02	.974880	50 37	.544310	6.75	.455690	42
19	.519551	6.00	.974836		.544715	6.73	.455285	41
20	9.519911	6.00	9.974792		9.545119	6.75	0.454881	40
21	.520271	6.00	.974748		.545524	6.73	.454476	39
22	.520631	5.98	.974703		.545928	6.72	.454072	38
23	.520990	5.98	.974659		.546331	6.73	.453669	37
24	.521349	5.98	.974614		.546735	6.73	.453265	36
25	9.521707	5.97	9.974570		9.547138	6.72	0.452862	35
26	.522066	5.98	.974525		.547540	6.70	.452460	34
27	.522424	5.97	.974481		.547943	6.70	.452057	33
28	.522781	5.95	.974436		.548345	6.70	.451655	32
29	.523138	5.95	.974391		.548747	6.70	.451253	31
30	9.523495	5.95	9.974347		9.549149	6.68	0.450851	30
31	.523852	5.93	.974302		.549550	6.68	.450450	29
32	.524208	5.93	.974257		.549951	6.68	.450049	28
33	.524564	5.93	.974212		.550352	6.67	.449648	27
34	.524920	5.92	.974167		.550752	6.68	.449248	26
35	9.525275	5.92	9.974122		9.551153	6.65	0.448847	25
36	.525630	5.90	.974077		.551552	6.67	.448448	24
37	.525984	5.92	.974032		.551952	6.65	.448048	23
38	.526339	5.90	.973987		.552351	6.65	.447649	22
39	.526693	5.88	.973942		.552750	6.65	.447250	21
40	9.527046	5.90	9.973897		9.553149	6.65	0.446851	20
41	.527400	5.88	.973852	" Corr.	.553548	6.63	.446452	19
42	.527753	5.87	.973807	10 8	.553946	6.63	.446054	18
43	.528105	5.88	.973761	15 11	.554344	6.62	.445656	17
44	.528458	5.87	.973716	20 15	.554741	6.63	.445259	16
45	9.528810	5.85	9.973671	30 23	9.555139	6.62	0.444861	15
46	.529161	5.87	.973625	40 30	.555536	6.62	.444464	14
47	.529513	5.85	.973580	45 34	.555933	6.60	.444067	13
48	.529864	5.85	.973535	50 38	.556329	6.60	.443671	12
49	.530215	5.83	.973489		.556725	6.60	.443275	11
50	9.530565	5.83	9.973444		9.557121	6.60	0.442879	10
51	.530915	5.83	.973398		.557517	6.60	.442483	9
52	.531265	5.82	.973352		.557913	6.58	.442087	8
53	.531614	5.82	.973307		.558308	6.58	.441692	7
54	.531963	5.82	.973261		.558703	6.57	.441297	6
55	9.532312	5.82	9.973169		9.559097	6.57	0.440903	5
56	.532661	5.80	.973169		.559491	6.57	.440509	4
57	.533009	5.80	.973124		.559885	6.57	.440115	3
58	.533357	5.78	.973078		.560279	6.57	.439721	2
59	.533704	5.80	.973032		.560673	6.55	.439327	1
60	9.534052		9.972986		9.561066		0.438934	0
	cos	D.1"	sin	Corr. for Sec.	cot	D.1"	tan	'

'	sin	Corr. for Sec.		cos	Corr. for Sec.		tan	Corr. for Sec.		cot	
0	9.534052			9.972986			9.561066			0.438934	60
1	.534399	" Corr.		.972940			.561459	" Corr.		.438561	59
2	.534745	10 58		.972894			.561851	10 65		.438149	58
3	.535092	15 86		.972848			.562244	15 98		.437756	57
4	.535438	20 115		.972802			.562636	20 131		.437364	56
5	9.535783	30 173		9.972755			9.563028	30 196		0.436972	55
6	.536129	40 230		.972709			.563419	40 261		.436581	54
7	.536474	45 259		.972663			.563811	45 294		.436189	53
8	.536818	50 288		.972617			.564202	50 326		.435798	52
9	.537163			.972570			.564593			.435407	51
10	9.537507			9.972524			9.564983			0.435017	50
11	.537851	" Corr.		.972478	" Corr.		.565373	" Corr.		.434627	49
12	.538194	10 57		.972431	10 8		.565763	10 65		.434237	48
13	.538538	15 86		.972385	15 12		.566153	15 97		.433847	47
14	.538880	20 114		.972338	20 16		.566542	20 130		.433458	46
15	9.539223	30 171		9.972291	30 23		9.566932	30 194		0.433068	45
16	.539565	40 228		.972245	40 31		.567320	40 259		.432680	44
17	.539907	45 257		.972198	45 35		.567709	45 292		.432291	43
18	.540249	50 285		.972151	50 39		.568098	50 324		.431902	42
19	.540590			.972105			.568486			.431514	41
20	9.540931			9.972058			9.568873			0..51127	40
21	.541272	" Corr.		.972011			.569261	" Corr.		.430739	39
22	.541613	10 57		.971964			.569648	10 64		.430352	38
23	.541953	15 85		.971917			.570035	15 97		.429965	37
24	.542293	20 113		.971870			.570422	20 129		.429578	36
25	9.542632	30 170		9.971823			9.570809	30 193		0.429191	35
26	.542971	40 226		.971776			.571195	40 258		.428805	34
27	.543310	45 255		.971729			.571581	45 290		.428419	33
28	.543649	50 283		.971682			.571967	50 322		.428033	32
29	.543987			.971635			.572352			.427648	31
30	9.544325			9.971588			9.572738			0.427262	30
31	.544663	" Corr.		.971540			.573123	" Corr.		.426877	29
32	.545000	10 56		.971493			.573507	10 64		.426493	28
33	.545338	15 84		.971446			.573892	15 96		.426108	27
34	.545674	20 112		.971398			.574276	20 128		.425724	26
35	9.546011	30 168		9.971351			9.574660	30 192		0.425340	25
36	.546347	40 224		.971303			.575044	40 256		.424956	24
37	.546683	45 252		.971256			.575427	45 288		.424573	23
38	.547019	50 280		.971208			.575810	50 320		.424190	22
39	.547354			.971161			.576193			.423807	21
40	9.547689			9.971113			9.576576			0.423424	20
41	.548024	" Corr.		.971066	" Corr.		.576959	" Corr.		.423041	19
42	.548359	10 56		.971018	10 8		.577341	10 64		.422659	18
43	.548693	15 83		.970970	15 12		.577723	15 95		.422277	17
44	.549027	20 111		.970922	20 16		.578104	20 127		.421896	16
45	9.549360	30 167		9.970874	30 24		9.578486	30 191		0.421514	15
46	.549693	40 222		.970827	40 32		.578867	40 254		.421133	14
47	.550026	45 250		.970779	45 36		.579248	45 286		.420752	13
48	.550359	50 278		.970731	50 40		.579629	50 318		.420371	12
49	.550692			.970683			.580009			.419991	11
50	9.551024			9.970635			9.580389			0.419611	10
51	.551356	" Corr.		.970586			.580769	" Corr.		.419231	9
52	.551687	10 55		.970538			.581149	10 63		.418851	8
53	.552018	15 83		.970490			.581528	15 95		.418472	7
54	.552349	20 110		.970442			.581907	20 126		.418093	6
55	9.552680	30 165		9.970394			9.582286	30 189		0.417714	5
56	.553010	40 220		.970345			.582665	40 252		.417335	4
57	.553341	45 248		.970297			.583044	45 284		.416956	3
58	.553670	50 275		.970249			.583422	50 316		.416578	2
59	.554000			.970200			.583800			.416200	1
60	9.554329			9.970152			9.584177			0.415823	0
	cos	Corr. for Sec.		sin	Corr. for Sec.		cot	Corr. for Sec.		tan	'

TABLE XXII.—LOGARITHMIC SINES,

'	sin	Corr. for Sec.	cos	Corr. for Sec.	tan	Corr. for Sec.	cot	
0	9.554329		9.970152		9.584177		0.415823	60
1	.554658	" Corr.	.970103		.584555	" Corr.	.415445	59
2	.554987	10 55	.970055		.584932	10 63	.415068	58
3	.555315	15 82	.970006		.585309	15 94	.414691	57
4	.555643	20 109	.969957		.585686	20 125	.414314	56
5	9.555971	30 164	9.969909		9.586062	30 188	0.413938	55
6	.556299	40 218	.969860		.586439	40 251	.413561	54
7	.556626	45 246	.969811		.586815	45 282	.413185	53
8	.556953	50 273	.969762		.587190	50 314	.412810	52
9	.557280		.969714		.587566		.412434	51
10	9.557606		9.969665		9.587941		0.412059	50
11	.557932	" Corr.	.969616	" Corr.	.588316	" Corr.	.411684	49
12	.558258	10 54	.969567	10 8	.588691	10 62	.411309	48
13	.558583	15 81	.969518	15 12	.589066	15 94	.410934	47
14	.558909	20 108	.969469	20 16	.589440	20 125	.410560	46
15	9.559234	30 162	9.969420	30 25	9.589814	30 187	0.410186	45
16	.559558	40 217	.969370	40 33	.590188	40 249	.409812	44
17	.559883	45 244	.969321	45 37	.590562	45 280	.409438	43
18	.560207	50 271	.969272	50 41	.590935	50 312	.409065	42
19	.560531		.969223		.591308		.408692	41
20	9.560855		9.969173		9.591681		0.408319	40
21	.561178	" Corr.	.969124		.592054	" Corr.	.407946	39
22	.561501	10 54	.969075		.592426	10 62	.407574	38
23	.561824	15 80	.969025		.592799	15 93	.407201	37
24	.562146	20 107	.968976		.593171	20 124	.406829	36
25	9.562468	30 161	9.968926		9.593542	30 186	0.406458	35
26	.562790	40 215	.968877		.593914	40 248	.406086	34
27	.563112	45 242	.968827		.594285	45 279	.405715	33
28	.563433	50 268	.968777		.594656	50 310	.405344	32
29	.563755		.968728		.595027		.404973	31
30	9.564075		9.968678		9.595398		0.404602	30
31	.564396	" Corr.	.968628		.595768	" Corr.	.404232	29
32	.564716	10 53	.968578		.596138	10 62	.403862	28
33	.565036	15 80	.968528		.596508	15 92	.403492	27
34	.565356	20 106	.968479		.596878	20 123	.403122	26
35	9.565676	30 160	9.968429		9.597247	30 185	0.402753	25
36	.565995	40 213	.968379		.597616	40 246	.402384	24
37	.566314	45 240	.968329		.597985	45 277	.402015	23
38	.566632	50 266	.968278		.598354	50 308	.401646	22
39	.566951		.968228		.598722		.401278	21
40	9.567269		9.968178		9.599091		0.400909	20
41	.567587	" Corr.	.968128	" Corr.	.599459	" Corr.	.400541	19
42	.567904	10 53	.968078	10 8	.599827	10 61	.400173	18
43	.568222	15 79	.968027	15 13	.600194	15 92	.399806	17
44	.568539	20 106	.967977	20 17	.600562	20 122	.399438	16
45	9.568856	30 158	9.967927	30 25	9.600929	30 184	0.399071	15
46	.569172	40 211	.967876	40 34	.601296	40 245	.398704	14
47	.569488	45 237	.967826	45 38	.601663	45 275	.398337	13
48	.569804	50 264	.967775	50 42	.602029	50 306	.397971	12
49	.570120		.967725		.602395		.397605	11
50	9.570435		9.967674		9.602761		0.397239	10
51	.570751	" Corr.	.967624		.603127	" Corr.	.396873	9
52	.571066	10 52	.967573		.603493	10 61	.396507	8
53	.571380	15 78	.967522		.603858	15 91	.396142	7
54	.571695	20 105	.967471		.604223	20 122	.395777	6
55	9.572009	30 157	9.967421		9.604588	30 182	0.395412	5
56	.572323	40 209	.967370		.604953	40 243	.395047	4
57	.572636	45 235	.967319		.605317	45 274	.394683	3
58	.572950	50 262	.967268		.605682	50 306	.394318	2
59	.573263		.967217		.606046		.393954	1
60	9.573575		9.967166		9.606410		0.393590	0
	cos	Corr. for Sec.	sin	Corr. for Sec.	cot	Corr. for Sec.	tan	'

'	sin	Corr. for Sec.	cos	Corr. for Sec.	tan	Corr. for Sec.	cot	
0	9.573575		9.967166		9.606410		0.393590	60
1	.573888	" Corr.	.967115		.606773	" Corr.	.393227	59
2	.574200	10 52	.967064		.607137	10 60	.392863	58
3	.574512	15 78	.967013		.607500	15 91	.392500	57
4	.574824	20 104	.966961		.607863	20 121	.392137	56
5	9.575136	30 156	9.966910		9.608225	30 181	0.391775	55
6	.575447	40 208	.966859		.608588	40 242	.391412	54
7	.575758	45 234	.966808		.608950	45 272	.391050	53
8	.576069	50 259	.966756		.609312	50 302	.390688	52
9	.576379		.966705		.609674		.390326	51
10	9.576688		9.966653		9.610036		0.389964	50
11	.576999	" Corr.	.966602	" Corr.	.610397	" Corr.	.389603	49
12	.577309	10 51	.966550	10 9	.610759	10 60	.389241	48
13	.577618	15 77	.966499	15 13	.611120	15 90	.388880	47
14	.577927	20 103	.966447	20 17	.611480	20 120	.388520	46
15	9.578236	30 154	9.966395	30 26	9.611841	30 180	0.388159	45
16	.578545	40 206	.966344	40 34	.612201	40 240	.387799	44
17	.578853	45 232	.966292	45 39	.612561	45 270	.387439	43
18	.579162	50 257	.966240	50 43	.612921	50 300	.387079	42
19	.579470		.966188		.613281		.386719	41
20	9.579777		9.966136		9.613641		0.386359	40
21	.580085	" Corr.	.966085		.614000	" Corr.	.386000	39
22	.580392	10 51	.966033		.614359	10 60	.385641	38
23	.580699	15 77	.965981		.614718	15 89	.385282	37
24	.581005	20 102	.965929		.615077	20 119	.384923	36
25	9.581312	30 153	9.965876		9.615435	30 179	0.384565	35
26	.581618	40 204	.965824		.615793	40 239	.384207	34
27	.581924	45 230	.965772		.616151	45 269	.383849	33
28	.582229	50 255	.965720		.616509	50 299	.383491	32
29	.582535		.965668		.616867		.383133	31
30	9.582840		9.965615		9.617224		0.382776	30
31	.583145	" Corr.	.965563		.617582	" Corr.	.382418	29
32	.583449	10 51	.965511		.617939	10 59	.382061	28
33	.583754	15 76	.965458		.618295	15 89	.381705	27
34	.584058	20 101	.965406		.618652	20 119	.381348	26
35	9.584361	30 152	9.965353		9.619008	30 178	0.380992	25
36	.584665	40 202	.965301		.619364	40 238	.380636	24
37	.584968	45 228	.965248		.619720	45 267	.380280	23
38	.585272	50 253	.965195		.620076	50 297	.379924	22
39	.585574		.965143		.620432		.379568	21
40	9.585877		9.965090		9.620787		0.379213	20
41	.586179	" Corr.	.965037	" Corr.	.621142	" Corr.	.378858	19
42	.586482	10 50	.964984	10 9	.621497	10 59	.378503	18
43	.586783	15 75	.964931	15 13	.621852	15 89	.378148	17
44	.587085	20 100	.964879	20 18	.622207	20 118	.377793	16
45	9.587386	30 151	9.964826	30 26	9.622561	30 177	0.377439	15
46	.587688	40 201	.964773	40 35	.622915	40 236	.377085	14
47	.587989	45 226	.964720	45 40	.623269	45 266	.376731	13
48	.588289	50 251	.964666	50 44	.623623	50 295	.376377	12
49	.588590		.964613		.623976		.376024	11
50	9.588890		9.964560		9.624330		0.375670	10
51	.589190	" Corr.	.964507		.624683	" Corr.	.375317	9
52	.589489	10 50	.964454	10 9	.625036	10 59	.374964	8
53	.589789	15 75	.964400	15 13	.625388	15 88	.374612	7
54	.590088	20 100	.964347	20 18	.625741	20 117	.374259	6
55	9.590387	30 149	9.964294	30 27	9.626093	30 176	0.373907	5
56	.590686	40 199	.964240	40 35	.626445	40 235	.373555	4
57	.590984	45 224	.964187	45 40	.626797	45 264	.373203	3
58	.591282	50 249	.964133	50 44	.627149	50 293	.372851	2
59	.591580		.964080		.627501		.372499	1
60	9.591878		9.964026		9.627852		0.372148	0
	cos	Corr. for Sec.	sin	Corr. for Sec.	cot	Corr. for Sec.	tan	'

TABLE XXII.—LOGARITHMIC SINES,

'	sin	Corr. for Sec.	cos	Corr. for Sec.	tan	Corr. for Sec.	cot	
0	9.591878		9.964026		9.627852		0.372148	60
1	.592176	" Corr.	.963972		.628203	" Corr.	.371797	59
2	.592473	10 49	.963919		.628554	10 58	.371446	58
3	.592770	15 74	.963865		.628905	15 88	.371095	57
4	.593067	20 99	.963811		.629255	20 117	.370745	56
5	9.593363	30 148	9.963757		9.629606	30 175	0.370394	55
6	.593659	40 198	.963704		.629956	40 234	.370044	54
7	.593955	45 222	.963650		.630306	45 263	.369694	53
8	.594251	50 247	.963596		.630656	50 292	.369344	52
9	.594547		.963542		.631005		.368995	51
10	9.594842		9.963488		9.631355		0.368645	50
11	.595137	" Corr.	.963434	" Corr.	.631704	" Corr.	.368296	49
12	.595432	10 49	.963379	10 9	.632053	10 58	.367947	48
13	.595727	15 74	.963325	15 14	.632402	15 87	.367598	47
14	.596021	20 98	.963271	20 18	.632750	20 116	.367250	46
15	9.596315	30 147	9.963217	30 27	9.633099	30 174	0.366901	45
16	.596609	40 196	.963163	40 36	.633447	40 232	.366553	44
17	.596903	45 221	.963108	45 41	.633795	45 261	.366205	43
18	.597196	50 245	.963054	50 45	.634143	50 290	.365857	42
19	.597490		.962999		.634490		.365510	41
20	9.597783		9.962945		9.634838		0.365162	40
21	.598075	" Corr.	.962890		.635185	" Corr.	.364815	39
22	.598368	10 49	.962836		.635532	10 58	.364468	38
23	.598660	15 73	.962781		.635879	15 87	.364121	37
24	.598952	20 97	.962727		.636226	20 115	.363774	36
25	9.599244	30 146	9.962672		9.636572	30 173	0.363428	35
26	.599536	40 194	.962617		.636919	40 231	.363081	34
27	.599827	45 219	.962562		.637265	45 260	.362735	33
28	.600118	50 243	.962508		.637611	50 289	.362389	32
29	.600409		.962453		.637956		.362044	31
30	9.600700		9.962398		9.638302		0.361698	30
31	.600990	" Corr.	.962343		.638647	" Corr.	.361353	29
32	.601280	10 48	.962288		.638992	10 57	.361008	28
33	.601570	15 72	.962233		.639337	15 86	.360663	27
34	.601860	20 96	.962178		.639682	20 115	.360318	26
35	9.602150	30 145	9.962123		9.640027	30 172	0.359973	25
36	.602439	40 193	.962067		.640371	40 230	.359629	24
37	.602728	45 217	.962012		.640716	45 258	.359284	23
38	.603017	50 241	.961957		.641060	50 287	.358940	22
39	.603305		.961902		.641404		.358596	21
40	9.603594		9.961846		9.641747		0.358253	20
41	.603882	" Corr.	.961791	" Corr.	.642091	" Corr.	.357909	19
42	.604170	10 48	.961735	10 9	.642434	10 57	.357566	18
43	.604457	15 72	.961680	15 14	.642777	15 86	.357223	17
44	.604745	20 96	.961624	20 19	.643120	20 114	.356880	16
45	9.605032	30 144	9.961569	30 28	9.643463	30 171	0.356537	15
46	.605319	40 191	.961513	40 37	.643806	40 228	.356194	14
47	.605606	45 215	.961458	45 42	.644148	45 257	.355852	13
48	.605892	50 239	.961402	50 46	.644490	50 286	.355510	12
49	.606179		.961346		.644832		.355168	11
50	9.606465		9.961290		9.645174		0.354826	10
51	.606751	" Corr.	.961235		.645516	" Corr.	.354484	9
52	.607036	10 47	.961179		.645857	10 57	.354143	8
53	.607322	15 71	.961123		.646199	15 85	.353801	7
54	.607607	20 95	.961067		.646540	20 114	.353460	6
55	9.607892	30 142	9.961011		9.646881	30 170	0.353119	5
56	.608177	40 190	.960955		.647222	40 227	.352778	4
57	.608461	45 214	.960899		.647562	45 256	.352438	3
58	.608745	50 237	.960843		.647903	50 284	.352097	2
59	.609029		.960786		.648243		.351757	1
60	9.609313		9.960730		9.648583		0.351417	0
	cos	Corr. for Sec.	sin	Corr. for Sec.	cot	Corr. for Sec.	tan	'

'	sin	Corr. for Sec.	cos	Corr. for Sec.	tan	Corr. for Sec.	cot	
0	9.609313		9.960730		9.648583		0.351417	60
1	.609597	" Corr.	.960674		.648923	" Corr.	.351077	59
2	.609880	10 47	.960618	10 9	.649263	10 56	.350737	58
3	.610164	15 71	.960561		.649602	15 85	.350398	57
4	.610447	20 94	.960505		.649942	20 113	.350058	56
5	9.610729	30 141	9.960448		9.650281	30 170	0.349719	55
6	.611012	40 188	.960392		.650620	40 226	.349380	54
7	.611294	45 212	.960335		.650959	45 254	.349041	53
8	.611576	50 236	.960279		.651297	50 283	.348703	52
9	.611858		.960222		.651636		.348364	51
10	9.612140		9.960165		9.651974		0.348026	50
11	.612421	" Corr.	.960109	" Corr.	.652312	" Corr.	.347688	49
12	.612702	10 47	.960052	10 9	.652650	10 56	.347350	48
13	.612983	15 70	.959995	15 14	.652988	15 84	.347012	47
14	.613264	20 93	.959938	20 19	.653326	20 112	.346674	46
15	9.613545	30 140	9.959882	30 28	9.653663	30 169	0.346337	45
16	.613825	40 187	.959825	40 38	.654000	40 225	.346000	44
17	.614105	45 210	.959768	45 43	.654337	45 253	.345663	43
18	.614385	50 234	.959711	50 47	.654674	50 281	.345326	42
19	.614665		.959654		.655011		.344989	41
20	9.614944		9.959596		9.655348		0.344652	40
21	.615223	" Corr.	.959539		.655684	" Corr.	.344316	39
22	.615502	10 46	.959482		.656020	10 56	.343980	38
23	.615781	15 69	.959425		.656356	15 84	.343644	37
24	.616060	20 93	.959368		.656692	20 112	.343308	36
25	9.616338	30 139	9.959310		9.657028	30 168	0.342972	35
26	.616616	40 186	.959253		.657364	40 224	.342636	34
27	.616894	45 209	.959195		.657699	45 252	.342301	33
28	.617172	50 232	.959138		.658034	50 280	.341966	32
29	.617450		.959080		.658369		.341631	31
30	9.617727		9.959023		9.658704		0.341296	30
31	.618004	" Corr.	.958965		.659039	" Corr.	.340961	29
32	.618281	10 46	.958908		.659373	10 56	.340627	28
33	.618558	15 69	.958850		.659708	15 83	.340292	27
34	.618834	20 92	.958792		.660042	20 111	.339958	26
35	9.619110	30 138	9.958734		9.660376	30 167	0.339624	25
36	.619386	40 184	.958677		.660710	40 223	.339290	24
37	.619662	45 207	.958619		.661043	45 250	.338957	23
38	.619938	50 230	.958561		.661377	50 278	.338623	22
39	.620213		.958503		.661710		.338290	21
40	9.620488		9.958445		9.662043		0.337957	20
41	.620763	" Corr.	.958387	" Corr.	.662376	" Corr.	.337624	19
42	.621038	10 46	.958329	10 10	.662709	10 55	.337291	18
43	.621313	15 69	.958271	15 15	.663042	15 83	.336958	17
44	.621587	20 91	.958213	20 19	.663375	20 111	.336625	16
45	9.621861	30 137	9.958154	30 29	9.663707	30 166	0.336293	15
46	.622135	40 183	.958096	40 39	.664039	40 222	.335961	14
47	.622409	45 206	.958038	45 44	.664371	45 249	.335629	13
48	.622682	50 228	.957979	50 49	.664703	50 277	.335297	12
49	.622956		.957921		.665035		.334965	11
50	9.623229		9.957863		9.665366		0.334634	10
51	.623502	" Corr.	.957804		.665698	" Corr.	.334302	9
52	.623774	10 45	.957746		.666029	10 55	.333971	8
53	.624047	15 68	.957687		.666360	15 83	.333640	7
54	.624319	20 91	.957628		.666691	20 110	.333309	6
55	9.624591	30 136	9.957570		9.667021	30 165	0.332979	5
56	.624863	40 181	.957511		.667352	40 220	.332648	4
57	.625135	45 204	.957452		.667682	45 248	.332318	3
58	.625406	50 227	.957393		.668013	50 275	.331987	2
59	.625677		.957335		.668343		.331657	1
60	9.625948		9.957276		9.668673		0.331327	0

	cos	Corr. for Sec.	sin	Corr. for Sec.	cot	Corr. for Sec.	tan	'

TABLE XXII.—LOGARITHMIC SINES,

25°   154°

'	sin	Corr. for Sec.	cos	Corr. for Sec.	tan	Corr. for Sec.	cot	
0	9.625948		9.957276		9.668673		0.331327	60
1	.626219	" Corr.	.957217		.669002	" Corr.	.330998	59
2	.626490	10 45	.957158		.669332	10 55	.330668	58
3	.626760	15 67	.957099		.669661	15 82	.330339	57
4	.627030	20 90	.957040		.669991	20 110	.330000	56
5	9.627300	30 135	9.956981		9.670320	30 164	0.329680	55
6	.627570	40 180	.956921		.670649	40 219	.329351	54
7	.627840	45 202	.956862		.670977	45 246	.329023	53
8	.628109	50 225	.956803		.671306	50 274	.328694	52
9	.628378		.956744		.671635		.328365	51
10	9.628647		9.956684		9.671963		0.328037	50
11	.628916	" Corr.	.956625	" Corr.	.672291		.327709	49
12	.629185	10 45	.956566	10 10	.672619		.327381	48
13	.629453	15 67	.956506	15 15	.672947		.327053	47
14	.629721	20 89	.956447	20 20	.673274		.326726	46
15	9.629989	30 134	9.956387	30 30	9.673602		0.326398	45
16	.630257	40 179	.956327	40 40	.673929	" Corr.	.326071	44
17	.630524	45 201	.956268	45 45	.674257	10 54	.325743	43
18	.630792	50 223	.956208	50 50	.674584	15 82	.325416	42
19	.631059		.956148		.674911	20 109	.325089	41
20	9.631326		9.956089		9.675237	30 163	0.324763	40
21	.631593	" Corr.	.956029		.675564	40 218	.324436	39
22	.631859	10 44	.955969		.675890	45 245	.324110	38
23	.632125	15 66	.955909		.676217	50 272	.323783	37
24	.632392	20 89	.955849		.676543		.323457	36
25	9.632658	30 133	9.955789		9.676869		0.323131	35
26	.632923	40 177	.955729		.677194		.322806	34
27	.633189	45 199	.955669		.677520		.322480	33
28	.633454	50 221	.955609		.677846		.322154	32
29	.633719		.955548		.678171		.321829	31
30	9.633984		9.955488		9.678496		0.321504	30
31	.634249	" Corr.	.955428		.678821	" Corr.	.321179	29
32	.634514	10 44	.955368		.679146	10 54	.320854	28
33	.634778	15 66	.955307		.679471	15 81	.320529	27
34	.635042	20 88	.955247		.679795	20 108	.320205	26
35	9.635306	30 132	9.955186		9.680120	30 162	0.319880	25
36	.635570	40 176	.955126		.680444	40 216	.319556	24
37	.635834	45 198	.955065		.680768	45 243	.319232	23
38	.636097	50 220	.955005		.681092	50 270	.318908	22
39	.636360		.954944		.681416		.318584	21
40	9.636623		9.954883		9.681740		0.318260	20
41	.636886	" Corr.	.954823	" Corr.	.682063		.317937	19
42	.637148	10 44	.954762	10 10	.682387		.317613	18
43	.637411	15 65	.954701	15 15	.682710		.317290	17
44	.637673	20 87	.954640	20 20	.683033		.316967	16
45	9.637935	30 131	9.954579	30 30	9.683356		0.316644	15
46	.638197	40 175	.954518	40 41	.683679	" Corr.	.316321	14
47	.638458	45 196	.954457	45 46	.684001	10 54	.315999	13
48	.638720	50 218	.954396	50 51	.684324	15 80	.315676	12
49	.638981		.954335		.684646	20 107	.315354	11
50	9.639242		9.954274		9.684968	30 161	0.315032	10
51	.639503	" Corr.	.954213		.685290	40 214	.314710	9
52	.639764	10 43	.954152		.685612	45 241	.314388	8
53	.640024	15 65	.954090		.685934	50 268	.314066	7
54	.640284	20 87	.954029		.686255		.313745	6
55	9.640544	30 130	9.953968		9.686577		0.313423	5
56	.640804	40 173	.953906		.686898		.313102	4
57	.641064	45 195	.953845		.687219		.312781	3
58	.641324	50 217	.953783		.687540		.312460	2
59	.641583		.953722		.687861		.312139	1
60	9.641842		9.953660		9.688182		0.311818	0

| | cos | Corr. for Sec. | sin | Corr. for Sec. | cot | Corr. for Sec. | tan | ' |

'	sin	Corr. for Sec.	cos	Corr. for Sec.	tan	Corr. for Sec.	cot	
0	9.641842		9.953660		9.688182		0.311818	60
1	.642101	" Corr.	.953599		.688502	" Corr.	.311498	59
2	.642360	10 43	.953537		.688823	10 53	.311177	58
3	.642618	15 65	.953475		.689143	15 80	.310857	57
4	.642877	20 86	.953413		.689463	20 106	.310537	56
5	9.643135	30 129	9.953352		9.689783	30 160	0.310217	55
6	.643393	40 172	.953290		.690103	40 213	.309897	54
7	.643650	45 194	.953228		.690423	45 240	.309577	53
8	.643908	50 215	.953166		.690742	50 266	.309258	52
9	.644165		.953104		.691062		.308938	51
10	9.644423		9.953042		9.691381		0.308619	50
11	.644680	" Corr.	.952980	" Corr.	.691700		.308300	49
12	.644936	10 43	.952918	10 10	.692019		.307981	48
13	.645193	15 64	.952855	15 16	.692338		.307662	47
14	.645450	20 85	.952793	20 21	.692656		.307344	46
15	9.645706	30 128	9.952731	30 31	9.692975		0.307025	45
16	.645962	40 171	.952669	40 42	.693293	" Corr.	.306707	44
17	.646218	45 192	.952606	45 47	.693612	10 53	.306388	43
18	.646474	50 213	.952544	50 52	.693930	15 79	.306070	42
19	.646729		.952481		.694248	20 106	.305752	41
20	9.646984		9.952419		9.694566	30 159	0.305434	40
21	.647240	" Corr.	.952356		.694883	40 212	.305117	39
22	.647494	10 42	.952294		.695201	45 238	.304799	38
23	.647749	15 64	.952231		.695518	50 264	.304482	37
24	.648004	20 85	.952168		.695836		.304164	36
25	9.648258	30 127	9.952106		9.696153		0.303847	35
26	.648512	40 170	.952043		.696470		.303530	34
27	.648766	45 191	.951980		.696787		.303213	33
28	.649020	50 212	.951917		.697103		.302897	32
29	.649274		.951854		.697420		.302580	31
30	9.649527		9.951791		9.697736		0.302264	30
31	.649781	" Corr.	.951728		.698053	" Corr.	.301947	29
32	.650034	10 42	.951665		.698369	10 53	.301631	28
33	.650287	15 63	.951602		.698685	15 79	.301315	27
34	.650539	20 84	.951539		.699001	20 105	.300999	26
35	9.650792	30 126	9.951476		9.699316	30 158	0.300684	25
36	.651044	40 168	.951412		.699632	40 210	.300368	24
37	.651297	45 189	.951349		.699947	45 236	.300053	23
38	.651549	50 210	.951286		.700263	50 263	.299737	22
39	.651800		.951222		.700578		.299422	21
40	9.652052		9.951159		9.700893		0.299107	20
41	.652304	" Corr.	.951096	" Corr.	.701208		.298792	19
42	.652555	10 42	.951032	10 11	.701523		.298477	18
43	.652806	15 63	.950968	15 16	.701837		.298163	17
44	.653057	20 84	.950905	20 21	.702152		.297848	16
45	9.653308	30 125	9.950841	30 32	9.702466		0.297534	15
46	.653558	40 167	.950778	40 42	.702781	" Corr.	.297219	14
47	.653808	45 188	.950714	45 48	.703095	10 52	.296905	13
48	.654059	50 209	.950650	50 53	.703409	15 78	.296591	12
49	.654309		.950586		.703722	20 104	.296278	11
50	9.654559		9.950522		9.704036	30 157	0.295964	10
51	.654808	" Corr.	.950458		.704350	40 209	.295650	9
52	.655058	10 41	.950394		.704663	45 235	.295337	8
53	.655307	15 62	.950330		.704976	50 261	.295024	7
54	.655556	20 83	.950266		.705290		.294710	6
55	9.655805	30 124	9.950202		9.705603		0.294397	5
56	.656054	40 166	.950138		.705916		.294084	4
57	.656302	45 187	.950074		.706228		.293772	3
58	.656551	50 207	.950010		.706541		.293459	2
59	.656799		.949945		.706854		.293146	1
60	9.657047		9.949881		9.707166		0.292834	0
	cos	Corr. for Sec.	sin	Corr. for Sec.	cot	Corr. for Sec.	tan	'

'	sin	Corr. for Sec.	cos	Corr. for Sec.	tan	Corr. for Sec.	cot	
0	9.657047		9.949881		9.707166		0.292834	60
1	.657295	" Corr.	.949816		.707478	" Corr.	.292522	59
2	.657542	10 41	.949752		.707790	10 52	.292210	58
3	.657790	15 62	.949688		.708102	15 78	.291898	57
4	.658037	20 82	.949623		.708414	20 104	.291586	56
5	9.658284	30 123	9.949558		9.708726	30 156	0.291274	55
6	.658531	40 164	.949494		.709037	40 207	.290963	54
7	.658778	45 185	.949429		.709349	45 233	.290651	53
8	.659025	50 205	.949364		.709660	50 259	.290340	52
9	.659271		.949300		.709971		.290029	51
10	9.659517		9.949235		9.710282		0.289718	50
11	.659763		.949170	" Corr.	.710593		.289407	49
12	.660009		.949105	10 11	.710904		.289096	48
13	.660255		.949040	15 16	.711215		.288785	47
14	.660501		.948975	20 22	.711525		.288475	46
15	9.660746	" Corr.	9.948910	30 33	9.711836		0.288164	45
16	.660991	10 41	.948845	40 43	.712146	" Corr.	.287854	44
17	.661236	15 61	.948780	45 49	.712456	10 51	.287544	43
18	.661481	20 81	.948715	50 54	.712766	15 77	.287234	42
19	.661726		.948650		.713076	20 103	.286924	41
20	9.661970	30 122	9.948584		9.713386	30 155	0.286614	40
21	.662214	40 163	.948519		.713696	40 206	.286304	39
22	.662459	45 183	.948454		.714005	45 232	.285995	38
23	.662703	50 203	.948388		.714314	50 258	.285686	37
24	.662946		.948323		.714624		.285376	36
25	9.663190		9.948257		9.714933		0.285067	35
26	.663433		.948192		.715242		.284758	34
27	.663677		.948126		.715551		.284449	33
28	.663920		.948060		.715860		.284140	32
29	.664163		.947995		.716168		.283832	31
30	9.664406		9.947929		9.716477		0.283523	30
31	.664648	" Corr.	.947863		.716785	" Corr.	.283215	29
32	.664891	10 40	.947797		.717093	10 51	.282907	28
33	.665133	15 60	.947731		.717401	15 77	.282599	27
34	.665375	20 80	.947665		.717709	20 102	.282291	26
35	9.665617	30 121	9.947600		9.718017	30 154	0.281983	25
36	.665859	40 161	.947533		.718325	40 205	.281675	24
37	.666100	45 181	.947467		.718633	45 231	.281367	23
38	.666342	50 201	.947401		.718940	50 256	.281060	22
39	.666583		.947335		.719248		.280752	21
40	9.666824		9.947269		9.719555		0.280445	20
41	.667065		.947203	" Corr.	.719862		.280138	19
42	.667305		.947136	10 11	.720169		.279831	18
43	.667546		.947070	15 17	.720476		.279524	17
44	.667786		.947004	20 22	.720783		.279217	16
45	9.668027		9.946937	30 33	9.721089		0.278911	15
46	.668267	" Corr.	.946871	40 44	.721396	" Corr.	.278604	14
47	.668506	10 40	.946804	45 50	.721702	10 51	.278298	13
48	.668746	15 60	.946738	50 55	.722009	15 76	.277991	12
49	.668986	20 80	.946671		.722315	20 102	.277685	11
50	9.669225	30 119	9.946604		9.722621	30 153	0.277379	10
51	.669464	40 159	.946538		.722927	40 204	.277073	9
52	.669703	45 179	.946471		.723232	45 229	.276768	8
53	.669942	50 199	.946404		.723538	50 255	.276462	7
54	.670181		.946337		.723844		.276156	6
55	9.670419		9.946270		9.724149		0.275851	5
56	.670658		.946203		.724454		.275546	4
57	.670896		.946136		.724760		.275240	3
58	.671134		.946069		.725065		.274935	2
59	.671372		.946002		.725370		.274630	1
60	9.671609		9.945935		9.725674		0.274326	0
	cos	Corr. for Sec.	sin	Corr. for Sec.	cot	Corr. for Sec.	tan	'

'	sin	Corr. for Sec.	cos	Corr. for Sec.	tan	Corr. for Sec.	cot	
0	9.671609		9.945935		9.725674		0.274326	60
1	.671847	" Corr.	.945868		.725979	" Corr.	.274021	59
2	.672084	10 39	.945800		.726284	10 51	.273716	58
3	.672321	15 59	.945735		.726588	15 76	.273412	57
4	.672558	20 79	.945666		.726892	20 101	.273108	56
5	9.672795	30 118	9.945598		9.727197	30 152	0.272803	55
6	.673032	40 158	.945531		.727501	40 203	.272499	54
7	.673268	45 177	.945464		.727805	45 228	.272195	53
8	.673505	50 197	.945396		.728109	50 253	.271891	52
9	.673741		.945328		.728412		.271588	51
10	9.673977		9.945261		9.728716		0.271284	50
11	.674213		.945193	" Corr.	.729020		.270980	49
12	.674448		.945125	10 11	.729323		.270677	48
13	.674684		.945058	15 17	.729626		.270374	47
14	.674919		.944990	20 23	.729929		.270071	46
15	9.675155		9.944922	30 35	9.730233		0.269767	45
16	.675390	" Corr.	.944854	40 45	.730535	" Corr.	.269465	44
17	.675624	10 39	.944786	45 52	.730838	10 50	.269162	43
18	.675859	15 58	.944718	50 57	.731141	15 76	.268859	42
19	.676094	20 78	.944650		.731444	20 101	.268556	41
20	9.676328	30 117	9.944582		9.731746	30 151	0.268254	40
21	.676562	40 156	.944514		.732048	40 201	.267952	39
22	.676796	45 175	.944446		.732351	45 227	.267649	38
23	.677030	50 195	.944377		.732653	50 252	.267347	37
24	.677264		.944309		.732955		.267045	36
25	9.677498		9.944241		9.733257		0.266743	35
26	.677731		.944172		.733558		.266442	34
27	.677964		.944104		.733860		.266140	33
28	.678197		.944036		.734162		.265838	32
29	.678430		.943967		.734463		.265537	31
30	9.678663		9.943899		9.734764		0.265236	30
31	.678895	" Corr.	.943830		.735066	" Corr.	.264934	29
32	.679128	10 39	.943761		.735367	10 50	.264633	28
33	.679360	15 58	.943693		.735668	15 75	.264332	27
34	.679592	20 77	.943624		.735969	20 100	.264031	26
35	9.679824	30 116	9.943555		9.736269	30 150	0.263731	25
36	.680056	40 154	.943486		.736570	40 200	.263430	24
37	.680288	45 174	.943417		.736870	45 225	.263130	23
38	.680519	50 193	.943348		.737171	50 250	.262829	22
39	.680750		.943279		.737471		.262529	21
40	9.680982		9.943210		9.737771		0.262229	20
41	.681213		.943141	" Corr.	.738071		.261929	19
42	.681443		.943072	10 12	.738371		.261629	18
43	.681674		.943003	15 17	.738671		.261329	17
44	.681905		.942934	20 23	.738971		.261029	16
45	9.682135		9.942864	30 35	9.739271		0.260729	15
46	.682365	" Corr.	.942795	40 46	.739570	" Corr.	.260430	14
47	.682595	10 38	.942726	45 52	.739870	10 50	.260130	13
48	.682825	15 57	.942656	50 58	.740169	15 75	.259831	12
49	.683055	20 76	.942587		.740468	20 100	.259532	11
50	9.683284	30 115	9.942517		9.740767	30 149	0.259233	10
51	.683514	40 153	.942448		.741066	40 199	.258934	9
52	.683743	45 172	.942378		.741365	45 224	.258635	8
53	.683972	50 191	.942308		.741664	50 249	.258336	7
54	.684201		.942239		.741962		.258038	6
55	9.684430		9.942169		9.742261		0.257739	5
56	.684658		.942099		.742559		.257441	4
57	.684887		.942029		.742858		.257142	3
58	.685115		.941959		.743156		.256844	2
59	.685343		.941889		.743454		.256546	1
60	9.685571		9.941819		9.743752		0.256248	0

	cos	Corr. for Sec.	sin	Corr. for Sec.	cot	Corr. for Sec.	tan	'

'	sin	Corr. for Sec.	cos	Corr. for Sec.	tan	Corr. for Sec.	cot	
0	9.685571		9.941819		9.743752		0.256248	60
1	.685799	" Corr.	.941749		.744050	" Corr.	.255950	59
2	.686027	10 38	.941679		.744348	10 49	.255652	58
3	.686254	15 57	.941609		.744645	15 74	.255355	57
4	.686482	20 76	.941539		.744943	20 99	.255057	56
5	9.686709	30 113	9.941469		9.745240	30 149	0.254760	55
6	.686936	40 151	.941398		.745538	40 198	.254462	54
7	.687163	45 170	.941328		.745835	45 223	.254165	53
8	.687389	50 189	.941258		.746132	50 248	.253868	52
9	.687616		.941187		.746429		.253571	51
10	9.687843		9.941117		9.746726		0.253274	50
11	.688069		.941046	" Corr.	747023		.252977	49
12	.688295		.940975	10 12	.747319		.252681	48
13	.688521		.940905	15 18	.747616		.252384	47
14	.688747		.940834	20 24	.747913		.252087	46
15	9.688972	" Corr.	9.940763	30 35	9.748209	" Corr.	0.251791	45
16	.689198	10 37	.940693	40 47	.748505	10 49	.251495	44
17	.689423	15 56	.940622	45 53	.748801	15 74	.251199	43
18	.689648	20 75	.940551	50 59	.749097	20 98	.250903	42
19	.689873		.940480		.749393		.250607	41
20	9.690098	30 112	9.940409		9.749689	30 148	0.250311	40
21	.690323	40 150	.940338		.749985	40 197	.250015	39
22	.690548	45 168	.940267		.750281	45 222	.249719	38
23	.690772	50 187	.940196		.750576	50 246	.249424	37
24	.690996		.940125		.750872		.249128	36
25	9.691220		9.940054		9.751167		0.248833	35
26	.691444		.939982		.751462		.248538	34
27	.691668		.939911		.751757		.248243	33
28	.691892		.939840		.752052		.247948	32
29	.692115		.939768		.752347		.247653	31
30	9.692339		9.939697		9.752642		0.247358	30
31	.692562	" Corr.	.939625		.752937	" Corr.	.247063	29
32	.692785	10 37	.939554		.753231	10 49	.246769	28
33	.693008	15 56	.939482		.753526	15 74	.246474	27
34	.693231	20 74	.939410		.753820	20 98	.246180	26
35	9.693453	30 111	9.939339		9.754115	30 147	0.245885	25
36	.693676	40 148	.939267		.754409	40 196	.245591	24
37	.693898	45 167	.939195		.754703	45 220	.245297	23
38	.694120	50 185	.939123		.754997	50 245	.245003	22
39	.694342		.939052		.755291		.244709	21
40	9.694564		9.938980		9.755585		0.244415	20
41	.694786		.938908	" Corr.	.755878		.244122	19
42	.695007		.938836	10 12	.756172		.243828	18
43	.695229		.938763	15 18	.756465		.243535	17
44	.695450		.938691	20 24	.756759		.243241	16
45	9.695671	" Corr.	9.938619	30 36	9.757052	" Corr.	0.242948	15
46	.695892	10 37	.938547	40 48	.757345	10 49	.242655	14
47	.686113	15 56	.938475	45 54	.757638	15 73	.242362	13
48	.696334	20 73	.938402	50 60	.757931	20 98	.242069	12
49	.696554		.938330		.758224		.241776	11
50	9.696775	30 110	9.938258		9.758517	30 146	0.241483	10
51	.696995	40 147	.938185		.758810	40 195	.241190	9
52	.697215	45 165	.938113		.759102	45 219	.240898	8
53	.697435	50 183	.938040		.759395	50 244	.240605	7
54	.697654		.937967		.759687		.240313	6
55	9.697874		9.937895		9.759979		0.240021	5
56	.698094		.937822		.760272		.239728	4
57	.698313		.937749		.760564		.239436	3
58	.698532		.937676		.760856		.239144	2
59	.698751		.937604		.761148		.238852	1
60	9.698970		9.937531		9.761439		0.238561	0
	cos	Corr. for Sec.	sin	Corr. for Sec.	cot	Corr. for Sec.	tan	'

'	sin	Corr. for Sec.	cos	Corr. for Sec.	tan	Corr. for Sec.	cot	
0	9.698970		9.937531		9.761439		0.238561	60
1	.699189	" Corr.	.937458		.761731		.238269	59
2	.699407	10 36	.937385		.762023		.237977	58
3	.699626	15 54	.937312		.762314		.237686	57
4	.699844	20 73	.937238		.762606		.237394	56
5	9.700062	30 109	9.937165		9.762897		0.237103	55
6	.700280	40 145	.937092		.763188	" Corr.	.236812	54
7	.700498	45 163	.937019		.763479	10 48	.236521	53
8	.700716	50 181	.936946		.763770	15 73	.236230	52
9	.700933		.936872		.764061	20 97	.235939	51
10	9.701151		9.936799		9.764352	30 145	0.235648	50
11	.701368		.936725	" Corr.	.764643	40 194	.235357	49
12	.701585		.936652	10 12	.764933	45 218	.235067	48
13	.701802		.936578	15 18	.765224	50 242	.234776	47
14	.702019		.936505	20 25	.765514		.234486	46
15	9.702236	" Corr.	9.936431	30 37	9.765805		0.234195	45
16	.702452	10 36	.936357	40 49	.766095		.233905	44
17	.702669	15 54	.936284	45 55	.766385		.233615	43
18	.702885	20 72	.936210	50 61	.766675		.233325	42
19	.703101		.936136		.766965		.233035	41
20	9.703317	30 108	9.936062		9.767255		0.232745	40
21	.703533	40 144	.935988		.767545		.232455	39
22	.703749	45 162	.935914		.767834		.232166	38
23	.703964	50 180	.935840		.768124		.231876	37
24	.704179		.935766		.768414		.231586	36
25	9.704395		9.935692		9.768703		0.231297	35
26	.704610		.935618		.768992	" Corr.	.231008	34
27	.704825		.935543		.769281	10 48	.230719	33
28	.705040		.935469		.769571	15 72	.230429	32
29	.705254		.935395		.769860	20 96	.230140	31
30	9.705469		9.935320		9.770148	30 144	0.229852	30
31	.705683	" Corr.	.935246		.770437	40 193	.229563	29
32	.705898	10 36	.935171		.770726	45 217	.229274	28
33	.706112	15 53	.935097		.771015	50 241	.228985	27
34	.706326	20 71	.935022		.771303		.228697	26
35	9.706539	30 107	9.934948		9.771592		0.228408	25
36	.706753	40 142	.934873		.771880		.228120	24
37	.706967	45 160	.934798		.772168		.227832	23
38	.707180	50 178	.934723		.772457		.227543	22
39	.707393		.934649		.772745		.227255	21
40	9.707606		9.934574		9.773033		0.226967	20
41	.707819		.934499	" Corr.	.773321		.226679	19
42	.708032		.934424	10 13	.773608		.226392	18
43	.708245		.934349	15 19	.773896		.226104	17
44	.708458		.934274	20 25	.774184		.225816	16
45	9.708670		9.934199	30 38	9.774471		0.225529	15
46	.708882	" Corr.	.934123	40 50	.774759	" Corr.	.225241	14
47	.709094	10 35	.934048	45 56	.775046	10 48	.224954	13
48	.709306	15 53	.933973	50 63	.775333	15 72	.224667	12
49	.709518	20 70	.933898		.775621	20 96	.224379	11
50	9.709730	30 106	9.933822		9.775908	30 144	0.224092	10
51	.709941	40 141	.933747		.776195	40 191	.223805	9
52	.710153	45 158	.933671		.776482	45 215	.223518	8
53	.710364	50 176	.933596		.776768	50 239	.223232	7
54	.710575		.933520		.777055		.222945	6
55	9.710786		9.933445		9.777342		0.222658	5
56	.710997		.933369		.777628		.222372	4
57	.711208		.933293		.777915		.222085	3
58	.711419		.933217		.778201		.221799	2
59	.711629		.933141		.778488		.221512	1
60	9.711839		9.933066		9.778774		0.221226	0
	cos	Corr. for Sec.	sin	Corr. for Sec.	cot	Corr. for Sec.	tan	'

TABLE XXII.—LOGARITHMIC SINES,

'	sin	Corr. for Sec.	cos	Corr. for Sec.	tan	Corr. for Sec.	cot	
0	9.711839		9.933066		9.778774		0.221226	60
1	.712050	" Corr.	.932990		.779060		.220940	59
2	.712260	10 35	.932914		.779346		.220654	58
3	.712469	15 52	.932838		.779632		.220368	57
4	.712679	20 70	.932762		.779918		.220082	56
5	9.712889	30 105	9.932685		9.780203		0.219797	55
6	.713098	40 140	.932609		.780489	" Corr.	.219511	54
7	.713308	45 157	.932533		.780775	10 48	.219225	53
8	.713517	50 174	.932457		.781060	15 71	.218940	52
9	.713726		.932380		.781346	20 95	.218654	51
10	9.713935		9.932304		9.781631	30 143	0.218369	50
11	.714144		.932228	" Corr.	.781916	40 190	.218084	49
12	.714352		.932151	10 13	.782201	45 214	.217799	48
13	.714561		.932075	15 19	.782486	50 238	.217514	47
14	.714769		.931998	20 26	.782771		.217229	46
15	9.714978		9.931921	30 38	9.783056		0.216944	45
16	.715186	" Corr.	.931845	40 51	.783341		.216659	44
17	.715394	10 35	.931768	45 58	.783626		.216374	43
18	.715602	15 52	.931691	50 64	.783910		.216090	42
19	.715809	20 69	.931614		.784195		.215805	41
20	9.716017	30 104	9.931537		9.784479		0.215521	40
21	.716224	40 138	.931460		.784764		.215236	39
22	.716432	45 155	.931383		.785048		.214952	38
23	.716639	50 173	.931306		.785332		.214668	37
24	.716846		.931229		.785616		.214384	36
25	9.717053		9.931152		9.785900		0.214100	35
26	.717259		.931075		.786184	" Corr.	.213816	34
27	.717466		.930998		.786468	10 47	.213532	33
28	.717673		.930921		.786752	15 71	.213248	32
29	.717879		.930843		.787036	20 95	.212964	31
30	9.718085		9.930766		9.787319	30 142	0.212681	30
31	.718291	" Corr.	.930688		.787603	40 189	.212397	29
32	.718497	10 34	.930611		.787886	45 213	.212114	28
33	.718703	15 51	.930533		.788170	50 236	.211830	27
34	.718909	20 68	.930456		.788453		.211547	26
35	9.719114	30 103	9.930378		9.788736		0.211264	25
36	.719320	40 137	.930300		.789019		.210981	24
37	.719525	45 154	.930223		.789302		.210698	23
38	.719730	50 171	.930145		.789585		.210415	22
39	.719935		.930067		.789868		.210132	31
40	9.720140		9.929989		9.790151		0.209849	20
41	.720345		.929911	" Corr.	.790434		.209566	19
42	.720549		.929833	10 13	.790716		.209284	18
43	.720754		.929755	15 20	.790999		.209001	17
44	.720958		.929677	20 26	.791281		.208719	16
45	9.721162		9.929599	30 39	9.791563		0.208437	15
46	.721366	" Corr.	.929521	40 52	.791846	" Corr.	.208154	14
47	.721570	10 34	.929442	45 59	.792128	10 47	.207872	13
48	.721774	15 51	.929364	50 65	.792410	15 70	.207590	12
49	.721978	20 68	.929286		.792692	20 94	.207308	11
50	9.722181	30 102	9.929207		9.792974	30 141	0.207026	10
51	.722385	40 135	.929129		.793256	40 188	.206744	9
52	.722588	45 152	.929050		.793538	45 211	.206462	8
53	.722791	50 169	.928972		.793819	50 235	.206181	7
54	.722994		.928893		.794101		.205899	6
55	9.723197		9.928815		9.794383		0.205617	5
56	.723400		.928736		.794664		.205336	4
57	.723603		.928657		.794946		.205054	3
58	.723805		.928578		.795227		.204773	2
59	.724007		.928499		.795508		.204492	1
60	9.724210		9.928420		9.795789		0.204211	0
	cos	Corr. for Sec.	sin	Corr. for Sec.	cot	Corr. for Sec.	tan	'

32°   147°

'	sin	Corr. for Sec.	cos	Corr. for Sec.	tan	Corr. for Sec.	cot	
0	9.724210		9.928420		9.795789		0.204211	60
1	.724412	" Corr.	.928342		.796070		.203930	59
2	.724614	10 34	.928263		.796351		.203649	58
3	.724816	15 50	.928183		.796632		.203368	57
4	.725017	20 67	.928104		.796913		.203087	56
5	9.725219	30 101	9.928025		9.797194	" Corr.	0.202806	55
6	.725420	45 134	.927946		.797474	10 47	.202526	54
7	.725622	45 151	.927867		.797755	15 70	.202245	53
8	.725823	50 168	.927787		.798036		.201964	52
9	.726024		.927708		.798316	20 93	.201684	51
10	9.726225		9.927629		9.798596	30 140	0.201404	50
11	.726426		.927549	" Corr.	.798877	40 187	.201123	49
12	.726626		.927470	10 13	.799157	45 210	.200843	48
13	.726827		.927390	15 20	.799437	50 234	.200563	47
14	.727027		.927310	20 27	.799717		.200283	46
15	9.727228		9.927231	30 40	9.799997		0.200003	45
16	.727428	" Corr.	.927151	40 53	.800277		.199723	44
17	.727628	10 33	.927071	45 60	.800557		.199443	43
18	.727828	15 50	.926991	50 66	.800836		.199164	42
19	.728027	20 66	.926911		.801116		.198884	41
20	9.728227	30 100	9.926831		9.801396		0.198604	40
21	.728427	40 133	.926751		.801675		.198325	39
22	.728626	45 149	.926671		.801955		.198045	38
23	.728825	50 166	.926591		.802234		.197766	37
24	.729024		.926511		.802513		.197487	36
25	9.729223		9.926431		9.802792		0.197208	35
26	.729422		.926351		.803072	" Corr.	.196928	34
27	.729621		.926270		.803351	10 46	.196649	33
28	.729820		.926190		.803630	15 70	.196370	32
29	.730018		.926110		.803909	20 93	.196091	31
30	9.730217		9.926029		9.804187	30 139	0.195813	30
31	.730415	" Corr.	.925949		.804466	40 186	.195534	29
32	.730613	10 33	.925868		.804745	45 209	.195255	28
33	.730811	15 49	.925788		.805023	50 232	.194977	27
34	.731009	20 66	.925707		.805302		.194698	26
35	9.731206	30 99	9.925626		9.805580		0.194420	25
36	.731404	40 132	.925545		.805859		.194141	24
37	.731602	45 148	.925465		.806137		.193863	23
38	.731799	50 164	.925384		.806415		.193585	22
39	.731996		.925203		.806693		.193307	21
40	9.732193		9.925222		9.806971		0.193029	20
41	.732390		.925141	" Corr.	.807249		.192751	19
42	.732587		.925060	10 14	.807527		.192473	18
43	.732784		.924979	15 20	.807805		.192195	17
44	.732980		.924897	20 27	.808083		.191917	16
45	9.733177		9.924816	30 41	9.808361		0.191639	15
46	.733373	" Corr.	.924735	40 54	.808638	" Corr.	.191362	14
47	.733569	10 33	.924654	45 61	.808916	10 46	.191084	13
48	.733765	15 49	.924572	50 68	.809193	15 69	.190807	12
49	.733961	20 65	.924491		.809471	20 92	.190529	11
50	9.734157	30 98	9.924409		9.809748	30 139	0.190252	10
51	.734353	40 130	.924328		.810025	40 185	.189975	9
52	.734549	45 147	.924246		.810302	45 208	.189698	8
53	.734744	50 163	.924164		.810580	50 231	.189420	7
54	.734939		.924083		.810857		.189143	6
55	9.735135		9.924001		9.811134		0.188866	5
56	.735330		.923919		.811410		.188590	4
57	.735525		.923837		.811687		.188313	3
58	.735719		.923755		.811964		.188036	2
59	.735914		.923673		.812241		.187759	1
60	9.736109		9.923591		9.812517		0.187483	0

| | cos | Corr. for Sec. | sin | Corr. for Sec. | cot | Corr. for Sec. | tan | ' |

TABLE XXII.—LOGARITHMIC SINES,
33°
146°

'	sin	Corr. for Sec.	cos	Corr. for Sec.	tan	Corr. for Sec.	cot	
0	9.736109		9.923591		9.812517		0.187483	60
1	.736303	" Corr.	.923509		.812794		.187206	59
2	.736498	10 32	.923427		.813070		.186930	58
3	.736692	15 48	.923345		.813347		.186653	57
4	.736886	20 65	.923263		.813623		.186377	56
5	9.737080	30 97	9.923181		9.813899		0.186101	55
6	.737274	40 129	.923098		.814176		.185824	54
7	.737467	45 145	.923016		.814452		.185548	53
8	.737661	50 161	.922933		.814728		.185272	52
9	.737855		.922851		.815004		.184996	51
10	9.738048		9.922768		9.815280		0.184720	50
11	.738241		.922686	" Corr.	.815555	" Corr.	.184445	49
12	.738434		.922603	10 14	.815831	10 46	.184169	48
13	.738627		.922520	15 21	.816107	15 69	.183893	47
14	.738820		.922438	20 28	.816382	20 92	.183618	46
15	9.739013		9.922355	30 41	9.816658	30 138	0.183342	45
16	.739206	" Corr.	.922272	40 55	.816933	40 184	.183067	44
17	.739398	10 32	.922189	45 62	.817209	45 207	.182791	43
18	.739590	15 48	.922106	50 69	.817484	50 230	.182516	42
19	.739783	20 64	.922023		.817759		.182241	41
20	9.739975	30 96	9.921940		9.818035		0.181965	40
21	.740167	40 128	.921857		.818310		.181690	39
22	.740359	45 144	.921774		.818585		.181415	38
23	.740550	50 160	.921691		.818860		.181140	37
24	.740742		.921607		.819135		.180865	36
25	9.740934		9.921524		9.819410		0.180590	35
26	.741125		.921441		.819684		.180316	34
27	.741316		.921357		.819959		.180041	33
28	.741508		.921274		.820234		.179766	32
29	.741699		.921190		.820508		.179492	31
30	9.741889		9.921107		9.820783		0.179217	30
31	.742080	" Corr.	.921023		.821057		.178943	29
32	.742271	10 32	.920939		.821332		.178668	28
33	.742462	15 48	.920856		.821606		.178394	27
34	.742652	20 63	.920772		.821880		.178120	26
35	9.742842	30 95	9.920688		9.822154		0.177846	25
36	.743033	40 127	.920604		.822429		.177571	24
37	.743223	45 142	.920520		.822703		.177297	23
38	.743413	50 158	.920436		.822977		.177023	22
39	.743602		.920352		.823251		.176749	21
40	9.743792		9.920268		9.823524		0.176476	20
41	.743982		.920184	" Corr.	.823798	" Corr.	.176202	19
42	.744171		.920099	10 14	.824072	10 46	.175928	18
43	.744361		.920015	15 21	.824345	15 68	.175655	17
44	.744550		.919931	20 28	.824619	20 91	.175381	16
45	9.744739		9.919846	30 42	9.824893	30 137	0.175107	15
46	.744928	" Corr.	.919762	40 56	.825166	40 182	.174834	14
47	.745117	10 31	.919677	45 63	.825439	45 205	.174561	13
48	.745306	15 47	.919593	50 70	.825713	50 228	.174287	12
49	.745494	20 63	.919508		.825986		.174014	11
50	9.745683	30 94	9.919424		9.826259		0.173741	10
51	.745871	40 125	.919339		.826532		.173468	9
52	.746060	45 141	.919254		.826805		.173195	8
53	.746248	50 157	.919169		.827078		.172922	7
54	.746436		.919085		.827351		.172649	6
55	9.746624		9.919000		9.827624		0.172376	5
56	.746812		.918915		.827897		.172103	4
57	.746999		.918830		.828170		.171830	3
58	.747187		.918745		.828442		.171558	2
59	.747374		.918659		.828715		.171285	1
60	9.747562		9.918574		9.828987		0.171013	0
	cos	Corr. for Sec.	sin	Corr. for Sec.	cot	Corr. for Sec.	tan	'

'	sin	Corr. for Sec.	cos	Corr. for Sec.	tan	Corr. for Sec.	cot	
0	9.747562		9.918574		9.828987		0.171013	60
1	.747749		.918489		.829260		.170740	59
2	.747936		.918404		.829532		.170468	58
3	.748123		.918318		.829805		.170195	57
4	.748310		.918233		.830077		.169923	56
5	9.748497		9.918147		9.830349		0.169651	55
6	.748683	" Corr.	.918062		.830621		.169379	54
7	.748870	10 31	.917976		.830893		.169107	53
8	.749056	15 47	.917891		.831165		.168835	52
9	.749243	20 62	.917805		.831437		.168563	51
10	9.749429	30 93	9.917719		9.831709		0.168291	50
11	.749615	40 124	.917634	" Corr.	.831981	" Corr.	.168019	49
12	.749801	45 140	.917548	10 14	.832253	10 45	.167747	48
13	.749987	50 155	.917462	15 22	.832525	15 68	.167475	47
14	.750172		.917376	20 29	.832796	20 91	.167204	46
15	9.750358		9.917290	30 43	9.833068	30 136	0.166932	45
16	.750543		.917204	40 57	.833339	40 181	.166661	44
17	.750729		.917118	45 64	.833611	45 204	.166389	43
18	.750914		.917032	50 72	.833882	50 226	.166118	42
19	.751099		.916946		.834154		.165846	41
20	9.751284		9.916859		9.834425		0.165575	40
21	.751469		.916773		.834696		.165304	39
22	.751654		.916687		.834967		.165033	38
23	.751839		.916600		.835238		.164762	37
24	.752023		.916514		.835509		.164491	36
25	9.752208		9.916427		9.835780		0.164220	35
26	.752392	" Corr.	.916341		.836051		.163949	34
27	.752576	10 31	.916254		.836322		.163678	33
28	.752760	15 46	.916167		.836593		.163407	32
29	.752944	20 61	.916081		.836864		.163136	31
30	9.753128	30 92	9.915994		9.837134		0.162866	30
31	.753312	40 123	.915907		.837405		.162595	29
32	.753495	45 138	.915820		.837675		.162325	28
33	.753679	50 153	.915733		.837946		.162054	27
34	.753862		.915646		.838216		.161784	26
35	9.754046		9.915559		9.838487		0.161513	25
36	.754229		.915472		.838757		.161243	24
37	.754412		.915385		.839027		.610973	23
38	.754595		.915297		.839297		.160703	22
39	.754778		.915210		.839568		.160432	21
40	9.754960		9.915123		9.839838		0.160162	20
41	.755143		.915035		.840108	" Corr.	.159892	19
42	.755326		.914948	10 15	.840378	10 45	.159622	18
43	.755508		.914860	15 22	.840648	15 67	.159352	17
44	.755690		.914773	20 29	.840917	20 90	.159083	16
45	9.755872		9.914686	30 44	9.841187	30 135	0.158813	15
46	.756054	" Corr.	.914598	40 58	.841457	40 180	.158543	14
47	.756236	10 30	.914510	45 66	.841727	45 202	.158273	13
48	.756418	15 45	.914422	50 73	.841996	50 225	.158004	12
49	.756600	20 61	.914334		.842266		.157734	11
50	9.756782	30 91	9.914246		9.842535		0.157465	10
51	.756963	40 121	.914158		.842805		.157195	9
52	.757144	45 136	.914070		.843074		.156926	8
53	.757326	50 151	.913982		.843343		.156657	7
54	.757507		.913894		.843612		.156388	6
55	9.757688		9.913806		9.843882		0.156118	5
56	.757869		.913718		.844151		.155849	4
57	.758050		.913630		.844420		.155580	3
58	.758230		.913541		.844689		.155311	2
59	.758411		.913453		.844958		.155042	1
60	9.758591		9.913365		9.845227		0.154773	0
	cos	Corr. for Sec.	sin	Corr. for Sec.	cot	Corr. for Sec.	tan	'

TABLE XXII.—LOGARITHMIC SINES,
35°
144°

'	sin	Corr. for Sec.	cos	Corr. for Sec.	tan	Corr. for Sec.	cot	
0	9.758591		9.913365		9.845227		0.154773	60
1	.758772		.913276		.845496		.154504	59
2	.758952		.913187		.845764		.154236	58
3	.759132		.913099		.846033		.153967	57
4	.759312		.913010		.846302		.153698	56
5	9.759492		9.912922		9.846570		0.153430	55
6	.759672	" Corr.	.912833		.846839		.153161	54
7	.759852	10 30	.912744		.847108		.152892	53
8	.760031	15 45	.912655		.847376		.152624	52
9	.760211	20 60	.912566		.847644		.152356	51
10	9.760390	30 90	9.912477		9.847913		0.152087	50
11	.760569	40 120	.912388	" Corr.	.848181	" Corr.	.151819	49
12	.760748	45 134	.912299	10 15	.848449	10 45	.151551	48
13	.760927	50 149	.912210	15 22	.848717	15 67	.151283	47
14	.761106		.912121	20 30	.848986	20 89	.151014	46
15	9.761285		9.912031	30 45	9.849254	30 134	0.150746	45
16	.761464		.911942	40 60	.849522	40 179	.150478	44
17	.761642		.911853	45 67	.849790	45 201	.150210	43
18	.761821		.911763	50 74	.850057	50 223	.149943	42
19	.761999		.911674		.850325		.149675	41
20	9.762177		9.911584		9.850593		0.149407	40
21	.762356		.911495		.850861		.149139	39
22	.762534		.911405		.851129		.148871	38
23	.762712		.911315		.851396		.148604	37
24	.762889		.911226		.851664		.148336	36
25	9.763067		9.911136		9.851931		0.148069	35
26	.763245	" Corr.	.911046		.852199		.147801	34
27	.763422	10 30	.910956		.852466		.147534	33
28	.763600	15 44	.910866		.852733		.147267	32
29	.763777	20 59	.910776		.853001		.146999	31
30	9.763954	30 89	9.910686		9.853268		0.146732	30
31	.764131	40 118	.910596		.853535		.146465	29
32	.764308	45 133	.910506		.853802		.146198	28
33	.764485	50 148	.910415		.854069		.145931	27
34	.764662		.910325		.854336		.145664	26
35	9.764838		9.910235		9.854603		0.145397	25
36	.765015		.910144		.854870		.145130	24
37	.765191		.910054		.855137		.144863	23
38	.765367		.909963		.855404		.144596	22
39	.765544		.909873		.855671		.144329	21
40	9.765720		9.909782		9.855938		0.144062	20
41	.765896		.909691	" Corr.	.856204	" Corr.	.143796	19
42	.766072		.909601	10 15	.856471	10 44	.143529	18
43	.766247		.909510	15 23	.856737	15 67	.143263	17
44	.766423		.909419	20 30	.857004	20 89	.142996	16
45	9.766598		9.909328	30 45	9.857270	30 133	0.142730	15
46	.766774	" Corr.	.909237	40 61	.857537	40 178	.142463	14
47	.766949	10 29	.909146	45 68	.857803	45 200	.142197	13
48	.767124	15 44	.909055	50 76	.858069	50 222	.141931	12
49	.767300	20 58	.908964		.858336		.141664	11
50	9.767475	30 88	9.908873		9.858602		0.141398	10
51	.767649	40 117	.908781		.858868		.141132	9
52	.767824	45 131	.908690		.859134		.140866	8
53	.767999	50 146	.908599		.859400		.140600	7
54	.768173		.908507		.859666		.140334	6
55	9.768348		9.908416		9.859932		0.140068	5
56	.768522		.908324		.860198		.139802	4
57	.768697		.908233		.860464		.139536	3
58	.768871		.908141		.860730		.139270	2
59	.769045		.908049		.860995		.139005	1
60	9.769219		9.907958		9.861261		0.138739	0
	cos	Corr. for Sec.	sin	Corr. for Sec.	cot	Corr. for Sec.	tan	'

'	sin	Corr. for Sec.	cos	Corr. for Sec.	tan	Corr. for Sec.	cot	
0	9.769219		9.907958		9.861261		0.138739	60
1	.769393		.907866		.861527		.138473	59
2	.769556		.907774		.861792		.138208	58
3	.769740		.907682		.862058		.137942	57
4	.769913		.907590		.862323		.137677	56
5	9.770087		9.907498		9.862589		0.137411	55
6	.770260	" Corr.	.907406		.862854		.137146	54
7	.770433	10 29	.907314		.863119		.136881	53
8	.770606	15 43	.907222		.863385		.136615	52
9	.770779	20 58	.907129		.863650		.136350	51
10	9.770952	30 86	9.907037		9.863915	" Corr.	0.136085	50
11	.771125	40 115	.906945	" Corr.	.864180	10 44	.135820	49
12	.771298	45 130	.906852	10 15	.864445	15 66	.135555	48
13	.771470	50 144	.906760	15 23	.864710	20 88	.135290	47
14	.771643		.906667	20 31	.864975	30 132	.135025	46
15	9.771815		9.906575	30 46	9.865240	40 177	0.134760	45
16	.771987		.906482	40 62	.865505	45 199	.134495	44
17	.772159		.906389	45 69	.865770	50 221	.134230	43
18	.772331		.906296	50 77	.866035		.133965	42
19	.772503		.906204		.866300		.133700	41
20	9.772675		9.906111		9.866564		0.133436	40
21	.772847		.906018		.866829		.133171	39
22	.773018		.905925		.867094		.132906	38
23	.773190		.905832		.867358		.132642	37
24	.773361		.905739		.867623		.132377	36
25	9.773533		9.905645		9.867887		0.132113	35
26	.773704	" Corr.	.905552		.868152		.131848	34
27	.773875	10 28	.905459		.868416		.131584	33
28	.774046	15 43	.905366		.868680		.131320	32
29	.774217	20 57	.905272		.868945		.131055	31
30	9.774388	30 85	9.905179		9.869209		0.130791	30
31	.774558	40 114	.905085		.869473		.130527	29
32	.774729	45 128	.904992		.869737		.130263	28
33	.774899	50 142	.904898		.870001		.129999	27
34	.775070		.904804		.870265		.129735	26
35	9.775240		9.904711		9.870529		0.129471	25
36	.775410		.904617		.870793		.129207	24
37	.775580		.904523		.871057		.128943	23
38	.775750		.904429		.871321		.128679	22
39	.775920		.904335		.871585		.128415	21
40	9.776090		9.904241		9.871849		0.128151	20
41	.776259		.904147	" Corr.	.872112	" Corr.	.127888	19
42	.776429		.904053	10 16	.872376	10 44	.127624	18
43	.776598		.903959	15 24	.872640	15 66	.127360	17
44	.776768		.903864	20 31	.872903	20 88	.127097	16
45	9.776937		9.903770	30 47	9.873167	30 132	0.126833	15
46	.777106	" Corr.	.903676	40 63	.873430	40 176	.126570	14
47	.777275	10 28	.903581	45 71	.873694	45 198	.126306	13
48	.777444	15 42	.903487	50 79	.873957	50 220	.126043	12
49	.777613	20 56	.903392		.874220		.125780	11
50	9.777781	30 84	9.903298		9.874484		0.125516	10
51	.777950	40 112	.903203		.874747		.125253	9
52	.778119	45 126	.903108		.875010		.124990	8
53	.778287	50 140	.903014		.875273		.124727	7
54	.778455		.902919		.875537		.124463	6
55	9.778624		9.902824		9.875800		0.124200	5
56	.778792		.902729		.876063		.123937	4
57	.778960		.902634		.876326		.123674	3
58	.779128		.902539		.876589		.123411	2
59	.779295		.902444		.876852		.123148	1
60	9.779463		9.902349		9.877114		0.122886	0

	cos	Corr. for Sec.	sin	Corr. for Sec.	cot	Corr. for Sec.	tan	'

TABLE XXII.—LOGARITHMIC SINES,

'	sin	Corr. for Sec.	cos	Corr. for Sec.	tan	Corr. for Sec.	cot	
0	9.779463		9.902349		9.877114		0.122886	60
1	.779631		.902253		.877377		.122623	59
2	.779798		.902158		.877640		.122360	58
3	.779966		.902063		.877903		.122097	57
4	.780133		.901967		.878165		.121835	56
5	9.780300		9.901872		9.878428		0.121572	55
6	.780467	" Corr. 10 28	.901776		.878691		.121309	54
7	.780634	15 42	.901681		.878953		.121047	53
8	.780801	20 56	.901585		.879216		.120784	52
9	.780968		.901490		.879478		.120522	51
10	9.781134	30 83	9.901394		9.879741		0.120259	50
11	.781301	40 111	.901298	" Corr. 10 16	.880003	" Corr. 10 44	.119997	49
12	.781468	45 125	.901202		.880265		.119735	48
13	.781634	50 139	.901106	15 24	.880528	15 66	.119472	47
14	.781800		.901010	20 32	.880790	20 87	.119210	46
15	9.781966		9.900914	30 48	9.881052	30 131	0.118948	45
16	.782132		.900818	40 64	.881314	40 175	.118686	44
17	.782298		.900722	45 72	.881577	45 197	.118423	43
18	.782464		.900626	50 80	.881839	50 218	.118161	42
19	.782630		.900529		.882101		.117899	41
20	9.782796		9.900433		9.882363		0.117637	40
21	.782961		.900337		.882625		.117375	39
22	.783127		.900240		.882887		.117113	38
23	.783292		.900144		.883148		.116852	37
24	.783458		.900047		.883410		.116590	36
25	9.783623		9.899951		9.883672		0.116328	35
26	.783788	" Corr. 10 27	.899854		.883934		.116066	34
27	.783953	15 41	.899757		.884196		.115804	33
28	.784118	20 55	.899660		.884457		.115543	32
29	.784282		.899564		.884719		.115281	31
30	9.784447	30 82	9.899467		9.884980		0.115020	30
31	.784612	40 110	.899370		.885242		.114758	29
32	.784777	45 123	.899273		.885504		.114496	28
33	.784941	50 137	.899176		.885765		.114235	27
34	.785105		.899079		.886026		.113974	26
35	9.785269		9.898981		9.886288		0.113712	25
36	.785433		.898884		.886549		.113451	24
37	.785597		.898787		.886811		.113189	23
38	.785761		.898689		.887072		.112928	22
39	.785925		.898592		.887333		.112667	21
40	9.786089		9.898494		9.887594		0.112406	20
41	.786252		.898397	" Corr. 10 16	.887855	" Corr. 10 43	.112145	19
42	.786416		.898299	15 24	.888116	15 65	.111884	18
43	.786579		.898202	20 33	.888378	20 87	.111622	17
44	.786742		.898104		.888639		.111361	16
45	9.786906		9.898006	30 49	9.888900	30 130	0.111100	15
46	.787069	" Corr. 10 27	.897908	40 65	.889161	40 174	.110839	14
47	.787232	15 41	.897810	45 73	.889421	45 196	.110579	13
48	.787395	20 54	.897712	50 82	.889682	50 217	.110318	12
49	.787557		.897614		.889943		.110057	11
50	9.787720	30 81	9.897516		9.890204		0.109796	10
51	.787883	40 108	.897418		.890465		.109535	9
52	.788045	45 122	.897320		.890725		.109275	8
53	.788208	50 135	.897222		.890986		.109014	7
54	.788370		.897123		.891247		.108753	6
55	9.788532		9.897025		9.891507		0.108493	5
56	.788694		.896926		.891768		.108232	4
57	.788856		.896828		.892028		.107972	3
58	.789018		.896729		.892289		.107711	2
59	.789180		.896631		.892549		.107451	1
60	9.789342		9.896532		9.892810		0.107190	0
	cos	Corr. for Sec.	sin	Corr. for Sec.	cot	Corr. for Sec.	tan.	'

'	sin	Corr. for Sec.	cos	Corr. for Sec.	tan	Corr. for Sec.	cot	
0	9.789342		9.896532		9.892810		0.107190	60
1	.789504		.896433		.893070		.106930	59
2	.789665		.896335		.893331		.106669	58
3	.789827		.896236		.893591		.106409	57
4	.789988		.896137		.893851		.106149	56
5	9.790149		9.896038		9.894111		0.105889	55
6	.790310	" Corr.	.895939		.894372		.105628	54
7	.790471	10 27	.895840		.894632		.105368	53
8	.790632	15 40	.895741		.894892		.105108	52
9	.790793	20 54	.895641		.895152		.104848	51
10	9.790954	30 80	9.895542		9.895412		0.104588	50
11	.791115	40 107	.895443	" Corr.	.895672	" Corr.	.104328	49
12	.791275	45 121	.895343	10 17	.895932	10 43	.104068	48
13	.791436	50 134	.895244	15 25	.896192	15 65	.103808	47
14	.791596		.895145	20 33	.896452	20 87	.103548	46
15	9.791757		9.895045	30 50	9.896712	30 130	0.103288	45
16	.791917		.894945	40 66	.896971	40 173	.103029	44
17	.792077		.894846	45 75	.897231	45 195	.102769	43
18	.792237		.894746	50 83	.897491	50 216	.102509	42
19	.792397		.894646		.897751		.102249	41
20	9.792557		9.894546		9.898010		0.101990	40
21	.792716		.894446		.898270		.101730	39
22	.792876		.894346		.898530		.101470	38
23	.793035		.894246		.898789		.101211	37
24	.793195		.894146		.899049		.100951	36
25	9.793354		9.894046		9.899308		0.100692	35
26	.793514	" Corr.	.893946		.899568		.100432	34
27	.793673	10 26	.893846		.899827		.100173	33
28	.793832	15 40	.893745		.900087		.099913	32
29	.793991	20 53	.893645		.900346		.099654	31
30	9.794150	30 79	9.893544		9.900605		0.099395	30
31	.794308	40 106	.893444		.900864		.099136	29
32	.794467	45 119	.893343		.901124		.098876	28
33	.794626	50 132	.893243		.901383		.098617	27
34	.794784		.893142		.901642		.098358	26
35	9.794942		9.893041		9.901901		0.098099	25
36	.795101		.892940		.902160		.097840	24
37	.795259		.892839		.902420		.097580	23
38	.795417		.892739		.902679		.097321	22
39	.795575		.892638		.902938		.097062	21
40	9.795733		9.892536		9.903197		0.096803	20
41	.795891		.892435	" Corr.	.903456	" Corr.	.096544	19
42	.796049		.892334	10 17	.903714	10 43	.096286	18
43	.796206		.892233	15 25	.903973	15 65	.096027	17
44	.796364		.892132	20 34	.904232	20 86	.095768	16
45	9.796521		9.892030	30 51	9.904491	30 129	0.095509	15
46	.796679	" Corr.	.891929	40 68	.904750	40 173	.095250	14
47	.796836	10 26	.891827	45 76	.905008	45 194	.094992	13
48	.796993	15 39	.891726	50 84	.905267	50 216	.094733	12
49	.797150	20 52	.891624		.905526		.094474	11
50	9.797307	30 78	9.891523		9.905785		0.094215	10
51	.797464	40 105	.891421		.906043		.093957	9
52	.797621	45 118	.891319		.906302		.093698	8
53	.797777	50 131	.891217		.906560		.093440	7
54	.797934		.891115		.906819		.093181	6
55	9.798091		9.891013		9.907077		0.092923	5
56	.798247		.890911		.907336		.092664	4
57	.798403		.890809		.907594		.092406	3
58	.798560		.890707		.907853		.092147	2
59	.798716		.890605		.908111		.091889	1
60	9.798872		9.890503		9.908369		0.091631	0
	cos	Corr. for Sec.	sin	Corr. for Sec.	cot	Corr. for Sec.	tan	'

TABLE XXII.—LOGARITHMIC SINES,

39°　　　　　　　　　　　　　　　　　　　　　　　　　　　　　　　　　140°

′	sin	Corr. for Sec.	cos	Corr. for Sec.	tan	Corr. for Sec.	cot	
0	9.798872		9.890503		9.908369		0.091631	60
1	.799028		.890400		.908628		091372	59
2	.799184		.890298		.908886		.091114	58
3	.799339		.890195		.909144		.090856	57
4	.799495		.890093		.909402		.090598	56
5	9.799651		9.889990		9.909660		0.090340	55
6	.799806	″ Corr.	.889888		.909918		.090082	54
7	.799962	10 26	.889785		.910177		.089823	53
8	.800117	15 39	.889682		.910435		.089565	52
9	.800272	20 52	.889579		.910693		.089307	51
10	9.800427	30 78	9.889477		9.910951		0.089049	50
11	.800582	40 103	.889374	″ Corr.	.911209	″ Corr.	.088791	49
12	.800737	45 116	.889271	10 17	.911467	10 43	.088533	48
13	.800892	50 129	.889168	15 26	.911725	15 64	.088275	47
14	.801047		.889064	20 34	.911982	20 86	.088018	46
15	9.801201		9.888961	30 52	9.912240	30 129	0.087760	45
16	.801356		.888858	40 69	.912498	40 172	.087502	44
17	.801511		.888755	45 77	.912756	45 193	.087244	43
18	.801665		.888651	50 86	.913014	50 215	.086986	42
19	.801819		.888548		.913271		.086729	41
20	9.801973		9.888444		9.913529		0.086471	40
21	.802128		.888341		.913787		.086213	39
22	.802282		.888237		.914044		.085956	38
23	.802436		.888134		.914302		.085698	37
24	.802589		.888030		.914560		.085440	36
25	9.802743		9.887926		9.914817		0.085183	35
26	.802897	″ Corr.	.887822		.915075		.084925	34
27	.803050	10 26	.887718		.915332		.084668	33
28	.803204	15 38	.887614		.915590		.084410	32
29	.803357	20 51	.887510		.915847		.084153	31
30	9.803511	30 77	9.887406		9.916104		0.083896	30
31	.803664	40 102	.887302		.916362		.083638	29
32	.803817	45 115	.887198		.916619		.083381	28
33	.803970	50 128	.887093		.916877		.083123	27
34	.804123		.886989		.917134		.082866	26
35	9.804276		9.886885		9.917391		0.082609	25
36	.804428		.886780		.917648		.082352	24
37	.804581		.886676		.917906		.082094	23
38	.804734		.886571		.918163		.081837	22
39	.804886		.886466		.918420		.081580	21
40	9.805039		9.886362		9.918677		0.081323	20
41	.805191		.886257	″ Corr.	.918934	″ Corr.	.081066	19
42	.805343		.886152	10 18	.919191	10 43	.080809	18
43	.805495		.886047	15 26	.919448	15 64	.080552	17
44	.805647		.885942	20 35	.919705	20 86	.080295	16
45	9.805799		9.885837	30 53	9.919962	30 128	0.080038	15
46	.805951	″ Corr.	.885732	40 70	.920219	40 171	.079781	14
47	.806103	10 25	.885627	45 79	.920476	45 193	.079524	13
48	.806254	15 38	.885522	50 88	.920733	50 214	.079267	12
49	.806406	20 50	.885416		.920990		.079010	11
50	9.806557	30 76	9.885311		9.921247		0.078753	10
51	.806709	40 101	.885205		.921503		.078497	9
52	.806860	45 114	.885100		.921760		.078240	8
53	.807011	50 126	.884994		.922017		.077983	7
54	.807163		.884889		.922274		.077726	6
55	9.807314		9.884783		9.922530		0.077470	5
56	.807465		.884677		.922787		.077213	4
57	.807615		.884572		.923044		.076956	3
58	.807766		.884466		.923300		.076700	2
59	.807917		.884360		.923557		.076443	1
60	9.808067		9.884254		9.923814		0.076186	0
	cos	Corr. for Sec.	sin	Corr. for Sec.	cot	Corr. for Sec.	tan	′

'	sin	Corr. for Sec.	cos	Corr. for Sec.	tan	Corr. for Sec.	cot	
0	9.808067		9.884254		9.923814		0.076186	60
1	.808218		.884148		.924070		.075930	59
2	.808368		.884042		.924327		.075673	58
3	.808519		.883936		.924583		.075417	57
4	.808669		.883829		.924840		.075160	56
5	9.808819		9.883723		9.925096		0.074904	55
6	.808969		.883617		.925352		.074648	54
7	.809119		.883510		.925609		.074391	53
8	.809269		.883404		.925865		.074135	52
9	.809419		.883297		.926122		.073878	51
10	9.809569		9.883191		9.926378		0.073622	50
11	.809718		.883084		.926634		.073366	49
12	.809868		.882977		.926890		.073110	48
13	.810017		.882871		.927147		.072853	47
14	.810167		.882764		.927403		.072597	46
15	9.810316		9.882657		9.927659		0.072341	45
16	.810465		.882550		.927915		.072085	44
17	.810614		.882443		.928171		.071829	43
18	.810763		.882336		.928427		.071573	42
19	.810912		.882229		.928684		.071316	41
20	9.811061		9.882121		9.928940		0.071060	40
21	.811210		.882014		.929196		.070804	39
22	.811358		.881907		.929452		.070548	38
23	.811507		.881799		.929708		.070292	37
24	.811655		.881692		.929964		.070036	36
25	9.811804		9.881584		9.930220		0.069780	35
26	.811952		.881477		.930475		.069525	34
27	.812100		.881369		.930731		.069269	33
28	.812248		.881261		.930987		.069013	32
29			.881153		.931243		.068757	31
30	9.812544		9.881046		9.931499		0.068501	30
31	.812692		.880938		.931755		.068245	29
32	.812840		.880830		.932010		.067990	28
33	.812988		.880722		.932266		.067734	27
34	.813135		.880613		.932522		.067478	26
35	9.813283		9.880505		9.932778		0.067222	25
36	.813430		.880397		.933033		.066967	24
37	.813578		.880289		.933289		.066711	23
38	.813725		.880180		.933545		.066455	22
39	.813872		.880072		.933800		.066200	21
40	9.814019		9.879963		9.934056		0.065944	20
41	.814166		.879855		.934311		.065689	19
42	.814313		.879746		.934567		.065433	18
43	.814460		.879637		.934822		.065178	17
44	.814607		.879529		.935078		.064922	16
45	9.814753		9.879420		9.935333		0.064667	15
46	.814900		.879311		.935589		.064411	14
47	.815046		.879202		.935844		.064156	13
48	.815193		.879093		.936100		.063900	12
49	.815339		.878984		.936355		.063645	11
50	9.815485		9.878875		9.936611		0.063389	10
51	.815632		.878766		.936866		.063134	9
52	.815778		.878656		.937121		.062879	8
53	.815924		.878547		.937377		.062623	7
54	.816069		.878438		.937632		.062368	6
55	9.816215		9.878328		9.937887		0.062113	5
56	.816361		.878219		.938142		.061858	4
57	.816507		.878109		.938398		.061602	3
58	.816652		.877999		.938653		.061347	2
59	.816798		.877890		.938908		.061092	1
60	9.816943		9.877780		9.939163		0.060837	0

| | cos | Corr. for Sec. | sin | Corr. for Sec. | cot | Corr. for Sec. | tan | ' |

Correction tables (upper, near 11–18):

sin — " Corr.
10 25 · 15 37 · 20 50 · 30 75 · 40 99 · 45 112 · 50 124

cos — " Corr.
10 18 · 15 27 · 20 36 · 30 53 · 40 71 · 50 89

tan — " Corr.
10 43 · 15 64 · 20 85 · 30 128 · 40 171 · 45 192 · 50 213

Correction tables (lower, near 41–48):

sin — " Corr.
10 24 · 15 37 · 20 49 · 30 73 · 40 98 · 45 110 · 50 122

cos — " Corr.
10 18 · 15 27 · 20 36 · 40 73 · 45 82 · 50 91

tan — " Corr.
10 43 · 15 64 · 20 85 · 30 128 · 40 170 · 45 192 · 50 213

TABLE XXII.—LOGARITHMIC SINES,

41°

138°

'	sin	Corr. for Sec.	cos	Corr. for Sec.	tan	Corr. for Sec.	cot	
0	9.816943		9.877780		9.939163		0.060837	60
1	.817088		.877670		.939418		.060582	59
2	.817233		.877560		.939673		.060327	58
3	.817379		.877450		.939928		.060072	57
4	.817524		.877340		.940183		.059817	56
5	9.817668		9.877230		9.940439		0.059561	55
6	.817813		.877120		.940694		.059306	54
7	.817958		.877010		.940949		.059051	53
8	.818103		.876899		.941204		.058796	52
9	.818247		.876789		.941459		.058541	51
10	9.818392		9.876678		9.941713		0.058287	50
11	.818536	" Corr.	.876568	" Corr.	.941968	" Corr.	.058032	49
12	.818681	10 24	.876457	10 18	.942223	10 42	.057777	48
13	.818825	15 36	.876347	15 28	.942478	15 64	.057522	47
14	.818969	20 48	.876236	20 37	.942733	20 85	.057267	46
15	9.819113	30 72	9.876125	30 55	9.942988	30 127	0.057012	45
16	.819257	40 96	.876014	40 74	.943243	40 170	.056757	44
17	.819401	45 108	.875904	45 83	.943498	45 191	.056502	43
18	.819545	50 120	.875793	50 92	.943752	50 212	.056248	42
19	.819689		.875682		.944007		.055993	41
20	9.819832		9.875571		9.944262		0.055738	40
21	.819976		.875459		.944517		.055483	39
22	.820120		.875348		.944771		.055229	38
23	.820263		.875237		.945026		.054974	37
24	.820406		.875126		.945281		.054719	36
25	9.820550		9.875014		9.945535		0.054465	35
26	.820693		.874903		.945790		.054210	34
27	.820836		.874791		.946045		.053955	33
28	.820979		.874680		.946299		.053701	32
29	.821122		.874568		.946554		.053446	31
30	9.821265		9.874456		9.946808		0.053192	30
31	.821407		.874344		.947063		.052937	29
32	.821550		.874232		.947318		.052682	28
33	.821693		.874121		.947572		.052428	27
34	.821835		.874009		.947827		.052173	26
35	9.821977		9.873896		9.948081		0.051919	25
36	.822120		.873784		.948335		.051665	24
37	.822262		.873672		.948590		.051410	23
38	.822404		.873560		.948844		.051156	22
39	.822546		.873448		.949099		.050901	21
40	9.822688		9.873335		9.949353		0.050647	20
41	.822830	" Corr.	.873223	" Corr.	.949608	" Corr.	.050392	19
42	.822972	10 24	.873110	10 19	.949862	10 42	.050138	18
43	.823114	15 35	.872998	15 28	.950116	15 64	.049884	17
44	.823255	20 47	.872885	20 38	.950371	20 85	.049629	16
45	9.823397	30 71	9.872772	30 56	9.950625	30 127	0.049375	15
46	.823539	40 94	.872659	40 75	.950879	40 170	.049121	14
47	.823680	45 106	.872547	45 85	.951133	45 191	.048867	13
48	.823821	50 118	.872434	50 94	.951388	50 212	.048612	12
49	.823963		.872321		.951642		.048358	11
50	9.824104		9.872208		9.951896		0.048104	10
51	.824245		.872095		.952150		.047850	9
52	.824386		.871981		.952405		.047595	8
53	.824527		.871868		.952659		.047341	7
54	.824668		.871755		.952913		.047087	6
55	9.824808		9.871641		9.953167		0.046833	5
56	.824949		.871528		.953421		.046579	4
57	.825090		.871414		.953675		.046325	3
58	.825230		.871301		.953929		.046071	2
59	.825371		.871187		.954183		.045817	1
60	9.825511		9.871073		9.954437		0.045563	0

	cos	Corr. for Sec.	sin	Corr. for Sec.	cot	Corr. for Sec.	tan	'

'	sin	Corr. for Sec.	cos	Corr. for Sec.	tan	Corr. for Sec.	cot	
0	9.825511		9.871073		9.954437		0.045563	60
1	.825651		.870960		.954691		.045309	59
2	.825791		.870846		.954946		.045054	58
3	.825931		.870732		.955200		.044800	57
4	.826071		.870618		.955454		.044546	56
5	9.826211		9.870504		9.955708		0.044292	55
6	.826351		.870390		.955961		.044039	54
7	.826491		.870276		.956215		.043785	53
8	.826631		.870161		.956469		.043531	52
9	.826770		.870047		.956723		.043277	51
10	9.826910		9.869933		9.956977		0.043023	50
11	.827049	" Corr.	.869818	" Corr.	.957231	" Corr.	.042769	49
12	.827189	10 23	.869704	10 19	.957485	10 42	.042515	48
13	.827328	15 35	.869589	15 29	.957739	15 63	.042261	47
14	.827467	20 46	.869474	20 38	.957993	20 85	.042007	46
15	9.827606	30 70	9.869360	30 57	9.958247	30 127	0.041753	45
16	.827745	40 93	.869245	40 76	.958500	40 169	.041500	44
17	.827884	45 104	.869130	45 86	.958754	45 190	.041246	43
18	.828023	50 116	.869015	50 96	.959008	50 211	.040992	42
19	.828162		.868900		.959262		.040738	41
20	9.828301		9.868785		9.959516		0.040484	40
21	.828439		.868670		.959769		.040231	39
22	.828578		.868555		.960023		.039977	38
23	.828716		.868440		.960277		.039723	37
24	.828855		.868324		.960530		.039470	36
25	9.828993		9.868209		9.960784		0.039216	35
26	.829131		.868093		.961038		.038962	34
27	.829269		.867978		.961292		.038708	33
28	.829407		.867862		.961545		.038455	32
29	.829545		.867747		.961799		.038201	31
30	9.829683		9.867631		9.962052		0.037948	30
31	.829821		.867515		.962306		.037694	29
32	.829959		.867399		.962560		.037440	28
33	.830097		.867283		.962813		.037187	27
34	.830234		.867167		.963067		.036933	26
35	9.830372		9.867051		9.963320		0.036680	25
36	.830509		.866935		.963574		.036426	24
37	.830646		.866819		.963828		.036172	23
38	.830784		.866703		.964081		.035919	22
39	.830921		.866586		.964335		.035665	21
40	9.831058		9.866470		9.964588		0.035412	20
41	.831195	" Corr.	.866353	" Corr.	.964842	" Corr.	.035158	19
42	.831332	10 23	.866237	10 19	.965095	10 42	.034905	18
43	.831469	15 34	.866120	15 29	.965349	15 63	.034651	17
44	.831606	20 46	.866004	20 39	.965602	20 84	.034398	16
45	9.831742	30 68	9.865887	30 58	9.965855	30 127	0.034145	15
46	.831879	40 91	.865770	40 78	.966109	40 169	.033891	14
47	.832015	45 103	.865653	45 88	.966362	45 190	.033638	13
48	.832152	50 114	.865536	50 97	.966616	50 211	.033384	12
49	.832288		.865419		.966869		.033131	11
50	9.832425		9.865302		9.967123		0.032877	10
51	.832561		.865185		.967376		.032624	9
52	.832697		.865068		.967629		.032371	8
53	.832833		.864950		.967883		.032117	7
54	.832969		.864833		.968136		.031864	6
55	9.833105		9.864716		9.968389		0.031611	5
56	.833241		.864598		.968643		.031357	4
57	.833377		.864481		.968896		.031104	3
58	.833512		.864363		.969149		.030851	2
59	.833648		.864245		.969403		.030597	1
60	9.833783		9.864127		9.969656		0.030344	0
	cos	Corr. for Sec.	sin	Corr. for Sec.	cot	Corr. for Sec.	tan	'

'	sin	Corr. for Sec.	cos	Corr. for Sec.	tan	Corr. for Sec.	cot	
0	9.833783		9.864127		9.969656		0.030344	60
1	.833919		.864010		.969909		.030091	59
2	.834054		.863892		.970162		.029838	58
3	.834189		.863774		.970416		.029584	57
4	.834325		.863656		.970669		.029331	56
5	9.834460		9.863538		9.970922		0.029078	55
6	.834595		.863419		.971175		.028825	54
7	.834730		.863301		.971429		.028571	53
8	.834865		.863183		.971682		.028318	52
9	.834999		.863064		.971935		.028065	51
10	9.835134		9.862946		9.972188		0.027812	50
11	.835269	" Corr.	.862827	" Corr.	.972441	" Corr.	.027559	49
12	.835403	10 22	.862709	10 20	.972695	10 42	.027305	48
13	.835538	15 34	.862590	15 30	.972948	15 63	.027052	47
14	.835672	20 45	.862471	20 40	.973201	20 84	.026799	46
15	9.835807	30 67	9.862353	30 59	9.973454	30 127	0.026546	45
16	.835941	40 90	.862234	40 79	.973707	40 169	.026293	44
17	.836075	45 101	.862115	45 89	.973960	45 190	.026040	43
18	.836209	50 112	.861996	50 99	.974213	50 211	.025787	42
19	.836343		.861877		.974466		.025534	41
20	9.836477		9.861758		9.974720		0.025280	40
21	.836611		.861638		.974973		.025027	39
22	.836745		.861519		.975226		.024774	38
23	.836878		.861400		.975479		.024521	37
24	.837012		.861280		.975732		.024268	36
25	9.837146		9.861161		9.975985		0.024015	35
26	.837279		.861041		.976238		.023762	34
27	.837412		.860922		.976491		.023509	33
28	.837546		.860802		.976744		.023256	32
29	.837679		.860682		.976997		.023003	31
30	9.837812		9.860562		9.977250		0.022750	30
31	.837945		.860442		.977503		.022497	29
32	.838078		.860322		.977756		.022244	28
33	.838211		.860202		.978009		.021991	27
34	.838344		.860082		.978262		.021738	26
35	9.838477		9.859962		9.978515		0.021485	25
36	.838610		.859842		.978768		.021232	24
37	.838742		.859721		.979021		.020979	23
38	.838875		.859601		.979274		.020726	22
39	.839007		.859480		.979527		.020473	21
40	9.839140		9.859360		9.979780		0.020220	20
41	.839272	" Corr.	.859239	" Corr.	.980033	" Corr.	.019967	19
42	.839404	10 22	.859119	10 20	.980286	10 42	.019714	18
43	.839536	15 33	.858998	15 30	.980538	15 63	.019462	17
44	.839668	20 44	.858877	20 40	.980791	20 84	.019209	16
45	9.839800	30 66	9.858756	30 60	9.981044	30 126	0.018956	15
46	.839932	40 88	.858635	40 81	.981297	40 169	.018703	14
47	.840064	45 99	.858514	45 91	.981550	45 190	.018450	13
48	.840196	50 110	.858393	50 101	.981803	50 211	.018197	12
49	.840328		.858272		.982056		.017944	11
50	9.840459		9.858151		9.982309		0.017691	10.
51	.840591		.858029		.982562		.017438	9
52	.840722		.857908		.982814		.017186	8
53	.840854		.857786		.983067		.016933	7
54	.840985		.857665		.983320		.016680	6
55	9.841116		9.857543		9.983573		0.016427	5
56	.841247		.857422		.983826		.016174	4
57	.841378		.857300		.984079		.015921	3
58	.841509		.857178		.984332		.015668	2
59	.841640		.857056		.984584		.015416	1
60	9.841771		9.856934		9.984437		0.015163	0
	cos	Corr. for Sec.	sin	Corr. for Sec.	cot	Corr. for Sec.	tan	'

'	sin	Corr. for Sec.	cos	Corr. for Sec.	tan	Corr. for Sec.	cot	
0	9.841771		9.856934		9.984837		0.015163	60
1	.841902		.856812		.985090		.014910	59
2	.842033		.856690		.985343		.014657	58
3	.842163		.856568		.985596		.014404	57
4	.842294		.856446		.985848		.014152	56
5	9.842424		9.856323		9.986101		0.013899	55
6	.842555		.856201		.986354		.013646	54
7	.842685		.856078		.986607		.013393	53
8	.842815		.855956		.986860		.013140	52
9	.842946		.855833		.987112		.012888	51
10	9.843076		9.855711		9.987365		0.012635	50
11	.843206	" Corr.	.855588	" Corr.	.987618	" Corr.	.012382	49
12	.843336	10 22	.855465	10 21	.987871	10 42	.012129	48
13	.843466	15 32	.855342	15 31	.988123	15 63	.011877	47
14	.843595	20 43	.855219	20 41	.988376	20 84	.011624	46
15	9.843725	30 65	9.855096	30 62	9.988629	30 126	0.011371	45
16	.843855	40 86	.854973	40 82	.988882	40 169	.011118	44
17	.843984	45 97	.854850	45 92	.989134	45 190	.010866	43
18	.844114	50 108	.854727	50 103	.989387	50 211	.010613	42
19	.844243		.854603		.989640		.010360	41
20	9.844372		9.854480		9.989893		0.010107	40
21	.844502		.854356		.990145		.009855	39
22	.844631		.854233		.990398		.009602	38
23	.844760		.854109		.990651		.009349	37
24	.844889		.853986		.990903		.009097	36
25	9.845018		9.853862		9.991156		0.008844	35
26	.845147		.853738		.991409		.008591	34
27	.845276		.853614		.991662		.008338	33
28	.845405		.853490		.991914		.008086	32
29	.845533		.853366		.992167		.007833	31
30	9.845662		9.853242		9.992420		0.007580	30
31	.845790		.853118		.992672		.007328	29
32	.845919		.852994		.992925		.007075	28
33	.846047		.852869		.993178		.006822	27
34	.846175		.852745		.993431		.006569	26
35	9.846304		9.852620		9.993683		0.006317	25
36	.846432		.852496		.993936		.006064	24
37	.846560		.852371		.994189		.005811	23
38	.846688		.852247		.994441		.005559	22
39	.846816		.852122		.994694		.005306	21
40	9.846944		9.851997		9.994947		0.005053	20
41	.847071	" Corr.	.851872	" Corr.	.995199	" Corr.	.004801	19
42	.847199	10 21	.851747	10 21	.995452	10 42	.004548	18
43	.847327	15 32	.851622	15 31	.995705	15 63	.004295	17
44	.847454	20 42	.851497	20 41	.995957	20 84	.004043	16
45	9.847582	30 64	9.851372	30 63	9.996210	30 126	0.003790	15
46	.847709	40 85	.851246	40 83	.996463	40 168	.003537	14
47	.847836	45 96	.851121	45 94	.996715	45 190	.003285	13
48	.847964	50 106	.850996	50 104	.996968	50 211	.003032	12
49	.848091		.850870		.997221		.002779	11
50	9.848218		9.850745		9.997473		0.002527	10
51	.848345		.850619		.997726		.002274	9
52	.848472		.850493		.997979		.002021	8
53	.848599		.850368		.998231		.001769	7
54	.848726		.850242		.998484		.001516	6
55	9.848852		9.850116		9.998737		0.001263	5
56	.848979		.849990		.998989		.001011	4
57	.849106		.849864		.999242		.000758	3
58	.849232		.849738		.999495		.000505	2
59	.849359		.849611		.999747		.000253	1
60	9.849485		9.849485		0.000000		0.000000	0
	cos	Corr. for Sec.	sin	Corr. for Sec.	cot	Corr. for Sec.	tan	'

Angles Less Than 6°.—Owing to the rapid variation in the versine of small angles, the usual straight-line method of interpolation for seconds may not be precise enough. A closer method is based upon the relation vers $A = 2 \sin^2 \frac{1}{2}A$. Since natural sines of small angles are closely proportional to the angles, natural versines of small angles are closely proportional to their squares.

In this table, v refers to the versine, and s refers to the number of seconds in an angle. Although $\log v$ varies rapidly, $(\log v - 2 \log s)$ varies so slowly that it may be determined from values at 1′ intervals.

Example.—Find long vers 2° 17′ 35″.

$$\frac{\text{vers } 2° \ 17′ \ 35″}{\text{vers } 2° \ 17′} = \frac{(2° \ 17′ \ 35″)^2}{(2° \ 17′)^2} = \frac{(8255″)^2}{(8220″)^2}$$

or

log vers 2° 17′ 35″ = 2 log 8255 + (log vers 8220″ − 2 log 8220)

or

$$\log v = 2 \log s \qquad + (\log v - 2 \log s)$$
$$2 \log s = 7.833434$$
$$\log v - 2 \log s = 9.070061 \ (-20)$$
$$\log \text{vers } 2° \ 17′ \ 35″ = \overline{6.903495} \ (-10)$$

In the reverse process of finding an angle to seconds when its logarithmic versine is given, first determine by inspection the value of $\log v - 2 \log s$. Then subtract it from $\log v$, giving $2 \log s$, and find the required angle.

Angles Greater Than 6°.—In the bulk of the table the use of the Diff. per 1″ is replaced by a quicker method in the form of sets of corrections for multiples of 10″ and 15″. The number of these sets varies so as to limit the maximum error for a 50″ correction to one in the sixth place of the logarithm anywhere within the indicated range.

Thus, log vers 48° 20′ 50″ is found quickly to be 9.525309 +234 = 9.525543. Because the sets of corrections are exact at the middle of the indicated range, slightly greater precision would be obtained in this example by adding a correction of 235, since the 50″ correction at 48° 10′ is 236. This gives log vers 48° 20′ 50″ = 9.525544. Many computers subtract the 10″ correction of 47 from log vers 48° 21′.

Obviously, corrections for any number of seconds could be obtained speedily, if the field work justifies, by combining the tabulated corrections and shifting the decimal point.

TABLE XXIII.—LOGARITHMIC VERSINES

	0°				1°				2°		
'	"	vers	log v - 2 log s	'	"	vers	log v - 2 log s	'	"	vers	log v - 2 log s
	s	log v	9.070		s	log v	9.070		s	log v	9.070
0	0	Inf.	120	0	3600	6.182714	109	0	7200	6.784741	076
1	60	2.626422	120	1	3660	.197071	108	1	7260	.791948	075
2	120	3.228482	120	2	3720	.211194	108	2	7320	.799096	074
3	180	3.580665	120	3	3780	.225091	108	3	7380	.806186	073
4	240	3.830542	120	4	3840	.238770	107	4	7440	.813219	073
5	300	4.024362	120	5	3900	6.252236	107	5	7500	6.820194	072
6	360	.182725	120	6	3960	.265497	106	6	7560	.827115	071
7	420	.316618	120	7	4020	.278558	106	7	7620	.833980	070
8	480	.432602	120	8	4080	.291426	106	8	7680	.840792	070
9	540	.534907	119	9	4140	.304106	105	9	7740	.847551	069
10	600	4.626422	119	10	4200	6.316603	105	10	7800	6.854257	068
11	660	.709207	119	11	4260	.328923	104	11	7860	.860912	067
12	720	.784784	119	12	4320	.341071	104	12	7920	.867517	066
13	780	.854308	119	13	4380	.353052	103	13	7980	.874071	066
14	840	.918678	119	14	4440	.364869	103	14	8040	.880577	065
15	900	4.978604	119	15	4500	6.376528	103	15	8100	6.887034	064
16	960	5.034661	119	16	4560	.388032	102	16	8160	.893443	063
17	1020	.087319	119	17	4620	.399386	102	17	8220	.899806	062
18	1080	.136966	119	18	4680	.410593	101	18	8280	.906122	061
19	1140	.183928	119	19	4740	.421657	101	19	8340	.912393	061
20	1200	5.228481	118	20	4800	6.432583	100	20	8400	6.918618	060
21	1260	.270859	118	21	4860	.443372	100	21	8460	.924800	059
22	1320	.311266	118	22	4920	.454029	099	22	8520	.930937	058
23	1380	.349876	118	23	4980	.464557	099	23	8580	.937032	057
24	1440	.386843	118	24	5040	.474959	098	24	8640	.943084	056
25	1500	5.422300	118	25	5100	6.485238	098	25	8700	6.949094	055
26	1560	.456367	118	26	5160	.495396	097	26	8760	.955063	054
27	1620	.489148	118	27	5220	.505438	097	27	8820	.960991	054
28	1680	.520736	117	28	5280	.515364	096	28	8880	.966879	053
29	1740	.551216	117	29	5340	.525178	095	29	8940	.972727	052
30	1800	5.580662	117	30	5400	6.534882	095	30	9000	6.978536	051
31	1860	.609143	117	31	5460	.544480	094	31	9060	.984306	050
32	1920	.636719	117	32	5520	.553972	094	32	9120	.990039	049
33	1980	.663447	116	33	5580	.563362	093	33	9180	.995733	048
34	2040	.689377	116	34	5640	.572651	093	34	9240	7.001391	047
35	2100	5.714555	116	35	5700	6.581842	092	35	9300	7.007012	046
36	2160	.739023	116	36	5760	.590936	092	36	9360	.012597	045
37	2220	.762821	116	37	5820	.599937	091	37	9420	.018146	044
38	2280	.785985	115	38	5880	.608845	090	38	9480	.023660	043
39	2340	.808547	115	39	5940	.617663	090	39	9540	.029139	042
40	2400	5.830537	115	40	6000	6.626392	089	40	9600	7.034584	041
41	2460	.851985	115	41	6060	.635034	089	41	9660	.039995	040
42	2520	.872915	114	42	6120	.643591	088	42	9720	.045372	039
43	2580	.893353	114	43	6180	.652064	087	43	9780	.050716	038
44	2640	.913322	114	44	6240	.660456	087	44	9840	.056028	037
45	2700	5.932841	114	45	6300	6.668767	086	45	9900	7.061307	036
46	2760	.951931	113	46	6360	.677000	085	46	9960	.066554	035
47	2820	.970611	113	47	6420	.685155	085	47	10020	.071770	034
48	2880	.988898	113	48	6480	.693234	084	48	10080	.076954	033
49	2940	6.006807	112	49	6540	.701239	083	49	10140	.082108	032
50	3000	6.024355	112	50	6600	6.709171	083	50	10200	7.087232	031
51	3060	.041555	112	51	6660	.717030	082	51	10260	.092325	030
52	3120	.058421	111	52	6720	.724820	081	52	10320	.097389	029
53	3180	.074965	111	53	6780	.732540	081	53	10380	.102423	028
54	3240	.091201	111	54	6840	.740192	080	54	10440	.107428	027
55	3300	6.107138	110	55	6900	6.747777	079	55	10500	7.112405	026
56	3360	.122789	110	56	6960	.755297	079	56	10560	.117353	025
57	3420	.138162	110	57	7020	.762752	078	57	10620	.122273	024
58	3480	.153268	109	58	7080	.770144	077	58	10680	.127165	023
59	3540	.168116	109	59	7140	.777473	076	59	10740	.132030	022
60	3600	6.182714	109	60	7200	6.784741	076	60	10800	7.136868	021

TABLE XXIII.—LOGARITHMIC VERSINES

	3°				4°				5°		
'	"	vers	log v − 2 log s	'	"	vers	log v − 2 log s	'	"	vers	log v − 2 log s
	s	log v	9.070		s	log v	9.069		s	log v	9.069
0	10800	7.136868	021	0	14400	7.386668	943	0	18000	7.580389	844
1	10860	.141679	019	1	14460	.390278	942	1	18060	.583278	842
2	10920	.146464	018	2	14520	.393874	940	2	18120	.586157	840
3	10980	.151222	017	3	14580	.397454	939	3	18180	.589026	839
4	11040	.155954	016	4	14640	.401020	937	4	18240	.591886	837
5	11100	7.160661	015	5	14700	7.404571	936	5	18300	7.594737	835
6	11160	.165342	014	6	14760	.408107	934	6	18360	.597578	833
7	11220	.169998	013	7	14820	.411629	933	7	18420	.600410	831
8	11280	.174630	011	8	14880	.415137	931	8	18480	.603233	829
9	11340	.179236	010	9	14940	.418631	930	9	18540	.606047	827
10	11400	7.183819	009	10	15000	7.422111	928	10	18600	7.608851	825
11	11460	.188377	008	11	15060	.425577	927	11	18660	.611647	824
12	11520	.192912	007	12	15120	.429029	925	12	18720	.614433	822
13	11580	.197423	006	13	15180	.432467	924	13	18780	.617211	820
14	11640	.201910	004	14	15240	.435892	922	14	18840	.619980	818
15	11700	7.206375	003	15	15300	7.439303	921	15	18900	7.622739	816
16	11760	.210817	002	16	15360	.442701	919	16	18960	.625491	814
17	11820	.215236	001	17	15420	.446086	917	17	19020	.628233	812
18	11880	.219633	000	18	15480	.449458	916	18	19080	.630967	810
19	11940	.224007	•998	19	15540	.452816	914	19	19140	.633692	808
20	12000	7.228360	997	20	15600	7.456162	913	20	19200	7.636409	806
21	12060	.232691	996	21	15660	.459495	911	21	19260	.639117	804
22	12120	.237000	995	22	15720	.462815	910	22	19320	.641816	802
23	12180	.241288	994	23	15780	.466122	908	23	19380	.644508	800
24	12240	.245555	992	24	15840	.469417	906	24	19440	.647191	798
25	12300	7.249801	991	25	15900	7.472699	905	25	19500	7.649865	796
26	12360	.254027	990	26	15960	.475969	903	26	19560	.652532	794
27	12420	.258232	989	27	16020	.479226	901	27	19620	.655190	792
28	12480	.262416	987	28	16080	.482472	900	28	19680	.657840	790
29	12540	.266581	986	29	16140	.485705	898	29	19740	.660483	788
30	12600	7.270726	985	30	16200	7.488927	896	30	19800	7.663117	786
31	12660	.274851	983	31	16260	.492136	895	31	19860	.665743	784
32	12720	.283043	982	32	16320	.495333	893	32	19920	.668361	782
33	12780	.283043	981	33	16380	.498519	891	33	19980	.670971	780
34	12840	.287110	980	34	16440	.501693	890	34	20040	.673574	778
35	12900	7.291158	978	35	16500	7.504856	888	35	20100	7.676168	776
36	12960	.295187	977	36	16560	.508007	886	36	20160	.678755	774
37	13020	.299197	976	37	16620	.511147	885	37	20220	.681334	772
38	13080	.303190	974	38	16680	.514275	883	38	20280	.683906	770
39	13140	.307164	973	39	16740	.517392	881	39	20340	.686470	768
40	13200	7.311119	972	40	16800	7.520498	880	40	20400	7.689026	766
41	13260	.315057	970	41	16860	.523593	878	41	20460	.691575	764
42	13320	.318977	969	42	16920	.526677	876	42	20520	.694116	762
43	13380	.322880	967	43	16980	.529750	874	43	20580	.696650	759
44	13440	.326765	966	44	17040	.532812	873	44	20640	.699177	757
45	13500	7.330632	965	45	17100	7.535863	871	45	20700	7.701696	755
46	13560	.334483	963	46	17160	.538904	869	46	20760	.704208	753
47	13620	.338316	962	47	17220	.541934	867	47	20820	.706712	751
48	13680	.342133	961	48	17280	.544953	866	48	20880	.709210	749
49	13740	.345933	959	49	17340	.547962	864	49	20940	.711700	747
50	13800	7.349716	958	50	17400	7.550961	862	50	21000	7.714183	745
51	13860	.353483	956	51	17460	.553949	860	51	21060	.716659	742
52	13920	.357233	955	52	17520	.556927	859	52	21120	.719128	740
53	13980	.360968	953	53	17580	.559895	857	53	21180	.721590	738
54	14040	.364686	952	54	17640	.562852	855	54	21240	.724045	736
55	14100	7.368389	951	55	17700	7.565800	853	55	21300	7.726493	734
56	14160	.372076	949	56	17760	.568737	851	56	21360	.728934	732
57	14220	.375747	948	57	17820	.571665	850	57	21420	.731368	729
58	14280	.379403	946	58	17880	.574583	848	58	21480	.733796	727
59	14340	.383043	945	59	17940	.577491	846	59	21540	.736216	725
60	14400	7.386668	943	60	18000	7.580389	844	60	21600	7.738630	722
			9.069								

256

TABLE XXIII.—LOGARITHMIC VERSINES

′	6° vers	D.1″	7° vers	D.1″	′	8° vers	D.1″	9° vers	D.1″
0	7.738630	40.13	7.872381	34.38	0	7.988199	30.08	8.090317	26.72
1	.741038	40.00	.874444	34.30	1	.990004	30.02	.091920	26.68
2	.743438	39.90	.876502	34.22	2	.991805	29.95	.093521	26.63
3	.745832	39.78	.878555	34.13	3	.993602	29.88	.095119	26.58
4	.748219	39.68	.880603	34.07	4	.995395	29.83	.096714	26.52
5	7.750600	39.57	7.882647	33.98	5	7.997185	29.77	8.098305	26.48
6	.752974	39.47	.884686	33.90	6	.998971	29.72	.099894	26.43
7	.755342	39.35	.886720	33.82	7	8.000754	29.63	.101480	26.40
8	.757703	39.25	.888749	33.73	8	.002532	29.60	.103064	26.33
9	.760058	39.13	.890773	33.67	9	.004308	29.52	.104644	26.28
10	7.762406	39.05	7.892793	33.58	10	8.006079	29.47	8.106221	26.25
11	.764749	38.92	.894808	33.50	11	.007847	29.40	.107796	26.18
12	.767084	38.83	.896818	33.43	12	.009611	29.35	.109367	26.15
13	.769414	38.72	.898824	33.35	13	.011372	29.28	.110936	26.15
14	.771737	38.62	.900825	33.27	14	.013129	29.22	.112502	26.10
15	7.774054	38.52	7.902821	33.20	15	8.014882	29.17	8.114065	26.05
16	.776365	38.42	.904813	33.12	16	.016632	29.10	.115625	26.00
17	.778670	38.30	.906800	33.05	17	.018378	29.05	.117182	25.95
18	.780968	38.22	.908783	32.97	18	.020121	29.00	.118737	25.92
19	.783261	38.10	.910761	32.90	19	.021861	28.93	.120289	25.82
20	7.785547	38.02	7.912735	32.82	20	8.023597	28.87	8.121838	25.77
21	.787828	37.90	.914704	32.73	21	.025329	28.82	.123384	25.72
22	.790102	37.82	.916668	32.68	22	.027058	28.75	.124927	25.68
23	.792371	37.70	.918629	32.58	23	.028783	28.70	.126468	25.63
24	.794633	37.62	.920584	32.53	24	.030505	28.65	.128006	25.58
25	7.796890	37.52	7.922536	32.45	25	8.032224	28.58	8.129541	25.55
26	.799141	37.40	.924483	32.37	26	.033939	28.53	.131074	25.50
27	.801385	37.33	.926425	32.32	27	.035651	28.47	.132604	25.45
28	.803625	37.22	.928364	32.22	28	.037359	28.42	.134131	25.40
29	.805858	37.13	.930297	32.17	29	.039064	28.37	.135655	25.37
30	7.808086	37.03	7.932227	32.08	30	8.040766	28.30	8.137177	25.32
31	.810308	36.93	.934152	32.02	31	.042464	28.25	.138696	25.27
32	.812524	36.83	.936073	31.95	32	.044159	28.20	.140212	25.23
33	.814734	36.75	.937990	31.88	33	.045851	28.13	.141726	25.18
34	.816939	36.67	.939903	31.80	34	.047539	28.08	.143237	25.13
35	7.819139	36.55	7.941811	31.73	35	8.049224	28.03	8.144745	25.10
36	.821332	36.48	.943715	31.67	36	.050906	27.98	.146251	25.05
37	.823521	36.37	.945615	31.60	37	.052585	27.92	.147754	25.02
38	.825703	36.28	.947511	31.52	38	.054260	27.87	.149255	24.95
39	.827880	36.20	.949402	31.47	39	.055932	27.82	.150752	24.93
40	7.830052	36.10	7.951290	31.38	40	8.057601	27.75	8.152248	24.88
41	.832218	36.02	.953173	31.32	41	.059266	27.72	.153741	24.83
42	.834379	35.93	.955052	31.27	42	.060929	27.65	.155231	24.78
43	.836535	35.83	.956928	31.18	43	.062588	27.60	.156718	24.75
44	.838685	35.75	.958799	31.12	44	.064244	27.55	.158203	24.72
45	7.840830	35.65	7.960666	31.05	45	8.065897	27.48	8.159686	24.67
46	.842969	35.58	.962529	30.98	46	.067546	27.45	.161166	24.62
47	.845104	35.48	.964388	30.92	47	.069193	27.38	.162643	24.58
48	.847233	35.40	.966243	30.85	48	.070836	27.33	.164118	24.53
49	.849357	35.30	.968094	30.78	49	.072476	27.30	.165590	24.50
50	7.851475	35.23	7.969941	30.73	50	8.074114	27.23	8.167060	24.45
51	.853589	35.13	.971785	30.65	51	.075748	27.18	.168527	24.42
52	.855697	35.05	.973624	30.58	52	.077379	27.13	.169992	24.37
53	.857800	34.97	.975459	30.53	53	.079007	27.07	.171454	24.33
54	.859898	34.88	.977291	30.45	54	.080631	27.03	.172914	24.30
55	7.861991	34.80	7.979118	30.40	55	8.082253	26.98	8.174372	24.25
56	.864079	34.72	.980942	30.33	56	.083872	26.93	.175827	24.20
57	.866162	34.63	.982762	30.27	57	.085488	26.87	.177279	24.17
58	.868240	34.55	.984578	30.22	58	.087100	26.83	.178729	24.13
59	.870313	34.47	.986391	30.13	59	.088710	26.78	.180177	24.08
60	7.872381		7.988199		60	8.090317		8.181622	

TABLE XXIII.—LOGARITHMIC VERSINES

'	10° vers	D.1"	11° vers	D.1"	'	12° vers	D.1"	13° vers	D.1"
0	8.181622	24.05	8.264176	21.85	0	8.339499	20.02	8.408748	18.47
1	.183065	24.00	.265487	21.82	1	.340700	20.00	.409856	18.43
2	.184505	23.97	.266796	21.78	2	.341900	19.95	.410962	18.42
3	.185943	23.93	.268103	21.75	3	.343097	19.95	.412067	18.40
4	.187379	23.88	.269408	21.72	4	.344294	19.95	.413171	18.38
5	8.188812	23.85	8.270711	21.68	5	8.345488	19.90	8.414274	18.35
6	.190243	23.80	.272012	21.65	6	.346681	19.88	.415375	18.32
7	.191671	23.77	.273311	21.62	7	.347872	19.85	.416474	18.30
8	.193097	23.73	.274608	21.58	8	.349061	19.82	.417572	18.28
9	.194521	23.68	.275903	21.57	9	.350249	19.80	.418669	18.25
10	8.195942	23.65	8.277197	21.52	10	8.351435	19.77	8.419764	18.23
11	.197361	23.62	.278488	21.48	11	.352620	19.75	.420858	18.22
12	.198778	23.57	.279777	21.47	12	.353803	19.72	.421951	18.18
13	.200192	23.53	.281065	21.42	13	.354984	19.68	.423042	18.17
14	.201604	23.50	.282350	21.40	14	.356164	19.67	.424132	18.13
15	8.203014	23.45	8.283634	21.37	15	8.357342	19.63	8.425220	18.12
16	.204421	23.42	.284916	21.33	16	.358518	19.60	.426307	18.10
17	.205826	23.38	.286196	21.28	17	.359693	19.58	.427393	18.07
18	.207229	23.35	.287473	21.27	18	.360866	19.55	.428477	18.05
19	.208630	23.30	.288749	21.25	19	.362038	19.53	.429560	18.02
20	8.210028	23.27	8.290024	21.20	20	8.363208	19.50	8.430641	18.02
21	.211424	23.23	.291296	21.17	21	.364377	19.48	.431722	17.97
22	.212818	23.18	.292566	21.15	22	.365543	19.43	.432800	17.97
23	.214209	23.18	.293835	21.10	23	.366709	19.43	.433878	17.93
24	.215599	23.12	.295101	21.08	24	.367872	19.38	.434954	17.92
25	8.216986	23.12	8.296366	21.05	25	8.369034	19.37	8.436029	17.88
26	.218371	23.08	.297629	21.02	26	.370195	19.35	.437102	17.87
27	.219753	23.03	.298890	20.98	27	.371354	19.32	.438174	17.85
28	.221133	22.98	.300149	20.95	28	.372511	19.28	.439245	17.82
29	.222512	22.93	.301406	20.93	29	.373667	19.27	.440314	17.80
30	8.223888	22.88	8.302662	20.90	30	8.374822	19.25	8.441382	17.78
31	.225261	22.87	.303916	20.85	31	.375974	19.20	.442449	17.75
32	.226633	22.82	.305167	20.85	32	.377125	19.18	.443514	17.73
33	.228002	22.78	.306418	20.80	33	.378275	19.17	.444578	17.72
34	.229369	22.77	.307666	20.77	34	.379423	19.13	.445641	17.68
35	8.230735	22.70	8.308912	20.75	35	8.380570	19.12	8.446702	17.68
36	.232097	22.68	.310157	20.72	36	.381715	19.08	.447763	17.63
37	.233458	22.65	.311400	20.68	37	.382858	19.05	.448821	17.63
38	.234817	22.60	.312641	20.65	38	.384000	19.03	.449879	17.60
39	.236173	22.57	.313880	20.62	39	.385141	19.02	.450935	17.58
40	8.237527	22.55	8.315117	20.60	40	8.386280	18.98	8.451990	17.55
41	.238880	22.50	.316353	20.57	41	.387417	18.95	.453043	17.55
42	.240230	22.47	.317587	20.53	42	.388553	18.93	.454096	17.52
43	.241578	22.43	.318819	20.50	43	.389688	18.92	.455147	17.48
44	.242924	22.38	.320049	20.48	44	.390821	18.88	.456196	17.48
45	8.244267	22.37	8.321278	20.45	45	8.391952	18.85	8.457245	17.45
46	.245609	22.32	.322505	20.42	46	.393082	18.83	.458292	17.43
47	.246948	22.30	.323730	20.38	47	.394211	18.82	.459338	17.40
48	.248286	22.25	.324953	20.37	48	.395338	18.78	.460382	17.40
49	.249621	22.23	.326175	20.33	49	.396463	18.75	.461426	17.37
50	8.250955	22.18	8.327395	20.30	50	8.397587	18.73	8.462468	17.35
51	.252286	22.15	.328613	20.27	51	.398710	18.72	.463509	17.32
52	.253615	22.12	.329829	20.25	52	.399831	18.68	.464548	17.30
53	.254942	22.10	.331044	20.22	53	.400951	18.67	.465586	17.28
54	.256268	22.05	.332257	20.18	54	.402069	18.63	.466623	17.27
55	8.257591	22.02	8.333468	20.17	55	8.403186	18.62	8.467659	17.23
56	.258912	21.98	.334678	20.13	56	.404301	18.58	.468693	17.23
57	.260231	21.95	.335886	20.10	57	.405415	18.57	.469727	17.20
58	.261548	21.92	.337092	20.07	58	.406527	18.53	.470759	17.17
59	.262863	21.88	.338296	20.05	59	.407638	18.52	.471789	17.17
60	8.264176		8.339499		60	8.408748	18.50	8.472819	

TABLE XXIII.—LOGARITHMIC VERSINES

'	14° vers	D.1"	15° vers	D.1"	'	16° vers	D.1"	17° vers	D.1"
0	8.472819	17.13	8.532425	15.98	0	8.588141	14.97	8.640434	14.08
1	.473847	17.12	.533384	15.97	1	.589039	14.95	.641279	14.07
2	.474874	17.10	.534342	15.95	2	.589936	14.95	.642123	14.05
3	.475900	17.08	.535299	15.93	3	.590833	14.93	.642966	14.05
4	.476925	17.05	.536255	15.92	4	.591729	14.90	.643809	14.02
5	8.477948	17.03	8.537210	15.88	5	8.592623	14.90	8.644650	14.02
6	.478970	17.02	.538165	15.88	6	.593517	14.88	.645491	14.00
7	.479991	17.00	.539116	15.88	7	.594410	14.87	.646331	13.98
8	.481011	16.97	.540068	15.83	8	.595302	14.83	.647170	13.97
9	.482029	16.95	.541018	15.83	9	.596192	14.83	.648008	13.95
10	8.483046	16.93	8.541968	15.80	10	8.597082	14.82	8.648845	13.95
11	.484062	16.92	.542916	15.78	11	.597971	14.82	.649682	13.93
12	.485077	16.90	.543863	15.78	12	.598860	14.78	.650518	13.92
13	.486091	16.87	.544810	15.75	13	.599747	14.77	.651353	13.90
14	.487103	16.87	.545755	15.73	14	.600633	14.75	.652187	13.88
15	8.488115	16.83	8.546699	15.72	15	8.601518	14.75	8.653020	13.87
16	.489125	16.82	.547642	15.70	16	.602403	14.72	.653852	13.87
17	.490134	16.78	.548584	15.68	17	.603286	14.72	.654684	13.85
18	.491141	16.78	.549525	15.67	18	.604169	14.70	.655515	13.83
19	.492148	16.75	.550465	15.65	19	.605051	14.67	.656345	13.82
20	8.493153	16.73	8.551404	15.63	20	8.605931	14.67	8.657174	13.82
21	.494157	16.72	.552342	15.62	21	.606811	14.65	.658003	13.78
22	.495160	16.70	.553279	15.60	22	.607690	14.63	.658830	13.78
23	.496162	16.67	.554215	15.58	23	.608568	14.62	.659657	13.77
24	.497162	16.67	.555150	15.57	24	.609445	14.60	.660483	13.75
25	8.498162	16.63	8.556084	15.55	25	8.610321	14.60	8.661308	13.73
26	.499160	16.62	.557017	15.53	26	.611197	14.57	.662132	13.73
27	.500157	16.60	.557949	15.50	27	.612071	14.57	.662956	13.72
28	.501153	16.58	.558879	15.50	28	.612945	14.53	.663779	13.70
29	.502148	16.57	.559809	15.48	29	.613817	14.53	.664601	13.68
30	8.503142	16.53	8.560738	15.47	30	8.614689	14.52	8.665422	13.67
31	.504134	16.52	.561666	15.43	31	.615560	14.50	.666242	13.67
32	.505125	16.52	.562592	15.43	32	.616430	14.48	.667062	13.65
33	.506116	16.48	.563518	15.42	33	.617299	14.47	.667881	13.63
34	.507105	16.45	.564443	15.40	34	.618167	14.45	.668699	13.62
35	8.508092	16.45	8.565367	15.37	35	8.619034	14.45	8.669516	13.60
36	.509079	16.43	.566289	15.37	36	.619901	14.42	.670332	13.60
37	.510065	16.40	.567211	15.35	37	.620766	14.42	.671148	13.58
38	.511049	16.40	.568132	15.33	38	.621631	14.40	.671963	13.57
39	.512033	16.37	.569052	15.30	39	.622495	14.38	.672777	13.55
40	8.513015	16.35	8.569970	15.30	40	8.623358	14.37	8.673590	13.55
41	.513996	16.33	.570888	15.28	41	.624220	14.35	.674403	13.53
42	.514976	16.28	.571805	15.27	42	.625081	14.33	.675215	13.52
43	.515955	16.28	.572721	15.25	43	.625941	14.33	.676026	13.50
44	.516932	16.28	.573636	15.22	44	.626801	14.30	.676836	13.48
45	8.517909	16.25	8.574549	15.22	45	8.627659	14.30	8.677645	13.48
46	.518884	16.25	.575462	15.20	46	.628517	14.29	.678454	13.47
47	.519859	16.22	.576374	15.18	47	.629374	14.27	.679262	13.45
48	.520832	16.20	.577285	15.17	48	.630230	14.25	.680069	13.43
49	.521804	16.18	.578195	15.15	49	.631085	14.23	.680875	13.43
50	8.522775	16.17	8.579104	15.13	50	8.631939	14.22	8.681681	13.42
51	.523745	16.15	.580012	15.12	51	.632792	14.22	.682486	13.40
52	.524714	16.13	.580919	15.10	52	.633645	14.18	.683290	13.38
53	.525682	16.13	.581825	15.08	53	.634496	14.18	.684093	13.38
54	.526648	16.10	.582730	15.07	54	.635347	14.17	.684896	13.35
55	8.527614	16.07	8.583634	15.05	55	8.636197	14.15	8.685697	13.35
56	.528578	16.07	.584537	15.05	56	.637046	14.13	.686498	13.35
57	.529542	16.03	.585440	15.02	57	.637894	14.13	.687299	13.32
58	.530504	16.03	.586341	15.02	58	.638742	14.10	.688098	13.32
59	.531465	16.02	.587241	15.00	59	.639588	14.10	.688897	13.30
60	8.532425	16.00	8.588141	15.00	60	8.640434	14.10	8.689695	13.30

TABLE XXIII.—LOGARITHMIC VERSINES

'	18° vers	D.1"	19° vers	D.1"	'	20° vers	D.1"	21° vers	D.1"
0	8.689695	13.28	8.736248	12.58	0	8.780370	11.95	8.822296	11.35
1	.690492	13.28	.737003	12.57	1	.781087	11.92	.822977	11.35
2	.691289	13.25	.737757	12.55	2	.781802	11.92	.823658	11.33
3	.692084	13.25	.738510	12.55	3	.782517	11.90	.824338	11.33
4	.692879	13.25	.739263	12.53	4	.783231	11.90	.825018	11.33
5	8.693674	13.25	8.740015	12.52	5	8.783945	11.88	8.825697	11.32
6	.694467	13.22	.740766	12.50	6	.784658	11.88	.826376	11.32
7	.695260	13.22	.741516	12.50	7	.785371	11.87	.827054	11.30
8	.696052	13.20	.742266	12.50	8	.786083	11.85	.827731	11.28
9	.696843	13.18	.743016	12.47	9	.786794	11.85	.828408	11.28
		13.18					11.85		11.28
10	8.697634	13.17	8.743764	12.47	10	8.787505	11.83	8.829085	11.27
11	.698424	13.15	.744512	12.45	11	.788215	11.82	.829761	11.25
12	.699213	13.13	.745259	12.45	12	.788924	11.82	.830436	11.25
13	.700001	13.13	.746006	12.43	13	.789633	11.82	.831111	11.23
14	.700789	13.12	.746752	12.42	14	.790342	11.78	.831785	11.23
15	8.701576	13.10	8.747497	12.42	15	8.791049	11.78	8.832459	11.22
16	.702362	13.08	.748242	12.40	16	.791756	11.78	.833132	11.20
17	.703147	13.08	.748986	12.38	17	.792463	11.77	.833804	11.20
18	.703932	13.07	.749729	12.38	18	.793169	11.75	.834476	11.20
19	.704716	13.05	.750472	12.37	19	.793874	11.75	.835148	11.18
20	8.705499	13.05	8.751214	12.35	20	8.794579	11.73	8.835819	11.17
21	.706282	13.02	.751955	12.35	21	.795283	11.73	.836489	11.17
22	.707063	13.02	.752696	12.33	22	.795987	11.72	.837159	11.17
23	.707844	13.02	.753436	12.32	23	.796690	11.70	.837829	11.15
24	.708625	12.98	.754175	12.32	24	.797392	11.70	.838498	11.13
25	8.709404	12.98	8.754914	12.30	25	8.798094	11.68	8.839166	11.13
26	.710183	12.97	.755652	12.28	26	.798795	11.68	.839834	11.12
27	.710961	12.97	.756389	12.28	27	.799496	11.67	.840501	11.12
28	.711739	12.95	.757126	12.27	28	.800196	11.67	.841168	11.10
29	.712516	12.93	.757862	12.27	29	.800896	11.63	841834	11.10
30	8.713292	12.92	8.758598	12.25	30	8.801594	11.65	8.842500	11.08
31	.714067	12.92	.759333	12.23	31	.802293	11.63	.843165	11.07
32	.714842	12.90	.760067	12.23	32	.802991	11.62	.843829	11.07
33	.715616	12.88	.760801	12.22	33	.803688	11.60	.844493	11.07
34	.716389	12.87	.761534	12.20	34	.804384	11.60	.845157	11.05
35	8.717161	12.87	8.762266	12.20	35	8.805080	11.60	8.845820	11.05
36	.717933	12.85	.762998	12.18	36	.805776	11.58	.846483	11.03
37	.718704	12.85	.763729	12.17	37	.806471	11.57	.847145	11.02
38	.719475	12.82	.764459	12.17	38	.807165	11.57	.847806	11.02
39	.720244	12.82	.765189	12.15	39	.807859	11.55	.848467	11.00
40	8.721013	12.82	8.765918	12.15	40	8.808552	11.53	8.849127	11.00
41	.721782	12.82	.766647	12.12	41	.809244	11.53	.849787	11.00
42	.722549	12.78	.767374	12.13	42	.809936	11.53	.850447	10.98
43	.723316	12.78	.768102	12.10	43	.810628	11.52	.851106	10.97
44	.724083	12.75	.768828	12.10	44	.811319	11.50	.851764	10.97
45	8.724848	12.75	8.769554	12.10	45	8.812009	11.50	8.852422	10.95
46	.725613	12.73	.770280	12.08	46	.812699	11.48	.853079	10.95
47	.726377	12.72	.771005	12.07	47	.813388	11.48	.853736	10.93
48	.727140	12.72	.771729	12.05	48	.814077	11.47	.854392	10.93
49	.727903	12.70	.772452	12.05	49	.814765	11.45	.855048	10.92
50	8.728665	12.70	8.773175	12.02	50	8.815452	11.45	8.855703	10.92
51	.729427	12.67	.773898	12.02	51	.816139	11.43	.856358	10.90
52	.730187	12.67	.774619	12.02	52	.816825	11.43	.857012	10.90
53	.730947	12.67	.775340	12.00	53	.817511	11.42	.857666	10.88
54	.731707	12.63	.776061	11.98	54	.818196	11.42	.858319	10.88
55	8.732465	12.63	8.776781	11.97	55	8.818881	11.40	8.858972	10.87
56	.733223	12.63	.777500	11.97	56	.819565	11.40	.859624	10.87
57	.733981	12.60	.778218	11.97	57	.820249	11.38	.860276	10.85
58	.734737	12.60	.778936	11.93	58	.820932	11.37	.860927	10.85
59	.735493	12.58	.779654		59	.821614	11.37	.861578	10.83
60	8.736248		8.780370		60	8.822296		8.862228	

TABLE XXIII.—LOGARITHMIC VERSINES

'	22° vers	D.1"	23° vers	D.1"	'	24° vers	D.1"	25° vers	D.1"
0	8.862228	10.82	8.900341	10.33	0	8.936788	9.90	8.971703	9.50
1	.862877	10.83	.900961	10.35	1	.937382	9.90	.972273	9.48
2	.863527	10.80	.901582	10.32	2	.937976	9.88	.972842	9.48
3	.864175	10.80	.902201	10.33	3	.938569	9.88	.973411	9.48
4	.864823	10.80	.902821	10.32	4	.939162	9.88	.973980	9.47
5	8.865471	10.78	8.903440	10.30	5	8.939754	9.87	8.974548	9.47
6	.866118	10.78	.904058	10.30	6	.940346	9.87	.975116	9.45
7	.866765	10.77	.904676	10.30	7	.940938	9.85	.975683	9.45
8	.867411	10.77	.905293	10.28	8	.941529	9.85	.976250	9.43
9	.868057	10.75	.905910	10.28	9	.942120	9.83	.976816	9.43
10	8.868702	10.73	8.906527	10.27	10	8.942710	9.83	8.977382	9.43
11	.869346	10.75	.907143	10.27	11	.943300	9.82	.977948	9.43
12	.869991	10.72	.907759	10.25	12	.943889	9.83	.978514	9.40
13	.870634	10.72	.908374	10.25	13	.944479	9.80	.979078	9.42
14	.871277	10.72	.908989	10.23	14	.945067	9.80	.979643	9.40
15	8.871920	10.70	8.909603	10.23	15	8.945655	9.80	8.980207	9.40
16	.872562	10.70	.910217	10.22	16	.946243	9.80	.980771	9.40
17	.873204	10.68	.910830	10.22	17	.946831	9.78	.981335	9.38
18	.873845	10.68	.911443	10.22	18	.947418	9.77	.981898	9.37
19	.874486	10.67	.912056	10.20	19	.948004	9.77	.982460	9.38
20	8.875126	10.67	8.912668	10.18	20	8.948590	9.77	8.983023	9.37
21	.875766	10.65	.913279	10.20	21	.949176	9.75	.983585	9.35
22	.876405	10.65	.913891	10.17	22	.949761	9.75	.984146	9.35
23	.877044	10.63	.914501	10.17	23	.950346	9.75	.984707	9.35
24	.877682	10.63	.915111	10.17	24	.950931	9.73	.985268	9.33
25	8.878320	10.62	8.915721	10.17	25	8.951515	9.73	8.985828	9.33
26	.878957	10.62	.916331	10.15	26	.952099	9.72	.986388	9.33
27	.879594	10.60	.916940	10.13	27	.952682	9.72	.986948	9.33
28	.880230	10.60	.917548	10.13	28	.953265	9.70	.987507	9.32
29	.880866	10.58	.918156	10.13	29	.953847	9.70	.988066	9.32
30	8.881501	10.58	8.918764	10.12	30	8.954429	9.70	8.988625	9.30
31	.882136	10.58	.919371	10.10	31	.955011	9.68	.989183	9.28
32	.882771	10.57	.919977	10.12	32	.955592	9.68	.989740	9.30
33	.883405	10.55	.920584	10.10	33	.956173	9.67	.990298	9.28
34	.884038	10.55	.921190	10.08	34	.956753	9.68	.990855	9.27
35	8.884671	10.53	8.921795	10.08	35	8.957334	9.65	8.991411	9.28
36	.885303	10.55	.922400	10.07	36	.957913	9.65	.991968	9.25
37	.885935	10.53	.923004	10.07	37	.958492	9.65	.992523	9.27
38	.886567	10.52	.923608	10.07	38	.959071	9.65	.993079	9.25
39	.887198	10.52	.924212	10.05	39	.959650	9.62	.993634	9.25
40	8.887829	10.50	8.924815	10.05	40	8.960227	9.63	8.994189	9.23
41	.888459	10.48	.925418	10.03	41	.960805	9.62	.994743	9.23
42	.889088	10.46	.926020	10.03	42	.961382	9.62	.995297	9.23
43	.889717	10.48	.926622	10.03	43	.961959	9.60	.995851	9.23
44	.890346	10.47	.927224	10.02	44	.962535	9.60	.996404	9.22
45	8.890974	10.47	8.927825	10.00	45	8.963111	9.60	8.996957	9.22
46	.891602	10.45	.928425	10.00	46	.963687	9.58	.997509	9.20
47	.892229	10.45	.929025	10.00	47	.964262	9.58	.998062	9.22
48	.892856	10.43	.929625	9.98	48	.964837	9.57	.998613	9.18
49	.893482	10.43	.930224	9.98	49	.965411	9.57	.999165	9.20
50	8.894108	10.42	8.930823	9.97	50	8.965985	9.57	8.999716	9.18
51	.894733	10.42	.931421	9.97	51	.966559	9.55	9.000266	9.17
52	.895358	10.42	.932019	9.97	52	.967132	9.55	.000817	9.18
53	.895983	10.40	.932617	9.95	53	.967705	9.53	.001367	9.17
54	.896607	10.38	.933214	9.95	54	.968277	9.53	.001916	9.15
55	8.897230	10.38	8.933811	9.93	55	8.968849	9.53	9.002466	9.17
56	.897853	10.38	.934407	9.93	56	.969421	9.53	.003014	9.13
57	.898476	10.37	.935003	9.92	57	.969992	9.52	.003563	9.15
58	.899098	10.35	.935598	9.92	58	.970563	9.52	.004111	9.13
59	.899719	10.37	.936193	9.92	59	.971133	9.50	.004659	9.13
60	8.900341		8.936788		60	8.971703		9.005206	9.12

TABLE XXIII.—LOGARITHMIC VERSINES

'	26° vers	D.1"	27° vers	D.1"	'	28° vers	D.1"	29° vers	D.1"
0	9.005206	9.12	9.037401	8.77	0	9.068380	8.45	9.098229	8.15
1	.005753	9.12	.037927	8.75	1	.068887	8.43	.098718	8.13
2	.006300	9.10	.038452	8.77	2	.069393	8.43	.099206	8.12
3	.006846	9.10	.038978	8.75	3	.069899	8.43	.099693	8.13
4	.007392	9.10	.039503	8.75	4	.070405	8.42	.100181	8.12
5	9.007938	9.08	9.040027	8.73	5	9.070910	8.42	9.100668	8.12
6	.008483	9.08	.040552	8.75	6	.071415	8.42	.101155	8.12
7	.009028	9.07	.041076	8.73	7	.071919	8.40	.101642	8.10
8	.009572	9.07	.041599	8.73	8	.072424	8.42	.102128	8.10
9	.010116	9.07	.042123	8.72	9	.072928	8.40	.102614	8.10
10	9.010660	9.05	9.042646	8.72	10	9.073432	8.40	9.103100	8.10
11	.011203	9.05	.043168	8.70	11	.073935	8.38	.103585	8.08
12	.011746	9.05	.043691	8.72	12	.074438	8.38	.104070	8.08
13	.012289	9.05	.044213	8.70	13	.074941	8.38	.104555	8.08
14	.012831	9.03	.044735	8.70	14	.075443	8.37	.105040	8.08
15	9.013373	9.03	9.045256	8.68	15	9.075946	8.38	9.105524	8.07
16	.013915	9.03	.045777	8.68	16	.076447	8.35	.106008	8.07
17	.014456	9.02	.046298	8.68	17	.076949	8.37	.106491	8.05
18	.014997	9.02	.046818	8.67	18	.077450	8.35	.106975	8.07
19	.015538	9.02	.047338	8.67	19	.077951	8.35	.107458	8.05
20	9.016078	9.00	9.047858	8.67	20	9.078452	8.35	9.107941	8.05
21	.016618	9.00	.048377	8.65	21	.078952	8.33	.108423	8.03
22	.017157	8.98	.048896	8.65	22	.079452	8.33	.108906	8.05
23	.017697	9.00	.049415	8.65	23	.079952	8.33	.109388	8.03
24	.018235	8.97	.049933	8.63	24	.080451	8.32	.109869	8.02
25	9.018774	8.98	9.050451	8.63	25	9.080950	8.32	9.110351	8.03
26	.019312	8.97	.050969	8.63	26	.081449	8.32	.110832	8.02
27	.019850	8.97	.051487	8.63	27	.081948	8.32	.111313	8.02
28	.020387	8.95	.052004	8.62	28	.082446	8.30	.111793	8.00
29	.020924	8.95	.052520	8.60	29	.082944	8.30	.112273	8.00
30	9.021461	8.95	9.053037	8.62	30	9.083441	8.28	9.112753	8.00
31	.021997	8.93	.053553	8.60	31	.083939	8.30	.113233	8.00
32	.022533	8.93	.054069	8.60	32	.084436	8.28	.113713	8.00
33	.023069	8.93	.054584	8.58	33	.084932	8.27	.114192	7.98
34	.023604	8.92	.055099	8.58	34	.085429	8.28	.114671	7.98
35	9.024139	8.92	9.055614	8.58	35	9.085925	8.27	9.115149	7.97
36	.024673	8.90	.056129	8.58	36	.086420	8.25	.115627	7.97
37	.025208	8.92	.056643	8.57	37	.086916	8.27	.116105	7.97
38	.025742	8.90	.057157	8.57	38	.087411	8.25	.116583	7.97
39	.026275	8.88	.057670	8.55	39	.087906	8.25	.117061	7.97
40	9.026808	8.88	9.058183	8.55	40	9.088400	8.23	9.117538	7.95
41	.027341	8.88	.058696	8.55	41	.088895	8.25	.118015	7.95
42	.027874	8.88	.059209	8.55	42	.089389	8.22	.118491	7.93
43	.028406	8.87	.059721	8.53	43	.089882	8.22	.118968	7.95
44	.028938	8.87	.060233	8.53	44	.090376	8.23	.119444	7.93
45	9.029469	8.85	9.060745	8.53	45	9.090869	8.22	9.119919	7.92
46	.030000	8.85	.061256	8.52	46	.091362	8.22	.120395	7.93
47	.030531	8.85	.061767	8.52	47	.091854	8.20	.120870	7.92
48	.031062	8.85	.062277	8.50	48	.092346	8.20	.121345	7.92
49	.031592	8.83	.062788	8.52	49	.092838	8.20	.121820	7.92
50	9.032122	8.83	9.063298	8.50	50	9.093330	8.20	9.122294	7.90
51	.032651	8.82	.063807	8.48	51	.093821	8.18	.122768	7.90
52	.033180	8.82	.064317	8.50	52	.094312	8.18	.123242	7.90
53	.033709	8.82	.064826	8.48	53	.094803	8.18	.123715	7.88
54	.034237	8.80	.065335	8.48	54	.095293	8.17	.124189	7.90
55	9.034765	8.80	9.065843	8.47	55	9.095783	8.17	9.124662	7.88
56	.035293	8.80	.066351	8.47	56	.096273	8.17	.125134	7.87
57	.035820	8.78	.066859	8.47	57	.096763	8.17	.125607	7.88
58	.036347	8.78	.067366	8.45	58	.097252	8.15	.126079	7.87
59	.036874	8.78	.067874	8.47	59	.097741	8.15	.126551	7.87
60	9.037401	8.78	9.068380	8.43	60	9.098229	8.13	9.127022	7.85

TABLE XXIII.—LOGARITHMIC VERSINES

'	30° vers	Corr.	Corr.	31° vers	32° vers	Corr.	Corr.	33° vers	'
0	9.127022			9.154828	9.181706			9.207714	0
1	.127494	Corr.	Corr.	.155283	.182147	Corr.	Corr.	.208140	1
2	.127965	10 78	10 76	.155738	.182587	10 73	10 71	.208566	2
3	.128436	15 118	15 114	.156193	.183027	15 110	15 106	.208992	3
4	.128906	20 157	20 151	.156648	.183466	20 146	20 142	.209418	4
5	9.129376	30 235	30 227	9.157102	9.183906	30 220	30 213	9.209843	5
6	.129846	40 313	40 303	.157556	.184345	40 293	40 284	.210268	6
7	.130316	45 353	45 341	.158010	.184784	45 330	45 319	.210693	7
8	.130785	50 392	50 378	.158464	.185223	50 366	50 354	.211118	8
9	.131255			.158917	.185662			.211543	9
10	9.131724			9.159370	9.186100			9.211967	10
11	.132192	Corr.	Corr.	.159823	.186538	Corr.	Corr.	.212391	11
12	.132660	10 78	10 75	.160276	.186976	10 73	10 71	.212815	12
13	.133129	15 117	15 113	.160728	.187413	15 109	15 106	.213239	13
14	.133596	20 156	20 151	.161180	.187851	20 146	20 141	.213662	14
15	9.134064	30 234	30 226	9.161632	9.188288	30 218	30 212	9.214085	15
16	.134531	40 312	40 301	.162083	.188724	40 291	40 282	.214508	16
17	.134998	45 350	45 339	.162535	.189161	45 328	45 317	.214931	17
18	.135465	50 389	50 376	.162986	.189597	50 364	50 353	.215354	18
19	.135931			.163437	.190034			.215776	19
20	9.136397			9.163887	9.190469			9.216198	20
21	.136863	Corr.	Corr.	.164338	.190905	Corr.	Corr.	.216620	21
22	.137329	10 77	10 75	.164788	.191341	10 72	10 70	.217042	22
23	.137794	15 116	15 112	.165237	.191776	15 109	15 105	.217463	23
24	.138260	20 155	20 150	.165687	.192211	20 145	20 140	.217884	24
25	9.138724	30 232	30 225	9.166136	9.192645	30 217	30 210	9.218305	25
26	.139189	40 310	40 299	.166585	.193080	40 290	40 281	.218726	26
27	.139653	45 349	45 337	.167034	.193514	45 326	45 316	.219146	27
28	.140117	50 387	50 374	.167483	.193948	50 362	50 351	.219567	28
29	.140581			.167931	.194382			.219987	29
30	9.141045			9.168379	9.194815			9.220407	30
31	.141508	Corr.	Corr.	.168827	.195249	Corr.	Corr.	.220826	31
32	.141971	10 77	10 74	.169275	.195682	10 72	10 70	.221246	32
33	.142434	15 116	15 112	.169722	.196115	15 108	15 105	.221665	33
34	.142896	20 154	20 149	.170169	.196547	20 144	20 140	.222084	34
35	9.143358	30 231	30 223	9.170616	9.196980	30 216	30 209	9.222503	35
36	.143820	40 308	40 298	.171062	.197412	40 288	40 279	.222921	36
37	.144282	45 347	45 335	.171509	.197844	45 324	45 314	.223340	37
38	.144743	50 385	50 372	.171955	.198275	50 360	50 349	.223758	38
39	.145204			.172400	.198707			.224176	39
40	9.145665			9.172846	9.199138			9.224593	40
41	.146126	Corr.	Corr.	.173291	.199569	Corr.	Corr.	.225011	41
42	.146586	10 77	10 74	.173736	.200000	10 72	10 70	.225428	42
43	.147046	15 115	15 111	.174181	.200430	15 107	15 104	.225845	43
44	.147506	20 153	20 148	.174626	.200861	20 143	20 139	.226262	44
45	9.147966	30 230	30 222	9.175070	9.201291	30 215	30 208	9.226678	45
46	.148425	40 306	40 296	.175514	.201720	40 287	40 278	.227095	46
47	.148884	45 345	45 333	.175958	.202150	45 322	45 312	.227511	47
48	.149343	50 383	50 370	.176402	.202579	50 358	50 347	.227927	48
49	.149801			.176845	.203008			.228342	49
50	9.150259			9.177288	9.203437			9.228758	50
51	.150717	Corr.	Corr.	.177731	.203866	Corr.	Corr.	.229173	51
52	.151175	10 76	10 74	.178174	.204294	10 71	10 69	.229588	52
53	.151633	15 114	15 110	.178616	.204723	15 107	15 104	.230003	53
54	.152090	20 152	20 147	.179058	.205151	20 143	20 138	.230418	54
55	9.152547	30 228	30 221	9.179500	9.205578	30 214	30 207	9.230832	55
56	.153003	40 305	40 295	.179942	.206006	40 285	40 276	.231246	56
57	.153460	45 343	45 331	.180383	.206433	45 321	45 311	.231660	57
58	.153916	50 381	50 368	.180825	.206860	50 356	50 345	.232074	58
59	.154372			.181265	.207287			.232487	59
60	9.154828			9.181706	9.207714			9.232901	60

TABLE XXIII.—LOGARITHMIC VERSINES

'	34° vers	Corr.	Corr.	35° vers	36° vers	Corr.	Corr.	37° vers	'
0	9.232901			9.257314	9.280995			9.303983	0
1	.233314	* Corr.	# Corr.	.257714	.281383	* Corr.	# Corr.	.304360	1
2	.233727	10 69	10 67	.258115	.281772	10 65	10 63	.304738	2
3	.234139	15 103	15 100	.258515	.282160	15 97	15 94	.305115	3
4	.234552	20 137	20 133	.258915	.282548	20 129	20 126	.305492	4
5	9.234964	30 206	30 200	9.259314	9.282936	30 194	30 188	9.305868	5
6	.235376	40 275	40 266	.259714	.283324	40 259	40 251	.306245	6
7	.235788	45 309	45 300	.260113	.283712	45 291	45 282	.306621	7
8	.236199	50 343	50 333	.260512	.284099	50 323	50 314	.306998	8
9	.236611			.260911	.284486			.307374	9
10	9.237022			9.261310	9.284873			9.307749	10
11	.237433	* Corr.	# Corr.	.261709	.285260	* Corr.	# Corr.	.308125	11
12	.237844	10 68	10 66	.262107	.285647	10 64	10 62	.308501	12
13	.238254	15 102	15 99	.262505	.286033	15 96	15 94	.308876	13
14	.238665	20 137	20 133	.262903	.286419	20 129	20 125	.309251	14
15	9.239075	30 205	30 199	9.263301	9.286805	30 193	30 187	9.309626	15
16	.239485	40 273	40 265	.263698	.287191	40 257	40 250	.310001	16
17	.239894	45 308	45 298	.264096	.287577	45 290	45 281	.310375	17
18	.240304	50 342	50 331	.264493	.287962	50 322	50 312	.310750	18
19	.240713			.264890	.288348			.311124	19
20	9.241122			9.265287	9.288733			9.311498	20
21	.241531	* Corr.	# Corr.	.265683	.289118	* Corr.	# Corr.	.311872	21
22	.241940	10 68	10 66	.266080	.289502	10 64	10 62	.312245	22
23	.242348	15 102	15 99	.266476	.289887	15 96	15 93	.312619	23
24	.242756	20 136	20 132	.266872	.290271	20 128	20 124	.312992	24
25	9.243164	30 204	30 198	9.267267	9.290655	30 192	30 186	9.313365	25
26	.243572	40 272	40 264	.267663	.291039	40 257	40 249	.313738	26
27	.243980	45 306	45 297	.268058	.291423	45 288	45 280	.314111	27
28	.244387	50 340	50 330	.268453	.291807	50 320	50 311	.314484	28
29	.244794			.268848	.292190			.314856	29
30	9.245201			9.269243	9.292573			9.315228	30
31	.245608	* Corr.	# Corr.	.269638	.292956	* Corr.	# Corr.	.315600	31
32	.246014	10 68	10 66	.270032	.293339	10 64	10 62	.315972	32
33	.246421	15 101	15 98	.270426	.293722	15 96	15 93	.316344	33
34	.246827	20 135	20 131	.270820	.294104	20 127	20 124	.316716	34
35	9.247233	30 203	30 197	9.271214	9.294486	30 191	30 186	9.317087	35
36	.247639	40 271	40 262	.271608	.294868	40 255	40 248	.317458	36
37	.248044	45 304	45 295	.272001	.295250	45 287	45 278	.317829	37
38	.248449	50 338	50 328	.272394	.295632	50 318	50 309	.318200	38
39	.248854			.272787	.296014			.318571	39
40	9.249259			9.273180	9.296395			9.318941	40
41	.249664	* Corr.	# Corr.	.273572	.296776	* Corr.	# Corr.	.319311	41
42	.250068	10 67	10 65	.273965	.297157	10 63	10 62	.319682	42
43	.250473	15 101	15 98	.274357	.297538	15 95	15 92	.320051	43
44	.250877	20 135	20 131	.274749	.297918	20 127	20 123	.320421	44
45	9.251281	30 202	30 196	9.275141	9.298299	30 190	30 185	9.320791	45
46	.251684	40 269	40 261	.275532	.298679	40 254	40 246	.321160	46
47	.252088	45 303	45 294	.275924	.299059	45 285	45 277	.321530	47
48	.252491	50 336	50 326	.276315	.299439	50 317	50 308	.321899	48
49	.252894			.276706	.299819			.322267	49
50	9.253297			9.277097	9.300198			9.322636	50
51	.253699	* Corr.	# Corr.	.277488	.300577	* Corr.	# Corr.	.323005	51
52	.254102	10 67	10 65	.277878	.300957	10 63	10 61	.323373	52
53	.254504	15 100	15 97	.278268	.301335	15 95	15 92	.323741	53
54	.254906	20 134	20 130	.278658	.301714	20 126	20 123	.324109	54
55	9.255308	30 201	30 195	9.279048	9.302093	30 189	30 184	9.324477	55
56	.255709	40 268	40 260	.279438	.302471	40 252	40 245	.324845	56
57	.256111	45 301	45 292	.279827	.302849	45 284	45 276	.325212	57
58	.256512	50 335	50 325	.280217	.303227	50 315	50 306	.325580	58
59	.256913			.280606	.303605			.325947	59
60	9.257314			9.280995	9.303983			9.326314	60

TABLE XXIII.—LOGARITHMIC VERSINES

'	38° vers	Corr.	Corr.	39° vers	40° vers	Corr.	Corr.	41° vers	'
0	9.326314			9.348021	9.369133			9.389681	0
1	.326681			.348377	.369480			.390018	1
2	.327047	10 61	10 59	.348734	.369827	10 58	10 56	.390356	2
3	.327414	15 91	15 89	.349090	.370174	15 86	15 84	.390694	3
4	.327780	20 122	20 118	.349446	.370520	20 115	20 112	.391031	4
5	9.328146	30 183	30 178	9.349802	9.370867	30 173	30 168	9.391368	5
6	.328512	40 244	40 237	.350158	.371213	40 231	40 224	.391705	6
7	.328878	45 274	45 267	.350514	.371559	45 259	45 253	.392042	7
8	.329243	50 305	50 296	.350869	.371905	50 288	50 281	.392379	8
9	.329609			.351225	.372251			.392716	9
10	9.329974			9.351580	9.372596			9.393052	10
11	.330339			.351935	.372942			.393388	11
12	.330704			.352290	.373287			..393724	12
13	.331069			.352644	.373632			.394061	13
14	.331433			.352999	.373977			.394396	14
15	9.331798			9.353353	9.374322			9.394732	15
16	.332162	10 60	10 59	.353707	.374667	10 57	10 56	.395068	16
17	.332526	15 91	15 88	.354062	.375011	15 86	15 84	.395403	17
18	.332890	20 121	20 118	.354415	.375356	20 115	20 111	.395738	18
19	.333254			.354769	.375700			.396074	19
20	9.333617	30 182	30 177	9.355123	9.376044	30 172	30 167	9.396409	20
21	.333981	40 242	40 235	.355476	.376388	40 229	40 223	.396743	21
22	.334344	45 272	45 265	.355829	.376732	45 258	45 251	.397078	22
23	.334707	50 302	50 294	.356182	.377075	50 286	50 279	.397413	23
24	.335070			.356535	.377419			.397747	24
25	9.335432			9.356888	9.377762			9.398081	25
26	.335795			.357241	.378105			.398415	26
27	.336157			.357593	.378448			.398749	27
28	.336519			.357945	.378791			.399083	28
29	.336881			.358297	.379133			.399417	29
30	9.337243			9.358649	9.379476			9.399750	30
31	.337605	10 60	10 58	.359001	.379818	10 57	10 55	.400084	31
32	.337966	15 90	15 88	.359353	.380161	15 85	15 84	.400417	32
33	.338328	20 120	20 117	.359704	.380503	20 114	20 111	.400750	33
34	.338689	30 180	30 175	.360056	.380845	30 171	30 166	.401083	34
35	9.339050	40 240	40 234	9.360407	9.381186	40 228	40 222	9.401416	35
36	.339411	45 270	45 263	.360758	.381528	45 256	45 249	.401748	36
37	.339771	50 300	50 292	.361108	.381869	50 284	50 277	.402081	37
38	.340132			.361459	.382211			.402413	38
39	.340492			.361810	.382552			.402745	39
40	9.340852			9.362160	9.382893			9.403077	40
41	.341212			.362510	.383234			.403409	41
42	.341572			.362860	.383574			.403741	42
43	.341932			.363210	.383915			.404073	43
44	.342291			.363560	.384255			.404404	44
45	9.342651			9.363909	9.384595			9.404736	45
46	.343010	10 60	10 58	.364259	.384935	10 57	10 55	.405067	46
47	.343369	15 90	15 87	.364608	.385275	15 85	15 83	.405398	47
48	.343728	20 119	20 116	.364957	.385615	20 113	20 110	.405729	48
49	.344086			.365306	.385955			.406059	49
50	9.344445	30 179	30 174	9.365655	9.386294	30 170	30 165	9.406390	50
51	.344803	40 239	40 232	.366003	.386634	40 226	40 220	.406721	51
52	.345161	45 268	45 261	.366352	.386973	45 254	45 248	.407051	52
53	.345519	50 298	50 290	.366700	.387312	50 283	50 275	.407381	53
54	.345877			.367048	.387651			.407711	54
55	9.346235			9.367396	9.387989			9.408041	55
56	.346592			.367744	.388328			.408371	56
57	.346950			.368091	.388666			.408700	57
58	.347307			.368439	.389005			.409030	58
59	.347664			.368786	.389343			.409359	59
60	9.348021			9.369133	9.389681			9.409688	60

TABLE XXIII.—LOGARITHMIC VERSINES

'	42°			43°	44°			45°	'
	vers	" Corr.	" Corr.	vers	vers	" Corr.	" Corr.	vers	
0	9.409688			9.429181	9.448181			9.466709	0
1	.410017	" Corr.	" Corr.	.429502	.448493	" Corr.	" Corr.	.467014	1
2	.410346	10 55	10 53	.429822	.448806	10 52	10 51	.467319	2
3	.410675	15 82	15 80	.430142	.449118	15 78	15 78	.467623	3
4	.411004	20 109	20 107	.430463	.449431	20 104	20 101	.467928	4
5	9.411332	30 164	30 160	9.430783	9.449743	30 156	30 152	9.468233	5
6	.411660	40 219	40 213	.431103	.450055	40 208	40 203	.468537	6
7	.411989	45 246	45 240	.431422	.450366	45 234	45 228	.468841	7
8	.412317	50 273	50 267	.431742	.450678	50 260	50 253	.469145	8
9	.412644			.432062	.450990			.469449	9
10	9.412972			9.432381	9.451301			9.469753	10
11	.413300			.432700	.451612			.470057	11
12	.413627			.433020	.451924			.470360	12
13	.413955			.433339	.452235			.470664	13
14	.414282			.433657	.452546			.470967	14
15	9.414609			9.433976	9.452856			9.471270	15
16	.414936	" Corr.	" Corr.	.434295	.453167	" Corr.	" Corr.	.471573	16
17	.415263	10 54	10 53	.434613	.453478	10 52	10 50	.471876	17
18	.415589	15 81	15 79	.434932	.453788	15 77	15 76	.472179	18
19	.415916	20 109	20 106	.435250	.454098	20 103	20 101	.472482	19
20	9.416242	30 163	30 159	9.435568	9.454408	30 155	30 151	9.472784	20
21	.416568	40 217	40 212	.435886	.454718	40 207	40 201	.473087	21
22	.416894	45 244	45 238	.436204	.455028	45 232	45 227	.473389	22
23	.417220	50 272	50 265	.436521	.455338	50 258	50 252	.473691	23
24	.417546			.436839	.455648			.473993	24
25	9.417871			9.437156	9.455957			9.474295	25
26	.418197			.437473	.456267			.474597	26
27	.418522			.437790	.456576			.474899	27
28	.418848			.438107	.456885			.475200	28
29	.419173			.438424	.457194			.475502	29
30	9.419498			9.438741	9.457503			9.475803	30
31	.419822	" Corr.	" Corr.	.439058	.457811	" Corr.	" Corr.	.476104	31
32	.420147	10 54	10 53	.439374	.458120	10 51	10 50	.476405	32
33	.420471	15 81	15 79	.439690	.458429	15 77	15 75	.476706	33
34	.420796	20 108	20 105	.440007	.458737	20 103	20 100	.477007	34
35	9.421120	30 162	30 158	9.440323	9.459045	30 154	30 150	9.477308	35
36	.421444	40 216	40 210	.440639	.459353	40 205	40 200	.477608	36
37	.421768	45 243	45 237	.440954	.459661	45 231	45 225	.477909	37
38	.422092	50 270	50 263	.441270	.459969	50 256	50 250	.478209	38
39	.422416			.441586	.460277			.478509	39
40	9.422739			9.441901	9.460584			9.478809	40
41	.423063			.442216	.460892			.479109	41
42	.423386			.442531	.461199			.479409	42
43	.423709			.442846	.461506			.479709	43
44	.424032			.443161	.461813			.480009	44
45	9.424355			9.443476	9.462120			9.480308	45
46	.424677	" Corr.	" Corr.	.443790	.462427	" Corr.	" Corr.	.480608	46
47	.425000	10 54	10 52	.444105	.462734	10 51	10 50	.480907	47
48	.425322	15 80	15 78	.444419	.463040	15 76	15 75	.481206	48
49	.425645	20 107	20 105	.444733	.463347	20 102	20 99	.481505	49
50	9.425967	30 161	30 157	9.445047	9.463653	30 153	30 149	9.481804	50
51	.426289	40 214	40 209	.445361	.463959	40 204	40 199	.482103	51
52	.426611	45 241	45 235	.445675	.464265	45 229	45 224	.482401	52
53	.426933	50 268	50 261	.445989	.464571	50 255	50 249	.482700	53
54	.427254			.446302	.464877			.482998	54
55	9.427576			9.446616	9.465183			9.483296	55
56	.427897			.446929	.465488			.483595	56
57	.428218			.447242	.465794			.483893	57
58	.428539			.447555	.466099			.484191	58
59	.428860			.447868	.466404			.484488	59
60	9.429181			9.448181	9.466709			9.484786	60

TABLE XXIII.—LOGARITHMIC VERSINES

′	46° vers	Corr.	Corr.	47° vers	48° vers	Corr.	Corr.	49° vers	′
0	9.484786			9.502429	9.519657			9.536484	0
1	.485084			.502720	.519940			.536761	1
2	.485381			.503010	.520224			.537038	2
3	.485678			.503300	.520507			.537315	3
4	.485976			.503591	.520791			.537592	4
5	9.486273			9.503881	9.521074			9.537869	5
6	.486570	■ Corr. 10 49	■ Corr. 10 48	.504171	.521357	■ Corr. 10 47	■ Corr. 10 46	.538145	6
7	.486866	15 74	15 72	.504460	.521640	15 71	15 69	.538422	7
8	.487163	20 99	20 96	.504750	.521923	20 94	20 92	.538698	8
9	.487460			.505040	.522206			.538974	9
10	9.487756	30 148	30 145	9.505329	9.522488	30 141	30 138	9.539251	10
11	.488053	40 198	40 193	.505618	.522771	40 188	40 184	.539527	11
12	.488349	45 222	45 217	.505908	.523054	45 212	45 207	.539803	12
13	.488645	50 247	50 241	.506197	.523336	50 236	50 230	.540079	13
14	.488941			.506486	.523618			.540354	14
15	9.489237			9.506775	9.523900			9.540630	15
16	.489533			.507063	.524182			.540906	16
17	.489828			.507352	.524464			.541181	17
18	.490124			.507640	.524746			.541456	18
19	.490419			.507929	.525028			.541732	19
20	9.490714			9.508217	9.525309			9.542007	20
21	.491010			.508505	.525591			.542282	21
22	.491305			.508793	.525872			.542557	22
23	.491600			.509081	.526153			.542832	23
24	.491894			.509369	.526435			.543106	24
25	9.492189			9.509657	9.526716			9.543381	25
26	.492484	■ Corr. 10 49	■ Corr. 10 48	.509945	.526997	■ Corr. 10 47	■ Corr. 10 46	.543655	26
27	.492778	15 74	15 72	.510232	.527277	15 70	15 68	.543930	27
28	.493072	20 98	20 96	.510520	.527558	20 93	20 91	.544204	28
29	.493367			.510807	.527839			.544478	29
30	9.493661	30 147	30 144	9.511094	9.528119	30 140	30 137	9.544752	30
31	.493955	40 196	40 191	.511381	.528400	40 187	40 183	.545026	31
32	.494249	45 220	45 215	.511668	.528680	45 210	45 206	.545300	32
33	.494542	50 245	50 239	.511955	.528960	50 234	50 228	.545574	33
34	.494836			.512241	.529240			.545848	34
35	9.495130			9.512528	9.529520			9.546121	35
36	.495423			.512815	.529800			.546395	36
37	.495716			.513101	.530080			.546668	37
38	.496009			.513387	.530359			.546941	38
39	.496302			.513673	.530639			.547214	39
40	9.496595			9.513959	9.530918			9.547487	40
41	.496888			.514245	.531198			.547760	41
42	.497181			.514531	.531477			.548033	42
43	.497473			.514817	.531756			.548306	43
44	.497766			.515102	.532035			.548579	44
45	9.498058			9.515388	9.532314			9.548851	45
46	.498350	■ Corr. 10 49	■ Corr. 10 47	.515673	.532592	■ Corr. 10 46	■ Corr. 10 45	.549124	46
47	.498643	15 73	15 71	.515959	.532871	15 70	15 68	.549396	47
48	.498935	20 97	20 95	.516244	.533150	20 93	20 91	.549668	48
49	.499226			.516529	.533428			.549940	49
50	9.499518	30 146	30 142	9.516814	9.533706	30 139	30 136	9.550212	50
51	.499810	40 194	40 190	.517098	.533985	40 186	40 181	.550484	51
52	.500101	45 219	45 214	.517383	.534263	45 209	45 204	.550756	52
53	.500393	50 243	50 237	.517668	.534541	50 232	50 227	.551028	53
54	.500684			.517952	.534819			.551299	54
55	9.500975			9.518236	9.535097			9.551571	55
56	.501266			.518521	.535374			.551842	56
57	.501557			.518805	.535652			.552113	57
58	.501848			.519089	.535929			.552384	58
59	.502139			.519373	.536207			.552656	59
60	9.502429			9.519657	9.536484			9.552927	60

TABLE XXIII.—LOGARITHMIC VERSINES

'	50° vers	Corr.	Corr.	51° vers	52° vers	Corr.	Corr.	53° vers	'
0	9.552927			9.568999	9.584714			9.600085	0
1	.553197			.569264	.584973			.600338	1
2	.553468			.569528	.585232			.600591	2
3	.553739			.569793	.585491			.600845	3
4	.554009			.570057	.585749			.601098	4
5	9.554280			9.570322	9.586008			9.601351	5
6	.554550	10 45	10 44	.570586	.586266	10 43	10 42	.601603	6
7	.554820	15 67	15 66	.570850	.586525	15 64	15 63	.601856	7
8	.555091	20 90	20 88	.571114	.586783	20 86	20 84	.602109	8
9	.555361			.571378	.587041			.602362	9
10	9.555631	30 135	30 132	9.571642	9.587299	30 129	30 126	9.602614	10
11	.555900	40 180	40 176	.571906	.587557	40 172	40 168	.602866	11
12	.556170	45 202	45 198	.572170	.587815	45 194	45 189	.603119	12
13	.556440	50 225	50 220	.572434	.588073	50 215	50 210	.603371	13
14	.556709			.572697	.588331			.603623	14
15	9.556979			9.572960	9.588588			9.603875	15
16	.557248			.573224	.588846			.604127	16
17	.557517			.573487	.589103			.604379	17
18	.557786			.573750	.589361			.604631	18
19	.558055			.574013	.589618			.604883	19
20	9.558324			9.574276	9.589875			9.605134	20
21	.558593			.574539	.590132			.605386	21
22	.558862			.574802	.590389			.605637	22
23	.559131			.575064	.590646			.605888	23
24	.559399			.575327	.590903			.606140	24
25	9.559667			9.575589	9.591160			9.606391	25
26	.559936	10 45	10 44	.575852	.591416	10 43	10 42	.606642	26
27	.560204	15 67	15 65	.576114	.591673	15 64	15 63	.606893	27
28	.560472	20 89	20 87	.576376	.591929	20 85	20 84	.607144	28
29	.560740			.576638	.592185			.607394	29
30	9.561008	30 134	30 131	9.576900	9.592442	30 128	30 125	9.607645	30
31	.561276	40 179	40 175	.577162	.592698	40 171	40 167	.607896	31
32	.561544	45 201	45 196	.577424	.592954	45 192	45 188	.608146	32
33	.561811	50 223	50 218	.577685	.593210	50 213	50 209	.608397	33
34	.562079			.577947	.593466			.608647	34
35	9.562346			9.578208	9.593721			9.608897	35
36	.562613			.578470	.593977			.609147	36
37	.562881			.578731	.594233			.609397	37
38	.563148			.578992	.594488			.609647	38
39	.563415			.579253	.594743			.609897	39
40	9.563682			9.579514	9.594999			9.610147	40
41	.563948			.579775	.595254			.610397	41
42	.564215			.580036	.595509			.610646	42
43	.564482			.580297	.595764			.610896	43
44	.564748			.580557	.596019			.611145	44
45	9.565015			9.580818	9.596274			9.611394	45
46	.565281	10 44	10 43	.581078	.596528	10 42	10 41	.611644	46
47	.565547	15 66	15 65	.581339	.596783	15 64	15 62	.611893	47
48	.565813	20 89	20 87	.581599	.597038	20 85	20 83	.612142	48
49	.566079			.581859	.597292			.612391	49
50	9.566345	30 133	30 130	9.582119	9.597546	30 127	30 124	9.612640	50
51	.566611	40 177	40 173	.582379	.597801	40 170	40 166	.612888	51
52	.566877	45 199	45 195	.582639	.598055	45 191	45 187	.613137	52
53	.567142	50 221	50 217	.582898	.598309	50 212	50 207	.613386	53
54	.567408			.583158	.598563			.613634	54
55	9.567673			9.583418	9.598817			9.613883	55
56	.567938			.583677	.599071			.614131	56
57	.568204			.583936	.599324			.614379	57
58	.568469			.584196	.599578			.614627	58
59	.568734			.584455	.599831			.614876	59
60	9.568999			9.584714	9.600085			9.615124	60

TABLE XXIII.—LOGARITHMIC VERSINES

'	54° vers	▪ Corr.	▪ Corr.	55° vers	56° vers	▪ Corr.	▪ Corr.	57° vers	'
0	9.615124			9.629841	9.644249			9.658356	0
1	.615371			.630084	.644486			.658588	1
2	.615619			.630326	.644724			.658821	2
3	.615867			.630569	.644961			.659053	3
4	.616115			.630811	.645198			.659286	4
5	9.616362			9.631054	9.645436			9.659518	5
6	.616610	▪ Corr.	▪ Corr.	.631296	.645673	▪ Corr.	▪ Corr.	.659750	6
7	.616857	10 41	10 40	.631538	.645910	10 39	10 39	.659983	7
8	.617104	15 62	15 60	.631780	.646147	15 59	15 58	.660215	8
9	.617351	20 82	20 81	.632022	.646384	20 79	20 77	.660447	9
10	9.617598	30 124	30 121	9.632264	9.646620	30 118	30 116	9.660679	10
11	.617845	40 164	40 161	.632505	.646857	40 158	40 155	.660910	11
12	.618092	45 185	45 181	.632747	.647094	45 178	45 174	.661142	12
13	.618339	50 206	50 201	.632989	.647330	50 197	50 193	.661374	13
14	.618586			.633230	.647567			.661605	14
15	9.618833			9.633472	9.647803			9.661837	15
16	.619079			.633713	.648039			.662068	16
17	.619326			.633954	.648276			.662300	17
18	.619572			.634196	.648512			.662531	18
19	.619818			.634437	.648748			.662762	19
20	9.620065			9.634678	9.648984			9.662993	20
21	.620311			.634919	.649220			.663224	21
22	.620557			.635159	.649456			.663455	22
23	.620803			.635400	.649691			.663686	23
24	.621048			.635641	.649927			.663917	24
25	9.621294			9.635881	9.650163			9.664148	25
26	.621540	▪ Corr.	▪ Corr.	.636122	.650398	▪ Corr.	▪ Corr.	.664378	26
27	.621786	10 41	10 40	.636362	.650633	10 39	10 38	.664609	27
28	.622031	15 61	15 60	.636603	.650869	15 59	15 58	.664839	28
29	.622276	20 82	20 80	.636843	.651104	20 78	20 77	.665070	29
30	9.622522	30 123	30 120	9.637083	9.651339	30 118	30 115	9.665300	30
31	.622767	40 164	40 160	.637323	.651574	40 157	40 154	.665530	31
32	.623012	45 184	45 180	.637563	.651809	45 176	45 173	.665760	32
33	.623257	50 204	50 200	.637803	.652044	50 196	50 192	.665990	33
34	.623502			.638043	.652279			.666220	34
35	9.623747			9.638283	9.652514			9.666450	35
36	.623992			.638522	.652748			.666680	36
37	.624237			.638762	.652983			.666910	37
38	.624461			.639001	.653217			.667139	38
39	.624726			.639241	.653452			.667369	39
40	9.624970			9.639480	9.653686			9.667599	40
41	.625215			.639719	.653920			.667828	41
42	.625459			.639958	.654155			.668057	42
43	.625703			.640197	.654389			.668287	43
44	.625947			.640436	.654623			.668516	44
45	9.626191			9.640675	9.654857			9.668745	45
46	.626435	▪ Corr.	▪ Corr.	.640914	.655090	▪ Corr.	▪ Corr.	.668974	46
47	.626679	10 41	10 40	.641153	.655324	10 39	10 38	.669203	47
48	.626923	15 61	15 60	.641391	.655558	15 58	15 57	.669432	48
49	.627166	20 81	20 79	.641630	.655792	20 78	20 76	.669661	49
50	9.627410	30 122	30 119	9.641868	9.656025	30 117	30 114	9.669889	50
51	.627654	40 162	40 159	.642107	.656258	40 156	40 152	.670118	51
52	.627897	45 183	45 179	.642345	.656492	45.175	45 171	.670347	52
53	.628140	50 203	50 199	.642583	.656725	50 195	50 190	.670575	53
54	.628384			.642822	.656958			.670804	54
55	9.628627			9.643060	9.657191			9.671032	55
56	.628870			.643298	.657424			.671260	56
57	.629113			.643535	.657657			.671488	57
58	.629356			.643773	.657890			.671716	58
59	.629598			.644011	.658123			.671945	59
60	9.629841			9.644249	9.658356			9.672172	60

TABLE XXIII.—LOGARITHMIC VERSINES

'	58° vers	Corr.	Corr.	59° vers	60° vers	Corr.	Corr.	61° vers	'
0	9.672172			9.685708	9.698970			9.711968	0
1	.672400			.685931	.699189			.712182	1
2	.672628			.686154	.699407			.712397	2
3	.672856			.686377	.699626			.712611	3
4	.673083			.686600	.699845			.712825	4
5	9.673311			9.686823	9.700063			9.713039	5
6	.673538			.687046	.700282			.713253	6
7	.673765			.687269	.700500			.713467	7
8	.673993			.687492	.700718			.713681	8
9	.674220			.687714	.700936			.713895	9
10	9.674448	* Corr.	* Corr.	9.687937	9.701154	* Corr.	* Corr.	9.714109	10
11	.674675			.688159	.701372			.714323	11
12	.674902	10 38	10 37	.688382	.701590	10 36	10 36	.714536	12
13	.675129	15 57	15 56	.688604	.701808	15 54	15 53	.714750	13
14	.675356	20 76	20 74	.688826	.702026	20 73	20 71	.714963	14
15	9.675582	30 113	30 111	9.689048	9.702244	30 109	30 107	9.715177	15
16	.675809	40 151	40 148	.689271	.702462	40 145	40 142	.715390	16
17	.676036	45 170	45 167	.689493	.702679	45 163	45 160	.715603	17
18	.676262	50 189	50 185	.689715	.702897	50 181	50 178	.715817	18
19	.676489			.689937	.703114			.716030	19
20	9.676715			9.690158	9.703332			9.716243	20
21	.676941			.690380	.703549			.716456	21
22	.677168			.690602	.703766			.716669	22
23	.677394			.690823	.703983			.716882	23
24	.677620			.691045	.704200			.717095	24
25	9.677846			9.691266	9.704417			9.717307	25
26	.678072			.691488	.704634			.717520	26
27	.678298			.691709	.704851			.717732	27
28	.678523			.691930	.705068			.717945	28
29	.678749			.692151	.705285			.718157	29
30	9.678975			9.692372	9.705501			9.718370	30
31	.679200			.692593	.705718			.718582	31
32	.679426			.692814	.705935			.718794	32
33	.679651			.693035	.706151			.719007	33
34	.679876			.693256	.706367			.719219	34
35	9.680102			9.693477	9.706584			9.719431	35
36	.680327			.693697	.706800			.719643	36
37	.680552			.693918	.707016			.719855	37
38	.680777			.694138	.707232			.720066	38
39	.681002			.694359	.707448			.720278	39
40	9.681227	* Corr.	* Corr.	9.694579	9.707664	* Corr.	* Corr.	9.720490	40
41	.681451			.694799	.707880			.720701	41
42	.681676	10 37	10 37	.695019	.708096	10 36	10 35	.720913	42
43	.681901	15 56	15 55	.695240	.708311	15 54	15 53	.721124	43
44	.682125	20 75	20 73	.695460	.708527	20 72	20 70	.721336	44
45	9.682350	30 112	30 110	9.695680	9.708743	30 108	30 106	9.721547	45
46	.682574	40 150	40 147	.695899	.708958	40 144	40 141	.721758	46
47	.682798	45 168	45 165	.696119	.709174	45 162	45 158	.721970	47
48	.683023	50 187	50 183	.696339	.709389	50 180	50 176	.722181	48
49	.683247			.696559	.709604			.722392	49
50	9.683471			9.696778	9.709819			9.722603	50
51	.683695			.696998	.710035			.722814	51
52	.683919			.697217	.710250			.723024	52
53	.684143			.697437	.710465			.723235	53
54	.684367			.697656	.710680			.723446	54
55	9.684590			9.697875	9.710895			9.723657	55
56	.684814			.698094	.711109			.723867	56
57	.685037			.698313	.711304			.724078	57
58	.685261			.698532	.711539			.724288	58
59	.685484			.698751	.711753			.724498	59
60	9.685708			9.698970	9.711968			9.724709	60

TABLE XXIII.—LOGARITHMIC VERSINES

'	62° vers	" Corr.	" Corr.	63° vers	64° vers	" Corr.	" Corr.	65° vers	'
0	9.724709			9.737200	9.749449			9.761463	0
1	.724919			.737406	.749652			.761661	1
2	.725129			.737612	.749854			.761860	2
3	.725339			.737818	.750056			.762058	3
4	.725549			.738024	.750258			.762256	4
5	9.725759			9.738230	9.750459			9.762454	5
6	.725969			.738436	.750661			.762652	6
7	.726179			.738642	.750863			.762850	7
8	.726388			.738847	.751065			.763047	8
9	.726599			.739053	.751266			.763245	9
10	9.726808			9.739258	9.751468			9.763443	10
11	.727017	" Corr.	" Corr.	.739464	.751669	" Corr.	" Corr.	.763641	11
12	.727227	10 35	10 34	.739669	.751871	10 34	10 33	.763838	12
13	.727436	15 52	15 51	.739875	.752072	15 50	15 49	.764036	13
14	.727645	20 70	20 68	.740080	.752273	20 67	20 66	.764233	14
15	9.727855	30 105	30 103	9.740285	9.752475	30 101	30 99	9.764430	15
16	.728064	40 139	40 137	.740490	.752676	40 134	40 132	.764628	16
17	.728273	45 157	45 154	.740695	.752877	45 151	45 148	.764825	17
18	.728482	50 174	50 171	.740900	.753078	50 168	50 164	.765022	18
19	.728691			.741105	.753279			.765219	19
20	9.728900			9.741310	9.753480			9.765416	20
21	.729109			.741515	.753681			.765613	21
22	.729317			.741719	.753881			.765810	22
23	.729526			.741924	.754082			.766007	23
24	.729735			.742129	.754283			.766204	24
25	9.729943			9.742333	9.754483			9.766401	25
26	.730152			.742538	.754684			.766597	26
27	.730360			.742742	.754884			.766794	27
28	.730569			.742946	.755085			.766991	28
29	.730777			.743150	.755285			.767187	29
30	9.730985			9.743355	9.755485			9.767384	30
31	.731193			.743559	.755685			.767580	31
32	.731401			.743763	.755886			.767776	32
33	.731609			.743967	.756086			.767972	33
34	.731817			.744171	.756286			.768169	34
35	9.732025			9.744375	9.756486			9.768365	35
36	.732233			.744578	.756685			.768561	36
37	.732441			.744782	.756885			.768757	37
38	.732648			.744986	.757085			.768953	38
39	.732856			.745189	.757285			.769149	39
40	9.733064			9.745393	9.757484			9.769344	40
41	.733271	" Corr.	" Corr.	.745596	.757684	10 33	10 33	.769540	41
42	.733478	10 35	10 34	.745800	.757883	15 50	15 49	.769736	42
43	.733686	15 52	15 51	.746003	.758083	20 66	20 65	.769931	43
44	.733893	20 69	20 68	.746206	.758282	30 100	30 98	.770127	44
45	9.734100	30 104	30 102	9.746409	9.758481	40 133	40 130	9.770323	45
46	.734307	40 138	40 135	.746613	.758681	45 149	45 147	.770518	46
47	.734515	45 155	45 152	.746816	.758880	50 166	50 163	.770713	47
48	.734721	50 173	50 169	.747019	.759079			.770909	48
49	.734928			.747222	.759278			.771104	49
50	9.735135			9.747424	9.759477			9.771299	50
51	.735342			.747627	.759676			.771494	51
52	.735549			.747830	.759875			.771689	52
53	.735755			.748033	.760073			.771884	53
54	.735962			.748235	.760272			.772079	54
55	9.736169			9.748438	9.760471			9.772274	55
56	.736375			.748640	.760669			.772469	56
57	.736581			.748843	.760868			.772664	57
58	.736788			.749045	.761066			.772858	58
59	.736994			.749247	.761265			.773053	59
60	9.737200			9.749449	9.761463			9.773248	60

TABLE XXIII.—LOGARITHMIC VERSINES

'	66° vers	Corr	Corr	67° vers	68° vers	Corr	Corr	69° vers	'
0	9.773248			9.784809	9.796153			9.807286	0
1	.773442			.785000	.796341			.807470	1
2	.773636			.785191	.796528			.807654	2
3	.773831			.785381	.796715			.807837	3
4	.774025			.785572	.796902			.808021	4
5	9.774219			9.785763	9.797089			9.808204	5
6	.774414			.785953	.797276			.808388	6
7	.774608			.786144	.797463			.808571	7
8	.774802			.786334	.797650			.808755	8
9	.774996			.786524	.797837			.808938	9
10	9.775190	Corr	Corr	9.786715	9.798023	Corr	Corr	9.809121	10
11	.775384			.786905	.798210			.809305	11
12	.775577	10 32	10 32	.787095	.798397	10 31	10 30	.809488	12
13	.775771	15 48	15 48	.787285	.798583	15 47	15 46	.809671	13
14	.775965	20 65	20 63	.787475	.798770	20 62	20 61	.809854	14
15	9.776159	30 97	30 95	9.787665	9.798956	30 93	30 92	9.810037	15
16	.776352	40 129	40 127	.787855	.799142	40 124	40 122	.810220	16
17	.776546	45 145	45 142	.788045	.799329	45 140	45 137	.810403	17
18	.776739	50 161	50 158	.788235	.799515	50 155	50 152	.810585	18
19	.776933			.788425	.799701			.810768	19
20	9.777126			9.788614	9.799887			9.810951	20
21	.777319			.788804	.800074			.811134	21
22	.777512			.788993	.800260			.811316	22
23	.777705			.789183	.800446			.811499	23
24	.777899			.789372	.800631			.811681	24
25	9.778092			9.789562	9.800817			9.811864	25
26	.778285			.789751	.801003			.812046	26
27	.778477			.789940	.801189			.812228	27
28	.778670			.790130	.801375			.812410	28
29	.778863			.790319	.801560			.812593	29
30	9.779056			9.790508	9.801746			9.812775	30
31	.779248			.790697	.801931			.812957	31
32	.779441			.790886	.802117			.813139	32
33	.779634			.791075	.802302			.813321	33
34	.779826			.791264	.802487			.813503	34
35	9.780018			9.791453	9.802673			9.813685	35
36	.780211			.791641	.802858			.813866	36
37	.780403			.791830	.803043			.814048	37
38	.780595			.792019	.803228			.814230	38
39	.780787			.792207	.803413			.814411	39
40	9.780980	Corr	Corr	9.792396	9.803598	Corr	Corr	9.814593	40
41	.781172			.792584	.803783			.814775	41
42	.781364	10 32	10 31	.792772	.803968	10 31	10 30	.814956	42
43	.781556	15 48	15 47	.792961	.804153	15 46	15 45	.815137	43
44	.781747	20 64	20 63	.793149	.804338	20 62	20 60	.815319	44
45	9.781939	30 96	30 94	9.793337	9.804522	30 92	30 91	9.815500	45
46	.782131	40 128	40 125	.793525	.804707	40 123	40 121	.815681	46
47	.782323	45 144	45 141	.793714	.804892	45 139	45 136	.815862	47
48	.782514	50 160	50 157	.793902	.805076	50 154	50 151	.816044	48
49	.782706			.794090	.805261			.816225	49
50	9.782897			9.794277	9.805445			9.816406	50
51	.783089			.794465	.805629			.816587	51
52	.783280			.794653	.805814			.816767	52
53	.783471			.794841	.805998			.816948	53
54	.783663			.795028	.806182			.817129	54
55	9.783854			9.795216	9.806366			9.817310	55
56	.784045			.795404	.806550			.817490	56
57	.784236			.795591	.806734			.817671	57
58	.784427			.795779	.806918			.817852	58
59	.784618			.795966	.807102			.818032	59
60	9.784809			9.796153	9.807286			9.818213	60

TABLE XXIII.—LOGARITHMIC VERSINES

'	70° vers	Corr.	Corr.	71° vers	72° vers	Corr.	Corr.	73° vers	'
0	9.818213			9.828938	9.839467			9.849805	0
1	.818393			.829115	.839641			.849976	1
2	.818573			.829292	.839815			.850147	2
3	.818754			.829469	.839989			.850317	3
4	.818934			.829646	.840162			.850488	4
5	9.819114			9.829823	9.840336			9.850658	5
6	.819294			.830000	.840510			.850829	6
7	.819474			.830177	.840683			.850999	7
8	.819654			.830353	.840857			.851169	8
9	.819834			.830530	.841030			.851340	9
10	9.820014			9.830706	9.841204			9.851510	10
11	.820194	Corr.	Corr.	.830883	.841377	Corr.	Corr.	.851680	11
12	.820374	10 30	10 29	.831059	.841550	10 29	10 28	.851850	12
13	.820553	15 45	15 44	.831236	.841723	15 43	15 42	.852020	13
14	.820733	20 60	20 59	.831412	.841896	20 58	20 57	.852190	14
15	9.820913	30 90	30 88	9.831589	9.842070	30 87	30 85	9.852360	15
16	.821092	40 120	40 118	.831765	.842243	40 115	40 113	.852530	16
17	.821272	45 135	45 132	.831941	.842416	45 130	45 128	.852700	17
18	.821451	50 150	50 147	.832117	.842589	50 144	50 142	.852870	18
19	.821631			.832293	.842762			.853040	19
20	9.821810			9.832469	9.842934			9.853209	20
21	.821989			.832645	.843107			.853379	21
22	.822168			.832821	.843280			.853549	22
23	.822348			.832997	.843453			.853718	23
24	.822527			.833173	.843625			.853888	24
25	9.822706			9.833349	9.843798			9.854057	25
26	.822885			.833525	.843970			.854227	26
27	.823064			.833700	.844143			.854396	27
28	.823243			.833876	.844315			.854565	28
29	.823421			.834051	.844488			.854735	29
30	9.823600			9.834227	9.844660			9.854904	30
31	.823779			.834402	.844832			.855073	31
32	.823958			.834578	.845004			.855242	32
33	.824136			.834753	.845177			.855411	33
34	.824315			.834928	.845349			.855580	34
35	9.824493			9.835104	9.845521			9.855749	35
36	.824672			.835279	.845693			.855918	36
37	.824850			.835454	.845865			.856087	37
38	.825028			.835629	.846037			.856255	38
39	.825207			.835804	.846208			.856424	39
40	9.825385			9.835979	9.846380			9.856593	40
41	.825563	Corr.	Corr.	.836154	.846552	Corr.	Corr.	.856762	41
42	.825741	10 30	10 29	.836329	.846724	10 29	10 28	.856930	42
43	.825919	15 44	15 44	.836504	.846895	15 43	15 42	.857099	43
44	.826097	20 59	20 ·58	.836678	.847067	20 57	20 56	.857267	44
45	9.826275	30 89	30 87	9.836853	9.847238	30 86	30 84	9.857436	45
46	.826453	40 119	40 116	.837028	.847410	40 114	40 112	.857604	46
47	.826631	45 133	45 131	.837202	.847581	45 129	45 126	.857772	47
48	.826809	50 148	50 146	.837377	.847753	50 143	50 140	.857941	48
49	.826987			.837551	.847924			.858109	49
50	9.827164			9.837726	9.848095			9.858277	50
51	.827342			.837900	.848267			.858445	51
52	.827519			.838075	.848438			.858613	52
53	.827697			.838249	.848609			.858781	53
54	.827874			.838423	.848780			.858949	54
55	9.828052			9.838597	9.848951			9.859117	55
56	.828229			.838771	.849122			.859285	56
57	.828406			.838945	.849293			.859453	57
58	.828584			.839119	.849464			.859621	58
59	.828761			.839293	.849634			.859788	59
60	9.828938			9.839467	9.849805			9.859956	60

TABLE XXIII.—LOGARITHMIC VERSINES

'	74° vers	75° vers	76° vers	77° vers	'
0	9.859956	9.869924	9.879714	9.889329	0
1	.860124	.870089	.879876	.889488	1
2	.860291	.870253	.880037	.889647	2
3	.860459	.870418	.880199	.889805	3
4	.860626	.870582	.880360	.889964	4
5	9.860794	9.870747	9.880522	9.890123	5
6	.860961	.870911	.880683	.890281	6
7	.861128	.871076	.880845	.890440	7
8	.861296	.871240	.881006	.890598	8
9	.861463	.871404	.881167	.890757	9
10	9.861630	9.871568	9.881329	9.890915	10
11	.861797	.871732	.881490	.891073	11
12	.861964	.871896	.881651	.891232	12
13	.862131	.872060	.881812	.891390	13
14	.862298	.872224	.881973	.891548	14
15	9.862465	9.872388	9.882134	9.891706	15
16	.862632	.872552	.882295	.891864	16
17	.862799	.872716	.882456	.892022	17
18	.862965	.872880	.882617	.892180	18
19	.863132	.873043	.882777	.892338	19
20	9.863299	9.873207	9.882938	9.892496	20
21	.863465	.873371	.883099	.892654	21
22	.863632	.873534	.883260	.892812	22
23	.863799	.873698	.883420	.892969	23
24	.863965	.873861	.883581	.893127	24
25	9.864131	9.874025	9.883741	9.893285	25
26	.864298	.874188	.883902	.893442	26
27	.864464	.874351	.884062	.893600	27
28	.864630	.874515	.884223	.893758	28
29	.864797	.874678	.884383	.893915	29
30	9.864963	9.874841	9.884543	9.894072	30
31	.865129	.875004	.884703	.894230	31
32	.865295	.875167	.884864	.894387	32
33	.865461	.875330	.885024	.894544	33
34	.865627	.875493	.885184	.894702	34
35	9.865793	9.875656	9.885344	9.894859	35
36	.865959	.875819	.885504	.895016	36
37	.866124	.875982	.885664	.895173	37
38	.866290	.876145	.885824	.895330	38
39	.866456	.876308	.885983	.895487	39
40	9.866622	9.876470	9.886143	9.895644	40
41	.866787	.876633	.886303	.895801	41
42	.866953	.876796	.886463	.895958	42
43	.867118	.876958	.886622	.896115	43
44	.867284	.877121	.886782	.896272	44
45	9.867449	9.877283	9.886941	9.896428	45
46	.867614	.877445	.887101	.896585	46
47	.867780	.877608	.887260	.896742	47
48	.867945	.877770	.887420	.896898	48
49	.868110	.877932	.887579	.897055	49
50	9.868275	9.878095	9.887739	9.897211	50
51	.868441	.878257	.887898	.897368	51
52	.868606	.878419	.888057	.897525	52
53	.868771	.878581	.888216	.897680	53
54	.868936	.878743	.888375	.897837	54
55	9.869100	9.878905	9.888534	9.897993	55
56	.869265	.879067	.888693	.898149	56
57	.869430	.879229	.888852	.898305	57
58	.869595	.879390	.889011	.898461	58
59	.869760	.879552	.889170	.898618	59
60	9.869924	9.879714	9.889329	9.898774	60

Correction tables (74°, upper):

▪ Corr.		▪ Corr.	
10	28	10	27
15	42	15	41
20	56	20	55
30	83	30	82
40	111	40	109
45	125	45	123
50	139	50	137

Correction tables (74°, lower):

▪ Corr.		▪ Corr.	
10	28	10	27
15	41	15	41
20	55	20	54
30	83	30	81
40	110	40	108
45	124	45	122
50	138	50	135

Correction tables (76°, upper):

▪ Corr.		▪ Corr.	
10	27	10	26
15	40	15	40
20	54	20	53
30	80	30	79
40	107	40	105
45	121	45	119
50	134	50	132

Correction tables (76°, lower):

▪ Corr.		▪ Corr.	
10	27	10	26
15	40	15	39
20	53	20	52
30	80	30	78
40	106	40	104
45	120	45	118
50	133	50	131

TABLE XXIII.—LOGARITHMIC VERSINES

'	78° vers	* Corr.	* Corr.	79° vers	80° vers	* Corr.	* Corr.	81° vers	'
0	9.898774			9.908051	9.917165			9.926119	0
1	.898930			.908204	.917316			.926267	1
2	.899086			.908357	.917466			.926415	2
3	.899241			.908511	.917616			.926562	3
4	.899397			.908664	.917767			.926710	4
5	9.899553			9.908817	9.917917			9.926858	5
6	.899709			.908970	.918068			.927006	6
7	.899865			.909123	.918218			.927153	7
8	.900020			.909276	.918368			.927301	8
9	.900176			.909428	.918518			.927448	9
10	9.900331			9.909581	9.918668			9.927596	10
11	.900487	* Corr.	* Corr.	.909734	.918818	* Corr.	* Corr.	.927743	11
12	.900642	10 26	10 25	.909887	.918968	10 25	10 25	.927891	12
13	.900798	15 39	15 38	.910039	.919118	15 37	15 37	.928038	13
14	.900953	20 52	20 51	.910192	.919268	20 50	20 49	.928185	14
15	9.901108	30 78	30 76	9.910345	9.919418	30 75	30 74	9.928333	15
16	.901264	40 104	40 102	.910497	.919568	40 100	40 98	.928480	16
17	.901419	45 116	45 114	.910650	.919718	45 112	45 110	.928627	17
18	.901574	50 129	50 127	.910802	.919868	50 125	50 123	.928774	18
19	.901729			.910955	.920018			.928921	19
20	9.901884			9.911107	9.920167			9.929068	20
21	.902040			.911259	.920317			.929215	21
22	.902195			.911412	.920466			.929362	22
23	.902350			.911564	.920616			.929509	23
24	.902504			.911716	.920766			.929656	24
25	9.902659			9.911868	9.920915			9.929803	25
26	.902814			.912020	.921064			.929950	26
27	.902969			.912172	.921214			.930097	27
28	.903124			.912324	.921363			.930243	28
29	.903278			.912476	.921512			.930390	29
30	9.903433			9.912628	9.921662			9.930537	30
31	.903588			.912780	.921811			.930683	31
32	.903742			.912932	.921960			.930830	32
33	.903897			.913084	.922109			.930976	33
34	.904051			.913235	.922258			.931123	34
35	9.904206			9.913387	9.922407			9.931269	35
36	.904360			.913539	.922556			.931416	36
37	.904514			.913690	.922705			.931562	37
38	.904668			.913842	.922854			.931708	38
39	.904823			.913993	.923003			.931855	39
40	9.904977			9.914145	9.923152			9.932001	40
41	.905131	* Corr.	* Corr.	.914296	.923301	* Corr.	* Corr.	.932147	41
42	.905285	10 26	10 25	.914448	.923449	10 25	10 24	.932293	42
43	.905439	15 38	15 38	.914599	.923598	15 37	15 36	.932439	43
44	.905593	20 51	20 50	.914750	.923747	20 50	20 49	.932585	44
45	9.905747	30 77	30 76	9.914902	9.923895	30 74	30 73	9.932731	45
46	.905901	40 103	40 101	.915053	.924044	40 99	40 97	.932877	46
47	.906055	45 115	45 113	.915204	.924192	45 111	45 110	.933023	47
48	.906209	50 128	50 126	.915355	.924341	50 124	50 122	.933169	48
49	.906363			.915506	.924489			.933315	49
50	9.906516			9.915657	9.924637			9.933460	50
51	.906670			.915808	.924786			.933606	51
52	.906824			.915959	.924934			.933752	52
53	.906977			.916110	.925082			.933897	53
54	.907131			.916261	.925231			.934043	54
55	9.907284			9.916412	9.925379			9.934189	55
56	.907438			.916562	.925527			.934334	56
57	.907591			.916713	.925675			.934480	57
58	.907744			.916864	.925823			.934625	58
59	.907898			.917014	.925971			.934770	59
60	9.908051			9.917165	9.926119			9.934916	60

TABLE XXIII.—LOGARITHMIC VERSINES

'	82° vers	" Corr.	" Corr.	83° vers	84° vers	" Corr.	" Corr.	85° vers	'
0	9.934916			9.943559	9.952052			9.960397	0
1	.935061			.943702	.952192			.960535	1
2	.935206			.943845	.952332			.960672	2
3	.935352			.943987	.952473			.960810	3
4	.335497			.944130	.952613			.960948	4
5	9.935642			9.944273	9.952753			9.961086	5
6	.935787			.944415	.952893			.961223	6
7	.935932			.944558	.953033			.961361	7
8	.936077			.944700	.953173			.961498	8
9	.936222			.944843	.953313			.961636	9
10	9.936367			9.944985	9.953453			9.961773	10
11	.936512	" Corr.	" Corr.	.945127	.953593	" Corr.	" Corr.	.961911	11
12	.936657	10 24	10 24	.945270	.953732	10 23	10 23	.962048	12
13	.936801	15 36	15 36	.945412	.953872	15 35	15 34	.962186	13
14	.936946	20 48	20 47	.945554	.954012	20 47	20 46	.962323	14
15	9.937091	30 72	30 71	9.945696	9.954152	30 70	30 69	9.962460	15
16	.937236	40 96	40 95	.945838	.954291	40 93	40 92	.962597	16
17	.937380	45 109	45 107	.945981	.954431	45 105	45 103	.962735	17
18	.937525	50 121	50 118	.946123	.954571	50 116	50 114	.962872	18
19	.937669			.946265	.954710			.963009	19
20	9.937814			9.946407	9.954850			9.963146	20
21	.937958			.946549	.954989			.963283	21
22	.938103			.946690	.955129			.963420	22
23	.938247			.946832	.955268			.963557	23
24	.938391			.946974	.955407			.963694	24
25	9.938536			9.947116	9.955547			9.963831	25
26	.938680			.947258	.955686			.963968	26
27	.938824			.947399	.955825			.964104	27
28	.938968			.947541	.955964			.964241	28
29	.939112			.947683	.956103			.964378	29
30	9.939257			9.947824	9.956243			9.964515	30
31	.939401			.947966	.956382			.964651	31
32	.939545			.948107	.956521			.964788	32
33	.939688			.948249	.956660			.964924	33
34	.939832			.948390	.956799			.965061	34
35	9.939976			9.948531	9.956937			9.965197	35
36	.940120			.948673	.957076			.965334	36
37	.940264			.948814	.957215			.965470	37
38	.940408			.948955	.957354			.965607	38
39	.940551			.949096	.957493			.965743	39
40	9.940695			9.949237	9.957631			9.965879	40
41	.940839	" Corr.	" Corr.	.949379	.957770	" Corr.	" Corr.	.966016	41
42	.940982	10 24	10 23	.949520	.957909	10 23	10 23	.966152	42
43	.941126	15 36	15 35	.949661	.958047	15 35	15 34	.966288	43
44	.941269	20 48	20 47	.949802	.958186	20 46	20 45	.966424	44
45	9.941413	30 72	30 70	9.949943	9.958324	30 69	30 68	9.966560	45
46	.941556	40 96	40 94	.950083	.958463	40 92	40 91	.966696	46
47	.941699	45 108	45 106	.950224	.958601	45 104	45 102	.966832	47
48	.941843	50 119	50 117	.950365	.958739	50 115	50 113	.966968	48
49	.941986			.950506	.958878			.967104	49
50	9.942129			9.950647	9.959016			9.967240	50
51	.942272			.950787	.959154			.967376	51
52	.942415			.950928	.959292			.967512	52
53	.942559			.951069	.959431			.967647	53
54	.942702			.951209	.959569			.967783	54
55	9.942845			9.951350	9.959707			9.967919	55
56	.942988			.951490	.959845			.968054	56
57	.943131			.951631	.959983			.968190	57
58	.943273			.951771	.960121			.968326	58
59	.943416			.951911	.960259			.968461	59
60	9.943559			9.952052	9.960397			9.968597	60

TABLE XXIII.—LOGARITHMIC VERSINES

'	86° vers	87° vers	88° vers	89° vers	'
0	9.968597	9.976654	9.984573	9.992354	0
1	.968732	.976788	.984703	.992482	1
2	.968868	.976921	.984834	.992611	2
3	.969003	.977054	.984965	.992739	3
4	.969138	.977187	.985096	.992868	4
5	9.969274	9.977320	9.985226	9.992996	5
6	.969409	.977452	.985357	.993124	6
7	.969544	.977585	.985487	.993253	7
8	.969679	.977718	.985618	.993381	8
9	.969814	.977851	.985748	.993509	9
10	9.969949	9.977984	9.985879	9.993637	10
11	.970084	.978116	.986009	.993765	11
12	.970219	.978249	.986140	.993894	12
13	.970354	.978382	.986270	.994022	13
14	.970489	.978514	.986400	.994150	14
15	9.970624	9.978647	9.986531	9.994278	15
16	.970759	.978779	.986661	.994406	16
17	.970894	.978912	.986791	.994534	17
18	.971029	.979044	.986921	.994662	18
19	.971164	.979177	.987051	.994789	19
20	9.971298	9.979309	9.987181	9.994917	20
21	.971433	.979442	.987311	.995045	21
22	.971568	.979574	.987441	.995173	22
23	.971702	.979706	.987571	.995301	23
24	.971837	.979838	.987701	.995428	24
25	9.971971	9.979970	9.987831	9.995556	25
26	.972106	.980103	.987961	.995683	26
27	.972240	.980235	.988091	.995811	27
28	.972374	.980367	.988221	.995939	28
29	.972509	.980499	.988350	.996066	29
30	9.972643	9.980631	9.988480	9.996193	30
31	.972777	.980763	.988610	.996321	31
32	.972912	.980895	.988739	.996448	32
33	.973046	.981026	.988869	.996576	33
34	.973180	.981158	.988998	.996703	34
35	9.973314	9.981290	9.989128	9.996830	35
36	.973448	.981422	.989257	.996957	36
37	.973582	.981554	.989387	.997085	37
38	.973716	.981685	.989516	.997212	38
39	.973850	.981817	.989646	.997339	39
40	9.973984	9.981949	9.989775	9.997466	40
41	.974118	.982080	.989904	.997593	41
42	.974252	.982212	.990034	.997720	42
43	.974386	.982343	.990163	.997847	43
44	.974519	.982475	.990292	.997974	44
45	9.974653	9.982606	9.990421	9.998101	45
46	.974787	.982737	.990550	.998228	46
47	.974920	.982869	.990679	.998355	47
48	.975054	.983000	.990808	.998481	48
49	.975188	.983131	.990937	.998608	49
50	9.975321	9.983262	9.991066	9.998735	50
51	.975455	.983394	.991195	.998862	51
52	.975588	.983525	.991324	.998988	52
53	.975722	.983656	.991453	.999115	53
54	.975855	.983787	.991582	.999241	54
55	9.975988	9.983918	9.991710	9.999368	55
56	.976121	.984049	.991839	.999494	56
57	.976255	.984180	.991968	.999621	57
58	.976388	.984311	.992096	.999747	58
59	.976521	.984442	.992225	.999874	59
60	9.976654	9.984573	9.992354	0.000000	60

Correction tables (86°, rows 11–18):

Corr.		Corr.	
10	22	10	22
15	34	15	33
20	45	20	44
30	67	30	66
40	90	40	88
45	101	45	99
50	112	50	110

Correction tables (88°, rows 11–18):

Corr.		Corr.	
10	22	10	21
15	33	15	32
20	43	20	43
30	65	30	64
40	87	40	85
45	98	45	96
50	108	50	107

Correction tables (86°, rows 42–48):

Corr.		Corr.	
10	22	10	22
15	33	15	33
20	45	20	44
30	67	30	66
40	89	40	88
45	100	45	99
50	111	50	109

Correction tables (88°, rows 42–48):

Corr.		Corr.	
10	22	10	21
15	32	15	32
20	43	20	42
30	65	30	63
40	86	40	85
45	97	45	95
50	108	50	106

TABLE XXIV.—STADIA REDUCTIONS

Minutes	0°		1°		2°		3°	
	Hor. Dist.	Diff. Elev.	Hor. Dist.	Diff. Elev.	Hor. Dist.	Diff. Elev.	Hor. Dist.	Diff. Elev.
0	100.00	.00	99.97	1.74	99.88	3.49	99.73	5.23
2	100.00	.06	99.97	1.80	99.87	3.55	99.72	5.28
4	100.00	.12	99.97	1.86	99.87	3.60	99.71	5.34
6	100.00	.17	99.96	1.92	90.87	3.66	99.71	5.40
8	100.00	.23	99.96	1.98	99.86	3.72	99.70	5.46
10	100.00	.29	99.96	2.04	99.86	3.78	99.69	5.52
12	100.00	.35	99.96	2.09	99.85	3.84	99.69	5.57
14	100.00	.41	99.95	2.15	99.85	3.89	99.68	5.63
16	100.00	.47	99.95	2.21	99.84	3.95	99.68	5.69
18	100.00	.52	99.95	2.27	99.84	4.01	99.67	5.75
20	100.00	.58	99.95	2.33	99.83	4.07	99.66	5.80
22	100.00	.64	99.94	2.38	99.83	4.13	99.66	5.86
24	100.00	.70	99.94	2.44	99.82	4.18	99.65	5.92
26	99.99	.76	99.94	2.50	99.82	4.24	99.64	5.98
28	99.99	.81	99.93	2.56	99.81	4.30	99.63	6.04
30	99.99	.87	99.93	2.62	99.81	4.36	99.63	6.09
32	99.99	.93	99.93	2.67	99.80	4.42	99.62	6.15
34	99.99	.99	99.93	2.73	99.80	4.47	99.61	6.21
36	99.99	1.05	99.92	2.79	99.79	4.53	99.61	6.27
38	99.99	1.11	99.92	2.85	99.79	4.59	99.60	6.32
40	99.99	1.16	99.92	2.91	99.78	4.65	99.59	6.38
42	99.99	1.22	99.91	2.97	99.78	4.71	99.58	6.44
44	99.98	1.28	99.91	3.02	99.77	4.76	99.58	6.50
46	99.98	1.34	99.90	3.08	99.77	4.82	99.57	6.56
48	99.98	1.40	99.90	3.14	99.76	4.88	99.56	6.61
50	99.98	1.45	99.90	3.20	99.76	4.94	99.55	6.67
52	99.98	1.51	99.89	3.26	99.75	4.99	99.55	6.73
54	99.98	1.57	99.89	3.31	99.74	5.05	99.54	6.79
56	99.97	1.63	99.89	3.37	99.74	5.11	99.53	6.84
58	99.97	1.69	99.88	3.43	99.73	5.17	99.52	6.90
60	99.97	1.74	99.88	3.49	99.73	5.23	99.51	6.96
C = .75	.75	.01	.75	.02	.75	.03	.75	.05
C = 1.00	1.00	.01	1.00	.03	1.00	.04	1.00	.06
C = 1.25	1.25	.02	1.25	.03	1.25	.05	1.25	.08

TABLE XXIV.—STADIA REDUCTIONS

Minutes	4°		5°		6°		7°	
	Hor. Dist.	Diff. Elev.	Hor. Dist.	Diff. Elev.	Hor. Dist.	Diff. Elev.	Hor. Dist.	Diff. Elev.
0	99.51	6.96	99.24	8.68	98.91	10.40	98.51	12.10
2	99.51	7.02	99.23	8.74	98.89	10.45	98.50	12.15
4	99.50	7.07	99.22	8.80	98.88	10.51	98.49	12.21
6	99.49	7.13	99.21	8.85	98.87	10.57	98.47	12.27
8	99.48	7.19	99.20	8.91	98.86	10.62	98.46	12.32
10	99.47	7.25	99.19	8.97	98.85	10.68	98.44	12.38
12	99.46	7.30	99.18	9.03	98.83	10.74	98.43	12.43
14	99.46	7.36	99.17	9.08	98.82	10.79	98.41	12.49
16	99.45	7.42	99.16	9.14	98.81	10.85	98.40	12.55
18	99.44	7.48	99.15	9.20	98.80	10.91	98.39	12.60
20	99.43	7.53	99.14	9.25	98.78	10.96	98.37	12.66
22	99.42	7.59	99.13	9.31	98.77	11.02	98.36	12.72
24	99.41	7.65	99.11	9.37	98.76	11.08	98.34	12.77
26	99.40	7.71	99.10	9.43	98.74	11.13	98.33	12.83
28	99.39	7.76	99.09	9.48	98.73	11.19	98.31	12.88
30	99.38	7.82	99.08	9.54	98.72	11.25	98.30	12.94
32	99.38	7.88	99.07	9.60	98.71	11.30	98.28	13.00
34	99.37	7.94	99.06	9.65	98.69	11.36	98.27	13.05
36	99.36	7.99	99.05	9.71	98.68	11.42	98.25	13.11
38	99.35	8.05	99.04	9.77	98.67	11.47	98.24	13.17
40	99.34	8.11	99.03	9.83	98.65	11.53	98.22	13.22
42	99.33	8.17	99.01	9.88	98.64	11.59	98.20	13.28
44	99.32	8.22	99.00	9.94	98.63	11.64	98.19	13.33
46	99.31	8.28	98.99	10.00	98.61	11.70	98.17	13.39
48	99.30	8.34	98.98	10.05	98.60	11.76	98.16	13.45
50	99.29	8.40	98.97	10.11	98.58	11.81	98.14	13.50
52	99.28	8.45	98.96	10.17	98.57	11.87	98.13	13.56
54	99.27	8.51	98.94	10.22	98.56	11.93	98.11	13.61
56	99.26	8.57	98.93	10.28	98.54	11.98	98.10	13.67
58	99.25	8.63	98.92	10.34	98.53	12.04	98.08	13.73
60	99.24	8.68	98.91	10.40	98.51	12.10	98.06	13.78
c = .75	.75	.06	.75	.07	.75	.08	.74	.10
c = 1.00	1.00	.08	1.00	.10	.99	.11	.99	.13
c = 1.25	1.25	.10	1.24	.12	1.24	.14	1.24	.16

TABLE XXIV.—STADIA REDUCTIONS

Minutes	8°		9°		10°		11°	
	Hor. Dist.	Diff. Elev.	Hor. Dist.	Diff. Elev.	Hor. Dist.	Diff. Elev.	Hor. Dist.	Diff. Elev.
0	98.06	13.78	97.55	15.45	96.98	17.10	96.36	18.73
2	98.05	13.84	97.53	15.51	96.96	17.16	96.34	18.78
4	98.03	13.89	97.52	15.56	96.94	17.21	96.32	18.84
6	98.01	13.95	97.50	15.62	96.92	17.26	96.29	18.89
8	98.00	14.01	97.48	15.67	96.90	17.32	96.27	18.95
10	97.98	14.06	97.46	15.73	96.88	17.37	96.25	19.00
12	97.97	14.12	97.44	15.78	96.86	17.43	96.23	19.05
14	97.95	14.17	97.43	15.84	96.84	17.48	96.21	19.11
16	97.93	14.23	97.41	15.89	96.82	17.54	96.18	19.16
18	97.92	14.28	97.39	15.95	96.80	17.59	96.16	19.21
20	97.90	14.34	97.37	16.00	96.78	17.65	96.14	19.27
22	97.88	14.40	97.35	16.06	96.76	17.70	96.12	19.32
24	97.87	14.45	97.33	16.11	96.74	17.76	96.09	19.38
26	97.85	14.51	97.31	16.17	96.72	17.81	96.07	19.43
28	97.83	14.56	97.29	16.22	96.70	17.86	96.05	19.48
30	97.82	14.62	97.28	16.28	96.68	17.92	96.03	19.54
32	97.80	14.67	97.26	16.33	96.66	17.97	96.00	19.59
34	97.78	14.73	97.24	16.39	96.64	18.03	95.98	19.64
36	97.76	14.79	97.22	16.44	96.62	18.08	95.96	19.70
38	97.75	14.84	97.20	16.50	96.60	18.14	95.93	19.75
40	97.73	14.90	97.18	16.55	96.57	18.19	95.91	19.80
42	97.71	14.95	97.16	16.61	96.55	18.24	95.89	19.86
44	97.69	15.01	97.14	16.66	96.53	18.30	95.86	19.91
46	97.68	15.06	97.12	16.72	96.51	18.35	95.84	19.96
48	97.66	15.12	97.10	16.77	96.49	18.41	95.82	20.02
50	97.64	15.17	97.08	16.83	96.47	18.46	95.79	20.07
52	97.62	15.23	97.06	16.88	96.45	18.51	95.77	20.12
54	97.61	15.28	97.04	16.94	96.42	18.57	95.75	20.18
56	97.59	15.34	97.02	16.99	96.40	18.62	95.72	20.23
58	97.57	15.40	97.00	17.05	96.38	18.68	95.70	20.28
60	97.55	15.45	96.98	17.10	96.36	18.73	95.68	20.34
C = .75	.74	.11	.74	.12	.74	.14	.73	.15
C = 1.00	.99	.15	.99	.17	.98	.18	.98	.20
C = 1.25	1.24	.18	1.23	.21	1.23	.23	1.22	.25

TABLE XXIV.—STADIA REDUCTIONS

Minutes	12°		13°		14°		15°	
	Hor. Dist.	Diff. Elev.	Hor. Dist.	Diff. Elev.	Hor. Dist.	Diff. Elev.	Hor. Dist.	Diff. Elev.
0	95.68	20.34	94.94	21.92	94.15	23.47	93.30	25.00
2	95.65	20.39	94.91	21.97	94.12	23.52	93.27	25.05
4	95.63	20.44	94.89	22.02	94.09	23.58	93.24	25.10
6	95.61	20.50	94.86	22.08	94.07	23.63	93.21	25.15
8	95.58	20.55	94.84	22.13	94.04	23.68	93.18	25.20
10	95.56	20.60	94.81	22.18	94.01	23.73	93.16	25.25
12	95.53	20.66	94.79	22.23	93.98	23.78	93.13	25.30
14	95.51	20.71	94.76	22.28	93.95	23.83	93.10	25.35
16	95.49	20.76	94.73	22.34	93.93	23.88	93.07	25.40
18	95.46	20.81	94.71	22.39	93.90	23.93	93.04	25.45
20	95.44	20.87	94.68	22.44	93.87	23.99	93.01	25.50
22	95.41	20.92	94.66	22.49	93.84	24.04	92.98	25.55
24	95.39	20.97	94.63	22.54	93.82	24.09	92.95	25.60
26	95.36	21.03	94.60	22.60	93.79	24.14	92.92	25.65
28	95.34	21.08	94.58	22.65	93.76	24.19	92.89	25.70
30	95.32	21.13	94.55	22.70	93.73	24.24	92.86	25.75
32	95.29	21.18	94.52	22.75	93.70	24.29	92.83	25.80
34	95.27	21.24	94.50	22.80	93.67	24.34	92.80	25.85
36	95.24	21.29	94.47	22.85	93.65	24.39	92.77	25.90
38	95.22	21.34	94.44	22.91	93.62	24.44	92.74	25.95
40	95.19	21.39	94.42	22.96	93.59	24.49	92.71	26.00
42	95.17	21.45	94.39	23.01	93.56	24.55	92.68	26.05
44	95.14	21.50	94.36	23.06	93.53	24.60	92.65	26.10
46	95.12	21.55	94.34	23.11	93.50	24.65	92.62	26.15
48	95.09	21.60	94.31	23.16	93.47	24.70	92.59	26.20
50	95.07	21.66	94.28	23.22	93.45	24.75	92.56	26.25
52	95.04	21.71	94.26	23.27	93.42	24.80	92.53	26.30
54	95.02	21.76	94.23	23.32	93.39	24.85	92.49	26.35
56	94.99	21.81	94.20	23.37	93.36	24.90	92.46	26.40
58	94.97	21.87	94.17	23.42	93.33	24.95	92.43	26.45
60	94.94	21.92	94.15	23.47	93.30	25.00	92.40	26.50
C = .75	.73	.16	.73	.18	.73	.19	.72	.20
C = 1.00	.98	.22	.97	.23	.97	.25	.96	.27
C = 1.25	1.22	.27	1.22	.29	1.21	.31	1.20	.33

TABLE XXIV.—STADIA REDUCTIONS

Minutes	16° Hor. Dist.	16° Diff. Elev.	17° Hor. Dist.	17° Diff. Elev.	18° Hor. Dist.	18° Diff. Elev.	19° Hor. Dist.	19° Diff. Elev.
0	92.40	26.50	91.45	27.96	90.45	29.39	89.40	30.78
2	92.37	26.55	91.42	28.01	90.42	29.44	89.36	30.83
4	92.34	26.59	91.39	28.06	90.38	29.48	89.33	30.87
6	92.31	26.64	91.35	28.10	90.35	29.53	89.29	30.92
8	92.28	26.69	91.32	28.15	90.31	29.58	89.26	30.97
10	92.25	26.74	91.29	28.20	90.28	29.62	89.22	31.01
12	92.22	26.79	91.26	28.25	90.24	29.67	89.18	31.06
14	92.19	26.84	91.22	28.30	90.21	29.72	89.15	31.10
16	92.15	26.89	91.19	28.34	90.18	29.76	89.11	31.15
18	92.12	26.94	91.16	28.39	90.14	29.81	89.08	31.19
20	92.09	26.99	91.12	28.44	90.11	29.86	89.04	31.24
22	92.06	27.04	91.09	28.49	90.07	29.90	89.00	31.28
24	92.03	27.09	91.06	28.54	90.04	29.95	88.97	31.33
26	92.00	27.13	91.02	28.58	90.00	30.00	88.93	31.38
28	91.97	27.18	90.99	28.63	89.97	30.04	88.89	31.42
30	91.93	27.23	90.96	28.68	89.93	30.09	88.86	31.47
32	91.90	27.28	90.92	28.73	89.90	30.14	88.82	31.51
34	91.87	27.33	90.89	28.77	89.86	30.18	88.78	31.56
36	91.84	27.38	90.86	28.82	89.83	30.23	88.75	31.60
38	91.81	27.43	90.82	28.87	89.79	30.28	88.71	31.65
40	91.77	27.48	90.79	28.92	89.76	30.32	88.67	31.69
42	91.74	27.52	90.76	28.96	89.72	30.37	88.64	31.74
44	91.71	27.57	90.72	29.01	89.69	30.41	88.60	31.78
46	91.68	27.62	90.69	29.06	89.65	30.46	88.56	31.83
48	91.65	27.67	90.66	29.11	89.61	30.51	88.53	31.87
50	91.61	27.72	90.62	29.15	89.58	30.55	88.49	31.92
52	91.58	27.77	90.59	29.20	89.54	30.60	88.45	31.96
54	91.55	27.81	90.55	29.25	89.51	30.65	88.41	32.01
56	91.52	27.86	90.52	29.30	89.47	30.69	88.38	32.05
58	91.48	27.91	90.49	29.34	89.44	30.74	88.34	32.09
60	91.45	27.96	90.45	29.39	89.40	30.78	88.30	32.14
C = .75	.72	.21	.72	.23	.71	.24	.71	.25
C = 1.00	.96	.28	.95	.30	.95	.32	.94	.33
C = 1.25	1.20	.36	1.19	.38	1.19	.40	1.18	.42

TABLE XXIV.—STADIA REDUCTIONS

Minutes	20°		21°		22°		23°	
	Hor. Dist.	Diff. Elev.	Hor. Dist.	Diff. Elev.	Hor. Dist.	Diff. Elev.	Hor. Dist.	Diff. Elev.
0	88.30	32.14	87.16	33.46	85.97	34.73	84.73	35.97
2	88.26	32.18	87.12	33.50	85.93	34.77	84.69	36.01
4	88.23	32.23	87.08	33.54	85.89	34.82	84.65	36.05
6	88.19	32.27	87.04	33.59	85.85	34.86	84.61	36.09
8	88.15	32.32	87.00	33.63	85.80	34.90	84.57	36.13
10	88.11	32.36	86.96	33.67	85.76	34.94	84.52	36.17
12	88.08	32.41	86.92	33.72	85.72	34.98	84.48	36.21
14	88.04	32.45	86.88	33.76	85.68	35.02	84.44	36.25
16	88.00	32.49	86.84	33.80	85.64	35.07	84.40	36.29
18	87.96	32.54	86.80	33.84	85.60	35.11	84.35	36.33
20	87.93	32.58	86.77	33.89	85.56	35.15	84.31	36.37
22	87.89	32.63	86.73	33.93	85.52	35.19	84.27	36.41
24	87.85	32.67	86.69	33.97	85.48	35.23	84.23	36.45
26	87.81	32.72	86.65	34.01	85.44	35.27	84.18	36.49
28	87.77	32.76	86.61	34.06	85.40	35.31	84.14	36.53
30	87.74	32.80	86.57	34.10	85.36	35.36	84.10	36.57
32	87.70	32.85	86.53	34.14	85.31	35.40	84.06	36.61
34	87.66	32.89	86.49	34.18	85.27	35.44	84.01	36.65
36	87.62	32.93	86.45	34.23	85.23	35.48	83.97	36.69
38	87.58	32.98	86.41	34.27	85.19	35.52	83.93	36.73
40	87.54	33.02	86.37	34.31	85.15	35.56	83.89	36.77
42	87.51	33.07	86.33	34.35	85.11	35.60	83.84	36.80
44	87.47	33.11	86.29	34.40	85.07	35.64	83.80	36.84
46	87.43	33.15	86.25	34.44	85.02	35.68	83.76	36.88
48	87.39	33.20	86.21	34.48	84.98	35.72	83.72	36.92
50	87.35	33.24	86.17	34.52	84.94	35.76	83.67	36.96
52	87.31	33.28	86.13	34.57	84.90	35.80	83.63	37.00
54	87.27	33.33	86.09	34.61	84.86	35.85	83.59	37.04
56	87.24	33.37	86.05	34.65	84.82	35.89	83.54	37.08
58	87.20	33.41	86.01	34.69	84.77	35.93	83.50	37.12
60	87.16	33.46	85.97	34.73	84.73	35.97	83.46	37.16
C = .75	.70	.26	.70	.27	.69	.29	.69	.30
C = 1.00	.94	.35	.93	.37	.92	.38	.92	.40
C = 1.25	1.17	.44	1.16	.46	1.15	.48	1.15	.50

TABLE XXIV.—STADIA REDUCTIONS

Minutes	24°		25°		26°		27°	
	Hor. Dist.	Diff. Elev.	Hor. Dist.	Diff. Elev.	Hor. Dist.	Diff. Elev.	Hor. Dist.	Diff. Elev.
0	83.46	37.16	82.14	38.30	80.78	39.40	79.39	40.45
2	83.41	37.20	82.09	38.34	80.74	39.44	79.34	40.49
4	83.37	37.23	82.05	38.38	80.69	39.47	79.30	40.52
6	83.33	37.27	82.01	38.41	80.65	39.51	79.25	40.55
8	83.28	37.31	81.96	38.45	80.60	39.54	79.20	40.59
10	83.24	37.35	81.92	38.49	80.55	39.58	79.15	40.62
12	83.20	37.39	81.87	38.53	80.51	39.61	79.11	40.66
14	83.15	37.43	81.83	38.56	80.46	39.65	79.06	40.69
16	83.11	37.47	81.78	38.60	80.41	39.69	79.01	40.72
18	83.07	37.51	81.74	38.64	80.37	39.72	78.96	40.76
20	83.02	37.54	81.69	38.67	80.32	39.76	78.92	40.79
22	82.98	37.58	81.65	38.71	80.28	39.79	78.87	40.82
24	82.93	37.62	81.60	38.75	80.23	39.83	78.82	40.86
26	82.89	37.66	81.56	38.78	80.18	39.86	78.77	40.89
28	82.85	37.70	81.51	38.82	80.14	39.90	78.73	40.92
30	82.80	37.74	81.47	38.86	80.09	39.93	78.68	40.96
32	82.76	37.77	81.42	38.89	80.04	39.97	78.63	40.99
34	82.72	37.81	81.38	38.93	80.00	40.00	78.58	41.02
36	82.67	37.85	81.33	38.97	79.95	40.04	78.54	41.06
38	82.63	37.89	81.28	39.00	79.90	40.07	78.49	41.09
40	82.58	37.93	81.24	39.04	79.86	40.11	78.44	41.12
42	82.54	37.96	81.19	39.08	79.81	40.14	78.39	41.16
44	82.49	38.00	81.15	39.11	79.76	40.18	78.34	41.19
46	82.45	38.04	81.10	39.15	79.72	40.21	78.30	41.22
48	82.41	38.08	81.06	39.18	79.67	40.24	78.25	41.26
50	82.36	38.11	81.01	39.22	79.62	40.28	78.20	41.29
52	82.32	38.15	80.97	39.26	79.58	40.31	78.15	41.32
54	82.27	38.19	80.92	39.29	79.53	40.35	78.10	41.35
56	82.23	38.23	80.87	39.33	79.48	40.38	78.06	41.39
58	82.18	38.26	80.83	39.36	79.44	40.42	78.01	41.42
60	82.14	38.30	80.78	39.40	79.39	40.45	77.96	41.45
C = .75	.68	.31	.68	.32	.67	.33	.67	.35
C = 1.00	.91	.41	.90	.43	.89	.45	.89	.46
C = 1.25	1.14	.52	1.13	.54	1.12	.56	1.11	.58

TABLE XXIV.—STADIA REDUCTIONS

Minutes	28°		29°		30°	
	Hor. Dist.	Diff. Elev.	Hor. Dist.	Diff. Elev.	Hor. Dist.	Diff. Elev.
0	77.96	41.45	76.50	42.40	75.00	43.30
2	77.91	41.48	76.45	42.43	74.95	43.33
4	77.86	41.52	76.40	42.46	74.90	43.36
6	77.81	41.55	76.35	42.49	74.85	43.39
8	77.77	41.58	76.30	42.53	74.80	43.42
10	77.72	41.61	76.25	42.56	74.75	43.45
12	77.67	41.65	76.20	42.59	74.70	43.47
14	77.62	41.68	76.15	42.62	74.65	43.50
16	77.57	41.71	76.10	42.65	74.60	43.53
18	77.52	41.74	76.05	42.68	74.55	43.56
20	77.48	41.77	76.00	42.71	74.49	43.59
22	77.42	41.81	75.95	42.74	74.44	43.62
24	77.38	41.84	75.90	42.77	74.39	43.65
26	77.33	41.87	75.85	42.80	74.34	43.67
28	77.28	41.90	75.80	42.83	74.29	43.70
30	77.23	41.93	75.75	42.86	74.24	43.73
32	77.18	41.97	75.70	42.89	74.19	43.76
34	77.13	42.00	75.65	42.92	74.14	43.79
36	77.09	42.03	75.60	42.95	74.09	43.82
38	77.04	42.06	75.55	42.98	74.04	43.84
40	76.99	42.09	75.50	43.01	73.99	43.87
42	76.94	42.12	75.45	43.04	73.93	43.90
44	76.89	42.15	75.40	43.07	73.88	43.93
46	76.84	42.19	75.35	43.10	73.83	43.95
48	76.79	42.22	75.30	43.13	73.78	43.98
50	76.74	42.25	75.25	43.16	73.73	44.01
52	76.69	42.28	75.20	43.18	73.68	44.04
54	76.64	42.31	75.15	43.21	73.63	44.07
56	76.59	42.34	75.10	43.24	73.58	44.09
58	76.55	42.37	75.05	43.27	73.52	44.12
60	76.50	42.40	75.00	43.30	73.47	44.15
C = .75	.66	.36	.65	.37	.65	.38
C = 1.00	.88	.48	.87	.49	.86	.51
C = 1.25	1.10	.60	1.09	.62	1.08	.63

TABLE XXV.—TURNOUT AND CROSSOVER DATA

American Railway Engineering Association

TURNOUT AND CROSSOVER DATA FOR STRAIGHT SPLIT SWITCHES

PLAN NO. 910-41

Adopted March, 1941. Supersedes Plan No. 900, Revised March, 1934.

	Properties of Switches			Closure Distance		Lead Curve		Gage Line Offsets							
Col. (1)	Col. (2)	Col. (3)	Col. (4)	Col. (5)	Col. (6)	Col. (7)	Col. (8)	Col. (9)	Col. (10)	Col. (11)	Col. (12)	Col. (13)	Col. (14)	Col. (15)	Col. (16)
Frog Number	Length of Switch Rail	Switch Angle	Actual Lead	Straight Closure Rail	Curved Closure Rail	Radius of Center Line	Degree of Curve							Tangent adjacent to Switch Rail	Tangent adjacent to toe of Frog
	Ft In	° ′ ″	Ft In	Ft In	Ft In	Feet	° ′ ″	Ft In	Ft In	Ft In	Inches	Inches	Ft In	Feet	Feet
5	11-0	2-39-34	42-6 1/2	28-0	28-4	177.80	32-39-56	18-0	25-0	32-0	11 13/16	20 5/8	2-8 7/8	0.00	0.78
6	11-0	2-39-34	47-6	32-9	33-0	258.57	22-17-58	19-2 1/4	27-4 1/2	35-6 3/4	12 3/8	21 5/8	2-10	0.00	1.75
7	16-6	1-46-22	62-1	40-10 1/2	41-1 1/4	365.59	15-43-16	26-2 1/4	35-10 1/2	45-6 3/4	11 3/8	19 9/16	2-6 7/8	0.01	0.00
8	16-6	1-46-22	68-0	46-5	46-7 1/2	487.28	11-46-44	27-7 1/4	38-8 1/2	49-9 3/4	11 7/8	20 9/16	2-8 5/16	0.64	0.00
9	16-6	1-46-22	72-3 1/2	49-5	49-7 1/4	615.12	9-19-30	28-10 1/4	41-2 1/2	53-6 3/4	12 5/16	21 3/8	2-9 7/16	0.00	0.17
10	16-6	1-46-22	78-9	55-10	56-0	779.39	7-21-24	29-11 3/4	43-5 1/2	56-11 1/4	12 1/4	21	2-8 5/8	2.08	0.00
11	22-0	1-19-46	91-10 1/4	62-10 1/4	63-0	927.27	6-10-56	37-8 1/2	53-5	69-1 1/2	12 1/4	21 3/8	2-9 3/4	0.00	0.13
12	22-0	1-19-46	96-8	66-10 1/2	67-0	1104.63	5-11-20	38-8 1/2	55-5	72-1 1/2	12 7/16	21 5/8	2-9 7/8	0.00	0.50
14	22-0	1-19-46	107-0 3/4	76-5 1/4	76-6 3/4	1581.20	3-37-28	41-1 1/4	60-2 1/2	79-3 3/4	12 7/8	22 5/16	2-10 1/2	0.24	0.00
15	30-0	0-58-30	126-4 1/2	86-11 1/2	87-0 3/4	1720.77	3-19-48	51-9	73-6	95-3	12 1/8	21 1/4	2-9 3/4	1.56	0.00
16	30-0	0-58-30	131-4	91-11	92-0	2007.12	2-51-18	53-0	76-0	99-0	12 7/16	21 13/16	2-10 5/16	0.66	0.00
18	30-0	0-58-30	140-11 1/2	99-11	100-0	2578.79	2-13-20	55-0	80-0	105-0	12 3/4	22 1/8	2-10 7/16	0.57	0.00
20	30-0	0-58-30	151-11 1/2	110-11	111-0	3289.29	1-44-32	57-9	85-6	113-3	13 1/16	22 11/16	2-11 3/16	2.47	0.00

TABLE XXV.—TURNOUT AND CROSSOVER DATA

Frog Number Col.①	Frog Angle Col.⑰ ° ′ ″	Overall Length Col.⑱ Ft In	Toe Length Col.⑲ Ft In	Heel Length Col.⑳ Ft In	Toe Spread Col.㉑ Inches	Heel Spread Col.㉒ Inches	Data for Crossovers 13'-0" Track Centers Straight Track Col.㉓ Ft In	Crossover Track Col.㉔ Ft In	For change of 1'-0" in Track Centers Straight Track Col.㉕ Ft In	Crossover Track Col.㉖ Ft In
5	11-25-16	9-0	3-6½	5-5½	7 11/16	13 3/4	16-10 5/8	18-1 5/8	4-11 1/2	5-0 5/8
6	9-31-38	10-0	3-9	6-3	7	13	20-5 3/4	21-6 5/8	5-11 1/4	6-0 1/2
7	8-10-16	12-0	4-8½	7-3½	7 7/8	13	24-0 7/8	24-11 5/8	6-11 1/8	7-0 1/8
8	7-09-10	13-0	5-1	7-11	7 5/8	12 7/8	27-7 5/8	28-4 5/8	7-11 1/8	8-0 1/8
9	6-21-35	16-0	6-4½	9-7½	8	13 3/8	31-1 5/8	31-10 1/2	8-11 1/8	9-0 5/8
10	5-43-29	16-6	6-5	10-1	7 3/4	12 5/8	34-8 3/4	35-3 5/8	9-11 1/8	10-0 1/8
11	5-12-18	18-8½	7-0	11-8½	7 5/8	13 3/8	38-2 1/2	38-9 1/2	10-11 1/4	11-0 1/8
12	4-46-19	20-4	7-9½	12-6½	7 5/8	13 1/8	41-8 3/4	42-3 1/4	11-11 1/4	12-0 1/8
14	4-05-27	23-7	8-7½	14-11½	6 5/8	13 3/8	48-9 3/4	49-2 5/8	13-11 1/8	14-0 1/8
15	3-49-06	24-4½	9-5	14-11½	7	12 1/8	52-3 7/8	52-8 1/4	14-11 1/8	15-0 1/8
16	3-34-47	26-0	9-5	16-7	7	12 1/8	55-9 5/8	56-2 1/4	15-11 3/4	16-0 1/8
18	3-10-56	29-3	11-0½	18-2½	6 7/8	12 1/4	62-9 5/8	63-2 1/8	17-11 1/8	18-0 1/8
20	2-51-51	30-10½	11-0½	19-10	6 7/8	12 1/8	69-10	70-2	19-11 1/8	20-0 1/8

NOTES

1. **TURNOUTS AND CROSSOVERS RECOMMENDED**
For main line high speed movements, No. 16 or No. 20. For main line slow speed movements, No. 12 or No. 10. For yards and sidings, to meet general conditions, No. 8.

2. The data shown are computed for turnouts out of straight standard 4′8½″ gage track. If the wheel base of the equipment used requires wider gage for the switch alinement or curvature shown, the lead and alinement of curved closure rail shall be maintained, and inside stock and curved rails shall be moved out the necessary amount. The gage of straight track through switch will then be increased and the straight closure rail shall be bent to true alinement in advance of toe of frog.

3. **FROG DESIGNS**
For short spring rail type frogs, the straight closure, and for solid manganese frogs, the straight and curved closures, shall be lengthened to conform.

4. **MODIFICATION OF ALINEMENT**
The alinement specified may be used without appreciable wear for switch points made in accordance either with Detail 4000 (thickness of point—¼″), or with Detail 5000 (thickness of point 0″).

5. For length of closure rails, see Plan Basic No. 911.

6. For bills of timber for various turnouts and crossovers see Plan Basic No. 912.

American Railway Engineering Association

LOCATION OF JOINTS FOR TURNOUTS WITH STRAIGHT SPLIT SWITCHES

PLAN NO. 911-41 Adopted March, 1941.

Supersedes in part Plans No. 901 to 908 Incl., Revised March, 1934.

NOTES

1. Type "L" turnouts are for general use, except for No. 5 and 6 turnouts.
2. Alternate Type "S" turnouts are for use with No. 5 and 6 turnouts, and where limited space requires location of joints ahead of switch nearer to switch point.
3. Insulated joints shown thus —■— on plans are located to conform to AAR Signal Section Plans No. 1634–B, 1635–B and 1637–B, approved in July, 1937, and if other rail lengths are used, the stagger of the joints must not exceed 4′ 6″.
4. Rail lengths provide for ⅜″ end posts at insulated joints.
5. For additional turnout data see Plan Basic No. 910.
6. For bills of timber for various turnouts see Plan Basic No. 912.

* Distances from stock rail joints to point of switch are 13′ 11″ on curved stock rail; 12′ 3″ on straight stock rail. These distances are reversed for left hand turnouts. (See sketch on next page.)

CLOSURE RAILS AND JOINT LOCATION FOR RIGHT HAND TURNOUT TYPE "L"

Frog Number	Length of Switch Rail	Toe Length to ½″ Pt.	Lead P.S. to ½″ Pt.	Closure Rails, Length in Feet and Inches: Straight Rail, Rail "A"	Rail "B"	Rail "C"	Curved Rail, Rail "D"	Rail "E"	Rail "F"	Turnout Rails, Length in Feet and Inches: Straight Rail, Rail "G"	Rail "H"	Rail "J"	Curved Rail, Rail "K"	Rail "M"	Rail "N"	Straight Stock Rail	Curved Stock Rail	Plus Stagger	Minus Stagger	Lap "X"	Lap "Y"
5	11′-0″	3′-6½″	42′-6½″	28′-0″			19′-6″	8′-9⅝″		15′-0″			15′-0″			30′-0″	30′-0″	1′-3¾″		10′-10 3/16″	9′-9½″
6	11′-0″	3′-9″	47′-6″	32′-9″			19′-6″	13′-5⅝″		19′-6″			15′-0″			30′-0″	30′-0″	1′-1⅞″		15′-10 9/16″	10′-3″
7	16′-6″	4′-8½″	62′-1″	27′-0″	13′-10½″		27′-0″	14′-0⅞″		27′-0″			16′-0″			39′-0″	39′-0″		1′-11⅛″	20′-6 11/16″	8′-4″
8	16′-6″	5′-1″	68′-0″	30′-0″	16′-5″		27′-0″	19′-7⅛″		30′-0″			19′-6″			39′-0″	39′-0″	1′-5 13/16″		23′-0 7/16″	11′-3″
9	16′-6″	6′-4½″	72′-3½″	30′-0″	19′-5″		27′-0″	22′-6⅞″		33′-0″			16′-0″	19′-6″		39′-0″	39′-0″		2′-0¾″	11′-4⅛″	12′-6½″
10	16′-6″	6′-5″	78′-9″	33′ 0″	22′-10″		25′-11⅝″	30′-0″		39′-0″			16′-0″	27′-0″		39′-0″	39′-0″		1′-1⅛″	10′-4″	13′-0″
11	22′-0″	7′-0″	91′-10¼″	39′-0″	23′-10¼″		39′-0″	23′-11⅝″		33′-0″			16′-6″	19′-6″		60′-0″	60′-0″	1′-10 11/16″		9′-5½″	11′-1¼″
12	22′-0″	7′-9½″	96′-8″	39′-0″	27′ 10½″		39′-0″	27′-11⅝″		33′-0″			16′-6″	19′-6″		60′-0″	60′-0″	1′-10 5/16″		14′-3 7/16″	15′-11″
14	22′-0″	8′-7½″	107′-0¾″	30′-0″	16′-5¼″	30′-0″	30′-0″	19′-6⅜″	27′-0″	39′-0″			27′-0″	19′-6″		60′-0″	60′-0″	1′-9 11/16″		14′-2 13/16″	20′-3¾″
15	30′-0″	9′-5″	126′-4½″	39′-0″	33′-0″	14′-11½″	33′-0″	24′-0⅜″	30′-0″	33′-0″	30′-0″		19′-6″	39′-0″		60′-0″	60′-0″	2′-9″		21′-6⅝″	15′-7½″
16	30′-0″	9′-5″	131′-4″	33′-0″	33′-0″	25′-11″	33′-0″	19′-11⅝″	39′-0″	33′-0″	33′-0″		33′-0″	33′-0″		60′-0″	60′-0″		3′-8 1/16″	19′-0⅛″	17′-7″
*18	30′-0″	11′-0½″	140′-11½″	39′-0″	33′-0″	27′-11″	39′-0″	33′-0″	27′-11⅝″	39′-0″	39′-0″		19′-6″	27′-0″	33′-0″	60′-0″	60′-0″		3′-3 3/16″	15′-2″	15′-2½″
20	30′-0″	11′-0½″	151′-11½″	39′-0″	39′-0″	32′-11″	39′-0″	39′-0″	32′-11⅝″	30′-0″	30′-0″	30′-0″	19′-6″	30′-0″	39′-0″	60′-0″	60′-0″		3′-3⅜″	19′-2 5/16″	14′-2½″

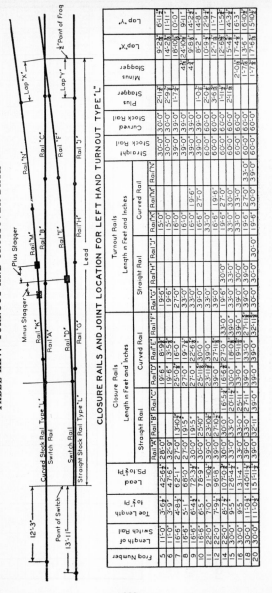

TABLE XXV.—TURNOUT AND CROSSOVER DATA

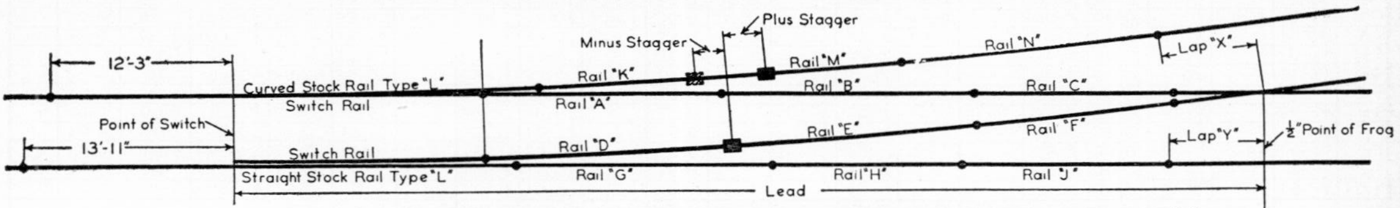

CLOSURE RAILS AND JOINT LOCATION FOR LEFT HAND TURNOUT TYPE "L"

Frog Number	Length of Switch Rail	Toe Length to ½" Pt	Lead P.S. to ½" Pt	Closure Rails, Length in Feet and Inches: Straight Rail			Curved Rail			Turnout Rails, Length in Feet and Inches: Straight Rail			Curved Rail			Straight Stock Rail	Curved Stock Rail	Plus Stagger	Minus Stagger	Lap "X"	Lap "Y"
				Rail "A"	Rail "B"	Rail "C"	Rail "D"	Rail "E"	Rail "F"	Rail "G"	Rail "H"	Rail "J"	Rail "K"	Rail "M"	Rail "N"						
5	11'-0"	3'-6$\frac{1}{2}$"	42'-6$\frac{1}{2}$"	28'-0"			19'-6"	8'-9$\frac{5}{8}$"		19'-6"			15'-0"			30'-0"	30'-0"	2'-11$\frac{3}{4}$"		9'-2$\frac{3}{16}$"	6'-11$\frac{1}{2}$"
6	11'-0"	3'-9"	47'-6"	32'-9"			19'-6"	13'-5$\frac{5}{8}$"		19'-6"			15'-0"			30'-0"	30'-0"	2'-9$\frac{7}{8}$"		14'-2$\frac{9}{16}$"	11'-11"
7	16'-6"	4'-8$\frac{1}{2}$"	62'-1"	27'-0"	13'-10$\frac{1}{2}$"		25'-0$\frac{7}{8}$"	16'-0"		27'-0"			16'-0"			39'-0"	39'-0"	1'-7$\frac{3}{4}$"		18'-10$\frac{11}{16}$"	10'-0"
8	16'-6"	5'-1"	68'-0"	27'-0"	19'-5"		27'-0"	19'-7$\frac{1}{8}$"		33'-0"			16'-0"			39'-0"	39'-0"		4$\frac{3}{16}$"	24'-10$\frac{7}{16}$"	9'-11"
9	16'-6"	6'-4$\frac{1}{2}$"	72'-3$\frac{1}{2}$"	30'-0"	19'-5"		27'-0"	22'-6$\frac{7}{8}$"		33'-0"			16'-0"	19'-6"		39'-0"	39'-0"		4$\frac{3}{4}$"	9'-8$\frac{1}{8}$"	14'-2$\frac{1}{2}$"
10	16'-6"	6'-5"	78'-9"	30'-0"	25'-10"		25'-11$\frac{5}{8}$"	30'-0"		39'-0"			16'-6"	27'-0"		39'-0"	39'-0"	1'-0$\frac{7}{8}$"		8'-2"	14'-8"
11	22'-0"	7'-0"	91'-10$\frac{1}{4}$"	39'-0"	23'-10$\frac{1}{4}$"		23'-11$\frac{5}{8}$"	39'-0"		33'-0"			33'-0"			60'-0"	60'-0"	2'-0$\frac{1}{8}$"		10'-9$\frac{1}{2}$"	12'-9$\frac{1}{4}$"
12	22'-0"	7'-9$\frac{1}{2}$"	96'-8"	39'-0"	27'-10$\frac{1}{2}$"		39'-0"	27'-11$\frac{5}{8}$"		39'-0"			16'-6"	19'-6"		60'-0"	60'-0"	3'-6$\frac{5}{16}$"		12'-7$\frac{7}{16}$"	11'-7"
14	22'-0"	8'-7$\frac{1}{2}$"	107'-0$\frac{3}{4}$"	30'-0"	30'-0"	16'-5$\frac{1}{4}$"	16'-6$\frac{3}{8}$"	27'-0"	33'-0"	19'-6"	30'-0"		19'-6"	27'-0"		60'-0"	60'-0"	1'-11$\frac{1}{2}$"		12'-6$\frac{13}{16}$"	11'-5$\frac{3}{4}$"
15	30'-0"	9'-5"	126'-4$\frac{1}{2}$"	33'-0"	33'-0"	20'-11$\frac{1}{2}$"	30'-0"	18'-0$\frac{3}{8}$"	39'-0"	33'-0"	33'-0"		33'-0"	30'-0"		60'-0"	60'-0"	2'-11$\frac{3}{16}$"		15'-4$\frac{5}{8}$"	14'-3$\frac{1}{2}$"
16	30'-0"	9'-5"	131'-4"	33'-0"	33'-0"	25'-11"	33'-0"	19'-11$\frac{5}{8}$"	39'-0"	39'-0"	30'-0"		33'-0"	33'-0"		60'-0"	60'-0"		2'-0$\frac{1}{16}$"	17'-4$\frac{1}{8}$"	16'-3"
18	30'-0"	11'-0$\frac{1}{2}$"	140'-11$\frac{1}{2}$"	39'-0"	33'-0"	27'-11"	39'-0"	33'-0"	27'-11$\frac{5}{8}$"	39'-0"	39'-0"		19'-6"	27'-0"	33'-0"	60'-0"	60'-0"		1'-7$\frac{3}{16}$"	13'-6"	16'-10$\frac{1}{2}$"
20	30'-0"	11'-0$\frac{1}{2}$"	151'-11$\frac{1}{2}$"	39'-0"	32'-11"	39'-0"	39'-0"	39'-0"	32'-11$\frac{5}{8}$"	30'-0"	30'-0"	30'-0"	19'-6"	30'-0"	39'-0"	60'-0"	60'-0"		1'-7$\frac{3}{8}$"	17'-6$\frac{5}{16}$"	15'-10$\frac{1}{2}$"

TABLE XXV.—TURNOUT AND CROSSOVER DATA

American Railway Engineering Association

LOCATION OF JOINTS FOR TURNOUTS WITH STRAIGHT SPLIT SWITCHES

PLAN NO. 911-41 Adopted March, 1941.

Supersedes in part Plans No. 901 to 908 Incl., Revised March, 1934.

NOTES

1. Type "L" turnouts are for general use, except for No. 5 and 6 turnouts.
2. Alternate Type "S" turnouts are for use with No. 5 and 6 turnouts, and where limited space requires location of joints ahead of switch nearer to switch point.
3. Insulated joints shown thus —■— on plans are located to conform to AAR Signal Section Plans No. 1634–B, 1635–B and 1637–B, approved in July, 1937, and if other rail lengths are used, the stagger of the joints must not exceed 4′ 6″.
4. Rail lengths provide for ⅛″ end posts at insulated joints.
5. For additional turnout data see Plan Basic No. 910.
6. For bills of timber for various turnouts see Plan Basic No. 912.

* Distances from stock rail joints to point of switch are 7′ 3″ on curved stock rail; 5′ 7″ on straight stock rail. These distances are reversed for left hand turnouts. (See sketch on next page.)

CLOSURE RAILS AND JOINT LOCATION FOR RIGHT HAND TURNOUT TYPE "S"

Frog Number	Length of Switch Rail	Toe Length to ½″ Pt.	Lead P.S. to ½″ Pt.	Closure Rails, Length in Feet and Inches: Straight Rail			Closure Rails: Curved Rail			Turnout Rails, Length in Feet and Inches: Straight Rail			Turnout Rails: Curved Rail			Straight Stock Rail	Curved Stock Rail	Plus Stagger	Minus Stagger	Lap "X"	Lap "Y"
				Rail "A"	Rail "B"	Rail "C"	Rail "D"	Rail "E"	Rail "F"	Rail "G"	Rail "H"	Rail "J"	Rail "K"	Rail "M"	Rail "N"						
5	11′-0″	3′-6 1/2″	42′-6 1/2″	28′-0″			13′-3 5/8″	15′-0″								30′-0″	30′-0″		11 9/16″	19′-2 3/16″	18′-1 1/2″
6	11′-0″	3′-9″	47′-6″	32′-9″			13′-5 5/8″	19′-6″		16′-0″			16′-0″			30′-0″	30′-0″		1′-3″	8′-2 9/16″	7′-1″
7	16′-6″	4′-8 1/2″	62′-1″	27′-0″	13′-10 1/2″		18′-0 7/8″	23′-0″		19′-6″			19′-6″			39′-0″	39′-0″		2′-5 3/8″	10′-4 1/16″	9′-2″
8	16′-6″	5′-1″	68′-0″	27′-0″	19′-5″		30′-0″	16′-7 1/8″		19′-6″			16′-0″			39′-0″	39′-0″	1′-8 1/8″		19′-10 7/16″	15′-1″
9	16′-6″	6′-4 1/2″	72′-3 1/2″	30′-0″	19′-5″		30′-0″	19′-6 7/8″		27′-0″			16′-0″			39′-0″	39′-0″	1′-7 1/2″		24′-2 1/2″	11′-10 1/2″
10	16′-6″	6′-5″	78′-9″	33′-0″	22′-10″		30′-0″	25′-11 5/8″		33′-0″			16′-0″	19′-6″		39′-0″	39′-0″	1′-6 3/4″		11′-2″	12′-4″
11	22′-0″	7′-0″	91′-10 1/4″	23′-10 1/4″	39′-0″		29′-11 5/8″	33′-0″		27′-0″			27′-0″			60′-0″	60′-0″	1′-0 1/2″		11′-9 1/2″	10′-5 1/4″
12	22′-0″	7′-9 1/2″	96′-8″	39′-0″	27′-10 1/2″		27′-11 5/8″	39′-0″		30′-0″			33′-0″			60′-0″	60′-0″	3′-0 1/8″		10′-7 7/16″	12′-3″
14	22′-0″	8′-7 1/2″	107′-0 3/4″	30′-0″	16′-5 1/4″	30′-0″	22′-6 3/8″	27′-0″	27′-0″	39′-0″			19′-6″	19′-6″		60′-0″	60′-0″	11 11/16″		15′-0 13/16″	13′-7 3/4″
15	30′-0″	9′-5″	126′-4 1/2″	39′-0″	33′-0″	14′-11 1/2″	39′-0″	18′-0 3/8″	30′-0″	30′-0″	27′-0″		33′-0″	27′-0″		60′-0″	60′-0″		1′-0 9/16″	13′-4 5/8″	14′-11 1/2″
16	30′-0″	9′-5″	131′-4″	33′-0″	33′-0″	25′-11″	39′-0″	19′-11 5/8″	33′-0″	30′-0″	30′-0″		19′-6″	39′-0″		60′-0″	60′-0″	3′-5″		19′-10 1/8″	16′-11″
18	30′-0″	11′-0 1/2″	140′-11 1/2″	39′-0″	27′-11″	33′-0″	39′-0″	33′-0″	27′-11 5/8″	33′-0″	39′-0″		19′-6″	33′-0″	19′-6″	60′-0″	60′-0″	3′-4 13/16″		16′-0″	14′-6 1/2″
20	30′-0″	11′-0 1/2″	151′-11 1/2″	39′-0″	39′-0″	32′-11″	39′-0″	39′-0″	32′-11 5/8″	30′-0″	30′-0″	19′-6″	19′-6″	27′-0″	39′-0″	60′-0″	60′-0″	3′-4 5/8″		13′-6 5/16″	18′-0 1/2″

TABLE XXV.—TURNOUT AND CROSSOVER DATA

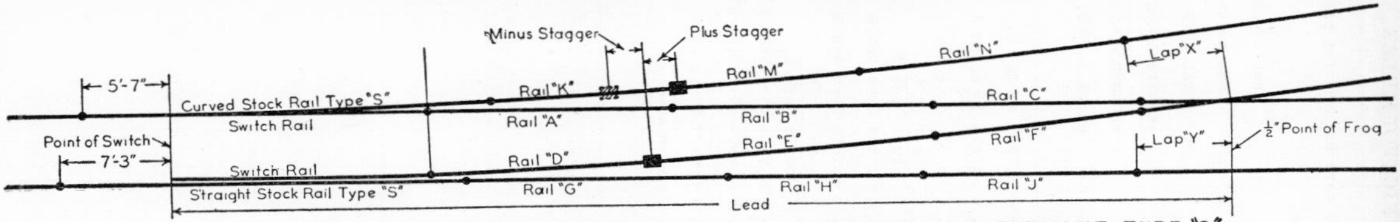

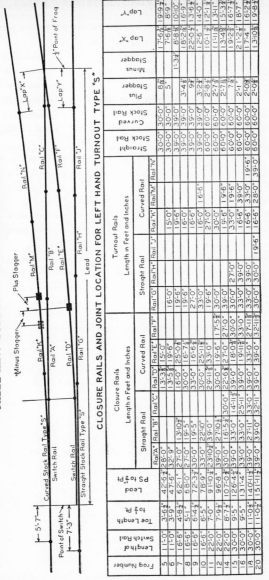

CLOSURE RAILS AND JOINT LOCATION FOR LEFT HAND TURNOUT TYPE "S"

Frog Number	Length of Switch Rail	Toe Length to ½ Pt.	Lead PS to ½" Pt	Closure Rails Length in Feet and Inches						Turnout Rails Length in Feet and Inches						Straight Stock Rail	Curved Stock Rail	Plus Stagger	Minus Stagger	Lap "X"	Lap "Y"
				Straight Rail			Curved Rail			Straight Rail			Curved Rail								
				Rail "A"	Rail "B"	Rail "C"	Rail "D"	Rail "E"	Rail "F"	Rail "G"	Rail "H"	Rail "J"	Rail "K"	Rail "M"	Rail "N"						
5	11'-0"	3'-6 1/2"	42'-6 1/2"	28'-0"			13'-3 5/8"	15'-0"								30'-0"	30'-0"	8 7/16"		17'-6 3/16"	19'-9 1/2"
6	11'-0"	3'-9"	47'-6"	32'-9"			13'-5 5/8"	19'-6"		16'-0"			15'-0"			30'-0"	30'-0"	5"		7'-6 9/16"	8'-9"
7	16'-6"	4'-8 1/2"	62'-1"	27'-0"	13'-10 1/2"		16'-0"	25'-0 7/8"		19'-6"			19'-6"			39'-0"	39'-0"		1'-3 1/4"	8'-8 11/16"	10'-10"
8	16'-6"	5'-1"	68'-0"	27'-0"	19'-5"		30'-0"	16'-7 1/8"		19'-6"			16'-0"			39'-0"	39'-0"	3'-4 1/8"		18'-2 7/16"	16'-9"
9	16'-6"	6'-4 1/2"	72'-3 1/2"	30'-0"	19'-5"		33'-0"	16'-6 7/8"		27'-0"			16'-6"			39'-0"	39'-0"	9 3/4"		22'-0 1/2"	13'-6 1/2"
10	16'-6"	6'-5"	78'-9"	33'-0"	22'-10"		30'-0"	25'-11 5/8"		33'-0"			16'-0"	16'-6"		39'-0"	39'-0"	3'-2 3/4"		12'-6"	14'-0"
11	22'-0"	7'-0"	91'-10 1/4"	23'-10 1/4"	39'-0"		29'-11 5/8"	33'-0"		19'-6"			27'-0"			60'-0"	60'-0"	2'-8 1/2"		10'-1 1/2"	12'-1 1/4"
12	22'-0"	7'-9 1/2"	96'-8"	39'-0"	27'-10 1/2"		30'-0"	19'-6"	17'-5 5/8"	30'-0"			30'-0"			60'-0"	60'-0"	2'-7 7/8"		11'-11 7/16"	13'-11"
14	22'-0"	8'-7 1/2"	107'-0 3/4"	30'-0"	16'-5 1/4"	30'-0"	22'-6 3/8"	27'-0"	27'-0"	39'-0"			19'-6"	19'-6"		60'-0"	60'-0"	2'-7 11/16"		13'-4 13/16"	15'-3 3/4"
15	30'-0"	9'-5"	126'-4 1/2"	39'-0"	33'-0"	14'-11 1/2"	39'-0"	18'-0 3/8"	30'-0"	30'-0"	27'-0"		33'-0"	19'-6"		60'-0"	60'-0"	7 7/16"		19'-2 5/8"	16'-7 1/2"
16	30'-0"	9'-5"	131'-4"	33'-0"	33'-0"	25'-11"	39'-0"	19'-11 5/8"	33'-0"	33'-0"	39'-0"		16'-6"	39'-0"		60'-0"	60'-0"	2'-1"		21'-2 1/8"	18'-7"
18	30'-0"	11'-0 1/2"	140'-11 1/2"	39'-0"	27'-11"	33'-0"	39'-0"	33'-0"	27'-11 5/8"	33'-0"	39'-0"		16'-6'	33'-0"	19'-6"	60'-0"	60'-0"	2'-0 13/16"		17'-4"	16'-2 1/2"
20	30'-0"	11'-0 1/2"	151'-11 1/2"	39'-0"	39'-0"	32'-11"	39'-0"	39'-0"	32'-11 5/8"	30'-0"	30'-0"	19'-6"	16'-6"	28'-0"	39'-0"	60'-0"	60'-0"	2'-0 5/8"		13'-10 5/16"	19'-8 1/2"

TABLE XXVI.—TRIGONOMETRIC FORMULAS

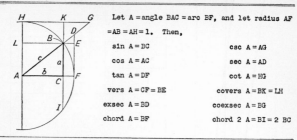

Let A = angle BAC = arc BF, and let radius AF = AB = AH = 1. Then,

sin A = BC   csc A = AG

cos A = AC   sec A = AD

tan A = DF   cot A = HG

vers A = CF = BE   covers A = BK = LH

exsec A = BD   coexsec A = BG

chord A = BF   chord 2 A = BI = 2 BC

In the right-angled triangle ABC, let AB = c, BC = a, CA = b. Then,

1. $\sin A = \dfrac{a}{c}$

2. $\cos A = \dfrac{b}{c}$

3. $\tan A = \dfrac{a}{b}$

4. $\cot A = \dfrac{b}{a}$

5. $\sec A = \dfrac{c}{b}$

6. $\csc A = \dfrac{c}{a}$

7. vers $A = 1 - \cos A = \dfrac{c-b}{c} = $ covers B

8. exsec $A = \sec A - 1 = \dfrac{c-b}{b} = $ coexsec B

9. covers $A = \dfrac{c-a}{c} = $ vers B

10. coexsec $A = \dfrac{c-a}{a} = $ exsec B

11. $a = c \sin A = b \tan A$

12. $b = c \cos A = a \cot A$

13. $c = \dfrac{a}{\sin A} = \dfrac{b}{\cos A}$

14. $a = c \cos B = b \cot B$

15. $b = c \sin B = a \tan B$

16. $c = \dfrac{a}{\cos B} = \dfrac{b}{\sin B}$

17. $a = \sqrt{c^2 - b^2} = \sqrt{(c-b)(c+b)}$

18. $b = \sqrt{c^2 - a^2} = \sqrt{(c-a)(c+a)}$

19. $c = \sqrt{a^2 + b^2}$

20. $C = 90° = A + B$

21. Area $= \frac{1}{2} ab$

TABLE XXVI.—TRIGONOMETRIC FORMULAS

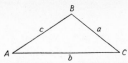

No.	Given	Sought	Formula
22	A, B, a	C, b, c	$C = 180° - (A+B)$
			$b = \dfrac{a}{\sin A} \times \sin B$
			$c = \dfrac{a}{\sin A} \times \sin (A+B) = \dfrac{a}{\sin A} \times \sin C$
		Area	$\text{Area} = \frac{1}{2}ab \sin C = \dfrac{a^2 \sin B \sin C}{2 \sin A}$
23	A, a, b	B, C, c	$\sin B = \dfrac{\sin A}{a} \times b$
			$C = 180° - (A+B)$
			$c = \dfrac{a}{\sin A} \times \sin C$
		Area	$\text{Area} = \frac{1}{2}ab \sin C$
24	C, a, b	c	$c = \sqrt{a^2 + b^2 - 2ab \cos C}$
25		$\frac{1}{2} (A+B)$	$\frac{1}{2} (A+B) = 90° - \frac{1}{2}C$
26		$\frac{1}{2} (A-B)$	$\tan \frac{1}{2} (A-B) = \dfrac{a-b}{a+b} \times \tan \frac{1}{2} (A+B)$
27		A, B	$A = \frac{1}{2}(A+B) + \frac{1}{2}(A-B)$ $B = \frac{1}{2}(A+B) - \frac{1}{2}(A-B)$
28		c	$c = (a+b) \times \dfrac{\cos \frac{1}{2}(A+B)}{\cos \frac{1}{2}(A-B)} = (a-b) \times \dfrac{\sin \frac{1}{2}(A+B)}{\sin \frac{1}{2}(A-B)}$
29		Area	$\text{Area} = \frac{1}{2}ab \sin C$
30	a, b, c	A	Let $s = \dfrac{a+b+c}{2}$
31			$\sin \frac{1}{2} A = \sqrt{\dfrac{(s-b)(s-c)}{bc}}$
			$\cos \frac{1}{2} A = \sqrt{\dfrac{s(s-a)}{bc}}$
			$\tan \frac{1}{2} A = \sqrt{\dfrac{(s-b)(s-c)}{s(s-a)}}$
32			$\sin A = \dfrac{2 \sqrt{s(s-a)(s-b)(s-c)}}{bc}$
			$\cos A = \dfrac{b^2 + c^2 - a^2}{2bc}$
33		Area	$\text{Area} = \sqrt{s(s-a)(s-b)(s-c)}$

TABLE XXVI.—TRIGONOMETRIC FORMULAS

General Formulas

34. $\sin A = 2 \sin \frac{1}{2}A \cos \frac{1}{2}A = \sqrt{1 - \cos^2 A} = \tan A \cos A$

35. $\cos A = 2 \cos^2 \frac{1}{2}A - 1 = 1 - 2 \sin^2 \frac{1}{2}A = \cos^2 \frac{1}{2}A - \sin^2 \frac{1}{2}A$

36. $\tan A = \dfrac{\sin A}{\cos A} = \dfrac{\sin 2A}{1 + \cos 2A} = \dfrac{\text{vers } 2A}{\sin 2A}$

37. $\cot A = \dfrac{\cos A}{\sin A} = \dfrac{\sin 2A}{1 - \cos 2A} = \dfrac{\sin 2A}{\text{vers } 2A}$

38. $\text{vers } A = 1 - \cos A = \sin A \tan \frac{1}{2}A = 2 \sin^2 \frac{1}{2}A$

39. $\text{exsec } A = \sec A - 1 = \tan A \tan \frac{1}{2}A = \dfrac{\text{vers } A}{\cos A}$

40. $\sin 2A = 2 \sin A \cos A$

41. $\cos 2A = 2 \cos^2 A - 1 = \cos^2 A - \sin^2 A = 1 - 2 \sin^2 A$

42. $\tan 2A = \dfrac{2 \tan A}{1 - \tan^2 A}$

43. $\cot 2A = \dfrac{\cot^2 A - 1}{2 \cot A}$

44. $\text{vers } 2A = 2 \sin^2 A = 2 \sin A \cos A \tan A$

45. $\text{exsec } 2A = \dfrac{2 \tan^2 A}{1 - \tan^2 A}$

46. $\sin (A \pm B) = \sin A \cos B \pm \sin B \cos A$

47. $\cos (A \pm B) = \cos A \cos B \mp \sin A \sin B$

48. $\sin A + \sin B = 2 \sin \frac{1}{2}(A + B) \cos \frac{1}{2}(A - B)$

49. $\sin A - \sin B = 2 \cos \frac{1}{2}(A + B) \sin \frac{1}{2}(A - B)$

50. $\cos A + \cos B = 2 \cos \frac{1}{2}(A + B) \cos \frac{1}{2}(A - B)$

51. $\cos A - \cos B = -2 \sin \frac{1}{2}(A + B) \sin \frac{1}{2}(A - B)$

52. $\tan A \pm \tan B = \dfrac{\sin (A \pm B)}{\cos A \cos B}$

TABLE XXVII.—SQUARES, CUBES, SQUARE ROOTS, CUBE ROOTS AND RECIPROCALS

No.	Squares.	Cubes.	Square Roots.	Cube Roots.	Recipro-cals.	No.
1	1	1	1.0000000	1.0000000	1.000000000	1
2	4	8	.4142136	.2599210	.500000000	2
3	9	27	.7320508	.4422496	.333333333	3
4	16	64	2.0000000	.5874011	.250000000	4
5	25	125	2.3606680	1.7099759	.200000000	5
6	36	216	.4494897	.8171206	.166666667	6
7	49	343	.6457513	.9129312	.142857143	7
8	64	512	.8284271	2.0000000	.125000000	8
9	81	729	3.0000000	.0800837	.111111111	9
10	100	1000	3.1622777	2.1544347	.100000000	10
11	121	1331	.3166248	.2239801	.090909091	11
12	144	1728	.4641016	.2894286	.083333333	12
13	169	2197	.6055513	.3513347	.076923077	13
14	196	2744	.7416574	.4101422	.142857¹	14
15	225	3375	3.8729833	2.4662121	.066666667	15
16	256	4096	4.0000000	.5198421	.062500000	16
17	289	4913	.1231056	.5712816	.058823529	17
18	324	5832	.2426407	.6207414	.055555556	18
19	361	6859	.3588989	.6684016	.052631579	19
20	400	8000	4.4721360	2.7144177	.050000000	20
21	441	9261	.5825757	.7589243	.047619048	21
22	484	10648	.6904158	.8020393	.045454545	22
23	529	12167	.7958315	.8438670	.043478261	23
24	576	13824	.8989795	.8844991	.041666667	24
25	625	15625	5.0000000	2.9240177	.040000000	25
26	676	17576	.0990195	.9624960	.038461538	26
27	729	19683	.1961524	3.0000000	.037037037	27
28	784	21952	.2915026	.0365889	.035714286	28
29	841	24389	.3851648	.0723168	.034482759	29
30	900	27000	5.4772256	3.1072325	.033333333	30
31	961	29791	.5677644	.1413806	.032258065	31
32	1024	32768	.6568542	.1748021	.031250000	32
33	1089	35937	.7445626	.2075343	.030303030	33
34	1156	39304	.8309519	.2396118	.029411765	34
35	1225	42875	5.9160798	3.2710663	.028571429	35
36	1296	46656	6.0000000	.3019272	.027777778	36
37	1369	50653	.0827625	.3322218	.027027027	37
38	1444	54872	.1644140	.3619754	.026315789	38
39	1521	59319	.2449980	.3912114	.025641026	39
40	1600	64000	6.3245553	3.4199519	.025000000	40
41	1681	68921	.4031242	.4482172	.024390244	41
42	1764	74088	.4807407	.4760266	.023809524	42
43	1849	79507	.5574385	.5033981	.023255814	43
44	1936	85184	.6332496	.5303483	.022727273	44
45	2025	91125	6.7082039	3.5568933	.022222222	45
46	2116	97336	.7823300	.5830479	.021739130	46
47	2209	103823	.8556546	.6088261	.021276600	47
48	2304	110592	.9282032	.6342411	.020833333	48
49	2401	117649	7.0000000	.6593057	.020408163	49
50	2500	125000	7.0710678	3.6840314	.020000000	50
51	2601	132651	.1414284	.7084298	.019607843	51
52	2704	140608	.2111026	.7325111	.019230769	52
53	2809	148877	.2801099	.7562858	.018867925	53
54	2916	157464	.3484692	.7797631	.018518519	54
55	3025	166375	7.4161985	3.8029525	.018181818	55
56	3136	175616	.4833148	.8258624	.017857143	56
57	3249	185193	.5498344	.8485011	.017543860	57
58	3364	195112	.6157731	.8708766	.017241379	58
59	3481	205379	.6811457	.8929965	.016949153	59

TABLE XXVII.—SQUARES, CUBES, SQUARE ROOTS,

No.	Squares.	Cubes.	Square Roots.	Cube Roots.	Reciprocals.	No.
60	3600	216000	7.7459667	3.9148676	.016666667	60
61	3721	226981	.8102497	.9364972	6393443	61
62	3844	238328	.8740079	.9578915	6129032	62
63	3969	250047	.9372539	.9790571	5873016	63
64	4096	262144	8.0000000	4.0000000	5625000	64
65	4225	274625	8.0622577	4.0207256	.015384615	65
66	4356	287496	.1240384	.0412401	5151515	66
67	4489	300763	.1853528	.0615480	4925373	67
68	4624	314432	.2462113	.0816551	4705882	68
69	4761	328509	.3066239	.1015661	4492754	69
70	4900	343000	8.3666003	4.1212853	.014285714	70
71	5041	357911	.4261498	.1408178	4084507	71
72	5184	373248	.4852814	.1601676	3888889	72
73	5329	389017	.5440037	.1793392	3698630	73
74	5476	405224	.6023253	.1983364	3513514	74
75	5625	421875	8.6602540	4.2171633	.013333333	75
76	5776	438976	.7177979	.2358236	3157895	76
77	5929	456533	.7749644	.2543210	2987013	77
78	6084	474552	.8317609	.2726586	2820513	78
79	6241	493039	.8881944	.2908404	2658228	79
80	6400	512000	8.9442719	4.3088695	.012500000	80
81	6561	531441	9.0000000	.3267487	2345679	81
82	6724	551368	.0553851	.3444815	2195122	82
83	6889	571787	.1104336	.3620707	2048193	83
84	7056	592704	.1651514	.3795191	1904762	84
85	7225	614125	9.2195445	4.3968296	.011764706	85
86	7396	636056	.2736185	.4140049	1627907	86
87	7569	658503	.3273791	.4310476	1494253	87
88	7744	681472	.3808315	.4479602	1363636	88
89	7921	704969	.4339811	.4647451	1235955	89
90	8100	729000	9.4868330	4.4814047	.011111111	90
91	8281	753571	.5393920	.4979414	0989011	91
92	8464	778688	.5916630	.5143574	0869565	92
93	8649	804357	.6436508	.5306549	0752688	93
94	8836	830584	.6953597	.5468359	0638298	94
95	9025	857375	9.7467943	4.5629026	.010526316	95
96	9216	884736	.7979590	.5788570	0416667	96
97	9409	912673	.8488578	.5947009	0309278	97
98	9604	941192	.8994949	.6104363	0204082	98
99	9801	970299	.9498744	.6260650	0101010	99
100	10000	1000000	10.0000000	4.6415888	.010000000	100
101	10201	1030301	.0498756	.6570095	.009900990	101
102	10404	1061208	.0995049	.6723287	9803922	102
103	10609	1092727	.1488916	.6875482	9708738	103
104	10816	1124864	.1980390	.7026694	9615385	104
105	11025	1157625	10.2469508	4.7176940	.009523810	105
106	11236	1191016	.2956301	.7326235	9433962	106
107	11449	1225043	.3440804	.7474594	9345794	107
108	11664	1259712	.3923048	.7622032	9259259	108
109	11881	1295029	.4403065	.7768562	9174312	109
110	12100	1331000	10.4880885	4.7914199	.009090909	110
111	12321	1367631	.5356538	.8058955	9009009	111
112	12544	1404928	.5830052	.8202845	8928571	112
113	12769	1442897	.6301458	.8345881	8849558	113
114	12996	1481544	.6770783	.8488076	8771930	114
115	13225	1520875	10.7238053	4.8629442	.008695652	115
116	13456	1560896	.7703296	.8769990	8620690	116
117	13689	1601613	.8166538	.8909732	8547009	117
118	13924	1643032	.8627805	.9048681	8474576	118
119	14161	1685159	.9087121	.9186847	8403361	119

No.	Squares.	Cubes.	Square Roots.	Cube Roots.	Recipro- cals.	No.
120	14400	1728000	10.9544512	4.9324242	.008333333	120
121	14641	1771561	11.0000000	.9460874	8264463	121
122	14884	1815848	.0453610	.9596757	8196721	122
123	15129	1860867	.0905365	.9731898	8130081	123
124	15376	1906624	.1355287	.9866310	8064516	124
125	15625	1953125	11.1803399	5.0000000	.008000000	125
126	15876	2000376	.2249722	.0132979	7936508	126
127	16129	2048383	.2694277	.0265257	7874016	127
128	16384	2097152	.3137085	.0396842	7812500	128
129	16641	2146689	.3578167	.0527743	7751938	129
130	16900	2197000	11.4017543	5.0657970	.007692308	130
131	17161	2248091	.4455231	.0787531	7633588	131
132	17424	2299968	.4891253	.0916434	7575758	132
133	17689	2352637	.5325626	.1044687	7518797	133
134	17956	2406104	.5758369	.1172299	7462687	134
135	18225	2460375	11.6189500	5.1299278	.007407407	135
136	18496	2515456	.6619038	.1425632	7352941	136
137	18769	2571353	.7046999	.1551367	7299270	137
138	19044	2628072	.7473401	.1676493	7246377	138
139	19321	2685619	.7898261	.1801015	7194245	139
140	19600	2744000	11.8321596	5.1924941	.007142857	140
141	19881	2803221	.8743421	.2048279	7092199	141
142	20164	2863288	.9163753	.2171034	7042254	142
143	20449	2924207	.9582607	.2293215	6993007	143
144	20736	2985984	12.0000000	.2414828	6944444	144
145	21025	3048625	12.0415946	5.2535879	.006896552	145
146	21316	3112136	.0830460	.2656374	6849315	146
147	21609	3176523	.1243557	.2776321	6802721	147
148	21904	3241792	.1655251	.2895725	6756757	148
149	22201	3307949	.2065556	.3014592	6711409	149
150	22500	3375000	12.2474487	5.3132928	.006666667	150
151	22801	3442951	.2882057	.3250740	6622517	151
152	23104	3511808	.3288280	.3368033	6578947	152
153	23409	3581577	.3693169	.3484812	6535948	153
154	23716	3652264	.4096736	.3601084	6493506	154
155	24025	3723875	12.4498996	5.3716854	.006451613	155
156	24336	3796416	.4899960	.3832126	6410256	156
157	24649	3869893	.5299641	.3946907	6369427	157
158	24964	3944312	.5698051	.4061202	6329114	158
159	25281	4019679	.6095202	.4175015	6289308	159
160	25600	4096000	12.6491106	5.4288352	.006250000	160
161	25921	4173281	.6885775	.4401218	6211180	161
162	26244	4251528	.7279221	.4513618	6172840	162
163	26569	4330747	.7671453	.4625556	6134969	163
164	26896	4410944	.8062485	.4737037	6097561	164
165	27225	4492125	12.8452326	5.4848066	.006060606	165
166	27556	4574296	.8840087	.4958647	6024096	166
167	27889	4657463	.9228480	.5068784	5988024	167
168	28224	4741632	.9614814	.5178484	5952381	168
169	28561	4826809	13.0000000	.5287748	5917160	169
170	28900	4913000	13.0384048	5.5396583	.005882353	170
171	29241	5000211	.0766968	.5504991	5847953	171
172	29584	5088448	.1148770	.5612978	5813953	172
173	29929	5177717	.1529464	.5720546	5780347	173
174	30276	5268024	.1909060	.5827702	5747126	174
175	30625	5359375	13.2287566	5.5934447	.005714286	175
176	30976	5451776	.2664992	.6040787	5681818	176
177	31329	5545233	.3041347	.6146724	5649718	177
178	31684	5639752	.3416641	.6252263	5617978	178
179	32041	5735339	.3790882	.6357408	5586592	179

TABLE XXVII.—SQUARES, CUBES, SQUARE ROOTS,

No.	Squares.	Cubes.	Square Roots.	Cube Roots.	Reciprocals.	No.
180	32400	5832000	13.4164079	5.6462162	.005555556	180
181	32761	5929741	.4536240	.6566528	5524862	181
182	33124	6028568	.4907376	.6670511	5494505	182
183	33489	6128487	.5277493	.6774114	5464481	183
184	33856	6229504	.5646600	.6877340	5434783	184
185	34225	6331625	13.6014705	5.6980192	.005405405	185
186	34596	6434856	.6381817	.7082675	5376344	186
187	34969	6539203	.6747943	.7184791	5347594	187
188	35344	6644672	.7113092	.7286543	5319149	188
189	35721	6751269	.7477271	.7387936	5291005	189
190	36100	6859000	13.7840488	5.7488971	.005263158	190
191	36481	6967871	.8202750	.7589652	5235602	191
192	36864	7077888	.8564065	.7689982	5208333	192
193	37249	7189057	.8924440	.7789966	5181347	193
194	37636	7301384	.9283883	.7889604	5154639	194
195	38025	7414875	13.9642400	5.7988900	.005128205	195
196	38416	7529536	14.0000000	.8087857	5102041	196
197	38809	7645373	.0356688	.8186479	5076142	197
198	39204	7762392	.0712473	.8284767	5050505	198
199	39601	7880599	.1067360	.8382725	5025126	199
200	40000	8000000	14.1421356	5.8480355	.005000000	200
201	40401	8120601	.1774469	.8577660	4975124	201
202	40804	8242408	.2126704	.8674643	4950495	202
203	41209	8365427	.2478068	.8771307	4926108	203
204	41616	8489664	.2828569	.8867653	4901961	204
205	42025	8615125	14.3178211	5.8963685	.004878049	205
206	42436	8741816	.3527001	.9059406	4854369	206
207	42849	8869743	.3874946	.9154817	4830918	207
208	43264	8998912	.4222051	.9249921	4807692	208
209	43681	9129329	.4568323	.9344721	4784689	209
210	44100	9261000	14.4913767	5.9439220	.004761905	210
211	44521	9393931	.5258390	.9533418	4739336	211
212	44944	9528128	.5602198	.9627320	4716981	212
213	45369	9663597	.5945195	.9720926	4694836	213
214	45796	9800344	.6287388	.9814240	4672897	214
215	46225	9938375	14.6628783	5.9907264	.004651163	215
216	46656	10077696	.6969385	6.0000000	4629630	216
217	47089	10218313	.7309199	.0092450	4608295	217
218	47524	10360232	.7648231	.0184617	4587156	218
219	47961	10503459	.7986486	.0276502	4566210	219
220	48400	10648000	14.8323970	6.0368107	.004545455	220
221	48841	10793861	.8660687	.0459435	4524887	221
222	49284	10941048	.8996644	.0550489	4504505	222
223	49729	11089567	.9331845	.0641270	4484305	223
224	50176	11239424	.9666295	.0731779	4464286	224
225	50625	11390625	15.0000000	6.0822007	.004444444	225
226	51076	11543176	.0332966	.0911994	4424779	226
227	51529	11697083	.0665192	.1001702	4405286	227
228	51984	11852352	.0996689	.1091147	4385965	228
229	52441	12008989	.1327460	.1180332	4366812	229
230	52900	12167000	15.1657509	6.1269257	.004347826	230
231	53361	12326391	.1986842	.1357924	4329004	231
232	53824	12487168	.2315462	.1446337	4310345	232
233	54289	12649337	.2643375	.1534495	4291845	233
234	54756	12812904	.2970585	.1622401	4273504	234
235	55225	12977875	15.3297097	6.1710058	.004255319	235
236	55696	13144256	.3622915	.1797466	4237288	236
237	56169	13312053	.3948043	.1884628	4219409	237
238	56644	13481272	.4272486	.1971544	4201681	238
239	57121	13651919	.4596248	.2058218	4184100	239

No.	Squares.	Cubes.	Square Roots.	Cube Roots.	Reciprocals.	No.
240	57600	13824000	15.4919334	6.2144650	.004166667	240
241	58081	13997521	.5241747	.2230843	4149378	241
242	58564	14172488	.5563492	.2316797	4132231	242
243	59049	14348907	.5884573	.2402515	4115226	243
244	59536	14526784	.6204994	.2487998	4098361	244
245	60025	14706125	15.6524758	6.2573248	.004081633	245
246	60516	14886936	.6843871	.2658266	4065041	246
247	61009	15069223	.7162336	.2743054	4048583	247
248	61504	15252992	.7480157	.2827613	4032258	248
249	62001	15438249	.7797338	.2911946	4016064	249
250	62500	15625000	15.8113883	6.2996053	.004000000	250
251	63001	15813251	.8429795	.3079995	3984064	251
252	63504	16003008	.8745079	.3163596	3968254	252
253	64009	16194277	.9059737	.3247035	3952569	253
254	64516	16387064	.9373775	.3330256	3937008	254
255	65025	16581375	15.9687194	6.3413257	.003921569	255
256	65536	16777216	16.0000000	.3496042	3906250	256
257	66049	16974593	.0312195	.3578611	3891051	257
258	66564	17173512	.0623784	.3660968	3875969	258
259	67081	17373979	.0934769	.3743111	3861004	259
260	67600	17576000	16.1245155	6.3825043	.003846154	260
261	68121	17779581	.1554944	.3906765	3831418	261
262	68644	17984728	.1864141	.3988279	3816794	262
263	69169	18191447	.2172747	.4069585	3802281	263
264	69696	18399744	.2480768	.4150687	3787879	264
265	70225	18609625	16.2788206	6.4231583	.003773585	265
266	70756	18821096	.3095064	.4312276	3759398	266
267	71289	19034163	.3401346	.4392767	3745318	267
268	71824	19248832	.3707055	.4473057	3731343	268
269	72361	19465109	.4012195	.4553148	3717472	269
270	72900	19683000	16.4316767	6.4633041	.003703704	270
271	73441	19902511	.4620777	.4712736	3690037	271
272	73984	20123648	.4924225	.4792236	3676471	272
273	74529	20346417	.5227116	.4871541	3663004	273
274	75076	20570824	.5529454	.4950653	3649635	274
275	75625	20796875	16.5831240	6.5029572	.003636364	275
276	76176	21024576	.6132477	.5108300	3623188	276
277	76729	21253933	.6433170	.5186839	3610108	277
278	77284	21484952	.6733320	.5265189	3597122	278
279	77841	21717639	.7032931	.5343351	3584229	279
280	78400	21952000	16.7332005	6.5421326	.003571429	280
281	78961	22188041	.7630546	.5499116	3558719	281
282	79524	22425768	.7928556	.5576722	3546099	282
283	80089	22665187	.8226038	.5654144	3533569	283
284	80656	22906304	.8522995	.5731385	3521127	284
285	81225	23149125	16.8819430	6.5808443	.003508772	285
286	81796	23393656	.9115345	.5885323	3496503	286
287	82369	23639903	.9410743	.5962023	3484321	287
288	82944	23887872	.9705627	.6038545	3472222	288
289	83521	24137569	17.0000000	.6114890	3460208	289
290	84100	24389000	17.0293864	6.6191060	.003448276	290
291	84681	24642171	.0587221	.6267054	3436426	291
292	85264	24897088	.0880075	.6342874	3424658	292
293	85849	25153757	.1172428	.6418522	3412969	293
294	86436	25412184	.1464282	.6493998	3401361	294
295	87025	25672375	17.1755640	6.6569302	.003389831	295
296	87616	25934336	.2046505	.6644437	3378378	296
297	88209	26198073	.2336879	.6719403	3367003	297
298	88804	26463592	.2626765	.6794200	3355705	298
299	89401	26730899	.2916165	.6868831	3344482	299

TABLE XXVII.—SQUARES, CUBES, SQUARE ROOTS,

No.	Squares.	Cubes.	Square Roots.	Cube Roots.	Reciprocals.	No.
300	90000	27000000	17.3205081	6.6943295	.003333333	300
301	90601	27270901	.3493516	.7017593	3322259	301
302	91204	27543608	.3781472	.7091729	3311258	302
303	91809	27818127	.4068952	.7165700	3300330	303
304	92416	28094464	.4355958	.7239508	3289474	304
305	93025	28372625	17.4642492	6.7313155	.003278689	305
306	93636	28652616	.4928557	.7386641	3267974	306
307	94249	28934443	.5214155	.7459967	3257329	307
308	94864	29218112	.5499288	.7533134	3246753	308
309	95481	29503629	.5783958	.7606143	3236246	309
310	96100	29791000	17.6068169	6.7678995	.003225806	310
311	96721	30080231	.6351921	.7751690	3215434	311
312	97344	30371328	.6635217	.7824229	3205128	312
313	97969	30664297	.6918060	.7896613	3194888	313
314	98596	30959144	.7200451	.7968844	3184713	314
315	99225	31255875	17.7482393	6.8040921	.003174603	315
316	99856	31554496	.7763888	.8112847	3164557	316
317	100489	31855013	.8044938	.8184620	3154574	317
318	101124	32157432	.8325545	.8256242	3144654	318
319	101761	32461759	.8605711	.8327714	3134796	319
320	102400	32768000	17.8885438	6.8399037	.003125000	320
321	103041	33076161	.9164729	.8470213	3115265	321
322	103684	33386248	.9443584	.8541240	3105590	322
323	104329	33698267	.9722008	.8612120	3095975	323
324	104976	34012224	18.0000000	.8682855	3086420	324
325	105625	34328125	18.0277564	6.8753443	.003076923	325
326	106276	34645976	.0554701	.8823888	3067485	326
327	106929	34965783	.0831413	.8894188	3058104	327
328	107584	35287552	.1107703	.8964345	3048780	328
329	108241	35611289	.1383571	.9034359	3039514	329
330	108900	35937000	18.1659021	6.9104232	.003030303	330
331	109561	36264691	.1934054	.9173964	3021148	331
332	110224	36594368	.2208672	.9243556	3012048	332
333	110889	36926037	.2482876	.9313008	3003003	333
334	111556	37259704	.2756669	.9382321	2994012	334
335	112225	37595375	18.3030052	6.9451496	.002985075	335
336	112896	37933056	.3303028	.9520533	2976190	336
337	113569	38272753	.3575598	.9589434	2967359	337
338	114244	38614472	.3847763	.9658198	2958580	338
339	114921	38958219	.4119526	.9726826	2949853	339
340	115600	39304000	18.4390889	6.9795321	.002941176	340
341	116281	39651821	.4661853	.9863681	2932551	341
342	116964	40001688	.4932420	.9931906	2923977	342
343	117649	40353607	.5202592	7.0000000	2915452	343
344	118336	40707584	.5472370	.0067962	2906977	344
345	119025	41063625	18.5741756	7.0135791	.002898551	345
346	119716	41421736	.6010752	.0203490	2890173	346
347	120409	41781923	.6279360	.0271058	2881844	347
348	121104	42144192	.6547581	.0338497	2873563	348
349	121801	42508549	.6815417	.0405806	2865330	349
350	122500	42875000	18.7082869	7.0472987	.002857143	350
351	123201	43243551	.7349940	.0540041	2849003	351
352	123904	43614208	.7616630	.0606967	2840909	352
353	124609	43986977	.7882942	.0673767	2832861	353
354	125316	44361864	.8148877	.0740440	2824859	354
355	126025	44738875	18.8414437	7.0806988	.002816901	355
356	126736	45118016	.8679623	.0873411	2808989	356
357	127449	45499293	.8944436	.0939709	2801120	357
358	128164	45882712	.9208879	.1005885	2793296	358
359	128881	46268279	.9472953	.1071937	2785515	359

No.	Squares.	Cubes.	Square Roots.	Cube Roots.	Reciprocals.	No.
360	129600	46656000	18.9736660	7.1137866	.002777778	360
361	130321	47045881	19.0000000	.1203674	2770083	361
362	131044	47437928	.0262976	.1269360	2762431	362
363	131769	47832147	.0525589	.1334925	2754821	363
364	132496	48228544	.0787840	.1400370	2747253	364
365	133225	48627125	19.1049732	7.1465695	.002739726	365
366	133956	49027896	.1311265	.1530901	2732240	366
367	134689	49430863	.1572441	.1595988	2724796	367
368	135424	49836032	.1833261	.1660957	2717391	368
369	136161	50243409	.2093727	.1725809	2710027	369
370	136900	50653000	19.2353841	7.1790544	.002702703	370
371	137641	51064811	.2613603	.1855162	2695418	371
372	138384	51478848	.2873015	.1919663	2688172	372
373	139129	51895117	.3132079	.1984050	2680965	373
374	139876	52313624	.3390796	.2048322	2673797	374
375	140625	52734375	19.3649167	7.2112479	.002666667	375
376	141376	53157376	.3907194	.2176522	2659574	376
377	142129	53582633	.4164878	.2240450	2652520	377
378	142884	54010152	.4422221	.2304268	2645503	378
379	143641	54439939	.4679223	.2367972	2638522	379
380	144400	54872000	19.4935887	7.2431565	.002631579	380
381	145161	55306341	.5192213	.2495045	2624672	381
382	145924	55742968	.5448203	.2558415	2617801	382
383	146689	56181887	.5703858	.2621675	2610966	383
384	147456	56623104	.5959179	.2684824	2604167	384
385	148225	57066625	19.6214169	7.2747864	.002597403	385
386	148996	57512456	.6468827	.2810794	2590674	386
387	149769	57960603	.6723156	.2873617	2583979	387
388	150544	58411072	.6977156	.2936330	2577320	388
389	151321	58863869	.7230829	.2998936	2570694	389
390	152100	59319000	19.7484177	7.3061436	.002564103	390
391	152881	59776471	.7737199	.3123828	2557545	391
392	153664	60236288	.7989899	.3186114	2551020	392
393	154449	60698457	.8242276	.3248295	2544529	393
394	155236	61162984·	.8494332	.3310369	2538071	394
395	156025	61629875	19.8746069	7.3372339	.002531646	395
396	156816	62099136	.8997487	.3434205	2525253	396
397	157609	62570773	.9248588	.3495966	2518892	397
398	158404	63044792	.9499373	.3557624	2512563	398
399	159201	63521199	.9749844	.3619178	2506266	399
400	160000	64000000	20.0000000	7.3680630	.002500000	400
401	160801	64481201	.0249844	.3741979	2493766	401
402	161604	64964808	.0499377	.3803227	2487562	402
403	162409	65450827	.0748599	.3864373	2481390	403
404	163216	65939264	.0997512	.3925418	2475248	404
405	164025	66430125	20.1246118	7.3986363	.002469136	405
406	164836	66923416	.1494417	.4047206	2463054	406
407	165649	67419143	.1742410	.4107950	2457002	407
408	166464	67917312	.1990099	.4168595	2450980	408
409	167281	68417929	.2237484	.4229142	2444988	409
410	168100	68921000	20.2484567	7.4289589	.002439024	410
411	168921	69426531	.2731349	.4349938	2433090	411
412	169744	69934528	.2977831	.4410189	2427184	412
413	170569	70444997	.3224014	.4470342	2421308	413
414	171396	70957944	.3469899	.4530399	2415459	414
415	172225	71473375	20.3715488	7.4590359	.002409639	415
416	173056	71991296	.3960781	.4650223	2403846	416
417	173889	72511713	.4205779	.4709991	2398082	417
418	174724	73034632	.4450483	.4769664	2392344	418
419	175561	73560059	.4694895	.4829242	2386635	419

TABLE XXVII.—SQUARES, CUBES, SQUARE ROOTS,

No.	Squares.	Cubes.	Square Roots.	Cube Roots.	Reciprocals.	No.
420	176400	74088000	20.4939015	7.4888724	.002380952	420
421	177241	74618461	.5182845	.4948113	2375297	421
422	178084	75151448	.5426386	.5007406	2369668	422
423	178929	75686967	.5669638	.5066607	2364066	423
424	179776	76225024	.5912603	.5125715	2358491	424
425	180625	76765625	20.6155281	7.5184730	.002352941	425
426	181476	77308776	.6397674	.5243652	2347418	426
427	182329	77854483	.6639783	.5302482	2341920	427
428	183184	78402752	.6881609	.5361221	2336449	428
429	184041	78953589	.7123152	.5419867	2331002	429
430	184900	79507000	20.7364414	7.5478423	.002325581	430
431	185761	80062991	.7605395	.5536888	2320186	431
432	186624	80621568	.7846097	.5595263	2314815	432
433	187489	81182737	.8086520	.5653548	2309469	433
434	188356	81746504	.8326667	.5711743	2304147	434
435	189225	82312875	20.8566536	7.5769849	.002298851	435
436	190096	82881856	.8806130	.5827865	2293578	436
437	190969	83453453	.9045450	.5885793	2288330	437
438	191844	84027672	.9284495	.5943633	2283105	438
439	192721	84604519	.9523268	.6001385	2277904	439
440	193600	85184000	20.9761770	7.6059049	.002272727	440
441	194481	85766121	21.0000000	.6116626	2267574	441
442	195364	86350888	.0237960	.6174116	2262443	442
443	196249	86938307	.0475652	.6231519	2257336	443
444	197136	87528384	.0713075	.6288837	2252252	444
445	198025	88121125	21.0950231	7.6346067	.002247191	445
446	198916	88716536	.1187121	.6403213	2242152	446
447	199809	89314623	.1423745	.6460272	2237136	447
448	200704	89915392	.1660105	.6517247	2232143	448
449	201601	90518849	.1896201	.6574138	2227171	449
450	202500	91125000	21.2132034	7.6630943	.002222222	450
451	203401	91733851	.2367606	.6687665	2217295	451
452	204304	92345408	.2602916	.6744303	2212389	452
453	205209	92959677	.2837967	.6800857	2207506	453
454	206116	93576664	.3072758	.6857328	2202643	454
455	207025	94196375	21.3307290	7.6913717	.002197802	455
456	207936	94818816	.3541565	.6970023	2192982	456
457	208849	95443993	.3775583	.7026246	2188184	457
458	209764	96071912	.4009346	.7082388	2183406	458
459	210681	96702579	.4242853	.7138448	2178649	459
460	211600	97336000	21.4476106	7.7194426	.002173913	460
461	212521	97972181	.4709106	.7250325	2169197	461
462	213444	98611128	.4941853	.7306141	2164502	462
463	214369	99252847	.5174348	.7361877	2159827	463
464	215296	99897344	.5406592	.7417532	2155172	464
465	216225	100544625	21.5638587	7.7473109	.002150538	465
466	217156	101194696	.5870331	.7528606	2145923	466
467	218089	101847563	.6101828	.7584023	2141328	467
468	219024	102503232	.6333077	.7639361	2136752	468
469	219961	103161709	.6564078	.7694620	2132196	469
470	220900	103823000	21.6794834	7.7749801	.002127660	470
471	221841	104487111	.7025344	.7804904	2123142	471
472	222784	105154048	.7255610	.7859928	2118644	472
473	223729	105823817	.7485632	.7914875	2114165	473
474	224676	106496424	.7715411	.7969745	2109705	474
475	225625	107171875	21.7944947	7.8024538	.002105263	475
476	226576	107850176	.8174242	.8079254	2100840	476
477	227529	108531333	.8403297	.8133892	2096436	477
478	228484	109215352	.8632111	.8188456	2092050	478
479	229441	109902239	.8860686	.8242942	2087683	479

No.	Squares.	Cubes.	Square Roots.	Cube Roots.	Recipro-cals.	No.
480	230400	110592000	21.9089023	7.8297353	.002083333	480
481	231361	111284641	.9317122	.8351688	2079902	481
482	232324	111980168	.9544984	.8405949	2074689	482
483	233289	112678587	.9772610	.8460134	2070393	483
484	234256	113379904	22.0000000	.8514244	2066116	484
485	235225	114084125	22.0227155	7.8568281	.002061856	485
486	236196	114791256	.0454077	.8622242	2057613	486
487	237169	115501303	.0680765	.8676130	2053388	487
488	238144	116214272	.0907220	.8729944	2049180	488
489	239121	116930169	.1133444	.8783684	2044990	489
490	240100	117649000	22.1359436	7.8837352	.002040816	490
491	241081	118370771	.1585199	.8890946	2036660	491
492	242064	119095488	.1810730	.8944468	2032520	492
493	243049	119823157	.2036033	.8997917	2028398	493
494	244036	120553784	.2261108	.9051294	2024291	494
495	245025	121287375	22.2485955	7.9104599	.002020202	495
496	246016	122023936	.2710575	.9157832	2016129	496
497	247009	122763473	.2934968	.9210994	2012072	497
498	248004	123505992	.3159136	.9264085	2008032	498
499	249001	124251499	.3383079	.9317104	2004008	499
500	250000	125000000	22.3606798	7.9370053	.002000000	500
501	251001	125751501	.3830293	.9422931	1996008	501
502	252004	126506008	.4053565	.9475739	1992032	502
503	253009	127263527	.4276615	.9528477	1988072	503
504	254016	128024064	.4499443	.9581144	1984127	504
505	255025	128787625	22.4722051	7.9633743	.001980198	505
506	256036	129554216	.4944438	.9686271	1976285	506
507	257049	130323843	.5166605	.9738731	1972387	507
508	258064	131096512	.5388553	.9791122	1968504	508
509	259081	131872229	.5610283	.9843444	1964637	509
510	260100	132651000	22.5831796	7.9895697	.001960784	510
511	261121	133432831	.6053091	.9947883	1956947	511
512	262144	134217728	.6274170	8.0000000	1953125	512
513	263169	135005697	.6495033	.0052049	1949318	513
514	264196	135796744	.6715681	.0104032	1945525	514
515	265225	136590875	22.6936114	8.0155946	.001941748	515
516	266256	137388096	.7156334	.0207794	1937984	516
517	267289	138188413	.7376340	.0259574	1934236	517
518	268324	138991832	.7596134	.0311287	1930502	518
519	269361	139798359	.7815715	.0362935	1926782	519
520	270400	140608000	22.8035085	8.0414515	.001923077	520
521	271441	141420761	.8254244	.0466030	1919386	521
522	272484	142236648	.8473193	.0517479	1915709	522
523	273529	143055667	.8691933	.0568862	1912046	523
524	274576	143877824	.8910463	.0620180	1908397	524
525	275625	144703125	22.9128785	8.0671432	.001904762	525
526	276676	145531576	.9346899	.0722620	1901141	526
527	277729	146363183	.9564806	.0773743	1897533	527
528	278784	147197952	.9782506	.0824800	1893939	528
529	279841	148035889	23.0000000	.0875794	1890359	529
530	280900	148877000	23.0217289	8.0926723	.001886792	530
531	281961	149721291	.0434372	.0977589	1883239	531
532	283024	150568768	.0651252	.1028390	1879699	532
533	284089	151419437	.0867928	.1079128	1876173	533
534	285156	152273304	.1084400	.1129803	1872659	534
535	286225	153130375	23.1300670	8.1180414	.001869159	535
536	287296	153990656	.1516738	.1230962	1865672	536
537	288369	154854153	.1732605	.1281447	1862197	537
538	289444	155720872	.1948270	.1331870	1858736	538
539	290521	156590819	.2163735	.1382230	1855288	539

TABLE XXVII.—SQUARES, CUBES, SQUARE ROOTS,

No.	Squares.	Cubes.	Square Roots.	Cube Roots.	Reciprocals.	No.
540	291600	157464000	23.2379001	8.1432529	.001851852	540
541	292681	158340421	.2594067	.1482765	1848429	541
542	293764	159220088	.2808935	.1532939	1845018	542
543	294849	160103007	.3023604	.1583051	1841621	543
544	295936	160989184	.3238076	.1633102	1838235	544
545	297025	161878625	23.3452351	8.1683092	.001834862	545
546	298116	162771336	.3666429	.1733020	1831502	546
547	299209	163667323	.3880311	.1782888	1828154	547
548	300304	164566592	.4093998	.1832695	1824818	548
549	301401	165469149	.4307490	.1882441	1821494	549
550	302500	166375000	23.4520788	8.1932127	.001818182	550
551	303601	167284151	.4733892	.1981753	1814882	551
552	304704	168196608	.4946802	.2031319	1811594	552
553	305809	169112377	.5159520	.2080825	1808318	553
554	306916	170031464	.5372046	.2130271	1805054	554
555	308025	170953875	23.5584380	8.2179657	.001801802	555
556	309136	171879616	.5796522	.2228985	1798561	556
557	310249	172808693	.6008474	.2278254	1795332	557
558	311364	173741112	.6220236	.2327463	1792115	558
559	312481	174676879	.6431808	.2376614	1788909	559
560	313600	175616000	23.6643191	8.2425706	.001785714	560
561	314721	176558481	.6854386	.2474740	1782531	561
562	315844	177504328	.7065392	.2523715	1779359	562
563	316969	178453547	.7276210	.2572633	1776199	563
564	318096	179406144	.7486842	.2621492	1773050	564
565	319225	180362125	23.7697286	8.2670294	.001769912	565
566	320356	181321496	.7907545	.2719039	1766784	566
567	321489	182284263	.8117618	.2767726	1763668	567
568	322624	183250432	.8327506	.2816355	1760563	568
569	323761	184220009	.8537209	.2864928	1757469	569
570	324900	185193000	23.8746728	8.2913444	.001754386	570
571	326041	186169411	.8956063	.2961903	1751313	571
572	327184	187149248	.9165215	.3010304	1748252	572
573	328329	188132517	.9374184	.3058651	1745201	573
574	329476	189119224	.9582971	.3106941	1742160	574
575	330625	190109375	23.9791576	8.3155175	.001739130	575
576	331776	191102976	24.0000000	.3203353	1736111	576
577	332929	192100033	.0208243	.3251475	1733102	577
578	334084	193100552	.0416306	.3299542	1730104	578
579	335241	194104539	.0624188	.3347553	1727116	579
580	336400	195112000	24.0831891	8.3395509	.001724138	580
581	337561	196122941	.1039416	.3443410	1721170	581
582	338724	197137368	.1246762	.3491256	1718213	582
583	339889	198155287	.1453929	.3539047	1715266	583
584	341056	199176704	.1660919	.3586784	1712329	584
585	342225	200201625	24.1867732	8.3634466	.001709402	585
586	343396	201230056	.2074369	.3682095	1706485	586
587	344569	202262003	.2280829	.3729668	1703578	587
588	345744	203297472	.2487113	.3777188	1700680	588
589	346921	204336469	.2693222	.3824653	1697793	589
590	348100	205379000	24.2899156	8.3872065	.001694915	590
591	349281	206425071	.3104916	.3919423	1692047	591
592	350464	207474688	.3310501	.3966729	1689189	592
593	351649	208527857	.3515913	.4013981	1686341	593
594	352836	209584584	.3721152	.4061180	1683502	594
595	354025	210644875	24.3926218	8.4108326	.001680672	595
596	355216	211708736	.4131112	.4155419	1677852	596
597	356409	212776173	.4335834	.4202460	1675042	597
598	357604	213847192	.4540385	.4249448	1672241	598
599	358801	214921799	.4744765	.4296383	1669449	599

No.	Squares.	Cubes.	Square Roots.	Cube Roots.	Reciprocals.	No.
600	360000	216000000	24.4948974	8.4343267	.001666667	600
601	361201	217081801	.5153013	.4390098	1663894	601
602	362404	218167208	.5356883	.4436877	1661130	602
603	363609	219256227	.5560583	.4483605	1658375	603
604	364816	220348864	.5764115	.4530281	1655629	604
605	366025	221445125	24.5967478	8.4576906	.001652893	605
606	367236	222545016	.6170673	.4623479	1650165	606
607	368449	223648543	.6373700	.4670001	1647446	607
608	369664	224755712	.6576560	.4716471	1644737	608
609	370881	225866529	.6779254	.4762892	1642036	609
610	372100	226981000	24.6981781	8.4809261	.001639344	610
611	373321	228099131	.7184142	.4855579	1636661	611
612	374544	229220928	.7386338	.4901848	1633987	612
613	375769	230346397	.7588368	.4948065	1631321	613
614	376996	231475544	.7790234	.4994233	1628664	614
615	378225	232608375	24.7991935	8.5040350	.001626016	615
616	379456	233744896	.8193473	.5086417	1623377	616
617	380689	234885113	.8394847	.5132435	1620746	617
618	381924	236029032	.8596058	.5178403	1618123	618
619	383161	237176659	.8797106	.5224321	1615509	619
620	384400	238328000	24.8997992	8.5270189	.001612903	620
621	385641	239483061	.9198716	.5316009	1610306	621
622	386884	240641848	.9399278	.5361780	1607717	622
623	388129	241804367	.9599679	.5407501	1605136	623
624	389376	242970624	.9799920	.5453173	1602564	624
625	390625	244140625	25.0000000	8.5498797	.001600000	625
626	391876	245314376	.0199920	.5544372	1597444	626
627	393129	246491883	.0399681	.5589899	1594896	627
628	394384	247673152	.0599282	.5635377	1592357	628
629	395641	248858189	.0798724	.5680807	1589825	629
630	396900	250047000	25.0998008	8.5726189	.001587302	630
631	398161	251239591	.1197134	.5771523	1584786	631
632	399424	252435968	.1396102	.5816809	1582278	632
633	400689	253636137	.1594913	.5862047	1579779	633
634	401956	254840104	.1793566	.5907238	1577287	634
635	403225	256047875	25.1992063	8.5952380	.001574803	635
636	404496	257259456	.2190404	.5997476	1572327	636
637	405769	258474853	.2388589	.6042525	1569859	637
638	407044	259694072	.2586619	.6087526	1567398	638
639	408321	260917119	.2784493	.6132480	1564945	639
640	409600	262144000	25.2982213	8.6177388	.001562500	640
641	410881	263374721	.3179778	.6222248	1560062	641
642	412164	264609288	.3377189	.6267063	1557632	642
643	413449	265847707	.3574447	.6311830	1555210	643
644	414736	267089984	.3771551	.6356551	1552795	644
645	416025	268336125	25.3968502	8.6401226	.001550388	645
646	417316	269586136	.4165301	.6445855	1547988	646
647	418609	270840023	.4361947	.6490437	1545595	647
648	419904	272097792	.4558441	.6534974	1543210	648
649	421201	273359449	.4754784	.6579465	1540832	649
650	422500	274625000	25.4950976	8.6623911	.001538462	650
651	423801	275894451	.5147016	.6668310	1536098	651
652	425104	277167808	.5342907	.6712665	1533742	652
653	426409	278445077	.5538647	.6756974	1531394	653
654	427716	279726264	.5734237	.6801237	1529052	654
655	429025	281011375	25.5929678	8.6845456	.001526718	655
656	430336	282300416	.6124969	.6889630	1524390	656
657	431649	283593393	.6320112	.6933759	1522070	657
658	432964	284890312	.6515107	.6977843	1519757	658
659	434281	286191179	.6709953	.7021882	1517451	659

TABLE XXVII.—SQUARES, CUBES, SQUARE ROOTS,

No.	Squares.	Cubes.	Square Roots.	Cube Roots.	Reciprocals.	No.
660	435600	287496000	25.6904652	8.7065877	.001515152	660
661	436921	288804781	.7099203	.7109827	1512859	661
662	438244	290117528	.7293607	.7153734	1510574	662
663	439569	291434247	.7487864	.7197596	1508296	663
664	440896	292754944	.7681975	.7241414	1506024	664
665	442225	294079625	25.7875939	8.7285187	.001503759	665
666	443556	295408296	.8069758	.7328918	1501502	666
667	444889	296740963	.8263431	.7372604	1499250	667
668	446224	298077632	.8456960	.7416246	1497006	668
669	447561	299418309	.8650343	.7459846	1494768	669
670	448900	300763000	25.8843582	8.7503401	.001492537	670
671	450241	302111711	.9036677	.7546913	1490313	671
672	451584	303464448	.9229628	.7590383	1488095	672
673	452929	304821217	.9422435	.7633809	1485884	673
674	454276	306182024	.9615100	.7677192	1483680	674
675	455625	307546875	25.9807621	8.7720532	.001481481	675
676	456976	308915776	26.0000000	.7763830	1479290	676
677	458329	310288733	.0192237	.7807084	1477105	677
678	459684	311665752	.0384331	.7850296	1474926	678
679	461041	313046839	.0576284	.7893466	1472754	679
680	462400	314432000	26.0768096	8.7936593	.001470588	680
681	463761	315821241	.0959767	.7979679	1468429	681
682	465124	317214568	.1151297	.8022721	1466276	682
683	466489	318611987	.1342687	.8065722	1464129	683
684	467856	320013504	.1533937	.8108681	1461988	684
685	469225	321419125	26.1725047	8.8151598	.001459854	685
686	470596	322828856	.1916017	.8194474	1457726	686
687	471969	324242703	.2106848	.8237307	1455604	687
688	473344	325660672	.2297541	.8280099	1453488	688
689	474721	327082769	.2488095	.8322850	1451379	689
690	476100	328509000	26.2678511	8.8365559	.001449275	690
691	477481	329933971	.2868789	.8408227	1447178	691
692	478864	331373888	.3058929	.8450854	1445087	692
693	480249	332812557	.3248932	.8493440	1443001	693
694	481636	334255384	.3438797	.8535985	1440922	694
695	483025	335702375	26.3628527	8.8578489	.001438849	695
696	484416	337153536	.3818119	.8620952	1436782	696
697	485809	338608873	.4007576	.8663375	1434720	697
698	487204	340068392	.4196896	.8705757	1432665	698
699	488601	341532099	.4386081	.8748099	1430615	699
700	490000	343000000	26.4575131	8.8790400	.001428571	700
701	491401	344472101	.4764046	.8832661	1426534	701
702	492804	345948408	.4952826	.8874882	1424501	702
703	494209	347428927	.5141472	.8917063	1422475	703
704	495616	348913664	.5329983	.8959204	1420455	704
705	497025	350402625	26.5518361	8.9001304	.001418440	705
706	498436	351895816	.5706605	.9043366	1416431	706
707	499849	353393243	.5894716	.9085387	1414427	707
708	501264	354894912	.6082694	.9127369	1412429	708
709	502681	356400829	.6270539	.9169311	1410437	709
710	504100	357911000	26.6458252	8.9211214	.001408451	710
711	505521	359425431	.6645833	.9253078	1406470	711
712	506944	360944128	.6833281	.9294902	1404494	712
713	508369	362467097	.7020598	.9336687	1402525	713
714	509796	363994344	.7207784	.9378433	1400560	714
715	511225	365525875	26.7394839	8.9420140	.001398601	715
716	512656	367061696	.7581763	.9461809	1396648	716
717	514089	368601813	.7768557	.9503438	1394700	717
718	515524	370146232	.7955220	.9545029	1392758	718
719	516961	371694959	.8141754	.9586581	1390821	719

No.	Squares.	Cubes.	Square Roots.	Cube Roots.	Reciprocals.	No.
720	518400	373248000	26.8328157	8.9628095	.001388889	720
721	519841	374805361	.8514432	.9669570	1386963	721
722	521284	376367048	.8700577	.9711007	1385042	722
723	522729	377933067	.8886593	.9752406	1383126	723
724	524176	379503424	.9072481	.9793766	1381215	724
725	525625	381078125	26.9258240	8.9835089	.001379310	725
726	527076	382657176	.9443872	.9876373	1377410	726
727	528529	384240583	.9629375	.9917620	1375516	727
728	529984	385828352	.9814751	.9958829	1373626	728
729	531441	387420489	27.0000000	9.0000000	1371742	729
730	532900	389017000	27.0185122	9.0041134	.001369863	730
731	534361	390617891	.0370117	.0082229	1367989	731
732	535824	392223168	.0554985	.0123288	1366120	732
733	537289	393832837	.0739727	.0164309	1364256	733
734	538756	395446904	.0924344	.0205293	1362398	734
735	540225	397065375	27.1108834	9.0246239	.001360544	735
736	541696	398688256	.1293199	.0287149	1358696	736
737	543169	400315553	.1477439	.0328021	1356852	737
738	544644	401947272	.1661554	.0368857	1355014	738
739	546121	403583419	.1845544	.0409655	1353180	739
740	547600	405224000	27.2029410	9.0450417	.001351351	740
741	549081	406869021	.2213152	.0491142	1349528	741
742	550564	408518488	.2396769	.0531831	1347709	742
743	552049	410172407	.2580263	.0572482	1345895	743
744	553536	411830784	.2763634	.0613098	1344086	744
745	555025	413493625	27.2946881	9.0653677	.001342282	745
746	556516	415160936	.3130006	.0694220	1340483	746
747	558009	416832723	.3313007	.0734726	1338688	747
748	559504	418508992	.3495887	.0775197	1336898	748
749	561001	420189749	.3678644	.0815631	1335113	749
750	562500	421875000	27.3861279	9.0856030	.001333333	750
751	564001	423564751	.4043792	.0896392	1331558	751
752	565504	425259008	.4226184	.0936719	1329787	752
753	567009	426957777	.4408455	.0977010	1328021	753
754	568516	428661064	.4590604	.1017265	1326260	754
755	570025	430368875	27.4772633	9.1057485	.001324503	755
756	571536	432081216	.4954542	.1097669	1322751	756
757	573049	433798093	.5136330	.1137818	1321004	757
758	574564	435519512	.5317998	.1177931	1319261	758
759	576081	437245479	.5499546	.1218010	1317523	759
760	577600	438976000	27.5680975	9.1258053	.001315789	760
761	579121	440711081	.5862284	.1298061	1314060	761
762	580644	442450728	.6043475	.1338034	1312336	762
763	582169	444194947	.6224546	.1377971	1310616	763
764	583696	445943744	.6405499	.1417874	1308901	764
765	585225	447697125	27.6586334	9.1457742	.001307190	765
766	586756	449455096	.6767050	.1497576	1305483	766
767	588289	451217663	.6947648	.1537375	1303781	767
768	589824	452984832	.7128129	.1577139	1302083	768
769	591361	454756609	.7308492	.1616869	1300390	769
770	592900	456533000	27.7488739	9.1656565	.001298701	770
771	594441	458314011	.7668868	.1696225	1297017	771
772	595984	460099648	.7848880	.1735852	1295337	772
773	597529	461889917	.8028775	.1775445	1293661	773
774	599076	463684824	.8208555	.1815003	1291990	774
775	600625	465484375	27.8388218	9.1854527	.001290323	775
776	602176	467288576	.8567766	.1894018	1288660	776
777	603729	469097433	.8747197	.1933474	1287001	777
778	605284	470910952	.8926514	.1972897	1285347	778
779	606841	472729139	.9105715	.2012286	1283697	779

TABLE XXVII.—SQUARES, CUBES, SQUARE ROOTS,

No.	Squares.	Cubes.	Square Roots.	Cube Roots.	Reciprocals.	No.
780	608400	474552000	27.9284801	9.2051641	.001282051	780
781	609961	476379541	.9463772	.2090962	1280410	781
782	611524	478211768	.9642629	.2130250	1278772	782
783	613089	480048687	.9821372	.2169505	1277139	783
784	614656	481890304	28.0000000	.2208726	1275510	784
785	616225	483736625	28.0178515	9.2247914	.001273885	785
786	617796	485587656	.0356915	.2287068	1272265	786
787	619369	487443403	.0535203	.2326189	1270648	787
788	620944	489303872	.0713377	.2365277	1269036	788
789	622521	491169069	.0891438	.2404333	1267427	789
790	624100	493039000	28.1069386	9.2443355	.001265823	790
791	625681	494913671	.1247222	.2482344	1264223	791
792	627264	496793088	.1424946	.2521300	1262626	792
793	628849	498677257	.1602557	.2560224	1261034	793
794	630436	500566184	.1780056	.2599114	1259446	794
795	632025	502459875	28.1957444	9.2637973	.001257862	795
796	633616	504358336	.2134720	.2676798	1256281	796
797	635209	506261573	.2311884	.2715592	1254705	797
798	636804	508169592	.2488938	.2754352	1253133	798
799	638401	510082399	.2665881	.2793081	1251564	799
800	640000	512000000	28.2842712	9.2831777	.001250000	800
801	641601	513922401	.3019434	.2870440	1248439	801
802	643204	515849608	.3196045	.2909072	1246883	802
803	644809	517781627	.3372546	.2947671	1245330	803
804	646416	519718464	.3548938	.2986239	1243781	804
805	648025	521660125	28.3725219	9.3024775	.001242236	805
806	649636	523606616	.3901391	.3063278	1240695	806
807	651249	525557943	.4077454	.3101750	1239157	807
808	652864	527514112	.4253408	.3140190	1237624	808
809	654481	529475129	.4429253	.3178599	1236094	809
810	656100	531441000	28.4604989	9.3216975	.001234568	810
811	657721	533411731	.4780617	.3255320	1233046	811
812	659344	535387328	.4956137	.3293634	1231527	812
813	660969	537367797	.5131549	.3331916	1230012	813
814	662596	539353144	.5306852	.3370167	1228501	814
815	664225	541343375	28.5482048	9.3408386	.001226994	815
816	665856	543338496	.5657137	.3446575	1225490	816
817	667489	545338513	.5832119	.3484731	1223990	817
818	669124	547343432	.6006993	.3522857	1222494	818
819	670761	549353259	.6181760	.3560952	1221001	819
820	672400	551368000	28.6356421	9.3599016	.001219512	820
821	674041	553387661	.6530976	.3637049	1218027	821
822	675684	555412248	.6705424	.3675051	1216545	822
823	677329	557441767	.6879766	.3713022	1215067	823
824	678976	559476224	.7054002	.3750963	1213592	824
825	680625	561515625	28.7228132	9.3788873	.001212121	825
826	682276	563559976	.7402157	.3826752	1210654	826
827	683929	565609283	.7576077	.3864600	1209190	827
828	685584	567663552	.7749891	.3902419	1207729	828
829	687241	569722789	.7923601	.3940206	1286273	829
830	688900	571787000	28.8097206	9.3977964	.001204819	830
831	690561	573856191	.8270706	.4015691	1203369	831
832	692224	575930368	.8444102	.4053387	1201923	832
833	693889	578009537	.8617394	.4091054	1200480	833
834	695556	580093704	.8790582	.4128690	1199041	834
835	697225	582182875	28.8963666	9.4166297	.001197605	835
836	698896	584277056	.9136646	.4203873	1196172	836
837	700569	586376253	.9309523	.4241420	1194743	837
838	702244	588480472	.9482297	.4278936	1193317	838
839	703921	590589719	.9654967	.4316423	1191895	839

No.	Squares.	Cubes.	Square Roots.	Cube Roots.	Reciprocals.	No.
840	705600	592704000	28.9827535	9.4353880	.001190476	840
841	707281	594823321	29.0000000	.4391307	1189061	841
842	708964	596947688	.0172363	.4428704	1187648	842
843	710649	599077107	.0344623	.4466072	1186240	843
844	712336	601211584	.0516781	.4503410	1184834	844
845	714025	603351125	29.0688837	9.4540719	.001183432	845
846	715716	605495736	.0860791	.4577999	1182033	846
847	717409	607645423	.1032644	.4615249	1180638	847
848	719104	609800192	.1204396	.4652470	1179245	848
849	720801	611960049	.1376046	.4689661	1177856	849
850	722500	614125000	29.1547595	9.4726824	.001176471	850
851	724201	616295051	.1719043	.4763957	1175088	851
852	725904	618470208	.1890390	.4801061	1173709	852
853	727609	620650477	.2061637	.4838136	1172333	853
854	729316	622835864	.2232784	.4875182	1170960	854
855	731025	625026375	29.2403830	9.4912200	.001169591	855
856	732736	627222016	.2574777	.4949188	1168224	856
857	734449	629422793	.2745623	.4986147	1166861	857
858	736164	631628712	.2916370	.5023078	1165501	858
859	737881	633839779	.3087018	.5059980	1164144	859
860	739600	636056000	29.3257566	9.5096854	.001162791	860
861	741321	638277381	.3428015	.5133699	1161440	861
862	743044	640503928	.3598365	.5170515	1160093	862
863	744769	642735647	.3768616	.5207303	1158749	863
864	746496	644972544	.3938769	.5244063	1157407	864
865	748225	647214625	29.4108823	9.5280794	.001156069	865
866	749956	649461896	.4278779	.5317497	1154734	866
867	751689	651714363	.4448637	.5354172	1153403	867
868	753424	653972032	.4618397	.5390818	1152074	868
869	755161	656234909	.4788059	.5427437	1150748	869
870	756900	658503000	29.4957624	9.5464027	.001149425	870
871	758641	660776311	.5127091	.5500589	1148106	871
872	760384	663054848	.5296461	.5537123	1146789	872
873	762129	665338617	.5465734	.5573630	1145475	873
874	763876	667627624	.5634910	.5610108	1144165	874
875	765625	669921875	29.5803989	9.5646559	.001142857	875
876	767376	672221376	.5972972	.5682982	1141553	876
877	769129	674526133	.6141858	.5719377	1140251	877
878	770884	676836152	.6310648	.5755745	1138952	878
879	772641	679151439	.6479342	.5792085	1137656	879
880	774400	681472000	29.6647939	9.5828397	.001136364	880
881	776161	683797841	.6816442	.5864682	1135074	881
882	777924	686128968	.6984848	.5900939	1133787	882
883	779689	688465387	.7153159	.5937169	1132503	883
884	781456	690807104	.7321375	.5973373	1131222	884
885	783225	693154125	29.7489496	9.6009548	.001129944	885
886	784996	695506456	.7657521	.6045696	1128668	886
887	786769	697864103	.7825452	.6081817	1127396	887
888	788544	700227072	.7993289	.6117911	1126126	888
889	790321	702595369	.8161030	.6153977	1124859	889
890	792100	704969000	29.8328678	9.6190017	.001123596	890
891	793881	707347971	.8496231	.6226030	1122334	891
892	795664	709732288	.8663690	.6262016	1121076	892
893	797449	712121957	.8831056	.6297975	1119821	893
894	799236	714516984	.8998328	.6333907	1118568	894
895	801025	716917375	29.9165506	9.6369812	.001117318	895
896	802816	719323136	.9332591	.6405690	1116071	896
897	804609	721734273	.9499583	.6441542	1114827	897
898	806404	724150792	.9666481	.6477367	1113586	898
899	808201	726572699	.9833287	.6513166	1112347	899

TABLE XXVII.—SQUARES, CUBES, SQUARE ROOTS,

No.	Squares.	Cubes.	Square Roots.	Cube Roots.	Reciprocals.	No.
900	810000	729000000	30.0000000	9.6548938	.00111111	900
901	811801	731432701	.0166620	.6584684	1109878	901
902	813604	733870808	.0333148	.6620403	1108647	902
903	815409	736314327	.0499584	.6656096	1107420	903
904	817216	738763264	.0665928	.6691762	1106195	904
905	819025	741217625	30.0832179	9.6727403	.001104972	905
906	820836	743677416	.0998339	.6763017	1103753	906
907	822649	746142643	.1164407	.6798604	1102536	907
908	824464	748613312	.1330383	.6834166	1101322	908
909	826281	751089429	.1496269	.6869701	1100110	909
910	828100	753571000	30.1662063	9.6905211	.001098901	910
911	829921	756058031	.1827765	.6940694	1097695	911
912	831744	758550528	.1993377	.6976151	1096491	912
913	833569	761048497	.2158899	.7011583	1095290	913
914	835396	763551944	.2324329	.7046989	1094092	914
915	837225	766060875	30.2489669	9.7082369	.001092896	915
916	839056	768575296	.2654919	.7117723	1091703	916
917	840889	771095213	.2820079	.7153051	1090513	917
918	842724	773620632	.2985148	.7188354	1089325	918
919	844561	776151559	.3150128	.7223631	1088139	919
920	846400	778688000	30.3315018	9.7258883	.001086957	920
921	848241	781229061	.3479818	.7294109	1085776	921
922	850084	783777448	.3644529	.7329309	1084599	922
923	851929	786330467	.3809151	.7364484	1083424	923
924	853776	788889024	.3973683	.7399634	1082251	924
925	855625	791453125	30.4138127	9.7434758	.001081081	925
926	857476	794022776	.4302481	.7469857	1079914	926
927	859329	796597983	.4466747	.7504930	1078749	927
928	861184	799178752	.4630924	.7539979	1077586	928
929	863041	801765089	.4795013	.7575002	1076426	929
930	864900	804357000	30.4959014	9.7610001	.001075269	930
931	866761	806954491	.5122926	.7644974	1074114	931
932	868624	809557568	.5286750	.7679922	1072961	932
933	870489	812166237	.5450487	.7714845	1071811	933
934	872356	814780504	.5614136	.7749743	1070664	934
935	874225	817400375	30.5777697	9.7784616	.001069519	935
936	876096	820025856	.5941171	.7819466	1068376	936
937	877969	822656953	.6104557	.7854288	1067236	937
938	879844	825293672	.6267857	.7889087	1066098	938
939	881721	827936019	.6431069	.7923861	1064963	939
940	883600	830584000	30.6594194	9.7958611	.001063830	940
941	885481	833237621	.6757233	.7993336	1062699	941
942	887364	835896888	.6920185	.8028036	1061571	942
943	889249	838561807	.7083051	.8062711	1060445	943
944	891136	841232384	.7245830	.8097362	1059322	944
945	893025	843908625	30.7408523	9.8131989	.001058201	945
946	894916	846590536	.7571130	.8166591	1057082	946
947	896809	849278123	.7733651	.8201169	1055966	947
948	898704	851971392	.7896086	.8235723	1054852	948
949	900601	854670349	.8058436	.8270252	1053741	949
950	902500	857375000	30.8220700	9.8304757	.001052632	950
951	904401	860085351	.8382879	.8339238	1051525	951
952	906304	862801408	.8544972	.8373695	1050420	952
953	908209	865523177	.8706981	.8408127	1049318	953
954	910116	868250664	.8868904	.8442536	1048218	954
955	912025	870983875	30.9030743	9.8476920	.001047120	955
956	913936	873722816	.9192497	.8511280	1046025	956
957	915849	876467493	.9354166	.8545617	1044932	957
958	917764	879217912	.9515751	.8579929	1043841	958
959	919681	881974079	.9677251	.8614218	1042753	959

No.	Squares.	Cubes.	Square Roots.	Cube Roots.	Reciprocals.	No.
960	921600	884736000	30.9838668	9.8648483	.001041667	960
961	923521	887503681	31.0000000	.8682724	1040583	961
962	925444	890277128	.0161248	.8716941	1039501	962
963	927369	893056347	.0322413	.8751135	1038422	963
964	929296	895841344	.0483494	.8785305	1037344	964
965	931225	898632125	31.0644491	9.8819451	.001036269	965
966	933156	901428696	.0805405	.8853574	1035197	966
967	935089	904231063	.0966236	.8887673	1034126	967
968	937024	907039232	.1126984	.8921749	1033058	968
969	938961	909853209	.1287648	.8955801	1031992	969
970	940900	912673000	31.1448230	9.8989830	.001030928	970
971	942841	915498611	.1608729	.9023835	1029866	971
972	944784	918330048	.1769145	.9057817	1028807	972
973	946729	921167317	.1929479	.9091776	1027749	973
974	948676	924010424	.2089731	.9125712	1026694	974
975	950625	926859375	31.2249900	9.9159624	.001025641	975
976	952576	929714176	.2409987	.9193513	1024590	976
977	954529	932574833	.2569992	.9227379	1023541	977
978	956484	935441352	.2729915	.9261222	1022495	978
979	958441	938313739	.2889757	.9295042	1021450	979
980	960400	941192000	31.3049507	9.9328839	.001020408	980
981	962361	944076141	.3209195	.9362613	1019368	981
982	964324	946966168	.3368792	.9396363	1018330	982
983	966289	949862087	.3528308	.9430092	1017294	983
984	968256	952763904	.3687743	.9463797	1016260	984
985	970225	955671625	31.3847097	9.9497479	.001015228	985
986	972196	958585256	.4006369	.9531138	1014199	986
987	974169	961504803	.4165561	.9564775	1013171	987
988	976144	964430272	.4324673	.9598389	1012146	988
989	978121	967361669	.4483704	.9631981	1011122	989
990	980100	970299000	31.4642654	9.9665549	.001010101	990
991	982081	973242271	.4801525	.9699095	1009082	991
992	984064	976191488	.4960315	.9732619	1008065	992
993	986049	979146657	.5119025	.9766120	1007049	993
994	988036	982107784	.5277655	.9799599	1006036	994
995	990025	985074875	31.5436206	9.9833055	.001005025	995
996	992016	988047936	.5594677	.9866488	1004016	996
997	994009	991026973	.5753068	.9899900	1003009	997
998	996004	994011992	.5911380	.9933289	1002004	998
999	998001	997002999	.6069613	.9966656	1001001	999
1000	1000000	1000000000	31.6227766	10.0000000	.001000000	1000
1001	1002001	1003003001	.6385840	.0033322	0999001	1001
1002	1004004	1006012008	.6543836	.0066622	0998004	1002
1003	1006009	1009027027	.6701752	.0099899	0997009	1003
1004	1008016	1012048064	.6859590	.0133155	0996016	1004
1005	1010025	1015075125	31.7017349	10.0166389	.000995025	1005
1006	1012036	1018108216	.7175030	.0199601	0994036	1006
1007	1014049	1021147343	.7332633	.0232791	0993049	1007
1008	1016064	1024192512	.7490157	.0265958	0992063	1008
1009	1018081	1027243729	.7647603	.0299104	0991080	1009
1010	1020100	1030301000	31.7804972	10.0332228	.000990099	1010
1011	1022121	1033364331	.7962262	.0365330	0989120	1011
1012	1024144	1036433728	.8119474	.0398410	0988142	1012
1013	1026169	1039509197	.8276609	.0431469	0987167	1013
1014	1028196	1042590744	.8433666	.0464506	0986193	1014
1015	1030225	1045678375	31.8590647	10.0497521	.000985222	1015
1016	1032256	1048772096	.8747549	.0530514	0984252	1016
1017	1034289	1051871913	.8904374	.0563485	0983284	1017
1018	1036324	1054977832	.9061123	.0596435	0982318	1018
1019	1038361	1058089859	.9217794	.0629364	0981354	1019

INDEX

Aerial photography; *see also* Photogrammetry
  advantages of, 305, 306
  in canal surveys, 287, 305
  in highway location, 278-81
  miscellaneous uses o., 303, 304
  in pipe-line surveys, 286
  in route surveying, 290-308
Aero-cartograph, 294
Alignment design
  horizontal, on highways, 167, 215, 224
  by paper-location, 240-42
  vertical, on highways, 215-25
American Association of State Highway Officials, 267, 275
  design policies of, 161
American Railway Engineering Association
  formula for track super-elevation of, 247, 249
  recommendation for spiral length by, 192, 249, 250
  recommendation for vertical curves by, 58
  ten-chord spiral of, 91, 312
  trackwork plans of, 260, 261
American Road Builders' Association, 267
Areas
  of cross-sections; *see* Cross-sections
  of pavement on curves, 214, 215

Balance lines on mass diagram, 125-32
Balance points, 123, 124, 132
Ball bank indicator, 174-77

Base line, 235, 271
Body roll, 173-77
Borrow pits, 118-21
Broken-back curve, 149-51
Bureau of Public Roads, 266, 268, 269, 274

Canal surveys, 287, 305
Central angle
  of circular curve, 13
  of spiral, 71, 72, 84
Change-of-location problems
  examples of, 143-48
  hints for solving, 143-45
Checking
  of curve by middle ordinate, 26
  of field work on curves, 20, 25, 26
Chord; *see also* Subchords
  long (L.C.), of simple curve, 13
Chord-gradient method of calculating
  vertical curves, 56-60
Chord lengths on circular curves, 26, 27
Chord offsets, 31-34
Circular curve; *see* Simple curve
Clothoid, 70
Compound curve
  calculation of, 47, 48
  completely-spiraled, 85, 86
  definition of, 39
  location of, by trial, 50, 51
  notation for, 39, 40
  notes and field work for, 50, 51
  with P.I. inaccessible, 138, 139

Compound curve (*Cont.*)
problems on, 52
rigid solution of, 39
solution of
by construction, 41, 42
by traverse, 42-46
vertex triangle, 40, 41
summary of methods of
solving, 46
three-centered, 49
use of, 39

Construction survey
methods for
in highway location, 276, 277
in railroad location, 245-47
relation of, to other surveys, 6

Contour map
field sketches for, 238, 239
by photogrammetry, 295-98
purpose and limitations of, 8, 9

Contours; *see* Topography
Controlling points, 3, 4, 233
Controls
for horizontal alignment, 224
for vertical alignment, 225

Cross-section leveling, 106, 270, 272
Cross-sectioning
on highways, 270, 272
methods of, 105-9
on Pennsylvania Turnpike, 289

Cross-sections
areas of
by calculating machine, 103, 104
by formulas, 100, 103
by graphic methods, 105
location of, 99, 100
types of, 97-99, 104

Crown
adverse, 170, 171
favorable, 170, 171

Curvature
aesthetic importance of, 3
correction for, in earth-work, 116-18
use of, in route location, 3

Curve
broken-back, 149-51
by-passing obstacles on, 29, 30, 36
circular, length of, 18
compound; *see* Compound curve
degree of, 14-16
easement, 69-71
even-radius, 30, 89
highway; *see* Highway
horizontal; *see* Horizontal curves
with inaccessible P.I. or T.C., 138-41
measurements along, 16, 17, 25-29
metric, 30, 31
parabolic; *see* Parabolic curve, Vertical curve
primary purpose of, 12
reverse; *see* Reverse curve
simple; *see* Simple curve
spiraled; *see* Spiraled curve
stakes on, 27-29
staking, by deflection angles, 21-23
staking, by offsets, 31-36
stationing on, 17
through fixed point, 153-55
transit set-ups on, 23-25
vertical; *see* Vertical curve

Curve problems
in highway design, 159-230
special
examples of, 137-58
methods of solving, 137, 138

Curve tables [see tables in Part III of book]

Deflection angle
from set-up on spiral, 80-83
to spiral, 74, 75, 77, 78

Deflection-angle method for circular curves, 21-23

Degree of curve
arc definition of, 15
chord definition of, 15
formulas for, 15
selection of, 20

Design; see Office studies

Development, 3, 5

Distribution of earthwork, 122-32

Earthwork
analysis of
by mass diagram, 125-32
by station-to-station method, 124
balance lines in, 125-32
balance points in, 123, 124, 132
basis of payment for, 96
calculation of, 111-14
correction of, for curvature, 116-18
cross-sections of; see Cross-sections
estimate of, 241, 242, 300, 301
from aerial photographs, 300, 301
operations included under, 96
practice problems in, 132-34
shrinkage, swell, and settlement of, 121, 122
slope staking for, 107-10
tables for computation of, 111-14
volume of; see Volume of earthwork

Easement curves, 68-70; see also Spirals

Edge lengths on highway curves, 212-14

Elevations; see Leveling

Excavation; see Earthwork

External distance
of simple curve, 13
of spiral, 76

Field notes
for by-passing obstacles, 244
for compound curves, 50
for cross-section leveling, 106
for simple curve, 23
for slope staking, 108, 110
for spiraled curve, 79

Field work [see type of survey desired]

Floating mark, 294, 295

Free haul, 122-24, 127-31

General Motors Proving Ground, 171, 173, 177, 180

Grade
balance between curvature and, 3
profile, 53

Grade contour, 240, 287

Grade rod, 109

Ground control
in photogrammetric mapping, 293, 299, 304
by radar, 293

Hand level
in cross-sectioning, 106
topography by, 237-39

Headlight sight distances, 219, 220, 223

Highway
cross-sectioning on, 270, 272
curves in
edge lengths on, 212-14
pavement areas on, 214, 215
vehicle operation on, 171-73, 187, 189-95, 201, 202

Highway (*Cont.*)
  design elements of, in relation to speed, 160, 161
  design speed on, 161
  location of, examples of, 277, 278
  over-all travel speed on, 161
  preparation of plans for, 267-70, 274-76
  relocation of, survey methods in, 270-72
  running speed on, 161
  side friction factor on; *see* Side friction factor
  sight distances on; *see* Sight distances
  speed signs on, 177
  superelevation of; *see* Superelevation
  surveys for, 266-81
  widening, on curves; *see* Widening

Highway projects, magnitude of, 11

Highway Research Board, 267, 274

Inaccessible points on curves, 138-41

Intersection
  of line and curve, 155, 156
  point of, for horizontal curve, 13

Kelsh plotter, 294

L-line, 242, 243

Length of curve, definition of
  on horizontal curve, 18
  on vertical curve, 53

Leveling
  bench, 235, 236
  on location survey, 243
  on preliminary surveys, 235, 236
  profile, 236, 243

Limit of economic haul, 123, 129

Location controls, 3, 4, 233

Location survey
  function of, 9
  methods of, in railroad location, 242-44
  relation of, to other surveys, 5, 6

Maps
  accuracy of, 296, 303, 306
  base, 291
  photogrammetric, costs of, 301, 302
  planimetric, 291, 293, 299
  topographic, by photogrammetric methods, 291, 295-300

Mass diagram, 125-32

Merritt Parkway [see Frontispiece]

Metric curves, 30, 31

Middle ordinate of simple curve, 13

Middle-ordinate method of staking curve, 31, 34

Mosaic
  controlled, 291-93
  uncontrolled, 291, 292

Multiplex aero-projector, 294

National map-accuracy standards, 296

Notes; *see* Field notes

Obstacles, by-passing
  on tangents, 244, 245
  on curves, 29, 30, 36, 140-43

Office studies
  in highway design, 274-76
  in paper location, 240-42
  relation of, to field work, 5

Offset T.C., 72

Offsets
  formulas for, 32, 33
  staking curves by, 31-36

Ordinates from a long chord, 31, 35

Osculating circle, 80-82

Overhaul, 122-24, 127-32

Oversteering, 172-73

P-line, 235, 242, 243

Paper location procedure, 240-42

Parabolic curves
laying out, by taping, 65-67
uses of, 53

Pennsylvania Turnpike
aerial surveys on, 297
cross-sectioning on, 289
high-speed tests on, 173, 178, 194, 202
run-off design on, 199, 200
sight distances on, 220
spirals on, 193, 200

Photogrammetry; *see also* Aerial photography
definitions in, 290, 291
for detailed location studies, 278-81, 299-301
limitations of, 304, 305
plotting instruments in, 294
for reconnaissance, 279, 298, 299

Photographs, aerial, types of, 290

Pipe-line surveys, 285, 286, 299

Point of intersection, 13

Preliminary survey
earthwork estimate from, 241, 242
leveling on, 235, 236
plotting map of, 239
purposes of, 7, 8
in railroad location, 234-39
relation of, to other surveys, 5
topography on, 236-39
traverses on, 234, 235

Prismoidal formulas, 114-16

Property surveys, 247

Radius of circular arc, 13-15

Railroad location, economics of, 263

Railroad relocations, 262-64

Railroad surveys, 231-65

Railroad track
layouts for, 259-62
realignment problems with, 258, 259
string lining of, 250-57
supererelevation of, 247-49

Railroad turnout and crossover, 260 [see also Table XXV in Part III of book]

Railway; *see* Railroad

Reaction time, 162-64

Reconnaissance
aerial, 270, 271, 279, 298, 299
for highway location, 271, 279, 280
importance of, 6, 7
instruments for, 231
for railroad location, 231, 233
relation of, to other surveys, 5
by stadia method, 234

Relocation
by field location method, 8
problems on, examples of, 148-53
railroad, 262-64

Reverse curve
definition of, 39
limitations and use of, 48, 49
non-parallel-tangent, 50
notes and field work for, 50
parallel-tangent, 49
practice problems on, 52
replacement of, 151, 152

Route location; *see also* Route surveying

Route location (*Cont.*)
controlling points in, 3, 4, 233
cross-drainage line in, 5
importance of curves and grades in, 3
influence of terrain on, 4, 5
influence of type of project on, 4
proper use of topography in, 8, 9
ridge line in, 4
side-hill line in, 4
use of development in, 3, 5
valley line in, 4

Route surveying; *see also* Route location
aerial photography in, 290-308
accuracies required in, 10, 11
definition and purposes of, 1
and design, 2
and economics, 2
and engineering, 9
sequence of field and office work in, 5, 6

Rule of offsets, 55

Runoff; *see* Superelevation

Runout, 200

Seismic studies, 273

Semi-final location, 9

Settlement of embankment, 122

Shrinkage of earthwork, 121, 122

Side friction factor, 171
recommended values of, 179
research on, 173-80

Sight distance
headlight, 219, 220, 223
on horizontal curves, 210-12
at interchanges, 223, 224
passing, 162, 164-68

Sight distance (*Cont.*)
stopping, 162-64
at underpass, 223
on vertical curves, 215-23

Simple curve; *see also* Curve
computations for, 19, 22
field work in staking, 20-30
formulas for, 31-33
methods of superelevating, 200-202
methods of widening, 202-9
notation for, 13
practice problems on, 36-38
with spirals, 75-79

Slip angles, 172, 173

Slope-staking, 107-10

Soil surveys, 272-74

Special curve problems
examples of, 137-58
methods of solving, 137, 138

Speed on highways; *see* Highway

Spiral; *see also* Spiraled curve
A.R.E.A. ten-chord, 91, 312
between arcs of compound curve, 83-85
calculation of, 76-78, 80
calculation of, without special tables, 90, 91
central angle of, 71, 72, 84
with compound curve, 83-86
deflection angles to, 74, 75, 77, 78
double, 90
Euler, 70
external distance of, 76
field work for, 76, 77, 92
geometry of the, 70-75
importance of the, 202
laying out, by taping, 92, 93
length of, 187-95, 249
locating any point on, 78
long chord for, 75

Spiral (*Cont.*)
   long tangent for, 75
   minimum curvature for use of, 195, 196
   notation for, 68, 72-76
   offsets to, 74, 92
   on Pennsylvania Turnpike, 193, 200
   problems on, 93-95
   on railroad track, 249, 250
   short tangent for, 75
   with simple curve, 75-79
   tables on [see tables in Part III of book]
   tangent distance of, 75, 76
   theory of the, 311, 312
   throw of, 73
   transit set-ups on, 80-83
   types of, 70

Spiral angle, 71

Spiraled curve
   to fit given E_s or T_s, 86-88
   formulas for, with radius as parameter, 89, 90
   methods of superelevating, 197-200
   methods of widening, 204-7

Stadia, topography by, 236, 237

Stadia traverse, 234, 235

Stakes
   construction, 246, 276
   slope, 107-10, 276
   station, 28, 235, 246, 271, 276

Station equation, 143

Stationing
   of tangent points, 20
   on curves, 16, 17

Station-to-station method of earthwork analysis, 124

Station-yard, 122

Stereocomparator, 294

Stereo-planigraph, 294

Stereoscopic fusion, 292, 294

Stereoscopic overlap, 291

Stereoscopic pairs, 290, 292, 294, 295, 299, 301

Stereoscopic plotting instruments, 294

Stereoscopic vision, importance of, 292

String lining of railroad track, 250-57

Subchords
   formulas for, 18, 33
   nominal, 17
   subdeflections for, 21
   true, 17

Subdeflections for subchords, 21

Superelevation
   effect of, on spiral length, 191-93
   maximum rates of, 180-85
   methods of attaining, 197-202
   railroad-track, 247-49
   rate of, over range of curvature, 185
   rates of, for design, 185-87
   theory of, 167-71

Superelevation runoff, length of, 196, 197

Survey [see type of survey desired]
   relation of, to engineering, 9-11

Swell of earthwork, 121

Tables, use of, 18, 19 [see also tables in Part III of book]

Tangent
   back (initial), 13
   forward, 13

Tangent distance
   of simple curve, 13
   of spiral, 75, 76

Tangent offsets
   for horizontal curve, 31, 35

Tangent offsets (*Cont.*)
  for vertical curve, 60, 61
  to spiral, 74
Tangent points
  on simple curve, 13, 20
  on spiraled curve, 68
Terrain
  influence of, on route location, 4, 5
  interpretation of, 274, 303
  types of, 4, 5
Throw of spiral, 73
Ties between P-line and L-line, 242, 243
Topography
  by field-sketch method, 238, 239
  by hand level, 237, 238
  in highway relocation, 272
  by photogrammetry, 295, 299
  plotting, 237, 239
  proper use of, 8, 9
  by stadia, 236, 237
Transit set-ups
  rule for, on circular curve, 24
  on spiral, 80-83
Transmission lines
  location of, 4
  surveys for, 283-85, 299
Traverse solution of curve problems, 42-46, 139, 140, 144-46
  stadia, 234, 235
  transit-and-tape, 235
Tunnel surveys, 288, 289

Underpass, sight distances at, 223
Understeering, 172

Vertex of horizontal curve, 13
Vertical curve
  by chord gradients, 56-60
  drainage requirements on, 219, 223
  equal-tangent, 53-56
  length of, 53, 215-23
  lowest or highest point (turning point) on, 63, 64
  to pass through fixed point, 64, 65
  problems, 67
  reversed, 65
  sight distances on, 215-23
  by tangent offsets, 60, 61
  at underpass, 223
  unequal-tangent, 62, 63
Volume of earthwork
  by average end areas, 111-14
  from borrow pits, 118-21
  corrected for curvature, 116-18
  by prismoidal formula, 114-16
  by tables, 111-14

Wellington, A. M., 6
Widening of highway
  formulas for, 203
  methods of attaining, 204-9
  reasons for, 202, 203